D1191823

Atlas of
BREEDING
BIRDS
IN
NEW
HAMPSHIRE

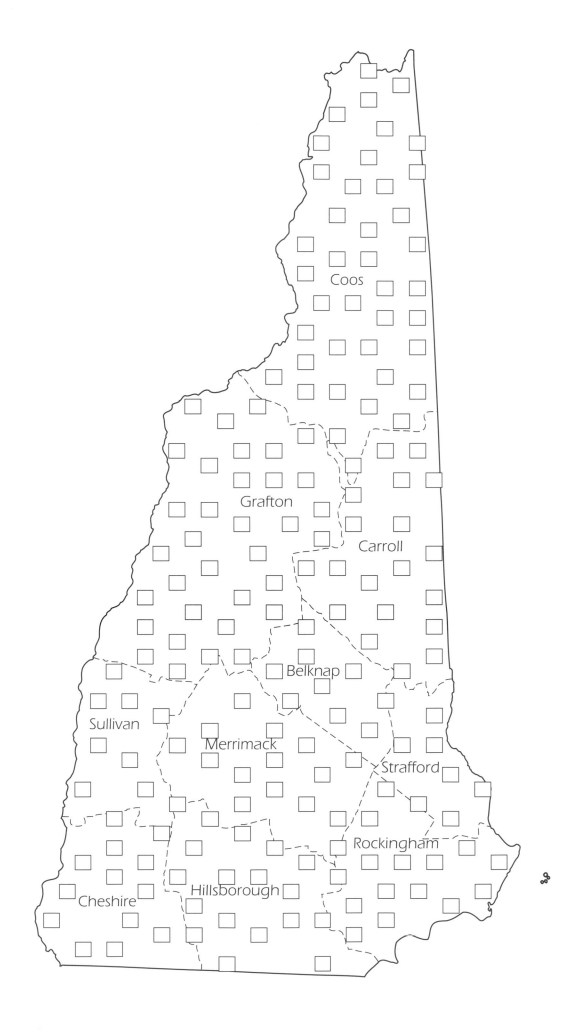

Atlas of
BREEDING BIRDS
IN
NEW HAMPSHIRE

Editor	Carol R. Foss
Associate Editors	Kimball C. Elkins
	Donald Miller
	Eileen Miller
	Tudor Richards
Project Coordinators	Sally Merrill Sutcliffe
	Alis G. Kuhn Ohlheiser
Technical Editor	Margaret B. Watkins
Publication Coordinator	Iain C. MacLeod

ARCADIA

Copyright © 1994 by Audubon Society of New Hampshire

All rights reserved. Except for brief quotations in critical articles or reviews, this book, or parts thereof, must not be reproduced in any form without permission in writing from the publisher.

Printed in Great Britain

Published for the Audubon Society of New Hampshire
by Arcadia, an imprint of
The Chalford Publishing Corporation
One Washington Center
Dover
NH 03820

ISBN 0–7524–0102–5

A set of transparent overlays depicting physical features of New Hampshire (figures 2.2, 2.3, 2.4, 2.6, 2.7, 2.8, 2.9) is available to accompany the atlas.
To obtain a set, send $3.00 to: Atlas Overlays, Audubon Society of New Hampshire, 3 Silk Farm Road, Concord, NH 03301.

Correspondence from the Sponsoring Organizations

University of New Hampshire

We are pleased that the Department of Natural Resources at the University of New Hampshire has been able to play an active role in the development of the New Hampshire Breeding Bird Atlas. The Atlas project was a unique opportunity for the University to work with volunteer bird enthusiasts from across the state who each year devoted long hours and extensive travel collecting the valuable information for the contents of this book. Dr. Harold Hocker, former Department Chair who provided most of the financial support, Dr. Donald Miller, the project initiator and Chris Neefus who did the entire data analysis deserve recognition for their efforts in this project. Alis Kuhn Ohlheiser played a key role as initial coordinator. Sally Merrill Sutcliffe, who served as coordinator after 1983, was instrumental in bringing this project to completion and deserves special recognition.

The Department of Natural Resources is a multidisciplinary department housing undergraduate and graduate majors in Environmental Conservation, Forestry, Soil Science, Water Resources Management and Wildlife. We are committed to providing young people with the skills necessary to become future leaders in the stewardship of our natural resources. We strive to introduce students to an integrated approach to natural resource management while at the same time ensuring they have the skills necessary to pursue successful careers in their chosen professional disciplines.

This atlas, which documents the distribution of nesting birds in New Hampshire from 1981 to 1986, should be useful in documenting future changes in New Hampshire's breeding bird populations. We are most pleased to see its publication.

William W. Mautz
Chair, Department of Natural Resources
University of New Hampshire

The Audubon society of New Hampshire is proud to present the Atlas of Breeding Birds in New Hampshire in cooperation with our colleagues at the New Hampshire Fish and Game Department and the University of New Hampshire's Department of Natural Resources. Our staff and volunteers have invested untold hours in this project, both in the collection of field data and in preparing the results for publication.

New Hampshire's bird life has been a major focus of our organization throughout its history, and we are delighted to have been a part of this effort. We hope that the information presented herein will inspire future efforts to further understand and conserve the bird life of this state.

D. Dickinson Henry, Jr.
President
Audubon Society of New Hampshire

The New Hampshire Fish and Game Department's Nongame and Endangered Species Program has been proud to support the efforts of the Audubon Society of New Hampshire in its work on the New Hampshire Breeding Bird Atlas.

We are pleased to have been part of this cooperative effort. It is a fine example of what can be accomplished, when governmental agencies and private non-profit organizations work together for a common goal.

Congratulations on this fine publication.

John I. Nelson, Jr.
Acting Executive Director
New Hampshire Fish and Game Department

*This book is dedicated to
the many individuals, past, present, and future,
whose interest and dedication contribute to
the on-going study and conservation of
New Hampshire's birds.*

To the Reader

We anticipate that individuals with a considerable range of interests and experience will find use for this volume. Potential readers include New Hampshire residents and visitors with widely varying knowledge of birds, environmental consultants in need of information for site reviews, and ornithology students and professionals from New England, elsewhere in North America, and more distant parts of the world. In attempting to meet the needs of such a diverse audience, we recognize that we are likely to satisfy none. Some readers undoubtedly will consider some of the included material unnecessary, while others may find some sections overly technical. Inevitably, readers will wish for greater detail on some topics and inclusion of others that were omitted entirely. Despite these realities, we sincerely hope that all readers will find something of interest, and use this book to increase their understanding of and appreciation for New Hampshire's bird life.

In Memoriam

Adelaide Berdeen

Milton Butterworth

Connie Casas

Vincent Hayden

Vera H. Hebert

George P. (Joe) Kent

John Morse

Helen W. Parker

Lawrence Rising

Clifford Rogers

Marilyn Woodman

Roy Wright

Contents

List of Tables. viii

List of Figures. viii

Foreword. ....
Chandler S. Robbins ix

Acknowledgements. xi

Introduction. ....
Carol R. Foss I-2

Geography of New Hampshire. ....
Carol R. Foss I-11

Major Changes in the Breeding Avifauna of New Hampshire Since Its First Settlement by Europeans in 1623.
Tudor Richards and Kimball C. Elkins I-18

A Proposed Division of New Hampshire into Avifaunal Regions Based Largely on the Altitudinal Distribution of Breeding Birds.
Tudor Richards I-25

Terms and Abbreviations. I-32

Species Accounts

Loons, *Gaviidae* 2

Grebes, *Podicipedidae* 4

Cormorants, *Phalacrocaracidae* 6

Bitterns and Herons, *Ardeidae* 8

Swans, Geese, and Ducks, *Anatidae* 16

Vultures, *Cathartidae* 40

Eagles and Hawks, *Accipitridae* 42

Falcons, *Falconidae* 58

Pheasants and Quails, *Phasianidae* 62

Rails and Coots, *Rallidae* 64

Plovers, *Charadriidae* 78

Sandpipers, *Scolopacidae* 82

Gulls and Terns, *Laridae* 92

Auks, *Alcidae* 100

Doves, *Columbidae* 102

Cuckoos, *Cuculidae* 219

Owls, *Strigidae* 110

Goatsuckers, *Caprimulgidae* 118

Swifts, *Apodidae* 122

Hummingbirds, *Trochilidae* 124

Kingfishers, *Alcedinidae* 126

Woodpeckers, *Picidae* 128

Tyrant Flycatchers, *Tyrannidae* 144

Larks, *Alaudidae* 164

Swallows, *Hirundinidae* 166

Jays and Crows, *Corvidae* 178

Titmice, *Paridae* 188

Nuthatches, *Sittidae* 194

Creepers, *Certhiidae* 198

Wrens, *Troglodytidae* 200

Kinglets to Thrushes, *Muscicapidae* 208

Mimic Thrushes, *Mimidae* 228

Waxwings, *Bombycillidae* 234

Starlings, *Sturnidae* 236

Vireos, *Vireonidae* 238

Warblers to Orioles, *Emberizidae* 250

Finches, *Fringillidae* 354

Old World Sparrows, *Passeridae* 368

Accounts of Historically or Potentially Breeding Species. 370

Appendix A:
Maps of Historical Records for Selected Species. 390

Appendix B:
Winter Distribution Maps of Selected Species. 392

Appendix C:
Level of Atlas Efforts by Priority Block. 393

Appendix D:
Plants Cited in the Text. 395

Appendix E:
Animals Cited in the Text. 396

References Cited. 397

Index of Bird Names. 410

List of Tables

1.1   Summary of Atlas results by number of years in which priority blocks were visited I-5

1.2   Summary by county of mean years in which priority blocks were visited I-6

1.3   Summary of Atlas results by documented hours of effort I-6

1.4   Summary by county of documented hours of effort I-7

1.5   Summary of number of months in which priority blocks were visited I-7

1.6   Distribution of species by frequency of detection in priority blocks I-8

1.7   Summary of occurrence frequency for species documented in more than
        50% of priority blocks I-8

1.8   Distribution of priority blocks by number of species detected and number
        of species confirmed I-9

1.9   Species detected and confirmed per priority block summarized by county I-9

1.10   Species detected per priority block summarized by length of growing season I-9

1.11   County summary of Atlas effort and results I-9

2.1   Drainage basins I-12

2.2   Size distribution of lakes and ponds by county I-12

2.3   Physical divisions of New Hampshire I-12

2.4   County size statistics I-15

2.5   Population data by county I-16

4.1   Counts of birds on Mt. Monadnock, Jaffrey, N.H. on 17 June 1962 .... I-28

4.2   Number of bird species counted in each 500 ft (152.5 m) interval of elevation
        in the White Mountains of New Hampshire I-28

4.3   Total individuals counted and altitudinal range of the 15 most frequently
        detected species in the White Mountains of New Hampshire I-29

4.4   Numbers of individuals counted of the 10 most frequently detected species in
        each 500 ft (152.5 m) interval in the White Mountains of New Hampshire I-29

4.5   A count of birds by 500 ft (152.5 m) intervals of elevation made on
        5 July 1972 from Carter Notch to Pinkham Notch via the Carter Range I-30

4.6   Counts of birds in long-since cut virgin spruce-fir flat above Norton Pool, East Inlet,
        Pittsburg, N.H. on 8 July 1953 .... I-31

List of Figures

1.1   Priority block selection I-2

1.2   Special areas I-3

1.3   Years of effort per priority block I-6

1.4   Documented hours of effort per priority block I-6

1.5   Number of species detected per priority block I-8

1.6   Number of species confirmed per priority block I-8

2.1   United States showing location of New Hampshire I-11

2.2   New Hampshire land elevations I-11

2.3   Distribution of major forest types in New Hampshire I-12

2.4   Drainage basins and major water bodies I-13

2.5   New Hampshire physiographic regions I-14

2.6   Mean annual precipitation I-14

2.7   Normal mean temperature (July) I-14

2.8   Summer rainfall I-15

2.9   Length of growing season I-15

2.10   Distribution of human population I-15

Foreword

Difficult to imagine are the great strides that have been made in understanding the distribution and ecology of New Hampshire's's bird life in a mere 2 centuries. It was in 1792 that Jeremy Belknap, in his *History of New Hampshire*, published the first list of New Hampshire birds, a mere 122 species plus 8 others reported by a Mr. Peck.

Although Belknap included the Latin and English names of his birds, nomenclature had not yet been standardized, and determining the identity of some of the birds on Belknap's list today is a challenge. His reporting of the "Penguin *Alca impennis*" and "Wild Pigeon *Columba migratoria*" is well understood as referring to the now extinct Great Auk and Passenger Pigeon. Equally intriguing, however, is the listing of "Crested Titmouse *Parus bicolor*" and "Carolina Woodpecker *Picus carolinus*," which evidently referred to the Tufted Titmouse and Red-bellied Woodpecker, 2 species that present-day naturalists consider recent immigrants to New Hampshire.

For 90 years, Glover Allen's *Birds of New Hampshire,* published in 1903, has been the definitive work on the distribution, migration, and habitat requirements of birds of the Granite State. Allen's list of 287 species, remarkably complete for its time, has been out of print for more than half a century.

As New Hampshire residents became more concerned over declining bird populations, environmental pollution, and the ever increasing demands on the state's open spaces, the Audubon Society of New Hampshire (ASNH) established a committee to explore possibilities of conducting an intensive bird survey of the entire state. The aim was to map the present distribution of every breeding species. The prospect of being able to conduct, over a six-year period, a thorough search of 178 randomly selected Atlas blocks of 25 square kilometers each seemed overwhelming at first, because many blocks were in uninhabited roadless areas. Yet, the need was pressing; therefore, ASNH members quickly volunteered to give priority to the project, and field work started in 1981.

Thanks to the coordinated efforts of amateur and professional ornithologists, every priority Atlas block and other designated blocks with habitats of special concern were satisfactorily searched. The resulting maps are supplemented with up-to-date information on the ecology, life history, and habitat needs of each species. This information is from published and unpublished New Hampshire sources, supplemented, as necessary, with data from other states.

The volume provides the first quantitative baseline data on the distribution, relative abundance, and ecology of New Hampshire's breeding birds. Much new information is furnished on the status of the state's Endangered and Threatened species. Some birds are more widely distributed than previously believed; others are unexpectedly missing from former haunts. Information on population trends alerts the reader to species in need of special attention, and habitat data assist in pinpointing conservation priorities. Each species account is enlivened with a drawing by a New Hampshire artist.

The success of this project is a tribute to the coordinated efforts of the Audubon Society of New Hampshire, the University of New Hampshire, New Hampshire Fish and Game Department, U.S. Forest Service, U.S. Fish and Wildlife Service, William Wharton Conservation Trust, New England Electric System, New Hampshire Fund for Women, Ellis L. Phillips Fund, New Hampshire Council on Humanities, the National Fish and Wildlife Foundation and several other contributors. We congratulate the Atlas Committee (Kimball Elkins, Carol Foss, Dr. Donald and Eileen Miller, and Tudor Richards); the State Coordinators (Alis Kuhn Ohlheiser, 1981–84, and Sally Merrill Sutcliffe, 1984–1994); the field observers, authors, artists, peer reviewers, and editors; and the landowners of New Hampshire who recognized the importance of the project and willingly granted access to their fields and forests. All may share the pride of this accomplishment.

New Hampshire is not alone in producing a breeding bird atlas. Sister state, Vermont, published a similar atlas in 1985. More recent atlases have been published for Maine and the Maritime Provinces of Canada. Atlas field work has now been completed for all the other Northeastern states, and the results for Ontario, New York, Ohio, Pennsylvania, Michigan, Alberta, and Rhode Island are published.

Together these atlas projects are providing a priceless tool for landuse planning and for the protection of high priority wildlife habitats.

Chandler S. Robbins

U.S. Fish and Wildlife Service
Patuxent Wildlife Research Center
Laurel, Maryland

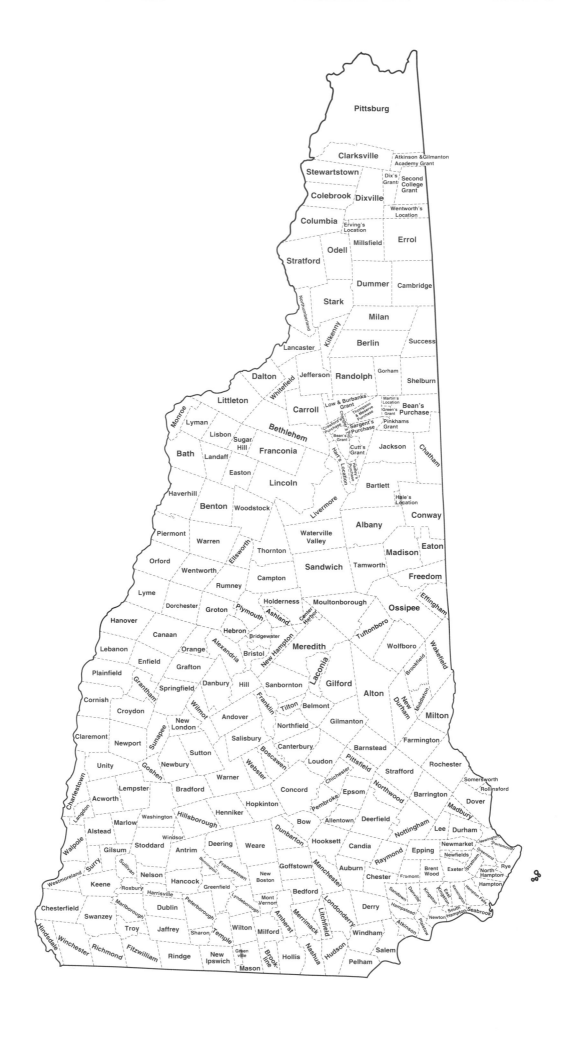

Acknowledgements

The New Hampshire Breeding Bird Atlas Project was sponsored by:
Department of Natural Resources, University of New Hampshire
Audubon Society of New Hampshire
New Hampshire Fish & Game Department

We deeply appreciate the financial contributions of the agencies, corporations, foundations, individuals, institutions, and organizations listed below, without whose support this project would not have been possible.

Anonymous
Ellis L. Phillips Foundation
Granite State Electric
National Fish & Wildlife Foundation
New England Electric System

New Hampshire Fund for Women
Dorothy B. Osborne
Peter Stettenheim
USDA Forest Service White Mountain National Forest
William P. Wharton Conservation Trust

The Atlas Committee
Kimball C. Elkins, Carol R. Foss, Donald Miller, Eileen Miller, Tudor Richards

Project Coordinators
Alis G. Kuhn Ohlheiser (1981-1984), Sally Merrill Sutcliffe (1984-1994)

Data Collection:

Regional Coordinators

Ralph Andrews, Thomas Bickel, Priscilla Didio, Kimball C. Elkins, Susan Fogleman, Wavell Fogleman, Carol R. Foss, George W. Gavutis, Jr., David Hoitt, George (Joe) Kent, David Killam, Deborah Kirwan, John Lanier, James McDermott, Harold P. (Flip) Nevers, Patrick O'Shaughnessy, Carleton Schaller, Steve Smith, Sally M. Sutcliffe, Sandra B. Turner, Robert Vernon, Marilyn Woodman.

Field volunteers

Dennis Abbott, Judi Abbott, Steve Abbott, Jane Abert, Karen Acerno, Rebecca Adams, Bob Addison, Susan Allen, Ellie Almstrom, Ralph Andrews, Tom Arter, Paul & Margaret Auger.

Nancy Bailey, Donald G. Baker, Vera Balch, Birgit Baldwin, Henry Baldwin, Dorothy Ball, Barbara Barrand, Jerome J. Barry, Mike Bauer, Irene Bay, Kay Beij, Barbara Benoit, Shirley Bentley, Barbara Benton, Adelaide Berdeen, Jim Berry, Tim Bertrand, Thomas Bickel, Elliot Birch, Richardson Blair, Ashton Bohanan, John D. Bonds, Arthur Borror, Mary Boswell, Sterling Brackett, Frankie Brackley, Bob Bradley, Doris Brainard, Jean Breed, Sally Brewer, Esther A. Brockelman, David Brooks, John Brooks, E. Brown, Maurice Brown, Edith Bunke, Anne Butler, Milton T. Butterworth.

Meade Cadot, Maxwell S. Campbell,Persis Campbell, Jr., Anne Carroll, Peggy Carter, Connie Casas, Linn Chao, Harriet Chaplin, Dana Charles, Robert H. Charnock, Michael Choukas, Neal Clark, Larry Clough, Mario Cohn-Haft, Albert A. Cole, Jr., Jeremy Coleman, Ken & Greta Collins, Les Corey, Alice Cormier, Annette & Bill Cottrell,

Gary Cress, Howard Crosby, Paul Crowley, Dorothy W. Crumb, Edwina Czajkowski.

Dorothy Day, John Day, Helen Dahl, Peggy Damon, Ray & Hildy Danforth, Rod & Carol Daugherty, Myra Davis, Barbara Delorey, Louise DeSousa, Mike & Priscilla Didio, Lala Dinsmore, Paul Doscher, Barbara Dowell, Sam Droege, Jim Duncan, Jessie Duston, Kay Dyment.

Francis Eames, Dave Eastman, Jean Eckhardt, Kimball C. Elkins, Margaret Ellis, Janice Ely, Edith Emery, Peggy Emery, Diane Evans.

Jeff Fair, Mary Farmat, Tony Federer, Davis Finch, Edith Finkel, Betty Fisher, Lynne Fitzsimmons, Bob Fox, Bob Flynn, Wavell & Susan A. Fogleman, Ken Folsom, Lynn Forsythe, Carol R. Foss, Tom French, Terry Frost, Dennis Furray, Denise Furtado.

Randy Gagne, Sally Gallagher, Ed Gardener, George W. Gavutis, Debi Giolito, Judy Golden, William Goodwill, Phoebe Googins, David Govatski, Richard Gracie, Jane Grant, Michael Greenwald, Cay Gregg, Frank & Eleanor Griffith, Tom Grogan, Ann Groth.

Bill Hancock, Lynn Harper, Norman & Joan Harris, Brian Hastings, Phyllis Hatch, Patricia Havumaki, Vin & Barbara Hayden, Carolyn Hayward, Vera Hebert, Bruce Hedin, Edie Hentcy, Keith Henney, Robert & Barbara Hilton, Peggy (Peters) Hines, Doris Hillier, Isabel Hoag, David Hoitt, The Holdens, Gloria Hotz, Lester Hotz, Richard Holmes, Jackie Howard, Paul B. Howes, Elizabeth Huggins.

Ginger Janenga, Augustis Janeway, Betsy & Harold Janeway, Willie Janeway, Guy Jaquith, Ron Joseph, Becky Johns, Mrs. Ray Johns, Curtis Jones, Mary Jones.

Field volunteers continued

Sean Kelly, Lydia Kennard, Ann Kent, David L. Kent, George N. Kent, David Killam, Hazel I. Killam, Alexandra Kilpatrick, Ann Kimball, Urling Kingery, Ralph Kirshner, Debbie Kirwan, Eugene Koch, Kevin Konieczny.

Carl Lacaillade, Paul LaCourse, Adelma Lajoie, Mary Lou Lambert, Lois Lamothe, John Lanier, Steve Lawrence, Connie Leighton, Cathy Leighty, Ted & Linny Levin, Jean Lockhart, Jody Longnecker, Lee Longnecker, Johanna Ludwig, L. Lutwack.

Gary McCool, Nancy McCool, Diann MacRae, Al Maley, Howard Mallett, Dave Mandell, Connie Manville, Hannah & Peter Martin, Marie Martin, Faith Mattison, Bonnie McCarthy, Jim McDermott, Micky McKinley, Jay McLaughlin, Jananne McNitt, Marta McWhorter, Malcolm & June Merrill, Marion Metcalf, Peggy Meyette, Alice Miksch, Donald & Eileen Miller, Steve Mirick, Bob Mitchell, Ed Morrier, Ruth Morris, Francesca Morrissey, John Morse, Louise P. Mullen, Marion Muller, Adair Mulligan, Diana Murphy, Mary Jo Murray, Frank Mynhan, Carolyn Myrick.

Harold P. Nevers, Gwen Newton, Jean Nichols, Karen Nielsen, Elizabeth Noel, Joe Noel, Robert Z. Norman, Frank Novak, Howard Nowell.

John O'Brien, Patrick O'Shaughnessy, Chet Ogan, Linda Ohlson, Alis Kuhn Ohlheiser.

Helen W. Parker, Northam Parr, Constance Patch, Claudia Payne, Chris Penniman, Elisabeth Phinney, Priscilla Phipps, Jean Polovchik, William C. Preston.

Robert Quinn.

Robert Rathbone, Barbara Rawson, Lorraine Rayburn, Bob Reeve, Grace N. Rhodes, Chris Ricardi, Barbara Richards, Tudor Richards, Beverly Ridgely, Robert Ridgely, Lawrence C.

Rising, Ann Robbins, Andrea & George Robbins, Chandler S. Robbins, Eleanor Robbins, William Roberts, Ed Robinson, Win Robinson, Clifford & Maida Rogers, T. Rogers, Pauline Roos, Dave Rowell, Debbie Rudis, Gordon Russell.

Jeanne Sargent, M. H. Sargent, Eloise Savi, Martha Schaffer, Carlton Schaller, Leo E. Schulten, Jr., Carl Schwartz, Doug Schwarz, Tom Sears, Pat Serrentino, Janice Smith Seufert, Mary Shields, Dorothy L. Skeels, John Skelton, Barbara Skuly, Alice Smith, Erna Smith, Mary Smith, Steve Smith, Arlene Soule, Particia Spenser, Raymond Sprague, Susan Absalom Staats, James Stalker, Karen Stan, J. Stark, Dawn Stavros, Elizabeth Steele, Frederic L. Steele, Roger Stephenson, Peter Stettenheim, Lea A. Stewart, Mrs. Stinson, The Stockmans, Mark & Becky Suomala, Carolyn Sutcliffe, Scott & Sally Merrill Sutcliffe, Gladys Sweetser, Guy A. Swenson, Jr., Byron Swift, Elizabeth F. Swift, Marjory Swope.

Charles & Jean Tewksbury, Andy Thompson, Sarah Thompson, Kim Titus, Roger Tournstrom, David Townsend, Clint Trefethen, Mark Turner, Sandra B. Turner.

Nancy Ulin, Harriet Underwood.

Tori Vallely, Henning Van der Lancken, Helen B. Varrieur, Arrolyn H. Vernon, Robert Vernon, Bette Verville, Jack & Jean Verville, Penny Verville.

Ted Walski, Ruth Walter, Jessie Ward, Tom Warren, Margaret Watkins, David Weber, Beverly Weeks, Annette Weinstroth, Gertrude Weir, Jane Westfall, Kenneth Whaley, Steve Wheeler, Ruth Wheldon, Jane White, Amy Whitlock, Johonet Wicks, Scot Williamson, Carolyn Van Wie, Joe Wiley, Marie Wolf, Brad Wood, Marilyn Woodman, Carleton A. Woodward, Mary Wright, Roy Wright, Vera Wright.

Peter Yankey, Jim Young, Jody Young.

Connie Zachman, Mike Zetteck, Michael Zwikelmaier.

Data Review Committee
Arthur C. Borror, Kimball C. Elkins, Robert A. Quinn, Tudor Richards.

Data Management Specialist
Chris Neefus

Computer Consultants:
James Cerney, William Costa, Chris Penniman

The following generously researched or provided additional data on New Hampshire breeding birds:
Arthur C. Borror, University of New Hampshire
Roger Clapp, U.S. Nat. Mus. of Nat. Hist., Washington, D.C.
George A. Clark, Jr., Univ. of Conn. Mus. of Nat. Hist.
Sam Droege, USFWS
Hannah Deweez, Montshire Museum, Norwich, Vt.
Greg Edinger, Bowman Hill Wildflower Preserve, Washington Crossing, Pa.
Kimball C. Elkins
Jeff Fair, Loon Preservation Committee (LPC)
Sean Kelly, USFWS
Lloyd Kiff, Western Foundation of Vertebrate Zoology, Los Angeles, Calif.

John Lanier, WMNF
Linny Levin, Montshire Museum
Loon Preservation Committee
June Merrill
Malcolm Merrill
Eileen Miller
NHFG Woodcock Survey
New Hampshire Natural Heritage Program
Cornell Laboratory of Ornithology, North American Nest Record Program
Kenneth C. Parkes, Carnegie Museum, Pittsburg, Pa.
Charles Platt, III
Betsy Poirier, LPC
Robert A. Quinn, ASNH
Tudor Richards
Chandler S. Robbins, Patuxent Wildlife Research Center, Laurel, Md.,
Edward Robinson, NHFG
Dawn B. Stavros, ASNH
Elizabeth F. Swift, ASNH
Theodore Walski, NHFG
D. Scott Wood, Carnegie Museum

Publication

Editor: Carol R. Foss
Associate Editors: Kimball C. Elkins, Donald Miller, Eileen Miller, Tudor Richards
Project Coordinators: Sally Merrill Sutcliffe, Alis G. Kuhn Ohlheiser
Technical Editor: Margaret B. Watkins
Publication Coordinator: Iain C. MacLeod
Word Processing: O. Douglas Schwarz, Janet Bourne

Contributing authors:
Ralph Andrews, Thomas H. Arter, Jim Berry, Rene M. Bollengier, Jr., Arthur C. Borror, Mario Cohn-Haft, Kimball C. Elkins, Diane Evans, Carol R. Foss, George W. Gavutis, Jr., Vera H. Hebert, Richard T. Holmes, Elizabeth C. Janeway, Lawrence Kilham, Harold C. Lacaillade, John Lanier, James McDermott, Iain C. MacLeod, Stephen R. Mirick, Harold P. Nevers, Tudor Richards, Andrea E. Robbins, Chandler S. Robbins, George C. Robbins, Edward G. Robinson, Patricia Serrentino, Thomas W. Sherry, Dennis Slate, Steve Smith, Susan Absalom Staats, Frederic L. Steele, Sally M. Sutcliffe, Elizabeth F. Swift, Sandra B. Turner, Robert C. Vernon, Charles Walcott, Theodore W. Walski, Margaret B. Watkins, Stephen H. Wheeler, Barry J. Wicklow.

Artists
Arthur C. Borror, William E. Davis, Jr., Susan Gonzalez Fogleman, Bea Gillette, Iain C. MacLeod, Eric Petersen, Andrea E. Robbins.

Text reviewers
Kenneth P. Able, Ralph Andrews, James Bendell, Gregory S. Butcher, Richard J. Clark, William E. Davis, Jr., Laura S. Deming, Ralph W. Dexter, William C. Dilger, William H. Drury, Erica H. Dunn, Kimball C. Elkins, R. Todd Engstrom, James D. Fraser, James Glidden, Jon S. Greenlaw, Michael J. Hamas, Frances N. Hamerstrom, Jerome A. Jackson, Ross D. James, Ellen D. Ketterson, Douglas P. Kibbe, Stephen W. Kress, John C. Kricher, Wesley E. Lanyon, Sarah B. Laughlin, Laurie H. MacIvor, Scott M. Melvin, Heinz Meng, M. Brooke Meanley, Tina M. Morris, Lynn Oliphant, David P. Olson, Wayne R. Petersen, Sergej Postupalski, Tudor Richards, Andrea E. Robbins, Chandler S. Robbins, Laird Shutt, Donald Slingerland, Charles R. Smith, C. Roy Smith, Walter R. Spofford, Peter Stettenheim, Scott A. Sutcliffe, Kimberly Titus, Nicholaas A. M. Verbeek, Daniel Welsh, D. Vaughn Weseloh.

Book design & layout
Iain C. MacLeod

Preliminary Cartography
Rodney Haywood

Map computerization and preparation
Iain C. MacLeod, Janet M. Bourne, Kathy Bouchard

Administrative support
Greta Collins, Paula Dimond, Lynn Harper, Edie Hentcy, Vicki Kerkel, Sandra B. Turner, Jean Verville, Roberta Whitlock

Proof-reading
Harold P. Nevers, O. Douglas Schwarz, M. Florence Randall, Marjorie Rolfe, Margaret B. Watkins

We deeply appreciate the use of office space, supplies, and equipment which have been provided by the Audubon Society of New Hampshire, the Cornell Laboratory of Ornithology, and the University of New Hampshire Wildlife Department during various phases of this project.

Special thanks are due Chan Robbins and Sally Laughlin for their leadership, guidance, and direct assistance through virtually every step of the process; to Tudor Richards and Kimball Elkins for their moral support, sage advice, and historical perspectives; to Doug Schwarz, Margaret Watkins, and Roberta Whitlock for their patience, perserverence, and untold hours of hard work during the many-staged editing process; and to Elizabeth Foss, Harold Hocker, June and Malcolm Merrill, Flip Nevers, Florence Randall, Isabel Rolfe, Marjorie Rolfe, and Scott Sutcliffe for various forms of logistical and moral support over the years.

The Atlas Committee wishes to thank the N.H. Department of Resources and Economic Development, Division of Parks, for enabling field staff to camp in State Park campgrounds at no cost during the block busting marathons of 1985 and 1986.

William Davis wishes to thank the Massachusetts Audubon Society for the loan of slides which served as models for many pen-and-ink drawings, and to the many photographers who contributed the slides to the Society's collection.

We especially want to thank the families and close friends of all who have been involved with the New Hampshire Breeding Bird Atlas for their patience, understanding, and sacrifices over the many years of this project. We also wish to acknowledge the individuals who quietly assisted this project behind the scenes, and whose names do not appear above.

Completion of the breeding bird atlas has been accomplished by donations of time and money from literally hundreds of individuals over a period of 14 years, spanning 3 different administrations at Audubon. We have done everything possible to give credit where credit is due. If we have left out anyone, please accept our apologies and let us know so that we can make amends in the next edition.

Atlas of BREEDING BIRDS IN NEW HAMPSHIRE

Introduction

by Carol R. Foss

&

Geography of New Hampshire

by Carol R. Foss

Figure 1.1 Priority Block Selection

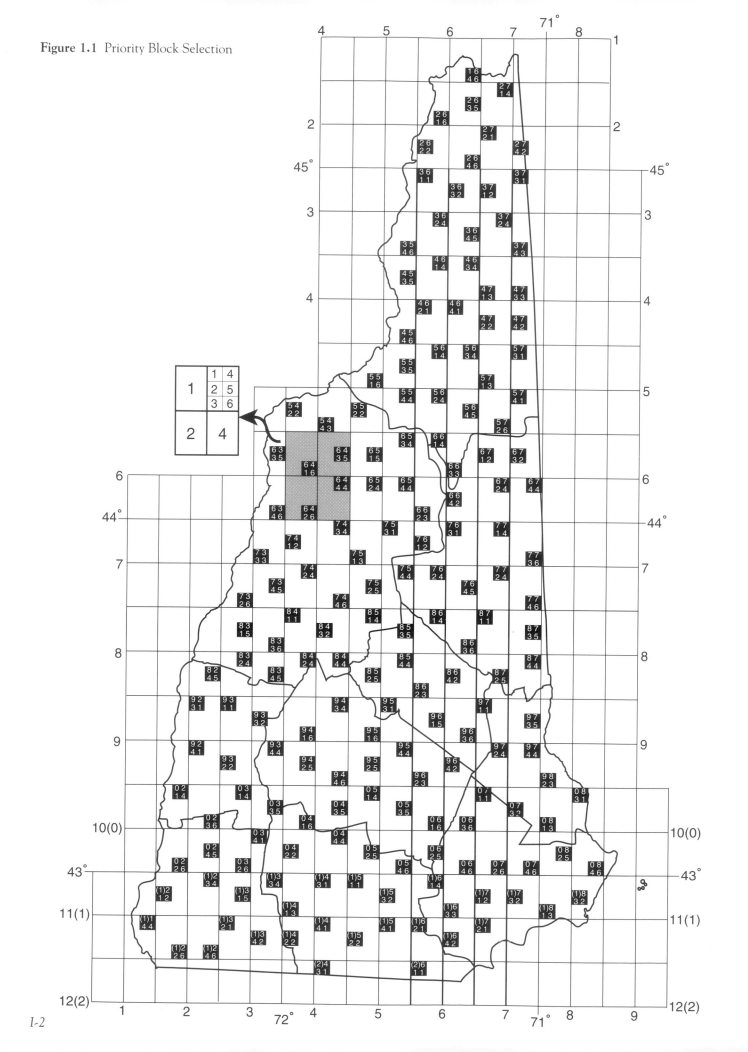

Introduction

The New Hampshire Breeding Bird Atlas (NHBBA) was a 6 year field study designed to determine the distribution of all bird species nesting within the boundaries of New Hampshire. This project followed the lead of the original breeding bird atlas effort in Great Britain (Sharrock 1976) and the concept's importation to North America (Laughlin and Kibbe 1985, Andrle and Carroll 1988).

Planning for the NHBBA began in 1980, when University of New Hampshire Wildlife Professor Donald Miller approached the Audubon Society of New Hampshire about collaborating on such a project. The idea met with enthusiasm from many quarters, a steering committee quickly formed, and preparations began for the first field season, conducted in 1981.

Methods

Grid Design

Survey blocks for the New Hampshire Breeding Bird Atlas were based on U.S. Geological Survey topographic maps covering 7.5 or 15 minutes of latitude and longitude. In areas of the state where 7.5-minute quadrangles were not available (primarily in northern New Hampshire), 15-minute quadrangles were bisected both horizontally and vertically to create 7.5-minute sections. Each 7.5-minute area was bisected longitudinally into 3.75-minute intervals and divided in thirds latitudinally into 2.5-minute intervals, forming 6 blocks of roughly equal size. This grid system generates 968 such blocks from the 62 15-minute topographic quadrangles which fall partially or entirely within the boundaries of the state.

Because New Hampshire extends over 2 degrees and 36 minutes of latitude, and longitude lines converge at the poles, the resulting blocks narrow in east-to-west dimension from south to north. Atlas blocks range in width from 3.21 mi (5.14 km) along the southern tier to 3.06 mi (4.90 km) at the northern tip of the state. The north-to-south dimension of Atlas blocks is consistently 2.87 mi (4.62 km). Total area of Atlas blocks ranges from 9.21 sq mi (23.75 sq km) for the southernmost blocks to 8.78 sq mi (22.64 sq km) for the northernmost.

Priority Blocks

As was the case in Vermont (Laughlin and Kibbe 1986), adequate personnel were not available to thoroughly cover all blocks, and a stratified random sample of priority blocks provided the focus for Atlas field work. This had the advantage of making our book comparable in most respects to *The Atlas of Breeding Birds of Vermont*, for which the field work was done according to a similar principle. Each 7.5-minute quadrangle with at least 50% of its area within New Hampshire qualified for priority block selection. Selections were made using a table of random numbers, with the stipulation that priority blocks in contiguous quadrangles could not touch. In several cases along the state border, areas of adjacent quadrangles were combined and were allowed one priority block to represent the combined areas. This selection process produced 178 priority blocks, representing approximately one sixth (16.7%) of the state's area. Figure 1.1 illustrates the priority blocks selected.

Special Areas

In addition to priority blocks, a number of "special areas" received particular attention from field volunteers. These areas comprised habitats in the state which were not well represented in priority blocks, and included: the Isles of Shoals; the mainland coast; the Great Bay estuary; the major complex of tidal rivers, including the Piscataqua and Salmon Falls rivers and Little Bay; several mountains above 2,500 ft (760 m) elevation in the southern part of the state, including Mt. Cardigan in Orange, Mt. Sunapee in Newbury, Mt. Kearsarge in Warner/Wilmot, and Mt. Monadnock in Jaffrey; the virgin spruce stand at Nancy Pond in the White Mountains; Whiteface Interval, a large, level area of extensive agricultural lands at the southern fringe of the White Mountains; a roughly 200 a (80 ha) protected area of mixed forest and wetland on the shore of Squam Lake; and several large wetland complexes, including East Inlet in Pittsburg, Church Pond Bog in Albany, and Danbury Bog and the Smith River meadows in Danbury. Figure 1.2 illustrates the locations of special areas, which are represented with triangles on the species maps.

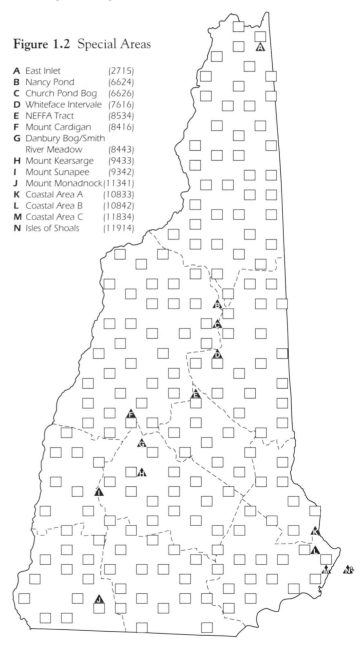

Figure 1.2 Special Areas

A East Inlet   (2715)
B Nancy Pond   (6624)
C Church Pond Bog   (6626)
D Whiteface Intervale   (7616)
E NEFFA Tract   (8534)
F Mount Cardigan   (8416)
G Danbury Bog/Smith
   River Meadow   (8443)
H Mount Kearsarge   (9433)
I Mount Sunapee   (9342)
J Mount Monadnock   (11341)
K Coastal Area A   (10833)
L Coastal Area B   (10842)
M Coastal Area C   (11834)
N Isles of Shoals   (11914)

Nonpriority Block Data

While Atlas field effort focused on priority blocks, the Atlas Committee actively solicited data from nonpriority blocks for rare, endangered, and secretive species, and accepted such data for other species as well. Available nonpriority block data is included in range-of-dates information presented on the map pages for all species, and is shown on the maps for 87 selected species. This data is available in the NH Breeding Bird Atlas data files at the Audubon Society of New Hampshire headquarters in Concord.

Project Administration

The Atlas Committee made the major policy decisions regarding the project throughout its duration. The project co-ordinators were responsible for coordinating implementation through the efforts of a dedicated corps of volunteers.

To facilitate coordination of the field effort, the state was divided into 20 regions, and experienced local birders were re-cruited to serve as regional coordinators. These invaluable in-dividuals recruited observers, matched observers with priority blocks, monitored progress towards coverage goals, generated and maintained local enthusiasm for the project, reviewed all field data for their region(s) annually, and provided the crucial link between the project coordinator and the field volunteers. Re-gional coordinators also were among the most dedicated field ob-servers, often taking on unclaimed blocks themselves when ad-equate numbers of local volunteers were lacking.

Breeding Codes

The basic premise of breeding bird "atlasing" is to deter-mine the likelihood that a species is nesting in a particular block as "possible," "probable," or "confirmed," by observing specific behaviors in the field. The breeding codes employed were adapted from those used by the British Trust for Ornithology (Sharrock 1976) and the Massachusetts Breeding Bird Atlas Project (unpubl.), and closely resemble the standardized codes subsequently recommended for North America (Laughlin et al. 1982) and those adopted by the North American Ornithologi-cal Atlas Committee (Sutcliffe et al. 1986). Breeding codes are detailed below, presented in order from least certain ("Possible") to most certain ("Confirmed"). The "Sighted" category enabled reporting of migratory overshoots, transients, early or late mi-grants, or other individuals for which there was no evidence of breeding activity. Species distribution maps published in this Atlas do not include "Sighted" records.

Breeding Codes

SI   "Sighted"
- o: species observed during its breeding season, but not in potential breeding habitat

PO   "Possible" breeding
- ✓:   individual observed in possible nesting habitat
- ♪:   singing male; OR courtship display of waterfowl or diurnal raptors

PR   "Probable" breeding
- P: pair observed in possible nesting habitat
- T: territory presumed from observations of territorial behavior
- C: courtship and display

- N: visiting probable nest site
- A: agitated behavior or anxiety calls
- B: brood patch or cloacal protuberance
- E: excavating nest hole: OR nest building by wrens

CO   "Confirmed" breeding
- DD: distraction display
- NB: nest building for species other than wrens
- UN: used nest
- FL: recently fledged young
- ON: adult leaving or entering cavity indicating occupied nest; OR adult on nest
- FF: adult carrying food or fecal sac
- NE: nest containing eggs
- NY: nest with young

Asterisk Species

Substantiating evidence was required for "probable" and "confirmed" records of selected species which were considered rare or of unknown breeding status in the state. "Asterisk Spe-cies Report Forms" (ASRFs) requested details about observation conditions, habitat, and field marks observed.

The Atlas Committee designated 80 species for ASRF submission. Observers documented 68 of those species (indicated with an asterisk [*] in the list below) during the Atlas project.

Species for which an ASRF was required included:

*Pied-billed Grebe Great Egret *Snowy Egret Cattle Egret Tri-colored Heron *Little Blue Heron *Green Heron *Black-crowned Night-Heron *Least Bittern *Glossy Ibis Gadwall *Green-winged Teal *Blue-winged Teal Northern Shoveler Red-breasted Merganser *Turkey Vulture *Sharp-shinned Hawk *Cooper's Hawk *Golden Eagle *Bald Eagle *Northern Harrier *Peregrine Falcon *Merlin *Northern Bobwhite King Rail *Clapper Rail *Virginia Rail *Sora Yellow Rail *Common Gallinule *Piping Plover *Upland Sandpiper *Wilson's Phalar-ope *Common Snipe *Ring-billed Gull *Common Tern *Arc-tic Tern Roseate Tern *Least Tern *Black Tern *Black Guil-lemot Barn Owl *Eastern Screech-Owl *Long-eared Owl Short-eared Owl *Common Nighthawk *Red-headed Woodpecker Red-bellied Woodpecker *Black-backed Woodpecker *Three-toed Woodpecker *Alder Flycatcher *Willow Flycatcher *Horned Lark *Rough-winged Swallow *Cliff Swallow *Purple Martin *Common Raven Carolina Wren *Marsh Wren *Sedge Wren *Blue-gray Gnatcatcher *Water Pipit *Loggerhead Shrike *White-eyed Vireo *Philadelphia Vireo *Golden-winged War-bler *Blue-winged Warbler *Tennessee Warbler *Cape May Warbler *Cerulean Warbler *Worm-eating Warbler *Palm Warbler *Louisiana Waterthrush *Pine Grosbeak *Red Cross-bill *Grasshopper Sparrow *Henslow's Sparrow *Sharp-tailed Sparrow *Seaside Sparrow *Vesper Sparrow

Goals & Standards for Field Effort and Coverage

The Atlas Committee adopted the standard set by the Vermont Breeding Bird Atlas project (Laughlin and Kibbe 1985) of considering a block adequately covered if 75 species had been recorded in the block and 35 of them had been "confirmed." This standard is based on the assumption that on average, about 100 species are likely to occur in any given block, and documentation of 75% of those species constitutes adequate coverage. This level of coverage is now generally accepted for the majority of breeding bird atlas projects in North America (Robbins and Geissler 1990).

While 100 likely represents a reasonable average of the number of species expected to breed in New Hampshire priority blocks, the number of breeding species certainly is larger in blocks with considerable habitat diversity, especially those in the southern part of the state. Conversely, heavily forested northern blocks would be expected to support fewer species of breeding birds.

Ideally, adequate coverage involved multiple visits to a block encompassing different stages of the breeding season and including time spent in all habitats present. Establishing, much less meeting such standards for every priority block was not feasible during this project.

Field Methods

Atlas field methods can be almost as varied as the species to be surveyed. The most commonly used method involves spending time in all the habitats present in a block, typically in the early morning hours between late May and early July, and observing the behavior of all birds encountered to determine their breeding status. While this approach is effective for the majority of species, thorough coverage of a block requires additional techniques. Crepuscular species such as American Woodcock, Common Nighthawk, and Whip-poor-will require evening visits. Owls are most reliably detected using nocturnal broadcasts of tape-recorded vocalizations, preferably in late winter. Broadcasts also provide the most effective means of detecting secretive marsh birds, such as rails and bitterns. "Confirmation" of most raptor species requires focused observation in appropriate habitat. Winter inspection of duck boxes can provide "confirmation" of Common Goldeneye, Hooded Merganser, and Wood Duck breeding from identification of eggshell fragments. Periodic newsletters mailed to Atlas participants provided suggestions on field methods and reminders to check for particular species at appropriate times.

Block Busting

For some remote blocks for which no local volunteers were available, coverage was achieved through "block busting." This approach involves recruitment of a number of volunteers who meet at the block on a given day and cover different portions of the block simultaneously, working as indiviuals or in small groups. Most blocks surveyed in this manner received a minimum of 2 block-busting visits. Block-busting visits were the primary or only source of Atlas data for a number of blocks in the southwestern and northern parts of the state.

Other Data Sources

A number of field studies on various species of New Hampshire birds were underway during the Atlas period, and project leaders were kind enough to allow incorporation of their data into the Atlas database. These projects included statewide surveys of Common Nighthawks, Whip-poor-wills, Peregrine Falcons, Ospreys, Bald Eagles, Common Terns, Upland Sandpipers, and Northern Harriers overseen by the New Hampshire Endangered Species Program, a cooperative project of NHFG and ASNH from 1981 to 1990; a Great Blue Heron rookery

inventory overseen by ASNH; duck box, waterfowl brood, Wild Turkey, and American Woodcock surveys overseen by NHFG; and Common Loon breeding surveys overseen by the Loon Preservation Committee (LPC).

Data Processing and Quality Control

At the conclusion of each field season, observers checked their field cards for entry errors, and regional coordinators reviewed all field cards for the priority blocks within their regions before forwarding them to the project coordinator. The regional coordinator or project coordinator transferred data for each priority block from field cards to a master summary sheet, and returned master summary sheets to regional coordinators for final review and editing.

The Data Review Committee reviewed each year's master summary sheets after each field season, prior to data entry, and identified species or habitats to target during subsequent field work in each block as well as questionable records requiring further documentation.

After all field work and data entry were completed, the Data Review and Atlas committees reviewed each species map and inspected documentation for all unusual or questionable records. Additional details were requested from observers as deemed necessary to accept or reject these records.

The computerized Atlas data is now stored at the New Hampshire Fish & Game Department headquarters in Concord. Access to the raw data may be granted with written permission from the Audubon Society of New Hampshire. Individuals may request such access in writing, and should include a detailed project proposal and justification.

Results and Discussion

Coverage and Field Effort

Field work for the New Hampshire Breeding Bird Atlas took place from 1981 to 1986. During this period, more than 390 observers logged in excess of 9,750 hours of field time, and generated more than 36,900 data records. All 178 priority blocks were visited in at least one year, and 86% of the priority blocks were visited in at least 3 years. Figure 1.5 presents the geographic distribution of priority block coverage by number of years visited; Table 1.1 summarizes block coverage and results by number of years visited; and Appendix C provides detail on years of coverage for individual priority blocks.

Table 1.1 Summary of Atlas results by number of years in which priority blocks were visited

# Yrs. Visited	# pri. blocks	Tot. spp. detected			Tot. spp. confirmed		
		Max	Min	Mean	Max	Min	Mean
1	6(3%)	79	38	69.3	43	13	30.8
2	25(14%)	102	62	81.2	55	22	39.4
3	45(25%)	107	43	78.8	64	14	35.9
4	39(22%)	109	53	86.4	64	20	42.2
5	55(31%)	118	42	89.0	92	13	46.2
6	8(4%)	107	80	92.5	64	41	48.4

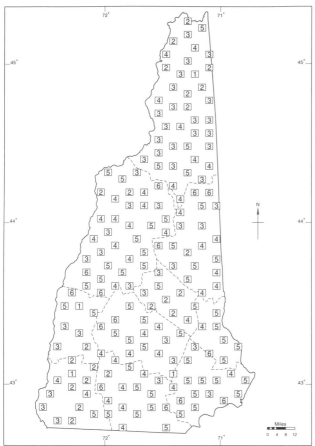

Figure 1.3 Years of effort per priority block

Documentation of hours of Atlas effort did not occur uniformly across blocks. While figures are reasonably accurate for blocks atlased during specific field trips or block-busting expeditions, blocks in which observers lived, worked, or visited frequently for other reasons gained records from serendipitous observations. For a few blocks, field time data was not recorded. Thus, the following analysis of hours of effort should be considered a general indication rather than an accurate assessment.

The mean hours of effort for the 174 priority blocks for which at least some time was documented was 56.07 hours. Of the 25 blocks with more than 100 documented hours of effort, 4 had in excess of 200 hours; the maximum was 320 hours. Figure 1.4 presents the geographic distribution of priority block coverage by documented hours of effort; Table 1.3 summarizes block coverage and results by documented hours; and Appendix C provides detail on documented hours of effort for individual priority blocks.

Table 1.3 Summary of Atlas results by documented hours of effort

Documented Hours	# pbs	Tot. spp. detected Max	Min	Mean	Tot. spp. confirmed Max	Min	Mean
<25	48	102	43	79.7	54	14	36.1
25-49.9	60	107	38	81.5	54	13	38.5
50-99.9	45	107	42	85.4	64	13	42.0
>=100	25	118	75	97.2	92	39	57.0

Mean years visited across all priority blocks was 3.9. Because New Hampshire's human population is largely concentrated in the southeastern part of the state, Atlas coverage was not evenly distributed geographically. Cheshire County, in the southwestern corner of the state, had the lowest mean years of visitation at 2.7, while Strafford County, in the southeast, had the highest at 5.0. Table 1.2 summarizes mean years visited by county.

Table 1.2 Summary by county of mean years in which priority blocks were visited

County	Total Priority blocks	1	2	3	4	5	6	Mean
Belknap	9	0	4	2	1	2	0	3.1
Carroll	19	0	1	4	6	5	3	4.3
Cheshire	13	1	6	3	2	1	0	2.7
Coos	40	1	7	20	8	4	0	3.2
Grafton	34	0	2	7	11	11	3	4.2
Hillsborough	18	0	1	1	7	7	2	4.4
Merrimack	16	1	0	2	5	6	2	4.3
Rockingham	14	0	0	2	1	9	2	4.8
Strafford	7	0	0	0	1	5	1	5.0
Sullivan	8	1	1	3	0	2	1	3.9

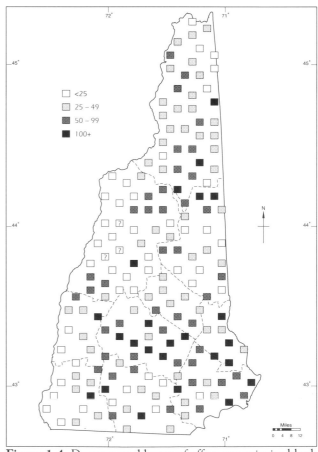

Figure 1.4 Documented hours of effort per priority block

As with the number of years in which blocks were visited, level of Atlas effort as indicated by documented hours of coverage was not evenly distributed. More than half the priority blocks in Merrimack, Rockingham, and Strafford counties received at least 50 documented hours of effort, while fewer than half the priority blocks in the other counties received this level of effort. Of the 25 priority blocks with more than 100 documented hours of effort, 71% were in the 4 southeastern counties, and 32% were in Merrimack County alone. Of the 48 blocks with less than 25 documented hours of effort, 70.9% were in the 3 northern counties, and 42% were in Grafton County alone.

Level of effort was highest overall in Merrimack County, where observers spent more than 100 hours in 50% of priority blocks, and more than 50 hours in 87.5% of priority blocks. Level of effort was lowest in Cheshire County, where observers spent less than 25 documented hours in 46.1% of priority blocks and less than 50 hours in 84.6% of priority blocks, and in Grafton County, where observers spent less than 25 hours in 58.8% of priority blocks and less than 50 hours in 73.5% of priority blocks. Table 1.4 summarizes documented hours of effort by county.

Table 1.4 Summary by county of documented hours of effort

County	# of Priority Blocks	Documented hours of effort			
		<25	25-49.9	50-99.9	>=100
Belknap	9	0	6(66.7%)	3(33.3%)	0
Carroll	19	7(36.8%)	5(26.3%)	5(26.3%)	2(10.5%)
Cheshire	13	6(46.1%)	5(38.5%)	1(7.7%)	1(7.7%)
Coos	40	7(17.5%)	21(52.5%)	9(22.5%)	3(7.5%)
Grafton	34	20(58.8%)	5(14.7%)	8(23.5%)	1(2.9%)
Hillsborough	18	5(27.8%)	6(33.3%)	4(22.2%)	3(16.7%)
Merrimack	16	0	2(12.5%)	6(37.5%)	8(50.0%)
Rockingham	14	1(7.1%)	4(28.6%)	7(50.0%)	2(14.3%)
Strafford	7	0	2(28.6%)	1(14.3%)	4(57.1%)
Sullivan	8	2(25.0%)	4(50.0%)	1(12.5%)	1(12.5%)

In addition to number of visits and length of time spent, timing of visits also can affect atlas results. While the ideal of multiple visits spaced across the breeding seasons of all native species was achieved for some blocks (observers gathered data in 32 priority blocks [18%] during 6-8 different months), most blocks fell short of this ideal. Since some breeding activity for most species occurs during May-July, visits in each of those months usually can provide adequate coverage for a block. This atlas project achieved good phenological coverage, with only 17 priority blocks (9%) visited in only one or 2 different months. Table 1.5 summarizes effort by number of months in which field work took place; Appendix C provides details on months in which individual blocks were visited.

Table 1.5 Summary of number of months in which priority blocks were visited

	Number of months in which block was visited							
	1	2	3	4	5	6	7	8
Number of Blocks	4	13	39	39	50	21	11	1

Species

The Atlas field effort obtained breeding evidence for 204 species, and "confirmed" breeding for 176. This project generated New Hampshire's first breeding "confirmations" for 6 species: Black Guillemot, Willet, Turkey Vulture, Fish Crow, Acadian Flycatcher, and Seaside Sparrow. Species previously known to breed in the state which were observed but not "confirmed" during the Atlas period include:

Black-crowned Night-Heron
Least Bittern
Green-winged Teal
Golden Eagle
Bald Eagle
Northern Bobwhite
Arctic Tern
Least Tern
Long-eared Owl
Three-toed Woodpecker
Sedge Wren
Loggerhead Shrike
White-eyed Vireo
Palm Warbler
Pine Grosbeak
White-winged Crossbill
Henslow's Sparrow

Observers documented breeding season activity, but not breeding "confirmation" of a number of species for which there are no documented breeding records for New Hampshire. These include:

Snowy Egret
Little Blue Heron
Glossy Ibis
Clapper Rail
Wilson's Phalarope
Ring-billed Gull
Black Tern
American Pipit
Cerulean Warbler
Worm-eating Warbler

Two species, Merlin and American Pipit, were documented as "possible" or "probable" breeders during the Atlas and have been "confirmed" in the years since Atlas field work was completed.

Only one species, the Black-capped Chickadee, was recorded in all 178 priority blocks; all but one priority block have records for Blue Jay, Cedar Waxwing, Red-eyed Vireo, and American Robin. Table 1.6 summarizes the distribution of species by frequency of detection in priority blocks. Table 1.7 presents species which were documented in more than 50% of priority blocks. Within each percentage category, species are listed in order of increasing frequency of records, with species recorded most frequently within each category at the bottom of the column.

Table 1.6 Distribution of species by frequency of detection in priority blocks

# of priority blocks	% of priority blocks	Number of species
1-17	1-10%	50
18-45	10-25%	28
46-89	26-50%	25
90-134	51-75%	25
135-161	76-90%	29
162-177	91-99%	28
178	100%	1

Table 1.7 Summary of occurrence frequency for species documented in more than 50% of priority blocks

Number and (%) of priority blocks with records for species

90-134 (51-75%)	135-161 (76-90%)	162-177 (91-100%)
Common Raven	Great Blue Heron	Broad-winged Hawk
Wood Duck	Pileated Woodpecker	Ruffed Grouse
Barred Owl	Swamp Sparrow	Eastern Wood-Pewee
Bank Swallow	Dark-eyed Junco	Least Flycatcher
Spotted Sandpiper	Yellow Warbler	American Goldfinch
Field Sparrow	Canada Warbler	Wood Thrush
Eastern Bluebird	Mourning Dove	Yellow-rumped Warbler
Mallard	Brown Creeper	Common Grackle
Warbling Vireo	Solitary Vireo	Chimney Swift
American Kestrel	Blackburnian Warbler	Scarlet Tanager
Alder Flycatcher	Black-throated Blue Warbler	Tree Swallow
Northern Waterthrush	European Starling	Black-and-White Warbler
Brown Thrasher	Brown-headed Cowbird	Northern Flicker
American Woodcock	Northern Oriole	Downy Woodpecker
American Black Duck	Great Crested Flycatcher	Veery
Red-tailed Hawk	Nashville Warbler	Purple Finch
Killdeer	Black-throat Green Warbler	Song Sparrow
House Wren	Barn Swallow	Chestnut-sided Warbler
House Sparrow	Ruby-thr. Hummingbird	Rose-breasted Grosbeak
Rufous-sided Towhee	Eastern Kingbird	American Redstart
Magnolia Warbler	Red-breasted Nuthatch	Ovenbird
Winter Wren	White-breasted Nuthatch	Common Yellowthroat
Bobolink	Belted Kingfisher	White-throated Sparrow
Yellow-bellied Sapsucker	Eastern Phoebe	Hairy Woodpecker
Indigo Bunting	Red-winged Blackbird	Blue Jay
	American Crow	Cedar Waxwing
	Chipping Sparrow	American Robin
	Hermit Thrush	Red-eyed Vireo
	Gray Catbird	Black-capped Chickadee

The minimum, maximum, and mean numbers of species detected in a single priority block were 38, 118, and 84.2, respectively. Minimum, maximum, and mean numbers of species "confirmed" in a single priority block were 13, 92, and 41.3, respectively. Figure 1.5 presents the number of species documented in each priority block. Figure 1.6 presents the number of species "confirmed" in each priority block. Table 1.8 summarizes distribution of priority blocks by number of species detected and number of species "confirmed." Appendix C provides numbers of species recorded as "possible," "probable," and "confirmed" for individual priority blocks.

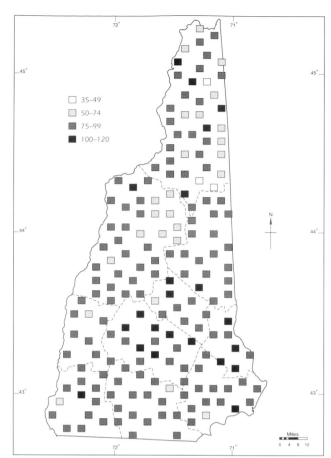

Figure 1.5 Number of species detected per priority block

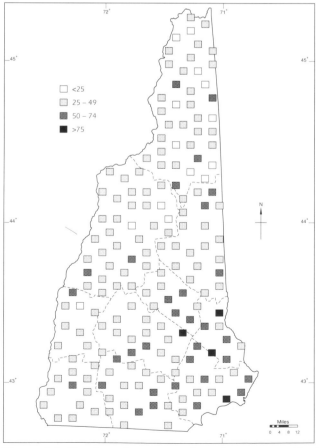

Figure 1.6 Number of species confirmed per priority block

Table 1.8 Distribution of priority blocks by number of species detected and number of species confirmed.

Number of species	10–19	20–29	30–39	40–49	50–59	60—69	70–79	80–89	90–99	100–109	110-119
# of priority blocks (total species)			1	2	8	15	31	61	38	20	2
# of blocks (confirmed species)	5	19	68	52	22	7	2	2	1		

Analyzed by county, the mean number of species documented per priority block ranged from 75 to 102. County averages were highest in central New Hampshire and lowest in the northern part of the state. Strafford, Merrimack, and Belknap counties produced the highest means, and Coos and Grafton counties the lowest. Maximum numbers of species detected per priority block for each county ranged from 96 to 118, with a mean of 105.2. This data showed no clear geographic pattern. Mean number of "confirmed" species per block ranged from 35 to 48. The geographic pattern was similar to that for mean total species, but the mean for Rockingham County exceeded those for Merrimack and Belknap counties. Table 1.9 summarizes data on number of detected and "confirmed" species per block by county.

Table 1.9 Species detected and confirmed per priority block summarized by county.

County	Blocks	Tot. spp. detected			Tot. spp. confirmed		
		Max	Min	Mean	Max	Min	Mean
Belknap	9	102	73	92.6	58	35	45.0
Carroll	19	102	77	86.4	62	35	42.8
Cheshire	13	101	69	80.9	55	29	39.7
Coos	40	109	22	75.2	55	13	35.0
Grafton	34	101	52	79.4	62	15	35.6
Hillsborough	18	96	74	87.2	64	29	44.3
Merrimack	16	118	78	94.7	76	31	45.4
Rockingham	14	117	68	87.6	92	38	48.7
Strafford	7	109	94	101.9	86	41	62.6
Sullivan	8	97	65	82.6	64	24	41.8

Space does not permit analysis in this volume of Atlas results with the various climatological and physiographic data sets available. This information will be published as a separate appendix which can be ordered from the Audubon Society of New Hampshire, 3 Silk Farm Road, Concord, NH 03301. We include in Table 1.10 a summary of results by length of growing season, which is of particular interest in a state with New Hampshire's range of elevation and latitude. As one would expect, number of species documented in priority blocks was directly correlated with the length of the growing season. Species occurrence by length of growing season will be available in the separately published appendix.

Table 1.1 Species detected per priority block summarized by length of growing season

Length of growing season (days)	≤105	105-120	110-120	120-140
Number of species documented	132	150	168	170

Biases and Limitations

A number of biases and limitations are common to atlas surveys which affect the quality of the final results. These include differences in observer ability, in level and timing of effort, and in abundance and detectability of the species being surveyed. Differences in detectability biased the survey against species which are rare, secretive, nocturnal, or early season nesters. These species were especially likely to be missed in blocks with limited effort, and those surveyed by block busting. Inclusion of data from other sources enhanced the final results for a number of rare and difficult to detect species, but introduced another source of bias in itself. Issues of detectability and inclusion of additional data are discussed in the pertinent species accounts.

Factors affecting level of effort include accessibility of blocks and of different habitats within blocks, number of observers living in or near blocks, and popularity of blocks as birding areas. These factors were particularly evident in New Hampshire, where effort was highest in the heavily populated southeastern part of the state. Despite the remoteness of many northern priority blocks, average effort in northern New Hampshire exceeded that in the southwestern part of the state. The opportunity to observe boreal species and the lure of wilderness attracted volunteers to northern blocks from long distances and often for extended stays. Southwestern blocks lacked similar allure. While summarizing results by county helps to mitigate the effects of coverage differences among blocks, the regional biases persist at the county level.

Areas of New Hampshire with lower habitat diversity and more severe climate are roughly correlated with areas of lower Atlas effort. Thus the relative effects of these factors on Atlas results are difficult to separate. Table 1.11 presents county information on effort, expressed as the percentage of a county's priority blocks with more than 50 documented hours of effort, and results for interested readers to compare and ponder.

Table 1.11 County summary of Atlas effort and results

County	Blocks	Mean Tot. Spp.	Max. Tot. Spp.	Mean CO Spp.	Effort Level
Belknap	9	93	102	45	33%
Carroll	19	86	102	42	37%
Cheshire	13	81	101	40	15%
Coos	40	75	109	35	30%
Grafton	34	86	101	36	26%
Hillsborough	18	87	96	44	39%
Merrimack	16	95	118	45	88%
Rockingham	14	88	117	48	64%
Strafford	7	102	109	63	71%
Sullivan	8	83	97	42	25%

Readers should constantly bear in mind that results reflect only what observers documented during the course of this project, and that the lack of a record for a given species in a given block does not necessarily imply the absence of that species in that block.

The Species Accounts

The species accounts in this book include several elements. Treatment of most species includes an illustration, text account, map, and data summary. Additional species, including historically nesting species not documented during the Atlas and those for which only "possible" records were obtained are treated at the end with a text account and, where appropriate, a small map. The text of the accounts provides basic habitat and natural history information about each species, as well as a synopsis of the species' history in New Hampshire and a discussion of Atlas results. The accompanying maps show priority (and in some cases, nonpriority) blocks and Special Areas in which the species was documented as a "possible," "probable," or "confirmed" breeder. The data summary includes the number of priority blocks in which the species was documented as "possible," "probable," or "confirmed," and the range of dates and number of records obtained for selected breeding codes.

References

Andrle, R.F. and J.R. Carroll, eds. 1988. The atlas of breeding birds of New York State. Cornell University Press, Ithaca, N.Y.

Laughlin, S.B., ed. 1982. Proc. Northeastern Breeding Bird Atlas Conference. Vermont Institute of Natural Science, Woodstock, Vt.

Laughlin, S.B. and D. Kibbe, eds. 1985. The atlas of breeding birds of Vermont. University Press of New England, Hanover, N.H.

Robbins, C.S. and P.H. Geissler. 1990. Survey methods and mapping grids. pp. 4.1-4.2 in C.R. Smith, ed. Handbook for atlasing American breeding birds. Vermont Institute of Natural Science, Woodstock, Vt.

Sharrock, J.T.R. 1976. The atlas of breeding birds in Great Britain and Ireland. T. & A.D. Poyser, Staffordshire, England.

Sutcliffe, S.M., R.E. Bonney, Jr., and J.D. Lowe, comps. 1986. Proc. Second Northeastern Breeding Bird Atlas Conference, April 25-27, 1986. Cornell University Press, Ithaca, N.Y.

Geography of New Hampshire

Carol R. Foss

New Hampshire, one of 6 states in the New England region, is a small, roughly triangular state in the northeastern U.S. (see Figure 2.1). It is bounded on the east by Maine, on the north by Quebec, Canada, on the west by Vermont, on the south by Massachusetts, and on the southeast by the Atlantic Ocean. Covering an area of 9,304 sq mi (3,592 sq km), the state extends roughly 180 mi (112 km) north to south. Elevations range from sea level to 6,288 ft (1,905 m).

Geological history

New Hampshire's present-day landforms are the product of a series of geological processes, including a major mountain-building episode more than 200 million years ago, a period of uplift within the last 8 million years, and the Wisconsin glaciation, which peaked 18-20,000 years ago, and covered the state's tallest mountains with ice (Jorgensen 1977, Van Diver 1987).

New Hampshire's bedrock consists largely of metamorphic shists and gneisses with origins 250-600 million years ago, and extensive areas of intrusive rocks, primarily granite, with origins 150-500 million years ago (Jorgensen 1977). Bedrock lies within 20 ft of the surface over much of the region.

The land

The topography of New Hampshire is hilly to mountainous, with a relatively small area of coastal plain. The Pemigewasset and Merrimack rivers nearly bisect the southern half of the state, separating highlands to the west from uplands to the east. Mountains in southern New Hampshire are isolated and relatively low. The most significant include: Mt. Monadnock, Jaffrey, at 3,165 ft (965 m); Mt. Cardigan, Orange, at 3,122

ft (952 m); Mt. Kearsage, Warner/Wilmot, at 2,937 ft (896 m); and Mt. Sunapee, at 2,743 ft (837 m). Further north, the White Mountains and Northern Highlands include 182 peaks exceeding 3,000 ft (915 m) in elevation, 10 of which exceed 5,000 ft (1,525 m). Figure 2.2 illustrates land elevations for the state.

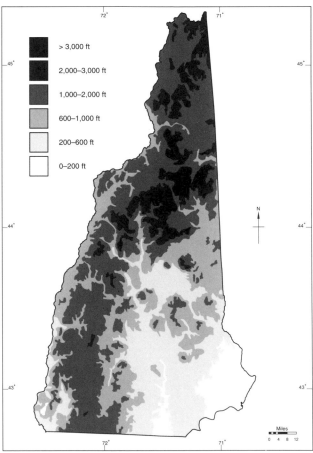

Figure 2.2 New Hampshire land elevations
(Source: N.H. Office of State Planning)

Soils are mostly of granite origin and are fairly acidic. Much of the state's area is covered by glacial tills, which are sandy in some areas and loamy in others. New Hampshire soils are very rocky, and contain a wide size range of stones and boulders. Productive soils occur primarily in the major river valleys, and consist of loamy or silty deposits from glacial runoff and postglacial floods.

Soil scientists recognize 4 soil orders (Spodosols, Inceptisols, Histosols, and Entisols) and 22 soil areas in New Hampshire (Pilgrim and Peterson 1979). Readers interested in detailed soil information are referred to Pilgrim and Peterson (1979) and more recent soil survey information available from the USDA Soil Conservation Service.

The natural vegetation over most of New Hampshire's upland area is forest of various types; exceptions include areas of

Figure 2.1 United States showing location of New Hampshire

alpine vegetation on the summits of higher peaks, and a small area of coastal sand dunes, much of which has been destroyed. While some upland areas are developed or in agricultural uses, the state presently is 86% forested (N.H. Div. For. and Lands 1980).

New Hampshire supports 8 major forest types: white pine/ red pine, spruce/fir, pitch pine, oak/pine, oak/hickory, elm/ash/ red maple, maple/beech/birch, and aspen/gray birch (Kingsley 1976). New Hampshire forests include more than 50 tree species, and considerable diversity exists within and among stands. The most common native trees include: balsam fir; eastern red cedar; white and red spruces; red and eastern white pines; eastern hemlock; red and sugar maples; American beech; yellow, black, and paper birches; white ash; eastern hophornbeam; bigtooth and quaking aspens; black cherry; white, northern red, and black oaks; and American elm (Kingsley 1977). Growing conditions and land use history can vary widely across relatively short distances, which increases forest diversity at the landscape scale. Figure 2.3 provides a general picture of major forest type distribution in New Hampshire.

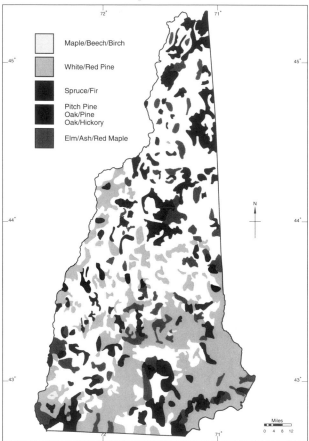

Figure 2.3 Distribution of major forest types in New Hampshire (Source: Kingsley 1973)

The waters

New Hampshire is rich in water resources, with about 40,000 mi (24,860 km) of rivers and streams (Division of Forests and Lands 1980), of which 1,227 mi (763.5 km) are fourth order streams (GRANIT GIS), and 780 great ponds (ie. lakes and ponds with a surface area of at least 10 a [4 ha]) (N.H. Dept. Resources and Economic Development 1977). The state has 5 major drainage basins, all of which extend into neighboring states. Figure 2.4 illustrates New Hampshire's drainage basins and major water bodies. Table 2.1 provides the areas of drainage basins within the state.

Table 2.1 Drainage basins

Drainage basin	Area in sq mi (sq km)	% of state
Androscoggin	743 (1,924)	8
Coastal	848 (2,196)	9
Connecticut	3,059 (7,923)	33
Merrimack	3,770 (9,764)	41
Saco	862 (2,233)	9

Lake Winnipesaukee is New Hampshire's largest water body, covering 44,586 a (17,834 ha). Squam and Umbagog lakes exceed 5,000 a (2,000 ha) in area. Table 2.2 summarizes the size distribution of New Hampshire lakes and ponds by county. Freshwater wetlands occur throughout the state, accounting for 1–2% of its area. Forested wetlands predominate, followed by scrub-shrub and emergent types.

Table 2.2 Size distribution of lakes and ponds by county

County	Size (acres)							
	10-24.9	25-49.9	50-149.9	150-299.9	300-499.9	500-999.9	1,000 & over	Total
Belknap	20	13	11	8	4	1	3	60
Carroll	31	14	25	9	5	4	5	93
Cheshire	30	24	26	13	1	4	0	98
Coos	17	20	15	8	2	0	4	66
Grafton	34	24	19	4	6	1	4	92
Hillsboro	29	31	17	7	3	1	0	88
Merrimack	44	36	20	10	3	2	0	115
Rockingham	30	15	16	9	4	2	1	77
Strafford	8	7	13	5	2	1	2	38
Sullivan	20	9	19	4	0	0	1	53
TOTAL	**263**	**193**	**181**	**77**	**30**	**16**	**20**	**780**

New Hampshire's 17.8 mi (11.1 km) coastline consists of rocky shore interspersed with sandy beaches. Development has destroyed all but a small fragment of dunes. Although much of the original salt marsh has been filled, some 6,000 a (2,400 ha) of tidal wetlands remain.

Physiographic regions

Chapman (1952) divides New Hampshire into 16 physical regions: 9 lowland areas, with elevations from 0 to 500 ft (0 to 152.5 m); a single upland area, the Eastern Uplands, with elevations up to about 1,500 ft (457.5 m); 2 highland areas, with elevations from 1,500 to 3,000 ft (457.5 to 915 m); and 4 mountain areas, with elevations exceeding 3,000 ft (915 m). Table 2.3 lists the physical divisions within each category. Figure 2.5 is adapted and simplified from Chapman's system.

Table 2.3 Physical divisions of New Hampshire

Lowlands
- Coastal Lowlands
- Merrimack Valley
- Connecticut Valley
- Keene Lowlands
- Winnipesaukee Lowlands
- Ossipee Lowlands
- Conway Lowlands
- Upper Androscoggin Lowlands
- Whitefield Lowlands

Uplands
- Eastern Uplands

Highlands
- Western Highlands
- Northern Highlands

Mountains
- Central White Mountains
- Southern White Mountains
- Ossipee Mountains
- Belknap Mountains

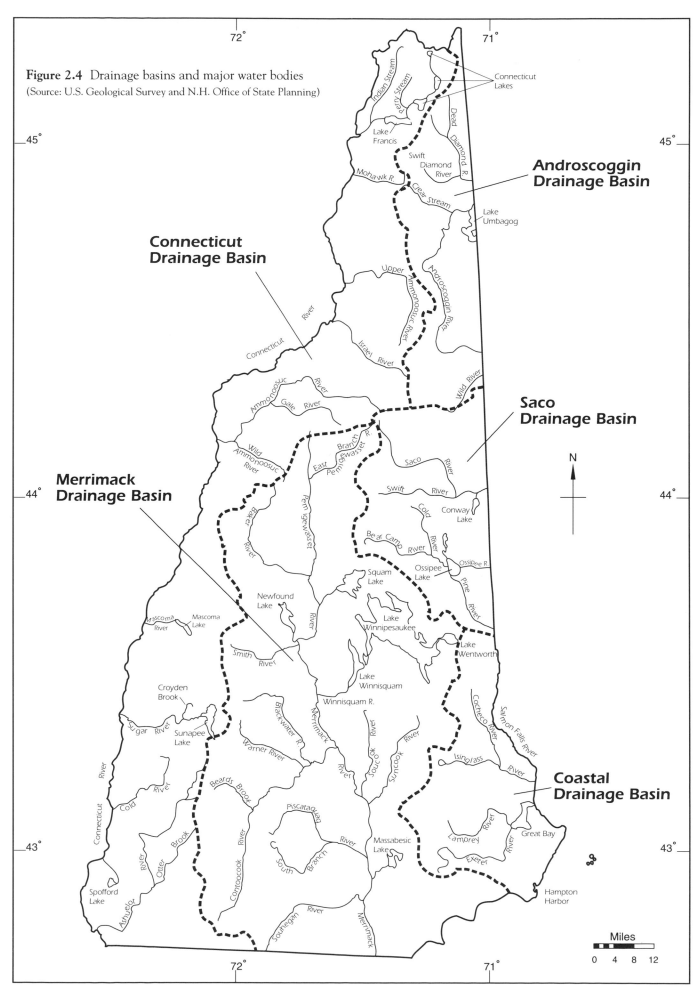

Figure 2.4 Drainage basins and major water bodies
(Source: U.S. Geological Survey and N.H. Office of State Planning)

**Connecticut
Drainage Basin**

**Androscoggin
Drainage Basin**

**Saco
Drainage Basin**

**Merrimack
Drainage Basin**

**Coastal
Drainage Basin**

Connecticut Lakes

Indian Stream

Perry Stream

Dead Diamond River

Lake Francis

Swift Diamond River

Mohawk R.

Clear Stream

Lake Umbagog

Upper Ammonoosuc River

Israel River

Androscoggin River

Wild River

Ammonoosuc River

Gale River

Wild Ammonoosuc River

East Branch

Pemigewasset R.

Saco River

Swift River

Cold River

Conway Lake

Bear Camp River

Ossipee Lake

Ossipee R.

Baker River

Pemigewasset River

Squam Lake

Newfound Lake

Pine River

Mascoma River

Mascoma Lake

Lake Winnipesaukee

Lake Wentworth

Smith River

Lake Winnisquam

Croyden Brook

Winnisquam R.

Sugar River

Sunapee Lake

Blackwater R.

Merrimack River

Soucook River

Suncook River

Cocheco River

Salmon Falls River

Warner River

Isinglass River

Connecticut River

Cold River

Beards Brook

Piscataquog River

Massabesic Lake

Lamprey River

Exeter River

Great Bay

Otter Brook

Contoocook River

South Branch River

Merrimack

Spofford Lake

Hampton Harbor

Ashuelot River

Southegan River

N

Miles

0   4   8   12

I-13

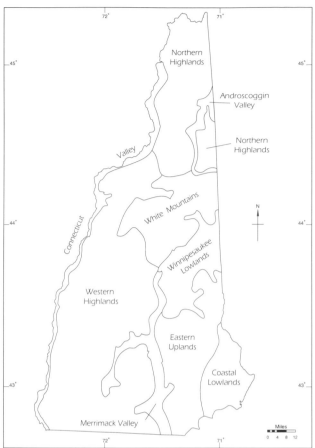

Figure 2.5 New Hampshire physiographic regions
(Source: Adapted from Chapman 1952)

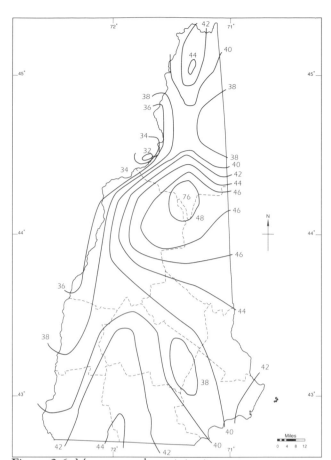

Figure 2.6 Mean annual precipitation
(Source: U.S. Weather Bureau and N.H. Office of State Planning)

Climatic Factors

New Hampshire lies within the north temperate zone, and has a four season climate with short, warm summers and long, cold winters. Snowfall typically begins by late November, and snowmelt in most years is complete by early May in all but the highest mountains. Mean annual precipitation ranges from 32 to 76 in (81 to 193 cm); summer rainfall ranges from less than 10 to more than 13 in (<25 to 33 cm). Normal mean July temperatures range from 64°F to 70°F (18°C to 21°C); mean maximum July temperatures range from 74°F to 84°F (23°C to 29°C). Mean minimum temperatures in January range form 0°F to 18°F (-8°C to -18°C). Dates of the last killing frosts in spring range from before 11 May to after 1 June, and dates of the first killing frost in the fall range from before 11 September to after 1 October. The resulting growing seasons extend for anywhere from less than 105 days to 140 days. Figures 2.6 – 2.9 present selected climatological information for New Hampshire.

Political Divisions

New Hampshire is divided politically into 10 counties and 258 townships. Because the counties are relatively large, their boundaries are well established both on maps and on the ground, and they can be grouped to approximate meaningful geographical and ecological regions of the state, they provide a useful framework for analyzing and discussing Atlas data. Several priority blocks overlap the boundaries of 2 or 3 counties. To simplify analysis, these blocks are considered to "belong" to the county encompassing the greatest portion of their areas. Table 2.4 provides per-

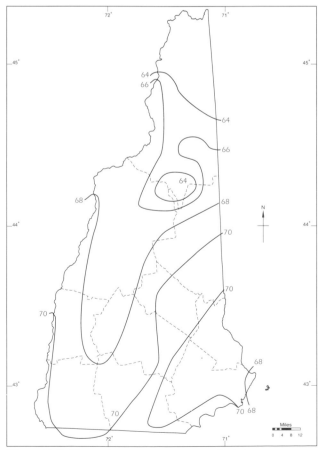

Figure 2.7 Normal mean temperature (July)
(Source: U.S. Weather Bureau and N.H. Office of State Planning)

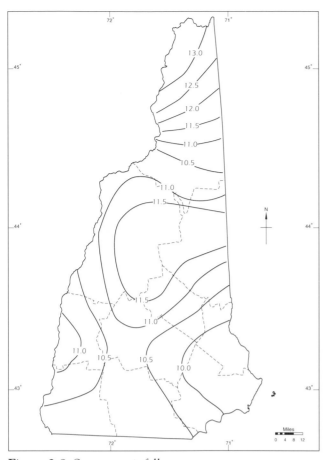

Figure 2.8 Summer rainfall
(Source: U.S. Weather Bureau and N.H. Office of State Planning)

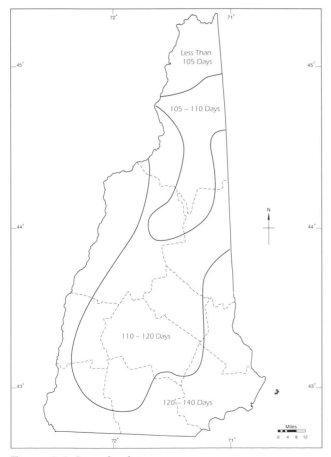

Figure 2.9 Length of growing season
(Source: U.S. Weather Bureau and N.H. Office of State Planning)

tinent information about each county. The map in the flyleaf outlines the locations of New Hampshire counties and townships.

Table 2.4 County size statistics

County	area (a)	area (ha)	number of townships	priority blocks
Belknap	299,384	121,250	11	9
Carroll	626,280	253,643	19	19
Cheshire	462,244	187,209	23	13
Coos	1,206,592	488,670	43	40
Grafton	1,117,952	452,771	39*[1]	34
Hillsborough	563,910	228,384	31	18
Merrimack	615,616	249,324	27*[2]	16
Rockingham	451,662	182,923	37	14
Strafford	242,301	98,132	13	7
Sullivan	351,270	142,264	15	8

*1 includes one unincorporated township
*2 includes 23 unincorporated townships

Human population density is greatest, and still growing rapidly, in Hillsborough, Strafford, and Rockingham counties, in the southeastern corner of the state. The 3 northern counties, Coos, Carroll, and Grafton, have the lowest population densities. While Coos County has consistently lost population over the past 3 decades, Carroll County has experienced rapid growth during this period. Figure 2.10 illustrates the distribution of human population in New Hampshire during the Atlas period. Table 2.5 presents population data by county.

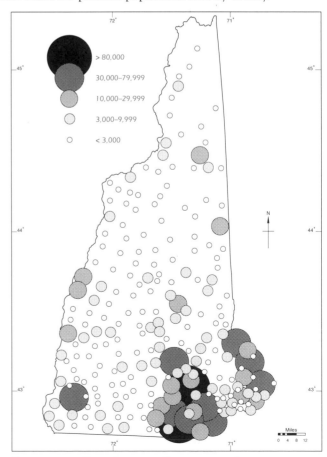

Figure 2.10 Distribution of human population
(Source: U.S. Census Bureau and N.H. Office of State Planning)

Table 2.5 Population data by county (from U.S. Census data)

County	Population 1980	Density 1980	% change 1960-80	% change 1980-90
Belknap	42,884	0.14/a (0.35/ha)	+48.3	+14.8
Carroll	27,979	0.04/a (0.11/ha)	+76.4	+26.8
Cheshire	62,116	0.13/a (0.33/ha)	+43.3	+12.9
Coos	35,147	0.03/a (0.07/ha)	-5.4	-0.9
Grafton	65,806	0.06/a (0.15/ha)	+34.7	+13.9
Hillsborough	276,608	0.49/a (1.21/ha)	+55.3	+21.4
Merrimack	98,302	0.16/a (0.39/ha)	+45.0	+22.3
Rockingham	190,345	0.42/a (1.04/ha)	+92.2	+50.2
Strafford	85,408	0.35/a (0.87/ha)	+42.8	+22.0
Sullivan	36,063	0.10/a (0.25/ha)	+28.5	+7.0

County Synopsis

Belknap County lies mostly within the Winnipesaukee Lowlands, and includes all of the Belknap Mountains and small areas of the Eastern Uplands and Western Highlands. Located in central New Hampshire, Belknap County is in the mid-range of elevations and climatic conditions in the state. Forest cover includes white pine/red pine, maple/beech/birch, and elm/ash/red maple as the predominant types, with small patches of aspen/gray birch and oak/pine.

Carroll County is the most diverse physiographically of all the 10 counties. It includes all of the Conway Lowlands, Ossipee Lowlands, and Ossipee Mountains, and portions of the Central White Mountains, Southern White Mountains, Winnipesaukee Lowlands, and Eastern Uplands. Although it is one of the northern 3 counties, its extensive lowlands provide areas of milder climatic conditions than occur elsewhere in northern New Hampshire. The forest cover of Carroll County is a complex pattern of all 8 forest types, and includes most of the state's acreage of the pitch pine type.

Cheshire County lies primarily within the Western Highlands, and encompasses the entire Keene Lowlands, a small area of the Merrimack Valley, and the southernmost portion of the Connecticut Valley. Located in the southwestern corner of the state, Cheshire County and Sullivan County to the north are similar in elevation and climate. Forest cover includes white pine/red pine, maple/beech/birch, and elm/ash/red maple as the predominant types, with smaller patches of spruce/fir, oak/pine, and oak/hickory.

Coos County encompasses all of the Northern Highlands and Androscoggin Lowlands, most of the Whitefield Lowlands, and some of the Central White Mountains. Encompassing the northern tip of New Hampshire and with most of its area at elevations exceeding 1,000 ft (305 m), Coos County experiences the most severe weather in New Hampshire. Most of the state's spruce/fir acreage is in Coos County; maple/beech/birch is the predominant forest type. Aspen/gray birch and elm/ash/red maple occur in scattered patches throughout the county; oak/pine and white pine/red pine types exist as a few small patches near the Connecticut River.

Grafton County lies largely within the Western Highlands, and includes some of the Central and Southern White Mountains, a small portion of the Whitefield Lowlands, and the northernmost portion of the Connecticut Valley. One of the 3 northern counties, Grafton includes considerable areas of higher elevations, and experiences relatively severe climatic conditions. Maple/beech/

birch and white pine/red pine are the primary forest types, but areas of spruce/fir, elm/ash/red maple, and oak/pine also occur.

Hillsborough County lies primarily within the Western Highlands, and includes 2 sections of the Merrimack Valley and a small corner of the Eastern Uplands. Centrally located in the southern tier of counties, Hillsborough County includes elevations from 200 to 2,000 ft (61 to 610 m) and experiences moderate climatic conditions. All the state's major forest types occur in Hillsborough County. White pine/red pine is the predominant type; pitch pine, spruce/fir, aspen/gray birch, and oak/pine are minor components.

Merrimack County encompasses portions of the Eastern Uplands, Western Highlands, and Merrimack Valley. Included as one of 3 or 5 southeastern counties, Merrimack County lies mostly below 1,000 ft (305 m) elevation and experiences moderate climatic conditions for New Hampshire. Forest cover is primarily white pine/red pine, maple/beech/birch, and elm/ash/red maple; small patches of the other types occur.

Rockingham County is comprised primarily of Coastal Lowlands and Eastern Uplands, and includes a small area of the Merrimack Valley. Located in the southeastern corner of New Hampshire and including the entire Seacoast, Rockingham County includes the state's lowest elevations and experiences its mildest climatic conditions. White pine/red pine is the predominant forest type; areas of oak/hickory, elm/ash/red maple, oak/pine, and beech/birch/maple also occur.

Strafford County includes portions of the Coastal Lowlands and Eastern Uplands. One of the southeastern counties, Strafford County lies almost entirely below 1,000 ft (305 m) elevation and experiences relatively mild climatic conditions. White pine/red pine is the predominant forest type; maple/beech/birch, elm/ash/red maple, oak/pine, and oak/hickory also occur.

Sullivan County lies almost entirely within the Western Highlands, and includes the central portion of the Connecticut Valley. One of the 2 southwestern counties, Sullivan lies mostly between 500 and 2,000 ft (152.5 and 610 m) and experiences moderate climatic conditions for New Hampshire. Forest cover includes all types except pitch pine.

References Cited

Chapman, D.H. 1952. Topographic map and physical divisions of New Hampshire. N.H. State Planning and Development Commission, Concord, N.H.

Jorgensen, N. 1977. A guide to New England's landscape. Globe Pequot Press, Chester, Conn.

N.H. Div. For. and Lands. 1980. Forests and forestry in New Hampshire action plan for the eighties. Forest Resources Status Report. Vol. 1, Div. For. and Lands, Dept. Resour. and Econ. Dev., Concord.

Kingsley, N.P. 1973. Forest resources of New Hampshire. USDA For. Serv. Resour. Bull. NE 43, USDA For.Serv., Upper Darby, Pa.

Pilgrim, S.A.L. and K.K. Peterson. 1979. Soils of New Hampshire. Res. Rep. 79, N.H. Agric. Exp. Station, Univ. N.H., Durham, N.H. and Soil Conserv. Serv., U.S. Dept. of Agric.

Van Diver, B.B. 1987. Roadside geology of Vermont and New Hampshire. Mountain Press Publishing Company, Missoula, Mont.

Major Changes in the Breeding Avifauna of New Hampshire Since Its First Settlements by Europeans, in 1623

Tudor Richards & Kimball C. Elkins

A Proposed Division of New Hampshire into Avifaunal Regions Based Largely on the Altitudinal Distribution of Breeding Birds

Tudor Richards

Major Changes in the Breeding Avifauna of New Hampshire Since Its First Settlements by Europeans, in 1623

Tudor Richards & Kimball C. Elkins

Virgin Forests, Indians, and First European Settlers

New Hampshire's breeding avifauna has had an interesting and remarkable history since 1623. The primeval forests had at that time long been somewhat altered by the Indians, who over several thousand years, especially in southern New Hampshire, had cut trees for their own uses, cleared small, usually temporary patches to grow crops, and set ground fires to clear out undergrowth in the forest to facilitate hunting and travel (Wood 1634 in Silver 1957). Despite these activities New Hampshire was still almost completely forested in 1623. Ancient trees of large size were common (Cline and Spurr 1942) and game, including Wild Turkeys and Passenger Pigeons, by all accounts, abundant.

The first white settlers, following in the steps of the Indians, undoubtedly took advantage of the abundance of sea and shore birds along the Coast. The Double-crested Cormorant, various members of the heron family, American Black Duck, Common Eider, and several species of gulls and terns probably all nested then on the New Hampshire Isles of Shoals or along the mainland coast, and the Leach's Storm-Petrel, American Oystercatcher, Willet, and one or more members of the auk family may well have done so, judging from the former ranges as given by Forbush (1916). These provided meat, eggs, feathers (including down), and probably also oil and fish bait and were exploited from the first. Eventually all were permanently or temporarily exterminated as breeding species in New Hampshire.

The early colonists made more complete and permanent clearings for their houses and farms than the Indians, but generally kept small areas as woodlots to provide firewood or as "sugar bushes." Uncontrolled hunting of turkeys and other game gradually reduced their numbers, but Passenger Pigeons remained abundant. Beavers were soon trapped out locally (Silver 1957), and the disintegration of their dams caused their ponds to turn into meadows, an advantage for the settlers' livestock (Belknap, 1792) but a disadvantage for water birds.

While hawks and owls no doubt were treated as vermin, the Common Raven evidently was regarded as more of a pest and was killed at every opportunity (Forbush 1927) and apparently disappeared from most of New Hampshire at a very early date. By the mid-1700s settlements had reached well inland and by 1800 were scattered over most of the state, which by then included much open farmland but, except very locally, still a lot less than the amount of forest land.

First New Hampshire Bird List (Jeremy Belknap, 1792)

Little is known about New Hampshire's breeding birds between 1623 and 1792, when Jeremy Belknap produced his famous History of New Hampshire, containing the first published list of New Hampshire birds. Unfortunately several of the 130 species listed have unrecognizable names or are apparent or definite duplicates, and there are comments for only a few. Wild Turkeys "formerly were numerous" but had "retired to the inland mountainous country." "Wild Pigeons" are described as arriving in Spring "in great flocks" and nesting in the "thickest parts of the forest" but having diminished in numbers since the clearing of the woods.

Already, the Barn Swallow had acquired its present name, and the Chimney Swift was called "Chimney Swallow." Some other birds typical of open land on Belknap's list are "Kildee" (Killdeer), "Turtle Dove" (Mourning Dove), "Marsh Lark" (Meadowlark), and "Boblincoln" (Bobolink). As for woodland birds, he describes the "Partridge" (Ruffed Grouse) as "very common" and the "Quail" (Northern Bobwhite), which by then had probably become more of an open land than a woodland species, as "equally prolific." A bird like the "Great Crested Woodpecker" (Pileated Woodpecker), on the other hand, may well have become uncommon because of the growing scarcity of extensive forests with old trees containing carpenter ants.

Farm Abandonment

Since almost nothing of consequence was published on the breeding avifauna of New Hampshire after Belknap's time until the 1870s, we have virtually no information on the subject for this long period. Nevertheless, enough is known about the land, forest, and wildlife history to allow us to make some assumptions about its breeding birds. In the first half of the century, employment opportunities increased in cities and towns, and construction of the Erie Canal and later the railroads enhanced migration to better farmland in the Middle West and gold fields in California. This led to some abandonment of farms, but continued land clearing more than offset the exodus, probably at least until 1850. This must have benefited birds breeding in open and semiopen land and caused most of them to increase. By this time, however, market hunting was becoming more important and causing declines of certain species. Although a forest breeder, the highly gregarious Passenger Pigeon long since had become a pest of grain fields and was also so delectable as food that it became a staple in the market. It suffered for both reasons and began to decline more noticeably.

By the middle of the century, agriculture approached its peak, with maximum areas of improved farmland being reached about 1850 in Cheshire, Hillsborough and Strafford counties; 1860 in Rockingham; 1870 in Sullivan, Merrimack, and Grafton; 1880 in Belknap and Carroll; and 1890 in Coos — a clear progression from south to north (U.S. Census in Silver 1957). At these peaks, from 55% to 63% of the total areas of each of the 7 southern counties and 40%, 29% and 13% of Grafton, Carroll and Coos, respectively, were improved farmland.

What seems to be the best information for this period on the breeding avifauna of southern New Hampshire other than the Seacoast is that in Goodhue's (1877) "Birds of Webster and Adjoining Towns." Even though it covers only a limited area, this probably was more or less typical of the larger region. Of open land species, Goodhue found the Upland "Plover" (Sandpiper) a common summer resident, but, surprisingly, the Killdeer (listed by Belknap) not even present, either having been already exterminated or not having occurred that far north before. He found the Bobolink abundant, the Eastern Meadowlark common, and the Vesper "the most common of the sparrows." He also listed Grasshopper and Henslow's sparrows, but, curiously, not the Savannah — presumably an oversight.

Goodhue also found the "Marsh Hawk" (Northern Harrier), Eastern Screech-Owl, and even the Passenger Pigeon common in summer but never saw a Mourning Dove or a Wood Thrush. He considered the Chestnut-sided Warbler (which was very rare in Massachusetts until "a marked increase after 1835," according to Griscom and Snyder [1955]) the most abundant warbler, breeding in "low bushes," and the Black-throated Green also abundant, breeding in "pine woods." This is almost certainly an indication of an abundance of these 2 stages of abandoned farmland. He found the Broad-winged Hawk and Pileated Woodpecker rare, however, suggesting that extensive woodlands containing old trees were largely gone.

Lumbering Becomes Big Business

Beginning in the mid-1800s, heavy logging of virgin white pine along the rivers and around the lakes of New Hampshire's North Country became a major activity, presumably with adverse effects on certain birds such as Bald Eagles, Ospreys, and other raptors as well as Great Blue Herons, which all like tall trees. The limited amount of pine didn't last very long and cutting of the much more widespread spruces followed. Nearer the end of the century, now in the White Mountains as well as the North Country, spruces of all sizes as well as balsam firs were cut for pulp wood for paper manufacture.

In the meantime, many fields and pastures in southern New Hampshire, abandoned several decades before, had grown up to stands of sizable white pines, giving rise to a thriving wooden box and lumber industry. Cutting of old field and pasture pines in the South and of virgin spruce and fir in the North both peaked shortly after 1900, with the volume of pine cut exceeding that of the northern conifers (USDA Census 1900). The damage, however, was far more extensive in the north, and left extensive clearcuts and burned over areas in contrast to the innumerable but mostly small and scattered cut-overs of the south. Of the many birds that lost habitat in the north, the Spruce Grouse, Three-toed Woodpecker, Gray Jay, Boreal Chickadee, certain of the warblers, and the crossbills presumably

suffered the most, while birds like the Mourning and Chestnut-sided warblers, Common Yellowthroat, and White-throated Sparrow benefited.

Market Hunting of Wild Pigeons

By far the greatest all time change in and disaster to the bird life of New Hampshire and eastern North America was the disappearance, largely due to market hunting, of the Passenger Pigeon, once the most abundant bird in the world. Weeks (1888) speaks of seeing "flocks of hundreds of thousands if not millions of wild pigeons" during his boyhood in Lancaster, and during the 1840s, when surveying, went at least half a mile through a nesting area where "in the tops of the trees, every place where sticks could be placed" had a nest, some trees having 20 or 30.

Brewster (1925) indicates that pigeons were still abundant around Lake Umbagog up to 1850, occurring in flocks a mile or more in length, and had to be kept out of fields of buckwheat by boys armed with guns. He found them still common there in summer up until 1875, as Goodhue did in Webster but gone except for a straggler or 2 by 1879. According to Silver (1957) New Hampshire's last official record dates from 1885, and the last of the species died of old age in the Cincinnati Zoo in 1914 (Forbush 1916).

Market Hunting of Other Birds

Market hunting also was devastating to waterfowl, upland game birds, and shore birds, including many migrants as well as the relatively few breeding species. It was especially hard on the Wood Duck, Northern Bobwhite, and Upland Plover (Sandpiper). Although most of the slaughter occurred outside of New Hampshire, it no doubt affected many migrants that would have nested in the state had they survived. At any rate, most if not all game birds and many other large birds declined drastically in numbers during the peak of market hunting, late in the century.

Another type of "market hunting" also became big business late in the last century — killing many kinds of birds from egrets, gulls, and terns to hummingbirds and song birds, to adorn ladies' hats. While this hardly became big business in New Hampshire, it involved many migrants that might have been headed this way. Many birds also were killed for private collections of mounted birds in glass cases, popular at the time. Egg collecting also was popular in that era, complete with dealers, catalogues, and high prices for rarities. Guides at Umbagog Lake once sold loon eggs for a dollar apiece (Brewster 1924).

Hawks and owls still were considered vermin and were killed at every opportunity. Shooting at birds for target practice or just sport was rampant. Examples include passengers on the Umbagog Lake steamer shooting at loons, and a "gang of vandals" coming regularly to the lake over a period of 10–12 years and killing (but not using) so many Hooded Mergansers that the species, which had been the most common nesting duck there, became the least common (Brewster 1924).

The last century ended with the formerly most abundant summer resident, the Passenger Pigeon, and 2 probable former winter visitors, the Great Auk and Labrador Duck, extinct; the Double-crested Cormorant, Common Eider, various shore birds, and several gulls and terns no longer nesting in New Hampshire; and many other birds, especially most breeding species of waterfowl, drastically reduced in numbers. Nevertheless, the reaction to such slaughter helped strengthen the bird protection movement, which had started in the 1880s with the formation of a bird protection committee of the AOU and the first Audubon Society.

Range Extensions into New Hampshire

Meanwhile other types of changes, some for the good, were occurring before the century ended and continuing after 1900. The Wood Thrush, which previously had been unknown in summer in New Hampshire, was first reported as occurring at that season in 1894, near Mt. Moosilauke, and in 1895, at North Woodstock, and about that year and several following in several different towns in the Monadnock Region Elkins (1957). The "Prairie" Horned Lark had first been reported in the state in the summer of 1891 (Allen 1903), following a gradual extension of its breeding range from the West. The Louisiana Waterthrush and Rough-winged Swallow seem to have been the next arrivals from the South, with first summer records in 1901 in Dublin and 1909 in Boscawen, respectively (Forbush 1929).

Better Bird Protection and the Response to it

The turn of the century saw the beginning of the end of market hunting with the passage of the federal Lacey Act, which outlawed the interstate transportation of game illegally taken in any state, at a time when legal protection and law enforcement was being improved in the various states. Then in 1913 the Weeks-McLean Act gave the federal government custody over all migratory birds except hawks and owls. These unfortunately, were not included until after New Hampshire had given them legal protection in 1958. Such protection and better law enforcement as well as the establishment of federal and state wildlife refuges together with the comeback of the beaver, especially after 1930, and expanded activities of Audubon societies and other private conservation organizations, gave a tremendous boost to bird protection in New Hampshire and elsewhere.

Loons to Herons

The results of all this have been spectacular, especially in the case of water birds, and among the greatest triumphs in the history of conservation. The Common Loon, for one, began to recover its former numbers at Umbagog remarkably early in the century according to records of the late William B. Cook (pers. comm.). Loons also increased in other parts of this state, having become more tolerant of people since receiving better protection. Along the Coast the Double-crested Cormorant began an extraordinary comeback in recent decades, eventually becoming an abundant summer resident though only recently a breeding species in New Hampshire. With better protection and the return of the beaver, the Great Blue Heron has thrived in recent decades, but for reasons unknown the Black-crowned Night-Heron has declined drastically in numbers. The American Bittern seems to be barely holding its own and the Least Bittern to be rarer than ever. Although the extraordinary increases and northeastern breeding range extensions of the egrets and Glossy Ibis have so far bypassed New Hampshire, both Snowy Egrets and

ibises (along with the Black-crowned Night-Heron) nest on Appledore Island, of the Maine Isles of Shoals, and regularly visit New Hampshire's salt marshes for feeding.

Waterfowl

Waterfowl also have recovered remarkably. The American Black Duck, which had become rare as a summer resident in southern New Hampshire (Allen 1903) and apparently no longer nested in the salt marshes (Dearborn 1903), recovered well and began to nest again in these marshes (Richards 1952). In recent years it has once more suffered a decline. The Wood Duck, which had become even scarcer than the Black Duck as a summer resident, by 1924 was "coming back" in the Concord area and by 1935 had recovered well (White 1937). Both the Wood Duck and the Hooded Merganser have benefited greatly from the increase in beavers and from duck boxes. The latter species presumably nested in Massachusetts and southern New Hampshire in the distant past but was unknown to do so definitely until 1936 and 1943, respectively (Richards 1952). Now it is well distributed and fairly common more or less throughout the Granite State. The Common Merganser also has expanded its nesting range considerably in southern New Hampshire and the Lakes Region in recent decades (Richards 1952).

Most remarkable is the case of the Ring-necked Duck, which first nested in New Hampshire in 1947, at Fish Pond, Columbia (Silver 1957). The next summer 6 families were found at the Cherry ponds, and since then it has nested occasionally even in the southern counties and regularly in numbers near Umbagog Lake (Richards 1952). Both teal have nested in the state in recent decades for the first time and still do so occasionally if not regularly, and the Northern Pintail has once (NHBBA data). Possibly because of increased boating, the small breeding range of the Common Goldeneye in the North Country has been getting even smaller in recent decades, while along the Coast just the opposite has happened in the case of the Common Eider. This species gradually has been recovering its former breeding range along the Maine coast and recently has been found breeding on the New Hampshire Isles of Shoals. The most spectacular changes of all among the waterfowl, however, involve the Canada Goose and Mallard, which were unknown as breeding species in the state until recent decades. Now, represented by birds apparently of feral origin, the goose is locally common and the Mallard generally common. Unfortunately the Mallard frequently hybridizes successfully with the Black Duck, confusing hunters and bird watchers alike.

Shore Birds

Shorebirds also have recovered well in general, a major exception being the Upland Sandpiper, which has continued to decline and now seems to be restricted as a breeding species in New Hampshire to a single location. While the continued loss of open farmland is undoubtedly a factor, heavy hunting along its migration routes and its wintering grounds also may be important. The Killdeer has made an extraordinary recovery starting in 1912. Unfortunately the Piping Plover, which started a fine comeback along the New England coast several decades ago and nested for several years at Hampton Harbor, seems to be struggling for survival in the face of increasing numbers of people, dogs, and predators on most beaches. Perhaps the Willet, which recently has started to nest in our coastal marshes, has a better chance. The Common Snipe also has rebounded in spectacular fashion in the last several decades. It is now a common summer resident in suitable habitat more or less throughout the North Country and nests locally in southern New Hampshire.

Gulls and Terns

The most remarkable recoveries of all, thanks both to protection and to the proliferation of garbage, have been those of the gulls, but at the expense of terns. The latter had made a fine recovery during the 1920s and 1930s. A colony of about 150 Common and a few Arctic terns nested at the mouth of Hampton Harbor in 1926, and about 1,000 pairs of Common Terns, 25 pairs of Arctic, and 50 to 60 pairs of Roseate terns nested on Lunging Island, Isles of Shoals, in 1938 (Borror 1980, Richards 1980). The mainland tern colony probably disappeared before or during World War II, presumably as a result of human disturbance, and the island colony was gone by 1955 (Borror 1980), apparently for the same reason combined with gull predation. At that time there were an estimated 700 pairs of Great Black-backed and 5,000 of Herring gulls nesting at the Isles of Shoals, but only a relatively small number of each on the New Hampshire islands. Since then the proportion of Great Black-backed Gulls has increased, and large numbers of mostly nonbreeding birds of both species have gathered at dumps all over the state. In very recent years there has been a great increase in the numbers of Ring-billed Gulls starting in the Lakes Region but soon becoming statewide, with Ring-bills now tending to outnumber other gulls in many inland localities.

Meanwhile, terns have been reduced to a few very small, scattered, struggling colonies of Common Terns in the Hampton Harbor marshes and islands in Great and Little bays. A small colony of Least Terns that survived for a number of years at Hampton Harbor starting in the early 1950s (Richards 1980) has been reduced to occasional pairs possibly trying, but failing, to nest there.

Continued Farm Abandonment, Logging, and Conservation

Farm abandonment has continued over the last several decades, providing continuous representation of all successional stages in southern and central New Hampshire. Resulting habitats range from weedy or brushy fields and pastures and pioneer gray and paper birches, aspens, and cherries, to intermediate stages of white pines, red maples, red oaks, and even some more or less "climax" stands of hemlock, beech, and sugar maple. Virtually all areas that were never cleared for agriculture have since been cut over, generally 2 or more times, with sprout red maples typically becoming the predominant trees.

In the north the situation has been similar except that spruce, fir, larch, northern white cedar, and white pine continue to be common on abandoned farmland, and beech, sugar maple, and yellow birch continue to be the prevailing hardwoods on the more extensive areas never farmed.

In recent decades, hardwoods have been cut heavily, especially for pulpwood. Continued cutting of spruce and fir mean-while has resulted in the more prolific fir gradually becoming more common than the originally predominant, longer-lived, and potentially larger spruce.

These forests are much better protected and better managed than formerly, notably in the White Mountains since establishment of the White Mountain National Forest about 80 years ago, and on numerous state forests and many private tree farms. In addition, various agencies and organizations have protected as natural areas many habitats of major importance for various uncommon or rare species of birds and other wildlife.

Introduced Birds

Altogether, there are far more different types of potential nesting and feeding habitat in New Hampshire today than in 1623 and so very probably more species of nesting birds. We should not overlook the introduction of 3 exotic species important for their large numbers and for being pests, especially about cities, towns, and farms — the Rock Dove, or domestic pigeon, European Starling, and House or English Sparrow. The first apparently was introduced in colonial days and has long been a general nuisance. The starling, after many failures, was introduced successfully into New York City about 1890 and soon spread rapidly, apparently first reaching New Hampshire in 1916 (Forbush 1929). It soon became one of the state's most abundant breeding species, which it continues to be, often competing with native birds for natural foods and nest sites and holes, as in Purple Martin houses. The House ("English") Sparrow apparently spread into New Hampshire from a colony established in Boston in 1869 (Forbush 1929) and subsequently became abundant but in recent decades has decreased in numbers.

Raptors

Among the diurnal raptors the most extraordinary change has been the comparatively recent establishment of the Turkey Vulture as a regular summer resident in much of southern New Hampshire. Of the accipiters, the Northern Goshawk has become much more common in the southern counties in recent decades, while the Cooper's and Sharp-shinned hawks seem to have made only modest recoveries since the use of DDT was banned in the early 1970s (ASNH records). Once "the most common hawk found in the state" (Goodhue 1922), the Red-shouldered Hawk clearly has become uncommon in recent years, but the Red-tailed seems to be more than holding its own as a fairly common species. The Broad-winged Hawk, long recovered from its scarcity of more than a century ago, continues to be our most common hawk, while the once common Northern Harrier has become scarce (ASNH records). The status of the Bald Eagle as even a rare summer resident seems to be in jeopardy, but the Osprey has recently not only increased its numbers in Coos County, but expanded its range to include the Great Bay area (ASNH records). Of the falcons the American Kestrel, which was considered "rather rare" by Allen (1903), appears to be more common than ever, while the Merlin was found to be nesting for the first time in the state (Coos County) only this year, 1994 (C.R. Foss, pers. comm.). The Peregrine's artificially assisted recovery after the species had been exterminated by DDT, appears to have been successful (ASNH records). The only clear, significant change of status of an owl seems to be that of the once common Eastern Screech-Owl, which already had become an uncommon resident by the turn of the century (Allen 1903) and in recent years has been a rare one (ASNH records).

Upland Game Species and Goatsuckers to the Raven

The Northern Bobwhite, which apparently was very common in Belknap's day, but evidently largely exterminated by a combination of market hunting and greatly reduced grain production in New Hampshire, never recovered (Silver 1957). Native birds were replaced by introduced birds, apparently of a weaker strain, those too disappearing completely except for occasional released birds that don't survive for long (Silver 1957). The Wild Turkey, on the other hand, has made a good comeback based entirely on introduced birds. Most remarkable has been the case of the once rare Mourning Dove, which was still considered to be uncommon in the Concord area in the 1930s (White, 1937), in recent years has become common to abundant throughout the state, regularly spending the winter in numbers (ASNH records). (*See* Appendix B, p. 392)

The Whip-poor-will, which was still a common summer resident within the memory of middle-aged people, has become very scarce in recent years for unknown reasons. The Common Nighthawk similarly has become scarce, having for breeding purposes long since forsaken open country for the flat city roofs that they have used successfully for many years but less often recently.

The once rare Pileated Woodpecker has made a fine comeback in recent decades thanks to better protection but principally because of the gradual return of the forest and the increasing age and size of many trees. Among the swallows the greatest changes have been the near disappearance of the Purple Martin, which was once common locally and nested as far north as Lancaster (Wright 1911); and the Rough-winged Swallow, which in recent years has extended its range well up into the North Country (ASNH records). Meanwhile the Barn Swallow has become less common and the Cliff Swallow uncommon, as many barns have disappeared.

While the Blue Jay has prospered with "civilization," including its bird feeders, the Gray Jay, once the more common of the 2 in the White Mountains (Chadbourne 1887), is now rare there. By contrast the Common Raven, one of the first birds to disappear completely from the state as a breeding species (Brewster 1937), has made a remarkable recovery, starting in the North Country less than half a century ago and recently extending its range into parts of southern New Hampshire.

Further Range Extensions

Other cases of similar range extensions of northern birds not previously known to breed in the state are those of the Ruby-crowned Kinglet, first found definitely breeding in 1947, in Rumney (Richards 1956), and since becoming a common summer resident even up to high elevations in the mountains and occasionally occurring in summer as far south as Andover and Mt. Kearsarge (ASNH records); American Pipit, first recorded in summer above timberline on the Presidential Range in 1938 (Palmer 1949) and finally found nesting there only a few years ago (ASNH records); Palm Warbler, first seen in summer in 1955 in an Errol bog and definitely breeding there a few years

later (Richards 1956); and Lincoln's Sparrow, first recorded as a summer resident in Pittsburg about 40 years ago and since summering regularly as far south as the Passaconaway Valley, in the White Mountains. The Tennessee Warbler in recent decades has been found at high elevations in the White Mountains several different summers, suggesting a southward extension of its breeding range from its former limit in the North Country; and the Rusty Blackbird has definitely extended its known breeding range from that region south to the high elevation ponds on the White Mountains and even to Mt. Sunapee and Dublin, if only temporarily.

Better known are the several range extensions north into New Hampshire besides the already mentioned earlier cases of the Wood Thrush, Louisiana Waterthrush and Rough-winged Swallow. The most striking are those of the Tufted Titmouse, Northern Mockingbird and Northern Cardinal, all 3 of which extended their ranges into the state rather suddenly in appreciable numbers starting around 1957 and soon becoming common summer residents throughout much of southern New Hampshire (ASNH records). While all 3 have benefited somewhat from feeders and suburbia in general, their general habitats are appreciably different, which makes their cases all the more remarkable, (*See* Appendix B, p. 392)

An even more recent and unique case is that of the House Finch, which spread north into southern New England and then New Hampshire from birds released from pet shops in New York City, becoming common in urban as well as suburban and rural areas over much of the state (Hebert 1968). The Blue-gray Gnatcatcher, Blue-winged Warbler, and Seaside Sparrow also have become regular summer residents of New Hampshire comparatively recently, and the Red-bellied Woodpecker, Carolina Wren, White-eyed Vireo, and Orchard Oriole may be starting to do so. The Prairie Warbler is another species worth mentioning since early in the century it was exceedingly rare (Allen 1903), but it has gradually become locally common and has extended its range north to the Lakes Region along powerlines rights-of-way (ASNH records).

The Evening Grosbeak is another remarkable case of a range extension from the West. First recorded in New Hampshire as a winter visitor in 1890 and not again until 1910–11, this species soon became regular in winter with the help of bird feeders. It was not until around 1950 that the species was first reported, in Pittsburg, as a summer resident (Richards 1953). Since then it has extended its breeding range into parts of southern New Hampshire (ASNH records).

A few other significant changes in status are worth mentioning. Birds that were once regular summer residents of New Hampshire and have declined to the point of barely or even no longer breeding here include the Sedge Wren, Loggerhead Shrike, Pine Grosbeak, and Grasshopper and Henslow's sparrows (ASNH records). Species that once were very common or abundant summer residents that clearly have become much less common in recent years include the Eastern Bluebird, Eastern Meadowlark, Bobolink, Purple Finch, Red Crossbill and Vesper Sparrow, the last, now scarce, being the most extreme case.

A Local Summary

Rather than finish this article with a summary of the changes in the bird life occurring since 1623 covering all of New Hampshire, we have chosen to mention a few outstanding examples from the one section of the state for which we have the longest continuous coverage — the general area including Webster and Andover, from the 1870s to the present. This has been made possible by Charles F. Goodhue's writings of 1877 and 1922, centered on Webster, and an article of 1961 and more recent unpublished comments by co-author Kimball C. Elkins regarding changes in the bird life that have occurred in the general Andover-Webster area.

During this nearly 120-year period 2 trends have been leading factors affecting bird populations in this area of New Hampshire and elsewhere. One is the gradual abandonment of farmland and consequent lack of open land and increase of woodland; the other, the climax of essentially uncontrolled slaughter of wildlife and its subsequent cessation due to growing scarcities of game, changing fashions, and especially better protection and education. Some other important factors include the introduction of exotic species, increases of surburban areas and bird feeders, proliferation of garbage, heavy cutting and fragmentation of forests, changing human attitudes toward wildlife, the comeback of the beaver, and possibly climatic warming. There follow examples of species that have decreased or increased in the Webster-Andover region as a result or apparent result of one or more of the above factors or for reasons unknown, with quoted or paraphased comments from Goodhue and Elkins.

Perhaps the most striking example of the effects (or apparent effects) of the loss of open land is the case of the Vesper Sparrow, "the most common of the sparrows" in 1877 and still a common summer resident in 1922, but which appeared to have declined greatly in numbers by 1961 and "now (1994) almost gone from the region." With some seemingly suitable habitat remaining but unused by the species, there evidently are also unknown reasons involved. At the other extreme, Goodhue found the Broad-winged Hawk to be "rare" in 1877, "scarce" to within 20 years of 1922, "more plenty" in the last few years before 1922, while Elkins found it "breeding in Andover in recent years" in 1961 and "in my time the most common nesting hawk." This seems to have been a definite response to the increase in woodland combined with protection and education.

A clear case of a response to better protection alone or nearly so is that of the Killdeer, which had not reappeared in Goodhue's area even by 1922 but became, "to a limited extent, a summer resident" of Andover by 1961. Elkins first recorded it in the area in 1947, confirmed it as a breeding species in 1954 in Danbury, and regards it as "conspicuous but not numerous" in 1994. This is an unusual case of a great recovery being made when the amount of apparently suitable habitat had greatly declined.

The proliferation of garbage in recent years has certainly been more to the advantage of the introduced Rock Dove, European Starling, and House Sparrow than to any native birds except the gulls, which do not nest in the Webster-Andover region.

The decline of the Upland Sandpiper, primarily as a result of market hunting, seems obvious, but its failure to recover, despite the great loss of potential habitat does not. A common summer resident in 1877, it had become "more and more scarce" since 1890 and by 1905 had "practically ceased to exist in this part of the state, though White (1937) found it still nesting in Concord in the 1930s. Since 1905 it has been seen in the Webster-Andover region only in migration — in 1916, 1922-23, and several times since 1960. Here, however, is another case with apparently suitable habitat remaining but unused by the species.

The Purple Martin in 1877 was apparently "not common" but did nest "in houses put up for them," often battling with bluebirds, with "one side and sometimes the other victorious." In 1922, however, they were described as having soon occupied every house erected for them 30 years previously, as occurring in "at least five or six large colonies in our immediate vicinity" 20 years before but as having "nearly disappeared in the last ten years." In 1961 martins appeared "to have declined greatly" and in 1994 were "rare, or perhaps gone." Elkins has not known of any in the area for several years. Martin houses today generally seem to be occupied by European Starlings or House Sparrows, which seem to be the main causes of the disappearance of martins. One of the best all-around additions to our breeding avifauna, the Northern Cardinal, was unknown anywhere in New Hampshire in 1877 and 1922 and "first reported in Andover in June 1967." Although warming of the climate may have been of some influence in the extraordinary range extension and increase of the cardinal, the growth of suburbia and great increase in the number of bird feeders seem to have been the principal factors involved.

Heavy cutting of forests has certainly benefited the White-throated Sparrow, which as a breeding species in the Webster area in 1877 seems to have been confined to Mt. Kearsarge, where "a large number stay through the summer." By 1922 it had increased considerably and by 1961 "made strong gains," but apparently had not increased further by 1994. The Common Grackle certainly seems to have benefited from forest fragmentation. "Not common" in 1877, it was still considered "a rather uncommon local summer resident" in 1922. By 1961, however, it had "on the evidence available, made strong gains."

The Hooded Merganser was a rare migrant in 1877 and still unknown as a summer resident in 1922 but was found breeding in 1943 and is "now (in 1994) a fairly common breeder." One of the most interesting and very positive cases is that of the Wood Thrush, which was unknown anywhere in the state in 1877. First seen in Andover in 1922, it was still uncommon in the period 1936–45, but after that gradually became one of the most common thrushes. This was possibly at the expense of the Hermit Thrush, which during the period 1951–60 appeared to have declined greatly in numbers. Now it appears the Wood Thrush may be declining too. The reasons for its range expansion into New Hampshire and wonderful increase and possible current decrease, as well as the definite decrease of the Hermit Thrush, are not well understood.

References

Allen, G.M. 1903. A list of the birds of New Hampshire. Nature Study Press, Manchester, N.H.

Belknap, J. 1792. The history of New Hampshire. Bradford and Read, Boston.

continued over . . .

Borror, A.C. 1980. Breeding Birds of the Isles of Shoals. Shoals Marine Lab., Cornell Univ., Ithaca, N.Y.

Brewster, W. 1924-38. The birds of the Lake Umbagog region of Maine. Pts. 1-4. Bull. Mus. Comp. Zool. 66. Harvard Coll., Cambridge.

Chadbourne, A.P. 1887. A list of the summer birds of the Presidential Range of the White Mountains, New Hampshire. Auk 4: 100-108.

Cline, A.C. and S.H. Spurr. 1942. The virgin upland forest of central New England. Harvard Forest, Petersham, Mass.

Dearborn, N. 1898. A preliminary list of the birds of Belknap and Merrimack counties, New Hampshire, with notes. M.S. thesis, N.H. Coll. Agric. and Mechanic Arts, Durham.

Dearborn, N. 1903. The birds of Durham and vicinity. Contrib. Zool Lab 6. N.H. Coll. Agric. and Mechanic Arts, Durham.

Elkins, K.C. 1957. The Wood Thrush in New Hampshire. N.H. Bird News 10(2): 33-36.

Elkins, K.C. 1961. Birds of Webster and vicinity in the 1870s and today. N.H. Audubon Quar. 14: 2-13.

Forbush, E.H. 1916. A history of the game birds, wild-fowl and shore birds of Massachusetts and adjacent states. Mass. State Board Agric., Boston.

Forbush, E.H. 1925-29. Birds of Massachusetts and other New England States. 3 vols. Mass. Dept. Agric., Boston.

Goodhue, C.F. 1877. The birds of Webster and adjoining towns. Forest and Stream 8: 33-34, 49, 96, 113, 146.

Goodhue, C.F. 1922. Fifty years among the birds of New Hampshire. Concord Public Library, Concord, N.H. Unpubl. ms.

Griscom, L. and D.E. Snyder. 1955. The Birds of Massachusetts. Peabody Mus., Salem, Mass.

Hebert, V.H. 1960. Purple Martins in New Hampshire. N.H. Bird News 13: 155.

Hebert, V.H. 1968. House Finches? Stop! Look! Listen. N.H. Audubon Quar. 21:43.

Howard. D.V. 1968. Range expansion of the cardinal into New Hampshire. N.H. Audubon Quar. 21:2-6.

Kennard, J.H. and L.L. Kennard. 1967. Notes on range extensions of Mourning Doves in New Hampshire. N.H. Audubon Quar. 20:136-137.

Palmer, R.S. 1949. Maine Birds. Bull. Mus. Comp. Zool. 102. Cambridge, Mass.

Richards, T. 1952. The waterfowl of New Hampshire. M.S. thesis, Univ. Mich., Ann Arbor.

Richards, T. 1954-56. Our changing bird life. N.H. Bird News 7(1):3-16, 8(2):43-52, 9(2):34-38.

Richards, T. 1980. A brief history of New Hampshire's coastal bird life. Pp. 13-21 in N.H. Audubon Ann., Concord.

Richards, T. and K.C. Elkins. 1989. Trends in New Hampshire bird populations, 1914-89. N.H. Audubon Ann., Concord.

Shaub, M.S. 1958. Evening Grosbeaks in the Northeastern U.S. and Eastern Canada. N.H. Bird News 11(1): 3-10.

Silver, H. 1957. A history of New Hampshire game and furbearers. N.H. Fish and Game Dept., Concord.

Weeks, J.W. 1888. Game of Coos County. In G.D. Merrill, History of Coos Co. W.A. Ferguson & Co., Syracuse, N.Y.

White, F.B. 1937. Local notes on the birds at Concord, New Hampshire. Rumford Press, Concord.

Wood, W. 1634. New England's prospect. Publ. Prince Soc., Boston, 1865.

Wright, H.W. 1911. The birds of the Jefferson Region in the White Mountains. Proc. Manchester Inst. Arts and Scien. 5. Pt. 1. Manchester, N.H.

A Proposed Division of New Hampshire into Avifaunal Regions Based Largely on the Altitudinal Distribution of Breeding Birds

Tudor Richards

Introduction

One of the more interesting and basic aspects of the distribution of birds in New Hampshire is the great, if indirect, influence of elevation on the areas where the different species nest. With every 1,000 foot increase in altitude, in fact, there is, other things being more or less equal, a drop in average temperature of about 3 degrees Fahrenheit (Brooks 1967) and corresponding changes in the vegetation and animal life. By comparing the 4,000 foot gain in elevation from the Saco Valley at North Conway, 500 feet above sea level, to the Alpine Garden on Mt. Washington, 4,500 feet above sea level, with the distance of more than 900 miles from there due north to the Arctic tundra, in Ungava, northern Quebec, at about the same elevation as North Conway, one can see that a 1,000 foot increase is roughly the equivalent of a gain of more than 200 miles of latitude.

Indeed, as one goes up Mt. Washington, starting at North Conway, one soon leaves woods of pine, hemlock, oak, and other hardwood species and passes through a northern hardwood (primarily sugar maple, beech, and yellow birch) forest on the way up to the top of Pinkham Notch. Here one begins to see some spruce and fir along the highway and then nearly solid stands of them bordering the Mt. Washington Auto Road. Higher up, just before one reaches the Alpine Garden, the forest becomes stunted, with fir predominant, but with some heart-leaved white birch as well as spruce (often black rather than red) present. All along the way from North Conway there have been corresponding changes in the bird life. Remarkably similar changes occur between New Hampshire and Ungava, but very gradually, and due primarily to an increase in latitude.

Changes in the vegetation and animal life between, say, Nashua and North Conway are almost imperceptible because the rise in elevation and the increase in latitude are so small, but there are some natural changes that are significant. These, however, are much greater and more obvious between Nashua and Mt. Monadnock, and similarly between Keene and Monadnock, primarily because of the cooling effects of the considerable increases in elevation.

This article, then, goes on to include mention of past descriptions of how the bird life changes with sizable increases in elevation and of early attempts at describing different avifaunal regions. A proposed division of New Hampshire into seven such regions follows. These are the Coastal Region, Southern Lowlands, Lakes Region, Southwestern Highlands, Connecticut Valley, White Mountains, and North Country. While these are based principally on more or less natural conditions, with much emphasis on elevation, it is obvious that the hand of man has directly or indirectly changed these conditions to a greater or lesser extent.

Past Studies of the Altitudinal Distribution of Birds in New Hampshire

Henry D. Thoreau unfortunately was not nearly as good an "ornithologist" as he was a botanist but he did note differences in the bird life of New Hampshire's mountains that he climbed (Monadnock, Lafayette, and Washington) and that of Concord, Mass. After discovering a junco's nest on the summit of Monadnock (1858) he wrote "It is the prevailing bird up there, i.e., on the summit. They are commonly said to go to the fir countries to breed . . . They probably are never seen in the surrounding low ground at this season."

Arthur P. Chadbourne (1887), after spending appreciable parts of 2 summers on the Presidential Range, compiled a list of the birds he recorded but also described the changes in the vegetation and bird life along the Carriage Road between "the Glen" and the summit of Mt. Washington. He mentions the Hermit Thrush, Red-eyed Vireo, Black-throated Blue, Black-throated Green and "Canadian" warblers as occurring in the first mile or two, "Olive-backed" Thrushes still occurring at the beginning of the fourth mile, there joined by the "Bicknell's" Thrush, Blackpoll Warbler, and "Hudson Bay" Chickadee; but only the junco present from the timber line to the summit of Washington. Glover Allen (1903), using the life zones of C. Hart Merriam (1898), divided New Hampshire into Transition, Canadian, Hudsonian, and Arctic-Alpine zones, listing appropriate bird species for each.

Gerald H. Thayer (1909), another good amateur ornithologist, compiled a list of the birds of Dublin, New Hampshire, and in it mentioned some species as occurring on Mt. Monadnock, such as the Swainson's Thrush, Golden-crowned Kinglet, and White-winged Crossbill. In Chapman (1907), however, are a number of observations made by Thayer on the altitudinal distribution of warblers on Monadnock — from the Northern Parula and Northern Waterthrush, about the base, and the Black-and-white and Chestnut-sided warblers, largely confined to the lower slopes, to the Black-throated Blue, common to 2,500 feet, the Canada, fairly common to 2,700 feet, the Magnolia, common up to 2,800 feet, the Black-throated Green, ranging up to the ridge, the "Myrtle", common on the ridge, and the Nashville, fairly common almost to the top of the mountain.

My interest in the altitudinal distribution of birds started on boyhood hikes in the White Mountains. After my move to New Hampshire as a resident in 1946, it was stimulated in the course of my job as a "ridge runner" for the US Forest Service on the Presidential Range. Work in the next several years on forest and wildlife surveys all over the state for the Forest Service and NH Fish & Game Dept., respectively, followed by many years of field work on my own, led to familiarity with the bird life of many areas from Pittsburg and Umbagog Lake, in the north, to Mt. Monadnock and the Coast, in the south.

Eventually I made mountain bird counts by 500 foot intervals, using an altimeter combined with close reading of a map's contour lines. These have provided data for each of the 13 different 500 foot intervals, from below 500 feet in the Saco Valley, to more than 6,000 on Mt. Washington. Counts were mostly of singing males or calling birds, but also of single birds, pairs, or family groups seen, each counted as one possible breeding record. In the case of trips repeated over the same route, even in different years, only the highest count for each species in each interval has been used, to avoid the possibility of counting the same birds more than once. A few of the counts were made in North Country, Southwestern Highlands, and Upper Connecticut Valley. Much of the later field work was made possible by a grant from the William P. Wharton Trust.

Altogether, with the addition of other records of birds at known altitudes, more than 150 species and 8,000 individual birds have been involved. Total counts per species for one interval range up to more than 100 and for all intervals to more than 500. The figures do provide information on the relative abundance of the different species at different elevations but have obvious limitations. The carrying power of songs and call notes and frequency and times of singing vary greatly per species, and there's the human factor, for example, the gradually decreasing ability of an aging observer to hear high notes. The most significant of all these records are probably those of particular trips that covered an appreciable amount of ground in each of several 500 foot intervals. While the records as a whole date back over many years, comparison of them with recent records of other observers indicate that they still apply fairly well to present conditions.

As to different avifaunal regions in New Hampshire, one could make a case for recognizing only 2 or 3, such as the highlands and the lowlands and perhaps a separate coastal region, but this would be over-simplifying the matter. In an article on the subject of bird distribution in the state (Richards, 1952) 7 major regions are recognized, and after rereading it, I decided to propose it again, with modifications such as placing more emphasis on elevation.

Coastal Region

New Hampshire has only about 18 miles of seashore, most of it consisting of alternating beaches and rocky headlands. The Coastal Region, however, also includes all the inshore and offshore waters under the State's jurisdiction; the New Hampshire Isles of Shoals; the Hampton River estuary, with its sand bars and spits, mud flats and great salt marsh (one of the largest in New England); estuaries and harbors around Portsmouth; the Piscataqua River and tidal portions of the Salmon Falls River, both shared with Maine; Great Bay (one of the finest estuaries of all); the tidal portions of 5 more rivers that flow into it or Little Bay; and much else.

Herring and Great Black-backed gulls have long since replaced terns as the dominant birds of the Isles of Shoals, though Double-crested Cormorants are also common there and, along with the gulls, on the mainland, too. A few Common Eiders also nest on the Isles, and Black-crowned Night-Herons, Snowy Egrets, and Glossy Ibises that nest on the Maine island of Appledore often feed in the New Hampshire marshes.

Common Terns in small numbers try to nest in the

marshes and on one or 2 islands between New Castle and Great Bay but often fail because of high tides or predation by gulls, night-herons or Great Horned Owls. Piping Plovers and Least Terns have nested until recently on the inner side of Hampton Harbor. Sharp-tailed Sparrows nest regularly in the marshes, and Willets and Seaside Sparrows also have done so in recent years.

Gulls actually are the predominant birds throughout the region and more or less throughout the year but depend more on garbage than natural foods for their meals. Shorebirds are numerous in migration, especially around Hampton Harbor; waterfowl are common in winter as well as on migration along the shore and on Great Bay, and small land bird migrants are sometimes abundant on Star Island, the largest New Hampshire Isle of Shoals. Thus the Coastal Region could be regarded as more important for migrating and wintering birds than for summer and year-round residents. At any rate, this region, low in elevation and small as it is, is just as distinctive and recognizable as the White Mountain Region.

Southern Lowlands

This region comprises the typical low country of southern New Hampshire, but it merges somewhat with the Southwestern Highlands and even more with the Lakes Region, and so its limits are hard to establish. It can perhaps best be recognized as the region bordered on the south by Massachusetts and the Coastal Region; on the east by Maine; and on the north and west where the 1,000 foot contour line becomes prominent at the southern edge of the Brookfield-Middleton hills, the Belknap-Gunstock range, and the hills just west of Franklin and at the eastern edge of a long line of highlands extending south from the latter to the New Ipswich hills, respectively.

Roughly half of the Southern Lowlands (the southeastern portion and the lower part of the Merrimack Valley) is below 500 feet, with only a few hills higher than that, and the Pawtuckaway Mountains just touching 1,000 feet. The remaining area above 500 feet has a few isolated hills exceeding 1,000 feet but none as high even as 1,500 feet.

Although this region still has a considerable amount of open farmland, it has much more scattered woodland and even continuous forest. The predominant tree species are white pine, hemlock, red and sugar maple, beech, paper and black birch and white ash, with aspens, cherries, hickories, white oak, red and pitch pine, red cedar, and other species occurring in lesser amounts.

Because of its good combination of evergreen and deciduous woods and great variety of habitat in general, the Southern Lowlands has a very rich avifauna. On the other hand, it is the one region of New Hampshire with by far the greatest extent of urban and suburban areas and the fastest rates of development and fragmentation of woodland. Consequently it almost certainly has the highest percentages of "trash" birds as well as such attractive suburban birds as Northern Mockingbirds, Northern Cardinals, and House Finches.

The Southern Lowlands has no common breeding bird species that don't occur in other regions but does have a few rarer species that don't occur in, or are definitely or probably less common than in other regions. Examples are the Common Moorhen, Yellow-billed Cuckoo, Eastern Screech-Owl, Fish Crow, Carolina Wren, White-eyed Vireo, Golden- and Blue- winged and Prairie warblers, and Orchard Oriole. In a walk around Turkey Pond,

Concord (elevation 350 feet; 7/5/74, 5:50 – 11:00 AM) I recorded 52 species and 250 individual birds. The 10 with the highest counts (or possible breeding records) were: Common Yellowthroat, 36; Red-eyed Vireo, 22; Gray Catbird, 15; Veery, 14; Song Sparrow, 13; Swamp Sparrow, 12; Ovenbird, 11; Chestnut-sided Warbler, 10; Rufous-sided Towhee, 10; Red-winged Blackbird, 9. Nine other warblers were recorded, 3 each of Black-and-white, Yellow, Pine and American Redstart, 2 of Blackburnian, and one each of Yellow-rumped, Black-throated Green, Black-throated Blue, and Northern Waterthrush. This is just an example of a count made in a typical area of the Southern Lowlands.

Lakes Region

This region could be considered just an extension of the Southern Lowlands but is perhaps different enough to deserve recognition as a separate region. It similarly is bordered on the East by Maine and on the North and West mostly by the 1,000 foot contour line, in this case one extending southwest from Redstone Ledge, in Conway, to the northwest corner of the Southern Lowlands, just east of Ragged Mountain, in Danbury Hill/Andover. Most of this region lies between 500 and 1,000 feet, but there are sizable sections below 500 around Ossipee Lake and along the Saco River, and some good monadnocks such as Mts. Belknap and Gunstock and the remarkable, ring-diked Ossipee Mountains, which reach almost 3,000 feet but are entirely separate from the White Mountains.

There is less open farmland than in the Southern Lowlands and only one small city (Laconia) and consequently a higher percentage of forest. The same tree species as in the Lowlands are predominant, and the land birds are also much the same. What gives the Lakes Region its character, however, are the many lakes, including several large and one very large one, Winnipesaukee, and the Common Loons and Common Mergansers that live on them. Other characteristic summering water birds of the Lakes Region are the now uncommon to rare Pied-billed Grebe, and the Great Blue Heron, American Bittern, Mallard, Black and Wood ducks, Hooded Merganser, Spotted Sandpiper and Great Black-backed, Herring and Ring-billed gulls.

The other main feature of the region, the Ossipee Mountains, which seem not to have been explored much if at all ornithologically, could be interesting if enough of its higher elevation spruce-fir timber remains. It is quite likely that such "northern" birds as the Yellow-bellied Flycatcher, Gray-cheeked Thrush, Ruby-crowned Kinglet, Philadelphia Vireo, Bay-breasted, Blackpoll and Mourning warblers and the crossbills nest there, but unlikely that the Spruce Grouse, Black-backed Woodpecker, Gray Jay, and Boreal Chickadee do.

In counts I made over the same route in Sandwich near Squam Lake, mostly, through mixed woodland, 6/17/51 and about 7/12/51, 44 species were tallied. Using the highest count per species on whichever trip it was, the 12 species with the highest counts were in order: Red-eyed Vireo, 32; American Redstart, 27; Blackburnian Warbler, 17; Ovenbird, 14; Chestnut-sided Warbler, 10; American Robin, 8; Veery, 7; Northern Parula Warbler, 7; Black-throated Blue Warbler, 7; Black-and-white Warbler, 6; Northern Waterthrush, 6; Common Yellowthroat, 6. Five other species of warblers were recorded: Pine, Black-throated Green, Yellow-rumped, Canada, and Louisiana Waterthrush. This count was made long enough ago so that habitat

changes alone would make a count over the same route today appreciably different.

Southwest Highlands

This region is fairly well defined in that most of it is above 1,000 feet, much above 1,500 and especially some, on seven different peaks, above 2,500 feet. These peaks are from north to south, Mt. Cube, 2,909 feet, near the region's northern border, the Baker River Valley; Smart's Mountain, 3,238 feet, Lyme; Mt. Cardigan, 3,121 feet, Mt. Cardigan State Park; Croydon Peak, 2,781 feet, closed to the public; Mt. Kearsarge, 2,931 feet, Winslow State Park; Mt. Sunapee, 2,743 feet, Mt. Sunapee State Park; and, after a long gap containing peaks only a little over 2,000 feet, and way to the South, Mt. Monadnock, 3,165 feet, Mt. Monadnock State Park. Although this region is one primarily of northern hardwoods (beech, sugar maple, and yellow birch), spruce grows at higher elevations and also in moist areas lower down. The peaks are all high enough to have substantial amounts of spruce forest and so do attract certain "northern" birds, though past forest fires combined with soil erosion have laid bare much of the summits of Mts. Cardigan, Kearsarge, and Monadnock.

No significant field work seems to have been carried out on Mt. Cube or Smart's Mountain, and very little on Croydon Peak. Mt. Cardigan, judging from my two early summer trips up the mountain, probably still has regular breeding populations of Yellow-bellied Flycatchers, Gray-cheeked Thrushes, and Blackpoll Warblers. Yellow-bellied Flycatcher, Gray-cheeked Thrush, Ruby-crowned Kinglet, Tennessee Warbler, and White-winged Crossbill all have been recorded in summer on Mt. Kearsarge by Kimball Elkins, and Blackpoll Warbler records for the mountain have been added by Jane Grant and myself.

Mt. Sunapee, which is lower than the other 7 and doesn't have a great deal of spruce, surprised me on my first ascent of it, in mid-June, 1953, with records of 2 separate Yellow-bellied Flycatchers, one each of Gray-cheeked Thrush, Blackpoll Warbler, and White-winged Crossbill, and a pair of Rusty Blackbirds, whose nest was found about a week later. The following summer in July, I recorded a Mourning Warbler and six Red Crossbills. Many years later, during the Atlas period, a Tennessee Warbler was added, though the northern element was otherwise missing, hopefully by oversight.

The 10 species with the highest counts on that first trip up Mt. Sunapee were in order: Red-eyed Vireo, 22; Swainson's Thrush, 12; American Redstart, 11; Canada Warbler, 10; Ovenbird, 9; Rose-breasted Grosbeak, 6; Dark-eyed Junco, 6; Black-throated Blue Warbler, 5; White-throated Sparrow, 5; Blackburnian Warbler, 4.

Following Thayer, several other observers reported seeing on Mt. Monadnock during the breeding season various birds of particular interest: Charles L. Whittle (1923), Bay-breasted Warbler; Leon Hausman (1935), Philadelphia Vireo, Blackpoll and Mourning warblers; Jacob B. Abbott (1949), Bay-breasted Warbler. On 7/2/51 I heard a Gray-cheeked Thrush on the upper spruce slope of the mountain and recorded 38 other species, not, however, including any of the above rarities. On a count made 6/17/62 48 species were recorded but not even including the Gray-cheek. The 15 species with the highest counts are shown in order, in the following table:

Table 4.1   Counts of birds on Mt. Monadnock, Jaffrey, N.H. on 17 June 1962

Species	Lower Slopes 1,400–2,000' *	Upper Slopes 2,000–3,000' **	Totals
Ovenbird	20	5	25
White-throated Sparrow	2	21	23
Red-eyed Vireo	19	0	19
Rufous-sided Towhee	0	19 (13 in scrub)	19
Yellow-rumped Warbler	1	16	17
Common Yellowthroat	6	11 (all in scrub)	17
Veery	12	4	16
Black-throated Blue Warbler	8	7	15
Blackburnian Warbler	11	4	15
Canada Warbler	1	12	13
Swainson's Thrush	0	11	11
Nashville Warbler	0	11	11
Magnolia Warbler	0	11	11
American Redstart	11	0	11
Dark-eyed Junco	0	10	10

* White pine, hemlock, and northern hardwoods
** Spruce, spruce-hardwoods, scrub

Although this count was made 32 years ago, a count covering the same ground today (Dublin and Pumpelly Trails) would probably be very similar because the forest hasn't changed very much. It seems possible that some of the rarities reported earlier by other observers might still occur as summer residents at least occasionally.

Connecticut Valley

The justification for recognizing this as a separate region is that it is completely separated by the Southwest Highlands and White Mountains from the other low elevation regions, the Lakes Region, and the Southern Lowlands. There is, in fact, only one pass across to the Connecticut Valley from the east (that along Rt. 4 in Grafton) which is below 1,000 feet, and it is only barely so. Another reason for recognizing this region is that it can be considered to stretch all the way up to Lancaster or even Colebrook. Near here the 1,000 foot contour crosses the Connecticut River, which, curiously enough, is all in New Hampshire, the west bank being the common boundary with Vermont.

Assuming the Valley as a region is bounded on the east more or less by the 1,000 foot contour, it merges quite a lot with the Southwestern Highlands and also the White Mountains and North Country. In any case, the Valley is very narrow. Nevertheless, it is very distinct from at least the higher parts of the Southwest Highlands, being more like the Southern Lowlands in having more open farmland and more tree species such as hickories, oaks, black birch, and cottonwood, that are scarce or missing from higher elevations. Ash-leaved maple or box elder is a common tree in the Connecticut Valley, occurring as far north as Columbia, but is not native elsewhere in New Hampshire.

In general the bird life of the Valley is much like that of the Southern Lowlands. Nearly 50 bird species typical of the Valley were tallied on an Audubon canoe trip along the river in Haverhill 6/12/71. The 10 species with the highest counts on the New Hampshire side were in order: Bank Swallow, 157

(holes); Red-eyed Vireo, 42; Common Grackle, 36; Song Sparrow, 36; Red-winged Blackbird, 33; Yellow Warbler, 29; American Redstart, 23; Eastern Kingbird, 15; Warbling Vireo, 13; Spotted Sandpiper and American Robin, 12 each. Among the others were: one Green Heron, 4 Belted Kingfishers, 4 Yellow-throated Vireos and one Vesper Sparrow.

By contrast further north, but at least as far south as Lancaster, are some heavily wooded tamarack-black spruce bogs that, at least in the past, have had as apparent breeding species (all recorded in late June or early July) Yellow-bellied Flycatcher, Boreal Chickadee, Ruby-crowned Kinglet, and Wilson's Warbler. Here the combination of latitude, rather than altitude, and bog is responsible for making the habitat cool enough and otherwise favorable for these birds.

White Mountain Region

This region could be divided into at least 4 well-defined regions if they were extensive enough — Valleys, Northern Hardwoods, Spruce-Fir, and Arctic Alpine, and even have a fifth zone of stunted trees, mostly firs, in contrast to the zone below it naturally dominated by spruce. As recognized here it is the region bounded on the east by Maine, on the south by the Lakes Region and Southwestern Highlands, on the west by the Connecticut River Valley and on the north by the North Country. In order to include the northern section of the White Mountain National Forest the common boundary with the North Country should probably be along the Upper Ammonoosuc River and North Branch, and, from Berlin down, the Androscoggin River. Along the Israel River and across to where the Androscoggin turns east might otherwise make a better boundary.

The counts of singing males and sightings made at 500 foot intervals and described earlier have at least produced some interesting figures. Unfortunately, there wasn't a desirable number of counts made in the 500 to 1,000 foot interval and especially in that below 500 feet, so little of the region being at these low elevations. It is also true of the highest interval, which is even less important because of the few species involved. Nevertheless, there are enough figures to give some idea of the status of the different species at these extremes.

The number of species counted in each interval is presented in Table 4.2.

Table 4.2   Number of bird species counted in each 500ft (152.5m) interval of elevation in the White Mountains of New Hampshire

under 500'	72
500–1,000'	101
1,000–1,500'	134
1,500–2,000'	116
2,000–2,500'	94
2,500–3,000'	70
3,000–3,500'	45
3,500–4,000'	41
4,000–4,500'	31
4,500–5,000'	20
5,000–5,500'	12
5,500–6,000'	1
over 6,000'	3

Excluding the first 2 sets of figures (because of the limited areas and consequent smaller number of species involved) one can still see that the greatest variety of species occurs at low elevations and that there is a steady drop in the number of species with every 500 foot gain in elevation, and only 3 occur in the >6,000 foot interval.

The leading species counted, with their numbers and range of 500 foot intervals, are shown in Table 4.3.

Table 4.3 Total individuals counted and altitudinal range of the 15 most commonly detected species in the White Mountains of New Hampshire

Species	#	Range of Intervals	Principal Range
White-throated Sparrow	559	500–1000' to 5000–5500'	500–5500'
Blackpoll Warbler	451	1000 –1500' to 5000–5500'	1500–5000'
Swainson's Thrush	400	500–1000' to 4500–5000'	1000–4500'
Red-eyed Vireo	350	<500' to 2500–3000'	<500–2500'
American Redstart	266	<500' to 4000–4500'	<500–2500'
Dark-eyed Junco	260	<500' to >6000'	1000 to >6000'
Common Yellowthroat	249	<500' to 3500–4000'	<500–2500'
Yellow-rumped Warbler	248	500–1000' to 5000–5500'	1000–5000'
American Robin	244	<500' to 5000–5500'	<500–2500'
Song Sparrow	202	<500' to 5000–5500'	<500–2500'
Red-winged Blackbird	198	<500' to 2500–3000'	<500–2500'
Gray-cheeked Thrush	194	1500–2000' to 5000–5500'	2500–5000'
Magnolia Warbler	192	500–1000' to 4500-5000'	1000–4000'
Purple Finch	175	<500' to 5000–5500'	<500–4500'
Veery	152	<500' to 2000–2500'	<500 –2000'

The above 15 common species can be divided into three groups. The White-throated Sparrow and Dark-eyed Junco each have an exceptionally great altitudinal range throughout which they are common, from below 1,000 feet to above timberline (with the junco the only species occurring in all intervals all the way to the summit of Mt. Washington), . The Purple Finch and Nashville Warbler (122 counted) have similar ranges. A second group consists of the Red-eyed Vireo, American Redstart, Common Yellowthroat, American Robin, Song Sparrow, Red-winged Blackbird, and Veery, which are principally birds of lower elevations and are common throughout much of southern New Hampshire. At least occasionally if not regularly a robin, a Song Sparrow, or perhaps a yellowthroat may occur and possibly even nest above the timberline. There are many other species in this general group ranging up to 2,000 – 3,000 feet.

The third group includes birds that are most common at medium to high elevations and are generally scarce in or absent from most of southern New Hampshire. These are the Swainson's and Gray-cheeked Thrushes and Blackpoll, Magnolia, and Yellow-rumped warblers, though the last 2 are more common than the other 2 south of the mountains. There are a number of other species that are somewhat less common such as the Yellow-bellied Flycatcher, Common Raven (another bird with a great altitudinal range), Winter Wren, both kinglets, Black-throated Green and Canada warblers, and Pine Siskin; also the uncommon Spruce Grouse, Black-backed Woodpecker, Boreal Chickadee, Philadelphia Vireo (probably more common that it seems), Bay-breasted Warbler, White-winged Crossbill, and Rusty Blackbird, and the rare Three-toed Woodpecker, Gray Jay, Tennessee Warbler, Pine Grosbeak (if it still occurs), and Red Crossbill.

Table 4.4 Numbers of individuals counted of the 10 most frequently detected species in each 500 ft (152.5 m) interval of elevation in the White Mountains of New Hampshire

Under 500'*: Bank Swallow, 162 (157 holes); Red-eyed Vireo, 71; Song Sparrow, 69; Common Grackle, 45; Red-winged Blackbird, 41; Yellow Warbler, 35; American Redstart, 30; American Robin, 28; Eastern Kingbird, 22; Veery, 20. * includes some Upper Connecticut Valley records.

500–1000': Red-eyed Vireo, 65; Bank Swallow, 60 holes; Veery, 49; Chestnut-sided Warbler, 40; Common Yellowthroat, 40; Song Sparrow, 39; American Robin, 35; American Redstart, 35; White-throated Sparrow, 33; Wood Thrush, 31.

1000–1500': Common Yellowthroat, 97; White-throated Sparrow, 88; Red-eyed Vireo, 83; Red-winged Blackbird, 65; American Robin, 64; Magnolia Warbler, 62; Veery, 59; Swamp Sparrow, 54; American Redstart: 53; Song Sparrow: 52.

1500–2000': Swainson's Thrush, 69; White-throated Sparrow, 59; Red-eyed Vireo, 53; American Robin, 49; American Redstart, 49; Common Grackle, 45; Common Yellowthroat, 40; Cedar Waxwing, 35; Blackpoll Warbler, 35; Purple Finch, 34.

2000–2500': Swainson's Thrush, 73; American Redstart, 61; Red-eyed Vireo, 58; White-throated Sparrow, 42; American Robin, 39; Red-winged Blackbird, 31; Ovenbird, 27; Common Yellowthroat, 25; Purple Finch, 25; Barn Swallow, 22.

2500–3000': Blackpoll Warbler, 78; Swainson's Thrush, 77; White-throated Sparrow, 70; Yellow-rumped Warbler, 39; Dark-eyed Junco, 37; Purple Finch, 29; Black-throated Green Warbler, 25; Red-breasted Nuthatch, 24; Magnolia Warbler, 24; Winter Wren, 22.

3000–3500': Blackpoll Warbler, 74; Swainson's Thrush, 61; White-throated Sparrow, 55; Gray-cheeked Thrush, 36; Dark-eyed Junco, 32; Yellow-rumped Warbler, 29; Magnolia Warbler, 25; Yellow-bellied Flycatcher, 22; Purple Finch, 21; Red-breasted Nuthatch, 15; Nashville Warbler, 15.

3500–4000': Blackpoll Warbler, 84; White-throated Sparrow, 58; Gray-cheeked Thrush, 53; Swainson's Thrush, 43; Dark-eyed Junco, 33; Yellow-rumped Warbler, 32; Nashville Warbler, 23; Magnolia Warbler, 16; Purple Finch, 16; Pine Siskin, 15.

4000–4500': Blackpoll Warbler, 122; White-throated Sparrow, 81; Gray-cheeked Thrush, 52; Yellow-rumped Warbler, 49; Swainson's Thrush, 36; Dark-eyed Junco, 32; Purple Finch, 28; Pine Siskin, 25; Spruce Grouse, 8; Magnolia Warbler, 8.

4500–5000': White-throated Sparrow, 52; Dark-eyed Junco, 37; Blackpoll Warbler, 32; Gray-cheeked Thrush, 28; Yellow-rumped Warbler, 22; Swainson's Thrush, 8; Purple Finch, 8; Pine Siskin, 8; Common Raven, 4; Ruby-crowned Kinglet, 4.

5000–5500': White-throated Sparrow, 21; Dark-eyed Junco, 20; American Robin, 6; Gray-cheeked Thrush, 5; Yellow-rumped Warbler, 3; Blackpoll Warbler, 3; American Kestrel, 1; Tree Swallow, 1; Common Raven, 1; Purple Finch, 1; Pine Siskin, 1; Song Sparrow, 1.

5500–6000': Dark-eyed Junco, 4.

>6000': Dark-eyed Junco, 3; Chimney Swift & Common Raven, 1

Although the figures in Table 4.4 were not obtained very systematically and should be used to make only rough rather than close comparisons of the numbers of the different species, they do show the altitudinal range and abundance at different elevations of each of the most common species probably with reasonable accuracy. The Red-eyed Vireo, for example, does appear to be the most abundant woodland species at lower elevations, the Swainson's Thrush in the mixed forests of low to medium elevations, the Blackpoll Warbler in the spruce-fir forests of high elevations, the White-throated Sparrow in the vicinity of timberline and the Dark-eyed Junco at highest elevations.

The figures also show the somewhat restricted range of the Blackpoll Warbler and especially the Gray-cheeked Thrush, which are largely absent below 1,500 and 2,500 feet, respectively. The more complete figures, which are too numerous to be included here, provide more information on the altitudinal distribution and abundance of many less common, uncommon, and rare species. The following table, however, shows the results of one particular trip.

The count shown in Table 4.5 started at an elevation above 3,000 feet so the lower elevations were not reached until late afternoon, when the birds were so quiet that few records were obtained for the intervals below 3,000 feet. The individual counts as far as they go seem on the whole to agree well with the overall figures in the previous table. The good count of Ruby-crowned Kinglets was, however, a surprise.

North Country

This region, since it consists largely of a string of mountains actually a little higher and more continuous than those of the Southwestern Highlands, could be regarded as a continuation of the White Mountains, as it often is. On the other hand, it is of the greatest interest to most people, including bird watchers, for the extensive, relatively level, often boggy areas of boreal forests and unspoiled lakes and ponds at lower elevations. For our purposes, then, it is worth recognizing as a separate region.

No significant bird studies seem to have been carried out on the higher peaks of the northern mountains, but it is probably safe to say that their avifauna, where the habitat hasn't been too disturbed, as by extensive clear-cutting, isn't essentially different at comparable elevations from that of the White Mountains proper.

A lot of field work, however, has been carried out in the past around the Connecticut Lakes, and even more and over a much longer period around Lake Umbagog. Here William Brewster began his nearly 40 years of intensive field work in 1871, and here also we expect soon to have an extensive National Wildlife Refuge established. Already the Audubon Society of New Hampshire, in cooperation with the Federal and State governments, has in recent years been conducting important research and management work in this area on behalf of the Common Loon, Bald Eagle, Osprey, and other species.

Although heavy logging combined with ravages of the spruce budworm has devastated much of the North Country in recent decades, wildlife populations have actually recovered remarkably since Brewster's day, and spectacularly with

Table 4.5 A count of birds by 500 ft (152.5 m) intervals of elevation made on 5 July 1972 from Carter Notch to Pinkham Notch via the Carter Range

Species	2000' to 2500'	2500' to 3000'	3000' to 3500'	3500' to 4000'	4000' to 4500'	>4500'	Totals	Rank
Spruce Grouse				1			1	
Yellow-bellied Flycatcher			3		1		4	12
Boreal Chickadee			1			1	2	14
Common Raven					1		1	
Winter Wren			3	2	2		7	9
American Robin	1		1				2	14
Swainson's Thrush			5	2	13	2	22	3
Gray-cheeked Thrush			4	3	11	7	25	2
Hermit Thrush					1		1	
Ruby-crowned Kinglet			1	1	6	2	10	7
Golden-crowned Kinglet		1			1		2	14
Philadelphia Vireo			1				1	
Nashville Warbler			1	2	4	2	9	8
Magnolia Warbler			1				1	
Yellow-rumped Warbler			1	1	11	7	20	5
Blackpoll Warbler			5	3	16	9	33	1
Black-throated Blue Warbler	1						1	
Black-throated Green Warbler		2	1	1			4	12
Ovenbird	1						1	
Purple Finch			1	1	1	3	6	10
Pine Siskin			1	2	2		5	11
Dark-eyed Junco			4	2	5	4	15	6
White-throated Sparrow			5	1	10	6	22	3

Counts were of singing males, nonsinging males, females, pairs or families or groups of young, each counting one ▪ Elevations were estimated as carefully as possible by altimeter readings checked against contour map readings ▪ Sixteen 500 foot intervals came out of the ups and downs of this trip ▪ Rusty Blackbird was missed at Carter Lakes but had been recorded there 7/11/70 ▪ 23 species (7 warblers) recorded, 21 (5 warblers) at >3000'. ▪ Best high elevation count of Ruby-crowned Kinglet.

the return of the moose and beaver, the latter providing innumerable ponds that are focal points for most of the wildlife around them. Waterfowl as a whole and snipe have also made extraordinary recoveries.

On all too many lower slopes of the North Country formerly covered with northern hardwoods only scattered culls remain, and on many higher slopes spruce and fir have been largely replaced by pin cherry, aspen and paper birch. On the lower flats, fir is now generally more common than spruce. There is in fact, very little virgin timber left, though there is a good remnant along East Inlet, Pittsburg, recently acquired by The Nature Conservancy. In 1953, when there was still an extensive area of old growth here, NH Fish & Game Conservation Officer Fred Scott and I made a bird count in it in early July. The results are shown in Table 4.6.

The count in perhaps most remarkable for the high number of Bay-breasted Warblers, leading all other species despite its rather weak songs. In an adjacent bog (which is still intact) on other occasions during the breeding season the following species also have been recorded: Spruce Grouse, Three-toed Woodpecker, Ruby-crowned Kinglet, Philadelphia Vireo, Wilson's Warbler, Pine Grosbeak, and Lincoln's Sparrow.

The Umbagog Lake section of the North Country is also interesting for its land birds, as New Hampshire's only known nesting site of the Palm Warbler, only recent nesting site of the Bald Eagle, and principal nesting area of the Osprey. This section, too, is New Hampshire's most important waterfowl nesting area. Besides the Mallard, Black and Wood ducks, and Hooded Merganser, the generally less common Ring-necked Duck and Common Goldeneye also nest in the wetlands near the Lake, and the Northern Pintail and both species of teal have done so in one or more recent years.

Conclusion

The several proposed avifaunal regions of New Hampshire just described are not, of course, much like what the Indians kept so nearly natural up until 1623. Nevertheless, there are a very few small stands of virgin forests left in protected or isolated areas and more old second-growth stands that resemble true "old growth." With more and more forest land becoming protected all the time, even from timber cutting, such areas can be expected to increase somewhat. The idea of "super sanctuaries," which has already started in the Southwestern Highlands, can be expanded and adapted to other regions. It would be especially appropriate in the North Country, where there are already nucleii at East Inlet and Umbagog.

Table 4.6 Counts of birds in long-since cut virgin spruce-fir flat above Norton Pool, East Inlet, Pittsburg, N.H. on 8 July 1953 (including brookside alders and beaver pond bog)

Species in order of Numbers	# seen or heard only	# squeaked to within view	Totals	# in Bog
Bay-breasted Warbler	25*	5	30	(2)
Swainson's Thrush	19	7	26	
Golden-crowned Kinglet	16	2	18	
Winter Wren	17*	0	17	
Black-throated Green Warbler	10	5	15	
White-throated Sparrow	12	3	15	(2+)
Red-breasted Nuthatch	9	5	14	
Yellow-rumped Warbler	11	3	14	(1)
American Redstart	8	6	14	(8)
Magnolia Warbler	6	6	12	(3)
Dark-eyed Junco	10	2	12	
Common Yellowthroat	9	0	9	(7)
Solitary Vireo	8	0	8	(2)
Blackburnian Warbler	5	2	7	(1)
Blackpoll Warbler	7	0	7	(4)
Yellow-bellied Flycatcher	4	1	5	
Boreal Chickadee	5	0	5	
Nashville Warbler	5	0	5	(3)
Black-throated Blue Warbler	4	0	4	
Rusty Blackbird	3	0	3	(3)
Chimney Swift	2+	0	2+	(2+)
Olive-sided Flycatcher	2	0	2	(1)
Barred Owl	1	0	1	
Downy Woodpecker	1	0	1	
Black-backed Woodpecker	1	0	1	(1)
Gray Jay	1 (group of 6)	0	1	
Black-capped Chickadee	1	0	1	
Cedar Waxwing	1	0	1	
Tennessee Warbler	1	0	1	(1)
Northern Parula Warbler	1	0	1	
Chestnut-sided Warbler	1	0	1	(1)
Purple Finch	1	0	1	(1)
Red Crossbill	1	0	1	
White-winged Crossbill	1	0	1	
Canada Warbler	1	0	1	(1)
TOTAL (35 species)	**210**	**47**	**257**	**(44)**

Singing males, lone females, pairs, families or single seperate young each counted as one.

* songs

References:

Abbott, J.B. 1949. Birds of the Grand Monadnock, Yankee Magazine, Oct. & Sept., 1949.

Allen, G. 1903. A list of the birds of N.H. Nature Study Press, Manchester, N.H.

Brooks, M. 1967. The life of the mountains. Publ. in coop. with World Book Encyclopedia by McGraw Hill, New York.

Chadbourne, A.P. 1887. A List of the summer birds of the Presidential Range of the White Mountains, N.H. Auk. 4: 100–105.

Chapman, F.M. 1907. The warblers of North America. Appleton & Co., New York.

Hausman, L. 1935. Summer bird life of Mount Monadnock. Appalachia, Nov., 1935.

Merriam, C.H. 1898. Life zones and crop zones of the United States. USDA Bull. 10.

Richards, T. 1952. The Distribution of bird life in New Hampshire. N.H. Bird News 5 (3): 3–14

Thayer. G.H. 1908 & 1909. A list of Dublin birds with brief notes, in Dublin News. Also reprinted in L.W. Leonard & J.C. Seward, History of Dublin, 1919, published by the town, and in Monadnock Sightings, E. & K. Allison, Dublin Conservation Commission, 1979.

Thoreau, H.D. 1910. Notes on New England birds. Arranged and edited by F.H. Allen, Houghton Mifflin Co., Boston.

Whittle, C.L. 1923. Bay-breasted Warbler, a regular summer resident on Mount Monadnock, NH. Auk 40 (4): 699.

Abbreviations Used in the Text

AOU	American Ornithologists' Union
ASNH	Audubon Society of New Hampshire
ASRF	Asterisk Species Report Form
Atlas	New Hampshire Breeding Bird Atlas Project
BBC	Breeding Bird Census
BBS	U.S. Fish and Wildlife Service Breeding Bird Survey
C	Centigrade
CBC	Christmas Bird Count(s)
CLO Nest Rec. Prog.	Cornell Laboratory of Ornithology North American Nest Record Program
cm	centimeter(s)
CTM	Audubon Society of New Hampshire Cardinal, Titmouse, Mockingbird Survey
dbh	Diameter at breast height (of tree[s])
F	Fahrenheit
ft	foot, feet
ha	hectare(s)
h	hour
in	inch(es)
km	kilometer(s)
LPC	Loon Preservation Committee of the Audubon Society of New Hampshire
m	meter(s)
mi	mile(s)
mph	miles per hour
Mt.	Mount
Mtn.	Mountain
mus. coll.	museum collections
NHAQ	New Hampshire Audubon Quarterly
NHBBA	New Hampshire Breeding Bird Atlas
NHESP	New Hampshire Endangered Species Program
NHFG	New Hampshire Fish and Game Department
pers. comm.	personal communication
pers. obs.	personal observation
RNEB	Records of New England Birds
sq	square
SRS	Species Report Slips
unpubl.	unpublished
USBS	U.S. Biological Survey
USFWS	U.S. Fish and Wildlife Service
WMNF	White Mountain National Forest
yd	yard(s)

Species
Accounts & Maps

Common Loon
Gavia immer

The extraordinary call notes of the Common Loon carrying across a northern lake reflect the very essence of wildness. This striking black and white bird is fascinating to watch, as it dives and eventually surfaces where one least expects it.

The Common Loon's breeding range extends from Alaska to Iceland, south to an irregular line extending from Washington to Massachusetts. In New Hampshire it is a Threatened Species, but is still a common summer resident of Squam, Winnipesaukee, and Umbagog lakes. Elsewhere, it nests at scattered lakes and larger ponds, except in the Lakes Region, where it is fairly well distributed. In migration the loon occurs widely inland and is common along the coast, where it is also fairly common in winter.

After wintering on the ocean, Common Loons arrive on New Hampshire lakes soon after the ice goes out, rarely before the first of April. Males ordinarily come first, but sometimes pairs arrive together (McIntyre 1988). Sutcliffe (1980) first saw pairs together on New Hampshire nesting lakes from 4 to 30 days after ice out. Loons may congregate on nearby open water to wait for ice out on their nesting lakes, as on 29 April 1992 when C. J. Martin (pers. comm.) saw 37 on the Androscoggin River just below Umbagog Lake. Spring migration apparently extends into June.

Nesting loons are strongly territorial. Although they may attempt to nest on ponds as small as 12 to 15 a (5 to 6 ha), lakes smaller than 198 a (80 ha) generally support a single pair. On large lakes, territories range from 22 to 415 a (9 to 168 ha) (McIntyre 1988). Loons defend their territories against other loons, Common Mergansers and other large ducks, and even Great Black-backed Gulls (Richards, pers. obs.).

Courtship is quiet and consists of rather simple displays by both sexes, such as bill dipping and other head movements, short dives, and soft calls. With the birds swimming together close to shore, the male invites the female to mate by climbing ashore, where mating eventually takes place (McIntyre 1988). Sutcliffe (1980) found 69% of New Hampshire loon nesting sites on islands, 71% of which were less than an acre in size. The remaining nests were about evenly divided between dry and swampy mainland shores. Nests were of 3 types: hummocks 22%, scrapes 36%, and wholly constructed nests 42%. Those closest to water were the most successful.

Incubation of the 2 eggs, which the adults share equally, takes 26 to 31 days (McIntyre 1988). Sutcliffe (1980) found 43% of 205 nesting attempts successful, with raccoon predation by far the leading cause of nest failure (37%).

Loons often accept artificial nesting rafts designed and constructed for their use. The Loon Preservation Committee (LPC) of ASNH placed 77 rafts on Squam Lake during 1980–89, of which 46 were used. Raft nests hatched 46 young, 55% of all chicks hatched on the lake in that period (Noon 1990). Raccoon predation was negligible on rafts, which rise and fall with fluctuating water levels and provide nesting sites in areas lacking natural ones. From 1977 to 1990, "raftlings" comprised 20% of loon chicks fledged in New Hampshire (LPC 1991).

Loon chicks leave the nest very soon after hatching and move, often on the backs or under the wings of their parents, to a "nursery" area of shallow water protected from strong winds and waves where small fish or other prey are abundant (McIntyre 1988). They have 2 downy plumages, the first black, the second brown, and acquire their juvenal plumage from about 4 to 13 weeks of age. Young loons depend entirely on their parents for food until almost 8 weeks of age (McIntyre 1988). They fledge at 11 or 12 weeks but require some parental care for 3 months and may stay with their parents for another month.

Loons often gather in loose flocks on large lakes before migrating (Palmer 1962). Adults migrate before the young (McIntyre 1988). Migration begins in September, peaks in late October, and winds down in December, with stragglers sometimes remaining into January (SRS).

Common Loon vocalizations include short "hoots," which help loons maintain contact with one another; the famous laughing "tremolos," which signify alarm; "wails" of one, 2, or 3 notes, which apparently call loons together; and the long territorial "yodels" of males (McIntyre 1988). Loon chicks peep like small chickens (Palmer 1962).

Loons once may have nested on most of New Hampshire's lakes and larger ponds, but they had become uncommon breeders by 1900, at least in the southern part of the state (Dearborn 1898, Allen 1903). Shooting and egg collecting continued to decimate their numbers in the early 1900s. Goodhue (1922) doubted if loons still nested at Lake Winnipesaukee, and Brewster (1924) wrote that they had "almost, if not wholly, ceased to breed" at Umbagog Lake, where visitors robbed the nests and sold the eggs for $1.00 each (Forbush 1912, Brewster 1924). Loons have been legally protected since 1918, but growing recreational use of lakes and ponds has affected nesting success. The LPC has helped bring about a substantial increase in the state's loon population since 1975 by promoting public interest in loons, locating and posting nesting territories, patrolling lakes, and providing nesting rafts. The numbers of nesting and territorial loon pairs in New Hampshire had risen to 86 and 132, respectively, in 1986, and to 127 and 176 in 1993. The Atlas map illustrates the species' concentrations in the Lakes Region and North Country, and scattered breeding sites elsewhere in the state. With continued success of protection efforts, future prospects for the Common Loon in New Hampshire appear to be positive.

Tudor Richards & Kimball C. Elkins

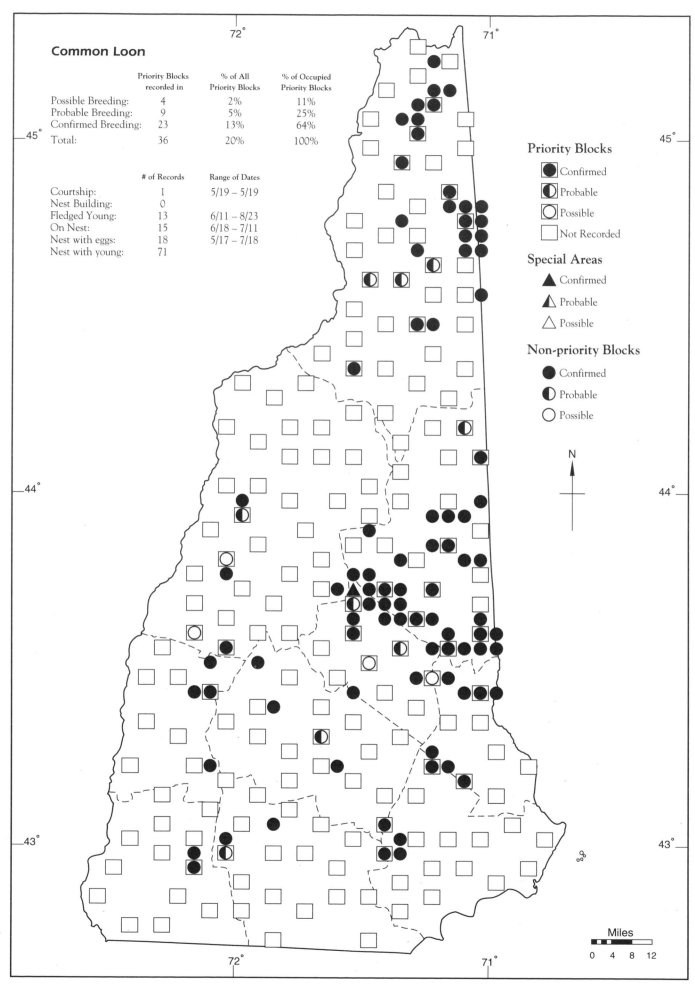

Common Loon

	Priority Blocks recorded in	% of All Priority Blocks	% of Occupied Priority Blocks
Possible Breeding:	4	2%	11%
Probable Breeding:	9	5%	25%
Confirmed Breeding:	23	13%	64%
Total:	36	20%	100%

	# of Records	Range of Dates
Courtship:	1	5/19 – 5/19
Nest Building:	0	
Fledged Young:	13	6/11 – 8/23
On Nest:	15	6/18 – 7/11
Nest with eggs:	18	5/17 – 7/18
Nest with young:	71	

Priority Blocks

- ◑ Confirmed
- ◐ Probable
- ○ Possible
- ☐ Not Recorded

Special Areas

- ▲ Confirmed
- ◥ Probable
- △ Possible

Non-priority Blocks

- ● Confirmed
- ◐ Probable
- ○ Possible

N

Miles
0 4 8 12

Pied-billed Grebe
Podilymbus podiceps

This secretive little "water witch" is hard to find in summer, when it often hides in thick marsh vegetation. Its ability to dive suddenly to escape being shot, and apparently to disappear completely have inspired the name "hell-diver." When disturbed, it may swim with only part of its body, even only its bill, above water. The species is most visible during spring and fall migration, when it occurs on water bodies throughout the state.

This grebe is widely distributed throughout North America, but is less common and more local in the Northeast than in other areas of the continent (Gibbs and Melvin 1990). The wintering range extends across the United States from New Jersey and Pennsylvania south, north in the West into Canada, and south into Mexico (Root 1988). It occurs in New Hampshire from ice out in April until November, and accidentally in winter.

The Pied-billed is the only grebe that nests in New Hampshire. This species is declining in the Northeast, at least in Vermont (Kibbe *in* Laughlin and Kibbe 1985), Massachusetts (Veit and Petersen, 1993; Mass. BBA proj., unpubl.) and New Jersey (Arbib 1982). It is listed as an Endangered Species in New Hampshire, and is considered a Migratory Bird of Management Concern in this region (Gibbs and Melvin 1992).

Nesting occurs in ponds with emergent vegetation and in marshes with large areas of open water (Palmer 1962, Chabreck 1963). In Maine this grebe requires wetlands of at least 12 a (5 ha) for nesting (Gibbs and Melvin 1990). The floating nest is hidden in vegetation, typically at least 50 ft (15.2 m) from shore and up to 20 ft (6.1 m) from open water. Water depth at the nest can range from a few inches to 4 ft (1.2 m) or more (Glover 1953).

In spring and summer the male frequently "sings" increasingly louder and slower sequences of "AH, kaow, kaow, kaow, kaoo" or "UH, cow-cow-cowp" (D.

D. Stavros, pers. comm.). A soft introduction consisting of rapid and increasingly intense "ow's" is audible at close range.

Courtship displays take many forms, and involve swimming, diving, splashing along the surface of the water, vocalizing, and ritualized postures (Palmer 1962). Copulation takes place on the nest (D. B. Stavros, pers. comm.). McAllister and Storer (1963) describe mating behavior in detail. Egg laying occurs from 12 April to 28 June in Massachusetts (Forbush 1925a), and in late May in southern Canada (Palmer 1962). Clutch size varies from 2 to 10 with a mean slightly over 6 (Glover 1953). Although the occurrence of second broods is not known, replacement clutches are found as late as August (Palmer 1962).

Both sexes share incubation, which begins after the fourth egg is laid (Forbes and Ankney 1988). When an adult leaves the nest, even to change places with its mate, it often covers the eggs with plant material. The adults usually approach from underwater and often dive and surface several times before hopping up to the rim of the nest (Deusing 1939). Hatching begins after about 23 days (Palmer 1962) and occurs over a period of 3 to 7 days (Forbes and Ankney 1987, 1988).

Newly hatched young have a complicated plumage pattern of black and white stripes and reddish brown spots. They sometimes crawl onto the back of an incubating or swimming adult (Deusing 1939). Adults usually divide their brood while the young are dependent; estimated age at first flight is 35 days (Forbes and Ankney 1987). A young grebe acquires juvenal plumage, which lacks stripes except on the head and upper neck, after up to 6 weeks. Molt into the dark grayish brown breeding plumage probably occurs by the first spring (Palmer 1962).

Grebes eat aquatic plants, small fish, amphibians, snails, leeches, and insects (Forbush 1925a). While preening they may consume some of their own feathers (Palmer 1962). Observed food items of grebes at New Hampshire breeding areas include crayfish and large tadpoles (D. B. Stavros, pers. comm.).

The Pied-billed Grebe apparently always has been rare to uncommon and very locally distributed as a nesting species in New Hampshire, although fairly common as a fall migrant (Coues 1868, Maynard 1871, Dearborn 1898, Allen 1903, Dearborn 1903, Wright 1911, White 1924, Goodhue 1877 *in* Elkins 1961, Ridgely 1977, Allison and Allison 1979). Around the turn of the century ornithologists knew it to breed on suitable ponds in southern New Hampshire (Allen 1903, Hoffmann 1904), and Goodhue (1877 *in* Elkins 1961) found it in Webster. Dearborn (1903), Wright (1911), and White (1937) knew it only as a migrant in the vicinities of Durham, Jefferson, and Concord, respectively. During the mid-1900s this grebe was widely distributed throughout the state during the breeding season, occurring as far north as Pittsburg and nesting in Errol (T. Richards, pers. comm.), where Brewster (1925) never found it in summer. Numbers began to decrease around 1960 (K. C. Elkins, T. Richards, pers. comm.).

Habitat loss and degradation are the primary threats to Pied-billed Grebe populations in the Northeast (Gibbs and Melvin 1990). Dredging and filling have destroyed numerous wetlands, while pollution and contamination have affected many others. Water level fluctuations on dammed ponds and increased predation may be factors in New Hampshire (Smith and Choate 1985).

Atlas field work confirmed the scarcity of breeding Pied- billed Grebes in New Hampshire. Other than a small cluster of confirmations in Strafford and northern Rockingham counties, records are widely scattered throughout the state. Protection of suitable breeding habitat will be important in maintaining a nesting population of this grebe in New Hampshire and the Northeast.

Robert C. Vernon

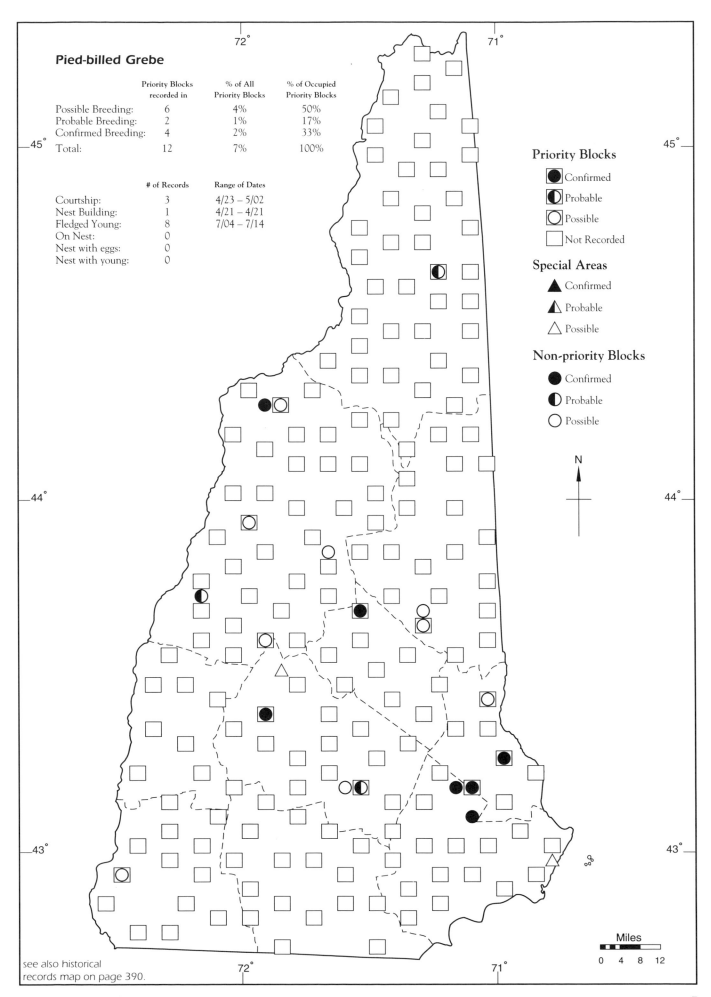

Pied-billed Grebe

	Priority Blocks recorded in	% of All Priority Blocks	% of Occupied Priority Blocks
Possible Breeding:	6	4%	50%
Probable Breeding:	2	1%	17%
Confirmed Breeding:	4	2%	33%
Total:	12	7%	100%

	# of Records	Range of Dates
Courtship:	3	4/23 – 5/02
Nest Building:	1	4/21 – 4/21
Fledged Young:	8	7/04 – 7/14
On Nest:	0	
Nest with eggs:	0	
Nest with young:	0	

Priority Blocks
- ◑ Confirmed
- ◐ Probable
- ○ Possible
- ☐ Not Recorded

Special Areas
- ▲ Confirmed
- ◣ Probable
- △ Possible

Non-priority Blocks
- ● Confirmed
- ◑ Probable
- ○ Possible

N

Miles
0 4 8 12

see also historical records map on page 390.

5

Double-crested Cormorant
Phalacrocorax auritus

Flying with heavy wing beats close to the wave crests, the cormorant increases its altitude, spreads its tail and feet, and lands awkwardly on a guano-streaked ledge. The bird then spreads its wings either to dry them or to allow loss of heat, a common sight along the New Hampshire coast.

Double-crested Cormorants are abundant along the coast during April-October. Adults fly at dawn from breeding islands at the Isles of Shoals to feed along the coast, then return in late afternoon to roost on the nesting ledges. They feed in estuaries on such sluggish fish as American eel and summer flounder. Offshore they also catch cunner. On the mainland cormorants perch on posts, rocky shoals, piers, or even utility lines near estuarine channels. Young of the year and nonbreeding adults also frequent inland lakes, ponds, and rivers.

The primary breeding site in New Hampshire is Square Rock, Rye, a ledge in the Isles of Shoals about 6 mi (10 km) east of Portsmouth. In 1986, one pair nested on nearby Lunging Island, Rye. A colony of about 1,500 pairs occurs on Duck Island, Kittery, Maine, about 2.5 mi (4 km) further north.

Double-crested Cormorants usually arrive at Square Rock from southern wintering areas in late March and early April. They wedge out gulls by sheer numbers and commence courtship. In April the double sets of plumes (the "double crests") are visible behind the eyes of both males and females; these usually disappear by the end of May. On Duck Island in April 1986, Borror observed several crouch displays, presumably of territorial males (Palmer 1962). In display, the bird elevates the tail and wing tips, lowers the breast, holds the head and bill upright, and vibrates the wings. Although Palmer (1962) described vocalizations under such conditions, Borror has heard only nestlings vocalize.

Both sexes construct well built nests on the bedrock of Square Rock, using sticks, dry weed stalks, algae, and debris plucked from the surface of the ocean. Nests become "glued" together with excreta, regurgitated fish, and dead young and may last several seasons, increasing in height with each use up to as much as 12 in (30 cm). Winter storms in 1978 eradicated all the nests on Square Rock, but the cormorants built new nests the following spring and had a successful season.

Cormorants usually are incubating by the end of May. Precise egg dates at this latitude are not documented. Nests on Square Rock are not synchronous; nests at the centers of colonies apparently are a few days earlier than those on the peripheries. The usual clutch is 3 eggs. Males and females incubate for 24.5 to 29 days (Palmer 1962).

Juveniles feed by inserting their heads and necks into the adults' mouths and gular pouches and swallowing fish their parents regurgitate. By July, dozens of young are visible on Square Rock, distinguished by their pale throats, breasts, and upper bellies. The young require about 6 weeks to fledge but can dive somewhat earlier. Young begin feeding offshore with yearlings and adults in August at the age of 7 weeks, and are independent at 10 weeks. Double-crested Cormorants require 2 years to reach reproductive maturity. The dark brown yearlings do not occur at the nesting colonies. Literature on cormorant nesting biology at our latitude includes studies of nestling physiology (e.g., Dunn 1975), predation effects (Kury and Gochfeld 1975), and range extension (Hatch 1982).

In early fall, several hundred roosting cormorants crowd onto Square Rock. Cormorants migrate during late August through November, forming long lines heading south along the coast. The highest counts of migrants occur during September and October (NHAQ, *passim*).

There are few predators on Square Rock, but predation by Great Black-backed Gulls is a major mortality factor for cormorants nesting on nearby Duck Island. Gulls may rob eggs or young from nests of absent or unwary cormorants at the perimeters of subcolonies. If humans enter such a colony, an influx of feeding gulls quickly follows the mass exodus of adult cormorants, with considerable loss of eggs and nestlings.

Cormorants probably nested along our coast at the time Europeans discovered it. In the 1600s, indigenous people visited offshore islands at night to capture cormorants by hand for food; in the last half of the 19th century, cormorants were slaughtered on the New England coast for oil and fish bait (Borror 1980). Samuels (1867) knew of no breeding population south of the Labrador coast. With changing public attitudes and protective federal legislation, New England's cormorants began to return in the 1920s.

The Double-crested Cormorant began breeding at the Isles of Shoals in the early 1940s with 18 pairs on Duck Island in 1943 (Gross 1945). That colony swelled to about 250 pairs by 1970, 300 pairs by 1975, 750 by 1980, and more than 1,600 in 1985 (Borror, unpubl. data). Borror found 8 pairs of cormorants breeding on Square Rock in 1974. The colony subsequently grew to 18 pairs in 1975, 30 in 1980, and 56 in 1985, and 80 in 1986.

There are no known inland nesting sites in New Hampshire, although the species recently (1982) began nesting on Lake Champlain in Vermont. Several growing colonies occur along the northern Massachusetts coast. The "shag" (as this species is commonly known along the Maine coastline) apparently is in the midst of a major population increase throughout its breeding range.

Arthur C. Borror

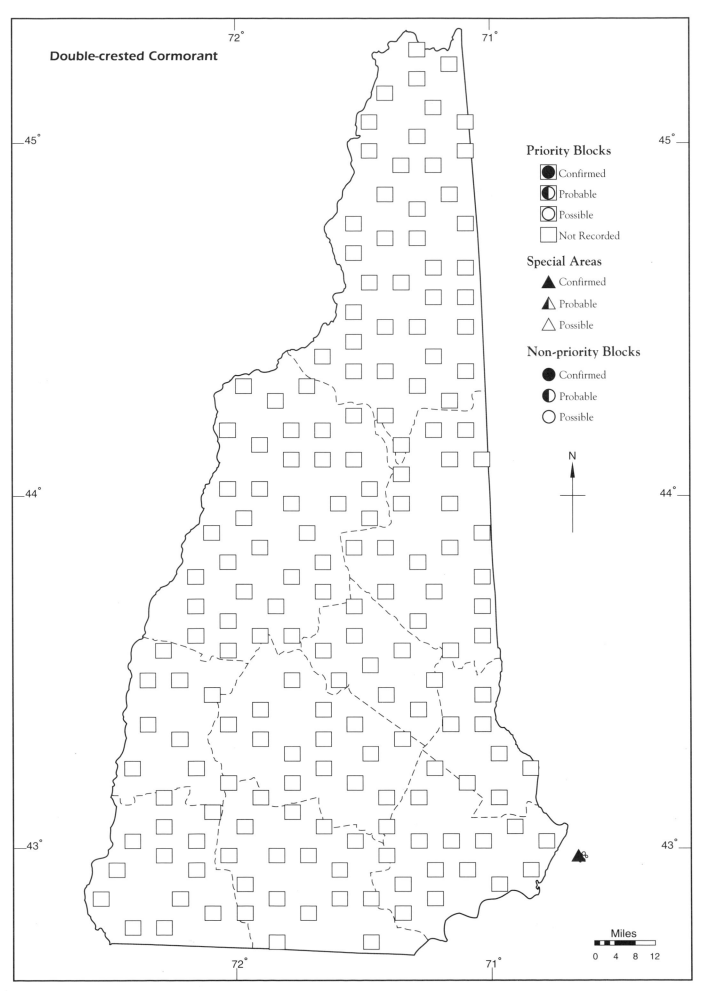

Double-crested Cormorant

Priority Blocks
- ● Confirmed
- ◐ Probable
- ○ Possible
- □ Not Recorded

Special Areas
- ▲ Confirmed
- ◮ Probable
- △ Possible

Non-priority Blocks
- ● Confirmed
- ◐ Probable
- ○ Possible

N

Miles
0   4   8   12

7

Great Blue Heron
Ardea herodias

This picturesque and stately bird is the largest and most common of New Hampshire's herons. When standing or perched, this bird's most conspicuous features are its long legs, neck, and bill. In flight the neck usually is folded back, the long legs trail behind, and the broad wings flap slowly and deliberately.

Great Blue Herons occur throughout New Hampshire, most commonly where lakes, ponds, and marshes are conspicuous features of the landscape. They usually forage by standing motionless or wading slowly in marshes or shallow water seeking fish, frogs, and other aquatic animals (Hancock and Kushlan 1984).

Great Blue Herons typically nest in colonies, sometimes (though seldom in New Hampshire) in association with other wading birds. The nests are usually high in dead trees. Years ago the colonies were often in wooded swamps (Samuels 1870, Forbush 1925a), but 90% of recent colonies were in beaver ponds (Swift, pers. obs.). These herons also nest in live trees on wooded islands in lakes, and even on upland ridges in mature deciduous trees. In northern New Hampshire they frequently nest in isolated pairs or small groups in live pine trees (ASNH data).

A vanguard of herons arrives in New Hampshire in late March. The earliest birds establish themselves in the largest and sturdiest nests. As more birds arrive, some may build new nests, which are usually on the edge of the nesting area, small, and flimsy. In nest building, the male usually brings the sticks, and the female fits them in place (Palmer 1962). Courtship, which includes stretching, bill clapping, and feather nibbling (Palmer 1962), and mating usually occur on or near the nest (Swift, pers. obs.). Egg laying may begin in mid-April or up to 3 weeks later, depending on the weather (Swift, pers. obs.). Both sexes incubate, for about 28 days. The normal clutch is 3 to 5 eggs, but 6 and even 7 are known (Palmer 1962). Cold rainy weather in May or June may cause nest failure, but the birds replace clutches lost early in the season.

Both parents feed nestlings, first by regurgitation and later with whole fish (Bent 1926). While the young are small, one parent usually guards the nest while the other forages. Later both hunt to feed the growing young, which stay in the nest until they are 7 to 8 weeks old and nearly full grown. Their parents continue to feed them for 2 or 3 weeks after fledging (Stokes and Stokes 1989).

Human activity near a colony early in the nesting season may cause the birds to abandon the site. Great Horned Owls sometimes take over a heron nest in February before the herons arrive, but the 2 species usually appear to coexist peacefully. Mammalian predation apparently is rare, but in one large colony in southwestern New Hampshire an animal thought to be a fisher killed at least 7 young herons in a single morning, and then slept off its feast in an empty nest (J. Ward, Swift, W. W. White, pers. obs.). Crows, ravens, grackles, gulls, and Turkey Vultures also consume eggs or small young (Bent 1926).

In New Hampshire most young herons have fledged by the end of July. Adults and young soon disperse in all directions. Fall migration begins in mid-September and lasts through October (Palmer 1962). Stragglers linger through November and December, and a few survive the winter, especially near the coast (SRS).

Great Blue Herons are usually silent, except at nesting colonies. Their most common calls are harsh and guttural: "frahnk" or "rah-rok." They also make loud clacking sounds by snapping their bills (Stokes and Stokes 1989).

Most early writers on New Hampshire birds regarded the Great Blue Heron as a more or less common summer resident (Goodhue 1877, Dearborn 1898, 1903, Allen 1903, Wright 1911, Goodhue 1922, White 1937, Thayer 1909 *in* Allison and Allison 1979). Its numbers no doubt have fluctuated, but observers have documented changes only locally, as at Umbagog Lake where Brewster (1924) observed a decline after 1885, and at Concord, where White (1937) noted an increase over the previous 25 years.

Volunteer efforts, principally that of the junior author, documented nearly 100 New Hampshire heronries during 1981–89 (Swift, unpubl. data). The great majority were small, several consisting of a single nest, and a number of them were short-lived. Six heronries, however, included more than 50 nests each, and some have existed in the same locality for many years.

Widespread nesting of Great Blue Herons in beaver ponds is comparatively recent in New Hampshire, for beavers were extirpated here in the 19th century and have reoccupied much of their former range in the state since the 1930s (Silver 1957). These nests presumably are less vulnerable to mammalian predation and human disturbance than nests in the forests.

The Atlas map includes "confirmed" and "possible" nesting records only. Because these birds range so widely, the frequent presence of one or more individuals at a particular locality is not reliable evidence of nesting close by. Moreover, 2 herons foraging near each other in late spring or early summer probably are not a pair. Thus, the "probable" nesting category is omitted. "Possible" nesting indicates at least one observation of a heron during the nesting season. Great Blue Herons seem to be doing well in New Hampshire. That they are more numerous now than 50 or 100 years ago is uncertain, but not improbable.

Kimball C. Elkins & Elizabeth F. Swift

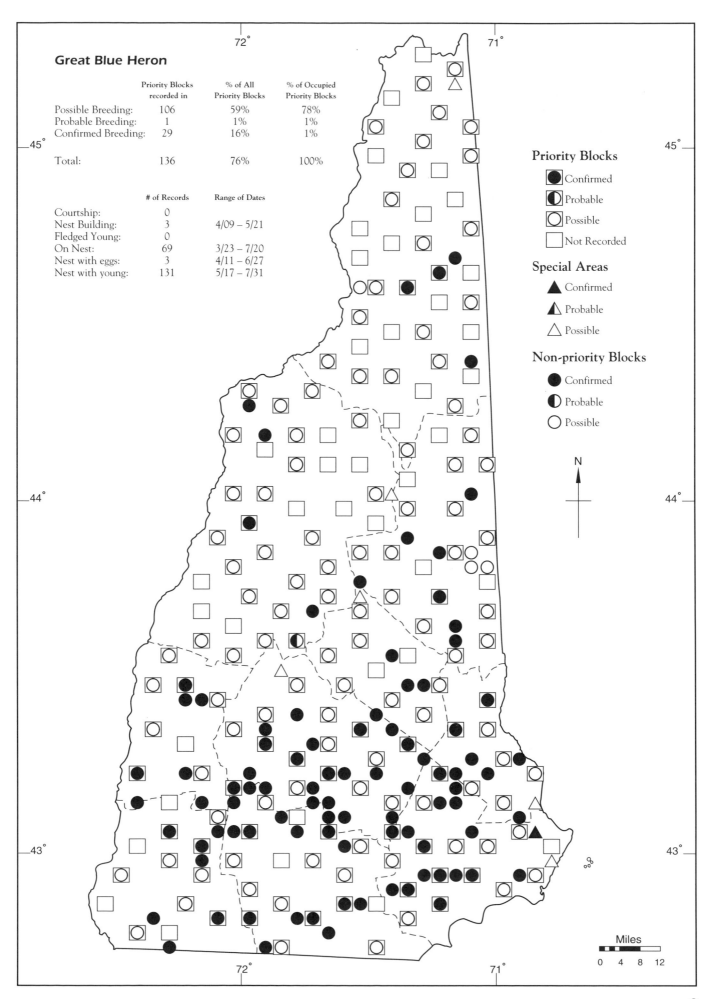

Great Blue Heron

	Priority Blocks recorded in	% of All Priority Blocks	% of Occupied Priority Blocks
Possible Breeding:	106	59%	78%
Probable Breeding:	1	1%	1%
Confirmed Breeding:	29	16%	1%
Total:	136	76%	100%

	# of Records	Range of Dates
Courtship:	0	
Nest Building:	3	4/09 – 5/21
Fledged Young:	0	
On Nest:	69	3/23 – 7/20
Nest with eggs:	3	4/11 – 6/27
Nest with young:	131	5/17 – 7/31

Priority Blocks

- Confirmed
- Probable
- Possible
- Not Recorded

Special Areas

- Confirmed
- Probable
- Possible

Non-priority Blocks

- Confirmed
- Probable
- Possible

N

Miles

0   4   8   12

American Bittern
Botaurus lentiginosus

This bird is best known by its hollow, guttural "oonck-ga-gloonk," which may carry more than half a mile. Stiletto beak pointed to the sky, the "stake-driver" in freeze posture is nearly invisible against its background of reeds and grasses. A black whisker mark, dark brown flight feathers, and more solidly warm brown back distinguish an adult bittern from the immature Black-crowned Night Heron, which is similarly streaked below but has white-spotted back and wings. An immature bittern is lighter than the adult and lacks the black whisker.

Suitable habitat includes emergent marshes with tall vegetation, such as cattails or reeds, and occasionally, wet fields. Marshes which supported territorial bitterns during the Atlas project ranged in size from a 3 a (1.2 ha) sewage lagoon in Rochester to the 722 a (292 ha) Merrymeeting Marsh in Alton/New Durham.

American Bitterns generally arrive in New Hampshire during the first or second week of April, departing again in October for the Southern states and Central America. An occasional bittern attempts to overwinter as far north as the Parker River NWR Newburyport, Mass. (Turner, pers. obs.).

Bitterns vocalize throughout the breeding season, from early April to mid-June. They call more commonly at twilight, but also call in early morning and at other times of day or night. From a tussock of grass, a "thunder-pumper" gulps air 5 or 6 times with an audible snap of the bill, producing a greatly enlarged neck, and belches its song several times, the neck diminishing in size with each undignified syllable (Turner, pers. obs.). Bitterns often emit a hoarse "kok-kok-kok" or a nasal "haink" as an alarm call after being flushed (Hancock and Kushlan 1984).

Seldom seen white plumes on each side of the male's neck are prominently displayed in a ruff during courtship. Johnsgard (1980) observed one male lowering his head to horizontal and shaking it from side to side repeatedly as he followed the female. He then mounted her, lowering his wings. Afterwards he kept his feathers fluffed with the white ruff still visible for most of the following hour.

Female American Bitterns gather reeds, grasses, and dried cattails to build the scanty nest (Harrison 1975). It usually is located a few inches above water line on the quaking margin of a pond, swamp, or marsh, or in a wet meadow. Males may be polygamous, having 2 or more females nesting within their territory, but this has not been verified (Palmer 1962, Harrison 1978).

Females incubate their 2 to 5 eggs for about 24 days, and tend the young alone (Palmer 1962, Harrison 1978). Atlas observers found recently fledged young from 20 June to 3 August, corresponding closely with Vermont's dates of 30 June to 25 July (Laughlin and Kibbe 1985).

An adult female sometimes will protect the nest from imminent attack by spreading her wings and fluffing every feather to increase her apparent size. With her daggerlike bill, she is indeed a formidable defender (Skutch 1976). Two immatures seen 29 June 1943 near a possible nest in Andover also showed this behavior, one "giving a sound between a snarl and a hiss, with frequent snappings of its beak" and striking at the observer (K. C. Elkins, unpubl. data). In July 1980 and 1981, a Strafford farmer left a patch of grass about 98 ft (30 m) square standing in a hayfield for a pair of nesting American Bitterns. No water was within sight. Three young with a mixture of down, bare skin, and erupting feather shafts hissed and clacked their beaks when intruders approached (A. Kimball and R. Lof, pers. comm.).

As an alternative to attack or flight, a frightened bittern will "freeze" instinctively into a posture resembling a stub or old stake. Even newly hatched young will crouch motionless with necks stretched and beaks straight up (V. H. Hebert, pers. comm.). This strategy is ludicrous, however, when a frightened bird is standing in the middle of a gravel pit or busy road (M. Jones and Turner, pers. obs.).

The American Bittern hunts by standing motionless or stalking in slow motion on the ground and seldom, if ever perches in trees or shrubs. It preys on fishes, snakes, grasshoppers, and small mammals, which the female swallows and regurgitates for her young. Young leave the nest at about 14 days and remain dependent for an unknown period (Terres 1980).

Historically, American Bitterns were considered locally common in marshes throughout New Hampshire (Samuels 1867, Dearborn 1898, Allen 1903, Comey 1904, Porter and Porter 1904, Thayer 1909 *in* Allison and Allison 1979). The National Audubon Society included this species on the *American Birds* Blue list in 1976 (Tate 1981), and BBS data suggest a current decline in New Hampshire (Robbins et al. 1986). This decline may reflect a general loss of suitable breeding habitat in the Northeast (Tate 1981).

Although reported sightings suggest a general decline of American Bitterns during the breeding season (SRS), Atlas observers found them in 43 priority blocks, which represent all major watersheds in the state. Observers also recorded this species on 12 of New Hampshire's 22 BBS routes during the Atlas period. These data suggest that the American Bittern may be more common than previously thought. Concerted efforts to protect American Bittern habitat in New Hampshire will go a long way toward ensuring its continued, if elusive, summer residency here.

Sandra B. Turner

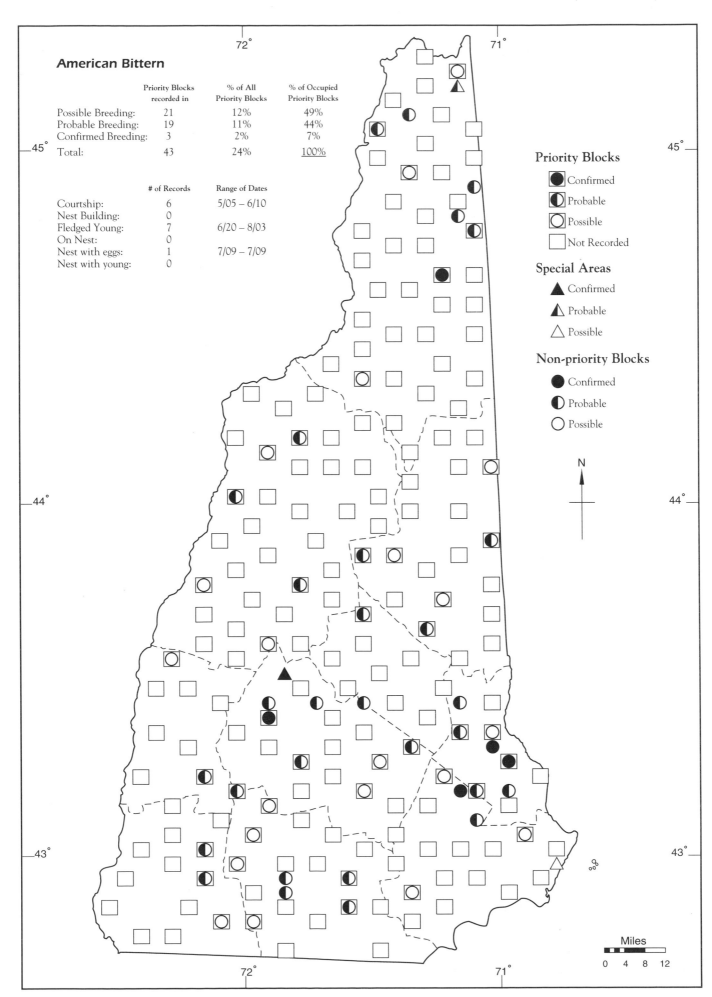

American Bittern

	Priority Blocks recorded in	% of All Priority Blocks	% of Occupied Priority Blocks
Possible Breeding:	21	12%	49%
Probable Breeding:	19	11%	44%
Confirmed Breeding:	3	2%	7%
Total:	43	24%	100%

	# of Records	Range of Dates
Courtship:	6	5/05 – 6/10
Nest Building:	0	
Fledged Young:	7	6/20 – 8/03
On Nest:	0	
Nest with eggs:	1	7/09 – 7/09
Nest with young:	0	

Priority Blocks

- ◕ Confirmed
- ◑ Probable
- ◔ Possible
- ☐ Not Recorded

Special Areas

- ▲ Confirmed
- ◣ Probable
- △ Possible

Non-priority Blocks

- ● Confirmed
- ◐ Probable
- ○ Possible

N

Miles
0 4 8 12

Green Heron
Butorides striatus

Distinctive with its bluish green back, orange legs, and chestnut neck, this small heron occurs in salt and fresh water, and frequents ponds, slow moving rivers, and coastal estuaries. The Green Heron, for a time known as the Green-backed Heron, is most often seen stealthily stalking along a tidal creek, or poised motionless beside a muddy beaver pond. When flushed, it is very vocal and often utters a "skeow" alarm note as it flies. This heron's habit of defecating in flight when startled has earned it the nickname "chalk line."

The Green Heron is widespread in the eastern U.S. However, it approaches the northern limit of its breeding range in New Hampshire and is rare as a nesting species in the White Mountains and in northern sections of the state. It occurs most often in the Coastal region and the Merrimack River valley.

Summer residents in New England, Green Herons return to southern New Hampshire in late April and May. Meyerriecks (1960) studied the pre-egglaying behavior of breeding Green Herons, and described 22 displays used in hostile and/or sexual encounters. Males establish territories soon after arrival, and females roam from one to another before selecting a mate; both sexes are highly vocal during this period. Males begin to repair an old nest or construct a new one before accepting a mate, and do not allow a female to enter the nest until relatively late in the pairing process (Meyerriecks 1960).

Once the female has entered the nest, the male brings nesting material while she finishes the nest (Harrison 1975). The adults may continue to add nest material until after the eggs have hatched (Harrison 1978). Atlas participants observed nest building as early as 19 May.

The nest itself is a frail, flimsy structure of sticks and twigs (Forbush 1925a) which typically is built in woods near water (Bent 1926). Nest height may vary greatly depending on available sites, but is typically between 10 and 30 ft (3 and 9.1 m). The only nest found during the Atlas period was 30 to 35 ft (9.1 to 10.7 m) up in a white pine. Herons reused it the following year. A nest found in 1989 was 18 ft (5.5 m) up in a red pine. Unlike most other herons, the Green Heron tends to be a solitary nester, although loose aggregations sometimes occur. The Atlas project documented only single nests, but more than one pair nested in a pine grove in southeastern New Hampshire in 1989.

Both parents incubate the 3 to 6 eggs during the 19 to 21 day incubation period (Forbush 1925a, Harrison 1978). Reported egg dates for this species range from 5 May to 17 June, and single broods are typical in the northern area of the species' range (Forbush 1925a).

The young birds hatch asynchronously (Hancock and Kushlan 1984). During the first week, both adults tend them, and brooding is constant (Harrison 1978). By the time they are 16 or 17 days old, they have developed excellent climbing skills and can run "through the tree-tops almost as nimbly as squirrels" (Dearborn 1898). The young first take flight at 21 to 23 days, can fly with the adults at 25 days, and probably are independent of the adults at 30 to 35 days (Harrison 1978).

Green Herons use a wide variety of foraging techniques, from standing in crouched posture and walking slowly in shallow water to plunging, jumping, and foot stirring (Hancock and Kushlan 1984). Prey includes fish, amphibians, insects, and other arthropods.

Postbreeding dispersal is less dramatic than for some herons, although late summer wanderings may take the birds northwards to Manitoba, Nova Scotia, and Newfoundland (Terres 1980). T. Richards (pers. comm.) observed 15 Green Herons along the Connecticut River valley in Hinsdale on 25 August 1988. Hancock and Kushlan (1984) believe that "eruptions" in postbreeding dispersals may help to explain this species' colonization of so many islands. Green Herons winter from the southern U.S. to Honduras (Bent 1926). They usually have left New Hampshire by the end of October (Elkins 1982).

The distribution and range of the Green Heron in New Hampshire appears to have changed only slightly since 1900. Brewster (1925) reported the species as a "rare summer visitor" around Umbagog Lake near the turn of the century, while Dearborn (1903) considered the species common along the Oyster and Piscataqua rivers during the same time period. Forbush (1925a) described the species as an "uncommon summer resident in southern half of New Hampshire" in 1925, but common further south into Massachusetts, Rhode Island, and Connecticut. Allen (1903) reported the Green Heron as occurring rarely in central areas of the state, occasionally to Ossipee, but not further north.

Atlas records for the Green Heron are concentrated in southeastern New Hampshire, and north along the Merrimack/Pemigewasset river valley. This species apparently is very local elsewhere in the state. It is essentially absent from the White Mountains, but occasionally occurs farther north along the Androscoggin and Ammonoosuc rivers. The several Atlas records north of the White Mountains suggest a possible northward expansion of this species in the state.

Stephen R. Mirick

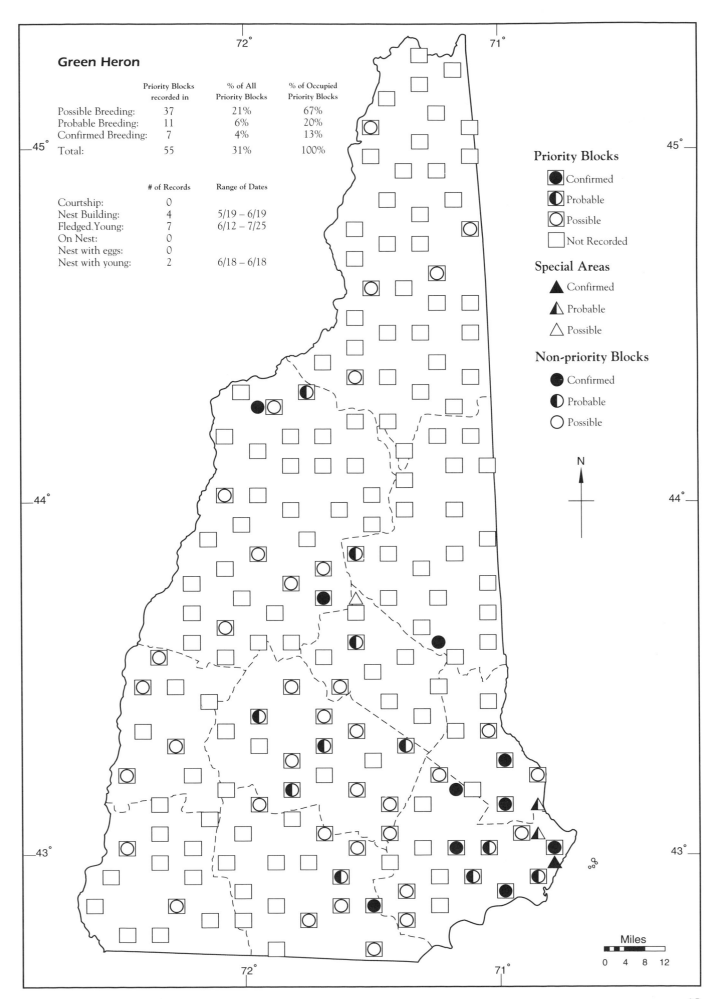

Green Heron

	Priority Blocks recorded in	% of All Priority Blocks	% of Occupied Priority Blocks
Possible Breeding:	37	21%	67%
Probable Breeding:	11	6%	20%
Confirmed Breeding:	7	4%	13%
Total:	55	31%	100%

	# of Records	Range of Dates
Courtship:	0	
Nest Building:	4	5/19 – 6/19
Fledged Young:	7	6/12 – 7/25
On Nest:	0	
Nest with eggs:	0	
Nest with young:	2	6/18 – 6/18

Priority Blocks

● Confirmed
◐ Probable
○ Possible
□ Not Recorded

Special Areas

▲ Confirmed
◮ Probable
△ Possible

Non-priority Blocks

● Confirmed
◑ Probable
○ Possible

N

Miles
0 4 8 12

13

Black-crowned Night-Heron
Nycticorax nycticorax

Black-crowned Night-Herons "work the night shift" along our coast, replacing Snowy Egrets along tidal creeks in the evening, returning to the breeding colony late at night or in the morning. They forage primarily at twilight and after dark, except when they have young to feed. Characteristic loud "kwok" calls quickly identify Black-crowned Night-Herons. Their rounded wings, stocky silhouettes, and distinctive, almost moth-like flight also aid in identification.

The Black-crowned Night-Heron is a colonial nester, often sharing a rookery with other herons and egrets. Woodlots adjacent to marshes, isolated stands of trees near the shore, and wooded islands are the most likely nesting habitats in New Hampshire.

Night-herons arrive on the New Hampshire coast in April, and begin nest building soon after arrival. Night-heron nests are generally bulkier than those of ibises and egrets. They are often on drier sites than ibis nests, and in taller, more isolated shrubs such as chokecherry or shadbush. In established rookeries, night-herons re-build on old stick nests year after year (Davis 1986).

Egg laying occurs between late April and early June. Black-crowned Night-Herons appear less synchronous in their nesting than our other small herons and seem to nest earlier. This species is very sensitive to disturbance and is quick to abandon a colony during the laying period (Borror, pers. obs.). Both sexes incubate the 3 to 5 eggs for 24 to 26 days, commencing with the first egg laid. This results in a substantial size difference among siblings. By early June, there are often 2- to 3-week-old young in the colony at Appledore Island, Isles of Shoals, Kittery, Maine, 7 mi (11 km) off the New Hampshire coast. Only 2 or 3 young usually survive per nest.

Most young fledge by mid-July, after about 4 weeks in the nest. At first they remain at the colony, where their parents return to feed them. By late August, the streaked brown immatures are visiting the mainland.

This species is well known for the wide-ranging postbreeding season dispersal of its young, and most of New Hampshire's inland records are of young birds in late summer (SRS). Black-crowned Night-Herons generally depart for warmer climates by October, but early winter records are not unknown along the New Hampshire coast (SRS).

The night-herons' primary food is small fish, especially killifish, but their diet includes many types of marsh fauna and even some flora (Bent 1925). In recent years, night-herons have been found to be predators on tern chicks when adult terns desert nesting colonies at night (Gavutis, pers. obs.; ASNH data).

Until recently, ornithologists considered the Black-crowned Night-Heron a common summer resident along the coast of New Hampshire and uncommon to rare inland (Dearborn 1898, 1903, Allen 1903, Brewster 1924, Forbush 1925a, Richards 1958, Thayer 1909 *in* Allison and Allison 1979). Several large rookeries existed near Great Bay in the late 1890s, but human persecution apparently caused their desertion (Dearborn 1903). Local residents reported a nesting colony near Back Channel of Little Harbor, Portsmouth, in the early to mid 1900s (E. Miller, pers. comm.).

The species continued to be common along the coast until a nationwide decline in the 1960s and 1970s. The Black-crowned Night-Heron was on the *American Birds* Blue List during 1972–81, and was downgraded to a species of Special Concern in 1982 and to Local Concern in 1986 (Tate 1986). It is currently a Special Concern Species in New Hampshire.

Night-heron numbers increased significantly in the early 1980s, with nesting sites known or strongly suspected in New Castle, Rye, and Hampton. A small rookery was present in a clump of scrubby pines between Rye Harbor and Locke Road, Rye until the summer of 1980. Observations also suggested possible nesting in Exeter, Lyme, Nashua, and Errol. However, verified breeding season observations during the Atlas period were limited to the Seacoast and Errol areas, and no active nests were found in New Hampshire.

Several reports suggest recent breeding on the New Hampshire mainland. On 10 July 1985, Gavutis saw 2 recently fledged birds following an adult from a woodlot adjacent to the Hampton marshes. During the summers of 1982 and 1986, one or 2 Black-crowned Night-Herons occurred in or near a Great Blue Heron colony in Derry (V. and B. Hayden, pers. comm.), and there was an unconfirmed report of a pair nesting near the Mill Pond, Stratham during 1986 or 1987. Finally, on 18 June 1988, Gavutis counted up to 10 adult night-herons in a Great Blue Heron rookery in Exeter, and on 17 July up to a dozen adults and one juvenal were present there.

Birds nesting on Appledore Island likely forage regularly in New Hampshire and undoubtedly contribute to the numerous sightings in our Seacoast area. The nesting population of night-herons on Appledore Island has remained fairly constant at about 50 pairs since 1978. A colony also occurs 10 mi (16.6 km) south of the New Hampshire border in the Parker River NWR, Ipswich, Mass.

Undisturbed wooded marsh edge and island nesting and roosting habitat are becoming increasingly rare in New Hampshire. Additional field work will be required to determine whether or not this species currently nests in New Hampshire.

George W. Gavutis, Jr. & Arthur C. Borror

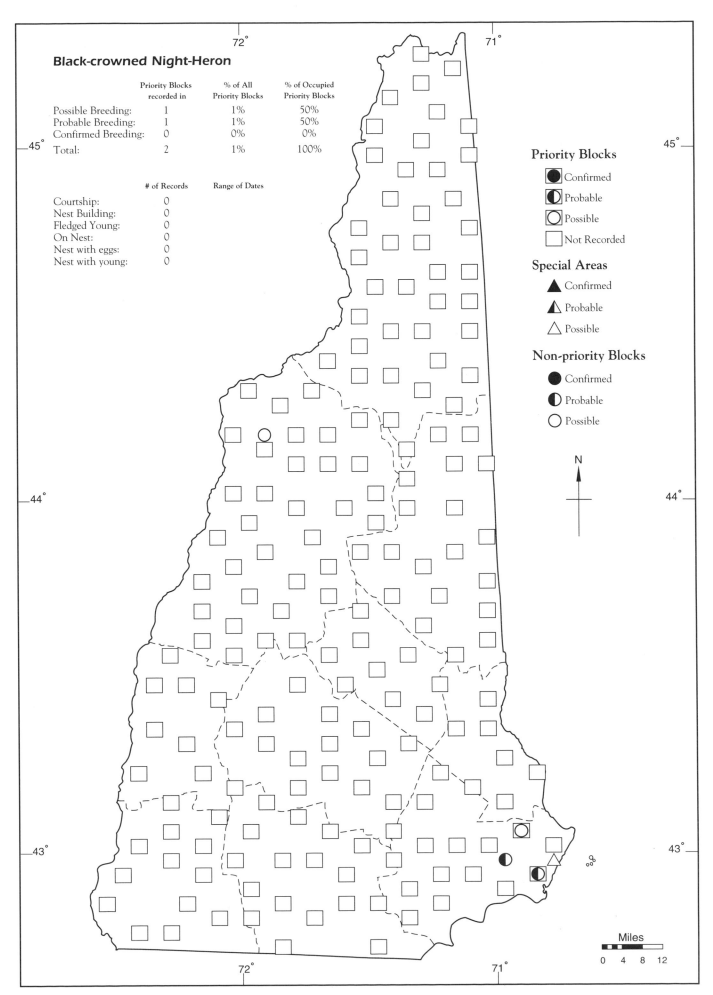

Black-crowned Night-Heron

	Priority Blocks recorded in	% of All Priority Blocks	% of Occupied Priority Blocks
Possible Breeding:	1	1%	50%
Probable Breeding:	1	1%	50%
Confirmed Breeding:	0	0%	0%
Total:	2	1%	100%

	# of Records	Range of Dates
Courtship:	0	
Nest Building:	0	
Fledged Young:	0	
On Nest:	0	
Nest with eggs:	0	
Nest with young:	0	

Priority Blocks

● Confirmed
◐ Probable
○ Possible
☐ Not Recorded

Special Areas

▲ Confirmed
◨ Probable
△ Possible

Non-priority Blocks

● Confirmed
◑ Probable
○ Possible

N

Miles
0 4 8 12

15

Mute Swan
Cygnus olor

The largest and most graceful of New Hampshire's birds has gained resident status since 1965, when a female Mute Swan landed in Durham's Mill Pond. A year later University of New Hampshire wildlife professor Dr. D. P. Olson and H. P. Nevers traveled to Rhode Island to obtain a mate for the Durham swan, courtesy of the Rhode Island Fish and Wildlife Department. Mute Swans now nest on a number of freshwater ponds and rivers in New Hampshire's Coastal Lowlands. In winter they move to sheltered, brackish and salt water bays and coves.

The Mute Swan's gracefully curved neck and orange bill with prominent black knob distinguish it from the straight-necked Tundra Swan, which occurs here rarely in migration. Territorial males frequently arch their secondary wing feathers over their backs, creating the illusion that they are much larger. Females ("pens") are smaller than males ("cobs"), but the sexes have identical plumage.

Mute Swans can fly at speeds of 50 to 55 mph (80 to 88 km/h) (Wood and Gelston 1972). In flight their wings produce a unique whistling sound audible for up to 1 mi (1.6 km) (Bellrose 1976). Mute Swans are generally silent but are not "mute" (Palmer 1976). Adults can utter a high-pitched "kiurr," an explosive exhalation with variants of a hiss, when disturbed on territory, and the pen uses a puppylike bark to summon her brood (Palmer 1976).

Mute Swan breeding habitat consists of still or slow-moving fresh or brackish water with an abundance of aquatic vegetation and some undisturbed shoreline. Breeding pairs in Rhode Island utilize a territory of 0.5 to 11.8 a (0.2 to 4.8 ha) (Willey 1968). When they nest on a pond, the cob will defend the entire pond against intruders. The cob initiates nest construction, with the pen assisting later on (Harrison 1978). The nest is usually on the shoreline or on a small island and consists of a depression lined with down and feathers

in a pile of aquatic plants, sticks, weeds, and roots that is 5 to 6 ft (1.5 to 1.8 m) in diameter.

The pen incubates her clutch of 5 to 7 eggs, laid on alternate days during late March to mid-June, for 34 to 38 days (Harrison 1978). The cob occasionally incubates for short periods and remains close by at all times (Halla 1966, Harrison 1978). Hatching peaks during the last week of May. Five Durham broods of 3 to 7 cygnets hatched from 22 May to 3 June (D. P. Olson, pers. comm.). Cygnets stay on the nest for a day or 2 before following the adults, and may ride on the adults' backs when small. The young feed themselves on vegetation which the pen pulls up and breaks into pieces for them (Harrison 1978). Cygnets are able to fly in 115 to 155 days, and stay with the adults until late fall (Bellrose 1976). The family may move together to an ice free overwintering area, but the young can be totally independent in about 4 months (Harrison 1978). A swan pair mates for life, and breeding can occur at 3 years of age (Willey 1968).

Mute Swans seldom dive for food but plunge their heads and necks below the water surface. In deeper water they may tip up like dabbling ducks to reach submerged aquatic plants and tubers. They feed at all hours during daylight and apparently to some extent on moonlit nights (Palmer 1976). Their natural diet is nearly all vegetable matter. They consume large amounts of aquatic vegetation and pass a tremendous amount of fecal matter, to the detriment of water quality (Willey 1968).

Mute Swans in New Hampshire are semidomestic and essentially nonmigratory. They are very protective of their young and can be aggressive toward other large waterfowl, dogs, and humans if aggravated within their territory, especially during the breeding season. Mute Swans originally were native to northern Europe and were domesticated in Great Britain before the 12th century (Harrison 1975). They were introduced to the United States from England beginning in the mid-nineteenth century and continuing into the early 1900s (Palmer 1976). Early sites of introduction included large private estates on Long Island and along the Hudson River, Duchess County, New York (Bull 1985). Escapes from these semidomestic populations became feral, and now small colonies occur along the coast from New Hampshire to Virginia, with the largest numbers in the vicinity of Long Island, New York. Feral Mute Swan numbers in the Atlantic Flyway from Maine to Georgia have increased from 200 in 1954 to 2,100 in 1967, 2,400 in 1977, and 6,100 in 1988 (USFWS 1988a).

The first confirmed New Hampshire breeding record of feral Mute Swans was that of the Durham pair in 1968. Few cygnets have survived in this state, primarily due to leucocytozoan infections, which are transmitted by black flies and characteristically decimate Mute Swan broods in northern areas (Davis et al. 1971; R. Strout, pers. comm.).

The Atlas project "confirmed" breeding at 5 locations in the Seacoast area, 3 of which were in priority blocks. A Mute Swan survey in midsummer 1986 documented a total of 25 Mute Swans in New Hampshire — 12 feral birds and 13 captive birds, including a brood of 5 cygnets owned by aviculturists (S. H. Wheeler, pers. comm.).

If Mute Swan populations continue to expand in Connecticut, Rhode Island, and Massachusetts, more feral swans may take up residence in New Hampshire's Seacoast area. However, disease will continue to prevent rapid expansion of Mute Swans in New Hampshire, and wherever black flies occur.

Harold P. Nevers

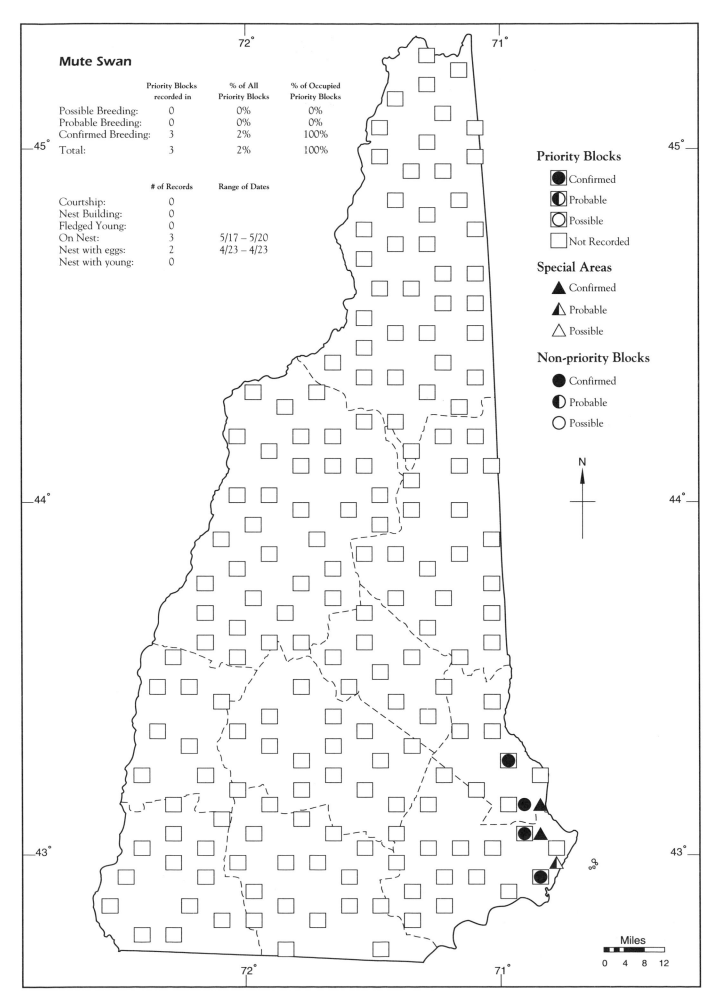

Mute Swan

	Priority Blocks recorded in	% of All Priority Blocks	% of Occupied Priority Blocks
Possible Breeding:	0	0%	0%
Probable Breeding:	0	0%	0%
Confirmed Breeding:	3	2%	100%
Total:	3	2%	100%

	# of Records	Range of Dates
Courtship:	0	
Nest Building:	0	
Fledged Young:	0	
On Nest:	3	5/17 – 5/20
Nest with eggs:	2	4/23 – 4/23
Nest with young:	0	

Priority Blocks

● Confirmed
◐ Probable
○ Possible
▢ Not Recorded

Special Areas

▲ Confirmed
◣ Probable
△ Possible

Non-priority Blocks

● Confirmed
◐ Probable
○ Possible

N

Miles
0 4 8 12

Canada Goose
Branta canadensis

The resonant honking of high flying flocks of Canada Geese in characteristic V-formation is a familiar trademark of the changing seasons. Flocks of these large birds with their black necks and heads and white cheeks have passed over New Hampshire for centuries during spring and fall migrations between nesting grounds in sub-Arctic Canada and coastal wintering areas of the mid-Atlantic states. Although these flocks occasionally stopped briefly on Great Bay or large lakes and rivers, until recently New Hampshire apparently provided neither suitable nesting nor wintering habitat.

Today, however, Canada Geese occur in parts of New Hampshire throughout the year, in ever-growing numbers. The recently established nesting population is the northern contingent of a semiwild population in adjacent Massachusetts. Before legislation outlawed commercial hunting, market hunters kept live decoys to lure flocks of wild migrants (Connett 1947). When live decoys were prohibited in the 1930s, some of the tame birds remained with other waterfowl on large estates. Offspring of those birds, augmented by geese which federal and state wildlife agencies stocked, gradually established small flocks. These readily adapted to artificial ponds and reservoirs amid expanses of mowed grass. In such suburban locations, where hunting usually is prohibited and large predators are scarce, the flocks have grown and lost any urge to migrate. Thus distinct migrant and breeding populations of Canada Geese now occur in New Hampshire. Migrant birds still fly over the state in spring and fall, and some winter on Great Bay. The migrants that winter here belong to the North Atlantic race (*B. c. canadensis*), which has not experienced the population increases of other races (D. P. Olson, pers. comm.). The resident population is similar in appearance but quite different in behavior.

Resident geese gather in small flocks and leave their nesting ponds to winter on open water, often near the coast. As soon as portions of the nesting ponds thaw, usually by late March, adult pairs return to defend their territories with much honking and posturing. Preferred breeding ponds are surrounded by open grasslands and have at least one small island. Many pairs now occupy our numerous beaver ponds, despite their lack of bordering grasslands.

Nests are always close to water. If small islands are unavailable, they may be on points of land, old stumps, old beaver lodges, or muskrat houses. Canada Geese sometimes will use artificial platforms filled with hay.

The female constructs the nest, a flat mound of dead vegetation. The Canada Goose nests early and in New Hampshire may lay eggs by mid-April. The female lays a clutch of 4 to 7 eggs over a period of about 1 week and incubates for 26 to 28 days (Bellrose 1976). As incubation progresses, she lines the nest with down from her breast. She covers the eggs with down during brief feeding trips. The gander is always nearby, ready to warn of potential danger or chase intruders.

Both parents guard their precocial young, which leave the nest within a day of hatching and feed themselves. Broods of downy young were observed as early as 15 May during the Atlas project. The female broods them at night and periodically during the day for the first week, less often as they get older. Food consists almost entirely of plant material, taken both in the water and on adjacent uplands.

Parents may attempt to distract an intruder with vigorous flapping and honking while the young "play possum" by remaining motionless (C. R. Foss, pers. comm.). Sometimes 2 or more families share the same feeding areas. An aggressive pair may take over the young of one or 2 other pairs, resulting in a combined brood of 10 to 15 young (Bellrose 1976).

The young grow rapidly but don't fly until they are 7 or 8 weeks old. Meanwhile, the adults molt all of their flight feathers and are flightless for nearly a month. Grown young look like adults and remain with their parents until the following spring. Canada Geese don't nest until they are 2 or 3 years old. Subadults remain together in small flocks, usually well separated from nesting birds (Johnsgard 1978).

Silver (1957) summarized historical records of Canada Geese in New Hampshire, based largely on the work of Richards (1952). Accounts from the 17th century indicated that hunters often shot large numbers during migration, but there is no indication that the species nested here before the mid-1900s. T. and B. Richards' observation of adults with a single downy young at World's End Pond, Salem, in 1951 provided the first documented breeding record, although a local farmer claimed the birds had nested there in 2 previous years (Silver 1957). This may have been a vanguard of semiwild geese from Massachusetts, which now nest throughout much of southern New Hampshire and have become a nuisance in some locations.

This species increased dramatically in southern New Hampshire during the Atlas project. NHFG biologists released 160 "nuisance" geese from southern New England in the Umbagog Lake area during 1978–83, and some pairs subsequently have nested there. All the other "confirmed" nesting records were from the southern part of the state. The status of this species in New Hampshire, as in most of its current range, is secure despite heavy hunting pressure in many areas. Nesting geese in New Hampshire are likely to continue to increase in numbers and distribution.

Ralph Andrews

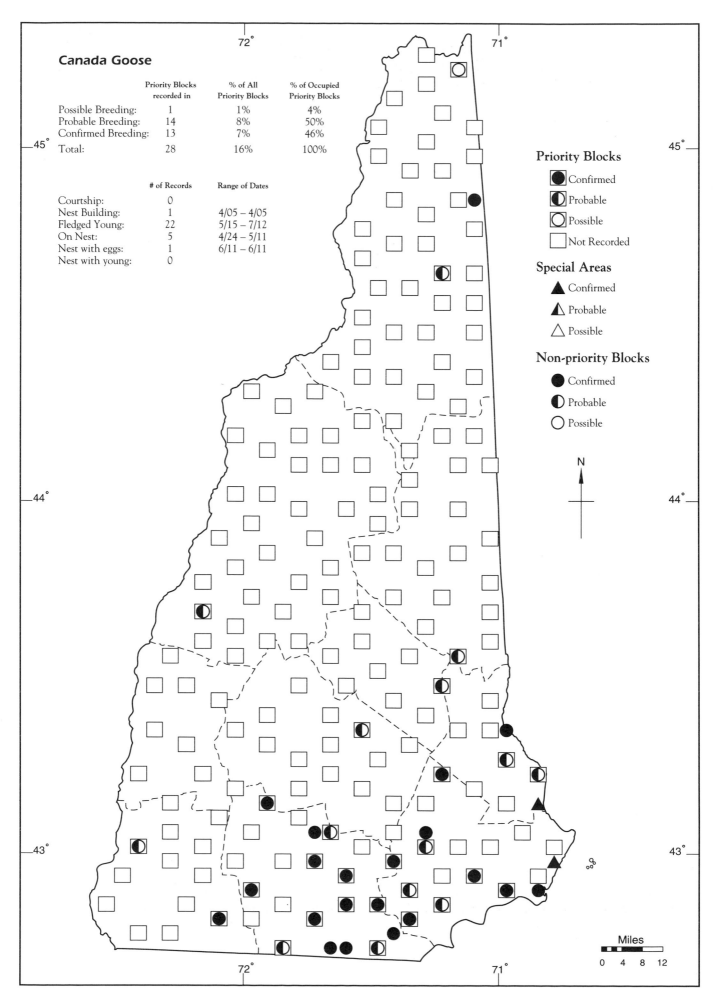

Canada Goose

	Priority Blocks recorded in	% of All Priority Blocks	% of Occupied Priority Blocks
Possible Breeding:	1	1%	4%
Probable Breeding:	14	8%	50%
Confirmed Breeding:	13	7%	46%
Total:	28	16%	100%

	# of Records	Range of Dates
Courtship:	0	
Nest Building:	1	4/05 – 4/05
Fledged Young:	22	5/15 – 7/12
On Nest:	5	4/24 – 5/11
Nest with eggs:	1	6/11 – 6/11
Nest with young:	0	

Priority Blocks

- ◑ Confirmed
- ◑ Probable
- ○ Possible
- □ Not Recorded

Special Areas

- ▲ Confirmed
- ◤ Probable
- △ Possible

Non-priority Blocks

- ● Confirmed
- ◑ Probable
- ○ Possible

N

Miles
0 4 8 12

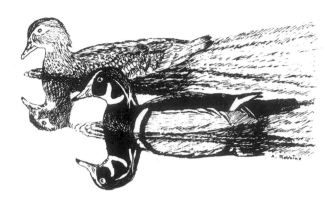

Wood Duck
Aix sponsa

One of the world's most colorful waterfowl species, the Wood Duck nests principally in the eastern half and far west of the United States and in Cuba. It winters from the southern parts of this range to central Mexico and the Bahamas (Bond 1971, Bellrose 1980). The Wood Duck breeds commonly at low elevations throughout New Hampshire, and occasionally up to about 2,000 ft (610 m) elevation. A dabbling duck and cavity nester, the Wood Duck flies skillfully in the woods, twisting rapidly between trees or stopping suddenly to perch in one.

Wood Ducks generally arrive in New Hampshire in late March or early April, often in pairs, though flocks of as many as 60 birds have occurred as late as 19 April (Richards, unpubl. data). A high percentage of hens return annually to the same breeding area, and mated pairs investigate small, weedy ponds or quiet backwaters for trees with potential nest holes (Palmer 1976).

Most Wood Ducks breed in their first year. In courtship the drake raises and lowers his head and crest while swimming around the hen; both sexes bill dip and preen (Bellrose 1980). The hen's loud, sharp "eek" alarm note is frequently heard in ponds and backwaters. Less commonly heard is the drake's softer whistle (Richards, pers. obs.).

Although Wood Ducks usually nest in natural cavities 30 ft (9 m) or more above the ground (Bellrose 1980), nest holes may be of almost any size or shape and at almost any height, in live or dead trees, near or far from water. Wood Ducks often use nest boxes, as do Hooded Mergansers. The Wood Duck's thinner egg shells crackle between the fingers while the merganser's snap, enabling their identification in nest boxes after the nesting season (H. P. Nevers, pers. comm.). The hen lines the nesting cavity with down.

A brood in Nottingham on 24 May 1983 (NHBBA data) suggests that egg laying may begin in mid-April, based on an average incubation period of 30+ days (Bellrose 1980). Clutch size averages about 12. Predation often results in renesting, occasionally with 2 or more females using the same "dump" nests (Bellrose 1980). Wood Ducks and Hooded Mergansers often compete for nest holes, and mixed broods may result. Richards has observed mother Wood Ducks with mixed broods in Penacook (Concord) and Swanzey.

A hen broods her young for about 24 hours after they hatch (Bellrose 1980). Then, in response to calls from their mother, the ducklings climb to the nest hole and jump to the water or ground below. Young Wood Ducks stay with the hen until they acquire their juvenal plumage and begin to fly, at 8 to 10 weeks. Hens with young are relatively easy to observe, and accounted for nearly all "confirmed" breeding records. Swimming "woodies," especially hens with young, are often recognized by their distinctive buoyancy and head-nodding motions. Baby Wood Ducks may dive when alarmed (Richards, pers. obs), and the hen typically performs distraction displays. Young almost immediately begin molting into their adult plumage, which may be complete as early as their fifth month (Bellrose 1980).

Drakes usually leave before the young hatch and congregate in marshes, wooded swamps, or ponds to molt. Richards (unpubl. data) observed 18 drakes on 6 June 1963 at Pool Pond, Rindge, and 15 on 30 June 1962 at Pontook Reservoir, Dummer. However, drakes accompanied families at Danbury on 21 June 1953 (K. C. Elkins, pers. comm.) and at Newfound Lake on 13 July 1953 (V. H. Hebert, pers. comm.). Drakes may regain their breeding plumage as early as 9 September (Richards, unpubl. data).

Wood Ducks ordinarily dabble for food without tipping up, but both sexes occasionally dive, submerging completely, while feeding. During their first 6 weeks or so ducklings gradually change their diet from insects and sometimes tiny fish to mostly vegetable matter (Bellrose 1980). Adults eat appreciable numbers of insects and spiders, but generally prefer seeds and tubers of aquatic vegetation, acorns, and other nuts (Kortright 1942).

Wood Ducks usually head south in late September or early October, often gathering in flocks. Richards (unpubl. data) has observed flocks of 24 to 75 birds on New Hampshire ponds between 15 September and 8 November. Individuals may linger into winter.

During the 1800s Wood Duck populations suffered heavily from egg collecting and hunting for food, feathers for fly-tying, and mounted specimens. Consequently they became scarce by about 1900. Allen (1903) describes the species as only an "occasional summer resident" in New Hampshire, and Wright (1911) saw only one Wood Duck during his 12-year studies of Jefferson's bird life. Brewster (1924) indicates that Wood Ducks had nearly disappeared from Umbagog Lake by about 1910.

Complete protection from 1913 until 1942 (Palmer 1976) and increasing habitat provided by abandoned farmland, the return of the beaver, and nest boxes have enabled the Wood Duck to make a remarkable recovery. This had begun in Concord by 1935 (White 1937). The species was generally common during the state waterfowl inventory of 1949–51 (NHFG data).

The Atlas map demonstrates that the Wood Duck is now a well-distributed summer resident throughout southern New Hampshire. It is less common in the north, where there is less suitable breeding habitat.

Current hunting seasons and bag limits appear to be adequately protecting Wood Duck populations. While a gradual decrease in suitable habitat seems inevitable with increasing development, the Wood Duck should continue to be a locally common summer resident of New Hampshire for a long time to come.

Tudor Richards

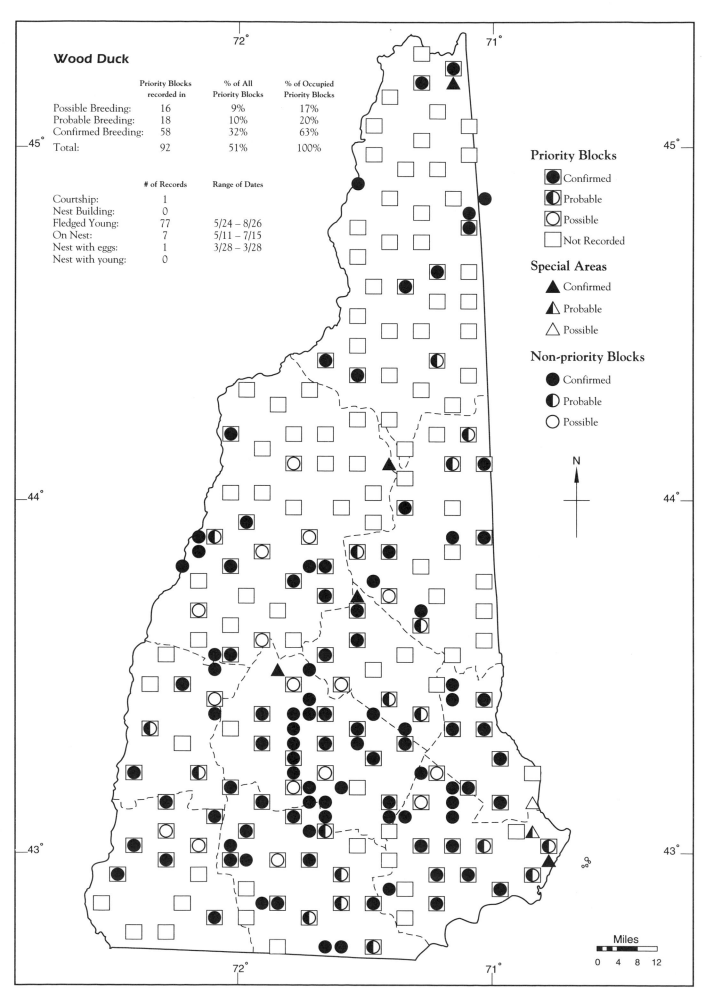

Wood Duck

	Priority Blocks recorded in	% of All Priority Blocks	% of Occupied Priority Blocks
Possible Breeding:	16	9%	17%
Probable Breeding:	18	10%	20%
Confirmed Breeding:	58	32%	63%
Total:	92	51%	100%

	# of Records	Range of Dates
Courtship:	1	
Nest Building:	0	
Fledged Young:	77	5/24 – 8/26
On Nest:	7	5/11 – 7/15
Nest with eggs:	1	3/28 – 3/28
Nest with young:	0	

Priority Blocks

● Confirmed
◐ Probable
○ Possible
□ Not Recorded

Special Areas

▲ Confirmed
◮ Probable
△ Possible

Non-priority Blocks

● Confirmed
◐ Probable
○ Possible

N

Miles
0 4 8 12

21

Green-winged Teal
Anas crecca

Green-wings are small, colorful, fast flying ducks. They typically dart in tight clusters, with white bellies showing and green wing patches flashing. While rare as summer residents in New Hampshire, they sometimes are locally common in migration. They occur in flooded fields in spring and in shallow fresh water with abundant vegetation in fall (Richards, pers. obs.). These little dabblers swim buoyantly. They dive well, but do so only to escape predators (Forbush 1925a).

The Green-winged Teal's breeding range extends from Arctic Alaska east to Labrador and south to Colorado and northern New England. Most of the population breeds in the Northwest, but breeding grounds in eastern Canada produce about 90% of the Green-wings migrating in the Atlantic Flyway (Bellrose 1980).

The drake's breeding plumage includes a broad, iridescent green stripe extending back from the eye on a reddish brown head. A white vertical bar which separates chest and back provides an excellent field mark for a swimming drake. The mottled brown hen resembles a pale, miniature black duck but, like the drake, has a green speculum. The drake's high-pitched whistle and the hen's quack are the most frequent calls (Richards, pers. obs.).

Green-winged Teal winter from the central U.S. to northern South America; most Atlantic Flyway birds winter from New Jersey to Florida (Bellrose 1976). They arrive in New Hampshire in late March or April. Large spring flocks observed in New Hampshire include 30 to about 100 Green-wings (Richards, unpubl. data).

Courtship, generally involving several swimming drakes circling a single hen, includes bobbing up and down and throwing the head back and peeping (Bent 1923; Richards, pers. obs.). Green-wings place their nests on dry ground up to 300 ft (91.5 m) from a fresh or brackish marsh, generally in shrub thickets with scattered trees, or in grasses and sedges (Palmer 1976).

Well hidden in tall grass at the base of a shrub, the nest is a hollow with grasses, weeds, and leaves lining its base (Harrison 1975). After laying several eggs, the hen thinly lines the nest with dark brown down and breast feathers. As incubation proceeds, she adds more down to the nest (Palmer 1976). One nest in Maine contained 9 eggs on 18 June (Palmer 1949).

While females incubate for 21 to 23 days, males gather on marshes or lakes in preparation for molt (Bellrose 1980). Hens generally leave the nest only to feed or rest, after covering the eggs. To distract intruders once broods have hatched, hens will beat their wings, make short flights, or run rapidly away while continuously quacking harshly (Palmer 1976).

Green-wings are most active early and late in the day. They often loaf along shores, standing on mud banks and stumps (Richards, pers. obs.). They usually feed on mud flats, seeking small seeds of plants such as nut grasses and smartweeds (Bellrose 1980). They also dabble in shallow marshes with submerged vegetation, where they often feed with Blue-winged Teal (Richards, pers. obs.).

Green-wings head south in early autumn (but later than Blue-wings), often in apparent family groups, such as 4 at Lonesome Lake, Lincoln, at more than 2,700 ft (820 m) in the White Mountains, on 10 September 1978 (Richards, pers. obs.). About 100, possibly including some late Blue-wings, were on Turkey Pond, Concord, on 4 October 1982 (Richards, unpubl. data). A few Green-wings occasionally winter in the Seacoast area.

Samuels (1870) suggested that this teal nested on secluded lakes of northern New England, but apparently there were no nesting records even for Maine until 1940 (Palmer 1949). Market hunting severely reduced populations of Green-winged Teal and other waterfowl in the last century. Coues (1868) considered the species a common spring and autumn migrant in New England. Brewster (1924) found Green-wings in the Umbagog Lake region on only 4 occasions during 1871–1909, all between 4 September and 12 October. Wright (1911) never saw Green-wings at the Cherry Ponds, Jefferson in the period 1899 to 1911.

Migrant Green-wings increased in New England beginning in the early 1900s (Silver 1957), and continuing into more recent decades (Richards 1952, Griscom and Snyder 1955, SRS). The continental breeding population increased during 1955–74, especially after 1959 (Bellrose 1978), and the nesting range expanded southward to Delaware by the early 1980s (AOU 1987).

The Green-winged Teal was not known to nest in New Hampshire until 1953. Richards (unpubl. data) subsequently observed a hen with 4 half-grown young and the drake close by at Pontook Reservoir, Dummer, on 7 July 1962. Breeding also may have occurred at Eel Pond, Rye, where 3 or 4 drakes, a pair, and another hen were present on 8 June 1961 (Richards, unpubl. data).

The Atlas project produced only 4 "probable" breeding records and 3 "possibles" in priority blocks. At least 3 subsequent confirmed breeding records exist, including a hen performing a broken wing act near the outlet of Umbagog Lake on 2 July 1987 (E. C. Janeway, unpubl. data), a hen with 5 young in Harpers Meadow, Errol, on 28 June 1988 (SRS), and a hen with at least one downy young at East Inlet, Pittsburg, on 8 July 1990 (Richards, unpubl. data). Since New Hampshire is near the southern edge of the Green-winged Teal's breeding range in the Northeast, continued sporadic breeding in the state seems most likely for the years to come.

Susan Absalom Staats & Tudor Richards

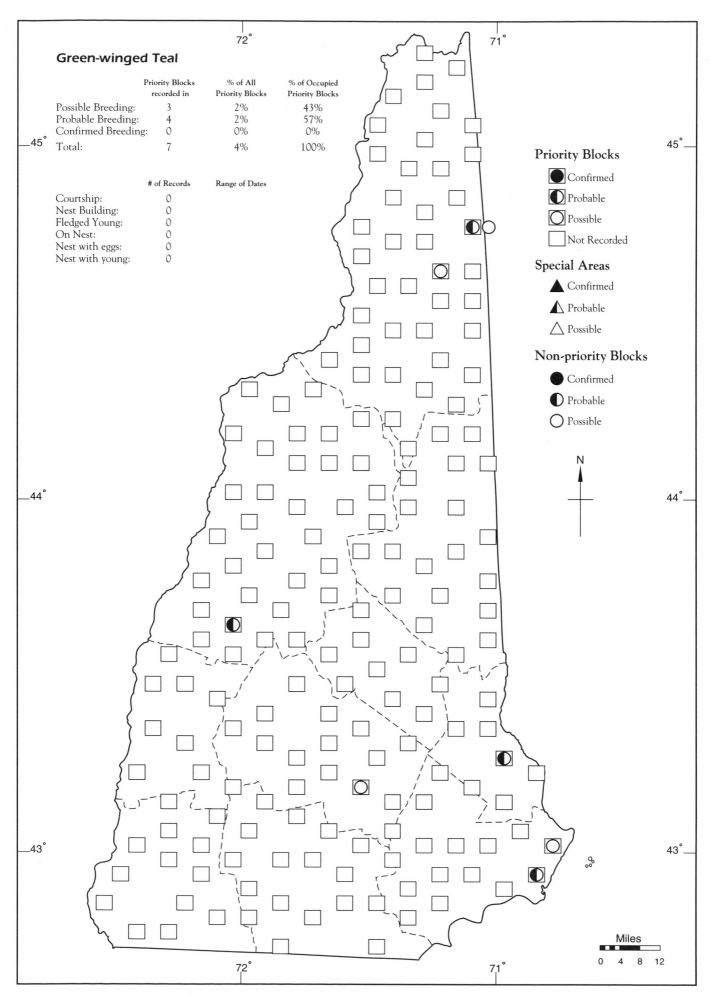

Green-winged Teal

	Priority Blocks recorded in	% of All Priority Blocks	% of Occupied Priority Blocks
Possible Breeding:	3	2%	43%
Probable Breeding:	4	2%	57%
Confirmed Breeding:	0	0%	0%
Total:	7	4%	100%

	# of Records	Range of Dates
Courtship:	0	
Nest Building:	0	
Fledged Young:	0	
On Nest:	0	
Nest with eggs:	0	
Nest with young:	0	

Priority Blocks
- ◑ Confirmed
- ◑ Probable
- ○ Possible
- ☐ Not Recorded

Special Areas
- ▲ Confirmed
- ◢ Probable
- △ Possible

Non-priority Blocks
- ● Confirmed
- ◑ Probable
- ○ Possible

N

Miles
0 4 8 12

American Black Duck
Anas rubripes

Rich brown plumage and the flash of white under-wings in flight distinguish this wary species from other ducks. Black ducks closely resemble Mallards in size, but are much darker in color than female Mallards. They breed throughout the state, from the Coastal region to northern wetlands. They apparently do not nest in tidal marshes here, however (G.W. Gavutis, D.P. Olson, pers. comm.).

Some black ducks overwinter in New Hampshire in coastal marshes, at Great Bay, and on open fresh water. Adults begin to pair in early September, and most are paired by January. Juveniles begin to pair in December or January and breed later in the spring than adults. Up to 10% of females do not breed as yearlings.

Black ducks appear in breeding areas as soon as the ice melts. Nesting habitat includes a variety of situations from thickets, briar patches, and woodland edges to grassy areas, bogs, and the borders of ponds, islands, or marshes. Built on dry ground of grasses, leaves, or other available litter and lined with down, the nest usually is well concealed. In areas subject to flooding, black ducks may nest in tree crotches, stubs, or cavities (Bellrose 1980).

Nesting typically begins in early April and extends into mid-June. The eggs, usually 8 to 10 in number, are indistinguishable from Mallard eggs (Harrison 1975), but breast feathers among the down can be used to identify the species (D. P. Olson, pers. comm.). The average incubation period for New Hampshire climates appears to be 28 days (Bellrose 1980). Males usually remain with their mates for up to 14 days after incubation begins (Stotts and Davis 1960 *in* Bellrose 1980).

Upon hatching and drying out, the downy young are immediately able to move about, swim, and feed for themselves. Hens with upland nests may lead their newly hatched broods for up to 2 mi (3.2 km) before reaching water (Wright 1954 *in* Bellrose 1980). Black duck broods are fairly terrestrial for the first 3 to 4

weeks after hatching and often seem to disappear from a wetland and suddenly reappear as half-grown ducklings (D.P. Olson, pers. comm.). The ducklings make their first flights at 58 to 63 days of age (Gollop and Marshall 1954). A female black duck raises a single brood annually, but females that lose nests may renest.

Male black ducks begin to congregate in large marshes and molt by mid-June. After regaining their flight feathers in early August, they concentrate by late August or early September at traditional staging areas, where first non-nesting females, then young, and finally the females that have nested successfully subsequently join them (Bellrose 1980). Most local black ducks have left their breeding areas for coastal wintering areas by the first week in October (Nevers 1968, Lacaillade 1975). Migrating black ducks from further north reach New England beginning in late September with peak migrations occurring along the coast in mid or late November (D.P. Olson, pers. comm.).

Black ducks have occupied acceptable breeding habitat throughout New Hampshire since records were first kept, but they rarely wintered here prior to the middle of this century (Silver 1957). In recent years, over-wintering black duck populations in New Hampshire have ranged from a few hundred to 3 or 4 thousand birds, of which about 80% are adults (USFWS, unpubl. data). Breeding populations in the state have fluctuated, with an apparent decline during the last quarter of the 19th century (Dearborn 1898, Allen 1903, Brewster 1938), a subsequent increase in the early 1900s (Richards 1952), and a current decline which began around 1955 (USFWS *in* Grandy 1983). If populations continue to decline at the present rate, it is possible that this species could disappear in the foreseeable future (Heusmann 1974).

Black duck populations have been declining steadily from the early 1950s to the present throughout most of the species' range, with the possible exception of the Canadian Maritimes. USFWS winter inventories during 1955-85 indicate an overall population decline of about 60%. Suggested causes include excessive hunting, habitat loss, hybridization and competition with Mallards, and effects of acid rain (Grandy 1983). Mallards are more tolerant of human disturbance than are black ducks and will nest closer to human activity (NHFG 1985). Mallards are increasing throughout New Hampshire and hybridize with American Black Ducks to produce fertile offspring. However, Mallards do not winter in our salt or brackish coastal habitats to the extent that black ducks do (D.P. Olson, pers. comm.), which somewhat reduces opportunities to hybridize.

The Atlas map shows that the black duck still is widely distributed in this state. Like many other wetland species, it is more common in southern New Hampshire, where suitable habitat is more plentiful, than in the more mountainous northern half of the state. Although some decrease in nesting habitat has occurred in southern New Hampshire, breeding habitat does not appear to be a limiting factor for black ducks in this state. Winter habitat in New Hampshire has decreased due to changing land uses and increasing human activity along the Coast and on the shores of Great Bay. The future of this species in New Hampshire and throughout its range may depend on biologists' ability to identify the true causes of the overall population decline and take steps to reverse the downward trend.

John Lanier

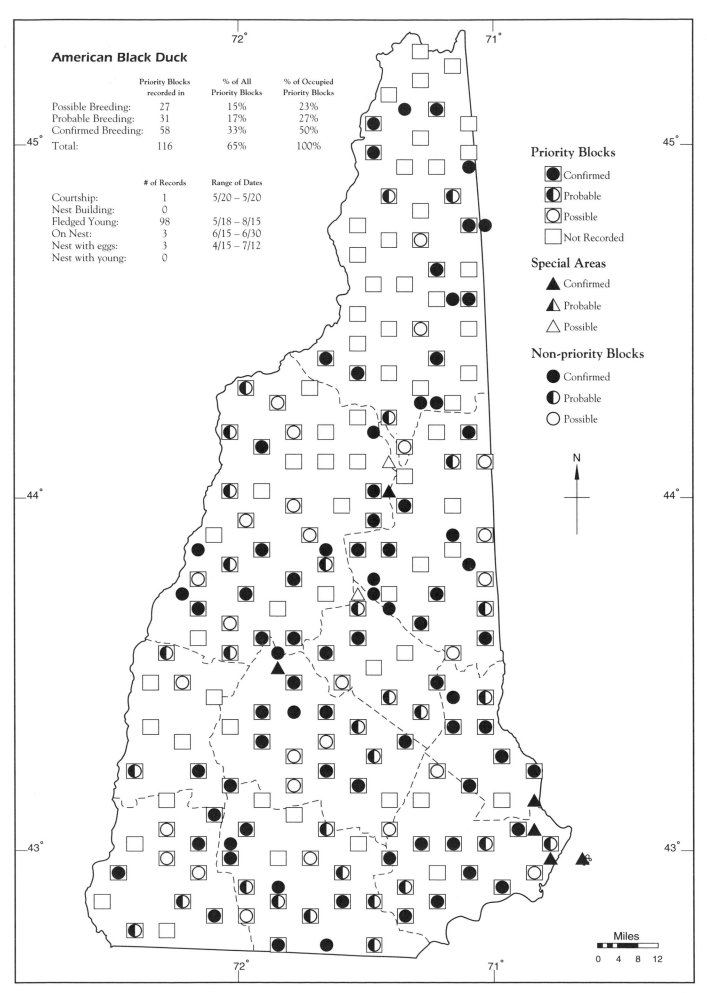

American Black Duck

	Priority Blocks recorded in	% of All Priority Blocks	% of Occupied Priority Blocks
Possible Breeding:	27	15%	23%
Probable Breeding:	31	17%	27%
Confirmed Breeding:	58	33%	50%
Total:	116	65%	100%

	# of Records	Range of Dates
Courtship:	1	5/20 – 5/20
Nest Building:	0	
Fledged Young:	98	5/18 – 8/15
On Nest:	3	6/15 – 6/30
Nest with eggs:	3	4/15 – 7/12
Nest with young:	0	

Priority Blocks

- Confirmed
- Probable
- Possible
- Not Recorded

Special Areas

- Confirmed
- Probable
- Possible

Non-priority Blocks

- Confirmed
- Probable
- Possible

N

Miles
0 4 8 12

25

Mallard

Anas platyrhynchos

The drake Mallard with its green head and white collar is a familiar duck throughout North America. Despite its abundance over a broad range, the Mallard is a relative newcomer in New Hampshire, and only recently has it become a resident of the state. Releases of game-farm stock give it a strong urban background with overtones of domesticity. The Romans domesticated this species before the birth of Christ (Phillips 1922), and all domestic ducks except the Muscovy are descendants of the Mallard (Terres 1980).

In North America, the Mallard was a common native duck that nested on prairie wetlands of the north central U.S. and adjacent Canada and wintered in southern marshes. The closely related American Black Duck inhabited forested wetlands of the Northeast. Only on the wintering grounds did the 2 species occupy the same wetlands. As Eastern woodlands were cleared for agriculture, the Mallard extended its range eastward, often replacing the black duck as the local breeding species. Frequently, the 2 hybridized. Unlike most hybrids, whose offspring are sterile, these close relatives produce fertile offspring (Heusmann 1974), and some ornithologists believe that the black duck should be included in the Mallard superspecies (Johnsgard 1978).

Mallards nest early, and most birds have paired by the time our wetlands become ice free in late March or early April. Many form pair bonds on the wintering grounds and migrate north together. They soon establish territories, and the drakes aggressively pursue intruding pairs of Mallards and/or black ducks (Hochbaum 1944). Subsequently the hens select nest sites and lay clutches of usually 9 to 12 eggs.

Nests generally are located in grassy cover close to water, but may be several hundred meters away (Bellrose 1976). They may be located under brush, on a stump or muskrat house, or in some other unusual site. The nest is merely a bowl-shaped depression when the hen lays the first egg, but she adds grass and other material and plucks down from her brood patch as she completes the clutch. During egg laying, she visits the nest briefly each day to deposit an egg and then rejoins the drake on the territory. After incubation begins, the drakes gather on a favorite molting marsh, sometimes a considerable distance away, leaving the hens to hatch and rear the young. Eggs hatch in about 28 days (Bellrose 1976), and the downy, precocial young leave the nest as soon as all are hatched and dry.

The young feed primarily on small aquatic invertebrates. The hen escorts them closely and broods them frequently. The brood disperses when the young become able to fly, at the age of 50 to 60 days (Bellrose 1976). Most Atlas confirmations were based on hens with broods. Identification of broods can be challenging because hybrid hens and hens of game-farm stock are variable in plumage. Young birds attain adult plumage by October. They pair and nest the following spring. Although a hen raises only a single brood each year, she may renest 2 or 3 times if clutches are destroyed.

Historical accounts indicate that the Mallard was no more than a rare to uncommon visitor in New Hampshire a century ago, and early records of the species in New Hampshire refer to migrants observed or shot during the hunting season, usually in association with black ducks (Silver 1957). Dearborn (1903) noted that they were taken not infrequently on Great Bay. White (1937) describes introduced Mallards breeding on a pond in Concord. Additional nesting records occurred during the 1950s, as the species became a more common summer resident. Silver (1957) attributed the sightings of many broods during the 1950s to large numbers of game-farm birds released in the Atlantic Flyway.

Today the Mallard is well established and increasing in New Hampshire and elsewhere in New England. Urban Mallards readily adapt to almost any type of natural or artificial wetland, readily accept handouts of food, and during the hunting season are quick to occupy city ponds and lakes that are closed to shooting (Heusmann 1974). As a result these birds and their offspring have spread and increased throughout the Northeast, where the native black duck has been declining for at least 3 decades. Wild Mallard populations also have declined recently in the prairie wetlands of their primary breeding range, and the continental population of 5.5 million in 1985 was the lowest since surveys began in 1955 (USFWS and CWS 1986).

Many Mallards now overwinter in New Hampshire despite deep snows and a scarcity of open water. Most concentrate where humans provide an ample food supply at inland sites of open water, but some occur along the Coast or on Great Bay. CBC data from the Nashua area show an increase from a few birds to more than 400 in 20 years, and Mallards recently have outnumbered black ducks.

As the Atlas map illustrates, the Mallard now nests throughout the southern half of New Hampshire, where it is widespread in the eastern portion of the state and somewhat local in the Western Highlands. It is largely absent from the White Mountains and occurs at only scattered locations in the North Country.

Considering recent trends, the cosmopolitan Mallards are likely to continue their increase in New Hampshire and keep pace with urbanizing habitats. They may even replace black ducks in many rural sites, either by out-competing them or by genetic swamping through repeated hybridization.

Ralph Andrews

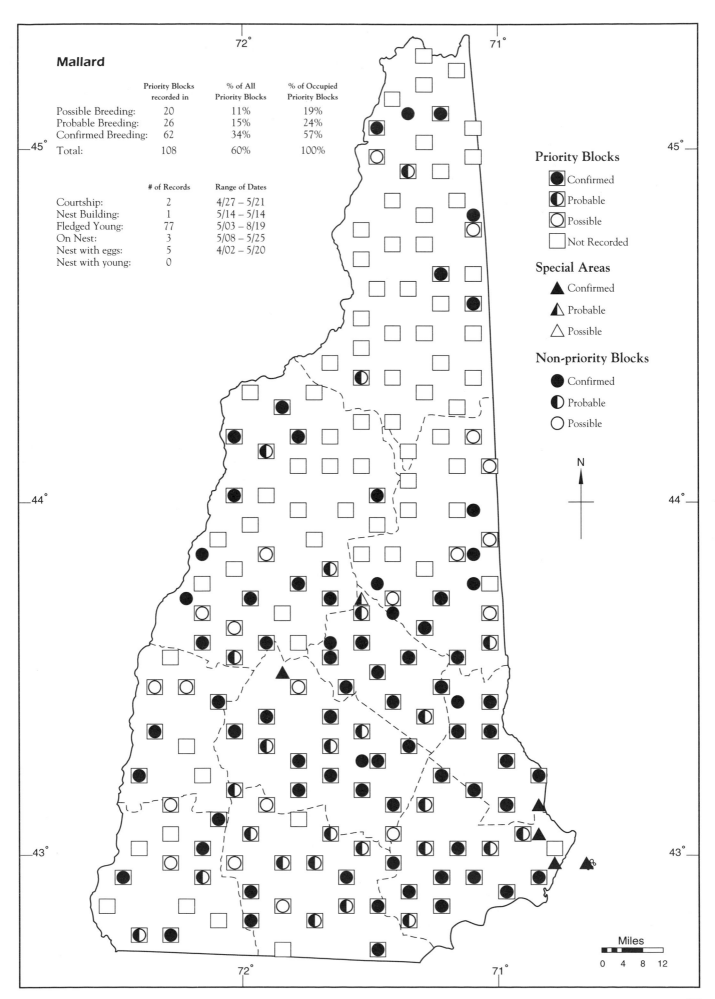

Mallard

	Priority Blocks recorded in	% of All Priority Blocks	% of Occupied Priority Blocks
Possible Breeding:	20	11%	19%
Probable Breeding:	26	15%	24%
Confirmed Breeding:	62	34%	57%
Total:	108	60%	100%

	# of Records	Range of Dates
Courtship:	2	4/27 – 5/21
Nest Building:	1	5/14 – 5/14
Fledged Young:	77	5/03 – 8/19
On Nest:	3	5/08 – 5/25
Nest with eggs:	5	4/02 – 5/20
Nest with young:	0	

Priority Blocks

- ◑ Confirmed
- ◐ Probable
- ○ Possible
- ▢ Not Recorded

Special Areas

- ▲ Confirmed
- ◣ Probable
- △ Possible

Non-priority Blocks

- ● Confirmed
- ◑ Probable
- ○ Possible

N

Miles
0 4 8 12

Blue-winged Teal
Anas discors

These small ducks of shallow wetlands fly rapidly on whistling wings. They typically circle several times before dropping into a marsh, where they may quickly disappear into the vegetation. Blue-wings are primarily ducks of northern prairies and parklands of the midwestern U.S. and Canada. They breed uncommonly in New Hampshire but migrate through the state in substantial numbers.

Blue-wings generally are the last waterfowl species to arrive in spring, from late April into May, and the first to leave in the autumn. These ducks begin to move south in August, and most have left the state by mid-October. Blue-winged Teal are reported to winter further south in greater numbers than any other North American duck. Those that migrate through and from New Hampshire usually winter in eastern Venezuela and Guyana (Bellrose 1980).

A white facial crescent, a steel-blue head and neck, and a tan chest and sides characterize the adult male. The hen is drab. Both sexes reveal a light blue shoulder patch in flight. These ducks are usually quiet, but the male utters a "keck-keck-keck" and the female, a mallard-like "quack" (Bellrose 1980).

Blue-winged Teal develop extremely strong pair bonds, which begin to form in early winter. Courtship, which consists primarily of aerial chases, continues during migration. Blue-wings have variable home ranges; Bellrose (1980) cites averages of 17 and 89 a (7 and 36 ha) and extremes of 1.4 a (0.6 ha) to 250 a (101 ha). They seldom return to the same breeding marsh, but are more likely to pioneer in new breeding areas (Bellrose 1980). This trait complicates efforts to monitor their status in areas, such as New Hampshire, where nesting pairs are few and widely scattered.

Pairs search for nest sites after arrival on the breeding grounds, flying low over areas which may exceed 100 a (40 ha), and often begin to nest within a week of arrival (Bellrose 1980). Blue-wings nest on the ground within 1 mi (1.7 km) of water; the average distance is 125 ft (38.1 m) (Bellrose 1980). Grassy areas, hayfields, and sedge meadows are favored nesting sites, but Blue-wings sometimes nest in wetlands on muskrat houses (Bent 1923).

The female lines the nest bowl with vegetation, usually grass, and adds down feathers after beginning the clutch (Bellrose 1980). Nest construction takes 2 to 7 days, and egg laying typically occurs from mid-May to mid-June, often beginning before the nest is complete (Harrison 1975, Bellrose 1980). Clutches average 6 to 12 eggs (Reed 1965). The male deserts the female soon after she has laid the eggs. Incubation takes 23 or 24 days, and young leave the nest within 24 hours of hatching (Harrison 1975). Blue-wings will renest if a clutch of eggs is lost before incubation begins, but as incubation proceeds, the probability of renesting decreases greatly (Bellrose 1980).

Hens often lead their broods over land a distance of 300 to 4,800 ft (91 to 1,463 m) to suitable brooding areas, which range from semipermanent 1 a (0.4 ha) marshes to large marsh systems. The young remain with the hens throughout the summer, feeding primarily on invertebrates during their first few weeks and gradually consuming more and more vegetation as they reach flight stage, about 40 days after hatching. The young, which resemble the adult female but are lighter below, can fly by the end of August. Drakes wander from the breeding home range in late June and early July and congregate to molt. They are flightless for 26 to 36 days, during which they usually remain concealed in emergent vegetation (Bellrose 1980).

Aquatic plants such as algae, duckweeds, and pondweeds in summer and seeds of sedges and other aquatic plants in autumn comprise the bulk of the Blue-wing's diet. One quarter of the diet consists of aquatic animals, such as snails, tadpoles, and insects (Bellrose 1980). Blue-wings seldom tip up while feeding, but skim the water's surface with their bills or reach below the surface with heads and necks extended.

Blue-winged Teal apparently were summer residents and abundant migrants in New England prior to a drastic decline in 1880 (Silver 1957, Palmer 1976). Belknap included them in his list of birds in 1790 (*in* Allen 1903), and they were common at Umbagog Lake until 1894 (Brewster 1925). The regional population has fluctuated during the 1900s, but this duck never has nested commonly in New Hampshire during the present century (Allen 1903, Silver 1957, Palmer 1976). Shelley (1933) observed a hen with 4 chicks in Westmoreland in 1932, which apparently is the first documented nesting in the state. USFWS and Canadian Wildlife Service breeding population data published since 1955 indicate an overall decline in the breeding population.

The Atlas project produced only 5 "confirmed" nesting records, including 2 from one priority block. A slight majority of records are from southeastern New Hampshire. This is consistent with Massachusetts, where the species is most common along the North Shore, is generally uncommon elsewhere in the eastern part of the state, and is rare in the western half (Veit and Petersen 1993).

Much of New Hampshire's waterfowl habitat consists of shrubby swamps and beaver flowages with forested shorelines, and includes relatively little preferred nesting habitat for Blue-winged Teal. It is unlikely that significant numbers of this species ever will breed in the state.

Edward G. Robinson

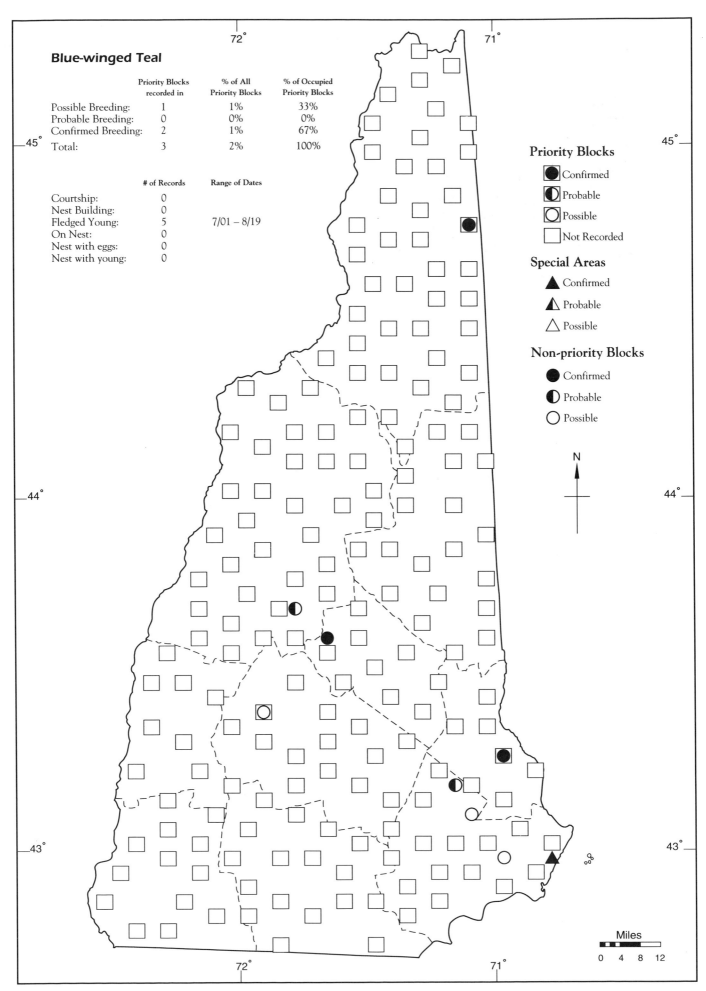

Blue-winged Teal

	Priority Blocks recorded in	% of All Priority Blocks	% of Occupied Priority Blocks
Possible Breeding:	1	1%	33%
Probable Breeding:	0	0%	0%
Confirmed Breeding:	2	1%	67%
Total:	3	2%	100%

	# of Records	Range of Dates
Courtship:	0	
Nest Building:	0	
Fledged Young:	5	7/01 – 8/19
On Nest:	0	
Nest with eggs:	0	
Nest with young:	0	

Priority Blocks
- Confirmed
- Probable
- Possible
- Not Recorded

Special Areas
- Confirmed
- Probable
- Possible

Non-priority Blocks
- Confirmed
- Probable
- Possible

N

Miles
0 4 8 12

Ring-necked Duck
Aythya collaris

The Ring-necked Duck nests only very locally in New Hampshire. Most common in summer in Canada's Prairie Provinces, it breeds from southeast Alaska to Newfoundland south to the northwestern U.S. and New England and winters from the Southern states to Mexico and the West Indies (Bellrose 1980). The drake Ring-neck's blackish purple head, chest and back contrast with its white to grayish sides and white belly. The white stripe across its blue bill and especially the white crescent next to its black chest are distinctive. The hen is brownish.

Ring-necked Ducks generally arrive in New Hampshire in late March or early April (SRS). They choose ponds and backwaters with boggy or marshy edges for breeding (Richards, pers. obs.) Although some form pair bonds in the fall, many arrive on the breeding grounds unpaired (Mendall 1958, Bellrose 1976). Audubon (1840 in Kortright 1942) described the drake's courtship performance as an almost constant raising of the head and occipital feathers accompanied by a muted call note.

A nest on the outlet of Little Cherry Pond, Jefferson, which contained 8 eggs on 29 May 1969, was on a floating island of sphagnum, sedges, and bog shrubs (Richards, unpubl. data). Mendall (1958) found this the most common type of nesting site in Maine. Nests may, however, be on solid ground near water, or in tussocks or clumps of tall plants in shallow water (Harrison 1978). Mendall (1958) found 86.3% of nests observed in Maine in marsh vegetation, averaging about 80 ft (24.4 m) from open water, with some nests as close together as 5 to 6 ft (1.5 to 1.8 m). Initial clutches averaged 9 eggs, renestings 7.

Early-nesting drakes remain with their mates until the fourth week of incubation or even until hatching, whereas late-nesting drakes usually leave by the second week (Mendall 1958 in Bellrose 1976). Hens usually leave their nests to feed in early morning or late after-noon. If they are still around, the drakes may join them (Bellrose 1980).

Incubation averages 26 days (Mendall 1958). Broods usually hatch in late June or July, the latest probably a result of renesting (Richards, pers. obs.). The earliest recorded New Hampshire brood apparently is one of 9 young on Cherry Pond, Jefferson on 9 June 1949, and the largest, one of 12 young at Scott's Bog, Pittsburg on 22 August 1952 (Richards, unpubl. data). Hen Ring-necks tend to keep their young more in open water than black or Wood ducks (Richards, pers. obs.). Richards (1952) provides counts of adults and young on Cherry and Little Cherry ponds, Jefferson, during surveys from 1949 to 1951.

Families tend to band together in late summer before migrating. Migration peaks in late October or early November, when flocks of up to 80 birds may occur in both northern and southern New Hampshire (Richards, unpubl. data). A record of 9 drakes and 2 hens at Chocorua Lake, Tamworth, on 7 December 1948 (Richards, unpubl. data) is unusually late.

In comparison with other diving ducks, Ring-necks seek food in relatively shallow water, usually less than 6 ft (1.8 m) deep. Ducklings first feed exclusively on animal matter such as aquatic insects, snails, and tiny fish. Adults feed mostly on pondweeds, duckweeds, sedges, bulrushes, and other aquatic plants (Bellrose 1980).

A rare breeder in Maine during the 1860s and 1870s, the Ring-necked Duck was a very rare migrant throughout New England then, and for many years afterwards, even in Maine (Forbush 1925a, Palmer 1949). Brewster (1924), during many long visits to the Umbagog Lake area in the period 1871–1909, encountered the species only 5 times, all in the fall. Allen (1903) cited but 2 records for the state: single birds taken at Concord and at Little Bay, Newington.

L. Nelson shot 6 Ring-necks out of a larger flock in Hinsdale on 27 October 1939, providing the first documentation for a flock in New Hampshire since Brewster's 1894 record (Richards 1952). H. Siegler's discovery of 2 flightless young at Fish Pond, Columbia, in 1947 established the state's first breeding record (Richards 1952).

Richards (1952) found 6 broods on the Cherry ponds in 1948 and during the next 3 years also saw broods on Mirror Lake, Whitefield; Leonard Pond, Errol; and Scott's Bog, Pittsburg. Successful nesting occurred in southern New Hampshire on Perkins Pond, Troy in 1962; on Turtle Pond, Concord in 1965 (Richards, unpubl. data); and on Cascade Marsh, Sutton in 1970 (K. C. Elkins, unpubl. data). Meanwhile, Ring-necks apparently ceased to breed successfully at the Cherry ponds. It seems impossible that there were even remotely 1,000 breeding Ring-necks in New Hampshire in 1965, as Sutherland (1971 in Bellrose 1980) calculated.

During the Atlas period, this species was the most common nesting duck in the backwaters of the Magalloway and Androscoggin rivers, Errol. Additional "confirmed" records came from elsewhere in Coos County and from George Pond, Enfield. Atlas field work produced "confirmed" breeding records from fewer areas than the number of breeding locations known in the past, strongly suggesting a recent decline in the state's breeding population.

Though scarce as a breeding species in New Hampshire, the Ring-neck remains a fairly common migrant. After highs estimated at 500 to 900 during 1980–87, hunters bagged only 94 in 1988 and 51 in 1989, suggesting a recent decline in migrant numbers. With much apparently suitable habitat unoccupied, the future of the Ring-necked Duck in New Hampshire looks bleak.

Tudor Richards

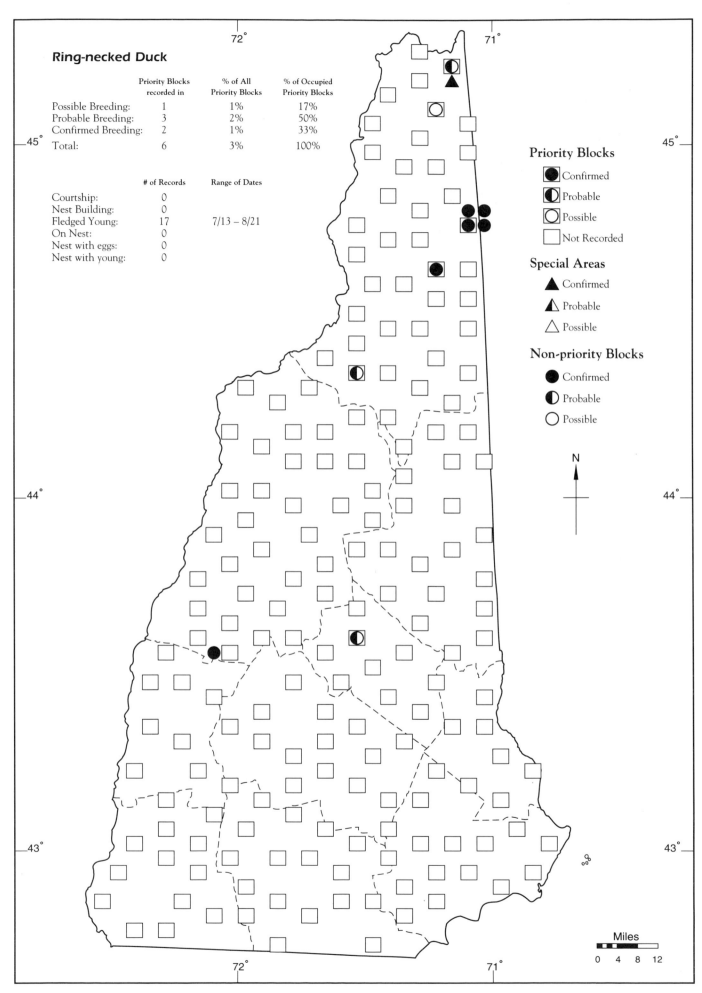

Ring-necked Duck

	Priority Blocks recorded in	% of All Priority Blocks	% of Occupied Priority Blocks
Possible Breeding:	1	1%	17%
Probable Breeding:	3	2%	50%
Confirmed Breeding:	2	1%	33%
Total:	6	3%	100%

	# of Records	Range of Dates
Courtship:	0	
Nest Building:	0	
Fledged Young:	17	7/13 – 8/21
On Nest:	0	
Nest with eggs:	0	
Nest with young:	0	

Priority Blocks

● Confirmed
◐ Probable
○ Possible
☐ Not Recorded

Special Areas

▲ Confirmed
◣ Probable
△ Possible

Non-priority Blocks

● Confirmed
◐ Probable
○ Possible

N

Miles
0   4   8   12

Common Eider
Somateria mollissima

Small rafts of these large, stocky ducks now occur year round near the breaking surf of the Isles of Shoals. They dive to the rocky bottom, feeding primarily on mussels. From time to time one can see them flying in lines low over the water, their sloping foreheads distinguishing them from other waterfowl. The Common Eider has had many colloquial names, including "Isle-of-Shoals duck" (Kortright 1953).

Eiders are present around the Isles of Shoals and along the New Hampshire coastline all winter. Courtship, not yet observed off our coast, apparently occurs in spring. Males actively elevate their heads and necks, flap their wings, and vocalize in the hens' presence (Bent 1923). One can see pairs of adults flying around Lunging Island, Isles of Shoals, Rye, in late May.

According to Korschgen (1979), egg laying occurs during mid-April to mid-July on the Maine Coast. At the Isles of Shoals, the earliest nest with eggs was on Duck Island, Kittery, Maine, 24 April 1986, and the latest were 5 nests with eggs on Lunging Island, 13 June 1986. The female constructs the nest of grasses with a lining of down. Nests occur on shore rocks and ledges as well as in near-shore terrestrial vegetation. They are sometimes semihidden by tufts of grass and may be situated among territories of nesting Great Black-backed or Herring gulls. More typically, nests are situated under low dense thickets of salt-spray rose, red raspberry, and/or poison ivy approximately 3 ft (1 m) high, beyond usual gull nesting areas.

The female incubates her 2 to 5 eggs for nearly 4 weeks (Bellrose 1976). On the rare occasions when she leaves the nest, she covers the eggs and/or downy young with down from the surface of the nest. According to Korschgen (1979), young eiders hatch from mid-May through mid-July. Borror has found young in the nest at Lunging Island as early as 25 May. The female leads her downy young into the water within a day or so of hatching; Borror has seen females with downy young in the water at the Isles of Shoals as early as 28 May (28 May to 13 June). Sometimes there are several females with combined broods. Young probably fly by 8 weeks of age (Bellrose 1976).

Flocks of immature eiders increase in size in late summer. By late August or early September, as many as 150 immature and postbreeding adult male eiders may be at the Isles of Shoals, mostly in rafts north of Duck Island. Eiders become less abundant at the Isles of Shoals in late fall. They migrate by day, traveling single file low over the water, sometimes in troughs of waves. The outer shore of Cape Cod is a major wintering area, and many winter along the coast of Maine, but only small numbers winter along rocky parts of the New Hampshire coast (Stott and Olson 1974). Diving over shallow, rocky, subtidal areas, they feed gregariously on invertebrates, especially blue mussels.

The Common Eider population has undergone major contraction and expansion in size and breeding range during the past century. Eiders may have bred regularly along the Maine and New Hampshire coasts in the distant past, but they were nearly extirpated in the 1800s, plundered for their feathers and eggs. Reduced by 1907 to a single colony, the population on the Maine coast gradually increased to approximately 2,000 pairs by 1943 (Korschgen 1979), and extended its range southwest to Franklin Island, Muscongus Bay by 1946 and to Bluff Island, Saco Bay by 1952 (Cruickshank 1950, Drury 1973).

Small flocks of immature males occurred in summer at the perimeter of the Isles of Shoals beginning in 1972. The first adults to spend the summer appeared in 1977. In early June 1977, Borror et al. observed an adult female Common Eider closely "herding" a group of 4 half-grown, but still downy, young eiders within a few meters of the shore of Lunging Island, providing the first New Hampshire breeding record. On 28 May 1980, Borror and P. McGill-Harelstad discovered and photographed a nest on Lunging Island. On the Maine Isles there were single nests on Appledore Island in 1985 and Duck Island in 1986.

The Common Eider currently is known to breed as far south as the Elizabeth Islands off Woods Hole, Mass. Given sufficient isolation during the critical breeding season in late spring and early summer, the population should continue to increase along the New Hampshire coast.

Arthur C. Borror

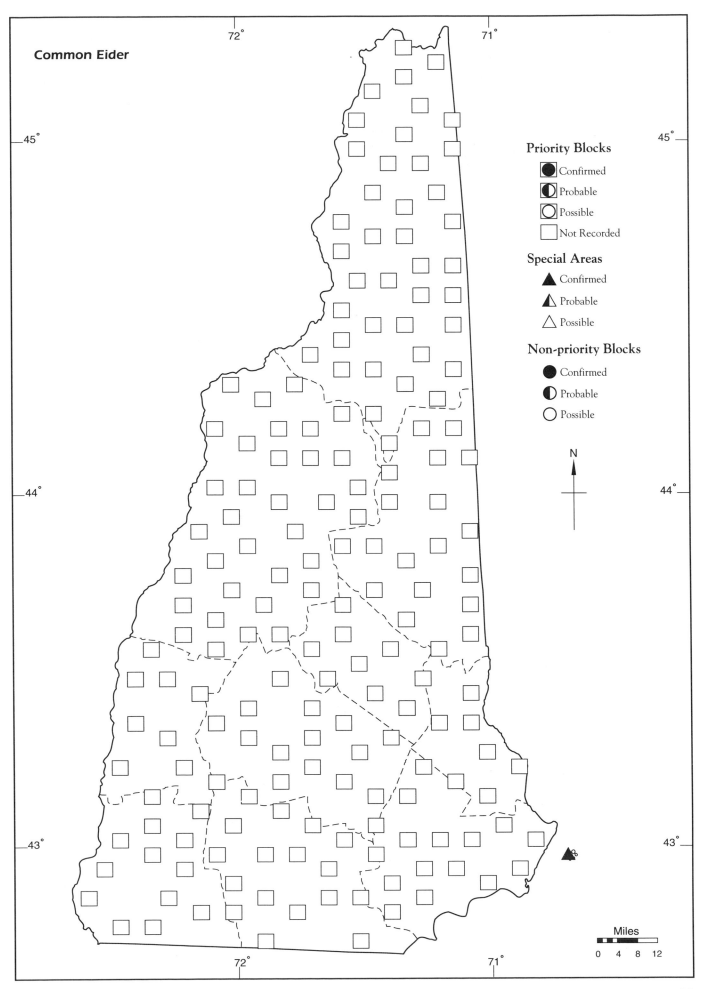

Common Eider

Priority Blocks
● Confirmed
◐ Probable
○ Possible
☐ Not Recorded

Special Areas
▲ Confirmed
◣ Probable
△ Possible

Non-priority Blocks
● Confirmed
◖ Probable
○ Possible

N

Miles
0 4 8 12

Common Goldeneye
Bucephala clangula

The "whistling" of rapidly beating wings announces the presence of a small group of Common Goldeneyes speeding overhead. Although most commonly referred to as the "whistler" for its musical flight, this species has earned many descriptive names, including "bull-head" for its large head ("*bucephala*") and "brass-eyed whistler" for its brilliant yellow eyes during the breeding season. This diving duck, distinguished from the rarer Barrow's Goldeneye by a round rather than crescent-shaped white facial patch and more extensive white on the wing, occurs in New Hampshire throughout the year.

The Common Goldeneye is distributed across North America from Alaska to Labrador (Bent 1925, Bellrose 1976) and reaches the southern extreme of its Eastern breeding range in northern New Hampshire, Maine, and New York. Nesting occurs on lakes and ponds in boreal forests.

A rather reluctant migrant, this species lingers on breeding areas longer than most waterfowl and winters along the Atlantic Coast from Maine to South Carolina and as far inland as open water allows (Bellrose 1976). The Common Goldeneye is the most widely distributed waterfowl species in New Hampshire during the winter months, occurring both along the Coast and inland on large open sections of rivers and lakes (Silver 1957).

Most Common Goldeneyes wait until their second year to breed (Bent 1925). The wooing of a female begins at wintering sites in January and February and continues after arrival at breeding areas. The courtship displays of the male are highly diverse and complex (Johnsgard 1975b). With his glossy green head accentuated by raised feathers, the male approaches a female, extends his head forward over the water, then snaps it far back as if to touch his tail. A buzzing vocalization completes the display. Two or more males may engage in buzzing and snapping around a female, which often leads to aggression. Goldeneyes may return to some breeding areas by late March (Ellis *in* Laughlin and Kibbe 1985).

Upon reaching the breeding grounds, goldeneyes seek a nest cavity on or near the shore. They will use an exposed or covered natural cavity or nest box from 6 to 60 ft (1.8 to 18.3 m) above the water (Bent 1925) and exhibit a strong tendency to reuse sites from year to year (Johnson 1967 *in* Bellrose 1976). A tuft of down snagged at the cavity entrance often indicates the goldeneye's presence inside (Harrison 1975).

The female lays her clutch of distinctive light green eggs (a unique color for cavity nesting ducks) during mid-April though May. The clutch includes 8 to 12 eggs on average (Bellrose 1976). Loss of eggs to predation is not common, but dump nesting by another female may result in a deserted clutch (Bellrose 1976). At least one Atlas confirmation resulted from discovery of abandoned eggs. The male guards a small territory during egg laying and early incubation, then departs to spend a flightless molt period in seclusion (Bellrose 1976). Adult males appear in eclipse plumage beginning in late July.

The distinctive dark brown and white chicks hatch after 28 to 32 days of incubation (Bent 1925, Bellrose 1976). After spending one or 2 days in the nest, the downy chicks tumble from the cavity and make their way to water. The female accompanies them through most of the brood period, warning them of danger with a distinctive hoarse croaking (Bent 1925). She departs when the chicks are about 50 days old, and the feathered but flightless young may congregate and move around in groups before fledging at 50 to 60 days (Belrose 1976, Cramp and Simmons 1977). When fully feathered at about 56 days, juveniles resemble adult females (Bellrose 1976). Common Goldeneye broods suffer comparatively high losses, for reasons which are unknown (Bellrose 1976). Presumably lack of food is not a problem, as this species is known for its diverse diet, which includes plant material, crustaceans, mollusks, and aquatic insects.

The status of the "whistler" in New Hampshire during the nonbreeding season apparently has changed little since the late 1800s. Dearborn (1898,1903) listed it as a common winter resident for the Winnipesaukee and Merrimack rivers and in the Great Bay estuary. Brewster found its numbers to be stable during the 40 years he frequented the Umbagog Lake area and identified a favored wintering spot on the Androscoggin River below the Errol Dam (Silver 1957). The goldeneye often is the most numerous wintering duck along the New Hampshire coast (K. C. Elkins, pers. comm.).

The Common Goldeneye's historical breeding status is less clear. New Hampshire is at the southern extreme of its nesting range, and its breeding distribution here has been restricted to a few sites in Coos County, including Weed's Pond, Whitefield; Nash Stream Bog, Stratford; Pontook Reservoir, Dummer; the Connecticut Lakes, Pittsburg; and Umbagog Lake, Errol (Richards 1952 *in* Silver 1957).

The Atlas map may reflect a decline in the state's breeding population, with nesting "confirmed" only in the Umbagog Lake area and at sites in Dixville and Pittsburg. Evans frequently encountered broods in shallow wetlands associated with Umbagog Lake throughout the mid-1980s, but these numbers may be declining (T. Richards, pers. comm.). Reasons for the apparent departure from former nesting areas are unknown.

Diane Evans

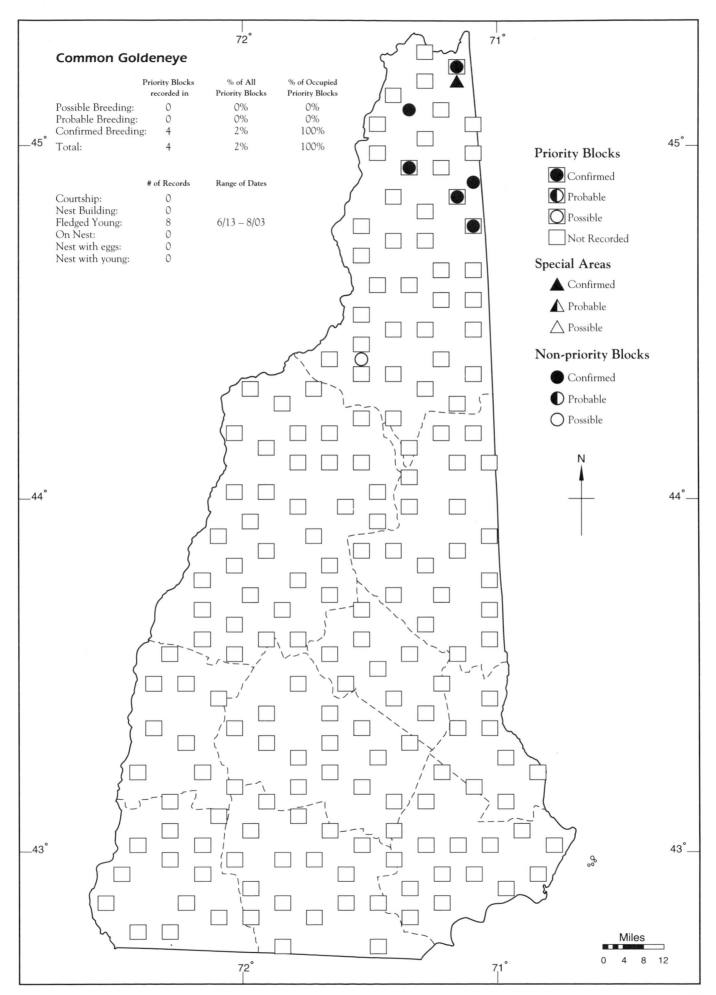

Common Goldeneye

	Priority Blocks recorded in	% of All Priority Blocks	% of Occupied Priority Blocks
Possible Breeding:	0	0%	0%
Probable Breeding:	0	0%	0%
Confirmed Breeding:	4	2%	100%
Total:	4	2%	100%

	# of Records	Range of Dates
Courtship:	0	
Nest Building:	0	
Fledged Young:	8	6/13 – 8/03
On Nest:	0	
Nest with eggs:	0	
Nest with young:	0	

Priority Blocks

- ◕ Confirmed
- ◑ Probable
- ○ Possible
- ▢ Not Recorded

Special Areas

- ▲ Confirmed
- ◤ Probable
- △ Possible

Non-priority Blocks

- ● Confirmed
- ◑ Probable
- ○ Possible

N

Miles
0 4 8 12

Hooded Merganser
Lophodytes cucullatus

The strikingly marked, swift-flying Hooded Merganser is the only diving duck to breed more or less throughout New Hampshire. This cavity-nesting species is locally common in areas with small ponds or quiet backwaters. It is the only merganser confined to North America, and its nesting range extends, with many gaps, from Alaska to New Brunswick and south to Florida (Bellrose 1980). Much of this area also is winter range. Only a few "hoodies" winter in New Hampshire, usually most of them in the Lakes Region.

From a distance Hooded Mergansers appear small and dark. Their white bellies and wing patches show in flight, which is fast and generally low over the water. Drakes are largely black above except for their beautiful, black-edged, white, fanlike crests, and largely white below. Even the brown and white hens have impressive crests.

Hooded Mergansers return to New Hampshire in March or April, usually in pairs, although flocks of 40 or more sometimes occur on ice free ponds early in the season (Richards, unpubl. data). The spectacular courtship, often performed by 2 drakes circling a hen on the water, involves opening the crest, stretching the neck, shaking the head, and snapping it to an inverted position over the back as the performer half rises out of the water and squawks (Bellrose 1980; Richards, pers. obs.).

Nests are in hollow trees or nest boxes. The lining consists of down from the female's breast mixed with cavity debris. Pairs often return to the same nest site or vicinity (Bellrose 1980), but competition for nest holes is keen between pairs and with Wood Ducks. Pileated Woodpeckers provide many of the natural holes. On 30 May 1953, near Turkey Pond, Concord, a hen Hooded Merganser investigated a tall snag containing a hole from which a hen Wood Duck and a Pileated Woodpecker had peered out on 30 April and 6 May, respectively, of the same year (Richards, pers. obs.).

Mixed broods of Wood Ducks and Hooded Mergansers sometimes occur. Hoodeds have laid eggs in Common Goldeneye nests (Harrison 1975) and vice versa (Brewster 1924).

Hens typically lay 7 to 13 eggs and incubate for 28 to 41 days (Bellrose 1980). Males usually disappear from nesting areas when incubation begins. When disturbed, hen Hoodeds feign injury or quack, signaling their young to seek cover. The young may become independent before fledging, but families sometimes group together in late summer. On 24 August 1950, on Little Diamond Pond, Stewartstown, elev. 2,200 ft (670 m), 5 families of 6, 8, 10, 10, and 14 birds each alternated between separating from each other and forming one large flock (Richards, unpubl. data).

Although this species eats appreciable amounts of plant material, it feeds mainly on aquatic animals such as small fish, frogs, tadpoles, crawfish, and insects (Kortright 1942).

Courting may begin as early as October. Five drakes performed full courtship displays around a hen on the Squam River, Ashland, on 21 October 1987, and several drakes in a flock of 27 Hooded Mergansers were raising their crests in display at Spofford Lake, Chesterfield, on 22 October 1959 (Richards, unpubl. data). Most Hooded Mergansers leave for the winter by mid-December (Richards, pers. obs.).

Probably once common in beaver ponds of New Hampshire's virgin forests, Hooded Mergansers declined greatly in the last century as forests were cleared, beaver ponds disappeared, and uncontrolled hunting increased. While there are no early breeding records of the species for southern New Hampshire, Brewster (1924) found it to be the most common nesting duck at Umbagog Lake in the early 1870s, and the least common after a few years of heavy shooting.

With better protection, the return of forests and beavers, and installation of duck boxes, the Hooded Merganser has made a remarkable recovery in the last half century. Observers found broods in Andover in 1942 (K.C. Elkins, unpubl. data), and in the next 2 years in New Hampton, Exeter, Eaton, Orange, and Millsfield (Richards 1952). The Millsfield brood, in 1944, apparently was the first breeding record in the Umbagog Lake area since Brewster's day, but by 1949, 8 of 37 broods recorded in a statewide survey were found at or near Umbagog, where the Hooded again became the most common nesting duck (Richards 1952). More recently, however, the Ring-necked Duck seems largely to have replaced this species along the Androscoggin River between the lake and the Errol dam.

In south-central New Hampshire, on the other hand, Hoodeds appear to nest in numbers almost comparable to those of the Wood Duck (NHBBA data). Of the 2 species, the mergansers are more sensitive to human disturbance and require clearer waters for foraging (Bellrose 1980). During 1981–89, Hooded Merganser occupation of nesting boxes inspected by NHFG personnel ranged from 27% to 42%, and rose almost steadily. Ratios of Hooded Merganser to Wood Duck occupation ranged from 1:1 to 3:1 (NHFG 1989b). During 1980–89, estimated Hooded Merganser harvests in New Hampshire averaged about 390 per year and comprised 0.42% to 2.73% of the total New Hampshire waterfowl harvest (USFWS 1990).

The Atlas map shows fairly wide distribution of the Hooded Merganser in southern New Hampshire. Most records are widely separated in the north, where suitable habitat is scarce or remote. Substantial beaver populations, continued availability of nest boxes and natural cavities, and adequate legal protection seem likely to favor the Hooded Merganser in New Hampshire for the foreseeable future.

Tudor Richards

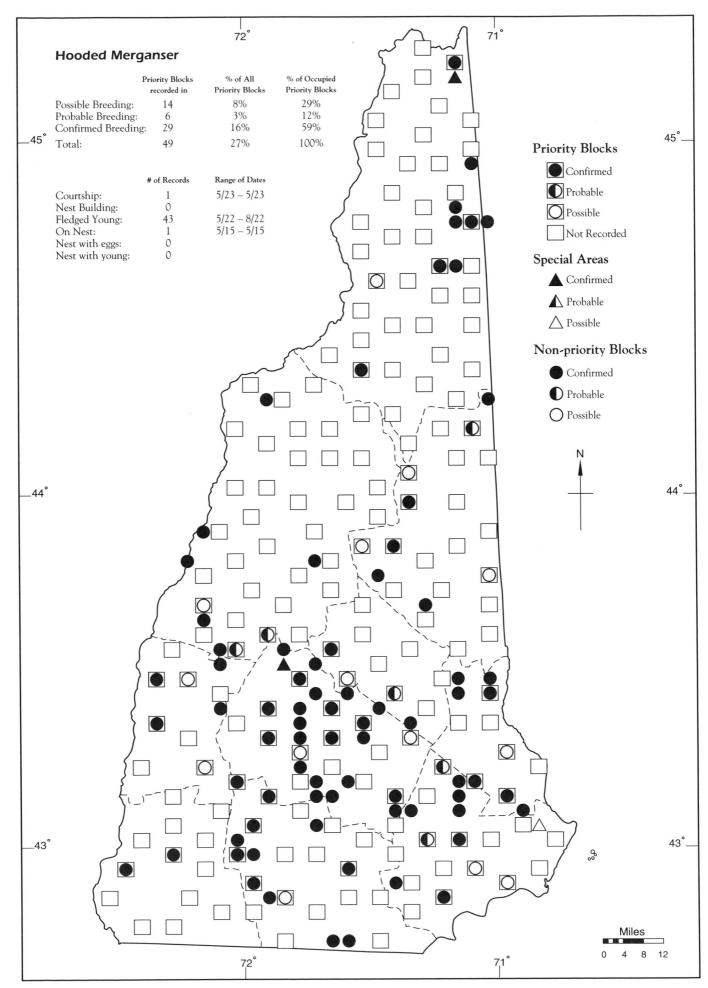

Hooded Merganser

	Priority Blocks recorded in	% of All Priority Blocks	% of Occupied Priority Blocks
Possible Breeding:	14	8%	29%
Probable Breeding:	6	3%	12%
Confirmed Breeding:	29	16%	59%
Total:	49	27%	100%

	# of Records	Range of Dates
Courtship:	1	5/23 – 5/23
Nest Building:	0	
Fledged Young:	43	5/22 – 8/22
On Nest:	1	5/15 – 5/15
Nest with eggs:	0	
Nest with young:	0	

Priority Blocks

● Confirmed
◑ Probable
○ Possible
□ Not Recorded

Special Areas

▲ Confirmed
◢ Probable
△ Possible

Non-priority Blocks

● Confirmed
◐ Probable
○ Possible

Miles
0 4 8 12

37

Common Merganser
Mergus merganser

The hardy, white-water and lake-loving Common Merganser, or Sheldrake is New Hampshire's largest nesting duck. It is a very local, uncommon to fairly common summer resident. Primarily a freshwater species, it is an even more local winter resident, but is very common in migration on lakes and larger rivers. It breeds from Alaska east to Labrador and south to New Mexico, the Lake states, and New England, and also in much of the Old World. Its winter range includes most of the United States and a little of Mexico.

With a greenish black head, long, bright red bill and creamy breast and sides sometimes tinged with pink, the drake Common Merganser is distinctive. Unlike the female and both sexes of our other mergansers, it lacks a crest. The hen's head and conspicuous crest are rufous, her back and sides gray. Her sharply defined white chin and breast help distinguish her from the similar hen Red-breasted Merganser.

Common Mergansers generally arrive from further south to join wintering birds in late March. They sometimes form large flocks, as one of about 210 on Massabesic Lake, Auburn, on 27 March 1954 and another of 146 on the Androscoggin River on 25 April 1950 (Richards, unpubl. data). Common Mergansers feed almost exclusively on fish, though they also eat shellfish and even some plant materials (Bellrose 1976).

Drakes arrive first on the breeding grounds. The hens follow a few weeks later and courtship begins while the birds are still in large flocks (Bent 1923). Mergansers first breed when 2 years old, shortly after the drakes attain adult plumage (Bent 1923). Courting drakes in mixed flocks vigorously chase rivals, rush across the water with slightly raised wings, bob or bow their heads while bill pointing and croaking, and sometimes raise themselves into an erect position. They also display their red feet while churning the water (Townsend in Bent 1923).

The nest usually is in a hollow tree or other protected site near a lakeshore or riverbank (Palmer 1976). Rarely one may be on the ground under overhanging vegetation (Bent 1923) or under a building (Richards, unpubl. data). Mergansers sometimes use large nest boxes. Tree nesters sit very tight but ground nesters slip away quietly when an intruder approaches (Bent 1923). The drake leaves the hen during egg laying and molts into eclipse plumage. Clutch size ranges from 6 to 12 eggs (Kortright 1942), but the many records of families with 18 to 28 young (usually with only one mother) indicate that "dump" nests and/or mergings of families are common.

Young may remain in the nest for a day or 2 before jumping to the ground and following the female to water. They become independent in about 5 weeks (Harrison 1978). Young merganser broods often are quite tame and are highly entertaining, rushing after schools of minnows in shallow water, climbing onto rafts (where they may roost at night), riding on their mother's back or, in rivers, bucking white water. They often cover considerable distances in the course of a day.

Mergansers and loons often nest on the same lakes, and confrontations between the 2 species occur frequently. When stalked by a loon, a merganser brood may hug the shore; when a loon surfaces suddenly in its midst and lunges, the family may "explode" and hydroplane away in several directions (Richards, pers. obs.). Raccoons probably are mergansers' primary predators in New Hampshire, though crows, gulls, water snakes, and snapping turtles also may take eggs or young.

Common Mergansers stay in New Hampshire through much of the autumn, gathering on big lakes in increasingly large flocks as migrants arrive and smaller water bodies freeze. By November drakes have regained their breeding plumage and joined hens and young in flocks of up to 250 and sometimes about 1,000 birds (Richards, unpubl. data). Most leave before freeze-up, though appreciable numbers winter on available open water even in the North Country, and some may go only as far as Great Bay.

Around the turn of the century Common Mergansers were "not uncommon" in summer from the White Mountains north (Allen 1903), and common summer residents at Umbagog Lake (Brewster 1924). Although they occurred on the lakes in spring and fall (Dearborn 1898), Common Mergansers apparently did not breed in the Lakes Region until 1920, when H. H. Richards (1920 in Richards 1952) observed a family on Squam Lake. The first breeding records for southern New Hampshire are from the Blackwater River in Andover in 1944 to 1946 (K. C. Elkins, unpubl. data) and from Allenstown; Great East Lake, Wakefield; and Dublin Lake, Dublin (NHFG data). More recent range expansion seems to have occurred within the Lakes Region, from Newfound Lake to Ossipee Lake, while some retraction apparently has occurred further south.

The majority of Atlas records are clustered in the Lakes Region and North Country. The southernmost New Hampshire record of "confirmed" breeding was from Lake Nubanusit, Hancock/Nelson. To a considerable extent the "Goosander" has adapted to human activity and may be able to survive in New Hampshire as a nesting species despite increasing recreational use of its breeding habitat.

Tudor Richards & Susan Absalom Staats

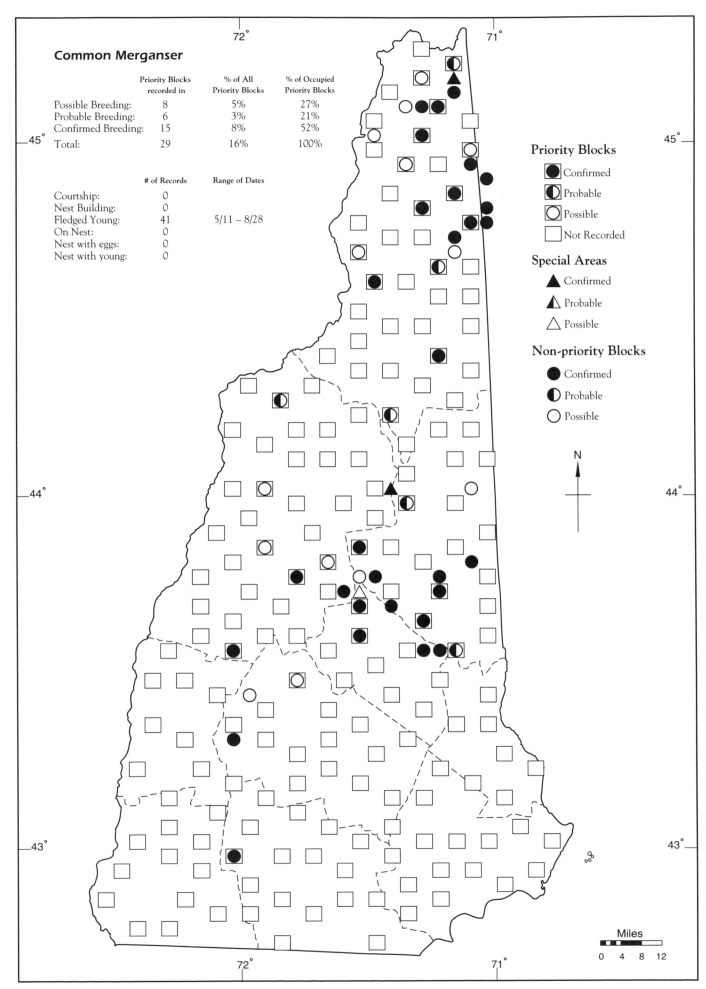

Common Merganser

	Priority Blocks recorded in	% of All Priority Blocks	% of Occupied Priority Blocks
Possible Breeding:	8	5%	27%
Probable Breeding:	6	3%	21%
Confirmed Breeding:	15	8%	52%
Total:	29	16%	100%

	# of Records	Range of Dates
Courtship:	0	
Nest Building:	0	
Fledged Young:	41	5/11 – 8/28
On Nest:	0	
Nest with eggs:	0	
Nest with young:	0	

Priority Blocks

- ◑ Confirmed
- ◐ Probable
- ○ Possible
- ☐ Not Recorded

Special Areas

- ▲ Confirmed
- ◩ Probable
- △ Possible

Non-priority Blocks

- ● Confirmed
- ◐ Probable
- ○ Possible

N

Miles
0 4 8 12

Turkey Vulture
Cathartes aura

Rocking awkwardly on enormous wings, these flying scavengers are relative newcomers to New Hampshire skies. With their dark brown plumage and soaring habits, Turkey Vultures resemble eagles. However, their V-shaped flight profile, longer tail, and inconspicuous, unfeathered head are distinctive.

A major range extension during the 1900s brought these formerly southern birds to the northern U.S. and southern Canada. Turkey Vultures are migratory north of Pennsylvania. Northern breeding populations begin to disperse from winter roosts in February (Coleman 1985) and drift northward, arriving in New Hampshire in March and April (SRS).

Turkey Vultures eat carrion and offal, usually from mammals. They occasionally feed on birds, turtles, and fish (Coleman and Fraser 1987). Turkey Vultures may travel up to 9 mi (15 km) a day in search of food (Coleman 1985). Foraging habitat includes agricultural lands, forest clearings, gravel pits, and roadsides, where roadkilled mammals are common. Turkey Vultures sometimes scavenge at fox dens and may take heron eggs and young from their nests (Brown and Amadon 1968). E. F. Swift and R. Coolidge (pers. comm.) have observed Turkey Vultures in New Hampshire Great Blue Heron rookeries but have not witnessed successful predation.

Turkey Vultures have enormous home ranges, which may exceed 400 sq mi (1,040 sq km) (Coleman and Fraser 1989). Breeding pairs are usually solitary, but may nest close together where food or nesting habitat is concentrated in a small area (Coleman 1985, Jackson *in* Palmer 1988). Nest sites typically are secluded from predators and human disturbance and close to food resources (Coleman 1985). All New Hampshire nests documented to date have been in caves or large crevices in cliffs, ledges, or boulder piles.

Pairs perform "follow flights," trailing one another at a distance of 66 to 165 ft (20 to 50 m), and individuals circle and glide over the nesting area in solo flights (Davis 1983). Courtship flights include aerial chases and twisting dives (Coleman 1985). Nonbreeding vultures and breeding individuals not attending the nest congregate at forested roosting areas at night. New Hampshire roosts often are on hillsides or ridges (Foss, pers. obs.).

The female typically sits on the nest site for up to several weeks before laying one to 4, usually 2 eggs, 36 to 72 hours apart (Jackson 1983). Egg dates from New Hampshire latitudes extend from early May to mid-June (Jackson 1983). Vultures bring no material to the nest site, and the eggs rest directly on the ground. Both adults incubate, exchanging places several times a day (Davis 1983). Turkey Vultures are likely to abandon their eggs after human disturbance during incubation (Coleman 1985), and are not known to renest after failure.

The eggs may hatch up to 72 hours apart after 28 to 41 days of incubation (Jackson 1983). Both adults brood nestlings continuously for their first 5 days and feed them by regurgitation (Davis 1983). By the time the young are 2 weeks old, the adults return to the nest only for brief and infrequent feedings, perching nearby for up to half an hour before entering, and staying less than a minute. One or both adults often perch or perform solo flights in the vicinity of the nest. Young usually remain in the nest for 56 to 88 days (Jackson 1983).

Turkey Vultures first fly at about 75 days of age and gather at communal perching areas within a week after leaving their nests (Coleman 1985). Adults and young feed together into late summer and fall. Migration through New Hampshire begins during early September, and most vultures have departed by mid-October.

New Hampshire's earliest Turkey Vulture records are from Hampton Falls in 1882, Weare in 1887, and Hampton Falls in 1898 (Bagg and Parker 1951). During 1900–50 observers documented only 5 more records: 30 April 1928 in Jaffrey, 10 August 1940 at Squam Lake, 9 April 1941 in Harrisville, and 13 April 1947 and 12 October 1948 in New Hampton (Bagg and Parker 1951).

The Turkey Vulture's range expansion into the Northeast has occurred mainly since 1925, when breeding first was documented in New York (Howes 1926 *in* Bull 1974). Reported nesting in Connecticut followed in 1930 (Mathers 1931 *in* Bagg and Eliot 1937) and in Massachusetts in 1954 (Veit and Petersen 1993). First breeding records in Vermont, New Hampshire and Maine occurred in 1979 (Martin *in* Laughlin and Kibbe 1985), 1981 (SRS), and 1982 (Tingley 1982), respectively.

In Antrim, 2 adults were at a potential nest ledge on 4 April 1981; 2 young were present on 6 August, and were nearly ready to fledge on 14 August (H. M. Cadot, pers. comm.). In Lebanon, T. Levin (pers. comm.) photographed a dead vulture chick and an unhatched egg on a ridge in June 1981. Subsequent nestings occurred in Hinsdale in 1983, in Warner in 1985 and 1986, and in Strafford and Weare in 1986.

Turkey Vultures now are common throughout much of New Hampshire south of the White Mountains, especially in major river valleys. With ample roadkills, numerous potential nest sites, and a continuing population increase throughout the Northeast, these winged scavengers likely will become even more widespread here.

Carol R. Foss

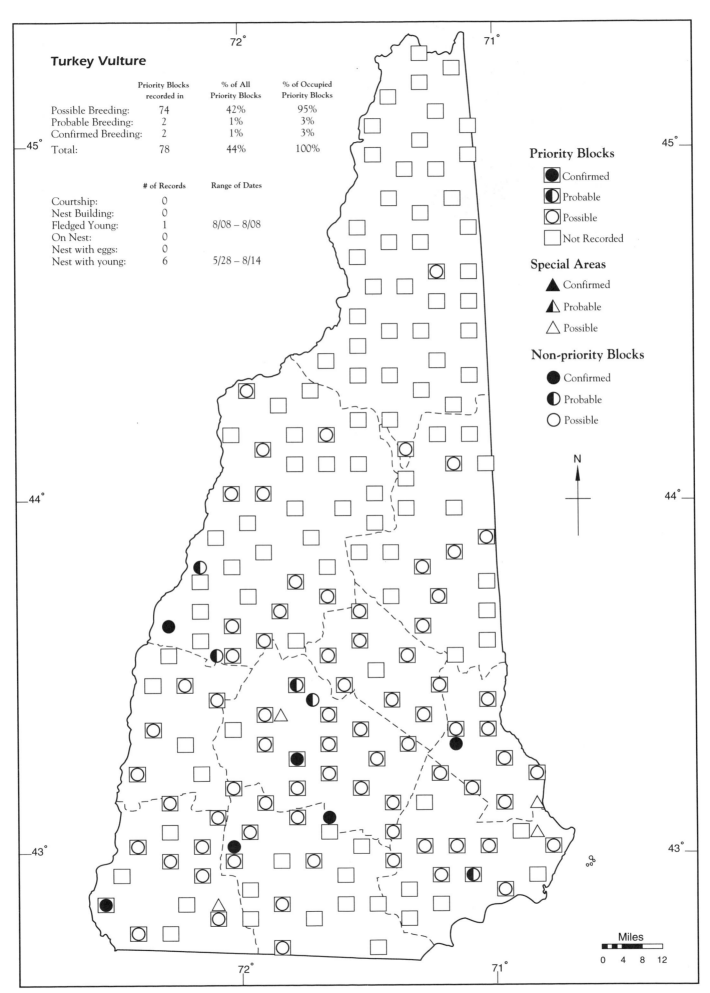

Turkey Vulture

	Priority Blocks recorded in	% of All Priority Blocks	% of Occupied Priority Blocks
Possible Breeding:	74	42%	95%
Probable Breeding:	2	1%	3%
Confirmed Breeding:	2	1%	3%
Total:	78	44%	100%

	# of Records	Range of Dates
Courtship:	0	
Nest Building:	0	
Fledged Young:	1	8/08 – 8/08
On Nest:	0	
Nest with eggs:	0	
Nest with young:	6	5/28 – 8/14

Priority Blocks

● Confirmed
◑ Probable
○ Possible
□ Not Recorded

Special Areas

▲ Confirmed
◤ Probable
△ Possible

Non-priority Blocks

● Confirmed
◐ Probable
○ Possible

N

Miles
0 4 8 12

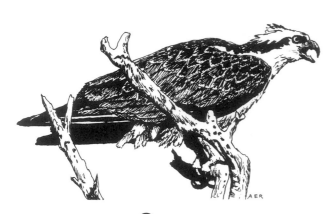

Osprey
Pandion haliaetus

A hover, a dive, an explosion of spray, then strong wings strain to lift bird and wriggling fish from the water. These dramatic food-capturing habits identify the Osprey, our only large raptor to feed exclusively on fish, and thus be restricted in breeding habitat to the vicinity of coastal and fresh water. This species often is confused with the adult Bald Eagle because both birds have white on their heads and dark backs and wings. The Osprey's white underparts, dark facial mask, less erect and slimmer profile when perched, and the stretched "M" shape of its wings when soaring distinguish it from the larger eagle.

Ospreys are long-distance migrants, traveling singly as far as Central and South America and back during an extended migration period (Henny and Van Velzen 1972). Early spring migrants occasionally appear in March (SRS), and experienced nesters may arrive on snow-covered northern nesting territories at least as early as 12 April (Evans, pers. obs.). Migrating Ospreys continue to travel through New Hampshire during April and May. The previous summer's young remain in wintering areas for another year (Henny and Van Velzen 1972).

The male's annual courtship calls and hovering flights over the breeding grounds break the silence of early spring. The pair's large stick nest, located in a tall stub or dead top of a live evergreen near the edge of a lake or river or in a bog, plays a strong role in the courtship ritual. During courtship the male ceremoniously delivers fish and new sticks to the female at the nest, reinforcing the pair bond.

Most Ospreys mate for life and return to the same nest year after year. Their annual additions of nesting material create immense structures, which may harbor nests of other species, including blackbirds (Scott 1921) and possibly red squirrels (Evans, pers. obs.).

Eggs, generally 3, are laid from about 28 April to 30 May (ASNH data), with experienced breeders nesting earlier. Incubation begins with the first egg laid, and although shared, falls mainly to the female. The male provides food for his mate during incubation and for the nestlings. Chicks hatch throughout June after about 35 to 43 days of incubation (Poole 1989). Families range in size from one to 3 young, with 2 most common.

Young Ospreys spend about 8 weeks in their lofty home, exercising their growing wings and experimenting with vocalizations. This educational experience continues after fledging and into the fall, as the young perfect their flying skills and learn to catch fish. The gradual exodus from northern New Hampshire breeding areas begins in late August and early September, with individuals still present as late as 4 November. Migrants continue to straggle through other parts of the state into late November (ASNH data). Migrating Ospreys may use any available fishing areas, including farm ponds, but gather and linger at particularly good spots.

Although Ospreys have been documented as migrants throughout New Hampshire since the late 1800s (Dearborn 1898, Allen 1902, Dearborn 1903), historically they were considered common summer residents only in the Umbagog Lake area (Maynard 1871, Brewster 1925). The Connecticut Lakes area supported at least one nesting pair until about 1970, and breeding season reports from elsewhere in the North Country suggest additional nesting activity (Smith 1979). Scott (1921) provides the only historical reference to nesting in the Great Bay area. The first documented nesting there since the 1930s occurred in 1989 (ASNH data), a possible result of expanding coastal populations in Massachusetts and Maine.

Osprey populations once suffered widely from the common belief that all large birds of prey were vermin, and more than a few were shot at fish hatcheries (R. Evans, pers. comm.). The effects of DDT and related pesticides caused a catastrophic decline of Osprey populations throughout the Northeast in the 1950s and 1960s (Ogden 1977). The Umbagog population included only 3 or 4 known pairs by 1977 (Smith 1979). The New Hampshire portion of this population increased to a minimum of 14 pairs during 1980–86, and rose to 21 pairs by 1989. Predator guards installed on nest trees beginning in 1985 have helped boost productivity significantly, and management agreements with industrial forest landowners now protect most nest sites.

The Osprey is currently listed as a Threatened Species in New Hampshire. The only known breeding population during the Atlas period was limited to Umbagog Lake and the Androscoggin River drainage in the northeastern part of the state. This inland population has recovered less rapidly than coastal breeding populations elsewhere in the East, which have rebounded to the point of being plentiful in some locations.

The Atlas map reflects data from annual ASNH Osprey monitoring efforts in the Umbagog Lake area. A few nests in remote bogs may have been missed, despite aerial surveys. "Probable" Atlas sightings in the upper Connecticut River valley and the Connecticut Lakes area may indicate nesting pairs or merely unmated third-year birds. With the help of active management efforts, this intriguing raptor should continue to increase and to expand its distribution in New Hampshire.

Diane Evans

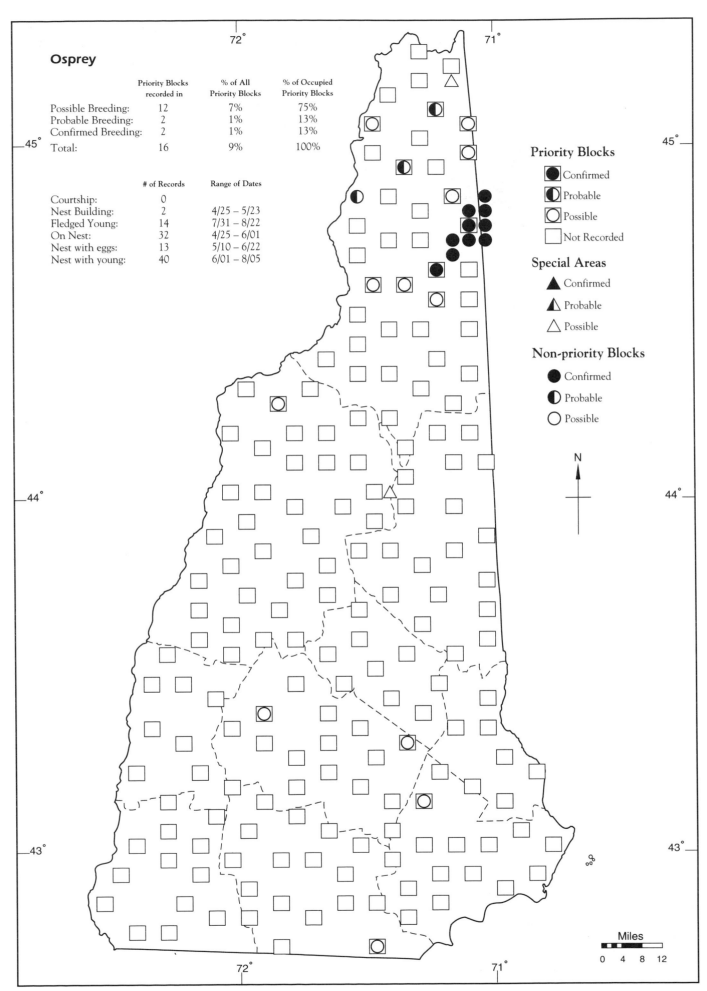

Osprey

	Priority Blocks recorded in	% of All Priority Blocks	% of Occupied Priority Blocks
Possible Breeding:	12	7%	75%
Probable Breeding:	2	1%	13%
Confirmed Breeding:	2	1%	13%
Total:	16	9%	100%

	# of Records	Range of Dates
Courtship:	0	
Nest Building:	2	4/25 – 5/23
Fledged Young:	14	7/31 – 8/22
On Nest:	32	4/25 – 6/01
Nest with eggs:	13	5/10 – 6/22
Nest with young:	40	6/01 – 8/05

Priority Blocks

● Confirmed
◐ Probable
○ Possible
☐ Not Recorded

Special Areas

▲ Confirmed
◭ Probable
△ Possible

Non-priority Blocks

● Confirmed
◑ Probable
○ Possible

N

Miles
0 4 8 12

Northern Harrier
Circus cyaneus

This graceful, low-flying raptor inhabits open lands, where it hunts "on the wing," weaving to and fro over hayfields, marshes, and shrub lands. The Northern Harrier, formerly called the "Marsh Hawk," is uncommon during the breeding season in New Hampshire. It is most easily seen flying over the farms of Coos County in mid-summer, when the fast-growing young require frequent food deliveries.

A harrier in flight can be identified by its white rump patch, long narrow wings, and characteristic hunting style. The brown female is larger than the light gray male, which has distinctive black wing tips. Juvenile birds resemble adult females but appear reddish below.

Migrating harriers return to New Hampshire between mid-March and early April, and court during May. The typical courtship "sky dance" is a series of nose dives or loop-the-loops of U-shaped dives, which the male usually performs (Bent 1937, Hamerstrom 1986). Sometimes both the male and female swoop through the air and fly side by side (D. Killam, pers. comm.). Harriers copulate on the ground or on a low perch (Brown and Amadon 1968, Clark 1972).

Harriers nest in open habitats, such as wetlands and old fields, with low shrubs and forbs. The nest is on the ground, usually in rather dense vegetation (Duebbert and Lokemoen 1977, Hamerstrom and Kopeny 1981). Nests in wet areas are usually larger and deeper than those in drier situations (Urner 1925, Sealy 1967). Although the female constructs the nest, both parents provide nesting material (Sealy 1967, Toland 1985). Four nests observed in Coos County were in thick patches of shrubs and forbs which were 3 to 5 ft (0.9 to 1.5 m) tall (Serrentino 1987). Nests were composed of dead grasses and small twigs.

Egg laying takes place between late May and early June, and hatch occurs from late June to early July (Serrentino 1987). Clutches range from 4 to 9, but average 4 or 5 eggs (Bent 1937, Hamerstrom 1969). The female incubates for 30 to 32 days (Urner 1925, Hamerstrom 1969). She often leaves the nest about 7:00 a.m. to preen for a short period of time (Hamerstrom 1969).

Throughout incubation and the first half of the nestling period the male drops prey to the female in midair above or near the nest. Young harriers remain in the nest for 30 to 35 days (Urner 1925, Hamerstrom 1969). When they are about 2 weeks old, the female leaves the nest more frequently (Hecht 1951, Serrentino 1987). She usually hunts closer to the nest than the male, who may cover about 1 to 7 sq mi (2.6 to 18.1 sq km) (Martin 1987). Harriers most commonly prey on small mammals and birds. Prey remains found in New Hampshire nests include voles, birds (Ruffed Grouse, Northern Flicker, American Robin, and Bobolink), and young garter snakes (Serrentino 1987).

Older nestlings make tunnels in the vegetation near the nest, which they may use as escape routes (Balfour and MacDonald 1970) and for roosting and eating prey (Serrentino 1987). Harriers are capable of short flights at 31 to 38 days (Scharf and Balfour 1971). In northern New Hampshire they leave the nest between the end of July and mid-August (Serrentino 1987). Newly fledged harriers often perch conspicuously in shrubs and trees near the nest. Young birds may remain near New Hampshire nest sites into early September (D. Killam, pers. comm.). Fall migration typically extends from the end of August through October or early November. A few harriers winter in southern New Hampshire, primarily in coastal marshes, and only rarely inland (CBC data).

Harriers have several distinct vocalizations. When protecting nests or young, adults use a fast chattering "ke-ke-ke" or "chek-chek-chek" (Brown and Amadon 1968). Juveniles also use this call when alarmed. The begging call can be described as a scream, "eeyah eeyah," and is given by the female to the male or by juveniles to either parent (Bildstein 1988).

The Northern Harrier benefited from clearing of forests for agriculture. At the peak of open land in New Hampshire between the late 1800s and early 1900s, the harrier nested locally throughout most of the state, with breeding sites reported in Hillsborough, Strafford, Belknap, Merrimack, and Coos counties (Dearborn 1898, Wright 1911, Blaisdell 1919, White 1937). With the decline of agriculture, harriers became less common during the early 1900s. Pesticide use after World War II and wetland destruction caused a subsequent drop in numbers of breeding harriers (Smith and Choate 1985, Hamerstrom 1986). From 1969-79 only 7 breeding records were reported in New Hampshire, most from Coos County (SRS). The harrier also has declined elsewhere in the region, and now has special management status in all the New England states except Maine.

The Atlas map reflects harrier activity documented by NHESP personnel (unpubl. data) and Serrentino (1987) during the Atlas period, some outside of priority blocks and most located north of the White Mountains. In Coos County about 10 pairs occur from Columbia north to southern Pittsburg at elevations from 1,000 to more than 2,000 ft (300 to 610 m), and there are scattered pairs in Errol, Dummer, and the Whitefield/Jefferson region. South of the White Mountains, harriers have nested successfully in Danbury and Sutton, and have been present in the Seacoast area during the breeding season.

The Northern Harrier has recovered somewhat from the adverse effects of the DDT era, but its numbers in New Hampshire are still low. The continuing decline in agriculture in its Coos County stronghold and the loss of wetlands and other open habitat throughout the state make its future here uncertain.

Patricia Serrentino

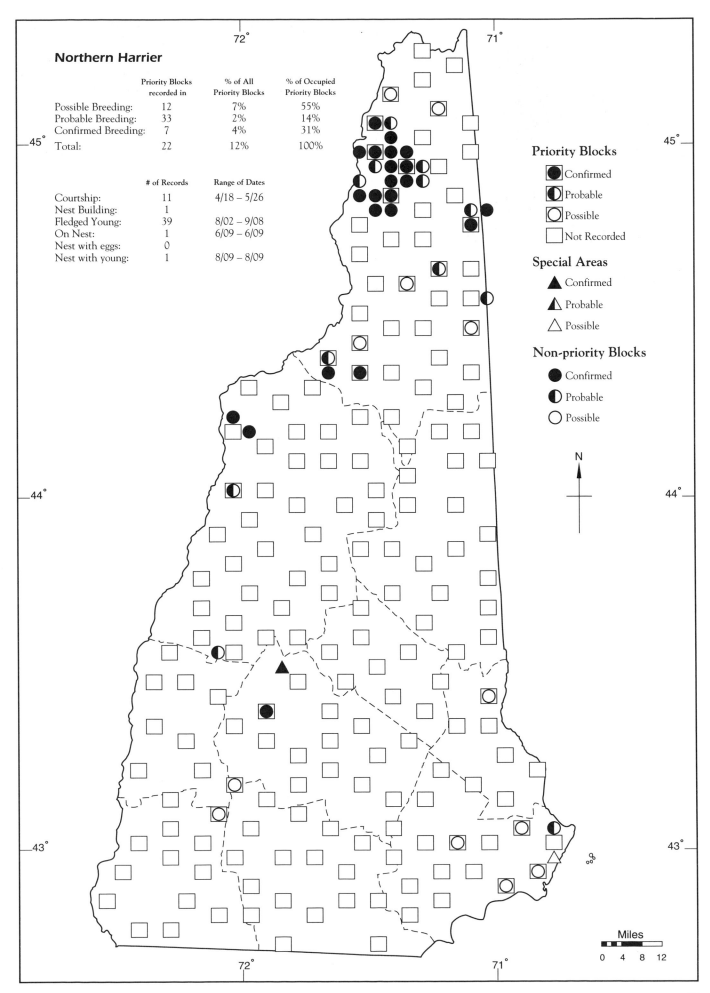

Northern Harrier

	Priority Blocks recorded in	% of All Priority Blocks	% of Occupied Priority Blocks
Possible Breeding:	12	7%	55%
Probable Breeding:	33	2%	14%
Confirmed Breeding:	7	4%	31%
Total:	22	12%	100%

	# of Records	Range of Dates
Courtship:	11	4/18 – 5/26
Nest Building:	1	
Fledged Young:	39	8/02 – 9/08
On Nest:	1	6/09 – 6/09
Nest with eggs:	0	
Nest with young:	1	8/09 – 8/09

Priority Blocks

- ◐ Confirmed
- ◑ Probable
- ○ Possible
- ☐ Not Recorded

Special Areas

- ▲ Confirmed
- ◪ Probable
- △ Possible

Non-priority Blocks

- ● Confirmed
- ◐ Probable
- ○ Possible

N

Miles
0 4 8 12

45

Sharp-shinned Hawk
Accipiter striatus

The Sharp-shinned Hawk is superbly adapted to forests, with its relatively short, rounded wings, long tail, and swift, graceful flight. It is well known for its ability to maneuver quickly through trees and brush, to wait in concealment and dart out after prey, and to pursue its target tenaciously. Its characteristic accipiter flight pattern alternates a series of quick wing beats with a short sail.

The adult Sharp-shin is dark blue-gray above and white below, with rufous barring on the breast. As with other accipiters, the male and female differ considerably in size. Close similarities in plumage between Sharp-shinned and Cooper's hawks create difficult field identification problems. Mueller et al. (1979), Clark and Wheeler (1987), and Kaufman (1990) discuss in detail the reliability of various field marks for distinguishing between the 2 species.

A foraging Sharp-shinned Hawk frequently perches on an open limb waiting for small songbirds to come near. Having spied its quarry, it is quite persistent in aerial chases and even may pursue its prey along the ground (Bent 1937). Like other accipiters, this hawk takes captured prey to a "butcher block" to pluck the feathers before eating.

The Sharp-shinned Hawk is a more common migrant than resident in New Hampshire. Some individuals overwinter in New Hampshire, but the majority move further south. Northward migrants begin to appear in March. Spring migration peaks during the first half of April (SRS) and usually ends during the first week of May.

Sharp-shinned Hawks often return annually to the same nesting area (Forbush 1927). Their primary habitat includes dense stands of conifers near open brushy areas and clearings (Brown *in* Bent 1937, Palmer 1988). Bent (1937) considered a typical nest site in southeastern Massachusetts to be in a "dense grove of medium sized white pines." Further north these hawks

nest in spruce (Brown *in* Bent 1937).

Pairs begin courtship and nest building upon arrival. Courtship consists primarily of aerial displays with the male soaring and darting down at the female, who drops in altitude and then rises again (Townsend 1920). During mid to late April adult Sharp-shins are relatively noisy, giving a "kik-kik-kik" alarm call and a squealing call note (Bent 1937). These vocalizations, best heard in early morning (Palmer 1988), often provide a clue to the general nest location. Calls of the Sharp-shinned Hawk are weaker, faster, and higher pitched than those of the Cooper's Hawk.

This accipiter nests principally in evergreens, but occasionally nests in deciduous trees (Bent 1937). The nest may be placed 10 to 60 ft (3 to 18 m) above ground but is most frequently located about 30 ft (9 m) up (Bent 1937, Harrison 1975). Documented New Hampshire nest sites include one 40 ft (12 m) up in a hemlock, one about 15 ft (4.5 m) up in a small hemlock (Dearborn 1898), and another 38 ft (11.5 m) up in a white pine (White 1937).

The broad platform of sticks, lined with twigs and sometimes bark, is built against the trunk on horizontal branches. It is large for the size of the bird, and incubating females often are not visible from below (Forbush 1927, Bent 1937). Sharp-shins usually build a new nest each year, but may reuse an old nest (Brown *in* Bent 1937, Reynolds and Wight 1978). New nests within a territory are generally within 300 ft (91.5 m) of former nests (Platt 1976).

Nest building is completed in early May, and incubation of the 4 or 5 eggs begins by early June. White (1937) observed a nest in Concord which was complete on 13 May and held 5 eggs on 27 May. The young hatch after 30 to 32 days of incubation (Reynolds and Wight 1978). The female tends the young, and the male brings food to the female near but not at the nest (Palmer 1988). Young Sharp-shins remain in the nest for 23 to 27 days (Platt 1976). After fledging, young birds remain in the vicinity of the nest for 2.5 to 3.5 weeks (Platt 1976, Snyder and Wiley 1976). Newly fledged young make characteristic peeping sounds, which resemble the calls of spring peepers (C. R. Foss, pers. comm.). Sharp-shins may breed as one-year-olds, but maintain a brown-backed plumage until the age of 2 (Bent 1937). Fall migration begins in early September and continues through October, peaking in the last half of September.

Observers in the mid-1800s (Coues 1868, Samuels 1870) considered the Sharp-shinned Hawk "common" to "abundant" throughout New England, but authors found the species a "rather common" or "uncommon" summer resident by the 1900s (Dearborn 1898, Allen 1903, Dearborn 1903). By the early 1920s this hawk had become uncommon to rare here in the breeding season (Forbush 1927, White 1937), a status which continues to the present day (Ridgely 1977, Allison and Allison 1979). The *American Birds* Blue List included this species in 1982 (Arbib 1982).

In a quantitative analysis of Hawk Mountain, PA, migration data from 1934 to 1986, Bednarz et al. (1990) noted a decrease in counts of Sharp-shinned Hawks during the 1946–72 DDT era, and a subsequent increase. More recently, Titus and Fuller (1990) detected no trend in counts of migrant Sharp-shinned Hawks at 6 observation sites in the eastern U.S. from 1972–87.

The Atlas effort obtained Sharp-shinned Hawk records for 22% of priority blocks statewide. Nearly half of those blocks are in northern New Hampshire, where Atlas effort was lower than in the more heavily populated southern part of the state. Future population trends of this small woodland raptor will be interesting to watch.

James McDermott

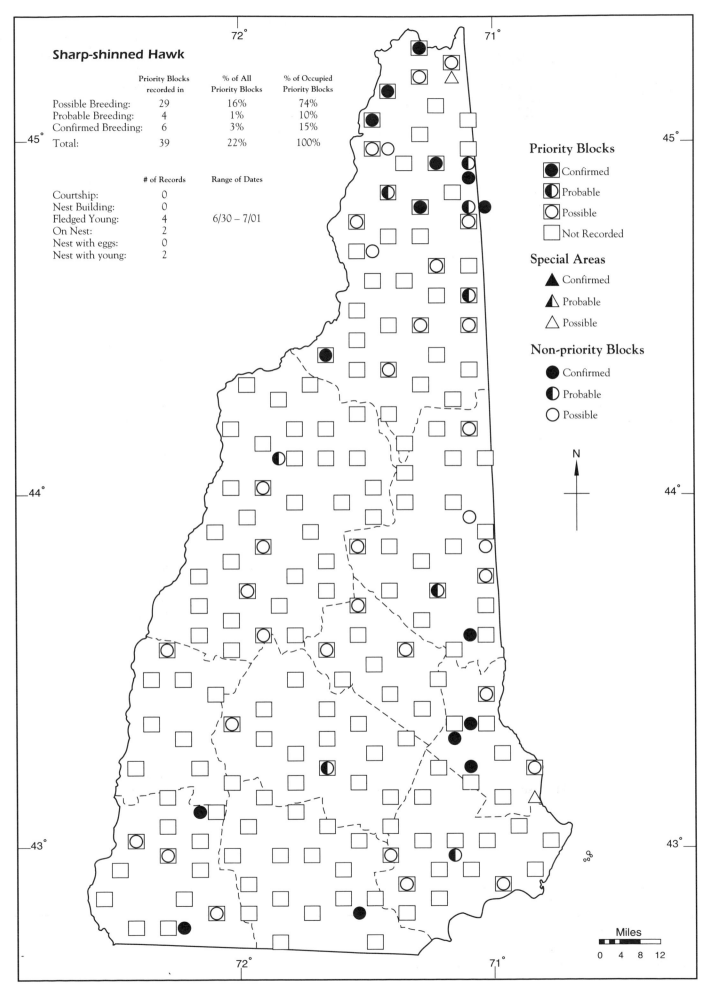

Sharp-shinned Hawk

	Priority Blocks recorded in	% of All Priority Blocks	% of Occupied Priority Blocks
Possible Breeding:	29	16%	74%
Probable Breeding:	4	1%	10%
Confirmed Breeding:	6	3%	15%
Total:	39	22%	100%

	# of Records	Range of Dates
Courtship:	0	
Nest Building:	0	
Fledged Young:	4	6/30 – 7/01
On Nest:	2	
Nest with eggs:	0	
Nest with young:	2	

Priority Blocks
- ● Confirmed
- ◑ Probable
- ◯ Possible
- □ Not Recorded

Special Areas
- ▲ Confirmed
- ◭ Probable
- △ Possible

Non-priority Blocks
- ● Confirmed
- ◐ Probable
- ◯ Possible

N

Miles
0 4 8 12

Cooper's Hawk
Accipiter cooperii

This slim, lithe, and dashing accipiter once was common in New Hampshire and well known to country people as the "chicken hawk." Older writings about it include many accounts of its exploits as a predator on free-ranging domestic fowl. The Cooper's Hawk is intermediate in size between the Sharp-shinned Hawk and Northern Goshawk. Its tail is slightly longer in relation to the bird's size than those of the other 2 accipiters and is distinctly rounded at the end. Clark and Wheeler (1987), Dunne et al. (1988), and Kaufman (1990) present detailed discussions of accipiter identification.

Although a few Cooper's Hawks winter in New Hampshire, most arrive in March or April, and migrants are still passing through in early May (Palmer 1949, Griscom and Snyder 1955). Adult males arrive first on breeding areas; adult females come a few days later (Meng 1951). The breeding range encompasses the entire state, but nests are difficult to find.

Cooper's Hawks usually nest in a dense canopy, yet often near an opening (Rosenfield in Palmer 1988). They may use the same nesting territory for several years. Once on territory the pair performs "sky dances" in which both birds soar high in the air, and the male moves with slow "rhythmic flapping" (Meng and Rosenfield in Palmer 1988). Bent (1937) found that Cooper's Hawks nested most often in white pine in southeastern Massachusetts, but Scott (1921) stated that they almost always chose hemlocks in southern New Hampshire, and spruce in the mountains. Elsewhere the species reportedly has nested most often in deciduous trees (Todd 1940, Meng 1951, Bull 1974). Documented New Hampshire nest sites include one 60 ft (18 m) up in a hemlock, another 30 ft (9 m) up in a pine (Dearborn 1898), and one about 50 ft (15 m) up in a yellow birch (Wright 1911).

The male usually builds a new nest each year, but may place it on an old nest of another species, such as a crow (Palmer 1949) or Broad-winged Hawk (K. Titus, pers. comm.). The nest is usually situated in, rather than below the canopy (Titus and Mosher 1981). It may be 26 to 50 ft (7.9 to 15.2 m) from the ground (Meng and Rosenfield in Palmer 1988). Several green hemlock or pine twigs may decorate the nest, though less commonly than in buteo nests (Harrison 1975).

During nest building, egg laying, and the early days of incubation, pairs perform early morning duets, consisting of variations on their usual calls: "cac-cac-cac" or "kuck-kuck-kuck" (Bent 1937), or "ca-ca-ca," "kek" (male), "kak" (female) (Meng 1951). Vermont egg dates range from 29 April to 15 June (Ellison in Laughlin and Kibbe 1985). The female does most of the incubation, which begins with the laying of the third egg and lasts about 36 days. Dearborn (1903) found that eggs in the Durham area hatched around the first of June. The clutch usually includes 4 or 5 eggs, but when 5 hatch, the last chick rarely survives.

Cooper's Hawks are secretive near their nests (K. Titus, pers. comm.). They are less aggressive towards human intruders than either Northern Goshawks or Sharp-shinned Hawks, but are fierce in attacking Great Horned Owls and will drive away crows (Meng and Rosenfield in Palmer 1988). Cooper's Hawk nests near Ithaca, N.Y. were almost never successful in woods where raccoons were abundant (Meng 1951).

The male does most of his hunting some distance from the nest (Rosenfield in Palmer 1988), and his hunting territory may extend from 0.5 mi (0.8 km) to as much as 2 mi (3.2 km) away (Meng 1951). The diet includes small birds and mammals (Meng 1951, Janik and Mosher 1982).

The male brings food to the nesting female, and she feeds the young (K. Titus, pers. comm.). A nest in Hopkinton held partly feathered young on 10 July (White 1937). The young leave the nest when 30 to 34 days old (Meng and Rosenfield in Palmer 1988), but return there to feed and rest for up to 10 days. Wright (1911) observed a young Cooper's Hawk on branches near a nest in Jefferson on 30 June. Fledglings remain near the nesting area into August. Migration may begin in late August, but occurs mainly in September and October (Meng 1951).

The Cooper's Hawk once was comparatively rare in New England, but by the latter half of the 19th century had become one of the region's most abundant birds of prey (Samuels 1870). New Hampshire ornithologists of the late 1800s and early 1900s considered the species a common summer resident (Goodhue 1877, Dearborn 1898, Allen 1903, Dearborn 1903, Blaisdell 1919, Goodhue 1922, Thayer 1909 in Allison and Allison 1979). A population decline throughout the eastern U.S. began before 1950 and became more pronounced thereafter (Rosenfield in Palmer 1988). Pesticide poisoning probably was a major contributing factor (Henny and Wight 1969, Rosenfield in Palmer 1988). The partial recovery observed in other states since the banning of DDT in 1972 (Ellison in Laughlin and Kibbe 1985) apparently has not occurred here, possibly due to competition with the Northern Goshawk, which has increased remarkably as a nesting bird in the state since about 1960.

Biologists "confirmed" only 2 successful Cooper's Hawk nests in New Hampshire during 1980–87 and found evidence of territorial pairs in only 4 additional locations (NHESP data). The species currently is Threatened in New Hampshire. The cluster of "possible" breeding reports from the North Country are from an area where goshawk records were surprisingly scarce, which may be significant. The group of "possible" records near Concord is from an area thoroughly covered by active birders.

Kimball C. Elkins

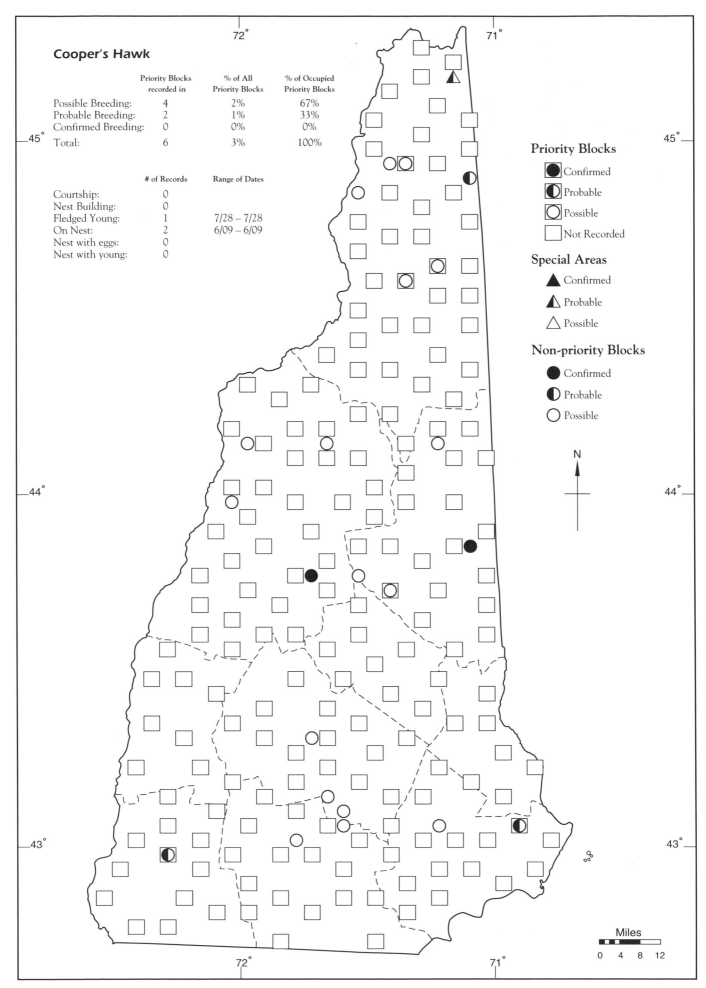

Cooper's Hawk

	Priority Blocks recorded in	% of All Priority Blocks	% of Occupied Priority Blocks
Possible Breeding:	4	2%	67%
Probable Breeding:	2	1%	33%
Confirmed Breeding:	0	0%	0%
Total:	6	3%	100%

	# of Records	Range of Dates
Courtship:	0	
Nest Building:	0	
Fledged Young:	1	7/28 – 7/28
On Nest:	2	6/09 – 6/09
Nest with eggs:	0	
Nest with young:	0	

Priority Blocks

● Confirmed
◐ Probable
○ Possible
☐ Not Recorded

Special Areas

▲ Confirmed
◣ Probable
△ Possible

Non-priority Blocks

● Confirmed
◑ Probable
○ Possible

N

Miles
0 4 8 12

Northern Goshawk
Accipiter gentilis

The Northern Goshawk is a large, powerful woodland hunter of secretive habits, known for fearless defense of its nest site. Our largest accipiter has this group's typical rounded wings, long tail, and flight pattern consisting of several flaps and a glide. The bushy, white undertail coverts are a good field mark in flight. An adult goshawk is blue-gray above and is the only accipiter with a pale gray breast, dark crown, and broad white line over the eye. Although not a buteo, or "soaring hawk," the goshawk soars regularly, especially during mornings, with wings held flat (Clark 1987). Goshawks occur year round in New Hampshire.

This raptor formerly nested principally in the forests of Canada and the northern parts of some northern states, but its breeding range has expanded south in recent decades (Peterson 1980). It now breeds throughout New Hampshire, and even in much of southern New England. New Hampshire's goshawks nest in mixed forests, often "in hilly country, and near the tops of ridges or knolls" (K. C. Elkins, pers. comm.). Descriptions of 24 New Hampshire nests indicate that nest trees are often beside roads, trails, clearings, or blowdown areas.

New Hampshire goshawks often nest in deciduous trees, especially white birch, red maple, and black birch, but they occasionally nest in white pines (ASNH data). Nests may be as high as 75 ft (23 m) above the ground, but many are within a range of 30 to 40 ft (9 to 12 m) (Bent 1937). K.C. Elkins (pers. comm.) describes a nest site in Andover at the top of a wooded ridge at about 900 ft (270 m) elevation. Dominant trees in the area were white pine, but some deciduous trees were present. Another nest visited in March 1981 was about 45 ft (13.6 m) up in a medium-sized white birch. A nest in Webster was 40 ft (12.2 m) up in the crotch of a red oak, 60 yd (54.5 m) from a trail (Janeway, pers. obs.). Intruding near a goshawk's nest may be perilous. Janeway once cowered beneath a bush with a packsack on her head while both adults took turns attacking, screaming what sounded like "Kill! Kill! Kill!"

Goshawks often use the same nest year after year or rebuild the nest of another hawk (Harrison 1975, ASNH data). The bulky stick nest may be in a crotch or on limbs against the trunk (Harrison 1975). Like many hawks, this species lines the nest with pine or hemlock twigs each spring (Forbush 1927). After the young are a few weeks old, the ground beneath an occupied nest may be littered with fur and feathers, as well as considerable whitewash.

The female incubates her 2 to 4 (rarely 5) eggs, laid in April or May, for an estimated 36 to 38 days (Brown and Amadon 1968). The female broods the young constantly for the first 8 to 10 days after hatching (Bent 1937). More than 2 chicks seldom survive, except in years of abundant prey (Lee 1980). Older nestlings and fledglings have a distinctive call, "qui-qui-qui-qui-qui" (Forbush 1927). K.C. Elkins (pers. comm.) observed a recently emptied nest on 25 June. Three young goshawks were in trees near their nest in Webster on 10 July 1987 (Janeway, pers. obs.). Young in an Alstead nest were "nearly full grown" on 21 July 1902 and were "taking short flights" on 29 July. Immature goshawks are heavily mottled above with tawny, rufous, and darker brown. Their underparts are heavily streaked. Some brown may remain in the plumage for up to 2 years (Clark 1987), and birds in juvenal plumage sometimes breed (Bent 1937).

The goshawk preys upon grouse, crows, waterfowl, and many smaller birds. It takes more mammals than do other accipiters, particularly hares, squirrels, and chipmunks. It may hunt from an inconspicuous tree perch or on the wing, pursuing its prey in low, swift, and relentless flight. Because its lines blend so well with the surroundings and present a slim silhouette to prey, a stooping goshawk is difficult to see when it is approaching head on (Sutton 1925 *in* Bent 1937; Janeway, pers. obs.). After killing with the powerful grip of its talons, the goshawk usually decapitates mammals and plucks birds. A typically bold goshawk once followed a hen "into a kitchen and seized her on the kitchen floor in the presence of an old man and his daughter" (Forbush 1927).

In the late 1800s and early 1900s the Northern Goshawk was a rare summer resident of northern forests (Allen 1903, Hoffmann 1904). Ornithologists in southern New Hampshire knew it primarily as a winter visitor (Dearborn 1898, 1903), although nests existed in Alstead (Allen 1903), Dunbarton Dearborn (1898), and Jaffrey (Thayer 1909 *in* Allison and Allison 1979). As late as the 1930s White (1937) found it a rare winter visitor in Concord. This hawk recently has increased in the state, perhaps as a result of widespread reforestation and a decline in Cooper's Hawk populations. Pesticides have affected the goshawk less than they have the other accipiters, probably because the goshawk diet is less likely to contain pesticide residues (Snyder et al. 1973).

The Atlas map shows an impressive number of goshawk records in the southeastern third of the state, including several "confirmed" records in the Coastal Lowlands. Records are surprisingly sparse in the Western Highlands, White Mountains, and North Country. However, most atlasing in these areas occurred in July, after the goshawk's nesting period. This species' future in New Hampshire will depend largely on the availability of adequate tracts of suitable habitat.

Elizabeth C. Janeway

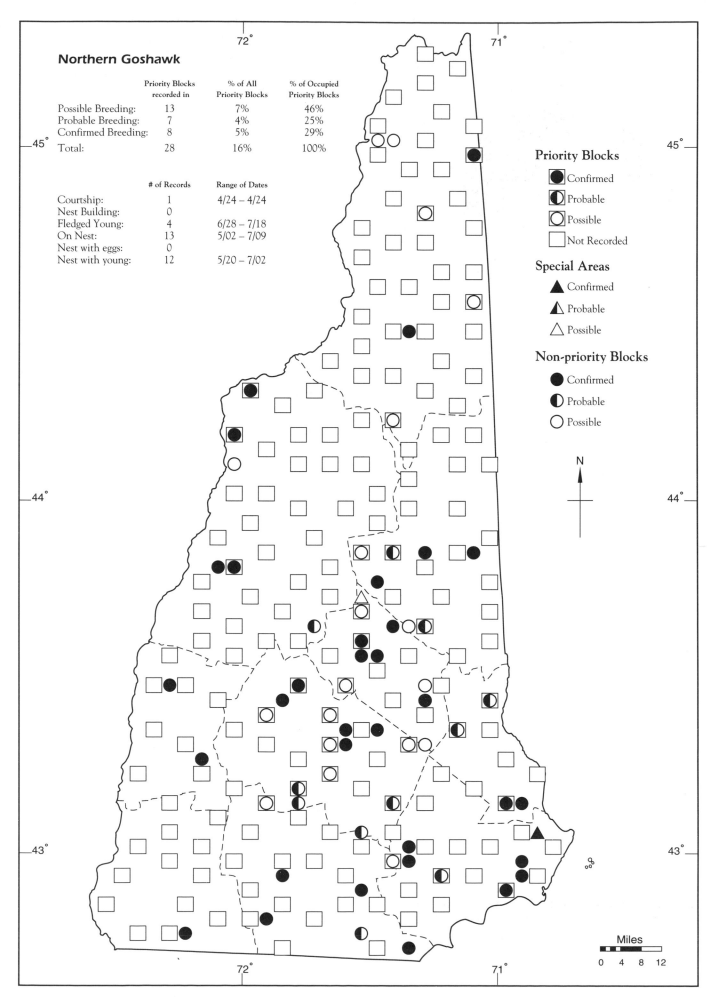

Northern Goshawk

	Priority Blocks recorded in	% of All Priority Blocks	% of Occupied Priority Blocks
Possible Breeding:	13	7%	46%
Probable Breeding:	7	4%	25%
Confirmed Breeding:	8	5%	29%
Total:	28	16%	100%

	# of Records	Range of Dates
Courtship:	1	4/24 – 4/24
Nest Building:	0	
Fledged Young:	4	6/28 – 7/18
On Nest:	13	5/02 – 7/09
Nest with eggs:	0	
Nest with young:	12	5/20 – 7/02

Priority Blocks

● Confirmed
◐ Probable
○ Possible
□ Not Recorded

Special Areas

▲ Confirmed
◢ Probable
△ Possible

Non-priority Blocks

● Confirmed
◐ Probable
○ Possible

N

Miles
0 4 8 12

Red-shouldered Hawk
Buteo lineatus

The "key-yeer" territorial call of the returning Red-shouldered Hawk is an avian equivalent of the spring peeper in New Hampshire's deciduous lowlands. The "red-shouldered buzzard" frequents swampy deciduous woods from March until November (Dearborn 1903). A few birds occasionally winter in New Hampshire, especially near the coast (SRS). Soaring Red-shoulders can be distinguished from Red-tailed and Broad-winged hawks by their longer black and white tails in which the white bands are much narrower than the black, and by the black and white checkerboard pattern on their wings.

This species began to decline in the Northeast during the 1960s (Henny 1972 and Campbell 1975 *in* Palmer 1988). It was on the *American Birds* Blue List (Tate 1986) throughout its range during 1972-86, and was on New Hampshire's list of Threatened Species from 1980 until 1986. Our state is near the northern limit of this species' range.

Red-shouldered Hawks usually appear in New Hampshire in mid-March, but sometimes arrive on territory in the Seacoast area in late February (SRS) following an early mild spell. They quickly establish territories, often returning to those of previous years, and engage in tumbling, erratic courtship flights. Courtship soaring occurs mainly within 0.5 mi. (0.8 km) of the nest and is most frequent in early morning and at midday (Gavutis, pers. obs.). Red-shoulders call most often on clear days during the 2 hours of midday (Portnoy and Dodge 1979).

Small wetlands or other natural openings are important for foraging (Bednarz and Dinsmore 1982), and Red-shoulders usually hunt from a tree perch with an open view. In March 1981, one adult made forays from a dead elm to capture several meadow voles (Gavutis, pers. obs.). Red-shouldered Hawks have a varied diet and prey on birds, mammals, reptiles, amphibians, and insects (Bent 1937). Hatching dates in mid-May coincide with the above-ground emergence of young chipmunks, a primary food for nestlings (Portnoy and Dodge 1979).

Nesting Red-shouldered Hawks usually inhabit mature wetland forests or upland forests adjacent to wetlands and select large trees for nest sites (Bent 1937, Portnoy and Dodge 1979, ASNH data). They occur at a density of approximately 1 pair/sq mi (2.6 sq km) in mixed forests near Kensington (ASNH data). Recent nests in southeastern New Hampshire were in mixed hardwood-pine-hemlock woods, part way up a slope above swampy woods (Gavutis, unpubl. data).

The majority of 31 recently observed New Hampshire nests were in maple, beech, or oak averaging 17 in (43 cm) dbh; only one was in a white pine (ASNH data). In a deciduous tree, the nest usually is in a main fork more than halfway up the tree but below the canopy, and in a pine tree it is on a whorl of branches against the trunk (Palmer 1988). Most active nests observed in the Kensington area contained fresh hemlock boughs and increasing amounts of white down in and near the nests as the season progressed (Gavutis, pers. obs.). Buzzing flies sometimes betray an active nest (E. Miller, pers. comm.). Red-shoulders may use the same nest in successive years, but more frequently return to old nests after an absence of 2 or more years (Dearborn 1898, Bent 1937, Jacobs et al. 1988). Barred Owls and Red-shouldered Hawks sometimes use the same nest in alternate years, or may nest in the same area (ASNH data).

Clutches include one to 6 eggs, averaging about 3 in northern areas of the range (Johnsgard 1990). Both adults share incubation, which lasts about 33 days (Palmer 1988). Hatching usually occurs around mid-May. The young begin to venture from the nest onto adjacent limbs at 5 to 6 weeks of age (Bent 1937, Portnoy and Dodge 1979). Young Red-shoulders respond to a calling adult with a very muted call, which can aid observers in locating nests or fledglings (Gavutis, pers. obs.; E. Miller, pers. comm.).

Historically the Red-shouldered Hawk was common in the vicinity of Durham and in the Merrimack River valley, where the Red-tailed Hawk was comparatively rare (Dearborn 1898, 1903, White 1924, Goodhue 1877 *in* Elkins 1961). The Red-shoulder was irregular and uncommon in many other parts of the state, especially in northern and southwestern sections (Allen 1903, Wright 1911, Forbush 1927, Thayer 1909 *in* Allison and Allison 1979). Ridgely (1977) reported Red-shouldered Hawks greatly reduced in the Squam Lakes region with a few pairs still nesting around beaver ponds.

The current distribution of the Red-shouldered Hawk, as illustrated by the Atlas map, generally follows that described in earlier times. Although Red-shouldered Hawks are far more common south of the White Mountains, they occur as far north as Pittsburg. The scarcity of northern records likely reflects both proximity to the fringe of the Red-shoulder's range and limited suitable habitat in the White Mountains and North Country. The valley separating the Presidential Range from the Pliny and Pilot ranges to the north shows clearly as a band of "possible" records across southern Coos County.

The relative abundance of Red-tailed and Red-shouldered hawks has changed in recent years. Atlasers found Red-tails in 32 more priority blocks than Red-shoulders statewide, and in 6 more priority blocks than Red-shoulders in the 5 southeastern counties.

The Red-shouldered Hawk is sensitive to logging and other significant habitat alterations (Bent 1937, Henny et al. 1973, Nelson and Titus 1989). Patterns of development, land protection, and silviculture, especially in the southern counties, will greatly influence the future distribution of this species in New Hampshire.

George W. Gavutis, Jr.

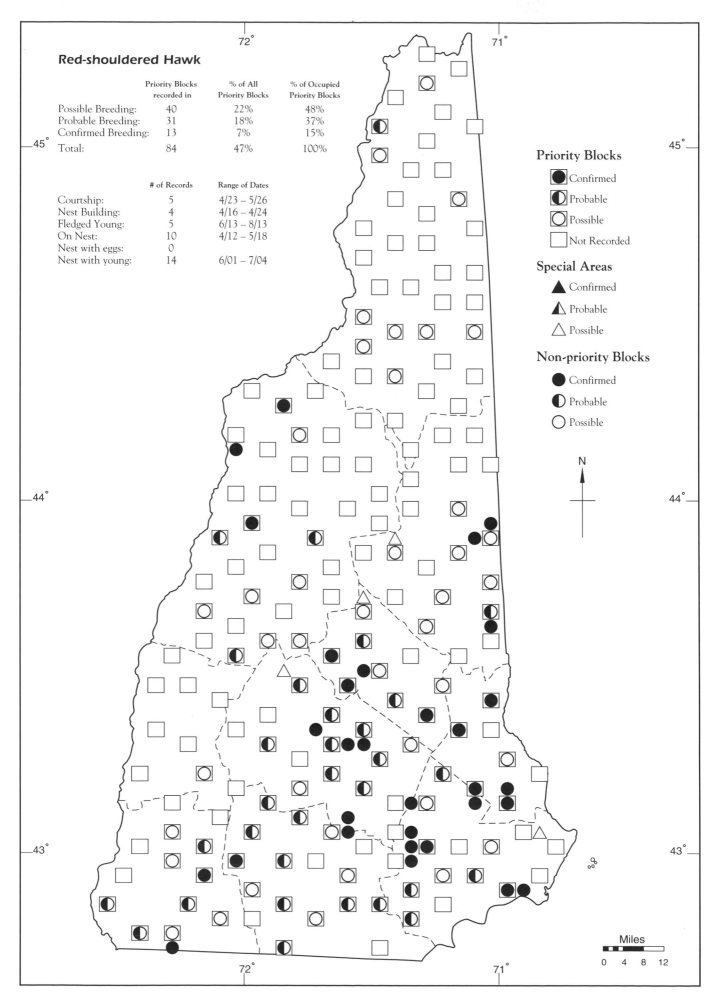

Red-shouldered Hawk

	Priority Blocks recorded in	% of All Priority Blocks	% of Occupied Priority Blocks
Possible Breeding:	40	22%	48%
Probable Breeding:	31	18%	37%
Confirmed Breeding:	13	7%	15%
Total:	84	47%	100%

	# of Records	Range of Dates
Courtship:	5	4/23 – 5/26
Nest Building:	4	4/16 – 4/24
Fledged Young:	5	6/13 – 8/13
On Nest:	10	4/12 – 5/18
Nest with eggs:	0	
Nest with young:	14	6/01 – 7/04

Priority Blocks
- Confirmed
- Probable
- Possible
- Not Recorded

Special Areas
- Confirmed
- Probable
- Possible

Non-priority Blocks
- Confirmed
- Probable
- Possible

N

Miles
0 4 8 12

Broad-winged Hawk

Buteo platypterus

This small buteo is the most common hawk in New Hampshire. A crow-sized, chunky body, broad wings mostly white underneath but narrowly bordered with black, a relatively short tail with black and white bands of nearly equal breadth, and a breast thickly covered with rufous bars (duller in color than a Red-shoulder's), are characteristic of the adult plumage. Immatures and subadults are difficult to tell from young Red-shouldered Hawks except by their smaller size. For perched adult and young Broad-winged Hawks, one of the best identification clues is their "round-shouldered" appearance.

Broad-winged Hawks are primarily birds of extensive but not necessarily mature forests (Bull 1974). They nest on wooded slopes and other dry locations near ponds or streams (Matray 1974, Crocoll and Parker 1989). In the White Mountains they breed up to the limits of large trees, at about 2,500 ft (760 m) (Allen 1903). They use deciduous or mixed forests more than coniferous stands (Brewster 1925). Although one can easily overlook them in forested habitats, Broad-wings often betray their presence by perching conspicuously, giving their plaintive, whistled cries while soaring overhead, and sometimes placing their nests near country roads (Elkins, pers. obs.).

Most Broad-winged Hawks winter in Central and South America. They arrive in New Hampshire in the latter half of April and early May. They return annually to the same home range, but usually nest at a different location each year (Palmer 1988). Breeding activities begin promptly after arrival in the spring (Fitch 1974). Courtship consists mainly of mutual soaring (Bent 1937).

Both sexes build the stick nest, which is small and poorly made compared to those of the other large hawks. They usually build a new nest each year, but sometimes repair an old nest of the same or another species (Matray 1974). The nest is made of twigs and may be lined with pieces of bark (Palmer 1988). The nest tree is likely to be near water and a forest opening (Titus and Mosher 1981). Yellow birch is a common nest tree (Burns 1911, Matray 1974). The nest is most often placed at the first main crotch of a large tree, 25 to 40 ft (7.6 to 12.2 m), sometimes more, above the ground (Palmer 1988). Active nests usually are decorated with fresh green sprigs (Lyons et al. 1986). During the Atlas period volunteers observed nest building as early as 29 April in Milan and Errol (NHBBA data).

The female lays her clutch of 2 or 3 (rarely 4) eggs at about the time deciduous trees are beginning to leaf out; in our latitude this rarely occurs before the first of May (Burns 1911). This makes Broad-winged Hawk nests more difficult to find than those of hawks that nest earlier. The female incubates for about a month (Palmer 1988). The male brings her food during incubation and provides all the food for the nestlings during the first week or so after they hatch, but the female feeds and broods them (Burns 1911, Matray 1974, Lyons and Mosher 1987). Most FF records before 1 June almost surely are of males bringing food to incubating females. Later both adults hunt.

The young may move out of the nest onto nearby branches at the beginning of their fifth week and fly at the age of 29 to 39 days (Matray 1974, Lyons and Mosher 1987, Crocoll and Parker 1989). In New Hampshire they usually fledge in July. Fledglings may stay in the vicinity of the nest for another 2 weeks (Matray 1974). Juveniles have dark brown streaks rather than reddish bars on their underparts and have light brown tails with several narrow dark bars. They keep this plumage nearly a year (Palmer 1988). Reports of fledged young before July almost certainly refer to yearlings.

Broad-wings usually hunt from perches at the edges of forest openings, country roads, or wetlands (Palmer 1988). Their varied diet includes frogs and toads, snakes, insects (especially large caterpillars), small mammals, and birds (Burns 1911, Palmer 1988).

Fall departure occurs almost entirely in September and is concentrated around the middle of the month. At this time hawkwatchers often count hundreds, sometimes thousands, passing over in a single day.

In the late 19th century when much of New Hampshire was open land, the Broad-winged Hawk was only locally common in the state, primarily in areas with extensive forests remaining. Dearborn (1898) had observed only 2 individuals in Belknap and Merrimack counties. Allen (1903) considered it the most common breeding hawk in the White Mountains and common in the Western Highlands, but less common to rare elsewhere. The Broad-wing began to be more plentiful before 1920 (Goodhue 1922). Forbush (1925a noted a recent increase, but still considered it less common south of the White Mountains than in the northern part of the state. By the 1930s, White (1937) considered it "somewhat common" around Concord and knew of several nests in the area. Subsequently this hawk has continued to increase, and now has become reasonably common in all sections of the state. Titus et al. (1989) considered Broad-wings common and stable in New Hampshire. While some analyses suggest a recent regional decline, available trend data are not consistent (Titus and Fuller 1990).

The Atlas map documents the Broad-winged Hawk's current statewide distribution. Atlas workers found this species in 91% of priority blocks, a remarkable record. Since this hawk is relatively tolerant of human activity and will nest in relatively young forests, it should remain common here for many years to come.

Kimball C. Elkins

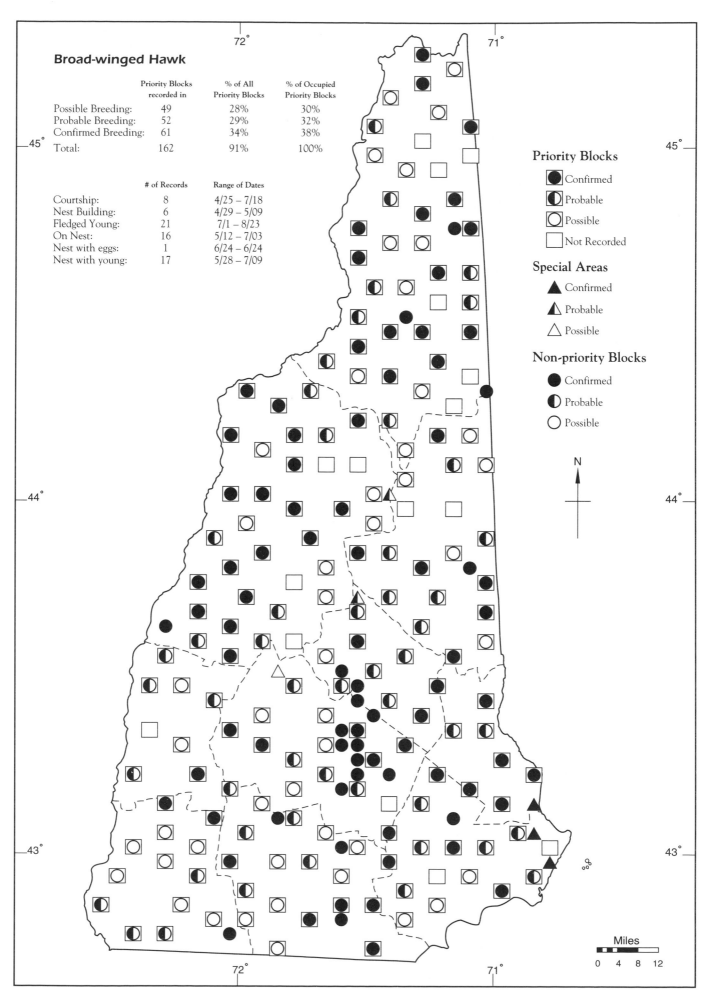

Broad-winged Hawk

	Priority Blocks recorded in	% of All Priority Blocks	% of Occupied Priority Blocks
Possible Breeding:	49	28%	30%
Probable Breeding:	52	29%	32%
Confirmed Breeding:	61	34%	38%
Total:	162	91%	100%

	# of Records	Range of Dates
Courtship:	8	4/25 – 7/18
Nest Building:	6	4/29 – 5/09
Fledged Young:	21	7/1 – 8/23
On Nest:	16	5/12 – 7/03
Nest with eggs:	1	6/24 – 6/24
Nest with young:	17	5/28 – 7/09

Priority Blocks

- ● Confirmed
- ◑ Probable
- ○ Possible
- □ Not Recorded

Special Areas

- ▲ Confirmed
- ◮ Probable
- △ Possible

Non-priority Blocks

- ● Confirmed
- ◑ Probable
- ○ Possible

N

Miles
0 4 8 12

Red-tailed Hawk
Buteo jamaicensis

The Red-tailed Hawk is a large, stocky buteo readily recognized in adult plumage by its fox-red tail, acquired during its second year. The combination of red tail and dark band on white belly are easily recognizable at great distances whether this hawk is soaring in characteristic large circles or perched against a tree line.

Red-tails utilize a wide range of habitats. They often nest in deciduous and mixed woodlands and hunt in nearby open lands with scattered large perch trees. Farmlands, pastures, meadows, wetlands, roadsides, and power-line rights-of-way all provide hunting habitat. Red-tails are opportunistic predators and frequently hunt from trees bordering fields. They prey principally on small mammals, especially rodents, and also take amphibians, reptiles, birds, and insects (Bent 1937, Orians and Kuhlman 1956, Petersen 1979).

The breeding range extends from Alaska and Canada south to Central America (Palmer 1988). In New Hampshire the Red-tail is a common breeding bird throughout open or agricultural lands at elevations up to about 2,500 ft (760 m) (Ridgely 1977). Other investigators have also noted a tendency of this species to nest at lower elevations within its range (Speiser and Bosakowski 1988).

Adult Red-tails frequently winter in New Hampshire south of the White Mountains and may be locally common in valley bottomlands and coastal regions. Wintering pairs in southern New Hampshire appear to be resident birds on permanent home ranges (Wheeler, unpubl. data). Observers elsewhere also have found wintering pairs to be permanent residents (Craighead and Craighead 1956, Gates 1972, Petersen 1979). Immature Red-tails are highly migratory and are rarely part of the northern wintering population (Orians and Kuhlman 1956; Gates 1972; Wheeler, unpubl. data).

Resident pairs may be conspicuous in early January, and aerial courtship subsequently occurs on warmer days (Wheeler, pers. obs.). During these courtship displays, which involve soaring in large circles to great heights, the male suddenly stoops towards the female, who flips over and presents her talons. The pair may vocalize with a long slurred "krrrr" as they return to the nest site, where they may copulate. The pair defends their territory as spring migrants begin to arrive in early March (Wheeler, pers. obs.).

Nests usually are located near or within mature woodland edges, frequently in the upper canopy of a large tree (Speiser and Bosakowski 1988), usually deciduous and frequently an oak or maple (Hager 1957). Red-tails occasionally use conifers, particularly white pines, and structures such as power-line towers for nest sites (Bent 1937; Wheeler, unpubl. data).

Resident pairs may begin nest construction by late February. They may either refurbish an old nest or select a new site within their territory (Hager 1957; Wheeler, unpubl. data). Both sexes build the nest, which is a large, flat, shallow, stick structure 2.5 to 3 ft (0.8 to 0.9 m) in diameter situated 30 to 70 ft (9.1 to 21.3 m) high in the tree's primary crotch or fork. It usually is lined with tree bark and decorated with evergreen sprigs (Bent 1937).

Egg laying extends from late March to mid-April (Wheeler, unpubl. data). Both sexes share incubation of the 2 to 4 eggs for approximately 30 days (Bent 1937). Although both parents hunt and provide food, the female assumes the dominant role in brooding young (Petersen 1979).

Young fledge at approximately 5 to 6 weeks of age. They remain near the nest site for up to 2.5 weeks, taking short flights with much wing flapping and crying for food. Some perch near hunting adults by 2 weeks of age (Petersen 1979). Young Red-tails disperse by early September as they learn to hunt on their own. Fall migration begins in September and extends into early November (Elkins 1982).

The status of the Red-tailed Hawk has fluctuated considerably in New Hampshire during the last 150 years. The species was common in New England during the 1860s and 1870s (Coues 1868, Maynard 1871, Forbush 1927), and likely had been so for many decades. This hawk declined drastically in numbers during the lifetime of Forbush (1927). Before the turn of the century it had become rare during the breeding season in the Merrimack Valley, and Allen (1903) considered it uncommon but generally distributed in New Hampshire as a whole. Dearborn (1903) knew of none nesting in the vicinity of Durham, and White (1937) observed this hawk only as a rare transient in Concord, where it had formerly nested.

Although analysis of hawk migration data from 1972 to 1987 for the Northeast indicated no significant trends (Titus and Fuller 1990), CBC data from 1962 to 1983 and BBS data from 1966 to 1987 document regional increases (Titus et al. 1989).

As the Atlas map demonstrates, the Red-tail is now well distributed throughout New Hampshire. It nests most commonly in the Coastal Lowlands and the Merrimack Valley and is more sparsely distributed in mountainous and upland areas elsewhere in the state. The decline of agriculture and legal protection likely have contributed to this increase, for soaring Red-tails provided easy targets for farmers seeking to protect their poultry, and many were shot in earlier times.

Atlas observers found the Red-tail in 66% of priority blocks, and documented no other large raptor in 27 of those. The majority of records were at elevations below 2,000 ft (610 m). Red-tailed Hawks are relatively tolerant of human activity. They likely will increase in available habitat and remain common for the foreseeable future.

Stephen H. Wheeler

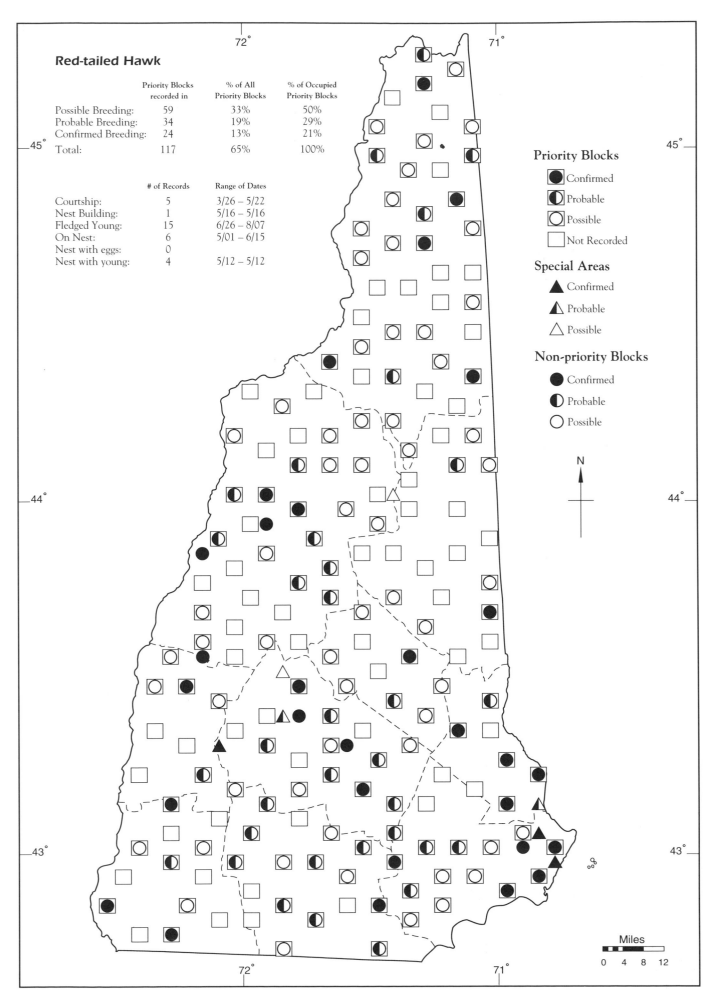

Red-tailed Hawk

	Priority Blocks recorded in	% of All Priority Blocks	% of Occupied Priority Blocks
Possible Breeding:	59	33%	50%
Probable Breeding:	34	19%	29%
Confirmed Breeding:	24	13%	21%
Total:	117	65%	100%

	# of Records	Range of Dates
Courtship:	5	3/26 – 5/22
Nest Building:	1	5/16 – 5/16
Fledged Young:	15	6/26 – 8/07
On Nest:	6	5/01 – 6/15
Nest with eggs:	0	
Nest with young:	4	5/12 – 5/12

Priority Blocks

◐ Confirmed
◑ Probable
○ Possible
□ Not Recorded

Special Areas

▲ Confirmed
◤ Probable
△ Possible

Non-priority Blocks

● Confirmed
◐ Probable
○ Possible

N

Miles
0 4 8 12

American Kestrel
Falco sparverius

The boldly marked American Kestrel, New Hampshire's smallest falcon, is easily recognized by its bright colors and habit of hovering on windy days. The female is larger but less boldly marked. This species breeds in open country or agricultural lands throughout the state.

Although most kestrels from the Northeast winter from the mid-Atlantic states south to Florida and the Gulf Coast (Bent 1925; Roest 1957; Lincer and Sherburn 1974; Wheeler, unpubl. data), a few winter in New Hampshire, where winter records are more frequent near the coast than inland (CBC data, SRS). Most kestrels wintering in New Hampshire are males (Wheeler, pers. obs.).

Kestrels are common migrants in spring and fall. Over most of New Hampshire, kestrels return to breeding territories during late March to mid-April. Roest (1957) suggests that males may arrive slightly ahead of females, but observations on established New Hampshire nesting territories indicate that either sex may return first (Wheeler, pers. obs.). There is a strong tendency for annual reoccupancy of nesting territories and nest sites (Balgooyen 1976; Wheeler, unpubl. data). Appropriate habitat consists of a wide variety of open terrain, including old fields, power-line rights-of-way, and large open bogs (Brewster 1925). Toland (1987) found open areas, principally mowed or grazed pastures and harvested hayfields, to be essential components of nesting season home ranges.

Kestrel pairs wintering in New Hampshire may copulate as early as 28 February, and courtship may occur over 6 to 8 weeks (Wheeler, pers. obs.). A pair frequently hunts together and perches on utility poles and dead treetops. The male defends his territory from other male kestrels, other cavity nesting species, and potential predators such as crows and owls (L. Shutt, pers. comm.). He initiates nest cavity examination, closely followed by his mate. The pair copulates fre-

quently throughout courtship. Other less frequently observed displays include courtship feeding, various vocalizations (the run-together series of "killy - killy - killy..." is most distinctive), and aerial displays (Willoughby and Cade 1964).

Kestrels nest in cavities in trees or buildings. One study in New Hampshire found Northern Flicker cavities in dead American Elms to be the most common natural kestrel nest sites (Wheeler 1979). Widespread mortality of large elms from Dutch elm disease over the past 3 decades has provided woodpeckers with extensive opportunities for cavity construction. Kestrels also accept other types of cavities, and commonly use barns, church steeples, or other buildings with holes or loose trim (Bent 1925). Kestrel nest boxes have been highly successful (Hamerstrom et al. 1973).

Egg laying in New Hampshire commences as early as mid-April and is completed by mid-May in most areas. Clutches normally include 3 to 5 eggs. In southwest Quebec, the mean incubation period is 27 to 29 days (L. Shutt, pers. comm.). Male kestrels occasionally incubate but primarily supply food to the incubating female. Young kestrels fledge after 29 to 31 days (Craighead and Craighead 1956). The peak fledging period in New Hampshire occurs from the last 2 weeks of June through the first week of July. A 10-year study of 101 successful kestrel nesting attempts in New Hampshire nest boxes from 1975 to 1985 indicated an average of 4.0 young per box (Wheeler, unpubl. data).

Young kestrels depend on their parents for at least 12 days after fledging (Balgooyen 1976). Newly fledged young are especially active and vocal, wing flapping and whining as adults approach with food. Older fledglings pursue adults which are carrying food. Insects are the major component of the diet, which also includes small mammals and occasionally birds (Sherrod 1978; L. Shutt, pers. comm.). Kestrel families remain together on the nesting territory into early August (Wheeler, pers. obs.). Young kestrels disperse before the adults (Balgooyen 1976), departing from New Hampshire during mid to late August. They may associate with other young kestrels before migrating (Lett and Bird 1987). Adults subsequently separate and disperse (Balgooyen 1976). Most kestrels migrate through New Hampshire during the first 2 weeks of September.

Some authorities considered kestrels uncommon to rare breeding birds in New Hampshire and New England during the late 19th century and early 20th century (Dearborn 1898, Allen 1903, Dearborn 1903, Goodhue 1922, Forbush 1927, Bagg and Eliot 1937, White 1937). Dearborn (1898) found them only "now and then" summer residents in Belknap and Merrimack counties. Allen (1903) and Forbush (1927) implied that their range in the state did not extend north of the White Mountains, but Brewster (1925) found kestrels to be locally common summer residents in the vicinity of Umbagog Lake.

Today this small falcon is locally common throughout New Hampshire. Atlas data indicate that it is least common in the White Mountains and southwestern highlands. Reforestation of New Hampshire during the present century seemingly would reduce kestrel populations. However, kestrels adapt well to civilization and populations should continue to remain stable or increase slightly in urban and agricultural areas.

Stephen H. Wheeler

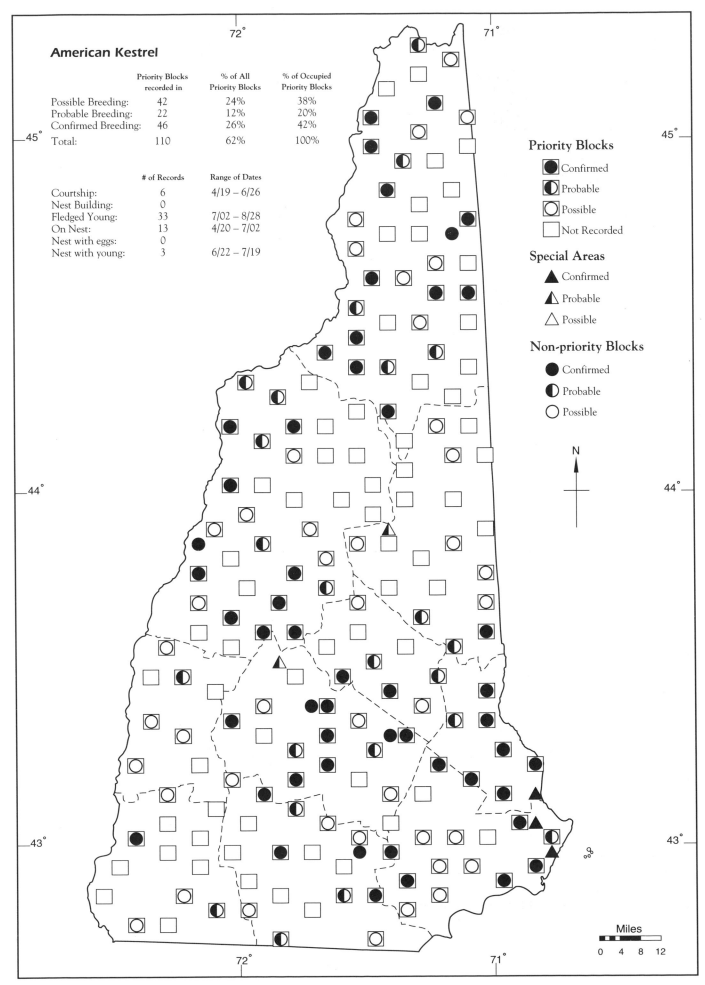

American Kestrel

	Priority Blocks recorded in	% of All Priority Blocks	% of Occupied Priority Blocks
Possible Breeding:	42	24%	38%
Probable Breeding:	22	12%	20%
Confirmed Breeding:	46	26%	42%
Total:	110	62%	100%

	# of Records	Range of Dates
Courtship:	6	4/19 – 6/26
Nest Building:	0	
Fledged Young:	33	7/02 – 8/28
On Nest:	13	4/20 – 7/02
Nest with eggs:	0	
Nest with young:	3	6/22 – 7/19

Priority Blocks

● Confirmed
◑ Probable
○ Possible
□ Not Recorded

Special Areas

▲ Confirmed
◩ Probable
△ Possible

Non-priority Blocks

● Confirmed
◑ Probable
○ Possible

N

Miles
0 4 8 12

Peregrine Falcon
Falco peregrinus

The Peregrine Falcon, formerly known as the Duck Hawk, is the ultimate "flying machine" among avian species. The Latin name of New Hampshire's native subspecies, *Falco peregrinus anatum*, means "wandering (or meandering) falcon of ducks." The Peregrine Falcon is a medium to large falcon distinguished by long, pointed wings and a moderately long, narrow tail. Adults are slate gray above with white underparts narrowly barred with black. The head has a dark cap and a distinct facial marking resembling a moustache. Immature birds are brown above and light with longitudinal brown streaks below. Male Peregrines are smaller than females. Calls include a rasping "cack-cack-cack" and a "WEEchew-WEEchew" wail repeated several times (Bull and Farrand 1977). The Peregrine Falcon is Federally listed as an Endangered Species and is State listed as Endangered in New Hampshire.

Peregrines nest on ledge shelves of sheer, rocky cliffs and occasionally on tall buildings and bridges. Peregrines often return year after year to their nest sites, called "aeries" or "eyries." Ravens may nest nearby on the same cliff, and the 2 species may use the same aerie in successive years. All currently known New Hampshire Peregrine aeries are on cliffs at elevations of 800 to 3,000 ft (240 to 910 m). Distances between neighboring aeries vary from 3 to 35 mi (4.8 to 56.4 km).

Upon returning to their breeding areas, Peregrines begin courtship and nesting rituals. In New Hampshire, first arrivals can be expected in late February or early March. Some individuals may visit a number of different cliffs in March and April before courtship begins. This is known as "cliff-hopping" and apparently is a search behavior for a suitable breeding site. Courtship flights take place near the selected aerie and involve dramatic diving and swooping, vocalizing, and talon grappling in midair. Courtship activity usually takes place from late March to early May.

Egg laying in New Hampshire usually occurs in April, but may be as late as early May (ASNH data). The 2 to 5 eggs, usually laid at 48-hour intervals, are placed in a shallow depression on the nest ledge (Bent 1938). Recent New Hampshire clutches have contained 2 to 4 eggs. Both sexes share incubation, beginning after the third egg is laid, for 33 or 34 days (H. Meng, pers. comm.). Both adults may store or "cache" food items in the vicinity of the scrape. When the hunting male is away for periods of several hours, the brooding female may visit a cache for food and a short stretch break. These breaks may last up to an hour if the weather is favorable. The female may resume hunting when the chicks are 3 weeks old.

At the age of 4 weeks the chicks become quite active and wander about the nest ledge, exercising their wings with vigorous flapping. The parents are extremely protective and may attack an intruder to the nest area. Female chicks fledge in approximately 45 days, and males in approximately 42 days (Sherrod 1983). Adults and fledglings may remain near the aerie until mid to late August, and occasionally until early November (Lanier, pers. obs.). Peregrines are uncommon in the eastern U. S. in winter, occurring mainly along the Atlantic Coast from New Jersey south (NGS 1983). However, an individual has wintered in downtown Manchester from 1987–88 to the present (1993–94) (ASNH data).

Peregrines prey on birds, which they take in the air by diving, "stooping" from above, or after a long chase. In either case, they grab their prey with their large feet. Stooping Peregrines have attained speeds in excess of 175 mi (280 km) per hour, (Lawson 1930 *in* Terres 1980). Favored prey include Blue Jays, flickers, doves, pigeons, waterfowl, and shorebirds.

The Peregrine Falcon nested throughout the mountainous regions of the eastern U.S. until the mid-1950s. J. Hickey (pers. comm.) documented 18 aeries in New Hampshire between the late 1800s and late 1930s from available literature and his own observations. After the 1950s, W. Spofford (pers. comm.) identified, located, and surveyed 25 historical nesting sites in the state, including Hickey's, most of which were located in the mountains, and none of which were then occupied.

Unrestricted use of chlorinated hydrocarbon insecticides, particularly DDT, subtly but effectively extirpated the Peregrine Falcon as a breeding bird in the eastern U. S. (Bollengier 1979). DDE, the principal breakdown product of DDT, accumulated in adult Peregrines and interfered with eggshell development, causing extensive reproductive failure (Cade et al. 1971).

Adult Peregrines began to disappear from traditional aeries during the 1950s, and by the early 1960s this falcon was no longer breeding east of the Mississippi River (Bollengier 1979). Use of DDT was banned in the United States in 1972. Since then, the release of captive-reared birds and reduced DDE levels have enabled Peregrines to reoccupy a number of historical aeries.

Beginning in 1976 and ending in 1986 biologists introduced to the wild more than 75 captive-reared Peregrines from 2 release sites on the WMNF through the cooperative efforts of the USFWS, WMNF, NHFG, and Peregrine Fund. During 1981–86, 7 known successful nesting attempts at 4 sites produced the first 16 wild Peregrines to be raised in New Hampshire since the early 1950s. As of the 1993 breeding season, 8 Peregrine pairs occupied New Hampshire cliffs. Further expansion of this population is anticipated in the coming years.

John Lanier & Rene M. Bollengier

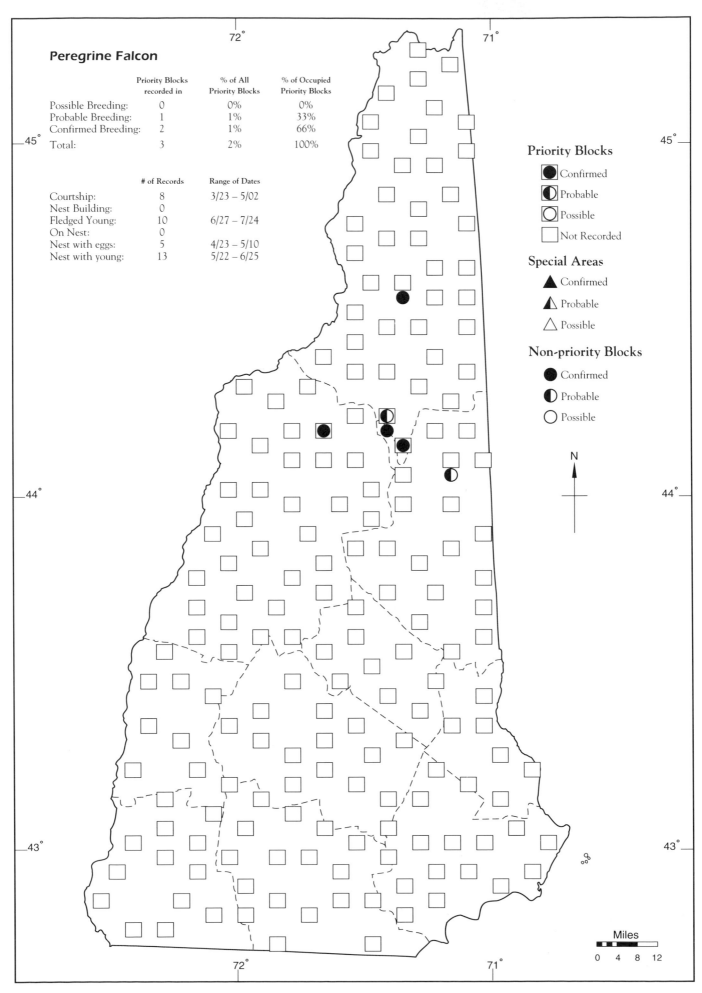

Peregrine Falcon

	Priority Blocks recorded in	% of All Priority Blocks	% of Occupied Priority Blocks
Possible Breeding:	0	0%	0%
Probable Breeding:	1	1%	33%
Confirmed Breeding:	2	1%	66%
Total:	3	2%	100%

	# of Records	Range of Dates
Courtship:	8	3/23 – 5/02
Nest Building:	0	
Fledged Young:	10	6/27 – 7/24
On Nest:	0	
Nest with eggs:	5	4/23 – 5/10
Nest with young:	13	5/22 – 6/25

Priority Blocks
- ● Confirmed
- ◑ Probable
- ○ Possible
- ☐ Not Recorded

Special Areas
- ▲ Confirmed
- ◮ Probable
- △ Possible

Non-priority Blocks
- ● Confirmed
- ◑ Probable
- ○ Possible

N

Miles
0 4 8 12

61

WED

Ring-necked Pheasant
Phasianus colchicus

The Ring-necked Pheasant is the most successfully introduced game bird in the United States. This introduced and nonmigratory species occasionally overwinters and breeds successfully in New Hampshire. Today's North American pheasant is a hybrid that usually resembles the Chinese Ring-necked Pheasant, *P. torquatus* (Goff et al. 1981). The large cock, 30 to 36 in (75 to 90 cm) long with a 21 in (53 cm) tail, is distinguished by his brilliant iridescent bronze body plumage, green head with scarlet eye and cheek patches, purple ear tufts, and white neck ring. The female is smaller 21 to 25 in (53 to 63 cm) long with an 11 to 12 in (28 to 30 cm) tail, and light brown in color. Both cock and hen have a long, pointed tail and short wings which enable them to burst into the air and accelerate very rapidly in flight, but such flights are only for short distances.

New Hampshire's pheasant population results from stocking efforts by NHFG and private clubs or individuals. Pheasants are most likely to overwinter and reproduce in agricultural lands in the Seacoast area, and at lower elevations and in river valleys elsewhere in the southern third of the state. New Hampshire's scarcity of grasslands and croplands, especially grain crops, limit naturalized pheasant populations in the state (Silver 1957; J. W. Glidden, pers. comm.).

Cock pheasants utter a loud "skwagook" crowing call year round but most often during the breeding season, and a "cackle" call when alarmed or flushed from cover. During March to early April the polygamous cock defends a territory of up to 2 a (0.8 ha) for courting, mating, and feeding activities (Allen 1956). One cock may mate with as many as 12 hens during the breeding season (Goff et al. 1981).

The hen pheasant constructs the nest, which is usually well concealed in a shallow depression in the grass in an open weedy field, brushy pasture, or hayfield, and is lined with grasses, weeds, or leaves (Harrison 1975).

An observer may pass within a few feet of an incubating bird without seeing her, and she will not leave the nest until almost stepped on. When she does leave, she generally skulks away quietly, rarely flushing (Bent 1932).

Egg laying occurs in May and June, and the hen incubates her 6 to 15, typically 10 to 12 eggs for 23 days (Goff et al. 1981). In New York, hatching may occur from May to September and peaks in early to mid-June (Goff et al. 1981). Pheasant chicks leave the nest as soon as their down has dried. The hen pheasant leads her brood within an area of 5 to 10 a (2 to 4 ha) around the nest site for 6 to 7 weeks, helping them to find food and cover, and brooding them at night and in cold or stormy weather (Bent 1932). The chicks are able to fly in 12 to 14 days and begin roosting in trees at night when half grown (Harrison 1978). White (1937) observed 6 young, all able to fly, with their parents in Concord on 12 June 1925. At 10 weeks of age the young disperse, often joining a flock which feeds and rests together during the fall and winter months (Bent 1932).

Adult pheasants forage on grains, seeds, berries, young herbaceous shoots, and insects (Goff et al. 1981). Some pheasants survive New Hampshire winters by eating cracked corn at winter feeding stations and using dense cover in nearby marshes.

Governor Wentworth brought the first pheasants to New Hampshire from England and released them in Wolfeboro around 1790. Belknap (1793 *in* Allen 1903) documented the event and wrote "they have not since been seen." Subsequent releases involved pheasants of various origins stocked in Concord in 1893, in Lebanon in 1895, and by NHFG in 1896 (Siegler 1949). New Hampshire's pheasant population increased during the early 1900s with releases by sportsmen's clubs and northward expansion from Massachusetts (Siegler 1949). In 1918 NHFG began buying grain for supplemental winter feeding and in 1920 initiated its own pheasant-rearing operation. Released birds numbered 98 in 1921 and had increased to 1,023 in 1935, when the farm was closed because of competition from private breeders (Silver 1957). Pheasants were common around Concord in the mid-1920s, but had declined considerably a decade later (White 1937). NHFG again produced pheasants from 1948 to 1975, stocking birds in both spring and fall. Since 1975, when the entire game-farm population was destroyed in response to an outbreak of equine encephalitis, the state has purchased up to 12,000 pheasants annually from out-of-state breeders for fall stocking in all 10 counties.

The first legislatively authorized pheasant hunting season occurred during 1–6 November 1923 in Hillsborough, Rockingham, and Strafford counties, with a 2 males per day limit and season limit of 5 birds. By 1945 the season had increased to 31 days, with a 10 bird season limit, and was open in all counties except Coos (Siegler 1949). A 1948 NHFG banding study concluded that hunters recovered only about 20% of stocked birds. Hessler et al. (1970) found that 81% of all stocked pheasants died within one month and that 92% of the mortality was attributable to predation.

Atlas field work documented pheasants in 18 priority blocks. The majority of records are from the southeastern part of the state, where milder winter conditions enhance survival. With the little remaining suitable pheasant habitat in New Hampshire under pressure from both development and natural vegetation changes, it is unlikely that the pheasant will become a self-perpetuating species in the state.

Harold P. Nevers

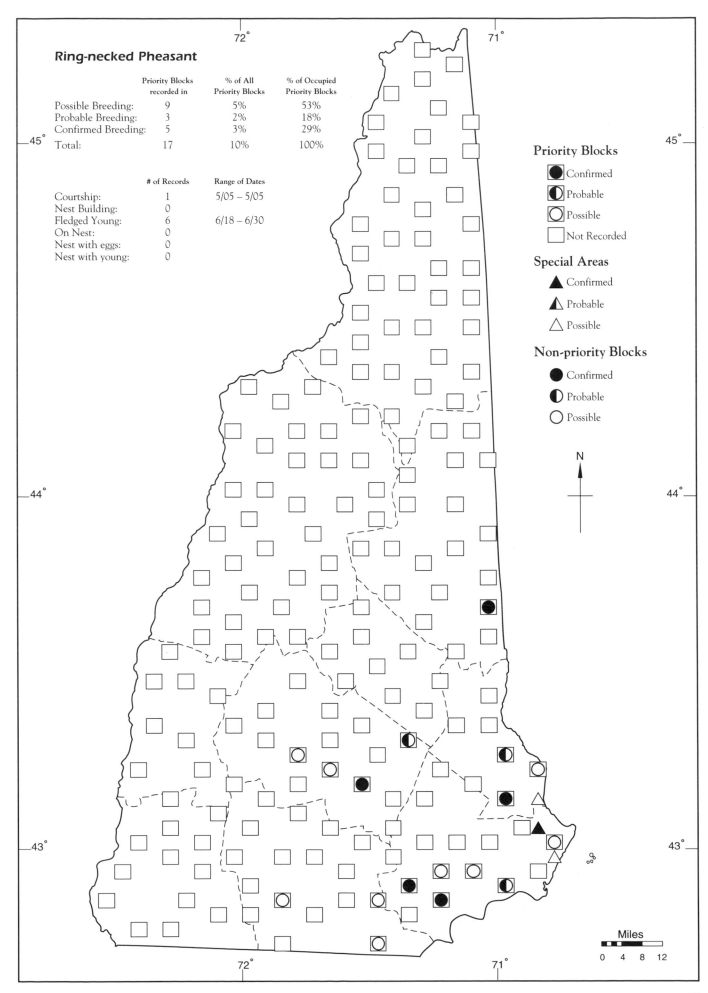

Ring-necked Pheasant

	Priority Blocks recorded in	% of All Priority Blocks	% of Occupied Priority Blocks
Possible Breeding:	9	5%	53%
Probable Breeding:	3	2%	18%
Confirmed Breeding:	5	3%	29%
Total:	17	10%	100%

	# of Records	Range of Dates
Courtship:	1	5/05 – 5/05
Nest Building:	0	
Fledged Young:	6	6/18 – 6/30
On Nest:	0	
Nest with eggs:	0	
Nest with young:	0	

Priority Blocks

● Confirmed
◐ Probable
○ Possible
▢ Not Recorded

Special Areas

▲ Confirmed
◩ Probable
△ Possible

Non-priority Blocks

● Confirmed
◐ Probable
○ Possible

N

Miles
0 4 8 12

Spruce Grouse
Dendragapus canadensis

The Spruce Grouse is an intriguing resident of northern coniferous forests. The male is easily recognized by its black breast patch, white barred sides, and red eye comb. The female is darker brown than the much more common and widespread Ruffed Grouse, and is barred with black.

Due in part to loss of coniferous forest and in part to its unsuspecting nature, the Spruce Grouse, or "fool hen," has disappeared from much of its former range in the northeastern U. S. (Silver 1957). In New Hampshire, the Spruce Grouse is now an uncommon permanent resident from the White Mountains north at elevations up to 4,500 ft (1,370 m)(Greenwald 1984). This species is tamer and more arboreal than the Ruffed Grouse, which prefers mixed or hardwood forests.

Spruce Grouse habitat consists of dense coniferous trees up to 46 ft (14 m) tall, with a well-developed midstory, regardless of the conifer species present (Boag and Schroeder 1992). In New England, Spruce Grouse reside in spruce-fir forests on mountain ridges and peaks, and in low-elevation bogs. Forest openings or bog edges are important habitat components (Greenwald 1984, Boag and Schroeder 1992). Population densities of 7 to 12 pairs/sq m (2.5 sq. km) are typical (Johnsgard 1973, Greenwald 1984). Individual birds use home ranges averaging less than 10 a (24 ha).

Spruce Grouse forage on the ground and in the midcrowns of conifers. They feed primarily on conifer needles, but also eat new growth of shrubs and forbs, fruits, flowers, fungi, land snails, and small arthropods (DeGraaf et al. 1980, Boag and Schroeder 1992).

The breeding season begins in late April. In Alaska, males establish territories of 3 to 21 a (1.2 to 8.5 ha) (Ellison 1971), and advertise them with strutting, tail flicking, and aerial courtship displays (Ellison 1971, Johnsgard 1973). The lone Atlas courtship record occurred on 26 April at 3,800 ft (1,160 m) on Mt.

Clinton, Beans Grant, near Crawford Notch, Harts Location (Greenwald 1984).

Males are polygamous and apparently take no part in nest building, incubation, or brood rearing. Females maintain independent territories during the breeding season and visit a male's territory only to mate (Ellison 1971).

The nest, usually in a shallow depression in the ground or atop a low, mossy mound, is sparingly lined with dead leaves, grasses, and conifer needles. Low-hanging conifer branches hide it well (Harrison 1975). The female typically lays 6 to 8 eggs in May or June and incubates for 17 to 25 days, starting after the last egg is laid. Well camouflaged, she sits very tight on the nest (Harrison 1975).

The precocial young leave the nest within a day of hatching and almost immediately begin foraging for themselves, feeding largely on insects. They are able to flutter from the ground after one week (Terres 1980). A hen with young chicks is very aggressive and may threaten an intruder. If threats fail, a distraction display may follow. Females with older broods may utter warning calls but are less aggressive towards intruders (Robinson and Maxwell 1968).

Encounters with a hen and her brood are most likely in late June and July, and provide the easiest way to "confirm" Spruce Grouse. Males sometimes accompany females and well-grown broods in early fall (Johnsgard 1973). Broods disperse when the chicks are about 9 to 12 weeks old (Alway and Boag 1979). Though generally sedentary, Spruce Grouse may wander in winter. Some adults migrate short distances between breeding and wintering range (Boag and Schroeder 1992), and yearlings may disperse more than 6 mi (10 km) (J. F. Bendell, pers. comm.).

This species once was common in the forests of northern New England, and a few birds may have occurred as far south as Massachusetts, presumably in higher elevation spruce forests (Coues 1868, Silver 1957). Maynard (1871) considered the White Mountains its southern limit. Allen (1903) reported Spruce Grouse in the Presidential, Carter-Moriah, Twin and Sandwich ranges, on Mt. Moosilauke, at Umbagog Lake, and along the East Branch of the Pemigewasset River.

Spruce Grouse apparently began to decline in Coos County around the turn of the century (Wright 1911, Forbush 1929, Weeks 1888 *in* Silver 1957). Logging, forest fires, market hunting (banned in New Hampshire in 1901), and casual killing probably were contributing factors (Bent 1932, Richards 1954 *in* Silver 1957, Silver 1957).

The Atlas map shows a clustering of Spruce Grouse records in the White Mountains. The Spruce Grouse likely occurs in more blocks than the map indicates, especially in the relatively inaccessible North Country, where its distribution is patchy. The southernmost record was of 2 males and a female at the 3,993 ft (1,217 m) summit of Sandwich Mtn. on the Waterville Valley/Sandwich town line (E. S. Daniell III, pers. comm.). Atlas observers reported several other sightings in the Sandwich Range and in the mountains around Waterville Valley.

The Spruce Grouse apparently has made a modest comeback here in the last several decades, after legal protection in 1941, and is now considered uncommon. Careful monitoring will be necessary to ensure that this fascinating bird maintains a stable or increasing population in New Hampshire in the coming years.

Steve Smith

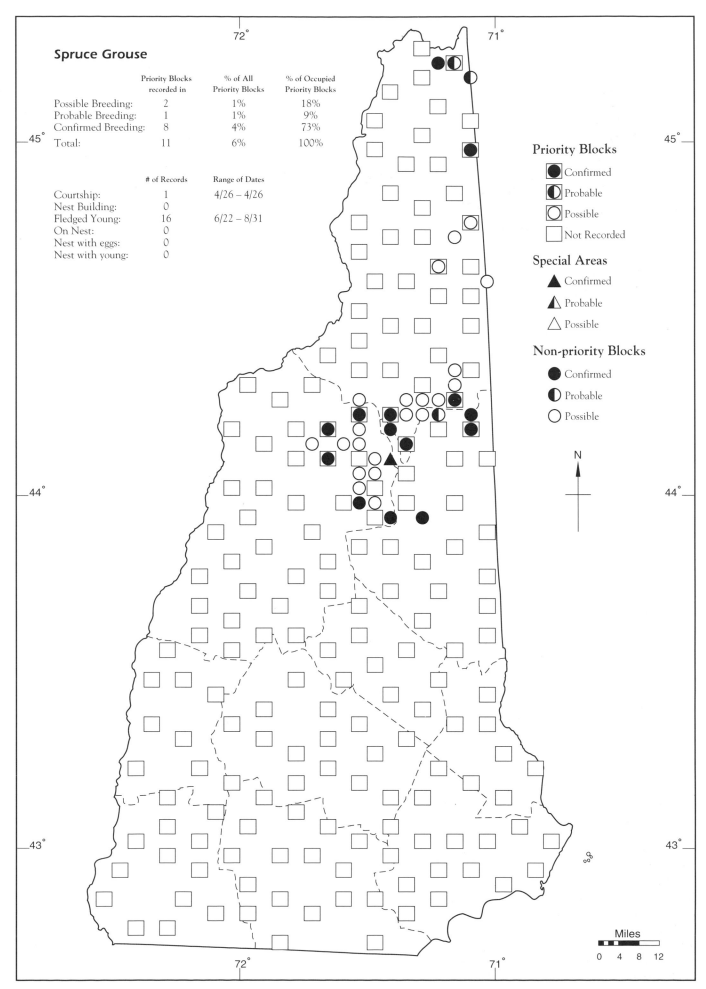

Spruce Grouse

	Priority Blocks recorded in	% of All Priority Blocks	% of Occupied Priority Blocks
Possible Breeding:	2	1%	18%
Probable Breeding:	1	1%	9%
Confirmed Breeding:	8	4%	73%
Total:	11	6%	100%

	# of Records	Range of Dates
Courtship:	1	4/26 – 4/26
Nest Building:	0	
Fledged Young:	16	6/22 – 8/31
On Nest:	0	
Nest with eggs:	0	
Nest with young:	0	

Priority Blocks

● Confirmed
◐ Probable
◑ Possible
□ Not Recorded

Special Areas

▲ Confirmed
◤ Probable
△ Possible

Non-priority Blocks

● Confirmed
◑ Probable
○ Possible

N

Miles
0 4 8 12

Ruffed Grouse
Bonasa umbellus

The Ruffed Grouse, or "partridge," as it is commonly called, is a wary bird that on takeoff will startle even the most seasoned woodsman with its loud, booming wing beats. However, until early in this century, this "fool hen" was so unaccustomed to humans that it could be killed with clubs (Silver 1957). Today one sees this behavior mostly in remote areas of northern New Hampshire.

These year-round residents of forests favor edges of clearings in moist, moderately sloped, mixed woodlands (Silver 1957). Ruffed Grouse occur from New Hampshire's coastal region to northern spruce-fir forests at elevations generally below 3,000 ft (915 m).

The Ruffed Grouse has 3 common color phases: a reddish phase more common in southern and especially coastal New Hampshire, a gray phase more common in the north, and an intermediate reddish gray phase which occurs statewide (Silver 1957). The sexes have similar plumage, but the male's black neck ruffs are more conspicuous than the female's, and the male has a small orange-red comb above the eye. The dark terminal band on the characteristic fan tail is interrupted on the female.

Biologists have focused considerable attention on Ruffed Grouse biology and habitat needs. Various authors (e.g., Gullion 1972, Chambers 1983, Vt. Fish & Wildlife Dept. 1986) have produced detailed guidelines for management of Ruffed Grouse habitat. This species is closely associated with young forests and depends heavily on trees associated with disturbance, such as aspens and birches, for winter food (Vt. Fish & Wildlife Dept. 1986). Ideal grouse habitat includes forests of several age classes to provide suitable breeding, nesting, brooding, and roosting habitat.

The Ruffed Grouse breeds at 10 months of age. In early March, the male establishes a "drumming territory" in a mature hardwood forest which usually includes some 40- to 50- year-old aspens (Johnsgard

1975a). There he displays for receptive females. A typical "drumming log" is moss covered, approximately 20 in (51 cm) in diameter, about 10 ft (3 m) long, and almost always located near an edge or opening in the forest. "Drumming" takes place on one spot on the log, which becomes worn; droppings accumulate nearby (Edminster 1947). When suitable logs are unavailable, moss-covered mounds, boulders, or stone walls serve the same purpose. A male grouse may drum in every month of the year and any hour of the day and night, but the most intense drumming occurs in early mornings and evenings in late March through April, tapering off in May (Edminster 1947). When a receptive female grouse approaches, the male struts with his tail fanned, black neck ruffs raised, and wings drooped (Johnsgard 1975a).

The nest is a hollow on the ground in dead leaves, usually located at the base of a tree, near a log, or under a shrub or brush pile, typically in a middle-aged stand of hardwood or mixed forest. The clutch size is usually 10 to 12, but may be 8 to 15 (Reed 1965). Clutches of more than 16 eggs probably are "dump nests," with eggs laid by 2 or more hens (Cringan 1970). The hen incubates for 24 or 25 days and raises only one brood per year, but may renest should the first clutch fail (Johnsgard 1975a).

After hatching in late May, the chicks typically spend several weeks with the hen, feeding on insects in moist, brushy woodlands, overgrown agricultural lands, or recently burned woodland. The hen may feign injury when danger approaches, or may rush at or even attack an intruder.

The family unit breaks up into small groups and individuals in mid-September, when the young are about 12 weeks old. The juvenile birds disperse from their summer habitat within 2.5 weeks, usually after a sudden change in weather. This dispersal has been described as "crazy flight," since juvenile birds often crash into buildings as they move into unfamiliar territories a mile or more from their brood habitat.

During spring and summer grouse feed on insects, grasses, and herbaceous vegetation. In fall and winter they switch to twigs, buds, and catkins of various trees and shrubs, especially aspen and birch (Vt. Fish & Wildlife Dept. 1986).

This species has been New Hampshire's most popular game bird since colonial times, and no doubt was an important staple for indigenous human populations. Belknap (1792) noted fears of the species' extinction due to overhunting. Harvest continued to be a limiting factor for grouse populations during the days of market hunting, but with controlled seasons this is no longer the case. Ruffed Grouse populations naturally experience irregularly cyclical booms and crashes, which vary geographically (Edminster 1947). Silver (1957) presents historical evidence of population fluctuations in New Hampshire from the era of market hunting and in more recent times, and summarizes the history of regulations on grouse hunting. Cyclical patterns aside, the species has been generally common in New Hampshire during the present century (Allen 1903, Dearborn 1903, Wright 1911).

Relatively few priority blocks lack Ruffed Grouse records. Additional effort, timed during the primary drumming period, likely would have filled in these gaps. Continuing development poses a significant threat to grouse habitat in southeastern New Hampshire, but pockets of grouse should persist there for the foreseeable future. The Western Highlands and northern two-thirds of the state continue to provide extensive grouse habitat. Continual harvesting of mature forests on the industrial timberlands of northern New Hampshire should ensure widespread, high quality grouse habitat for many decades to come.

Edward G. Robinson

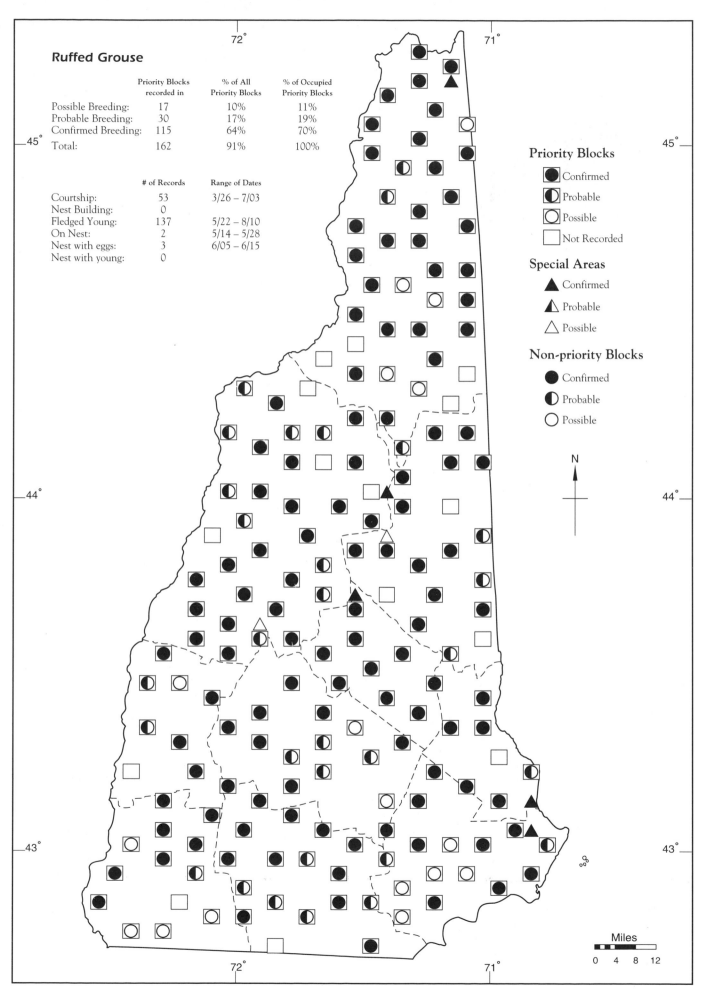

Ruffed Grouse

	Priority Blocks recorded in	% of All Priority Blocks	% of Occupied Priority Blocks
Possible Breeding:	17	10%	11%
Probable Breeding:	30	17%	19%
Confirmed Breeding:	115	64%	70%
Total:	162	91%	100%

	# of Records	Range of Dates
Courtship:	53	3/26 – 7/03
Nest Building:	0	
Fledged Young:	137	5/22 – 8/10
On Nest:	2	5/14 – 5/28
Nest with eggs:	3	6/05 – 6/15
Nest with young:	0	

Priority Blocks

● Confirmed
◑ Probable
○ Possible
□ Not Recorded

Special Areas

▲ Confirmed
◭ Probable
△ Possible

Non-priority Blocks

● Confirmed
◐ Probable
○ Possible

N

Miles
0 4 8 12

Wild Turkey

Meleagris gallapavo

Absent from the state for more than a century, the unmistakable Wild Turkey once again gobbles in agricultural areas of southern New Hampshire. Turkeys range widely, and a flock may cover 4 to 5 sq mi (1.5 to 1.9 sq km) during the course of a year (Pough 1951). Ideal habitat includes a combination of farmlands and hilly mixed woodlands with abundant mast-producing trees, springs, and seeps. Turkeys occur in flocks during most of the year, and groups of 30 to 50 are not uncommon around farms during the winter.

Turkeys appear dark brown or blackish from a distance. In full sunlight their chestnut plumage has a coppery, greenish and reddish sheen. Adult toms are longer legged, taller, and darker than hens and average about 18.5 lb (8.5 kg). Their heads and necks are reddish with pronounced wattles, and conspicuous 5 to 12 in (13 to 30 cm) "beards" hang down from their upper chests. In contrast, adult hens average about 10 lb (4.5 kg), and have bluish heads and necks with more feathers than males. Hens generally lack beards, but about 6% have thin ones.

Turkeys are polygamous. Older gobblers do most of the breeding, although one-year-old males, or "jakes," are physiologically able to breed. Most hens breed in their first year. Males begin gobbling and sparring in late February and early March, but the serious breeding activity occurs during April. Toms perform dramatic courtship displays throughout this period, strutting, gobbling, and drooping and rattling their wings, with tails fanned, body plumage expanded, and head ornaments swollen (Bent 1932). Wild Turkeys have a considerable "vocabulary" (McIlhenny 1914 *in* Bent 1932). The hens produce a variety of yelps, clucks, and gobbles, and the toms gobble and boom.

Hens choose nest sites by mid-April, often beside tree trunks or fallen logs (Harrison 1975). The nest is a depression on dry ground lined with dry leaves. Most New Hampshire nests are situated under overhanging branches in sites with an open overstory and a well developed understory (Thomas 1989). Cover at New Hampshire nest sites includes brambles, juniper, spirea, and coniferous (usually white pine) slash (Thomas 1989).

In New Hampshire, most hens begin incubating clutches of 8 to 14 eggs around 16 or 17 May (Thomas 1989). Incubation lasts 28 days. Hens usually desert if disturbed during early incubation. Nests located more than 66 ft (20 m) from a road or trail are most likely to be successful (Thomas 1989).

Turkey poults grow fast. At 10 days of age they can fly a little and begin to roost in low tree branches at night. Hens without young commonly join hens with broods, and several hens often band together with their broods.

Oak, beech, ash, and hickory mast are the Wild Turkey's primary food sources. Turkeys are omnivorous and opportunistic, however, and consume a variety of foods. During summer poults feed largely on insects, especially grasshoppers, and also eat large volumes of seeds and berries in late summer.

Nesting success in southeastern New Hampshire exceeds that in the southwestern part of the state (84% vs. 30%), while brood size averages higher in the soutwest (12) than in the southeast (7) (Thomas 1989). Turkey chicks are susceptible to pneumonia, and long rainy periods with cool temperatures during early June can decimate broods. Coyote, fox, and fisher are their major predators in New Hampshire. Lack of brood-rearing habitat also may limit poult survival here (Thomas 1989).

The species' greatest limiting factor in New Hampshire is winter food availability. Corn wastage in manure, a high protein source, may be the major winter food when the mast crop is poor or covered by snow. Seeps provide an important winter water source, and turkeys feed on the black, beady spore heads of sensitive ferns projecting above the snow.

Allen (1921) provides a thorough account of the Wild Turkey's history in New England. Most of New Hampshire's 7 southern counties were once turkey range. Historical accounts describe flocks of 40 to 100 turkeys as common in the early days of settlement (Silver 1957), when vast undisturbed tracts of mixed hardwood-coniferous forest with many mast-bearing trees provided extensive habitat. Deep snows and lack of oak trees were limiting factors in the North Country. European settlement adversely affected turkeys through habitat destruction and unrestricted hunting. Turkeys were essentially gone from New Hampshire by the end of the Revolutionary War. Apparently the last Wild Turkey report from New Hampshire is of a bird in Weare in 1854 (NHFG, unpubl. data).

NHFG unsuccessfully transplanted 26 live-trapped Wild Turkeys from West Virginia to Pawtuckaway State Park, Deerfield/Nottingham, during 1969–70. A second transplant of 25 turkeys from the Allegheny Mountains of southwestern New York to the Walpole area in 1975 was successful (NHFG 1975). Since then, NHFG biologists have trapped and transplanted turkeys from this nucleus to 8 additional sites. Limited spring gobbler hunting began in 1980, and hunters take up to 89 gobblers annually.

The Wild Turkey's present distribution in New Hampshire is somewhat more extensive than that illustrated by Atlas records. Turkeys now occur in 9 of New Hampshire's 10 counties. A few have reached as far north as Piermont/Haverhill, and the dairy farms along the Connecticut River probably will enable them to survive this far north. Otherwise their range is unlikely to expand north of Lake Winnipesaukee. Habitat availability and winter conditions will determine turkey distribution and abundance in the years to come.

Theodore W. Walski

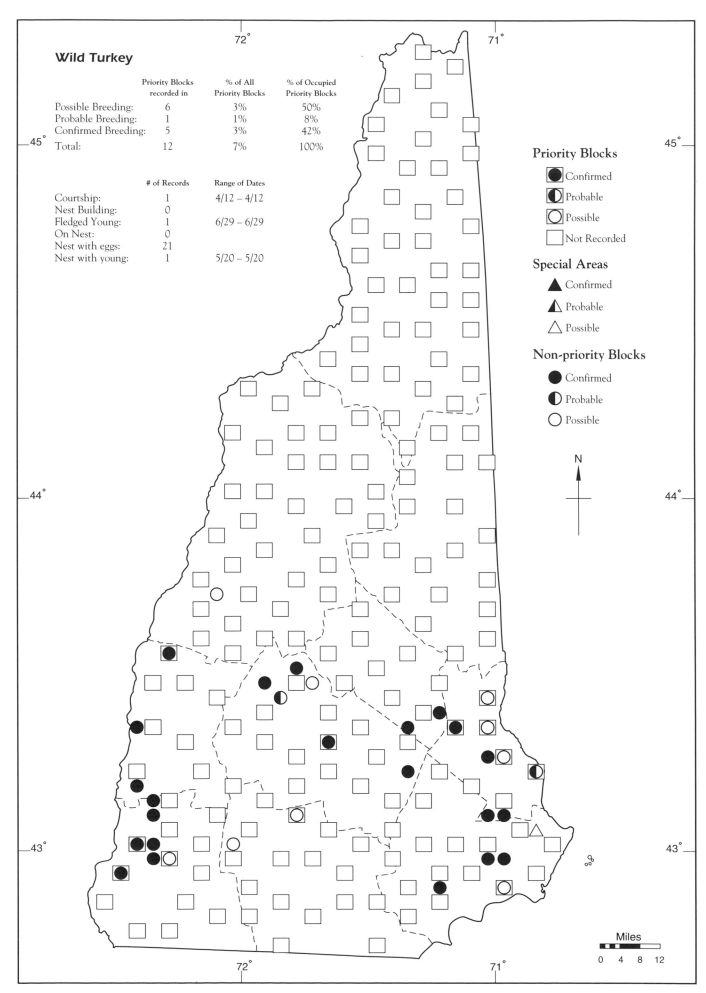

Wild Turkey

	Priority Blocks recorded in	% of All Priority Blocks	% of Occupied Priority Blocks
Possible Breeding:	6	3%	50%
Probable Breeding:	1	1%	8%
Confirmed Breeding:	5	3%	42%
Total:	12	7%	100%

	# of Records	Range of Dates
Courtship:	1	4/12 – 4/12
Nest Building:	0	
Fledged Young:	1	6/29 – 6/29
On Nest:	0	
Nest with eggs:	21	
Nest with young:	1	5/20 – 5/20

Priority Blocks

● Confirmed

◐ Probable

◖ Possible

□ Not Recorded

Special Areas

▲ Confirmed

◣ Probable

△ Possible

Non-priority Blocks

● Confirmed

◐ Probable

○ Possible

N

Miles
0 4 8 12

Northern Bobwhite

Colinus virginianus

The Northern Bobwhite is a small, reddish brown, chunky, chickenlike bird with a dark tail and a short, dark bill. The conspicuous eye-stripe and throat are white on the male and buffy on the female. The bobwhite, or quail, is easily identified by its clear whistled "I'm bob white" call, explosive flushes, and a "koilee" call (similar to a Sora's) used to reassemble the covey.

The native and now extirpated "Old New England Quail" was a larger, tawny version of today's stocked quail and occurred from southeast Ontario easterly into southwestern Maine (Silver 1957). In New Hampshire, the native quail was common in agricultural lands in the southern counties, and occasionally occurred north to the southern valleys of the White Mountains. Good quail habitat includes feeding grounds in weed patches and grain stubble, night roosts in thick, swampy tangles or briar patches, and escape cover in dense woodlots (Bent 1932).

A wintering quail covey begins to scatter in late March or April, as the birds move to breeding territories. The cock calls frequently, defends his territory from rivals, and listens for a female's response call from a low but prominent perch. Pairs are inseparable after mating but may not nest for several weeks (Harrison 1975).

The nesting season extends from late May well into September (Bull 1974), and a pair may raise 2 or more broods each year. The nest, a hollow lined with dead grasses or forbs, typically is located in thick vegetation in or on the edge of a pasture or field. The bobwhite weaves grasses or other vegetation into an arch over the nest, often leaving only a small entrance on the side (Stoddard 1931). An incubating female will not flush until nearly stepped on (Harrison 1975). The female typically lays 12 to 14 eggs and incubates for 23 or 24 days (Bent 1932). Newly hatched chicks leave the nest soon after hatching, and the parents carefully tend them. Young birds can fly 2 to 3 yd (1.8 to 2.7 m)

at 3 days of age (Stoddard 1931) and are fully mobile after 2 weeks.

Bobwhites are rapid and tireless runners, flying only when threatened with imminent danger. They typically forage in a weedy field or berry patch for several hours after sunrise, and resume again before sunset. Food includes seeds, berries, small acorns, wild fruits, and succulent leaves. In summer, insects may comprise up to 30% of their diet (Johnsgard 1973).

In late summer and fall bobwhites form coveys of up to 30 birds which remain together through winter, feeding and roosting in a 30 to 40 a (12 to 16 ha) territory (Pough 1951). At night the covey selects a sheltered spot under an evergreen tree or thick brush (Bent 1932) and roosts on the ground in a circle with heads pointed outward, tails pointed to the sky, and bodies closely pressed together. When flushed, a covey explodes into the air in all directions, rising swiftly with loudly whirring wings and scaling off to land and later regroup. Bent (1932) refers to quail as "feathered bombshells."

The native bobwhite quail originally occupied all 35 Eastern states from southern Maine to Florida (Silver 1957). Historical references to quail in New Hampshire date back to the late 1800s (Morrison 1883, Allen 1909). Quail hunting became popular in the latter part of the 19th century, but quail were not important game here as they never were numerous in the state (Silver 1957). Allen (1903) considered the bobwhite a rare permanent resident of the Transition valleys of southern New Hampshire, where native birds barely survived severe winters and introduced birds succumbed. The legislature enacted the first law protecting birds, including quail, in 1842 (Silver 1957), but quail populations continued to decline. The 1920 ASNH Checklist of Birds of New Hampshire classified the bobwhite as a rare permanent resident. White (1924) described quail as rare in Concord, and subject to winterkill. Forbush (1927) reported bobwhites to be uncommon, local, and rare throughout their former range.

Efforts to reestablish the birds met with little success. Restocking efforts included many introductions, notably of large numbers of southern quail up until 1935 (Allen 1954, Silver 1957). The decline of agriculture and subsequent loss of open lands, combined with severe winters, excessive hunting, and interbreeding with less hardy introduced stock brought about the complete extirpation of native quail from New Hampshire during the early decades of this century (Forbush 1912, Silver 1957, Bull 1985). The quail season was closed for 31 of the 44 years during 1923–66 and reopened in 1967 to allow incidental harvest of stocked birds.

The few Atlas records represent recently released captives. The northernmost record is from Conway, where 3 quail pairs foraged in and around a 100 a (40 ha) field adjacent to the Saco River throughout the summer of 1985. With the "native" bobwhite extirpated and its habitat essentially gone from New Hampshire, the Northern Bobwhite will continue to occur only as an uncommon and introduced species.

Harold P. Nevers

Atlas of Breeding Birds in New Hampshire

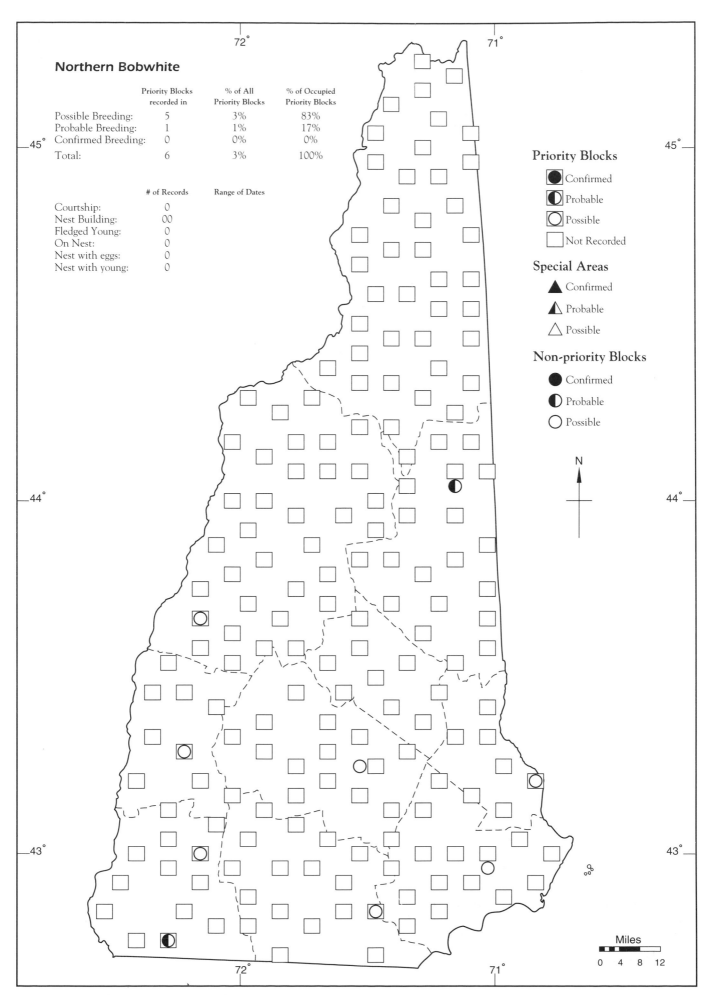

Northern Bobwhite

	Priority Blocks recorded in	% of All Priority Blocks	% of Occupied Priority Blocks
Possible Breeding:	5	3%	83%
Probable Breeding:	1	1%	17%
Confirmed Breeding:	0	0%	0%
Total:	6	3%	100%

	# of Records	Range of Dates
Courtship:	0	
Nest Building:	00	
Fledged Young:	0	
On Nest:	0	
Nest with eggs:	0	
Nest with young:	0	

Priority Blocks

● Confirmed
◑ Probable
○ Possible
▢ Not Recorded

Special Areas

▲ Confirmed
◮ Probable
△ Possible

Non-priority Blocks

● Confirmed
◑ Probable
○ Possible

N

Miles

0 4 8 12

Virginia Rail
Rallus limicola

Vocal but seldom seen, this rail occurs in much of the state where suitable wetland habitat exists, and probably is the most common rail in New Hampshire. With its gray cheeks, rusty breast, long bill, and small size, the Virginia Rail can be mistaken for no other North American rail.

The Virginia Rail is officially a game bird, but New Hampshire has had no open season since the mid-1970s. These birds are highly migratory, nesting throughout the northern half of the United States and southern Canada and wintering along the southeast, Gulf, and West coasts, and south to Guatemala (Zimmerman 1977). Virginia Rails arrive in New Hampshire in mid to late April. Although they occasionally breed in the upper reaches of salt or brackish marshes, fresh water emergent marshes seem more to their liking. Small wetlands of 0.3 a (0.1 ha) may sustain one or more Virginia Rail pairs (Kibbe *in* Laughlin and Kibbe 1985). Larger marshes may support 0.24 to 1.6 pairs/a (0.4 to 4.0 pairs/ha) (Zimmerman 1977). New Hampshire is within the species' area of highest breeding density (Zimmerman 1977).

Because their bodies are thin, Virginia Rails can travel through dense marsh vegetation with surprising speed and agility. They run swiftly when threatened, and even swim across or under water to escape. They also may hide under aquatic plants, with only their bills above the water (Forbush 1925a). When they are flushed, their flight is weak and fluttery. Legs dangling, they drop back into cover shortly after takeoff.

Despite their typically secretive behavior in marshes, Virginia Rails occasionally perch in trees. One which flushed from a small tree in a thicket of white pines on Hoag Island in Squam Lake, Sandwich in September 1949 flew successively to several other small trees and never landed on the ground (Richards 1951).

Both Soras and Virginia Rails may inhabit the same marsh, but Virginias tend to prefer drier nest sites than Soras (Townsend 1926, Kibbe *in* Laughlin and Kibbe 1985). The Virginia Rail's eggs are paler, less heavily marked, and duller, but empty nests are difficult to distinguish (Harrison 1975).

The nest is constructed of marsh vegetation in 3 to 4 days (Pospichal 1952), but the adults may add material after incubation begins (Townsend 1926, Walkinshaw 1937). A canopy of marsh grasses sometimes conceals the nest, which may have a ramp of vegetation leading up to it. The nest is usually 2 to 5 in (5 to 13 cm) above water that is 3 to 10 in (8 to 25 cm) deep (Zimmerman 1977).

Virginia Rails lay one egg per day until the clutch of 6 to 13, usually 8 to 10 eggs is complete (Harrison 1975). Most clutches are completed by mid-June, and reported incubation periods range from 13 to 22 days (Zimmerman 1977). The precocial young are covered with black down and leave the nest a few days after hatching (Kaufmann 1987). Chicks are able to feed themselves after their first week, but adults may continue to feed them for some time thereafter (Zimmerman 1977, Kaufmann 1987). The typical diet consists of worms, insects, slugs, snails, and small fish, as well as an occasional frog or small snake. Chicks can swim and dive at an early age (Harrison 1978) and are capable of flight at 6 to 7 weeks (Zimmerman 1977). Virginia Rails probably attempt only one brood in New Hampshire.

Typical calls include a series of "kid-ick" notes and a descending series of quacking sounds. A less common "kicker" call is more restricted to the breeding season (K. C. Elkins, pers. comm.). Virginia Rails usually respond well to tape-recorded vocalizations. They also respond to calls and recordings of other rails, especially Soras (Kibbe *in* Laughlin and Kibbe 1985, Andrle and Carroll 1988).

Virginia Rails may congregate in large marshes in early fall (Pospichal 1952 *in* Zimmerman 1977). Most migrate in early October, but a few linger and may overwinter (CBC data, SRS).

Historically, ornithologists considered the Virginia Rail a rare summer resident of New Hampshire (Allen 1909, Wright 1911, Forbush 1925a), but Forbush (1925a) acknowledged that it was more common than sightings suggested. There is no evidence of appreciable change in status over the past century.

Atlasers located only 2 nests: one containing young and one containing eggshell fragments. Most confirmations (78%) involved sightings of young. Robbins can attest to the difficulty of "confirming" the species. Several days and many hours of searching in two 20+ a (8+ ha) marshes, each of which supported 3 to 5 pairs of Virginia Rails, yielded many observations of agitated adult rails. Peeping sounds suggested nearby young, but may have come from the adults. An adult carrying a huge mouthful of food, scolding all the while, finally provided "confirmation."

Although the Atlas project documented Virginia Rails in all drainage basins, most records are from the southern half of the state. The concentration of records in Merrimack, Strafford, and Rockingham counties reflects both a high level of Atlas effort and a relatively high density of wetlands in southeastern New Hampshire. The Virginia Rail undoubtedly is more widespread than the Atlas map suggests. Specific surveys of potentially suitable wetlands will be needed to accurately assess the distribution and abundance of this species.

George C. Robbins

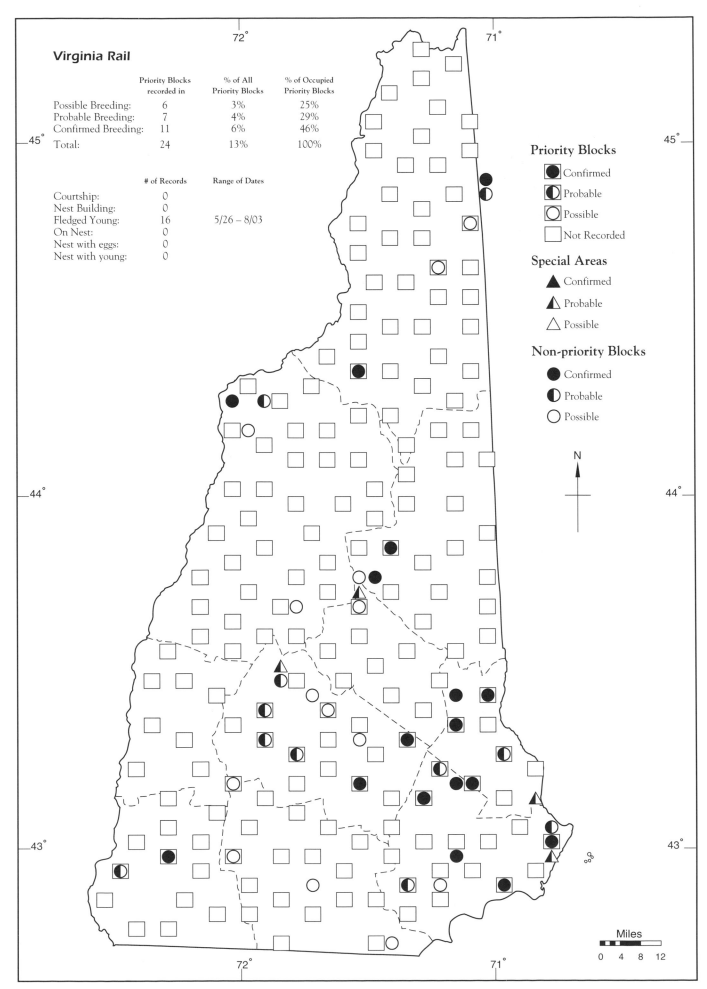

Virginia Rail

	Priority Blocks recorded in	% of All Priority Blocks	% of Occupied Priority Blocks
Possible Breeding:	6	3%	25%
Probable Breeding:	7	4%	29%
Confirmed Breeding:	11	6%	46%
Total:	24	13%	100%

	# of Records	Range of Dates
Courtship:	0	
Nest Building:	0	
Fledged Young:	16	5/26 – 8/03
On Nest:	0	
Nest with eggs:	0	
Nest with young:	0	

Priority Blocks
- Confirmed
- Probable
- Possible
- Not Recorded

Special Areas
- Confirmed
- Probable
- Possible

Non-priority Blocks
- Confirmed
- Probable
- Possible

N

Miles
0   4   8   12

73

Sora
Porzana carolina

The Sora is a plump, short-necked rail, with a conical yellow bill, and black face and chin patch. This species undoubtedly is more common than available data suggest, but because of its secretive nature and preferred habitat of almost impenetrable cattail marshes, it is seldom seen. Its distinctive "whinny" usually is the first clue to a Sora's presence. Soras arrive in New Hampshire by mid-May after a migration of up to 3,000 mi (5,000 km), belying their reputation as weak fliers. Once on the breeding grounds, however, they are extremely reluctant to fly and escape from danger by running through dense emergent vegetation.

Soras often feed along edges of channels and other openings, flicking their tails as they walk along plucking food from the water's surface (Sykes *in* Farrand 1983). Seeds comprise 73% of their diet, which also includes mollusks, crustaceans, and aquatic insects (Horak 1970).

Territorial behavior is little known (Ripley 1977), but probably consists largely of vocalizations. In early spring Soras utter a plaintive rising "er-we" (Terres 1980). Broadcast recordings of their descending whinny song sometimes draw Soras to an observer's feet (Turner, M. J. Murray, pers. obs.). Soras may vocalize in response to broadcast calls of other marsh birds (C.R. Foss, pers. comm.) or loud noises, such as hand clapping or the slamming of a car door (Sykes *in* Farrand 1983) or the splash of a stone thrown into the marsh (Forbush 1912, Walkinshaw 1940). The courtship display includes a posture with head lowered, body feathers fluffed, and tail feathers spread.

Soras first appear in New Hampshire in mid-April, and migration peaks during the first 3 weeks of May (Elkins 1982; RNEB, *passim*). Nesting begins about 2.5 weeks after arrival on the breeding grounds (Pospichal 1952). Soras build a small basket nest of dry grasses and dead cattail leaves, typically concealing it with overarching vegetation. The nest usually is located at least 6 in (15 cm) above fairly deep water and mud (Harrison 1975). Soras may construct nest "pyres" 17 to 19 in (42 to 48 cm) high to overcome flooding (Billard 1948 *in* Ripley 1977). A pathway or raised "gangway" often leads to the nest (Ripley 1977). Although empty Sora and Virginia Rail nests are nearly indistinguishable, the Sora typically nests over deeper water than the Virginia Rail and builds a more substantial nest; Sora eggs are glossier and more colorful than those of the Virginia Rail (Harrison 1975).

Eggs may number 4 to 17; dates reported for Massachusetts range from 20 May to 11 June (Forbush 1925a). Both sexes incubate, beginning after the first few eggs are laid. The incubation period lasts 16 to 20 days (Harrison 1978), depending on the size of the clutch. One adult often broods hatched chicks on a nearby platform or "dummy nest" while the other continues incubating (Skutch 1979). The juvenal plumage is browner than the adult, and lacks the black face and throat. Wright (1911) cites 2 immatures observed on the shore of Cherry Pond, Jefferson, with an adult calling nearby on 29 June 1910, and White (1937) mentions young observed in Concord in July. Sora families in Michigan left breeding marshes for other feeding areas by mid-July, a few weeks after hatching (Walkinshaw 1940), but the age at first flight is unknown (Terres 1980). Soras concentrate in marshes with abundant seeds during late summer and early fall, and most migrate before the first hard frost in late September or early October (Walkinshaw 1940, Odum 1977, Terres 1980).

In the late 1800s and early 1900s, Soras were considered uncommon and local in New Hampshire (Allen 1903, Forbush 1925a). Samuels (1867) suspected that they may have been more abundant in suitable habitat than people realized. Dearborn (1898) makes no mention of Soras even occurring in Belknap and Merrimack counties, and Dearborn (1903) had no evidence of nesting in the vicinity of Durham. However, they were fairly common at one time in backwaters of the Merrimack River in Concord (Moulton *in* White 1937).

In the early 1900s, Soras experienced tremendous hunting pressure during fall migration, with hundreds commonly taken in a day on the salt marshes of Massachusetts and Connecticut (Forbush 1925a). A few hunters still seek them in Massachusetts, but the current harvest appears to be insignificant (Odum 1977).

A Nottingham marsh of 90 to 100 a (36 to 40 ha) supports at least 2 Sora pairs along with several Virginia Rails and one pair of Pied-billed Grebes, but other marshes supporting Soras, in Rochester, Bedford, and Tilton, are only a few acres in extent. The only "confirmed" Atlas record was from the marsh in Nottingham, where a black, downy young skittered across an opening in the marsh toward an adult giving an alarm call on 20 July 1985. The "keek" alarm note was noticeably higher in pitch than the similar note of the Virginia Rail (T. Arter, L. Harper, and M. J. Murray, pers. comm.).

Further surveys of suitable habitat probably would produce additional records from many areas of New Hampshire. In the North Country, observers have found Soras in extensive marshes in Errol and Dummer since the Atlas Project (C.R. Foss, pers. comm.).

Fluctuating water levels in marshes regulated by dams, and habitat loss from dredging or filling may have adversely affected Soras in some areas. A significant loss of wild rice and extensive marsh drainage for mosquito control along the Atlantic Flyway have reduced available food during migration (Ripley 1977). Adequate understanding of Sora distribution and abundance in New Hampshire awaits further field research.

Sandra B. Turner

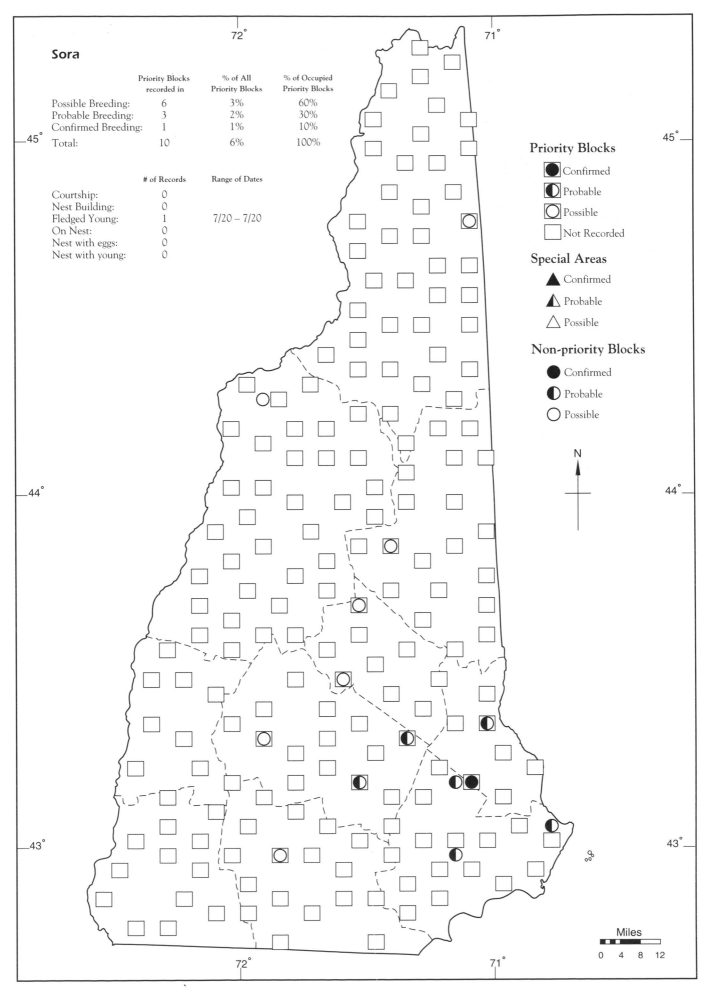

Sora

	Priority Blocks recorded in	% of All Priority Blocks	% of Occupied Priority Blocks
Possible Breeding:	6	3%	60%
Probable Breeding:	3	2%	30%
Confirmed Breeding:	1	1%	10%
Total:	10	6%	100%

	# of Records	Range of Dates
Courtship:	0	
Nest Building:	0	
Fledged Young:	1	7/20 – 7/20
On Nest:	0	
Nest with eggs:	0	
Nest with young:	0	

Priority Blocks

- Confirmed
- Probable
- Possible
- Not Recorded

Special Areas

- Confirmed
- Probable
- Possible

Non-priority Blocks

- Confirmed
- Probable
- Possible

N

Miles
0 4 8 12

Common Moorhen
Gallinula chloropus

The Common Moorhen is a secretive member of the rail family that readily swims and dives like a duck, for which it is often mistaken. It also resembles barnyard fowl, as the name *Gallinula*, which means "little hen," suggests. This bird long has been known as Moorhen in Britain, where it truly is common. In New Hampshire it is neither common nor found on moors. The earlier common names of Florida Gallinule and Common Gallinule were equally inappropriate here. The North American range includes the eastern U.S. from southern Maine to Florida west to southern Minnesota and eastern Texas, and the southwest from California to southern New Mexico, and extends down both coasts of Mexico.

The gray adult moorhen has a red, chickenlike bill with a yellow tip and a red frontal plate that extends onto the forehead. The juvenile's bill is brownish. The white undertail coverts are conspicuous. This bird walks and climbs in marsh vegetation as deftly as a rail. In swimming, it bobs its head forward and backward much like the closely related coot. It is somewhat less secretive than the rails, and often swims in open water.

On their home marshes moorhens appear to be weak flyers, but on long overland flights they travel directly and fairly swiftly, with heads and feet extended (Bent 1926). They are noisy during the breeding season, with an extensive vocabulary of henlike calls too numerous to describe here.

Moorhens breed in shallow ponds or deep marshes with extensive areas of dense emergent vegetation interspersed with open pools and channels. Sewage lagoons have supported successful pairs in New Hampshire. Suitable marshes are scarce in this state, which is near the northern edge of the breeding range, and the species always has been rare here.

Migrants may begin to appear in New Hampshire wetlands as early as 18 April, and sightings continue into the third week of May (SRS). Courtship begins on migration (Strohmeyer 1977) and continues after the birds arrive on their breeding marshes in late April or in May. The males swim in rapid circles around the females, displaying their red bills and shields and white undertail coverts, partly raising their wings and fanning their tails, and calling "ticket-ticket-ticket" (Brewster 1891, Bent 1926).

The moorhen's nest is usually close to water in dense vegetation. It consists of heaps of cattail stalks or other coarse plant stems with a shallow hollow in the center. Built either over water or on a small hummock in the marsh, it often has a sloping ramp or runway leading to the water (Harrison 1975). Additional platforms built nearby are used for mating, roosting, loafing, and brooding the young. Both sexes build the nest and share incubation, which takes 19 to 22 days (Harrison 1978). The usual clutch is 10 to 12 eggs, but as with other precocial birds predation is high; often only 2 or 3 chicks survive.

The downy young are black, like young rails, but have red skin at the base of their bills (Bent 1926). They may stay in the nest a few days or leave soon after hatching. Both parents brood and feed the young. Common foods are dragonfly and mayfly nymphs (Fredrickson 1971). The chicks become independent at about 5 weeks of age, and can fly at 6 or 7 weeks (Harrison 1978). Fall migration occurs mainly in September and October, but stragglers occasionally stay into December (SRS).

The first New Hampshire Common Moorhen record is of an immature bird taken at Rollinsford some years before 1902 (Dearborn 1903). Goodhue (1922) knew of an individual collected in Concord on an unspecified date. T. Richards (pers. comm.) first confirmed nesting in July 1960, with the observation of a family of 2 adults and at least 6 young on a small pond in Portsmouth. In 1962 he observed a single bird in a cattail marsh in Concord, where other observers later saw an adult with 3 young. Frequent breeding season sightings at an Exeter wetland throughout the 1970s strongly suggest nesting there. Single individuals seen at Cherry Pond, Jefferson, in late May and again in August and September 1962, and at Pontook Reservoir, Dummer, on 30 June 1962, were perhaps the first breeding season records for the White Mountain region and North Country, respectively (NHAQ *passim*).

In the U.S. as a whole, moorhens are said to be declining in numbers, owing to loss of habitat (Strohmeyer 1977). The observations noted above suggest that the birds were increasing and extending their range in New Hampshire in the 1960s. If this expansion has continued, it has been very slow. The pond where the first state breeding record occurred is no longer suitable habitat for the species, but Atlas workers "confirmed" breeding at marshes in Barrington, Concord, and Rochester, and observed pairs at sites in Rye and Exeter. Moorhens are less common in New Hampshire than in Vermont, where their range is mainly in the Champlain valley and almost entirely in western Vermont (Laughlin and Kibbe 1985). They are also rare breeders in Massachusetts (Veit and Petersen 1993) and in Maine (Adamus 1988), where their range extends well north of any known nesting localities in our state. Owing to its habitat requirements, the moorhen probably never will be a common breeding bird in New Hampshire, but it may become established as a regular breeder in a few suitable marshes.

Vera H. Hebert & Kimball C. Elkins

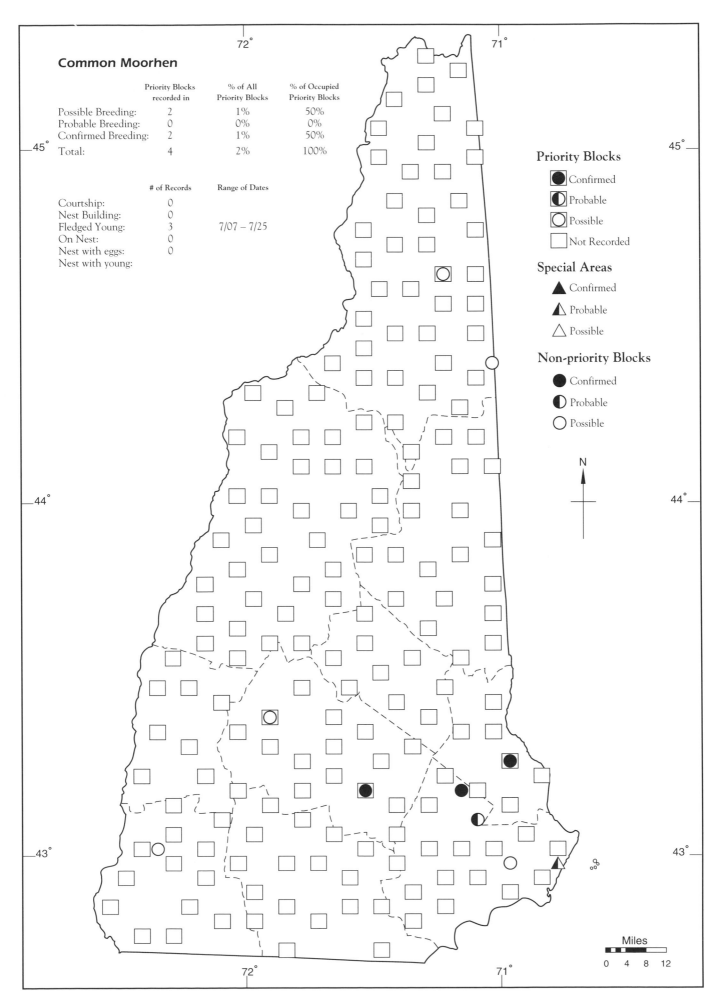

Common Moorhen

	Priority Blocks recorded in	% of All Priority Blocks	% of Occupied Priority Blocks
Possible Breeding:	2	1%	50%
Probable Breeding:	0	0%	0%
Confirmed Breeding:	2	1%	50%
Total:	4	2%	100%

	# of Records	Range of Dates
Courtship:	0	
Nest Building:	0	
Fledged Young:	3	7/07 – 7/25
On Nest:	0	
Nest with eggs:	0	
Nest with young:		

Priority Blocks
- ● Confirmed
- ◖ Probable
- ○ Possible
- □ Not Recorded

Special Areas
- ▲ Confirmed
- ◮ Probable
- △ Possible

Non-priority Blocks
- ● Confirmed
- ◖ Probable
- ○ Possible

N

Miles
0   4   8   12

Piping Plover
Charadrius melodus

This little beach bird is so near the color of the dry sand on which it makes its summer home that it would often go undetected if it were not for its mournful, whistled call. In breeding plumage the Piping Plover has a sometimes incomplete black breast band, a black bar across its forehead, and an orange bill with a black tip. In fall and winter the black areas are obscure or wanting, and the bill is dark.

Piping Plovers breed along the Atlantic Coast of North America from Newfoundland to South Carolina, and very locally on the Great Lakes and on the Great Plains (USFWS 1988b). A few arrive in New England in March, but most come in April, and they begin to depart in the latter half of July. Most are gone by mid-August, but some may remain into early October.

Piping Plovers leave their nesting habitat on dry sand to forage in the wet intertidal zone (Robbins 1919), feeding on insects, crustaceans, mollusks, and eggs of marine animals (Forbush 1912). Their principal foraging method is a short run, followed by a stop to look around.

Along the Atlantic Coast Piping Plovers nest on sandy beaches, barrier spits and islands, in open areas among sand dunes, and sometimes on dredge spoils (USFWS 1988b). Adults often return each year to the same nesting area (Harrison 1975, MacIver 1990). Nests typically are above the high-water mark along beaches and usually are closer to dunes or other vegetated areas than to the water (Burger 1987). Nests often are in flat areas with sand and gravel substrates littered with bits of shell (Burger 1987). On arrival males may fly circular formations over an area of beach to advertise their nesting territories, and may defend this area on the ground with aggressive horizontal threat displays and upright threat postures (Cairns 1982). Their common call resembles "peep, peep, peeplo." A territorial call is given on the wing (Tyler

1929). Nesting territories at a beach in Nova Scotia varied greatly in size, but averaged about an acre (0.4 ha). Distances between nests averaged 170 ft (52 m), but rarely were as small as 10 ft (3 m) (Cairns 1982).

In courtship the male digs shallow scrapes in the sand, and may squat briefly in a number of them; both male and female may toss in bits of shell (Cairns 1982; L. MacIver, pers. comm.). The nest is a shallow scrape, sometimes lined with pieces of shell or small pebbles (Tyler 1929). The normal clutch is 4 eggs. The earliest New Hampshire date for a complete clutch is 30 April (ASNH data), although a nest with 3 eggs on 26 April (ASNH data) probably would have had 4 by the 27th or 28th. Incubation, by both sexes, takes 27 to 29 days (Cairns 1982). Piping Plovers raise only a single brood each year.

The earliest New Hampshire hatching date appears to be 31 May (Phinney 1968). Chicks leave the nest within a few hours of hatching, and seldom return. They typically remain in or near the nesting territory until they can fly at about 30 days of age (Wilcox 1959). During this period they forage for themselves (Tyler 1929), but their parents guard and brood them (Wilcox 1959, Cairns 1982). Adults attempt to lead an approaching predator away from their chicks by feigning injury (Forbush 1925a). After fledging, Piping Plovers may form loose flocks with other individuals raised on the same beach (Robbins 1919).

Piping Plovers presumably nested on New Hampshire beaches prior to the present century (Richards 1954), for they once were common, even abundant, all along the New England coast (Samuels 1870, Forbush 1912). In the late 1800s, sport and market shooting decimated populations of Piping Plovers and many other shorebirds. By 1900 they were known in New Hampshire only as migrants (Dearborn 1903). The population began to recover after legal protection by the Migratory Bird Treaty Act in 1919. By the 1920s the Piping Plover was "fast becoming again a common local summer resident coastwise" in New England (Forbush 1925a). White (1927) saw young Piping Plovers in Seabrook on 9 July 1926. In 1928 he saw 9 adults there on 26 June and found a nest with 4 eggs on 1 July, and chicks on 19 July (White 1929). After an apparent absence of many years, the species again nested near the mouth of the Hampton River, Hampton, in the 1950s and 1960s, with as many as 12 adults present in 1957 (Hebert 1957). The most recent record of eggs or young is from 1971, but Piping Plovers have occurred at Seabrook irregularly since that time, primarily during spring and late summer (SRS). Observers witnessed a pair of Piping Plovers performing a distraction display there on 12 May 1984, which suggested a nest, but failed to find the birds again after a very high tide that night (NHBBA data).

The Piping Plover has declined throughout its range during the past 20 years and has been on the *American Birds* Blue List since 1973. The USFWS lists the Atlantic Coast population as threatened (USFWS 1988b), and the NHFG lists the species as Endangered. Habitat loss, human disturbance, and increasing predation are contributing causes. Protection of nesting areas has produced recent population gains in New England (A. Hecht, USFWS, pers. comm.).

The New Hampshire beach that once supported nesting Piping Plovers now receives heavy recreational use. Intensive management will be needed to protect any Piping Plovers that attempt to nest there in the future.

Kimball C. Elkins

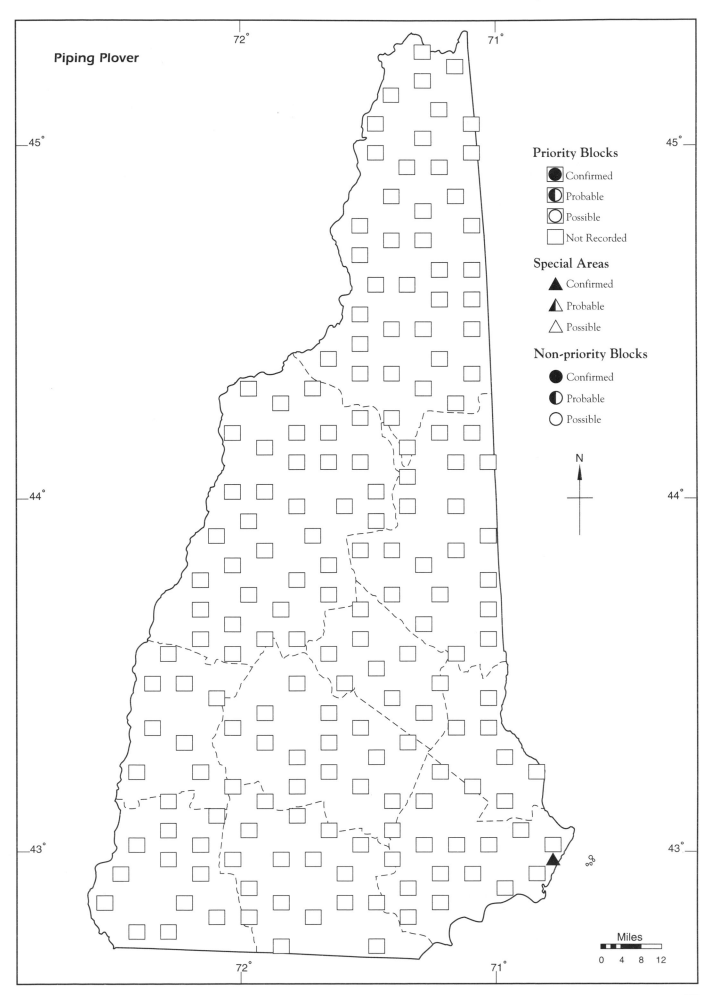

Piping Plover

Priority Blocks

● Confirmed
◑ Probable
○ Possible
□ Not Recorded

Special Areas

▲ Confirmed
◭ Probable
△ Possible

Non-priority Blocks

● Confirmed
◐ Probable
○ Possible

N

Miles
0 4 8 12

Killdeer

Charadrius vociferus

The Killdeer is a plover that has adapted to living away from shores. As its scientific name suggests, it is a very noisy bird, and its propensity for living in areas of human activity makes it easy to observe. It is most often seen running over open ground, and the 2 conspicuous black neck bands against its snowy white breast leave no doubt as to its identity. Of the few shorebirds that nest in New Hampshire, this is the best known.

Killdeer breed from Alaska and the southern half of Canada to northern Mexico. They winter primarily in the southern states, the West Indies, and Central America, but small numbers winter further north along the coast.

Killdeer commonly arrive in New Hampshire in March or early April. If most of the ground is still covered with snow, they cruise over the fields, calling "killdee, killdee," while searching for a bare patch on which to alight. When conditions permit, courtship begins promptly after the pair's arrival on the breeding territory and may last as long as 6 weeks (Townsend 1929, Lenington 1980). The male spreads his wings to display the cinnamon color on his rump and tail and makes long flights, often high in the air, while calling loudly. Often the female joins these flights. In this season the flight calls of Killdeer often are audible at night.

For nesting, which begins in April, Killdeer must have open land and bare ground or sparse or very short vegetation. Cultivated fields, pastures, golf courses, athletic fields, cemeteries, lawns, and parking lots all are suitable. The birds will tolerate considerable disturbance, as evidenced by a nest found in New Jersey between the rails of a railroad track over which trains passed at least twice a day (Stone 1937). In New Hampshire and elsewhere these birds sometimes nest on flat, gravel-covered roofs. Each pair defends both a nesting territory and one or more feeding territories (Lenington 1980).

The nest itself is a mere hollow in the soil or gravel that may be surrounded with pebbles, bits of wood, or weed stalks. There are almost always 4 eggs. Although totally unconcealed, the eggs blend in with their background. Both sexes incubate for a total of 24 to 26 days (Harrison 1975). Early nests may be subjected to wintry weather. An April storm in Michigan buried a nest containing 2 eggs under 6 in (15 cm) of snow. The female brushed the snow away and subsequently laid 2 more eggs to complete the clutch (Nickell 1943). Many nests are destroyed by predators or accidentally, but Killdeer will renest as many as 3 times, if necessary (Nickell 1943). Killdeer sometimes raise 2 broods in a season.

When a potential predator enters a Killdeer's nesting territory, the incubating bird usually will slip quietly off the nest and run away, but if the intruder comes close to the eggs, a parent may return and put on a distraction display or broken wing act. Killdeer regularly give this spectacular display when the chicks are threatened, often succeeding in luring the predator away.

Newly hatched chicks remain at the nest site overnight, but leave within 24 hours, even if they hatched on high rooftops (Pickwell 1925). Usually the adults lead the chicks to a feeding territory, which includes dense herbaceous vegetation where they can hide (Lenington 1980). The young can fly at ages variously reported as 29 to about 40 days (Harrison 1978, Lenington 1980). The families subsequently disband within 3 or 4 days (Lenington 1980).

Flocks of Killdeer often travel together in late summer, when they occur on beaches and shores more than in other seasons. Most leave New Hampshire in September and October, but often some remain into November and rarely a few winter along the coast.

The Killdeer probably was fairly common in New Hampshire in the first half of the 19th century (Forbush 1912, Griscom and Snyder 1955). Belknap (1792) included the "Killdee" on his list of New Hampshire birds, and Dearborn (1903) provided evidence that Killdeer nested regularly in southeastern New Hampshire within the memory of his generation. The Killdeer had become rare here by soon after 1850, presumably for the same reason as in Massachusetts, where shooting nearly exterminated the species (Forbush 1912). Allen (1903) listed the Killdeer as "formerly a rare migrant" in New Hampshire and referred to records from Rye in August 1868 and August 1871 and a specimen from Jefferson in December 1893. He also mentioned the great flight of 1888-89, when large numbers arrived at the Isles of Shoals and other New England coastal locations during a big storm in November, with some remaining into February.

In the Merrimack Valley, the Killdeer was rare in the breeding season as recently as the 1930s, and nested in Concord in 1916, 1936, and 1937 (Goodhue 1922, White 1937). Since then this species has increased enormously because of protective laws and its remarkable adaptability, despite a decrease in apparently suitable habitat. BBS data from 1966 to 1984 show a continuing increase in Killdeer numbers in New Hampshire through 1979, but lower numbers in the 1980s.

Today, the Killdeer breeds in most areas with suitable habitat south of the White Mountains, where the Atlas project produced records for all but 20 priority blocks. It is nearly absent as a nesting bird in the White Mountains, where little suitable habitat exists, and is very local in the North Country, where open land is limited.

Kimball C. Elkins

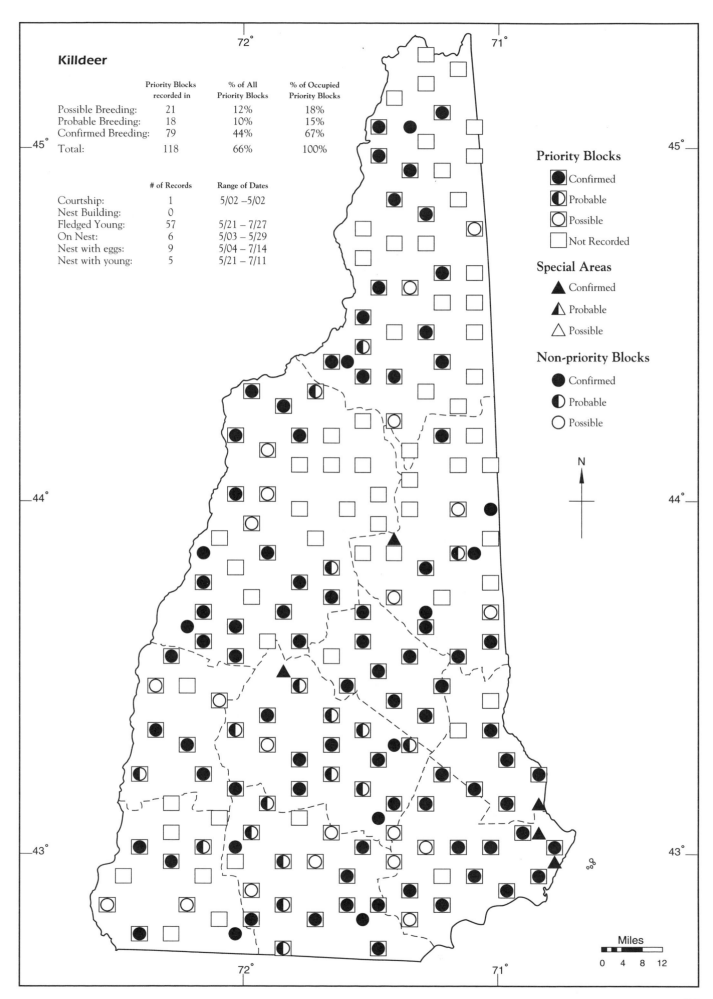

Killdeer

	Priority Blocks recorded in	% of All Priority Blocks	% of Occupied Priority Blocks
Possible Breeding:	21	12%	18%
Probable Breeding:	18	10%	15%
Confirmed Breeding:	79	44%	67%
Total:	118	66%	100%

	# of Records	Range of Dates
Courtship:	1	5/02 –5/02
Nest Building:	0	
Fledged Young:	57	5/21 – 7/27
On Nest:	6	5/03 – 5/29
Nest with eggs:	9	5/04 – 7/14
Nest with young:	5	5/21 – 7/11

Priority Blocks

● Confirmed
◐ Probable
○ Possible
□ Not Recorded

Special Areas

▲ Confirmed
◭ Probable
△ Possible

Non-priority Blocks

● Confirmed
◖ Probable
○ Possible

N

Miles
0   4   8   12

Willet

Catoptrophorus semipalmatus

Willets, while rather nondescript when standing quietly on tidal mud flats, are unmistakable in flight over bays and salt marshes with their striking black and white wing pattern. When their wings are closed, Willets can be distinguished from the similar Greater Yellowlegs by their thicker bills and gray legs. Willets are noisy on the breeding grounds, typically giving triple "wek" or "ker-wek" calls and occasionally a whistled "pill-will-willet."

This large, grayish brown shorebird only recently has expanded its range into New Hampshire, probably from newly reestablished populations in coastal Massachusetts or southern Maine. To date, Willets are known to nest only in Hampton and Seabrook, where they frequent coastal salt marshes, shallow salt ponds and exposed mud flats, sand bars, and tidal creek banks.

Willets arrive in New Hampshire salt marshes in late April or the first half of May and probably pair and begin nesting by late May to early June. Each pair defends an exclusive feeding territory, but bathes and loafs with other Willets on exposed tidal plats (Howe 1982). Willets often engage in aerial chases on their breeding grounds, and hold their wings open and straight up after landing. Before mating, males may stand behind the females waving their wings above their backs, and continuously giving ternlike calls (J. T. Nichols *in* Bent 1929).

New Hampshire Willets currently nest in salt marshes, perhaps for lack of suitable alternatives. Other known nesting habitats include shrubby islands, dunes, beaches, and upland fields (Forbush 1925a, Bent 1929). The first documented New Hampshire nest was amid a loose colony of Common Terns in Hampton on 21 June 1987 (Gavutis, pers. obs.). The site was on a slightly elevated expanse of *Spartina patens* near a tidal creek and several large salt pannes. The nest was a hollow in the marsh litter, similar to many nests found in New Jersey (Gavutis, pers. obs.). Residual cover from the previous year as well as new growth provided a canopy. A pair of adult Willets scolding intensely overhead suggested the presence of young nearby.

Willets typically lay 4 eggs and may begin shared incubation before the clutch is complete. Asynchronous hatching occurs after 22 to 29 days (Harrison 1975). Both adults tend the brood for 2 to 3 weeks, after which the female departs, and the male remains with the young for at least another 2 weeks (Howe 1982).

Like most shorebirds, Willets are very solicitous of their young. In June and July, adults vigorously protest intrusions into their territory by pedestrians or even boats. Incessantly calling, an adult rises from the marsh and flies directly at the intruder, then veers off at close range, often hovering effortlessly in the wind. Close approach to a hidden chick often instigates a distraction display (Gavutis, pers. obs.). The Willet may move its young one at a time by grasping a chick between its thighs and flying up to 0.24 mi (0.4 km) across channels and bays (Wayne 1910).

Willets forage primarily on exposed mud flats and sand bars, eating aquatic insects, marine worms, fiddler crabs and other small crabs, mollusks, fish, and some vegetable matter, such as grasses, tender roots, and seeds (Bent 1929). In New Hampshire, a popular feeding area is on the Blackwater River south of Rt. 286 in Seabrook, where up to 6 birds were flying back and forth on 25 June 1983 during 2 hours at low tide (Gavutis, pers. obs.).

Most New Hampshire Willets depart by late August (Gavutis, pers. obs.). A few September records exist for New Hampshire, the latest of which is for 28 September 1958 at Rye Harbor (RNEB, *passim*).

Little is known of the Willet's historical presence in New Hampshire. These birds formerly nested along the Atlantic Coast from Nova Scotia to Florida, but market and sport hunting and egg consumption extirpated the species from New England by the late 1800s. Substantial numbers of fall migrants still occurred in New England in the early 1900s (Forbush 1925a, Bent 1929). With passage of the Migratory Bird Treaty Act in 1918 the Willet began a slow recovery, which continues to this day.

Observers suspected breeding here in the early 1980s, when a few territorial adults were present along the New Hampshire coast between Rye and Seabrook, especially near Hampton Harbor. On 18 July 1985 a week-old chick along the Blackwater River, Seabrook, near 4 vociferous territorial pairs, provided the first confirmation of breeding in New Hampshire (Gavutis, pers. obs.). Two recently fledged and weakly flying young further "confirmed" breeding north of Rt. 152, Hampton, on 23 July 1985 (Gavutis, pers. obs.).

The Willet population is still expanding, and additional pairs may become established in the Hampton estuary and possibly elsewhere on the coast. New Hampshire is unlikely to sustain a large Willet population due to limited habitat and human encroachment.

George W. Gavutis, Jr.

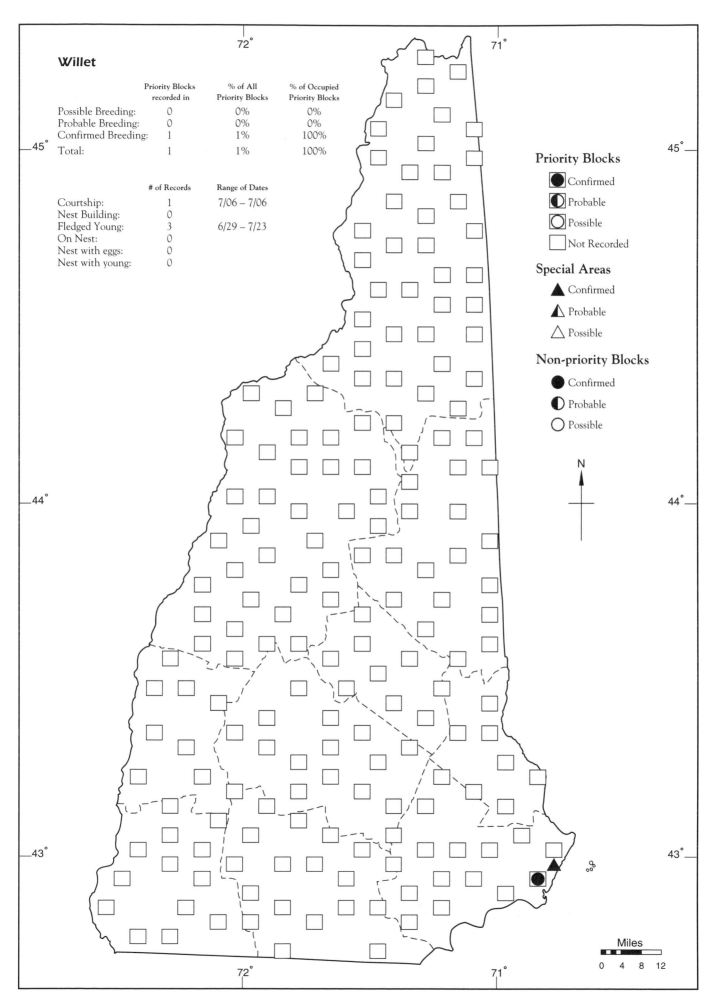

Willet

	Priority Blocks recorded in	% of All Priority Blocks	% of Occupied Priority Blocks
Possible Breeding:	0	0%	0%
Probable Breeding:	0	0%	0%
Confirmed Breeding:	1	1%	100%
Total:	1	1%	100%

	# of Records	Range of Dates
Courtship:	1	7/06 – 7/06
Nest Building:	0	
Fledged Young:	3	6/29 – 7/23
On Nest:	0	
Nest with eggs:	0	
Nest with young:	0	

Priority Blocks
- ● Confirmed
- ◐ Probable
- ○ Possible
- □ Not Recorded

Special Areas
- ▲ Confirmed
- ◤ Probable
- △ Possible

Non-priority Blocks
- ● Confirmed
- ◐ Probable
- ○ Possible

N

Miles
0   4   8   12

Spotted Sandpiper
Actitis macularia

The Spotted Sandpiper bobs its tail, then teeters its way along New Hampshire shorelines. This species occurs along lakeshores, riverbanks, and pond edges, breeding from sea level to at least 3,000 ft (915 m) elevation in the White Mountains (T. Richards, unpubl. data). Allen (1903) observed this species at about 3,100 ft (950 m) elevation on Mt. Washington on 8 July 1886, and Richards (unpubl. data) has found it at the same elevation at Norcross Pond, Lincoln.

Returning from Brazil, Central America, or perhaps as nearby as South Carolina, adult female "teeter-peeps" appear in late April or early May. They generally precede the males, which arrive throughout May (Oring and Lank 1982). In breeding plumage, both sexes have spotted, white breasts and brown upperparts. The female is slightly larger and more heavily spotted.

The female assumes the dominant role in the breeding cycle, both in maintaining territories and in initiating courtship. In courtship, after flying upward with vibrating wing strokes on stiffly held, bowed wings, she glides back to earth and fans her tail like a turkey for the benefit of a nearby male. The pair forms quickly, often within minutes (Oring and Knudsen 1972), although Shelley (1925) observed courtship which continued all afternoon. White (1937) observed a courtship performance in Concord on 14 May. The male becomes attached to a nest site, while a female may subsequently mate with up to 4 other males within her territory and lay additional clutches (Oring and Knudsen 1972, Hays 1972 *in* Johnsgard 1981, Johnsgard 1981).

The nest, which both female and male construct, is a depression in the ground lined with grasses and mosses. It may be located near the water's edge, or some distance away (Harrison 1975). It may be built beside a rotting log or overhanging rock, on open ground or in sparse vegetation. Atlasers discovered a nest with eggs in a sandy fallow field in Weare about 50 yd (45

m) from the Piscataquog River on 6 May 1985 (C.R. Foss, NHBBA data). Spotted Sandpipers have nested in colonies on small islands in Michigan (Johnsgard 1981).

The usual clutch is of 4 eggs, but 3 or 5 occasionally occur (Harrison 1975). Brewster (1925) wrote that at Umbagog Lake, eggs usually were laid during the last week in May. Four nests found in southern New Hampshire during the Atlas period had egg dates ranging from 6 May through 17 June. Males usually incubate, but a female may assist in incubating her final clutch if multiple clutches are involved (Harrison 1978). The incubation period is 20 to 24 days (Hays 1972).

Adults typically perform injury-feigning distraction displays from the laying of the second egg until the chicks leave the nest, although some Spotted Sandpipers do not display at all (Miller and Miller 1948). New Hampshire Atlas observers reported distraction displays from 11 June to 26 July. Spotted Sandpipers apparently require open ground without entangling vegetation for these displays (Skutch 1979).

Spotted Sandpiper chicks have white undersides and are light buff above with a dark band running over the backs of their heads and down the middle of their backs. As soon as their down dries, they are off and "teetering." Sometimes both parents tend the young, but often the male broods them alone. In Concord, White (1937) observed young with a pair of adults on 2 June 1934 and with a single adult on 7 July 1928. Most "confirmations" were based on sightings of young, despite their tendency to hide from danger by lying motionless on the ground (Tyler 1929; Turner, pers. obs.).

The brood scatters after 13 to 18 days, when the young begin to fly (Stout 1967, Harrison 1978, Johnsgard 1981). Winter plumage for adults and juveniles includes unspotted white underparts and duller bill and leg coloration. Buffy bars on the wing coverts of the juveniles are conspicuous (Farrand 1983).

Both adults and young can swim, dive, and run short distances along the bottom in shallow water (Forbush 1925a). T. Richards (pers. comm.) watched a Spotted Sandpiper escape 2 Peregrine Falcon attacks by diving into the water of a reservoir.

Along pond and stream edges, aquatic insects, crustaceans, and fish fry make up the bulk of this sandpiper's diet. In Durham, Rochester, and Alton, Spotted Sandpipers have searched for food among the algae in water coursing over dams (M. Davis and Turner, pers. obs.). Although one usually associates Spotted Sandpipers with water, they also forage in tilled fields, where they feed on grasshoppers, crickets, caterpillars, grubs, beetles, and occasionally flying insects, which they catch by snapping them out of the air (Terres 1980).

Historical writings suggest that the Spotted Sandpiper may have decreased somewhat in New Hampshire over the course of the past century. Samuels (1867) considered the species abundant in New England, and Dearborn (1898) described it as abundant in Belknap and Merrimack counties. Authors in the early 1900s found it "rather common" (Allen 1903, Wright 1911), but White (1937) described it as a "summer resident in small numbers" in the vicinity of Concord.

The Atlas map illustrates a widespread but local distribution in New Hampshire at the present time. The Spotted Sandpiper was one of only 10 species "confirmed" at the Isles of Shoals, where it has nested for many years (Jackson 1947, Borror 1980). Lack of public access to some ponds and lakes in southern New Hampshire may account for an apparent gap in evidence of breeding there. However, since shoreline development can adversely affect habitat availability and nesting success, this species bears watching in the years ahead.

Sandra B. Turner

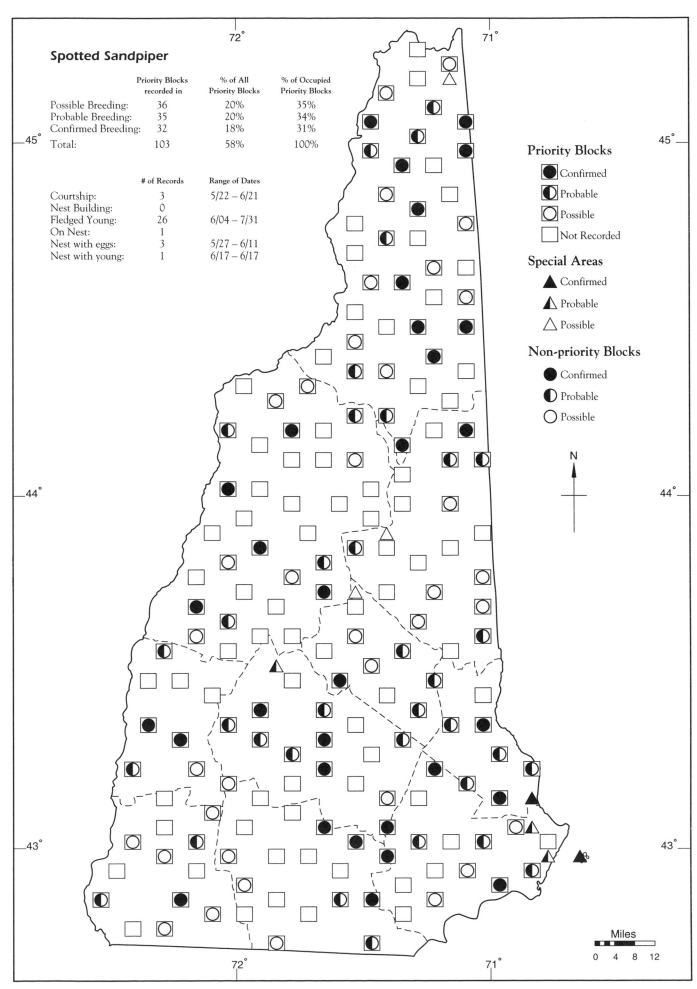

Spotted Sandpiper

	Priority Blocks recorded in	% of All Priority Blocks	% of Occupied Priority Blocks
Possible Breeding:	36	20%	35%
Probable Breeding:	35	20%	34%
Confirmed Breeding:	32	18%	31%
Total:	103	58%	100%

	# of Records	Range of Dates
Courtship:	3	5/22 – 6/21
Nest Building:	0	
Fledged Young:	26	6/04 – 7/31
On Nest:	1	
Nest with eggs:	3	5/27 – 6/11
Nest with young:	1	6/17 – 6/17

Priority Blocks

● Confirmed
◐ Probable
○ Possible
□ Not Recorded

Special Areas

▲ Confirmed
◣ Probable
△ Possible

Non-priority Blocks

● Confirmed
◐ Probable
○ Possible

N

Miles
0 4 8 12

Upland Sandpiper
Bartramia longicauda

Perched on a fence post, the Upland Sandpiper is unmistakable with its long legs and neck, small head, and short bill. The long wings are bowed stiffly in flight and held erect briefly after landing. This upland shorebird inhabits extensive grasslands and prairies. A loosely colonial species, it breeds from the northeastern U. S. and adjacent Canada west to the limits of the prairies (Robbins et al. 1986), and winters on the pampas of South America and in Surinam (White 1988).

Arriving in New Hampshire in mid-April, migrating Upland Sandpipers forage in large fields, especially in major river valleys and near the coast. White (1937) reported late April arrivals in Concord of individuals, pairs, and groups of up to 6. An apparent pair arrived on breeding grounds in Haverhill by 9 May in 1982 (R. Bradley and E. A. Emery, pers. comm.).

The Upland Sandpiper is conspicuous on arrival, uttering mellow, drawn out whistles and giving a variety of mournful liquid notes and trills while flying low on vibrating wings (Farrand 1983, Kibbe *in* Laughlin and Kibbe 1985). During courtship, the male struts with tail cocked, wings dragging, and throat puffed out (Todd 1940). Courtship flights involve vocalizing while soaring high in slow circles, then plummeting to earth with closed wings (Pierce *in* Bent 1929). The distinctive "wolf whistle" given during these flights is audible over long distances.

Upland Sandpipers sometimes forage in plowed and recently planted fields, especially on wet days (Foss, pers. obs.), but typically avoid tilled croplands for nesting (Kirsch and Higgins 1976). Preferred nesting habitat consists of grassy areas with little disturbance and vegetation 6 to 24 in (15 to 60 cm) tall (Higgins et al. 1969, Kirsch and Higgins 1976, Westemeier 1989).

Nest construction begins 14 to 20 days after arrival, and may continue into late June (Buss and Hawkins 1939, Higgins and Kirsch 1975, Westemeier 1989). The nest, well hidden in a shallow depression, consists of grass twisted into a neat circular cup, with vegetation arched over the top (Bent 1929). First nests usually are synchronized closely in mid to late May; renesting may occur if the initial clutch is lost (Buss and Hawkins 1939, Higgins and Kirsch 1975). Adults circle overhead if disturbed at the nest, giving an alarm call ("quip-ip-ip-ip"), and distract intruders by fluttering off with wings dragging; once young hatch, their parents may swoop near an intruder, calling anxiously (Todd 1940).

Both sexes incubate the single clutch of 4 (occasionally 3 or 5) eggs for 21 to 28 days. Eggs in a clutch hatch within 24 to 72 hours of one another, and adults usually carry off the empty shells (Higgins and Kirsch 1975). White (1937) observed a nest in Concord in 1934 in which one egg hatched on 7 June and another the next day, and saw recently hatched broods on 14 and 20 June and 31 July. Observers in North Haverhill documented adults with young on 12 June 1979 and 22 July 1983, and 3 young accompanied an adult at the Manchester Airport on 9 and 15 July 1979 (SRS).

Both parents tend the precocial young until they are fully grown at about 30 days (Harrison 1978). Juvenal plumage resembles the adult's but is darker above and deeper buff below, with less distinct streaking (Forbush 1925a). Migrants begin to appear at Pease Air Force Base, Newington/Portsmouth in mid-July, and nearly all depart by the end of August (Overtree et al. 1989, Foss and DeLuca 1990, DeLuca 1991). These birds forage on the ground, walking deliberately or running in short spurts, then stopping to pick up insects (Forbush 1912, Todd 1940).

After European settlement converted unbroken Eastern forests to extensive agricultural lands in the late 1700s and early 1800s, the Upland Sandpiper population expanded eastward from the prairies (Bagg and Eliot 1937, Silver 1957). These birds became abundant migrants and locally common breeders in central and southern New Hampshire (Allen 1903), where their abundance probably peaked between 1860 and 1880 (Silver 1957). Market hunting dramatically reduced the population during the next several decades (Forbush 1912, 1925a, Silver 1957), and overshooting and conversion of prairies to agriculture nearly exterminated the species by 1920 (Harrison 1975). It was uncommon, rare, or absent in former New Hampshire breeding areas by the early 1900s (Allen 1903, Goodhue 1922, White 1937, Silver 1957). New Hampshire law protected Upland Sandpipers in 1909 (Silver 1957), and federal protection followed in 1916, which brought some increases during the 1920s (Kirsch and Higgins 1976). Although BBS data from 1966 to 1979 suggests a population increase in the Eastern region (Robbins et al. 1986), this sandpiper is Threatened in Vermont, Endangered in New Hampshire and Massachusetts, and a Species of Concern in New York. It has appeared on the *American Birds* Blue List since 1975. Habitat loss continues in the heart of the species' range (Kirsch and Higgins 1976, Westemeier 1989), as well as in the Northeast, and factors on the wintering grounds also may have negative impacts on the species (White 1988).

Atlas observers documented "probable" or "confirmed" breeding at Pease Air Force Base and in large fields in Newington, Rochester, Dover, and Haverhill. The species' future in New Hampshire seems tenuous. The best opportunities for continued survival here may exist at large airports, where habitat conversion is unlikely and mowing can be timed to protect nests.

Carol R. Foss

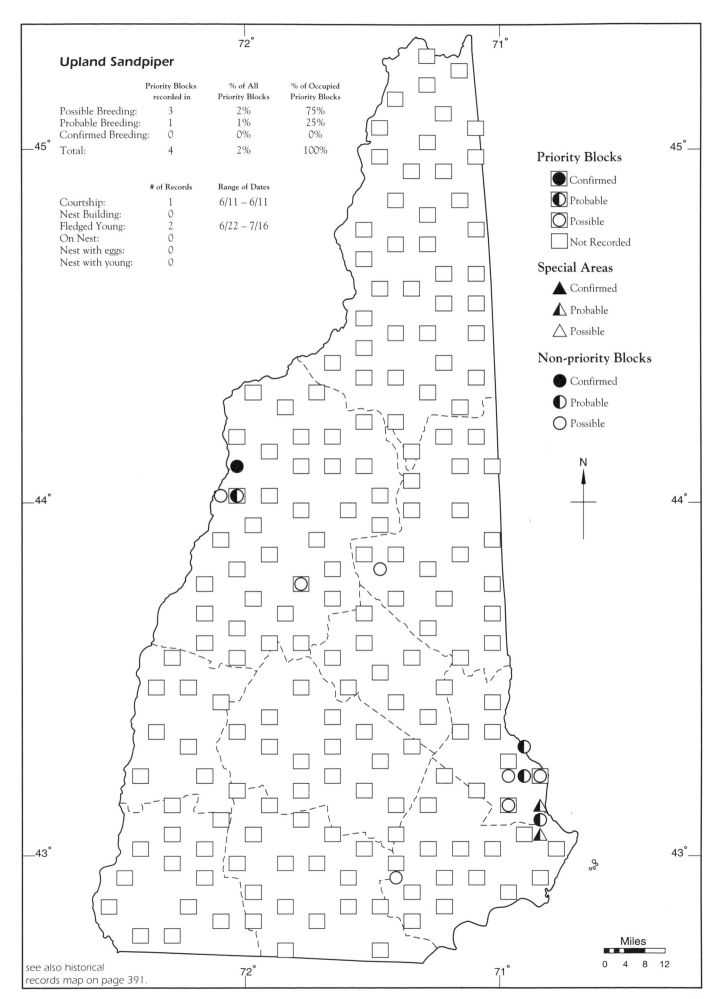

Upland Sandpiper

	Priority Blocks recorded in	% of All Priority Blocks	% of Occupied Priority Blocks
Possible Breeding:	3	2%	75%
Probable Breeding:	1	1%	25%
Confirmed Breeding:	0	0%	0%
Total:	4	2%	100%

	# of Records	Range of Dates
Courtship:	1	6/11 – 6/11
Nest Building:	0	
Fledged Young:	2	6/22 – 7/16
On Nest:	0	
Nest with eggs:	0	
Nest with young:	0	

Priority Blocks
- ● Confirmed
- ◐ Probable
- ○ Possible
- ☐ Not Recorded

Special Areas
- ▲ Confirmed
- ◭ Probable
- △ Possible

Non-priority Blocks
- ● Confirmed
- ◐ Probable
- ○ Possible

N

see also historical records map on page 391.

87

Common Snipe
Gallinago gallinago

The Common Snipe's winnowing flights over wetlands are among the most remarkable courtship and territorial performances of any North American bird. Like the woodcock, the snipe has an exceedingly long bill and cryptic coloration. Formerly called Wilson's Snipe, the Common Snipe currently is recognized as a subspecies of the Eurasian snipe, and is the only snipe native to North America.

Snipe breed in marshes, bogs, and wet meadows across northern Canada south to California and West Virginia, and winter from the southern part of the nesting range to Brazil (AOU 1957). Snipe are uncommon to locally common summer residents in northern and central New Hampshire, but are rare as breeders in southern sections.

Some snipe may return to New Hampshire as early as the third week of March, but most arrive in early to mid-April. At this time flocks of 15 to 30+ may occur in wet meadows in the southern part of the state (Richards, unpubl. data). Snipe move north when frost leaves the ground, males typically preceding females by a week or 2 (Bent 1927).

Their heavily striped brown plumage makes snipe difficult to spot. When foraging they probe deeply in the mud with their long, pliable bills in search of snails, worms, and insects. When flushed, usually at close range, snipe spring up quickly with erratic zigzags, giving harsh calls. On their breeding grounds males often perch on fence posts, tall dead stubs, and sometimes even in the tops of tall live trees, uttering a loud, measured "chip-a, chip-a, chip-a."

The spectacular courtship and territorial performance is generally given by the male but sometimes by both sexes at once (Terres 1980). Most often performed at dawn or dusk or on moonlit nights, winnowing may occur at any time when a female is present on the territory, including the middle of the day (Fogarty et al. 1977). The usual display consists of flights several

hundred feet in the air punctuated by deep undulations during which vibrating tail feathers produce loud, eerie winnowing sounds.

Males establish territories immediately after arrival, but winnowing intensifies when the females arrive (Fogarty et al. 1977). Snipe winnow throughout spring migration as well as during the nesting season (Bent 1927), and sometimes in the fall. Brewster (1924) observed winnowing at Umbagog Lake on 21 September 1894.

At the onset of pair formation, the male produces a "yakking" call while slowly dropping to the ground with wings held over his back and feet dangling. Once on the ground, he struts about (Fogarty et al. 1977). Just before copulation, the male struts before the female with tail spread and wings drooped on the ground (Gass 1891 *in* Bent 1927).

The female builds the nest of dried grasses and sometimes twigs, usually nestled in a relatively dry spot in the marsh (Terres 1980). She incubates her 4 eggs for 18 to 20 days. When disturbed from a nest with eggs or with young, a female snipe may feign injury (Kells 1906 and Sutton 1923 *in* Bent 1927). The parents feed the otherwise precocial young for about 10 days after hatching (Stout 1967). Young snipe make their first flights at about 15 days of age (Stout 1967).

Southbound snipe first appear in southern New Hampshire during late August and early September. Most depart by the end of October, though late migrants may be present in December; a few stragglers may linger into February, but apparently leave or succumb before spring (Elkins 1982).

Common Snipe nested in Massachusetts more than a century ago (Griscom 1949) and presumably nested in New Hampshire in the last century. Bent (1927) indicated that snipe formerly had been extremely abundant but that excessive shooting had depleted their populations over the previous 50 years. Brewster (1924) knew the species only as a migrant at Umbagog Lake in the period 1871–1909, and found them to be abundant in fall but rare in spring.

Following a totally closed season on snipe throughout the country in the years 1942–1953 and light hunting pressure since (Fogarty et al. 1977), Common Snipe appear to have made an extraordinary recovery and are again summer residents in New Hampshire. The first recent probable breeding record occurred in 1948, when D. Brainard (pers. comm.) observed one or more snipe several times at a site in Colebrook between 2 June and 7 July. Subsequently, H. R. Siegler reported a snipe at George Pond, Enfield on 18 July 1950 (Silver 1957).

On 6 July 1955, Richards observed a snipe calling and plummeting into Harper's Meadow near Umbagog Lake, Errol as if it had young, and Hebert (1956) located a pair with 2 to 4 young there in 1956. Subsequent summer records came from Pittsburg in 1957 (Hebert 1957); Dummer and Lancaster in 1962; and Canaan in 1966 (Richards, unpubl. data). Additional summer records gradually accumulated, especially in the North Country, where snipe have become well distributed and locally common in recent years.

As the Atlas map illustrates, the Common Snipe now is a fairly well-distributed summer resident in the wetlands of northern and west-central New Hampshire, but is still scarce or absent in summer from most of the southern part of the state. It is especially common in Harper's and Sweatt meadows and Leonard Marsh, Errol, as well as at Pontook Reservoir, Dummer (Richards, unpubl. data). It has not become an important game species in New Hampshire. With a further increase in southern New Hampshire likely, the species' future in the state seems secure.

Tudor Richards

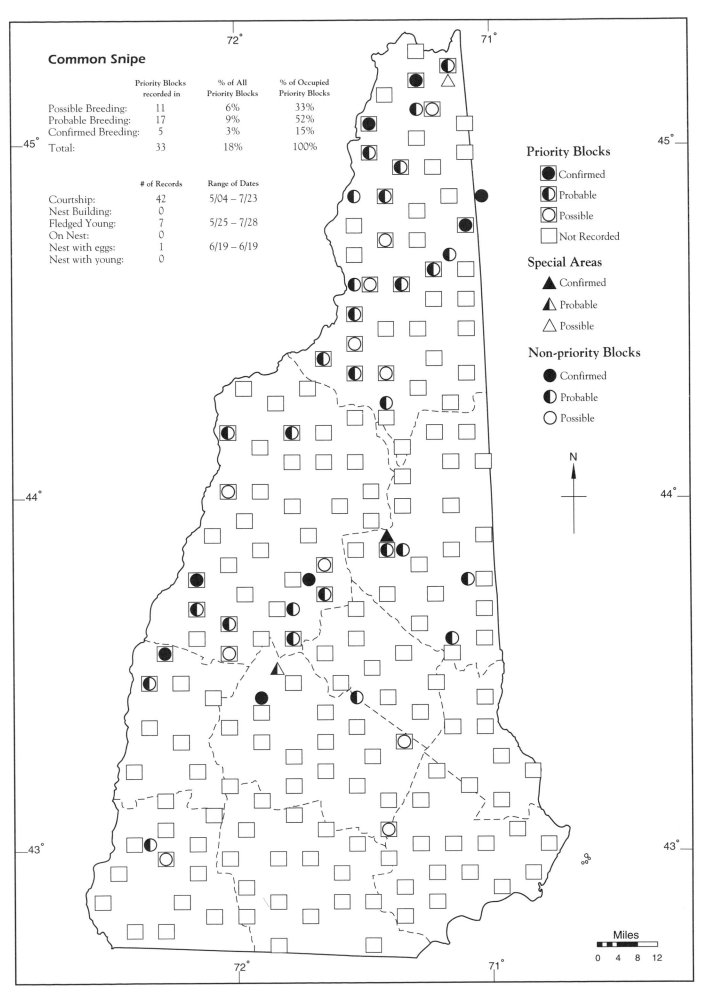

Common Snipe

	Priority Blocks recorded in	% of All Priority Blocks	% of Occupied Priority Blocks
Possible Breeding:	11	6%	33%
Probable Breeding:	17	9%	52%
Confirmed Breeding:	5	3%	15%
Total:	33	18%	100%

	# of Records	Range of Dates
Courtship:	42	5/04 – 7/23
Nest Building:	0	
Fledged Young:	7	5/25 – 7/28
On Nest:	0	
Nest with eggs:	1	6/19 – 6/19
Nest with young:	0	

Priority Blocks

● Confirmed
◑ Probable
○ Possible
□ Not Recorded

Special Areas

▲ Confirmed
◮ Probable
△ Possible

Non-priority Blocks

● Confirmed
◑ Probable
○ Possible

N

Miles
0 4 8 12

American Woodcock
Scolopax minor

This chunky, long-billed upland game bird blends perfectly with the dead leaves of the forest floor where it waits, motionless, until nearly stepped upon before exploding into flight. Breeding woodcock are well distributed and fairly common throughout New Hampshire at elevations below 2,000 ft (610 m) (T. Richards, unpubl. data), although their numbers have declined since the 1960s in much of the Eastern region (Bortner 1988). Woodcock favor areas of aspen or birch saplings, alders, or some combination thereof, and also use overgrown fields, burned or recently logged areas, and wetlands during both migration and the breeding season.

Woodcock usually arrive on their nesting grounds while patches of snow still blotch the earth. They commonly arrive in New Hampshire in mid-March, occasionally earlier (NHFG data). Upon arrival, males perform conspicuous courtship displays over open areas at evening and early morning twilight and on moonlit nights. These involve flights of 40 to 60 seconds, with aerobatics and wing twittering during the ascent and a variable but distinctive flight song of 5 or 6 chirps during the rapid descent. After alighting, the males utter a series of nasal "peent" calls during a brief ground display. They repeat this repertoire 10 to 20 times during courtship sessions of 30 to 60 minutes (Owen et al. 1977). It is not surprising that more than half of the Atlas records for woodcock were of courtship.

Males remain concealed in nearby woods during the day. Their conspicuous white droppings provide clues to their diurnal territories (Pettingill 1936). Females visit the males both on diurnal territories and on the singing grounds, but nest in areas up to 0.25 mi (0.4 km) away (Pettingill 1936).

Woodcock nest on the ground, and typically choose sites which are partially concealed by surrounding vegetation or debris. Nests often are located near the base of a shrub clump or small conifer, but some have no overhead cover (Pettingill 1936). The nest consists of a cup-shaped depression in dead leaves with a few twigs arranged around the rim, and is usually in a well-drained spot. Woodcock nests often are in wooded areas near the edge of a field or other opening, but also occur in forested wetlands and open fields (Pettingill 1936).

Confirmed breeding records are difficult to obtain due to the bird's inconspicuous behavior while nesting. Egg laying and incubation in New Hampshire occur mainly during April, and peak hatching occurs in late April and early May (NHFG data). Clutches usually include 4, but occasionally 3 and rarely 5 eggs (Pettingill 1936). The female does all the incubation, which lasts 20 to 21 days (Harrison 1978). Incubating females do not flush until danger is nearly upon them. Chicks leave the nest soon after hatching and fly 2 weeks later, becoming full grown at 4 weeks of age (Owen et al. 1977). Woodcock may renest if their initial nesting fails, but apparently produce only a single brood each year.

The female usually feigns injury when flushed with her brood, and seldom strays far from the chicks. The family spends time in open fields, brushy areas, alder thickets, birch and aspen groves, and young stands of mixed woods, foraging for earthworms in poorly drained soils (Sheldon 1967). They roost at night in fields and forest openings, sometimes in large groups (Owen et al. 1977).

Most woodcock migrate south through New Hampshire during October, although in mild autumns substantial numbers appear during the first half of November. Northeastern woodcock apparently winter in the South Atlantic states (Krohn 1973).

Beavers undoubtedly created extensive habitat for woodcock in the time before European settlement. Subsequent agriculture and wide-scale logging presumably favored this species. A severe drought in 1881, severe winters in the south in 1892, 1895, and 1899, combined with long open seasons and market hunting, which flourished between 1850 and 1900, took heavy tolls on woodcock populations, which had declined noticeably by 1895 (Silver 1957). Although enactment of the Migratory Bird Treaty Act enabled the species to begin recovery during the 1920s, another decline occurred during the 1930s, and woodcock never have regained the abundance of the mid-1800s (Silver 1957).

Annual counts of singing males along permanent, randomly selected routes in the central and northern portions of the breeding range since 1968 provide an index of the woodcock breeding population. Indices for New Hampshire and for the Eastern region indicate a long-term decline (Bortner 1987). Drainage of wetlands and development have destroyed breeding, migration, and wintering habitat, a likely cause of the decline. Also, pesticides have affected earthworm populations in many areas, decimating the woodcock's primary food source.

The Atlas map reveals that breeding woodcock are still well distributed throughout New Hampshire, and suggests that they are most common in the central and southeastern parts of the state. Singing Ground Survey data indicate that New Hampshire's highest woodcock concentrations occur in west central and southeastern regions of the state and in northern Coos County. Habitat changes and regional population trends do not bode well for the future of this unique and interesting species. Hopefully New Hampshire forests will continue to provide a stronghold for woodcock in the coming years.

Harold C. Lacaillade

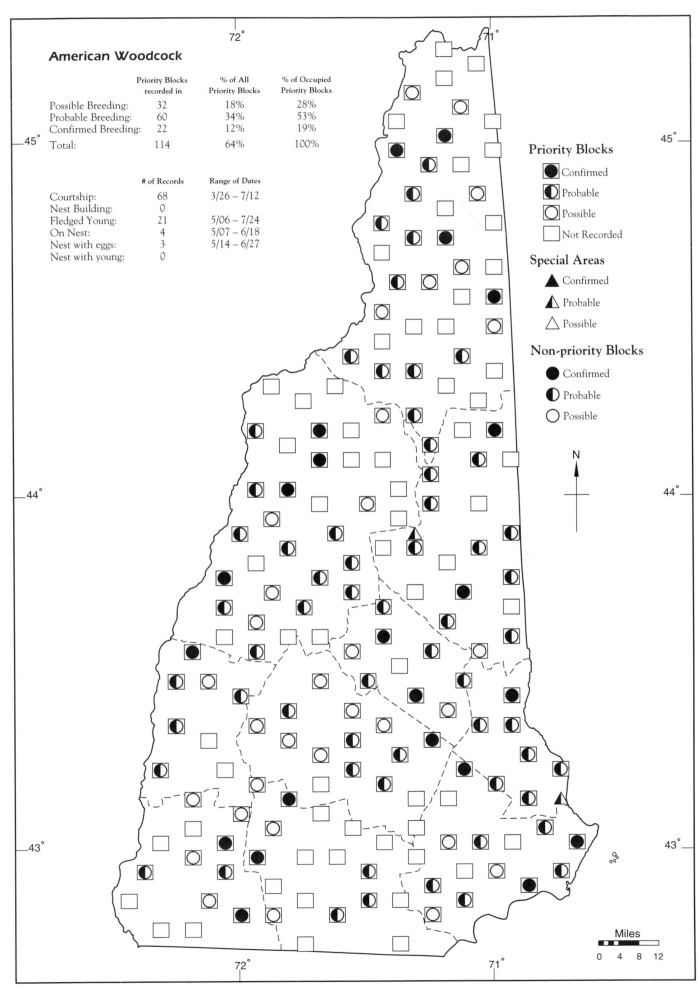

American Woodcock

	Priority Blocks recorded in	% of All Priority Blocks	% of Occupied Priority Blocks
Possible Breeding:	32	18%	28%
Probable Breeding:	60	34%	53%
Confirmed Breeding:	22	12%	19%
Total:	114	64%	100%

	# of Records	Range of Dates
Courtship:	68	3/26 – 7/12
Nest Building:	0	
Fledged Young:	21	5/06 – 7/24
On Nest:	4	5/07 – 6/18
Nest with eggs:	3	5/14 – 6/27
Nest with young:	0	

Priority Blocks
- Confirmed
- Probable
- Possible
- Not Recorded

Special Areas
- Confirmed
- Probable
- Possible

Non-priority Blocks
- Confirmed
- Probable
- Possible

N

Miles
0 4 8 12

Herring Gull
Larus argentatus

The plaintive cries and graceful forms of wheeling gulls are conspicuous features of the New England coast. The Herring Gull is handsome in adult breeding plumage, with snowy white head, tail, and underparts, pale gray mantle, black-tipped wings, and pinkish legs and feet. In fall and winter dark streaks on the head and neck give the bird a grizzled appearance. Immature plumages progress from chocolate brown to the adult plumage, attained in the fourth year.

Although they are migratory, Herring Gulls are numerous in all seasons on the New Hampshire coast and locally inland. "Spring" migration along the coast occurs mainly in February, and gulls arrive promptly after ice out on inland waters that freeze in winter (Palmer 1949). They are generally colonial nesters, and most large colonies are on islands.

Herring Gulls occupy nesting colonies 2 weeks or more after arrival in the vicinity (Palmer 1949). Most are paired upon arrival, for they probably mate for life (Tinbergen 1953). The female initiates pair formation by walking around the male while turning her head away and calling softly. Her food begging is an important part of courtship. Pairs defend small territories within the colony against other gulls with threatening displays and sometimes by fighting (Tinbergen 1953).

Both sexes build the bulky nests, which consist of grass, moss, seaweed or other plant material, and sometimes miscellaneous debris (Palmer 1949, Harrison 1978). In our area the nests usually are on the ground. Both sexes incubate the clutch of usually 3 eggs for 25 to 33 days (Harrison 1978), and feed the semiprecocial young, which become full grown and able to fly when about 6 weeks old (Tinbergen 1953). In late summer, gulls disperse from breeding areas in all directions, but chiefly along coasts or rivers (Palmer 1949, Hofslund 1959).

The natural foods of Herring Gulls are principally fish, crustaceans, and mollusks. They prey on the eggs and young of other seabirds, and eat insects, worms, small mammals, carrion, and refuse. They are notorious for swarming at municipal dumps and for following fishing boats. When not foraging, they rest on the ocean and coastal beaches, and in urban areas often on roofs. They visit fresh water to drink, and gather on ponds, rivers, and reservoirs, where they sometimes threaten water quality. Large flocks sometimes congregate and forage in fields (Palmer 1949).

Herring Gulls are noisy, especially in breeding colonies and when squabbling over food. Common calls include a loud "keew" and a "trumpeting" that consists of several subdued notes followed by loud screams. On the breeding grounds "kleeu" signifies alarm (Tinbergen 1953) and "ga ga ga" signifies annoyance (W.H. Drury, pers. comm.).

In earlier centuries, indigenous peoples of New England and subsequently European settlers ate Herring Gull eggs, which helped to keep gull numbers down (Palmer 1949). Beginning in 1896 these gulls were slaughtered in huge numbers for use in the millinery trade (Borror 1980). Soon after this practice was prohibited in 1901 gulls began to increase. By the 1930s gulls were abundant enough to be a nuisance. Temporary efforts to puncture and spray gulls' eggs briefly stopped population growth, but gulls again have increased in numbers, greatly expanding their nesting range southward.

During the 1800s the Herring Gull's principal breeding grounds in New England were islands off the Maine coast (Palmer 1949). Gulls probably nested on Duck Island, Kittery, Maine, at the Isles of Shoals, in the 1880s and possibly earlier (Borror 1980). The first New Hampshire breeding record is from Umbagog Lake, where a number of nests existed (some in trees and some on the ground) from the 1870s to the 1890s (Griscom *in* Brewster 1938).

At the turn of the century these birds were common along the New Hampshire coast from early October to late April, but were only occasional inland (Allen 1903, Dearborn 1903). By the 1920s they occurred on the coast throughout the year, and regularly in spring and fall on larger inland lakes and rivers (Goodhue 1922). Summer sightings inland still were rare during the 1930s (T. Richards, pers. comm.). Since then New Hampshire's gull population has expanded enormously. Nesting began on the New Hampshire Isles of Shoals at least as early as 1932 (Borror 1980). The Shoals colonies in Maine and New Hampshire grew to 4,654 pairs in 1977 (Borror 1980), but have declined since then, as Great Black-backed Gulls have increased.

Small numbers of Herring Gulls now breed along New Hampshire's mainland coast on salt marshes and small islands, and inland on buildings, bridge abutments, and islands in the larger lakes. A population which in 1980 produced 14 successful nests on the roof of a large mill in Manchester had grown to 59 pairs by 1984 (R.M. Bollengier, pers. comm.). The species also has nested in Concord and at Conway Lake, Conway/Eaton; Success Pond, Success; Second Connecticut Lake, Pittsburg; Squam Lake; and Lake Winnipesaukee (NHBBA data).

The Atlas map shows a concentration of records in the southeastern third of the state, where these gulls are abundant throughout the year, particularly near the Coast and in the Merrimack Valley and Lakes Region. Nesting sites remain limited to a few locations. If dumps and landfills have contributed to the great expansion in Herring Gull range and numbers, new refuse disposal techniques eventually may result in a drastic reduction in gull populations.

Kimball C. Elkins

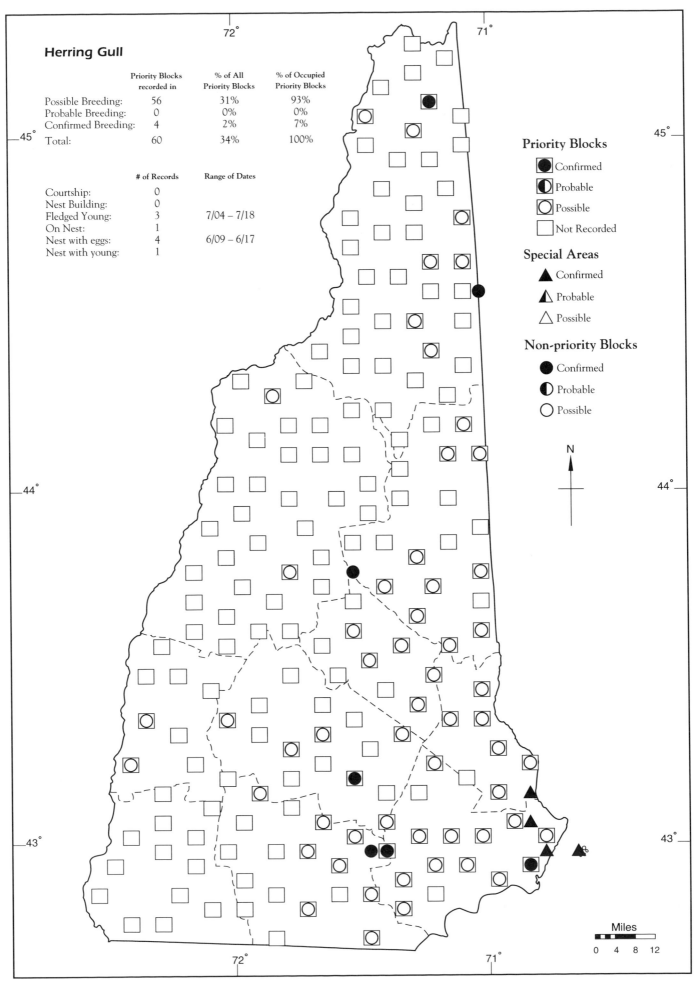

Herring Gull

	Priority Blocks recorded in	% of All Priority Blocks	% of Occupied Priority Blocks
Possible Breeding:	56	31%	93%
Probable Breeding:	0	0%	0%
Confirmed Breeding:	4	2%	7%
Total:	60	34%	100%

	# of Records	Range of Dates
Courtship:	0	
Nest Building:	0	
Fledged Young:	3	7/04 – 7/18
On Nest:	1	
Nest with eggs:	4	6/09 – 6/17
Nest with young:	1	

Priority Blocks

- ◉ Confirmed
- ◑ Probable
- ○ Possible
- ☐ Not Recorded

Special Areas

- ▲ Confirmed
- ◤ Probable
- △ Possible

Non-priority Blocks

- ● Confirmed
- ◐ Probable
- ○ Possible

N

Miles
0 4 8 12

Great Black-backed Gull

Larus marinus

Unmistakable because of their large size and contrasting black and white plumage, adult Great Black-backed Gulls occur throughout the year along the New Hampshire coast and occasionally on the state's larger inland lakes and rivers. Concentrations of juveniles occur annually during fall and early winter among the gulls at landfills in New Hampshire's lower Merrimack Valley (R. M. Bollengier, pers. comm.). Great Black-backed Gulls are common breeding birds on the Isles of Shoals, where their numbers now equal those of nesting Herring Gulls (Borror 1980).

Great Black-backed Gulls nest on the ground among boulders, in rock crevices, and on rocky ridges (Bent 1921). They usually nest in areas of low vegetation or exposed rock, and tend to avoid nesting under a canopy of shrubs or trees (Bent 1921). They frequently nest near Herring Gulls on New Hampshire's coastal islands, making nest identification difficult. Great Black-back nests usually are constructed of grasses and small weed stalks and seldom include turf, soil, or large sticks, which are common in Herring Gull nests (Gross 1945).

Great Black-backed Gulls initiate nesting at the Isles of Shoals an average of one week before Herring Gulls (McGill 1977), which likely affords the Great Black-backed Gulls easier access to preferred nesting sites. Great Black-back nests may be present there as early as mid-April, but most nest initiation occurs during early May to early June.

The Great Black-back's clutch usually consists of 3 eggs, but sometimes contains 2 and occasionally 4 eggs (Bent 1921, Harrison 1978). The eggs resemble those of the Herring Gull but are slightly larger and more coarsely spotted. When the clutch is complete, both sexes attend to incubation and territorial defense, but females invest more time in both activities than males (Butler and Janes-Butler 1983). Incubation takes 26 to 30 days (Bent 1921, Harrison 1978).

Adults become more aggressive toward intruders after hatching has occurred (Butler and Janes-Butler 1983). Both parents attend newly hatched chicks for approximately 7 weeks, feeding the young a wide variety of foods including fish, shellfish, and the eggs and young of other gulls, waterfowl, and seabirds (Bent 1921, Harrison 1978). When young Great Black-backs are large enough to run, they may prey on nearby eggs of other nesting birds (Bent 1921).

The young fledge and leave the breeding grounds 7 to 8 weeks after hatching (Gross 1945). Historically, young Black-backs migrated southward when they left the breeding grounds (Gross 1945). Now, they commonly travel inland, where they concentrate near landfills until late fall/early winter weather conditions force them to migrate (R.M. Bollengier, pers. comm.). Juveniles are mottled in a variety of buffy browns. The adult plumage does not become apparent until a spring molt in their third year.

There is no clear evidence that the Great Black-backed Gull nested in the United States prior to the early 1900s. Reports from the mid-1800s indicate that the southernmost limit of breeding was probably on the Grand Manan archipelago in the southwestern Bay of Fundy (Gross 1945). Bent (1921) described the North American breeding distribution as including the west central coast of Greenland and the North Atlantic coast from Labrador to southern Nova Scotia. Since the 1920s the species has undergone a remarkable population boom and range expansion (Drury 1973), due in part to legal protection of gulls, which previously had been overexploited by people harvesting eggs for food and adult birds for feathers used in the millinery trade.

Bent (1921) included Isle au Haute, Maine as the southernmost extent of this gull's breeding range. Jackson and Allan (1932) confirmed breeding activity at the Isles of Shoals on Duck Island, Kittery, Maine in 1928. Breeding activity on 10 islands along the Maine coast in 1931 confirmed the southward extension of the breeding range (Norton and Allen 1931). Later breeding records for Rhode Island (RNEB 1944), New York (Wilcox 1944), New Jersey (Burger 1978), and North Carolina (Parnell and Soots 1975) clearly document the range extension along the Atlantic Coast, which currently has its southern limit in North Carolina. The Great Black-back breeding range also has expanded westward to include the Great Lakes, where the species has nested sporadically since 1954 (Bull 1974). The wintering range has also expanded, and now extends south to Florida and the Gulf Coast and includes the Great Lakes (Gross 1945).

Black-backed gulls were nesting on the New Hampshire coast by 1965 (W.H. Drury, pers. comm.). In 1975, at the Isles of Shoals, Rye, 10 pairs nested on Star Island, 50 pairs on Lunging Island, and one pair on Square Rock (Borror 1980). The Great Black-backed Gull population on Star Island has increased about 10-fold over the 9 pairs Borror observed in 1979 (Borror and Holmes 1990), which constituted the largest breeding colony in the U.S. at the time (Erwin 1979). More than 2,800 breeding pairs of Great Black-backs nested at the Isles of Shoals in 1989, an increase of more than 500 pairs since the late 1970s (Borror and Holmes 1990).

"Confirmed" breeding sites during the Atlas period include the Isles of Shoals and Manchester, where a pair nested on an old bridge abutment in the Merrimack River in 1983 (Bollengier 1984). "Possible" records likely represent nonbreeding individuals. New nesting sites are likely on the mainland coast and inland, but the Isles of Shoals likely will continue to support the state's largest breeding population.

Dennis Slate

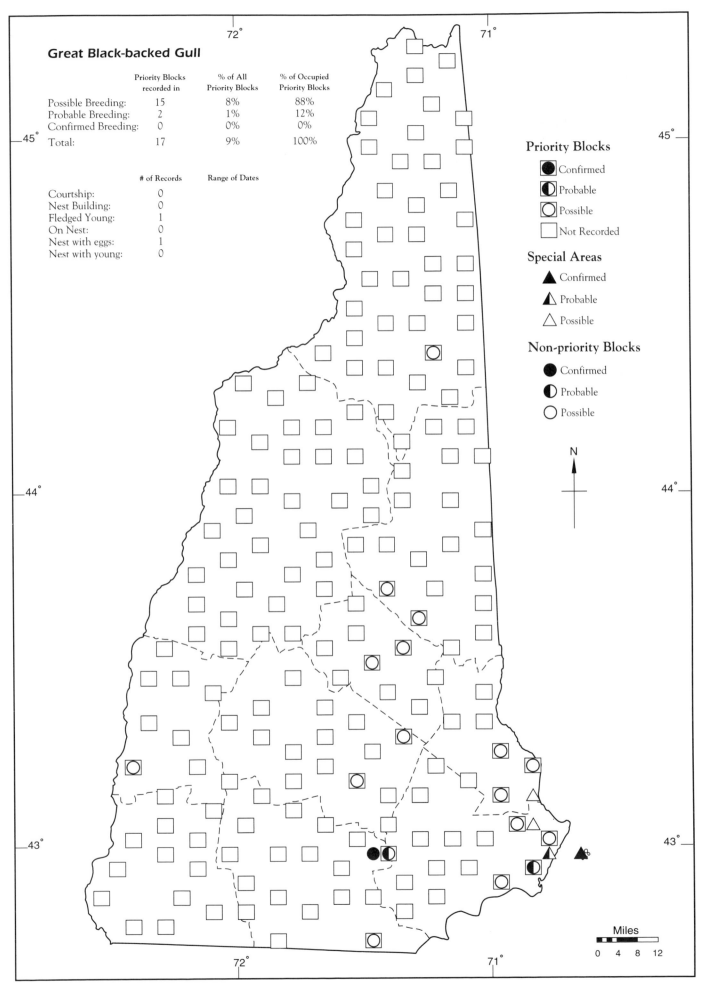

Great Black-backed Gull

	Priority Blocks recorded in	% of All Priority Blocks	% of Occupied Priority Blocks
Possible Breeding:	15	8%	88%
Probable Breeding:	2	1%	12%
Confirmed Breeding:	0	0%	0%
Total:	17	9%	100%

	# of Records	Range of Dates
Courtship:	0	
Nest Building:	0	
Fledged Young:	1	
On Nest:	0	
Nest with eggs:	1	
Nest with young:	0	

Priority Blocks
- ◐ Confirmed
- ◑ Probable
- ○ Possible
- ▢ Not Recorded

Special Areas
- ▲ Confirmed
- ◤ Probable
- △ Possible

Non-priority Blocks
- ● Confirmed
- ◐ Probable
- ○ Possible

N

Miles
0 4 8 12

Common Tern
Sterna hirundo

Fishermen long have followed the "mackerel gull" as it dives for sand lance, while schools of mackerel or bluefish herd and devour the small fish from the depths. The Common Tern breeds on islands, marshes, and shorelines of seacoasts and large bodies of fresh water throughout the Northern Hemisphere and winters in the Southern Hemisphere.

Common Terns arrive in New Hampshire in early to mid-May and usually depart by the end of September. They congregate at the Hampton Harbor estuary upon arrival before dispersing to their nesting areas, and again after the breeding season before departing on fall migration.

In courtship, the male postures with bill pointed upward, neck fully extended, chest protruding, and tail held erect while he waddles about on short legs. Eventually the female accepts a fish from the male of her choice (Bent 1921). Gavutis has observed courtship feeding along the Hampton River, Hampton, as early as 14 May.

Common Terns usually lay a clutch of 3 eggs in a shallow scrape in sand, gravel, or dried marsh grass, or in a shallow depression in bare rock, often constructing little, if any, actual nest. Most salt marsh nests are located on dense "thatch" mats of dead cordgrass. Terns also have accepted floatable nesting platforms covered with thatch (ASNH data). If the first clutch, usually laid in the first 2 weeks of June, is lost early in incubation, a second and even a third may follow. This occurs frequently in New Hampshire colonies, with late clutches sometimes hatching in early August (ASNH data).

Common Terns can be very intimidating in defense of their nests by day, when the entire colony repeatedly dives and scolds intruders with harsh "tee ar-r-r-r-r" calls. However, they are prone to night desertion of nesting colonies, usually triggered by owl predation. Often the eggs still hatch, but such interruptions may

prolong the usual 22-day incubation period to up to 32 days (I.C.T. Nisbet, pers. comm.), and increase susceptibility of eggs and chicks to chilling, flooding, predation, and attacks by predacious ants (NHESP, unpubl. data; Nisbet and Welton 1984).

Both sexes incubate the eggs and feed the young, which may leave the nest a few days after hatching, but generally return there for brooding (Bent 1921). Chicks hide in thick grass and easily blend in with bare sand or rock. They begin to fly at about 24 days. Their parents continue to feed them well after they can fly. Incomplete black caps, less deeply forked and darker tails, buffy wing coverts, and blackish bills distinguish juveniles from adults.

The Common Tern formerly was a common to abundant breeder along the New England coast on offshore islands, which were secure from most predators. Hunting for the feather trade greatly reduced the population by 1900, but it recovered with protection. Dearborn (1903) knew of no terns nesting on New Hampshire's mainland coast around the turn of the century. Following passage of the Migratory Bird Treaty Act in 1914, Common Terns were nesting on Lunging (formerly Londoners) Island, Rye, by 1922 (Borror 1980), and numbered about 1,000 pairs there by 1928. Nest and egg destruction reportedly began in 1927 (Jackson and Allan 1931), but 1,500 to 2,000 pairs nested there during 1928–48 (Jackson 1947, Drury 1973). Although 650 pairs were present in the late 1940s, T. Richards (pers. comm.) found nesting Herring and Black-backed gulls but no terns on 3 August 1951.

During recent decades, increasing numbers of Herring and Great Black-backed gulls have displaced Common Terns from many prime nesting habitats (Drury 1973, Erwin and Korschgen 1979). Many Common Terns have resorted to marshes and other mainland nesting sites where tidal overwash, predation, and human disturbance result in low reproductive success. White (1928, 1929, 1931, 1932a, 1932b, 1935) reported on a mainland colony at Hampton Harbor, Seabrook, which peaked with at least 120 pairs and existed until at least 1934. In 1953, a single nest with eggs was documented at this site (Wallace 1953). New Castle has supported a tern colony for at least 50 years, which fluctuated from 15 to 20 pairs in the early 1960s (ASNH data) to one pair in 1971 (E.W. Phinney, pers. comm.). Nannie's, Hen, Goat, and the 2 Footman islands in Great and Little bays also have supported tern populations, which peaked around 1970 with 12 pairs on the Footmans and 30 to 40 pairs on Nannie's (A. C. Borror and E. Whitaker, pers. comm.). Common Terns nested in the Hampton Falls salt marsh in 1964, 1966, and 1978 (SRS). H. C. Anderson reported a nest with 2 eggs there on 4 July 1966, and adults were feeding young there on 6 July 1973 (CLO Nest Rec. Prog.).

The Common Tern was on the *American Birds* Blue List from 1978 to 1981, but its status was reduced to Special Concern in 1982 and to Local Concern in 1986 (Tate 1986). Formerly a Threatened Species in New Hampshire, it is now listed as Endangered in the state.

Atlas surveys found terns nesting on the Hampton marshes in 1981, and 50 pairs nested there in 1982. E. W. Phinney (pers. comm.) reported adults feeding 2 unfledged chicks in the Seabrook marshes in 1982. In 1986, about 20 pairs nested in the Hampton marshes, 30 to 35 pairs on the islands in Back Channel of Little Harbor, New Castle, and 4 to 6 pairs on a small island in Little Bay, Newington (NHESP, unpubl. data). Predation and flooding have decimated recent production at these colonies. Management of nesting gulls could foster recolonization at the Isles of Shoals, which may be the best hope for maintaining this species on the New Hampshire coast over the long-term.

George W. Gavutis, Jr.

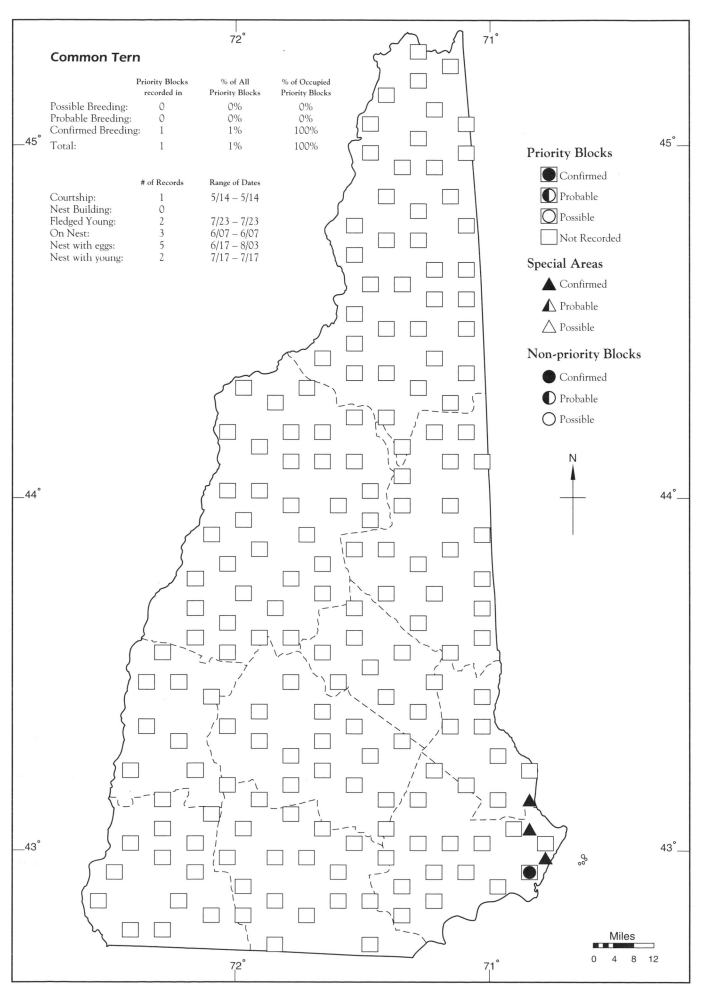

Common Tern

	Priority Blocks recorded in	% of All Priority Blocks	% of Occupied Priority Blocks
Possible Breeding:	0	0%	0%
Probable Breeding:	0	0%	0%
Confirmed Breeding:	1	1%	100%
Total:	1	1%	100%

	# of Records	Range of Dates
Courtship:	1	5/14 – 5/14
Nest Building:	0	
Fledged Young:	2	7/23 – 7/23
On Nest:	3	6/07 – 6/07
Nest with eggs:	5	6/17 – 8/03
Nest with young:	2	7/17 – 7/17

Priority Blocks
- ◐ Confirmed
- ◑ Probable
- ○ Possible
- ☐ Not Recorded

Special Areas
- ▲ Confirmed
- ◣ Probable
- △ Possible

Non-priority Blocks
- ● Confirmed
- ◐ Probable
- ○ Possible

N

Miles
0 4 8 12

97

Least Tern
Sterna antillarum

This graceful little "sea swallow" nests on unvegetated sandy beaches. Our smallest tern is readily identified by its black cap with white forehead, bright yellow, black-tipped bill, shrill "zree ee eeep" call, and rapid wing beats.

Least Tern populations were severely reduced to supply feathers for ladies' hats in the late 1800s. The species was on the *American Birds* Blue List during 1972–81 (Tate 1981), and the interior U.S. population was federally listed as an Endangered Species in 1982. This bird has been extirpated from New Hampshire in recent years, but there was evidence of "possible" breeding during the Atlas period. The species was officially listed as Endangered in the state in 1987.

Least Terns begin arriving on New England beaches around mid-May and promptly become involved in courtship and colony site selection (Bent 1921; Gavutis, pers. obs.). Colony members usually return faithfully to a nesting area. Precise colony sites often vary from year to year due to changes in beach profile, vegetative cover, human disturbance, predation, food supplies, and other factors known only to the terns themselves. The primary nesting site for this species in New Hampshire is several acres of sandy dredge spoils which form a spit near the mouth of the Hampton River, Hampton/Seabrook.

The nest is a shallow depression scraped in the sand, often just above the high tide line. Least Terns sometimes use sparsely vegetated sites further from the water, especially if beach front or unvegetated island sites are not available (Gavutis, pers. obs.). In some states, Least Terns have nested on large, flat, graveled roofs, sometimes considerable distances from the ocean.

During courtship the male captures a small fish and proffers it to a chosen female. Gavutis witnessed this behavior on the Hampton River, Hampton on 1 July 1984. The female generally lays 2 or 3 eggs by early June, which are usually all but invisible on the sand.

The eggs hatch after approximately 15 days (Bent 1921). The light, protectively colored chicks can move about as soon as they dry off and usually move within a few days to a nearby area where tide wrack and beach grass provide cover and essential shade. They fly at the age of 15 to 17 days (Harrison 1978). Least Tern fledglings are readily distinguishable from the adults by their darker plumage and lack of yellow bills and black caps. Observers saw 5 fledged young in New Hampshire on 12 July 1953 (Wallace 1953). Least Terns begin gathering in favorite feeding areas in August, and nearly all leave the Northeast by the end of that month (Bent 1921; Gavutis, pers. obs.).

Nocturnal predators, human disturbance, and high spring tides pushed by northeast gales often thwart Least Tern nesting attempts and can eliminate an entire colony's nesting effort in a very short time. Once a predator finds a nest, it often searches the general area until all the nests are found. Humans may prevent adults from feeding or shading their progeny by staying too close to a colony, in addition to causing direct losses by walking and driving in tern colonies.

Least Terns are very aggressive when intruders invade their nesting colonies. They dive boldly and repeatedly, uttering sharp scolding calls. They renest persistently if clutches are lost early in incubation and the season is not too far advanced. Sometimes, however, all or part of a colony will leave and renest at another site a considerable distance away.

Although Dearborn (1903) referred to this species as "uncommon at Hampton," individuals carrying fish in Portsmouth Harbor in July 1932 (Shelley 1932) provide the first evidence of breeding on the New Hampshire coast. A Least Tern observed at Rye Beach on 7 June 1950 provided "apparently the first record in some years" (ASNH 1950c). Richards (1958) considered Least Terns very rare and local summer residents. A colony of 2 to 10 pairs nested on the Hampton Harbor sand spit during 1953–59, and 2 individuals were present in 1960 (NHAQ, *passim*).

Of 69 Least Tern sightings reported to ASNH during 1963–80, 11 occurred in May (earliest 20 May), 1 in June, 14 in July, 38 in August, and 5 in September (latest 17 September). Sightings involved up to 5 individuals, and occurred primarily within the Hampton Harbor estuary, Hampton, although a few occurred in Rye.

The Least Tern now breeds at numerous sites in Massachusetts and several sites in Maine. Several colonies totaling up to 100 pairs annually nest on the beach at Plum Island, Newburyport, Mass., only 8 mi (13.3 km) south of the New Hampshire line. Dispersal from these colonies could account for sightings of prospecting pairs and fledged young on the New Hampshire coast.

All Least Tern observations during the Atlas project occurred in the Hampton Harbor estuary. Although these observations included adults feeding fledged young in 1982, 1984, and 1986, this activity most likely involved birds from successful colonies on Plum Island. This species may have attempted to nest in the Seabrook/Hampton area during the Atlas period, but observers were unable to locate a nesting colony in New Hampshire.

The historical nesting site at Hampton Harbor, now managed by NHFG, has strong potential to support a viable Least Tern colony again. The regional population has increased steadily during the last decade. If this trend continues, recolonization of the New Hampshire coast may be only a matter of time.

Geroge W. Gavutis, Jr.

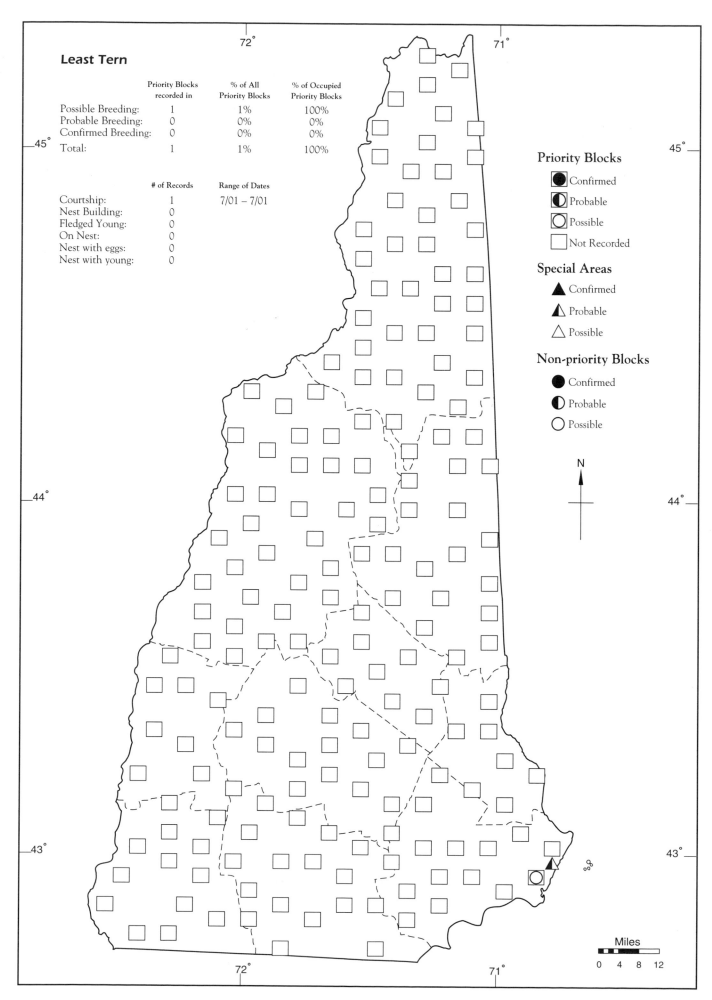

Least Tern

	Priority Blocks recorded in	% of All Priority Blocks	% of Occupied Priority Blocks
Possible Breeding:	1	1%	100%
Probable Breeding:	0	0%	0%
Confirmed Breeding:	0	0%	0%
Total:	1	1%	100%

	# of Records	Range of Dates
Courtship:	1	7/01 – 7/01
Nest Building:	0	
Fledged Young:	0	
On Nest:	0	
Nest with eggs:	0	
Nest with young:	0	

Priority Blocks
- Confirmed
- Probable
- Possible
- Not Recorded

Special Areas
- Confirmed
- Probable
- Possible

Non-priority Blocks
- Confirmed
- Probable
- Possible

N

Miles
0 4 8 12

Black Guillemot
Cepphus grylle

The Black Guillemot, with its unmistakable bumblebeelike flight, white wing patches, and bright red feet, has been known to generations of fishermen along the New England coast as the "sea pigeon." More so than other ocean birds, it often dips its bill into the water as if looking for fish.

This species has a holarctic distribution, nesting on rocky coasts and offshore islands. In June 1970, Dr. O. Hewitt and Borror recorded the guillemot nesting on Smuttynose Island, among the Maine islands of the Isles of Shoals. New Hampshire's first nesting record was established during the Atlas period and represents the southernmost extreme of the species' breeding range. The Black Guillemot breeds on remote coasts and offshore islands from the Canadian Arctic and Greenland south into northern New England and east across the British Isles, Scandinavia, and islands north of western Siberia (Nettleship and Birkhead 1985).

Guillemots occur at the Isles of Shoals throughout the year, feeding around Duck Island, Maine, as well as at a relatively shallow site about 0.6 m (1 km) west of Appledore Island, Maine. Some birds winter along the Massachusetts coast, heading north in early April. By late May, pairs are involved in courtship behavior. Borror has not witnessed the so-called "water dance" (Harrison 1983) at the Isles of Shoals, nor been close enough to hear the birds' high-pitched whistle, but has watched one member of the pair (presumably the male) arching its neck as it swims rapidly after the female. According to Nelson (1979), initial stages of courtship are not well defined. Guillemots display communally on water and land and exhibit a ritualized courtship flight in which the pair fly close together, often at surprising height, with unusually rapid wing beats. Groups of 10 or more often form a "military line formation" on the water, the function of which is unknown (S.W. Kress, pers. comm.). Guillemots mix surface display with diving and underwater pursuit.

Guillemots nest under huge storm-tossed rocks or in deep crevices above the average high-water mark. Such potential nest sites are common on outer islands of Muscongus and Penobscot bays, Maine, but are infrequent at the Isles of Shoals except on the east side of Appledore Island and the north side of Smuttynose Island in Maine, and the east side of New Hampshire's Star Island, Rye. In most of the guillemot's nesting range, nesting sites typically are well dispersed in small colonies.

The guillemot makes practically no nest, placing its 2 oval, white eggs (with small, dark speckles) directly on the rock surface or on a substrate of broken shells or stones. Egg dates at the Isles of Shoals are unknown, but are 28 May to 8 June on Kent Island in the Bay of Fundy, Canada (Nettleship and Birkhead 1985), and 12 June to 16 July on the coast of Maine (Bent 1919). There is a 28 to 31 day incubation period, followed by a 30 to 40 day nestling period. Two downy chicks were in a nest on Smuttynose Island on 30 June 1975.

Great Black-backed Gulls prey upon young guillemots in other parts of the Gulf of Maine and may do so at the Isles of Shoals. According to Fisher and Lockley (1954), young exercise their wings before fledging. Young are independent of their parents at the time of fledging. They usually fledge at night (S.W. Kress, pers. comm.). Adults begin to molt into winter plumage in August, about the time the young are fledging. Even in winter, adults have more white than juveniles, especially on the head (Bent 1919).

Nettleship and Birkhead (1985) indicate that the Black Guillemot is more of a generalist in its feeding than other members of the alcid family. At the Isles of Shoals, as well as further east on the coast, Borror has seen them bringing rock gunnels to the nest. However, guillemots also consume other bottom-dwelling marine animals, including crustaceans as well as fish (Nettleship and Birkhead 1985).

Celia Thaxter (1870) mentioned the Black Guillemot as a winter bird at the Isles of Shoals. Both Dearborn (1903) and Forbush (1925a) mentioned its occurrence along the New Hampshire coast in winter. None of the scientists at the Marine Zoological Laboratory at Appledore Island during 1928—40 observed this species at the Isles of Shoals. According to Nettleship and Birkhead (1985), the guillemot has been increasing in numbers in eastern Canada and New England (see also Korschgen 1979). Early in this century its breeding range in Maine extended eastward from Little Egg Rock (Forbush 1925a). By 1983 the species nested on at least 6 islands further south and west (Adamus 1988).

In 1985, visitors at Star Island observed a pair of Black Guillemots landing among the rocks on the island with fish in their bills and disappearing between boulders. This provided the first evidence of nesting in New Hampshire. None were observed nesting there in either 1986 or 1987, although they did nest on Smuttynose then.

Provided that the Great Black-backed Gull doesn't prove too great a predator and that major calamity doesn't destroy the limited nesting sites, the Black Guillemot should continue to breed in small numbers at the Isles of Shoals.

Arthur C. Borror

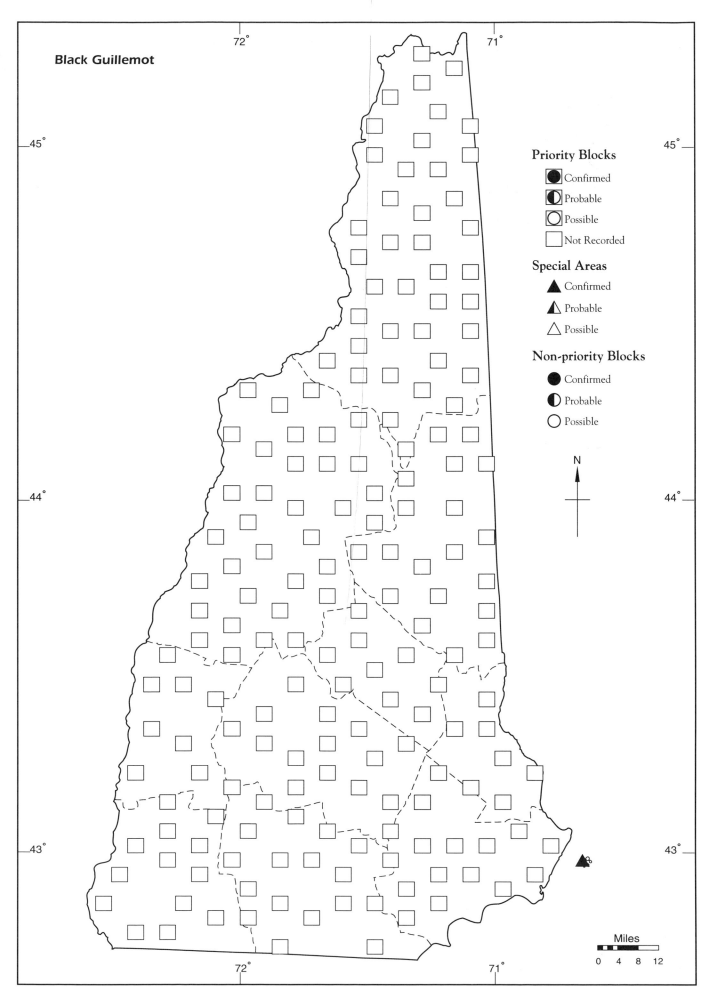

Black Guillemot

Priority Blocks
● Confirmed
◑ Probable
○ Possible
□ Not Recorded

Special Areas
▲ Confirmed
◩ Probable
△ Possible

Non-priority Blocks
● Confirmed
◐ Probable
○ Possible

N

Miles
0   4   8   12

101

Rock Dove
Columba livia

The common pigeon's sleek appearance, iridescent plumage, speedy flight, gentle trust in taking food from the hands of children, and melodious coo are familiar to many. Our pigeons are descendents of imported birds and are year-round residents wherever they occur. Although they vary considerably in plumage, all common pigeons are the same species, formally the Rock Dove.

Pigeons are most common where there are people; thus the largest cities support the largest numbers. Few, if any, pigeons occur in heavily forested sections of the state. In cities they feed on scraps and handouts and are quite tame; in rural areas they consume waste grain in fields, feed lots, or manure and are quite wild.

Pigeons in captivity breed all year long, but nesting in the wild is most frequent in spring and summer. The majority of Atlas reports indicate nesting from March to August in New Hampshire. Dedicated observers probably could find pigeons breeding in every month of the year with the possible exception of January and February.

Although their ancestors were cliff dwellers, pigeons now nest under bridges, on eaves and window sills of buildings, and on the rafters of barns and silos. Although there are no Atlas records of New Hampshire Rock Doves nesting in natural sites, rock climbers report them nesting on cliffs in Conway, and there are reports of cliff nests in Vermont as well.

Pigeons begin their reproductive cycle with a complex courtship (Levi 1963). A young cock approaches a hen and begins to coo, with neck feathers flattened and crop inflated with air. Once mated, pigeons are monogamous and generally stay mated for life. The male pigeon usually selects the nest site. He then begins a series of coos which attract the female to the shelf. There they may remain together for up to an hour before the cock goes off in search of nesting material. He brings back sticks, bits of string and any other odd objects he can find while the hen fashions a crude

nest. Once the nest is complete, the cock becomes extremely jealous of the female; if she leaves the nest he usually pursues her, often pecking her until she returns to the nest site. This behavior is called "driving."

The nest is seldom more than a loose aggregation of sticks which becomes liberally covered with pigeon manure. A pigeon lays 2 eggs, somewhat less than 24 hours apart. Incubation begins after the clutch is complete and continues for 17 to 19 days. The female incubates for 17 or 18 hours a day, and the male relieves her from roughly 10 a.m. to 4 p.m. (Maeterlinck 1936 *in* Levi 1963).

The parents first feed young squabs with "pigeon milk," a secretion of cells from the lining of the crop. As the squabs get older, they graduate to grain or other plant material. The young fledge in 30 to 35 days and begin foraging for themselves, but continue to beg food from their parents. Once the chicks are completely independent, usually 6 weeks after hatching, the parents begin another nest or lay another clutch in the old one. A young pigeon can breed at 20 weeks of age, so the potential for pigeon population growth is enormous. The major limit on pigeon populations is the availability of nest sites in close proximity to agricultural lands or other sources of food.

Pigeons were native to the Mediterranean basin and were domesticated for food by at least 4500 B.C. The French introduced them to North America at Port Royal, N.S. in 1606; subsequent introductions occurred in Virginia in 1621 and in Massachusetts in 1642 (Schorger 1952). New Hampshire pigeons presumably are descended from these early domesticated strains.

It is not clear when Rock Doves became established in New Hampshire. Ornithologists (Dearborn 1898, 1903, Allen 1903, Thayer 1909 *in* Allison and Allison 1979) writing of New Hampshire's bird life around the turn of the century failed to mention them, although it seems likely that pigeons were nesting here at that time. Early writers may not have considered them wild birds (K.C. Elkins, pers. comm.). Forbush (1927) states that they were common in towns and cities, and occurred in many rural areas as well. BBS data suggest a significant increase in the Rock Dove population in the Northeastern states over the past 15 years. The CBC ignored pigeons until 1974, so little historical information exists on their winter distribution.

Pigeons are among the favorite prey of Northern Goshawks, Red-tailed and Cooper's hawks, and Peregrine Falcons. Pigeons may comprise 20 to 60% of Peregrine prey during the breeding season (Cade 1982), and biologists have found some Peregrine nests liberally sprinkled with the aluminum bands of racing pigeons (A. Hager, pers. comm.).

The breeding distribution of Rock Doves in New Hampshire corresponds roughly with human distribution, with greater concentrations of nesting Rock Doves in the south, the west, and along the coast. The only Atlas reports of pigeon sightings in the White Mountains were in Carter Notch, Beans Purchase, and Crawford Notch, Harts Location. In the Northern Highlands, Atlas observers reported them from Gorham, Columbia, and the Hall Stream valley of Pittsburg. Pigeons also nest in Berlin, which does not fall within a priority block. Barring a major disease outbreak or extensive control measures, the future of the Rock Dove seems secure in New Hampshire.

Charles Walcott

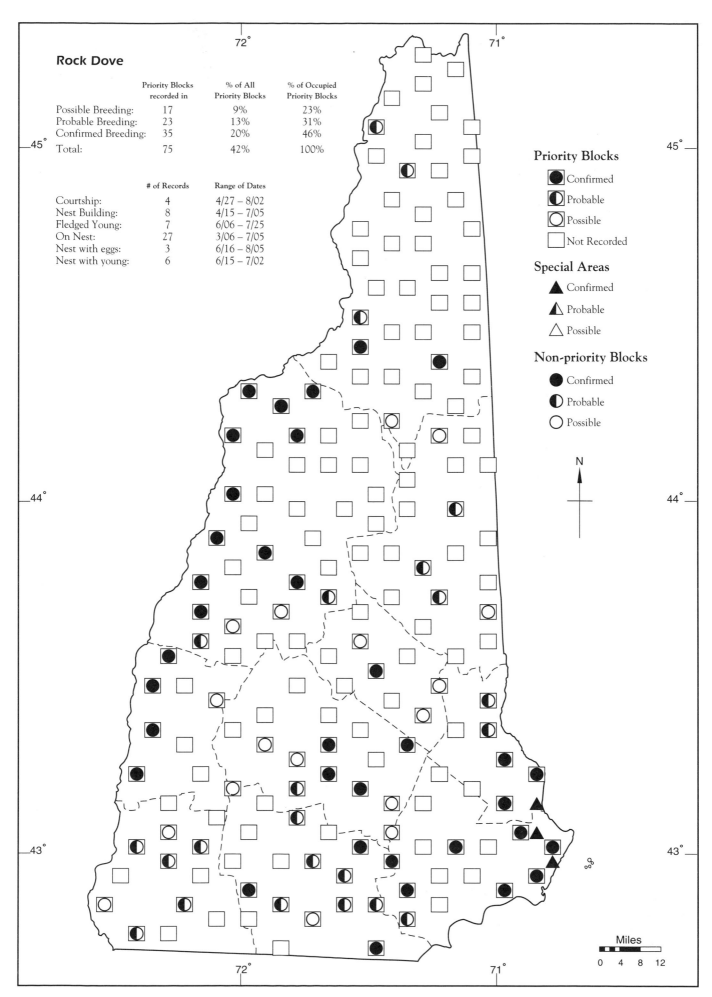

Rock Dove

	Priority Blocks recorded in	% of All Priority Blocks	% of Occupied Priority Blocks
Possible Breeding:	17	9%	23%
Probable Breeding:	23	13%	31%
Confirmed Breeding:	35	20%	46%
Total:	75	42%	100%

	# of Records	Range of Dates
Courtship:	4	4/27 – 8/02
Nest Building:	8	4/15 – 7/05
Fledged Young:	7	6/06 – 7/25
On Nest:	27	3/06 – 7/05
Nest with eggs:	3	6/16 – 8/05
Nest with young:	6	6/15 – 7/02

Priority Blocks

◕ Confirmed
◑ Probable
○ Possible
☐ Not Recorded

Special Areas

▲ Confirmed
◮ Probable
△ Possible

Non-priority Blocks

● Confirmed
◖ Probable
○ Possible

N

Miles
0 4 8 12

Mourning Dove
Zenaida macroura

The slender, graceful Mourning Dove is a common sight in fields and along roadsides. Perched on a utility wire, this species has a distinctive silhouette with its small head and long, pointed tail. Its rapid and direct flight is made on whistling wings. The Mourning Dove is gray brown above and blends easily into the background as it walks slowly along the ground in search of forb and grass seeds. This species occurs in a wide range of habitats, including parks, suburbs, orchards, cemeteries, cultivated lands, pastures, and woodlots.

The Mourning Dove currently is a year-round resident of New Hampshire, well distributed in summer but notably less so in winter. Most numerous in southern New Hampshire, the dove has extended its range northward in recent years and is now moderately common even in Coos, the state's northernmost county. The species breeds from southern Canada southward throughout North America and Mexico. Most Mourning Doves winter south to Central America and the West Indies (Keeler et al. 1977).

The presence of wintering doves makes it difficult to determine dates of spring migration, but numbers of doves in northern New Hampshire increase in late March (Elkins 1982). The beginning of breeding activity typically follows a rise in the average overnight low temperature (Madson 1978). Courtship includes cooing, bowing, self-preening, and the male's pursuit of the female. The male arches his neck, puffs out his throat, and fans his tail when uttering his low, mournful coo. This call, often mistaken for an owl's hoot, consists of 4 notes, the first of which has 2 syllables and rises in pitch. A cooing male is audible at surprising distances, which facilitates efforts to monitor populations. The male also performs a flapping/gliding flight with deep, exaggerated wing beats, rising to a hundred feet or more and descending in a long, slow, curving glide with wings extended. A pair may grasp beaks and bob heads several times just before copulating (Madson 1978).

The male attracts his mate to a potential nest site with a soft, 3-note coo (Madson 1978). Doves often nest in isolated trees and apparently prefer evergreens, though they sometimes nest in deciduous trees. Nests frequently are placed next to the trunk, often about 10 ft (3 m) from the ground, but sometimes up to 50 ft (15.2 m) above ground (Harrison 1975). Mourning Doves occasionally nest on roofs, fire escapes, eaves, balconies, wood piles, and other structures, and uncommonly even on the ground (Harrison 1975, Keeler et al. 1977).

The nest is a loose but strong platform of twigs with little or no lining and often is constructed on top of the old nest of another species such as a robin, catbird, or grackle (Harrison 1975, Harrison 1978). Nest building takes place in the morning; the male gathers twigs and the female constructs the platform (Bent 1932).

Most Mourning Doves attempt 3 to 5 nests between April and August (Madson 1978). The usual clutch is 2 eggs, but some are 3 or rarely 4. Incubation takes 14 or 15 days, and nestlings leave the nest when 13 to 15 days old. Males usually incubate during the day and females at night, and both parents tend the nestlings, with one adult usually present at the nest (Bent 1932). Mourning Doves regurgitate "pigeon's milk," a secretion from glands in their crops, to their young nestlings or "squabs," gradually introducing seeds before the young fledge (Bent 1932, Keeler et al. 1977).

Young doves remain in the vicinity of the nest for several days after fledging and continue to beg food from their parents. Some may come into breeding condition later the same year (Madson 1978). Immature doves begin associating in small groups before migration, occasionally as early as July. Cooling nights in late summer and early fall trigger the first stages of migration in August, and migrating doves have left northern New Hampshire by late October (Keeler et al. 1977, Madson 1978, Elkins 1982).

In the late 1800s, this species was an "irregular and rather uncommon visitor" in Belknap and Merrimack counties in spring and fall (Dearborn 1898) and rarely occurred north of Lake Winnipesaukee (Allen 1903). At the turn of the century the Mourning Dove was nesting in the Seacoast area and the Merrimack Valley (Goodhue, unpubl. data; Allen 1903; Dearborn 1903).

Mourning Dove numbers and distribution have been increasing since the 1940s. The USFWS initiated a Call-Count Survey in 1966, with 3 New Hampshire survey routes. This survey produced a low population index for the first 10 years, which escalated rapidly after 1977; the 5-year average for 1981–85 of 8.4 doves per route represents a 22% increase over the 20-year mean of 6.9 doves per route (Dolton 1985). BBS data during 1966–79 also suggest a significant increase in the Northeastern states, especially in parts of Maine, New Hampshire, and Massachusetts (Robbins et al. 1986). The dove's relative scarcity throughout the Northeast is attributed chiefly to extensive forests and cold, snowy winters. Doves have benefited from conversion of the vast Eastern deciduous forests to woodlots interspersed with clearings (Keeler et al. 1977).

As the Atlas map indicates, Mourning Doves are well distributed south of the White Mountains, with records in all but 3 priority blocks. The distribution is more scattered in Coos County, where about half of the priority blocks have records. Their compatibility with human communities probably will enable continued population increases in the coming years.

Harold C. Lacaillade

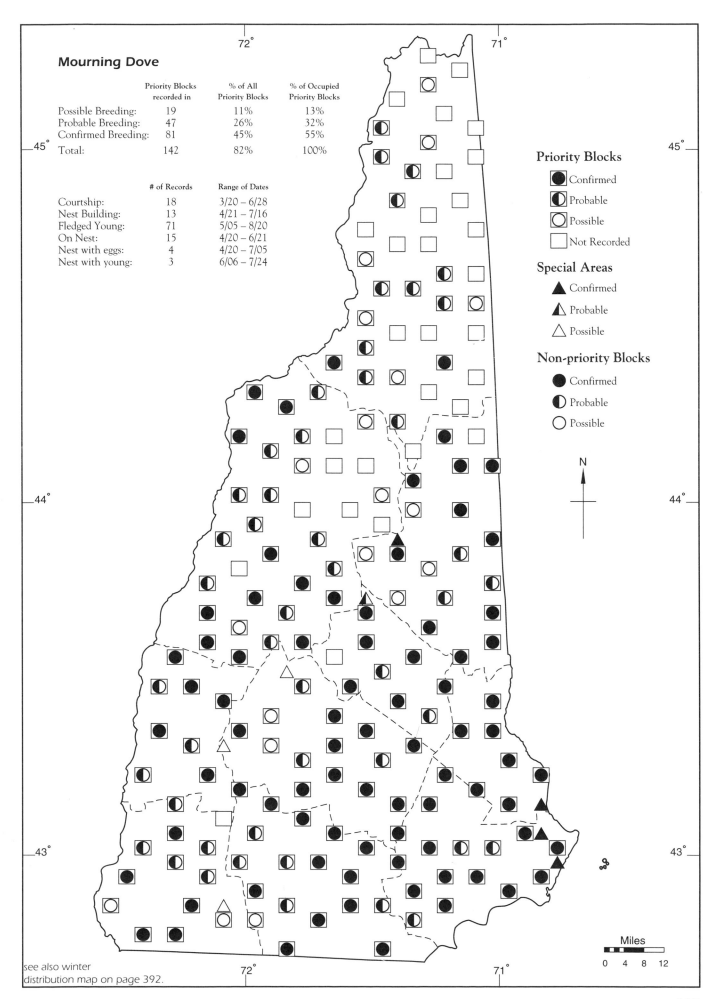

Mourning Dove

	Priority Blocks recorded in	% of All Priority Blocks	% of Occupied Priority Blocks
Possible Breeding:	19	11%	13%
Probable Breeding:	47	26%	32%
Confirmed Breeding:	81	45%	55%
Total:	142	82%	100%

	# of Records	Range of Dates
Courtship:	18	3/20 – 6/28
Nest Building:	13	4/21 – 7/16
Fledged Young:	71	5/05 – 8/20
On Nest:	15	4/20 – 6/21
Nest with eggs:	4	4/20 – 7/05
Nest with young:	3	6/06 – 7/24

Priority Blocks
- Confirmed
- Probable
- Possible
- Not Recorded

Special Areas
- Confirmed
- Probable
- Possible

Non-priority Blocks
- Confirmed
- Probable
- Possible

N

Miles			
0	4	8	12

see also winter
distribution map on page 392.

Black-billed Cuckoo
Coccyzus erythropthalmus

The Black-billed Cuckoo resembles its close relative, the Yellow-billed Cuckoo, but lacks the rufous primaries and large tail spots of the latter and has an all dark bill. This is the cuckoo one is most likely to encounter in New Hampshire, as well as elsewhere in New England. A bird of Eastern woodlands, it is a summer resident throughout New Hampshire except in the higher mountains, where it is scarce or absent. Although both cuckoos occur in similar habitats, including groves of trees, thickets, and the edges of deciduous or mixed forests, the Black-billed Cuckoo is more apt to be found in extensive upland woods (Bent 1940).

The local abundance of the Black-billed Cuckoo apparently is related to the population cycles of certain hairy caterpillars, its favorite insect prey. In southern New Hampshire, both cuckoos were noticeably more plentiful in the early 1980s, when gypsy moths were abundant, than later during the Atlas project. Most Atlas records (69% for Black-bills) were obtained during 1981 and 1982, when hairy caterpillars were particularly abundant. In Vermont, where the Atlas project took place during years when caterpillar populations peaked, this species was recorded in 75% of blocks and "confirmed" in 24% of those (Pistorius *in* Laughlin and Kibbe 1985).

Most Black-billed Cuckoos return to New Hampshire from tropical wintering areas at the end of May (Elkins 1982), but some may arrive as early as 15 May (White 1937, Allison and Allison 1979). Thayer (1909 *in* Allison and Allison 1979) heard migrants passing overhead at night in the Dublin area, including from the top of Mt. Monadnock, Jaffrey. Fall departure is less noticeable because these birds are not vocal in late summer. Most have left by mid-September, and October sightings are rare.

Breeding cuckoos are more likely to be located by their distinctive song than by sight. The typical song is a long and monotonous series of gutteral 3- or 4-note phrases. Less frequent is a series of single notes that resembles the song of the Yellow-billed Cuckoo, but never ends with the latter's slower, slurred "gulps." This species is known for singing at night and on calm, muggy mornings before rain. It sometimes sings while sitting on its nest or in flight (Bent 1940).

Black-billed Cuckoos build nests of twigs lined with ferns, grass, catkins, and other soft materials, which are usually more substantial than the similar nests of Yellow-billed Cuckoos. They are frequently only 2 to 4 ft (0.6 to 1.2 m) above the ground in bushes, thickets, or beside the trunks of small trees, including white pines (Bent 1940). Two nests which Bent (1940) found in New Hampshire were in thick clumps of mountain laurel. White (1937) describes a nest in a small pine which contained 3 eggs on 7 June 1925, and another, in a small spruce, which contained 3 young on 16 June 1932. Both were in Concord and at the edge of water.

Although North American cuckoos normally hatch and raise their own young, they sometimes lay their eggs in each others' nests and occasionally in the nests of other species (Bent 1940). In New Hampshire most Black-billed Cuckoo pairs initiate their first clutch by mid-June. During the Atlas project, however, the only egg dates were for 1 and 2 July. The female lays 2 to 4 greenish blue eggs at intervals of 1 to 3 days (Harrison 1975). Both parents share the 11 to 14 day incubation. Incubation often starts after the first egg is laid, resulting in young of different ages (Bent 1940). Nestlings leave the nest after only 7 to 9 days. Although they can not fly until 21 to 24 days, they move considerable distances by climbing and jumping from branch to branch (Harrison 1978). Despite records of exceptionally late nesting, the species apparently raises only a single brood (Pearson 1936). The juvenal plumage is similar to the adults' (Peterson 1980).

Most historic accounts of the Black-billed Cuckoo in New Hampshire refer to it as a common summer inhabitant, much more numerous than the Yellow-billed (Coues 1868, Dearborn 1898, 1903, White 1924). White (1937) notes several years of relative scarcity around Concord. BBS data show a significant population increase in the Eastern region and across North America during 1966–79, with a decline noted in southern New England (Robbins et al. 1986). The reversion of abandoned fields and pastures to shrubs and scattered trees provided ample habitat for this species earlier in this century, but the maturing forests support fewer cuckoos. Black-billed Cuckoos are noticeably less common in New Hampshire today than they were during the 1940s and 1950s (K. C. Elkins, T. Richards, pers. comm.). Urbanization is generally unfavorable to this species, although while apparently shy and reclusive, this cuckoo often nests close to human habitation in rural settings.

As the Atlas map indicates, the Black-billed Cuckoo is widely distributed in New Hampshire. Records are decidedly more plentiful in the southern part of the state, however, where hardwood forests predominate. All priority blocks with records for the species include elevations below 2,000 ft (610 m), and about two-thirds of them are in the Merrimack and Coastal drainages.

Ralph Andrews

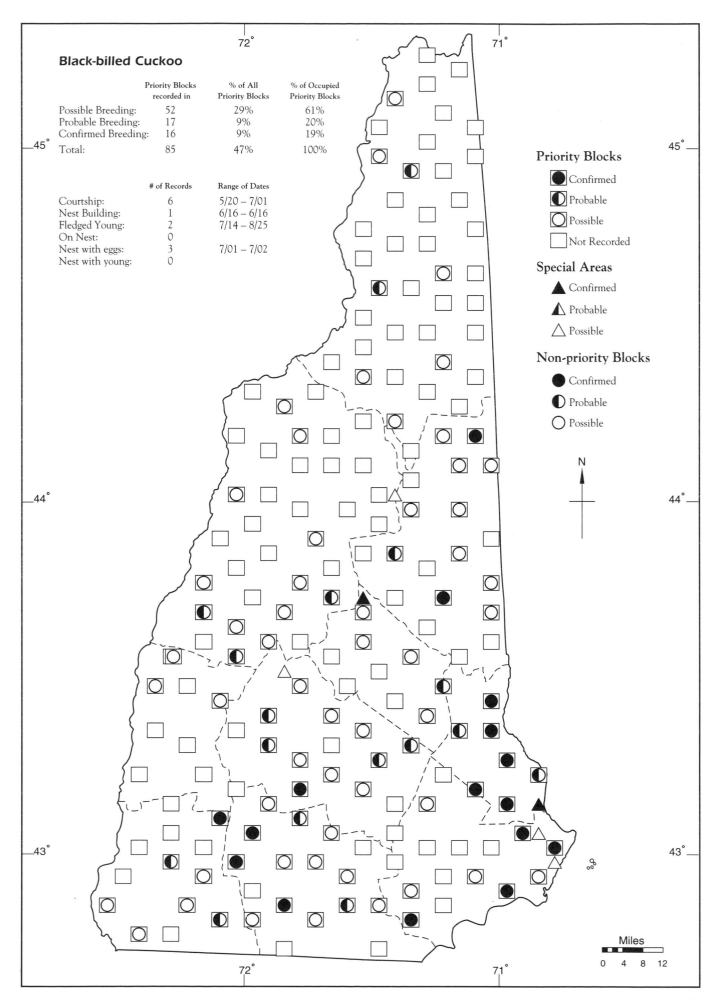

Black-billed Cuckoo

	Priority Blocks recorded in	% of All Priority Blocks	% of Occupied Priority Blocks
Possible Breeding:	52	29%	61%
Probable Breeding:	17	9%	20%
Confirmed Breeding:	16	9%	19%
Total:	85	47%	100%

	# of Records	Range of Dates
Courtship:	6	5/20 – 7/01
Nest Building:	1	6/16 – 6/16
Fledged Young:	2	7/14 – 8/25
On Nest:	0	
Nest with eggs:	3	7/01 – 7/02
Nest with young:	0	

Priority Blocks

● Confirmed
◐ Probable
○ Possible
☐ Not Recorded

Special Areas

▲ Confirmed
◤ Probable
△ Possible

Non-priority Blocks

● Confirmed
◑ Probable
○ Possible

N

Miles
0 4 8 12

Yellow-billed Cuckoo
Coccyzus americanus

North American cuckoos are slender, long-tailed birds with brownish backs and whitish underparts. Unlike the better known European cuckoo, Yellow-billed and Black-billed cuckoos neither sing like a cuckoo clock nor normally parasitize the nests of smaller birds. Occasionally both species lay their eggs in each other's nests, and rarely in other species' nests (Bent 1940).

The Yellow-billed Cuckoo is the more southern of the 2 cuckoo species that occur in New Hampshire, and reaches the northern limit of its breeding range in central New England (Peterson 1980). It resembles the Black-billed Cuckoo, but is distinguished by rufous primaries, large white spots on the tail, and a yellow lower mandible. It is much less common than the Black-billed Cuckoo in New Hampshire and is restricted to the southern part of the state, where it is rare to uncommon (Elkins 1982). It usually inhabits woodland edges, streamside thickets, brushy country roadsides, and run-down orchards where hairy caterpillars, its chief food, are abundant (Pough 1946). It is one of the few birds that regularly feeds on the hairy kinds, including tent caterpillars and gypsy moth larvae. The diet also includes birds' eggs, frogs, berries, and fruit.

Most cuckoos arrive in late May, when the annual crop of early caterpillars has already hatched. Cuckoo breeding distribution and abundance may change annually depending on local food resources. Nearly all Yellow-billed Cuckoo Atlas records and 10 of the 12 "probable" or "confirmed" breeding records in priority blocks were from 1981 and 1982, when both gypsy moths and tent caterpillars were abundant.

These furtive birds seldom perch in open sites, so one is much more likely to hear than to see them. The Yellow-billed Cuckoo's song is a guttural series of croaks that starts rapidly and slows at the end. Although slower, a chipmunk's clucking is sometimes mistaken for a cuckoo's. Cuckoos often "sing" in early morning, or even at night, particularly in calm, muggy weather. Potter (1980) observed that the female pumped her tail prior to copulation and the male passed her an insect during the act. Both sexes build the nest, gathering materials from about 1 a (0.4 ha) around the site (Potter 1980). The nest is a flimsy platform of twigs, lined with softer material such as rootlets and dried leaves. It is usually placed in a dense shrub or tree 4 to 8 ft (1.2 to 2.4 m) above the ground (Pough 1946), but may be as high as 20 ft (6.1 m) (Harrison 1975). Both adults incubate the 3 or 4 eggs for nearly 2 weeks, and may start before the clutch is complete (Potter 1980). During the first few days of incubation, the male brings new nesting material when relieving the female at the nest site (Potter 1980). They also share the duty of feeding young, foraging within about 2.5 a (1 ha) of the nest (Potter 1980). When young cuckoos are about a week old, they leave their nest and scramble about the branches for another 2 weeks until they are able to fly (Terres 1980).

Near the nest the adults are shy and secretive, and nestlings beg only briefly and rather quietly (Potter 1980). This behavior may explain why no nests were found during the Atlas period. Most "confirmed" nesting records were based on adults carrying food for young. Although records of late nesting are common among both cuckoos, there is no evidence that they raise more than one brood annually (Hamilton and Hamilton 1965, Nolan and Thompson 1975). The birds are quiet after the nesting season so records of departure dates for tropical wintering areas are scarce. Most have departed by mid-September, but a few may linger into October.

Historical records indicate that this cuckoo always has been an uncommon and irregular summer resident in southern New Hampshire (Coues 1868, Dearborn 1898, 1903, White 1924). The earliest nesting record may be from Webster in 1902 (Goodhue, 1922.). Although a prolonged population decline in California warranted its inclusion on the *American Birds* Blue List for that state (Tate 1986), BBS data from 1966 to 1979 indicate a significant increase elsewhere in its breeding range (Robbins et al. 1986). Apparently, annual crops of hairy caterpillars are sufficient to sustain cuckoos despite ill-advised campaigns for massive insecticide applications.

As the map shows, all 31 priority blocks with Atlas records for the Yellow-billed Cuckoo are south of the White Mountains or along the Connecticut River. The majority of records were from within or east of the Merrimack River valley. In Vermont, the species occurs primarily in the Champlain Lowlands (Pistorius *in* Laughlin and Kibbe 1985). In Massachusetts it is fairly widespread, with most records in the southeastern part of the state (Veit and Petersen 1993). It seems likely that this cuckoo will continue to be an uncommon breeding bird in New Hampshire, its numbers fluctuating with woolly caterpillar populations.

Ralph Andrews

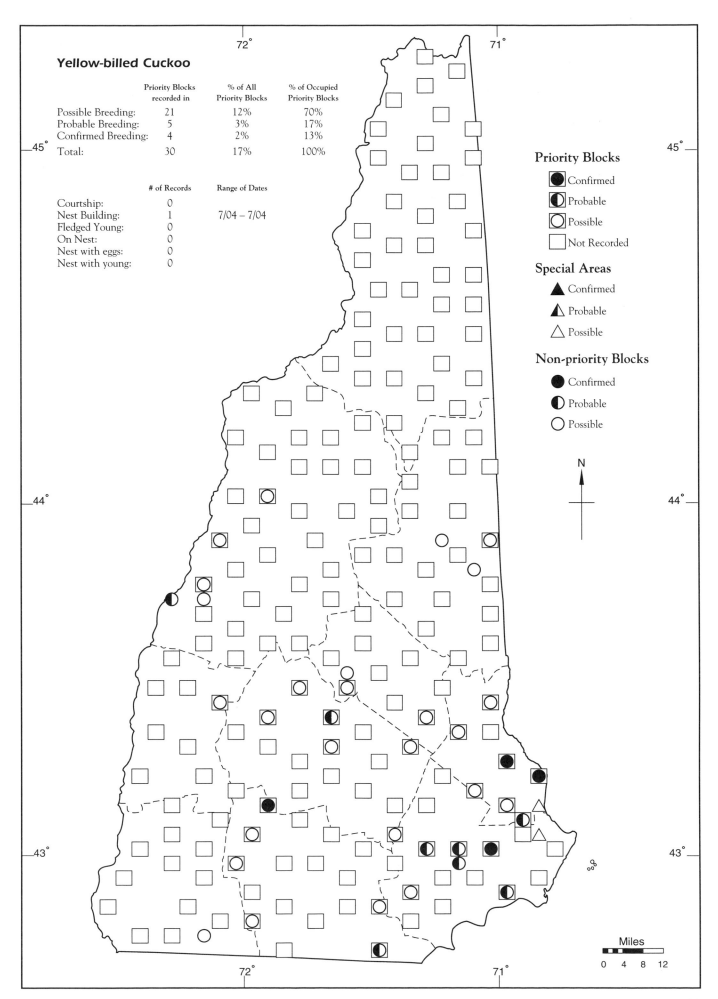

Yellow-billed Cuckoo

	Priority Blocks recorded in	% of All Priority Blocks	% of Occupied Priority Blocks
Possible Breeding:	21	12%	70%
Probable Breeding:	5	3%	17%
Confirmed Breeding:	4	2%	13%
Total:	30	17%	100%

	# of Records	Range of Dates
Courtship:	0	
Nest Building:	1	7/04 – 7/04
Fledged Young:	0	
On Nest:	0	
Nest with eggs:	0	
Nest with young:	0	

Priority Blocks
- Confirmed
- Probable
- Possible
- Not Recorded

Special Areas
- Confirmed
- Probable
- Possible

Non-priority Blocks
- Confirmed
- Probable
- Possible

Miles
0   4   8   12

Eastern Screech-Owl

Otis asio

The Eastern Screech-Owl is the only small owl in New Hampshire that has prominent ear tufts. It is sufficiently rare at the present time to be considered a Special Concern Species in the state. This owl occurs east of the Rocky Mountains from the northern U.S. and extreme southern Canada south to northeastern Mexico (Adam 1987). Marshall (1967) recognized 5 subspecies within this range. Screech-owls may have red or gray plumage; several intermediate colors also occur. Mosher and Henny (1976) concluded that red-plumaged birds have a significantly higher metabolic requirement below 23° F (-5° C) and thus are more suited to southern climates. Distributional data support this theory; gray birds are more common in the north, and red in the south (Owen 1963). Atlas workers found both red and gray birds in New Hampshire.

Screech-owls are year-round residents in New Hampshire and apparently reach the northern limit of their breeding range in the northern part of the state, although their current distribution and abundance here are not well documented. They occur in open hardwood stands, pine woods, cemeteries, old orchards, and even in suburban neighborhoods (Johnsgard 1988). Lynch and Smith (1984) found that areas of considerable habitat diversity, including high percentages of natural habitats, supported screech-owl populations in developed areas of southern Connecticut.

Courtship begins in early spring, which is the best time to hear this bird's distinctive calls. In advertising his territory, a male utters a quavering whinny, which ascends briefly and then descends in pitch (Johnsgard 1988). Especially during late winter and early spring, he gives a long trill on one pitch in responding to a female, and they may perform this song as a duet (Weyden 1975, Smith et al. 1987, Johnsgard 1988). Hungry nestlings utter chattering calls, which adults may use when being mobbed (Johnsgard 1988). Marshall (1967) describes a variety of additional vocalizations.

Screech-owls most often nest in old flicker or Pileated Woodpecker holes, or in natural cavities in trees, but also may use bird boxes and sometimes outbuildings (Scott 1921). Nest cavities may range from 5 to 30 ft (1.5 to 9.1 m) from the ground (Harrison 1975). Arter observed a red-phase screech-owl peering from a 3 in (8 cm) hole in a tall beech tree in response to gentle scratching on the trunk. Eastern Screech-Owls often breed in their first year (Van Camp and Henny 1975). Egg laying begins in April, and a full clutch consists of 2 to 7 eggs, most commonly 4 or 5 (Harrison 1975). The male does all the hunting during incubation and early brooding, and may roost in the nest cavity during the day while the female incubates (Harrison 1975). Incubation lasts for 21 to 30 days (Harrison 1975).

Both adults feed the young, which fledge 4 to 5 weeks after hatching (Bent 1938). The young depend on their parents for some time after fledging, and families remain together through the summer. Young birds disperse in late summer or early fall, 45 to 65 days after fledging (Belthoff and Ritchison 1986, Johnsgard 1988).

The Eastern Screech-Owl is an opportunist when hunting. Prey items include insects, fish, various small mammals, and at least 53 different species of birds (VanCamp and Henny 1975). VanCamp and Henny (1975) found that the diet of screech-owls in Ohio consisted of 64.8% birds in spring and suggested that timing of the nesting period may have evolved to coincide with the peak of spring migration.

The Eastern Screech-Owl was considered a common species in southern New Hampshire during the 1800s, but became rare in the vicinity of Webster and Concord around the turn of the century (Dearborn 1898, White 1937). It remained relatively common in the Durham area into the early 1900s (Dearborn 1903, Scott 1921). Allen (1903) considered it an uncommon permanent resident south from the valleys of the White Mountains. Early nesting records include 4 recently fledged young at Intervale (Bartlett/Conway) on 18 June 1900 (Allen 1903), and 4 young in a tree on Concord's North Main Street on 2 August 1905 (White 1937). In recent years, screech-owl records in New Hampshire have been infrequent and scattered. Sightings reported during 1936–70 came from 19 communities representing all counties except Coos (RNEB, NHAQ, *pass.*). The majority of sightings occurred in Hillsborough and Rockingham counties; Tamworth and Ossipee provided the northernmost records.

The status of this species in New Hampshire contrasts sharply with the situation in Massachusetts, where the screech-owl is considered the most common bird of prey (Andrew et al. 1982, Veit and Petersen 1993). While the decline of agriculture may be responsible for a population decline in New Hampshire, much apparently suitable habitat remains unoccupied.

Due to the screech-owl's strictly nocturnal nature, people often overlook this bird. This may partially explain the scarcity of Atlas records. Broadcast of tape-recorded calls is the most reliable method for locating this species, but does not "confirm" breeding. This technique should be used with caution as it may interfere with normal territory establishment and maintenance.

Atlas records for this species are rather scattered, but the majority are in the southeastern part of the state. Only one "confirmed" record, a nest with young observed in Newington on 18 May, emerged during the Atlas project. Further effort will be required to determine accurately the present distribution and abundance of this species.

Thomas H. Arter

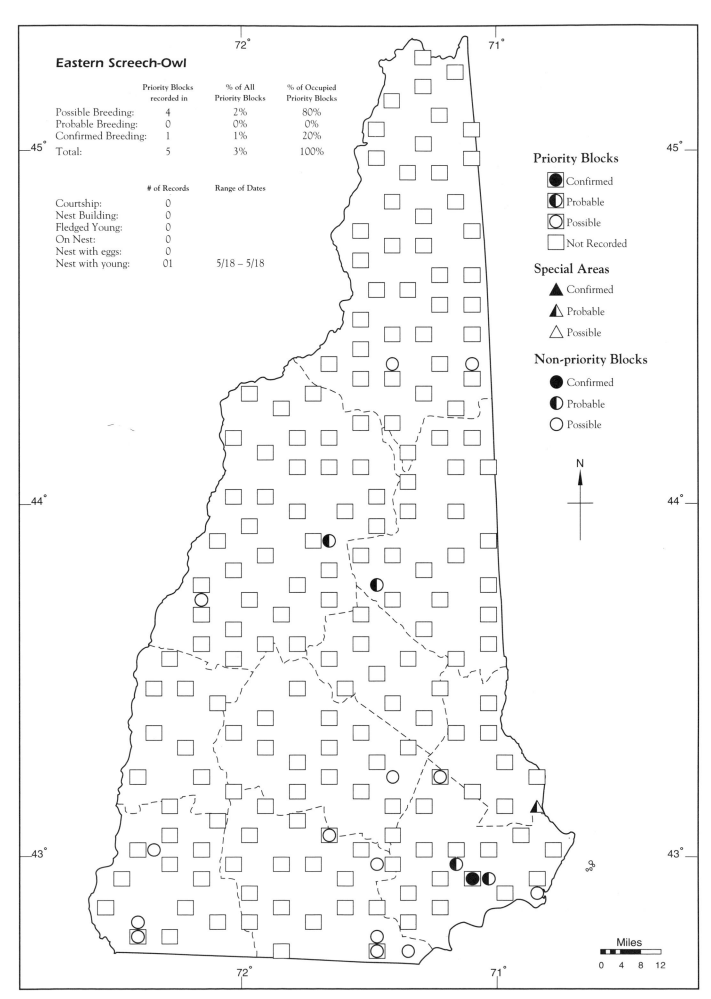

Eastern Screech-Owl

	Priority Blocks recorded in	% of All Priority Blocks	% of Occupied Priority Blocks
Possible Breeding:	4	2%	80%
Probable Breeding:	0	0%	0%
Confirmed Breeding:	1	1%	20%
Total:	5	3%	100%

	# of Records	Range of Dates
Courtship:	0	
Nest Building:	0	
Fledged Young:	0	
On Nest:	0	
Nest with eggs:	0	
Nest with young:	01	5/18 – 5/18

Priority Blocks
- Confirmed
- Probable
- Possible
- Not Recorded

Special Areas
- Confirmed
- Probable
- Possible

Non-priority Blocks
- Confirmed
- Probable
- Possible

N

Miles
0 4 8 12

Great Horned Owl
Bubo virginianus

Perched imposingly on a tree branch, New Hampshire's largest native owl is readily identified by its size, conspicuous ear tufts, and bright yellow eyes. The female is substantially larger than the male. Its dark coloration, long, rounded wings, and heavy, neckless head distinguish it in flight.

This widely distributed North American species ranges from Arctic treeline to the southern tip of South America (Johnsgard 1988). The Great Horned Owl is a year-round resident throughout New Hampshire, where it usually resides in woods near open areas, sometimes close to human dwellings. Nest and roost sites often are in dense woods, especially in white pine stands. This owl often occupies the same habitat as the Red-tailed Hawk (Forbush 1927).

Great Horned Owls typically remain in their home ranges year round. Petersen (1979) estimated average annual home ranges from telemetry data of 819 a (329 ha) for Great Horned Owls in Wisconsin. Several estimates of defended nesting territories have been about 150 to 162 a (60 to 65 ha) (Miller 1930, Baumgartner 1939, Fitch 1958).

Vocal throughout the year, Great Horned Owls produce a wide variety of sounds. The most familiar are deep, mellow hootings, often in a series of 5 or 6: "hoo, hoo-hoo, hoo, hoo" or "hoo, hoo-hoo-hoo, hoo, hoo." The deep booming hoots may carry for more than a mile. When both members of a pair are calling, the deeper voice of the male is easily distinguishable from the higher pitched notes of the female. Pairs often call synchronously on winter nights from late December through March (Emlen 1973). Other vocalizations include a variety of whistles, screams, barks, and meows. Great Horned Owls call most frequently at dusk and dawn and between dusk and midnight, and occasionally during the day (Bent 1938, Johnsgard 1988).

In courtship, the male bows his head, raises his spread wings, and dances along a limb or hops from branch to branch, snapping his bill loudly. Eventually he approaches the female and strokes her, rubbing bills and bowing (Bendire 1892, Bralliar 1922 *in* Bent 1938).

Great Horned Owls do not build nests of their own, but use old nests of crows, squirrels, Great Blue Herons, Red-shouldered Hawks, or more commonly, Red-tailed Hawks. They also have nested on broken-off tree trunks, on ledges, and within large cavities (Harrison 1975). Three nests in Concord observed during 1921-25 were in white pines, and one was in an elm (White 1924). A nest near Lancaster housed Great Horned Owls in 1894, 1895, and 1897, and Red-tailed Hawks in 1896 (Wright 1911). White (1937) noted that several nests in the Concord area were in pine groves within extensive mixed woods.

The female incubates the one to 3, usually 2 eggs for 28 to 35 days, beginning with the first egg (Bent 1938, Harrison 1978). White (1937) observed that in the Concord area, hatching occurred in the last 2 weeks of March (White 1924). A nest near Lancaster held 2 eggs on 11 April 1895 and 2 downy young on 21 April 1898. Two nests near Durham contained half-grown young on 26 April 1899 (Dearborn 1903).

The male does all the hunting during incubation and brooding, and is least vocal while there are young in the nest. An incubating female often gives a coarse, raspy, rising call note at dusk. The male generally responds and approaches the nest, frequently with prey. Some Great Horned Owls fly silently from the nest when people approach, while others may circle overhead or attack and even strike intruders (Forbush 1927).

Owlets venture out onto limbs near the nest 5 to 6 weeks after hatching. They may make short flights at the age of about 45 days, but don't fly well until they are 9 or 10 weeks old (Johnsgard 1988). An adult usually stays near the young but may remain hidden from observers. Responding to the owlets' shrill begging calls, the parents continue to provide food for a number of weeks after fledging, and families remain together through the summer. Young disperse in September or October and may travel widely.

The Great Horned Owl is an opportunistic hunter, preying on rodents, rabbits, birds, skunks and occasionally porcupines (Bent 1938, Akerley 1968). This owl often soars over marshes, swamps, or other open areas, especially at dusk or first light. It perches on the edge of a clearing and swoops silently after prey.

Around the turn of the century, Allen (1903) considered the Great Horned Owl common throughout "the well watered forest areas" of New Hampshire, but rare in the White Mountains. It was present, though uncommon in the vicinity of Jefferson (Wright 1911), and nested near Lancaster. Brewster (1925) found it resident in the Umbagog region. In central New Hampshire, Dearborn (1898) knew it to occur only occasionally in Belknap and Merrimack counties, although Goodhue (*in* Allen 1903) often encountered it around Webster. White (1937) noted that it was encountered frequently in the Concord area during 1919-29, but observed that either its distribution was erratic or it had "become definitely scarcer in recent years." Apparently it was most common in the coastal plain (Dearborn 1903, Scott 1921).

The Atlas map appears to corroborate Dearborn's (1903) statement that Great Horned Owls were more often seen in the Durham area than anywhere else in the state. Additional effort would clarify this owl's distribution, especially in the northern New Hampshire where most Atlas field work was done in June and July. Atlas results in New Hampshire and Vermont (Laughlin and Kibbe 1985) were strikingly similar both for this species and for the smaller Barred Owl. Both states documented Great Horned Owls in about one-third of all priority blocks, and Barred Owls in nearly twice as many.

James McDermott

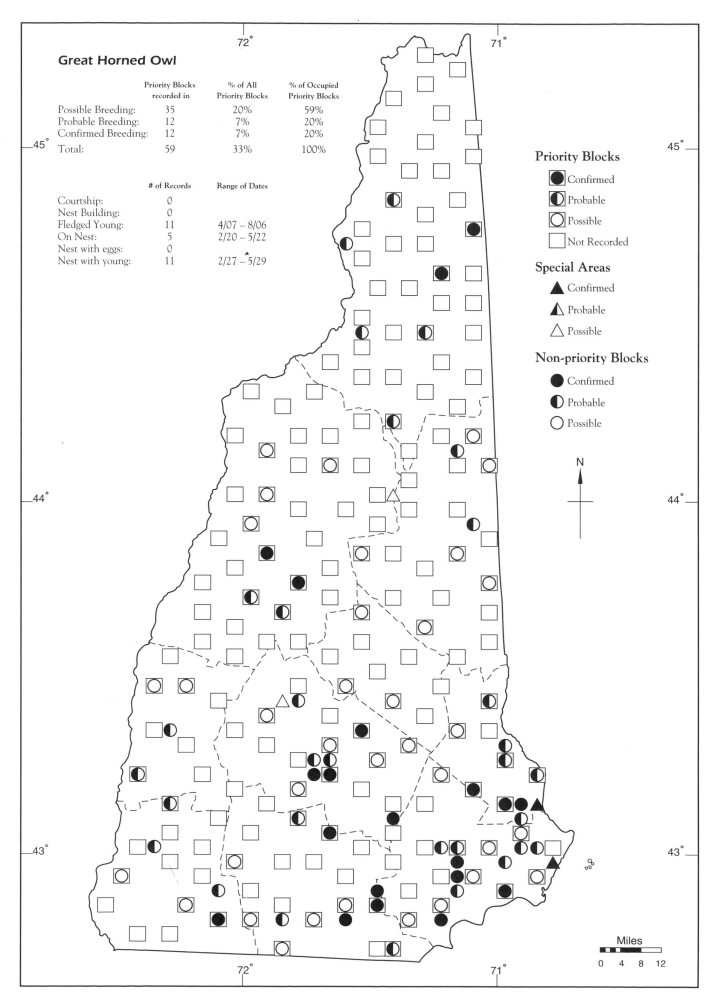

Great Horned Owl

	Priority Blocks recorded in	% of All Priority Blocks	% of Occupied Priority Blocks
Possible Breeding:	35	20%	59%
Probable Breeding:	12	7%	20%
Confirmed Breeding:	12	7%	20%
Total:	59	33%	100%

	# of Records	Range of Dates
Courtship:	0	
Nest Building:	0	
Fledged Young:	11	4/07 – 8/06
On Nest:	5	2/20 – 5/22
Nest with eggs:	0	
Nest with young:	11	2/27 – 5/29

Priority Blocks

● Confirmed
◑ Probable
○ Possible
□ Not Recorded

Special Areas

▲ Confirmed
◭ Probable
△ Possible

Non-priority Blocks

● Confirmed
◐ Probable
○ Possible

N

Miles
0 4 8 12

Barred Owl
Strix varia

This large, round-headed, grayish brown raptor is probably the most common owl in New Hampshire (Smith 1980). If well seen, the Barred Owl can be distinguished from other owls by its size, dark eyes, lack of feather "ear" tufts, and the distinctive pattern of bars and streaks on its underparts. Our other large woodland owl, the Great Horned Owl, has conspicuous "ear" tufts and a white "bib," but it is difficult to tell the 2 species apart in flight.

Barred Owls are permanent residents throughout New Hampshire and often remain in their home woods all year, but in winter when small mammals are hard to find, many may be forced to leave their home ranges in order to survive. When food is scarce some may enter towns and villages or perch conspicuously near bird feeders that attract mice and squirrels (Elkins, pers. obs.).

Extensive forests of mature trees constitute the preferred habitat of Barred Owls (McGarigal and Fraser 1984). They generally favor mixed forests over pure deciduous or coniferous stands. Deciduous trees provide more large cavities for nesting, but conifers offer better concealment and thermal cover for winter roosting. Woodlands that are somewhat open under the canopy make flight easier within the forest and provide better visibility for hunting (Nichols and Warner 1972).

In some regions these owls prefer low, wet woods and wooded swamps for nesting (Bull 1985), but in others they choose the hills (Bagg and Eliot 1937). Barred Owls often favor woodlands bordering lake or river shores (Brewster 1925). A radio telemetry study in Minnesota found that home ranges varied in size from 213 to 922 a (86 to 373 ha), and averaged 565 a (229 ha) (Nichols and Warner 1972). The territory defended during the nesting season is often smaller (Johnsgard 1988).

Breeding activities begin in February or early March. Forbush (1927), who witnessed Barred Owls courting by the light of a campfire, watched as "they nodded and bowed with half-spread wings, and wobbled and twisted their heads from side to side, meanwhile uttering the most weird and uncouth sounds imaginable," some very loud, others "soft and cooing."

Barred Owls prefer to nest in large cavities in trees or in the hollow tops of stubs, but will use old hawk or crow nests, squirrel dreys (Bent 1938), or nest boxes (Johnson 1987). They bring no nesting materials into the cavities and only minimally rearrange used nests, which sometimes are in such poor repair that the eggs roll out (Bent 1938). In our latitude the clutch of 2 or 3 (rarely 4) eggs is normally laid in March or April (Laughlin in Laughlin and Kibbe 1985). When a first clutch is lost a second may be laid 3 to 4 weeks later (Bent 1938). Incubation takes from 28 to 33 days (Johnsgard 1988). Incubation begins when the first egg is laid, and young do not hatch on the same day. A nest in Concord held one egg and one young owl on 19 April (White 1937).

Both parents feed the young, which stay in the nest for 28 to 35 days (DeGraaf and Rudis 1986), and then move to branches close by. A young owl was still in a nest in Madbury on 18 June (ASNH data), while another, in Durham, was a "brancher" on 23 May (ASNH data). The age at first flight is approximately 12 to 15 weeks (Bent 1938, Stokes and Stokes 1989). Parents continue to feed fledged young for several weeks (Bent 1938).

Barred Owls prey mainly on small mammals and birds up to the size of Ruffed Grouse, and to a lesser extent on amphibians, fish, reptiles, and insects (Bent 1938). Barred Owls sometimes kill and eat smaller owls (Bent 1938). Although mainly nocturnal, they sometimes hunt by day and can see well in broad daylight (Bolles 1890).

These owls are noisy at times. Their best known call, "hoo hoo hoohoo, hoo hoo hoohoo-aww," is often translated as "who cooks for you, who cooks for you-all." They often will respond to a crude imitation of their hooting, by day or night, and may approach and "converse" with the caller at length.

In some regions Barred Owls have been considered associates of Red-shouldered Hawks, inhabiting the same woods with apparent mutual toleration and often using the same nests in different years, exceptionally in the same year (Bent 1938). In New Hampshire Barred Owls are much more common than Red-shouldered Hawks and not as closely confined to low or swampy woods.

Early writers on New Hampshire birds generally considered the Barred the state's most common owl around the turn of the century (Dearborn 1898, Allen 1903, Goodhue 1922). Considering the extent of reforestation during this century, these owls may be even more numerous now than 90 years ago. Smith (1978) identified 11 occupied home ranges within an area of less than 18,100 a (7,320 ha) in Hebron, Bristol, Plymouth, and Alexandria in 1976.

Atlas workers found this species in slightly more than half of the priority blocks, a good record for a nocturnal and secretive species. An area of apparent rarity just north of our southern border is consistent with its uncommon status in eastern Massachusetts (Veit and Petersen 1993). Records are lacking from most priority blocks north of the White Mountains. Many of these blocks are remote and did not get thorough coverage, especially at night. Barred Owls likely will continue to be rather common residents of those parts of our state that have extensive and relatively undisturbed forests containing large trees.

Kimball C. Elkins

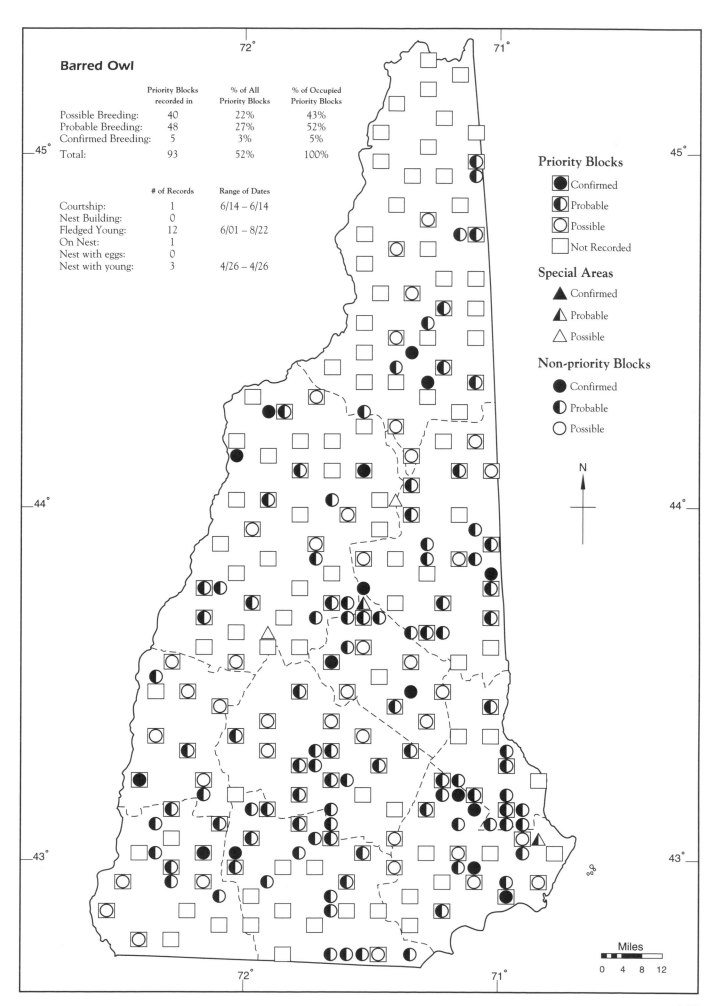

Barred Owl

	Priority Blocks recorded in	% of All Priority Blocks	% of Occupied Priority Blocks
Possible Breeding:	40	22%	43%
Probable Breeding:	48	27%	52%
Confirmed Breeding:	5	3%	5%
Total:	93	52%	100%

	# of Records	Range of Dates
Courtship:	1	6/14 – 6/14
Nest Building:	0	
Fledged Young:	12	6/01 – 8/22
On Nest:	1	
Nest with eggs:	0	
Nest with young:	3	4/26 – 4/26

Priority Blocks

● Confirmed
◐ Probable
○ Possible
□ Not Recorded

Special Areas

▲ Confirmed
◣ Probable
△ Possible

Non-priority Blocks

● Confirmed
◐ Probable
○ Possible

N

Miles
0 4 8 12

Northern Saw-whet Owl
Aegolius acadicus

Like most nocturnal birds, the Northern Saw-whet Owl is more often heard than seen. Our smallest owl may be more common than is realized, as it not only is nocturnal, but chooses well-hidden roosts. When seen, its squat shape and rounded head without ear tufts are easily recognizable. This owl's northernmost populations are migratory (Weir et al. 1980), but its summer and winter ranges overlap. It occurs in New Hampshire year round in thick evergreens or shrubs near wetlands. The elevation range of the saw-whet owl in New Hampshire extends to about 4,400 ft (1,333 m) (Allen 1903).

Although this owl may vocalize earlier, its regular calling season here begins in late February or early March. Even then it is difficult to locate, as it is a great ventriloquist. Its typical call consists of a series of short, whistled notes, usually at a rate of about 2 per second. Some liken this to the sound of a saw being filed, or "whetted." Others liken the sound to the beeping of a bus backing up. Vocalizing is most frequent in March, but continues sporadically throughout the spring and occurs again in the fall. In fall the saw-whet may give a "staccato whistle" singly or several times in rapid succession (K. C. Elkins, pers. comm.). It sometimes responds to imitations of its typical call with a squeal of varying pitch, lasting perhaps 2 seconds. Terrill (1931) describes a "tsch-wett" call of the adults. Brewster (1925) reported still other vocalizations. Behr (*in* Forbush 1927) reports that the young make a sound like a sniffing dog.

The nest site is commonly a woodpecker (especially a Northern Flicker) hole, but may be a natural cavity or even a birdhouse (DeGraaf and Rudis 1986). The home range is about 280 to 350 a (113 to 142 ha) (Forbes and Warner 1974, Simpson 1972 *in* DeGraaf and Rudis 1986). As with many cavity nesters, the adult may appear at the opening in response to tapping on the tree or stub.

The female lays 3 to 7 eggs, anytime from early April until well into June. Incubation lasts 21 to 28 days, and observers have documented eggs in New England and New York as late as 3 July. A month after hatching, the young leave the nest in their juvenal plumage, which includes reddish brown upper parts, a conspicuous buff belly, and a white, triangular patch on the forehead (Bent 1938, Farrand 1983). Goodhue (1922) observed fully fledged young in Webster on 20 May. By the end of summer juveniles have acquired the first winter plumage, which is almost the same as the adult plumage (Bent 1938).

Saw-whet owls occur most frequently in heavily wooded areas near water or other edges, but also use adjacent areas that are drier and more open (Forbes and Warner 1974). They roost in evergreens or other thick shrubbery, often near eye level. It is sometimes possible to approach within a few feet of roosting birds and even touch them (Scott 1938, Ridgely 1977).

Prey consists chiefly of mice, with a fair number of voles, shrews, bats, chipmunks, young squirrels, and occasional songbirds (Bent 1938). The summer diet includes many insects, primarily night-flying moths and beetles (Dearborn 1903, Forbush 1927). Although saw-whets typically are most active between sunset and sunrise (Forbes and Warner 1974), they sometimes hunt during the day (B. Ridgely and C. R. Foss, pers. comm.). Barred and Great Horned owls, and even screech-owls occasionally prey on saw-whet owls (Allison and Allison 1957).

Although Bent (1938) describes the saw-whet's migration as erratic, others have observed a definite fall migration in a number of places near the northern boundary of the species' range. Observations in southern Ontario showed a consistent pattern of southerly migration in October (Weir et al. 1980).

Accurate population data on the Northern Saw-whet Owl in New Hampshire are lacking. Ornithologists in the mid-1800s considered it common (Coues 1868, Maynard 1871). Dearborn (1898) considered it second in abundance to the Barred Owl in Belknap and Merrimack counties, and Scott (1921) considered it second in abundance to the Great Horned Owl in the vicinity of Durham. Allen (1903) did not believe it to be common anywhere in the state. The New Hampshire population may fluctuate from year to year. Winter incursions sometimes occur (Smith 1980), and this owl is more often seen in New Hampshire in fall and winter than in other seasons (White 1924, Allison and Allison 1979).

The New Hampshire Atlas Committee placed the Northern Saw-whet Owl on the "special effort" list in the third year of the project. Observers found the species in 28 of the 178 priority blocks, of which 13 also had both Great Horned and Barred owl records, and only 5 had records of neither large owl. The Atlas map should not be considered an accurate reflection of this species' distribution in New Hampshire. The apparent concentrations of saw-whet owls in the Saco River watershed and in the New London/Andover area likely result more from concerted efforts to locate them than from unusual saw-whet densities. Efforts targeting owls in 7 New London/Andover blocks yielded saw-whets in 5 of them. In the Saco River watershed, the saw-whet occurred in more blocks than did the Great Horned Owl. Since those blocks are typical of much of New Hampshire, similar densities may exist in much of the state, at least in some years.

Robert C. Vernon

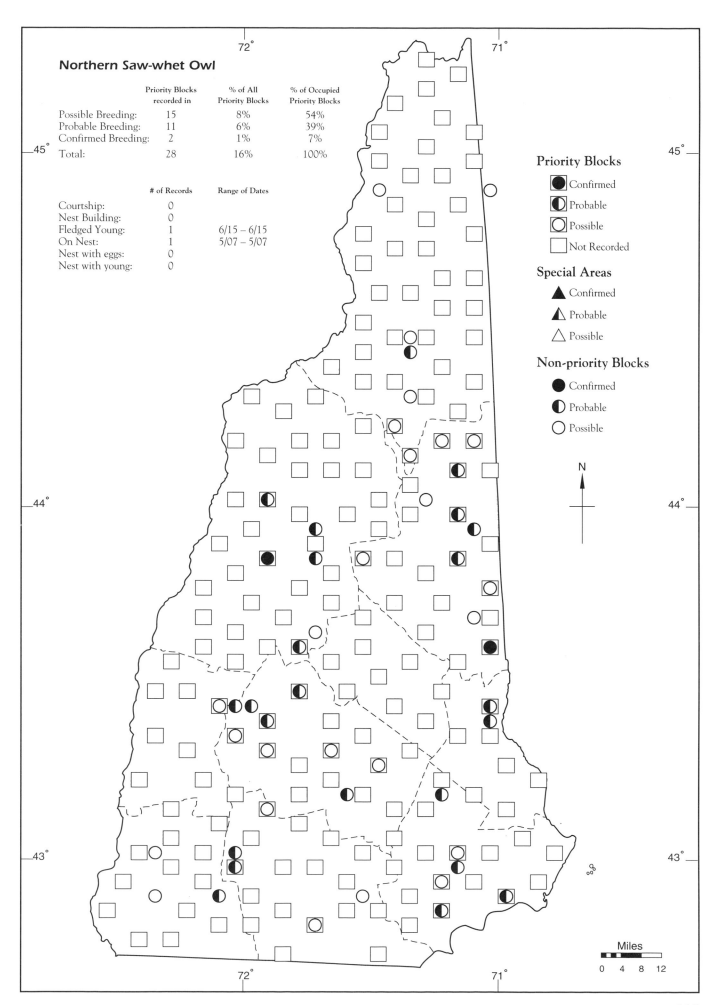

Northern Saw-whet Owl

	Priority Blocks recorded in	% of All Priority Blocks	% of Occupied Priority Blocks
Possible Breeding:	15	8%	54%
Probable Breeding:	11	6%	39%
Confirmed Breeding:	2	1%	7%
Total:	28	16%	100%

	# of Records	Range of Dates
Courtship:	0	
Nest Building:	0	
Fledged Young:	1	6/15 – 6/15
On Nest:	1	5/07 – 5/07
Nest with eggs:	0	
Nest with young:	0	

Priority Blocks
- Confirmed
- Probable
- Possible
- Not Recorded

Special Areas
- Confirmed
- Probable
- Possible

Non-priority Blocks
- Confirmed
- Probable
- Possible

N

Miles
0 4 8 12

117

Common Nighthawk
Chordeiles minor

The nighthawk's falconlike shape, prominent white wing bars, and loud, nasal call, similar to a woodcock's "peent," are diagnostic. Its presence in an area is hard to miss during the evening hours, when it forages conspicuously over towns, rivers, and open areas. This species has been on the *American Birds* Blue List since 1975, except in 1978 (Arbib 1977, Tate 1986), and it was added to New Hampshire's list of Threatened Species in 1987.

The breeding distribution in New Hampshire is widespread, though local (NHESP, unpubl. data). New Hampshire sightings are increasingly limited to urban areas, where nighthawks nest on flat-topped gravel roofs, often in the central downtown districts. Townsend (1916) documented rooftop nesting in Nashua in 1915.

Rural nesting habitat includes gravel beaches, open rocky ground, burned-over areas, and cultivated fields (Allen 1903). The only rural nest site in New Hampshire "confirmed" during the Atlas period was in a sandy area at the New London stump dump (NHESP, unpubl. data). In the early 1900s, nighthawks nested on the bare summit of Mt. Monadnock, Jaffrey, and on a few other barren hilltops nearby (Thayer 1909 *in* Allison and Allison 1979).

Nighthawks arrive in New Hampshire in early to mid-May. Courtship begins shortly after arrival and peaks during June. Males perform dramatic aerial dives, during which air rushing through their primaries causes a "booming" sound. These conspicuous flights occur throughout the summer in the immediate vicinity of the nest area (Bertrand 1984).

Nighthawks forage over towns, water bodies, and open areas, generally in the hours around dawn and dusk. They feed exclusively on a wide variety of insects, which may range in size from mosquitoes to beetles and large moths (Gross 1940).

Armstrong (1965) found that breeding nighthawks in Detroit maintained territories that averaged 25.7 a (10.4 ha) and included an average of 38 flat roofs. In Manchester, home to New Hampshire's largest nighthawk population, 8 territories had relatively consistent boundaries during 1983–85 (Bertrand 1984, Cherrington 1985). Females may return to the same roofs in successive years (Harrison 1975), and many observers eagerly anticipate the return of "their" nighthawks each spring. Display flights and consistent take offs and landings provide the best clues to nesting roofs.

Nighthawks make no nests or scrapes, but lay their eggs directly on the substrate. Nesting nighthawks respond to heat by panting, facing away from the sun, and fluffing their feathers (Weller 1958, Sutherland 1963, Laerm and Haney 1984), and may move their eggs and young into shade cast by chimneys, air conditioning vents, pipes, and other rooftop paraphernalia (Gross 1940; Watkins, pers. obs.).

The clutch may include 2 to 4 eggs (C.S. Robbins, pers. comm.), and incubation lasts for 16 to 20 days (Forbush 1927, Gross 1940). Both members of a pair may incubate the eggs and feed the young, although accounts of their roles differ, and there seems to be considerable variation among individuals (Gross 1940). The male may roost in a nearby deciduous tree when the female is on the nest and alight near the nest when she is away (Gross 1940). A bird with eggs or young is slow to flush, and the female will attempt to distract intruders by feigning a broken wing or other injury.

Chicks begin to fly 21 to 23 days after hatching, begin to feed themselves at 25 days, and are independent at about one month of age (Harrison 1978, Terres 1980). Phenology can be quite variable. While some young in New Hampshire are flying by mid-July, others haven't fledged by mid-August (NHESP, unpubl. data). Hatching occurred at a Nashua nest on 17 June 1916 (Townsend 1916), and young left an Exeter nest on 24 June 1902 (Selleck 1902). The voices of recently hatched nighthawks have a distinct tonal quality and are readily distinguishable from adults (M. Carr and Watkins, pers. obs.). Young may remain in the nest area into September (NHESP, unpubl. data).

Fall migration generally occurs from mid-August through mid-September. Flocks vary in size from half a dozen birds to more than 300. Nighthawks generally move in the late afternoon and at night (Forbush 1927), but may feed earlier in the day throughout migration.

Once a common summer resident in New Hampshire, this species always has been locally distributed (Goodhue 1877, Farmer 1892, Allen 1903, White 1924, Forbush 1927). Sightings reported to RNEB (*passim*) during 1937–67 include breeding season records from Andover, Hanover, Laconia, Littleton, Monroe, Nashua, New Ipswich, and Ragged Mtn., Danbury. By the 1950s, nighthawks had disappeared from most of their former rural breeding areas in New Hampshire, but continued to nest on roofs in cities and towns (Richards 1958, Elkins 1961, Allison and Allison 1979). Pesticides undoubtedly have had a major impact on this exclusively insectivorous species. Nighthawks disappeared from Portsmouth directly following implementation of a spraying regime (E.W. Phinney, C. M. Straus, pers. comm.).

During the 1980s, observers documented nighthawks nesting in 14 New Hampshire communities, from Berlin to Nashua. The map reflects both Atlas data and results from NHESP volunteer nighthawk surveys during the Atlas period. Records are concentrated in south central New Hampshire, and correspond with towns that have downtown areas with flat-roofed buildings. The only known or suspected rural nest sites documented were in New London and Ossipee.

Margaret B. Watkins

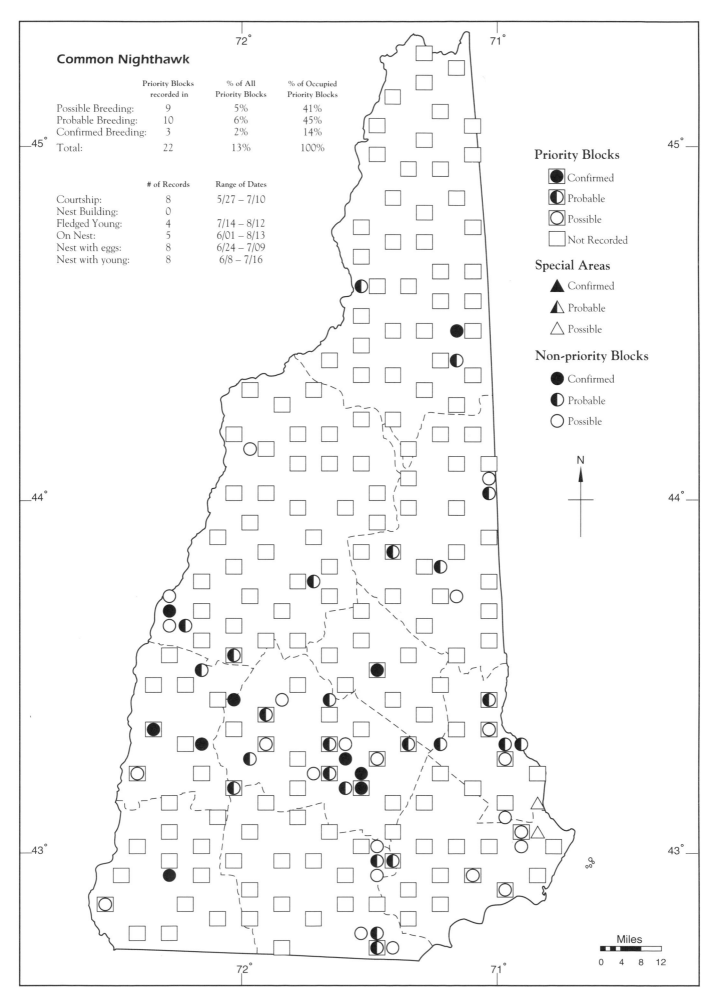

Common Nighthawk

	Priority Blocks recorded in	% of All Priority Blocks	% of Occupied Priority Blocks
Possible Breeding:	9	5%	41%
Probable Breeding:	10	6%	45%
Confirmed Breeding:	3	2%	14%
Total:	22	13%	100%

	# of Records	Range of Dates
Courtship:	8	5/27 – 7/10
Nest Building:	0	
Fledged Young:	4	7/14 – 8/12
On Nest:	5	6/01 – 8/13
Nest with eggs:	8	6/24 – 7/09
Nest with young:	8	6/8 – 7/16

Priority Blocks

- ● Confirmed
- ◑ Probable
- ○ Possible
- □ Not Recorded

Special Areas

- ▲ Confirmed
- ◭ Probable
- △ Possible

Non-priority Blocks

- ● Confirmed
- ◑ Probable
- ○ Possible

N

Miles
0 4 8 12

Whip-poor-will

Caprimulgus vociferus

Few birds are better known by song and less often seen than the Whip-poor-will. This descriptive name was in use in New Hampshire by 1792, when Belknap (1792) included this species in a list of the state's birds. Because the Whip-poor-will remains hidden until well after dark, early New England residents thought this species and the Common Nighthawk were the same. Most Whip-poor-will sightings occur when a bird flies across a road at night in the beam of headlights. Its steady flight and red eyeshine aid identification.

Whip-poor-wills arrive from wintering grounds in Central America, Mexico, and the Gulf Coast states from late April to mid-May. Typical breeding habitat includes a mix of forest and open areas such as fields, orchards, pastures, wetlands, or open water. Males sing during the hours of dusk and dawn and during moonlit nights (Mills 1986), often repeating their name hundreds of times without pause. Burroughs (1917) counted 1,088 consecutive songs. Forbush (1927) credits Mrs. C. Preston of Tamworth with a tally of 700. Each male uses various singing perches, such as rocks, roofs, tree limbs, or bare ground. They are usually on or near the ground and often 330 ft (100 m) or more apart. Singing perches are of little help in revealing the location of eggs or young.

Humans rarely have observed courtship and mating. Rauth (1979) watched a male, with wings arched and spread, hop on the ground toward his mate until their beaks were a few inches apart. They repeatedly raised and lowered their heads in unison before the male moved closer, flew behind her, and mounted. Short circular flights and more head bobbing followed the mounting.

The female places her 2 eggs directly on the ground, often on fallen leaves beneath dense underbrush or near a decaying log. The nest site usually is in dry, open woods, often near the forest edge, and is nearly impossible to find. Dearborn (1903) mentions several nests found in Hampton "among rank ferns in mixed woods." K. Stapelfeldt photographed 2 downy chicks at the only nest site discovered during the Atlas period, on 5 or 6 July 1984. The site was in Ossipee in the leaf litter of pitch pine woods with scrub oak understory, 9.8 ft (3 m) from a logging road.

Incubation requires about 19 days. Hatching is most likely to occur within 10 days before the full moon (Mills 1986). Young can hop from the nest site at 6 days of age (Bent 1940). They make their first flight in about 3 weeks and can capture prey by the age of about 30 days, but continue to accept food from their parents (Mills 1986). The diet consists of insects, especially large moths, captured on the wing. Singing becomes sporadic in August, but resumes briefly before departure in September.

Early writers (Coues 1868, Maynard 1871) referred to the Whip-poor-will as a common summer resident throughout New England. The earliest dated reference to New Hampshire seems to be that of Fox (1876), who gave arrival dates in Hollis as 15 May 1874, 11 May 1875, and 6 May 1876. In and north of the White Mountains, no authority has referred to the Whip-poor-will as more than uncommon and local. South of the mountains, however, it was formerly considered common (Goodhue 1877, Farmer 1892, Allen 1889, 1903, Comey 1904).

Several authors (Richards 1958, Elkins 1961, Ridgely 1977, Allison and Allison 1979, Smith 1979) have commented on a recent decrease in Whip-poor-wills, which began about the late 1950s or early 1960s (K.C. Elkins, pers. comm.). Observers have recorded Whip-poor-wills on 10 of the 15 BBS routes south of the White Mountains, and on 2 of the 7 routes in and north of the mountains, despite the fact that this survey is not particularly well suited for crepuscular birds. The number of birds heard per year dropped abruptly between 1969 (13 birds, 7 routes) and 1970 (5 birds, 3 routes), and has remained very low to the present time. Whip-poor-will sightings reported to ASNH decreased noticeably after 1973 (Smith 1979). This species was listed as Threatened in New Hampshire in 1980.

Atlas results show the northern limit of the breeding range in New Hampshire to coincide with the 68 ° F (18° C) isotherm as it does in Vermont. The pitch pine barrens near Ossipee Lake, Ossipee/Tamworth/Madison, still support a Whip-poor-will population, although the species apparently is absent from priority blocks in some of the nearby hills. The highest elevation recorded for this species during the Atlas was 1,200 ft (370 m), but Wright (1911) reported a pair at 1,400 ft (430 m) on Mt. Starr King, Jefferson, near the northern limit of the New Hampshire breeding range. However, Whip-poor-wills nest farther north at lower elevations in Quebec. Many "possible" records for this species, especially those in remote, northern blocks, reflect Atlasers' single nocturnal visits, rather than limited Whip-poor-will activity.

Some observers have suggested habitat changes and/or declining moth populations as possible reasons for apparent Whip-poor-will declines in the Northeast (N. Proctor *in* Laughlin and Kibbe 1985, Robbins et al. 1986), but the severity, extent, and contributing factors of a regional decline are unknown. The species has expanded its range recently in the Southern states (Cooper 1981). Clearly this will be a species to watch closely in the coming years.

Chandler S. Robbins

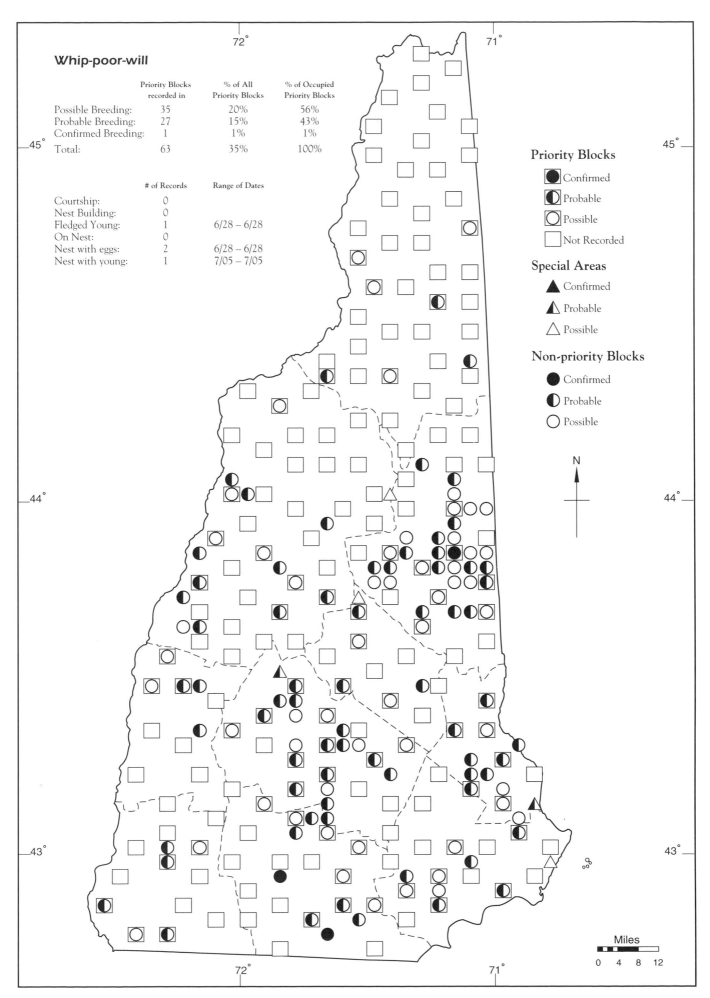

Whip-poor-will

	Priority Blocks recorded in	% of All Priority Blocks	% of Occupied Priority Blocks
Possible Breeding:	35	20%	56%
Probable Breeding:	27	15%	43%
Confirmed Breeding:	1	1%	1%
Total:	63	35%	100%

	# of Records	Range of Dates
Courtship:	0	
Nest Building:	0	
Fledged Young:	1	6/28 – 6/28
On Nest:	0	
Nest with eggs:	2	6/28 – 6/28
Nest with young:	1	7/05 – 7/05

Priority Blocks
- Confirmed
- Probable
- Possible
- Not Recorded

Special Areas
- Confirmed
- Probable
- Possible

Non-priority Blocks
- Confirmed
- Probable
- Possible

N

Miles
0   4   8   12

121

Chimney Swift
Chaetura pelagica

One need not look long to find Chimney Swifts twittering overhead in New Hampshire towns. Their incessant chattering, unique silhouette, and peculiar flight, in which the wings appear to (but do not in fact) beat alternately, are unmistakable. Food gathering, drinking, gathering of nest material, and even bathing is accomplished in flight. Swifts feed on live, airborne insects and "ballooning" spiders, and may travel several miles from their nest sites to feed (Norse and Kibbe in Laughlin and Kibbe 1985). They commonly forage over agricultural lands and wetlands, but occur in many habitats, especially in cities and towns.

Swifts generally arrive in New Hampshire in late April or early May. Courtship takes place on the wing, and involves 3 consecutive flight patterns, beginning within 2 weeks after arrival (Stokes 1979). Initially, 4 to 7 birds fly together in an oval or circular path. Subsequently, 3 birds fly together, with a leader noticeably ahead of the other 2. Finally, 2 birds fly very close together with the first bird slightly lower than the second, and both occasionally glide with wings in V-shape.

Mate and site fidelity vary widely among individuals. At Kent State University, Ohio, one female had the same mate and nested in the same air shaft for 9 consecutive years, while another female had 7 mates over the same course of time (Dexter 1969). Over a period of 40 years, 88.8% of resident swifts returned to the campus colony at least once.

Once paired, swifts begin nest building. Most Chimney Swifts long ago abandoned natural breeding sites in hollow trees and now nest largely in chimneys. A few pairs still nest in hollow trees in remote areas of northern New Hampshire. They also nest occasionally in barns, silos, cisterns, open wells, and old houses. The nests, which resemble semicircular pockets, are made of small twigs, gathered on the wing. Swifts initially grasp the twigs with their feet, but may transfer them to their bills in flight. They glue the twigs together with a gelatinous fluid secreted by their salivary glands, which are unusually large during the nest-building period. After the nests are built, the glands shrink rapidly, leaving cheek pouches in which the birds can pack a quantity of small insects for their young (Forbush 1927).

Laying of the 3 to 6, usually 4 eggs begins before the nest is complete, and both adults continue to add twigs and saliva during incubation. Both parents incubate for a total of 18 to 21 days (Harrison 1975). Up to 3 unmated individuals occasionally assist a pair at the nest, disgorging insects into the mouths of hungry nestlings (Dexter 1981). Swifts occasionally forage throughout the night to gather food for their young (Tyler 1940a). Chimney Swifts raise only one brood yearly (Forbush 1927).

Young Chimney Swifts fledge in late July and early August, 28 days after hatching (Harrison 1978). Large groups of swifts gather in late summer, and more than 100 may swarm above a large chimney at dusk before diving singly into the stack to roost. They leave New Hampshire for wintering grounds in the Peruvian Amazon in late August and early September (Terres 1980, Elkins 1982).

Although swifts on the wing are easy to observe, breeding is difficult to "confirm." Sometimes chirping nestlings in a chimney are audible in the house, and nests occasionally wash down into fireplaces during heavy rains (C.R. Foss, pers. comm.). Atlas workers most commonly "confirmed" nesting by observing birds consistently entering a chimney, presumably to incubate or feed young.

Early records from Gorham, Bethlehem, Webster, Amoskeag (Manchester), Bridgewater, and Belknap and Merrimack counties (Maynard 1871, Minot 1876, Goodhue 1877, Allen 1889, Farmer 1897, Dearborn 1898) indicate that the Chimney Swift was a common summer resident in New Hampshire. Swifts frequently foraged over the extensive wooded tracts of the Presidential Range (Wright 1911). They were considered common in Holderness (Comey 1904); Kearsarge, Bartlett/Conway (Porter and Porter 1904); Jefferson Highlands, Jefferson (Wright 1911); Concord (White 1924); and Durham (Scott 1921). In June 1903, substantial rainstorms in southern New England cleared the air of insects, decimating swift populations in the region (Porter 1903, Brewster 1906, Forbush 1927). Swifts recovered more quickly from losses suffered in several minor storms since 1903 (Tyler 1940a).

The Atlas map illustrates the Chimney Swift's widespread distribution in the 7 southern counties, where only 3 priority blocks lack records. Even in Grafton and Coos counties, which are heavily forested and sparsely populated, only 9 priority blocks lack records. Although there were no "confirmed" nesting records in the White Mountain region during the Atlas period, Chadbourne (1887) documented a specimen caught alive on 3 July 1886 in an unused chimney of the Halfway House on Mt. Washington at 3,840 ft (1,170 m), and a pair apparently nested in a large hollow tree on the WMNF in June 1992 (ASNH data).

During 1966–84, observers recorded Chimney Swifts on all but one (Northern Highlands) New Hampshire BBS route. BBS data indicate that the Chimney Swift has declined in parts of the Northeast in recent years (Robbins et al. 1986; J.S. Sauer, pers. comm.). Demolition of old factories with large smokestacks and renovation or removal of many residential chimneys have eliminated many urban and suburban nest sites, and few forests now contain large open-topped hollow trees suitable for nesting. Habitat changes on the wintering grounds also may be adversely affecting breeding populations. Despite its current widespread distribution in New Hampshire, this species will bear watching in the years to come.

Sally M. Sutcliffe

Atlas of Breeding Birds in New Hampshire

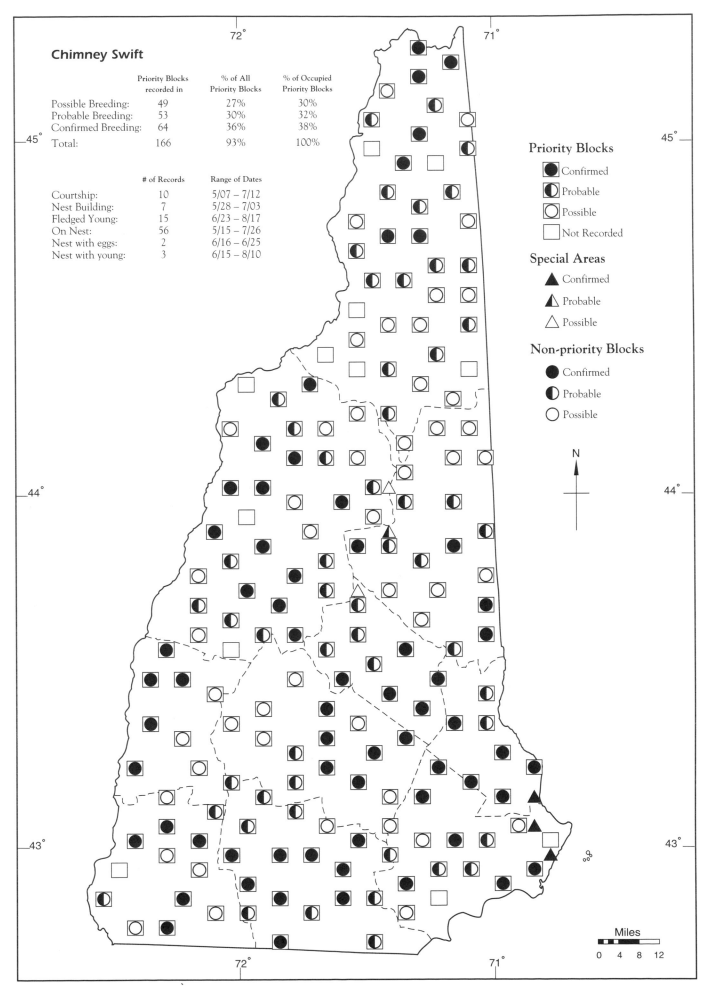

Chimney Swift

	Priority Blocks recorded in	% of All Priority Blocks	% of Occupied Priority Blocks
Possible Breeding:	49	27%	30%
Probable Breeding:	53	30%	32%
Confirmed Breeding:	64	36%	38%
Total:	166	93%	100%

	# of Records	Range of Dates
Courtship:	10	5/07 – 7/12
Nest Building:	7	5/28 – 7/03
Fledged Young:	15	6/23 – 8/17
On Nest:	56	5/15 – 7/26
Nest with eggs:	2	6/16 – 6/25
Nest with young:	3	6/15 – 8/10

Priority Blocks
- ◕ Confirmed
- ◑ Probable
- ○ Possible
- ☐ Not Recorded

Special Areas
- ▲ Confirmed
- ◥ Probable
- △ Possible

Non-priority Blocks
- ● Confirmed
- ◐ Probable
- ○ Possible

N

Miles
0 4 8 12

123

Ruby-throated Hummingbird
Archilochus colubris

A tiny jewel from the tropics, the Ruby-throated Hummingbird in its metallic brilliance shimmers in New Hampshire's gardens and forests. Although widely distributed throughout the state, it is not very common and has recently declined. Migrating from Central and South America, Ruby-throated Hummingbirds arrive here in May as the apple blossoms appear. They depart from mid-August through September en route to the Gulf Coast, where they rest and feed heavily before flying directly across the Gulf of Mexico to the Yucatan (Skutch 1976).

Hummingbirds are the only birds that can fly backwards. When frightened while feeding at flowers, they may somersault backwards and fly upside down. They hover while feeding and can ascend straight up like a helicopter.

The adult male's throat feathers may appear black when viewed from some angles and shimmery scarlet in other lighting. He has a slightly forked tail. The female lacks the scarlet throat and has a rounded tail with prominent white spots at the outer corners.

Ruby gorget glowing as he orients himself to the sun, the male performs a spectacular flight display in the shape of a 12 ft (3.7 m) U-shaped arc. Atlas observers recorded such displays from 26 May to 15 July. On 3 July 1984 a male swung with pendulum regularity over the edge of Dodge Pond, Lyman, where a female was sitting on the leaf of a daylily. He accompanied the flight with a squeaky "chippering" song (Turner, pers. obs.).

The female arrives after the male and begins nest building. The walnut-sized nest is saddled on a horizontal or down-sloping branch, usually 10 to 20 ft (3 to 6.1 m) but sometimes as much as 50 ft (15.2 m) above the ground (Harrison 1978). A nest observed in Barnstead was about 25 ft (7.6 m) up in a red oak tree, over a dirt road near a pond (Turner, pers. obs.). Dearborn (1903) found nests in beech, hemlock, and apple trees in the vicinity of Durham. The exquisite nest cup resembles a lichen-covered knot on the branch. Its soft lining and compact size efficiently insulate the 2 bean-sized eggs and later the nestlings.

When the nest is nearly complete, the female mates with a displaying male nearby. Males often mate with 2 or more females. During the mating period males are quite aggressive towards one another, using their beaks in "sword thrusts" at their opponents' eyes (Tyrell 1984). Showing little fear, they may join other species in mobbing owls and sometimes dive at approaching humans (Tyrell 1984).

The female incubates the eggs and broods and feeds the nestlings with no help from the male, often in a territory different from his (Tyrell 1984). A female often will nest in the same tree for more than one year (Terres 1980). She continues to add to and rebuild the nest during the incubation period of 14 to 17 days (Harrison 1975, Harrison 1978). A female in Benton was collecting dried cattail fluff on 10 July 1987 (Turner, pers. obs.).

The female regurgitates nectar and semidigested remains of minute insects, often gleaned from spider webs (Turner, pers. obs.), directly down the throats of newly hatched young. She takes their droppings in the tip of her bill and flings them from the nest or carries them away. When the nestlings are older, they forcefully squirt liquid excreta beyond the nest's rim (Skutch 1976). Shortly before fledging time the female feeds the nestlings soft whole insects, and the young begin to strike at insects within reach (Forbush and May 1939).

When the nestlings are almost ready to fly, 19 days after hatching (Harrison 1978), the nest is filled to bursting, quite literally. When raising 2 broods, the female constructs the second nest while continuing to care for the first brood (Tyrell 1984). A nest in Nottingham produced 2 fledglings on 18 August 1986 (M. J. Murray, pers. comm.).

Ruby-throated Hummingbirds frequently establish territories near active sapsucker trees (D. Kibbe, pers. comm.) and may attend the "wells" more frequently than the sapsuckers (Foster and Tate 1966). In Lyman, 3 sapsuckers and 12 hummingbirds, including recently fledged young and adult males and females, simultaneously fed at sapsucker wells in a large white birch on the edge of a pond in early July (L. Rayburn, pers. comm.).

The best way to locate these birds is to find flowers upon which they are feeding. They are frequently attracted to the color red, but sugar content of the nectar influences them more than color (Tyrell 1984). Hummingbirds, like bees, pollinate flowers as they travel from one to another.

Hummingbirds are conspicuous in flower gardens, but many live in forests where they are easily overlooked. Allen (1903), Wright (1911), and White (1937) considered them uncommon in New Hampshire, while Dearborn (1898) and Forbush (1927) deemed them common.

BBS data indicate a stable population during 1966 – 1979 (Robbins et al. 1986) but the *American Birds* Blue List has included this species since 1978. The Atlas project documented a wide distribution for this species in New Hampshire, with records in 88% of priority blocks. Both Atlas and BBS data suggest a scarcity of Ruby-throated Hummingbirds in southeastern New Hampshire, where a number of priority blocks lack hummingbird records. Future population trends of this species bear watching.

Sandra B. Turner

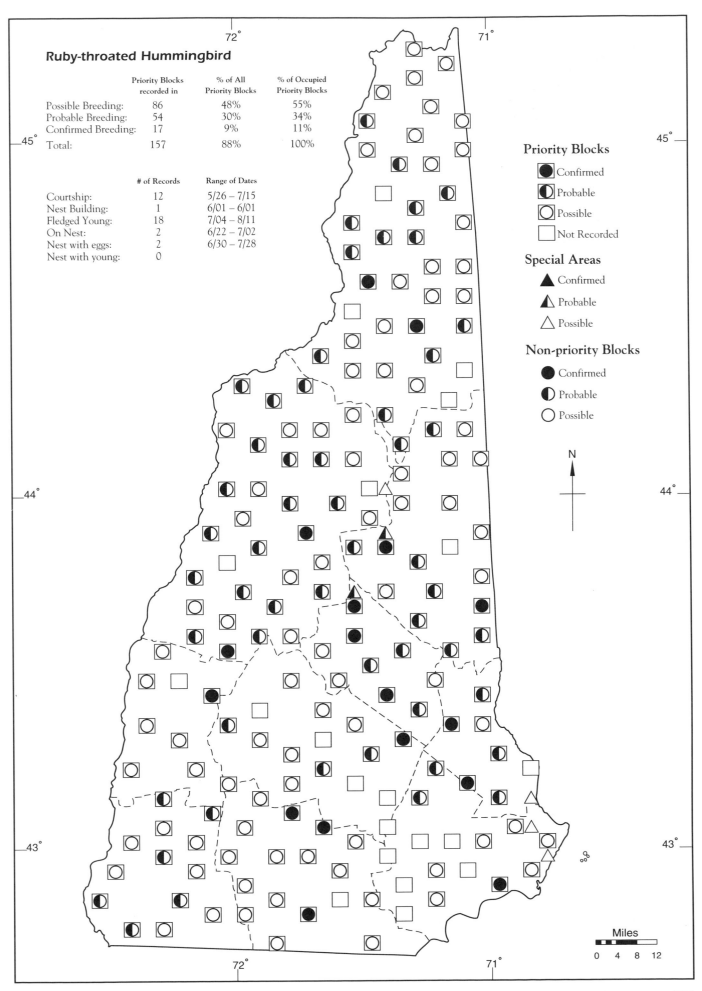

Ruby-throated Hummingbird

	Priority Blocks recorded in	% of All Priority Blocks	% of Occupied Priority Blocks
Possible Breeding:	86	48%	55%
Probable Breeding:	54	30%	34%
Confirmed Breeding:	17	9%	11%
Total:	157	88%	100%

	# of Records	Range of Dates
Courtship:	12	5/26 – 7/15
Nest Building:	1	6/01 – 6/01
Fledged Young:	18	7/04 – 8/11
On Nest:	2	6/22 – 7/02
Nest with eggs:	2	6/30 – 7/28
Nest with young:	0	

Priority Blocks

● Confirmed
◑ Probable
○ Possible
□ Not Recorded

Special Areas

▲ Confirmed
◮ Probable
△ Possible

Non-priority Blocks

● Confirmed
◐ Probable
○ Possible

N

Miles
0 4 8 12

125

Belted Kingfisher
Ceryle alcyon

With its large, crested head, slate-blue back and matching belt on a white breast, the kingfisher and its distinctive rattle are familiar to all who frequent New Hampshire waterways. The Belted Kingfisher fishes both from habitual perches and by hovering, then diving. This bird selects conspicuous perches, including wharf pilings, transmission wires, and snags. Sporting a second "belt" of chestnut and rufous flanks, the female is more colorful than the male. The species' distribution, dictated by adequate fish populations and suitable embankments for nest burrows, extends to an elevation of about 2,500 ft (760 m) in this state (Allen 1903, Ridgely 1977).

A few kingfishers traditionally have overwintered in parts of New Hampshire where open water persists year round (Dearborn 1898, 1903, White 1937). The Coastal CBC often records them in mid-December, and they may occur in winter even as far north as Moore Dam on the Connecticut River, Littleton (Turner, pers. obs.). Most kingfishers winter south of the state, however, and return in late March and April.

The kingfisher's rough, harsh cry has been likened to the whirlagig rattles used at New Year's Eve parties or hockey games. After establishing a territory, a kingfisher will fly from one favorite perch to another, just ahead of a canoe and "rattling" all the way, circling back when it reaches the end of its territory. Its courtship flight is a noisy affair. On 18 May 1985 a pair flew in tandem for more than an hour along a half-mile stretch of the Ammonoosuc River, Lisbon. Never more than a few feet apart, they sped around tall spruces and on a slalom course low over the water near boulders, chattering all the while (Turner, pers. obs.).

Although gravel pits, sand banks, or other earthen banks provide the usual nesting sites, occasionally Belted Kingfishers nest in tree cavities or in the tops of hollow stumps (Hamas 1974, Terres 1980). In 1984 a pair dug a nest burrow in a mound of sludge compost

at the Durham Sewage Treatment Plant. The male dug a roost hole nearby in the same mound (M. Davis, pers. comm.). When no sites are available near water, they will nest more than a mile away (Allen 1903).

Both adults excavate the burrow using their strong beaks, and push the loose material out of the tunnel with their feet (A. Kimball and Turner, pers. obs.). Excavation can take from a few days to 3 weeks, depending on soil type and the length of the burrow (Harrison 1975). Nest excavation has been underway in Concord as early as 22 April (White 1937). Kingfishers may use the same burrow for more than one year (Terres 1980). Although Bank Swallows may nest in the same sand bank, the entrances to their burrows are noticeably smaller than the kingfishers' (Harrison 1975). The adult kingfishers' shuffling feet eventually wear 2 grooves in the bottom of the burrow's opening, while the Bank Swallows leave no grooves (Mallett 1978). Rough-winged Swallows may nest in abandoned kingfisher holes in subsequent years (Harrison 1975, Harrison 1978).

An enlarged chamber at the end of a kingfisher's burrow holds the 5 to 8 white eggs, laid on the bare floor or on residue of fish bones and scales disgorged by the adults or by young of a previous year (Terres 1980; M.J. Hamas, pers. comm.). Incubation lasts 22 to 24 days (Skutch 1945, Hamas 1975). Three nestling kingfishers accidentally uncovered on 28 June during a gravel excavation in New Hampshire were of different sizes and obviously had hatched on different days (Kilham 1976a). One nest in Concord contained 5 eggs on 3 June 1927 and another held 7 young on 11 June 1925 (White 1937).

Both adults feed the nestlings by regurgitation for the first week or more after hatching. They then bring small fish, one at a time, to the young (Wheelock 1905 *in* Bent 1940, Skutch 1976). Always fairly conspicuous, these birds are relatively easy to "confirm." Adults carrying fish for the nestlings and adults entering and leaving their burrow provided most "confirmed" breeding records during the Atlas period.

The young leave the nest 27 to 29 days after hatching (Hamas 1975). The adults continue to feed the fledglings while they learn to fish, which takes about 10 days. Bralliar (1922 *in* Bent 1940) observed an adult teaching its young to fish by dropping a stunned fish into the water beneath them. Kilham (1976a) reports that young kingfishers in his care taught themselves to fish in a wading pool that held minnows and goldfish. Kingfishers are single brooded (Terres 1980). After the breeding season, they may wander widely from their nesting area (Allen 1903). Those that winter south of New Hampshire depart in mid to late October (Elkins 1982).

Belted Kingfishers have been fairly common along New Hampshire's waterways for centuries (Belknap 1762, Samuels 1867, Dearborn 1898, Allen 1903, Dearborn 1903, Wright 1911, Forbush 1927, White 1937). Their status apparently has undergone little change, despite the popularity of shooting them "just for fun" (Dearborn 1903) prior to protection under the Migratory Bird Treaty Act.

The Atlas map demonstrates that the Belted Kingfisher is broadly distributed in New Hampshire at the present time. Only 20 priority blocks lack records, and these are scattered throughout the state. This species was "confirmed" in all drainages and was recorded on 14 of New Hampshire's 22 BBS routes during the Atlas period. As long as our waters continue to support healthy fish populations and suitable nesting sites remain available, the kingfisher should continue to flourish here.

Sandra B. Turner

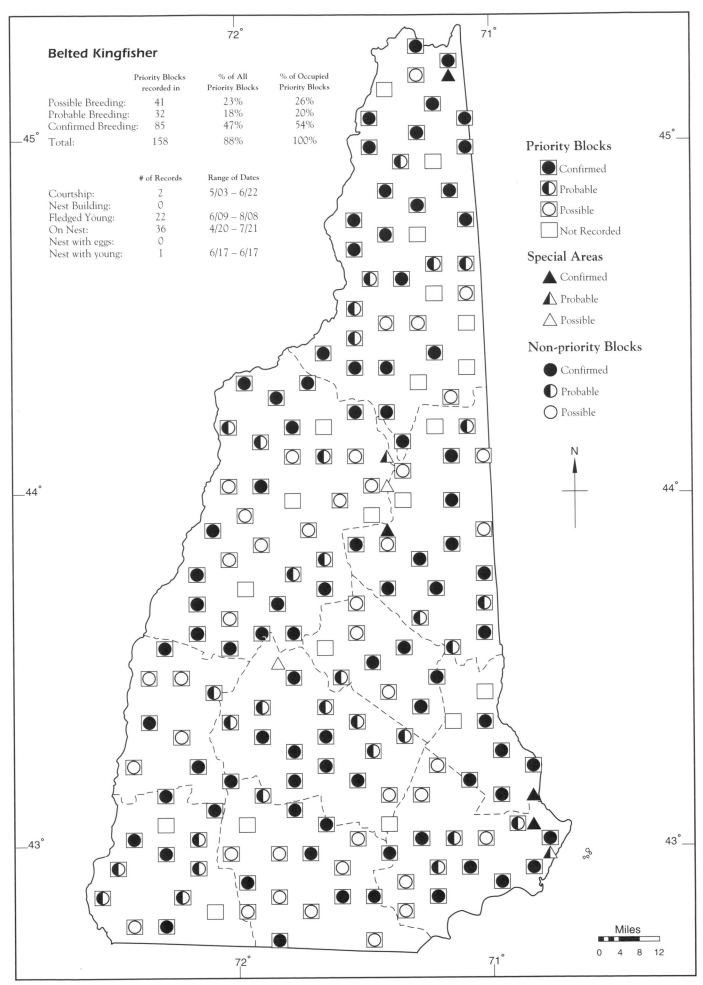

Belted Kingfisher

	Priority Blocks recorded in	% of All Priority Blocks	% of Occupied Priority Blocks
Possible Breeding:	41	23%	26%
Probable Breeding:	32	18%	20%
Confirmed Breeding:	85	47%	54%
Total:	158	88%	100%

	# of Records	Range of Dates
Courtship:	2	5/03 – 6/22
Nest Building:	0	
Fledged Young:	22	6/09 – 8/08
On Nest:	36	4/20 – 7/21
Nest with eggs:	0	
Nest with young:	1	6/17 – 6/17

Priority Blocks
- ● Confirmed
- ◑ Probable
- ○ Possible
- ☐ Not Recorded

Special Areas
- ▲ Confirmed
- ◪ Probable
- △ Possible

Non-priority Blocks
- ● Confirmed
- ◑ Probable
- ○ Possible

N

Miles
0 4 8 12

Red-headed Woodpecker
Melanerpes erythrocephalus

The colorful Red-headed Woodpecker occurs only occasionally in New Hampshire. This woodpecker's boldly black and white plumage and solid red head make it among the most conspicuous of North American birds. The sexes are alike in plumage. Juveniles lack the red heads and are duller than adults, with black bands on their white wing patches and obvious white rumps.

Red-headed Woodpeckers are only locally common throughout their range, and are scarce in New England. Typical breeding habitat includes open woods and open country with scattered trees (Harrison 1975). The breeding range extends from the Atlantic Coast to the foothills of the Rocky Mountains, from the Gulf Coast north to New England and southern Canada. The wintering range extends west to southern Minnesota and western Oklahoma, and north to southern New York (NGS 1983). They rarely winter in New Hampshire (K.C. Elkins, pers. comm.).

Red-headed Woodpeckers begin to drum and call on their wintering grounds in late April and leave in early May to nest elsewhere. Most New Hampshire records are from May, but few individuals remain to nest (Ridgely 1977; NHAQ, *passim*; SRS).

In courtship, the male calls "quee-ark, quee-ark" from a potential nest hole until his mate approaches, and then ducks out of sight. When she lands below the hole, he taps loudly on the inside and she on the outside (Kilham 1959c), by which they eventually agree on where to nest. Nest sites include trunks and large limbs of live and dead trees, stumps, utility poles, and fence posts, and may be up to 80 ft (24 m) from the ground (Harrison 1975, Harrison 1978). The cavity is usually in dead wood from which the bark has fallen (Jackson 1976, Harrison 1978). Unlike many woodpeckers, Red-heads will nest in stubs with many holes, and often use existing holes (L. Kilham, pers. comm.). When they do construct a new cavity, both sexes ex-

cavate, and excavation may take about 17 to 20 days (Jackson 1970b, Jackson 1976).

Red-heads drum in well-spaced or single bursts, usually when defending the nest stub against other pairs (L. Kilham, pers. comm.). Both sexes incubate the 3 to 8 eggs, beginning before the clutch is complete. The male and female share incubation by day, and the male incubates at night. The young hatch over several days, after 12 to 14 days of incubation (Harrison 1975, Jackson 1976). They fledge at about 27 to 30 days of age (Jackson 1970b, Harrison 1978). A northern New Hampshire nest with unfledged young in late August suggests the possibility of second broods at the northern limits of the breeding range.

Red-headed Woodpeckers hawk insects from the air, dig irregular places in tree trunks to feed on sap and cambium (Kilham 1959a), take sap from sapsucker holes, and prey on eggs and young of other birds. They take grasshoppers, crickets, and beetles, which adults dismember before feeding them to young (Bent 1939, Jackson 1970b). About half the diet consists of plant material, including corn, berries, acorns, and beechnuts. These woodpeckers may cache nuts and occasionally insects in cavities, knot holes, and cracks under bark (Forbush 1927).

Numerous New Hampshire sightings occur in late summer (SRS), when these opportunistic woodpeckers wander in search of acorns (Forbush 1927; Kilham, pers. comm.). Migration peaks in September (Bent 1939). Pairs that nest in New Hampshire may or may not winter nearby. A number of winter records exist, many of which involve sightings at feeders (SRS). Adults and juveniles maintain individual winter territories, each woodpecker aggressively protecting a large store of acorns (Kilham 1959d; L. Kilham, pers. comm.).

Allen (1903) cites a number of early New Hampshire records for the Red-headed Woodpecker, but provides no evidence of nesting. Forbush (1927) considered these birds "rare, irregular summer and fall visitors" to New Hampshire, and presumed that they nested here. Apparently the first breeding record for New Hampshire is of a pair which nested near the Fitzwilliam village green in 1939 (Fenn 1940). Taber (1953) found them in the same hole in 1940, with an egg present on 17 June, and again in July 1942.

Breeding season sightings occurred in Monroe, New Hampton, Pittsburg, and Woodstock during several ensuing decades (NHAQ, *passim*). The next documented nesting occurred in 1970. A pair enlarged a hole in a dead tree in Lyme for about 10 days in late May 1970 before beginning another about 3 ft (0.9 m) lower, and eventually nested 0.25 mi (0.4 km) away in a dead tree along the Connecticut River in Lyme. This nest contained young on 18 July, and an adult and a fledged young were in the vicinity on 30 July (SRS). A pair was present in the Littleton/Monroe area during 19 May – 13 July 1970 (SRS).

The Atlas project produced "confirmed" breeding records at 2 locations. In the Rumney area, documented breeding includes fledged young in 1981, a bird entering a nest hole on 10 June 1982, and a bird entering a nest hole on 5 June 1983 from which young had fledged by 7 July. In Monroe, young were calling from a nest on 19 August 1984, and 3 adults and 2 fledged young were in the vicinity on 26 August (SRS). These woodpeckers are by no means limited to New Hampshire's southern counties. They may enter the state from the west, where a breeding population exists in Vermont's Champlain Valley (Laughlin and Kibbe 1985).

Carol R. Foss

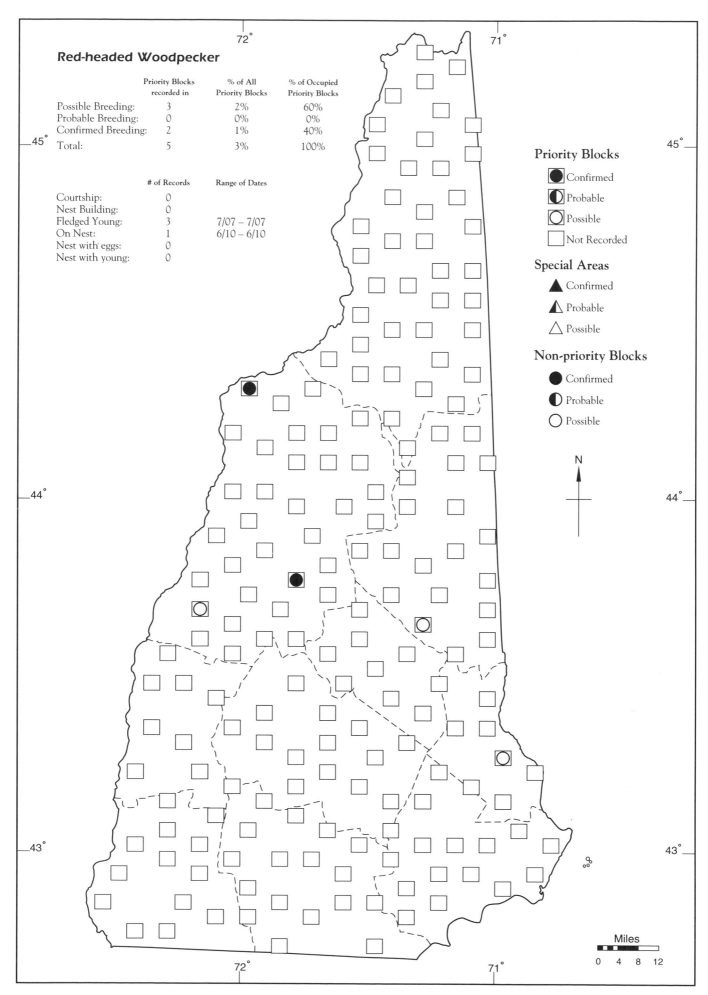

Red-headed Woodpecker

	Priority Blocks recorded in	% of All Priority Blocks	% of Occupied Priority Blocks
Possible Breeding:	3	2%	60%
Probable Breeding:	0	0%	0%
Confirmed Breeding:	2	1%	40%
Total:	5	3%	100%

	# of Records	Range of Dates
Courtship:	0	
Nest Building:	0	
Fledged Young:	3	7/07 – 7/07
On Nest:	1	6/10 – 6/10
Nest with eggs:	0	
Nest with young:	0	

Priority Blocks
● Confirmed
◑ Probable
○ Possible
□ Not Recorded

Special Areas
▲ Confirmed
◣ Probable
△ Possible

Non-priority Blocks
● Confirmed
◐ Probable
○ Possible

N

Miles
0 4 8 12

Yellow-bellied Sapsucker
Sphyrapicus varius

An irregular "rat-a-tat-tat" ringing through the woods signals the presence of the Yellow-bellied Sapsucker. Many people are more familiar with the parallel rows of small holes in tree trunks and large branches than with the bird that makes them. This colorful woodpecker has a red forehead, black and white face and wings, buffy barred back, and yellowish belly. A broad white patch on the wing is diagnostic of both adults and fledged young.

The Yellow-bellied Sapsucker breeds in deciduous, mixed, and boreal forests of northeastern North America and south in the Appalachian Mountains to Tennessee and Georgia (NGS 1983). The wintering range includes the southern U. S. (and occasionally southern New England), and extends south to Central America.

Sapsuckers feed on the sap of at least 258 tree species (McAtee 1911), and can do considerable damage to forest trees. In their first weeks on the breeding grounds they feed mostly in hemlocks and aspens (Kilham 1983). Deciduous trees that have been wounded repeatedly produce sap rich in nutrients to heal the wounds (Kilham 1964). A number of other wildlife species, including hummingbirds, red squirrels, and insects, feed on the oozing sap.

Male sapsuckers announce their arrival in early April with explosive bursts of erratic drumming. The distinctive tapping is rapid at the beginning, slowing down toward the end. Their shrill, territorial calls slur downward and somewhat resemble the cries of a Red-shouldered Hawk. Males winter farther north than females and return first. When the females arrive, the pair may engage in bobbing dances, in which the 2 birds jerk up and down giving scratchy "quirks" and, with crown feathers raised, display their red frontal shields (Kilham 1962a).

By the end of the month the pair seeks a suitable nest tree, which may be dead or alive, but always has decayed heartwood (Harrison 1978). Sapsuckers often nest in aspens infected with the false tinder fungus. Such trees provide a tough outer shell of living sapwood with a decayed heartwood that is easy to excavate (Shigo and Kilham 1968). The most suitable nest trees exceed 10 in (25 cm) in dbh (Thomas et al. 1979). A pair may use a suitable tree for 5 or 6 successive years (Kilham 1971a), excavating a new hole annually. Flying squirrels often occupy the old holes.

Once chosen, the nest site becomes the center of lively courtship. When the female approaches, the male taps at the side of the excavation, then flies away with winnowing wings (Kilham 1962a). The female inspects the site frequently, but the male does most of the excavating, which takes 15 to 28 days (Harrison 1978). The round nest hole may be located 5 to 60 ft (1.5 to 18.3 m) above the ground (Harrison 1978).

The male and female share incubation of the 5 or 6 eggs for 12 or 13 days (Harrison 1978), brooding the young when they are small, and feeding them with almost tireless energy, sometimes making visits every one or 2 minutes (Lawrence 1967). Adults are quite vocal when an intruder approaches their nest (Harrison 1975).

Sapsuckers are expert flycatchers. They can catch enough insects — in the air, from leafy branches, and on tree trunks — to stuff their bills in a very short time. They then may load up on sap before swooping back to their nestlings (Kilham 1983).

Nestlings begin making steady, harsh vocalizations as soon as they hatch. The male usually enlarges the cavity during nesting, and his rapid pecking sounds like a small motor within the tree. This provides sawdust to absorb the watery excreta of the young, which the adults then remove (Kilham 1962b). Young climb part way up the cavity to be fed within 18 days of hatching, and await food at the entrance hole by 20 days of age (Harrison 1978). They leave the nest at 24 to 26 days, and depend on their parents for the next week or 2 (Harrison 1978). The drab juveniles feed at their parents' main sap trees right away, but cannot drill their own holes until mid-August.

Sapsucker families remain on their nesting territories throughout the summer. Parents at this time often utter a mewing "waan." By summer's end they stop vocalizing, but drilling continues to betray their presence until migration south in October.

Yellow-bellied Sapsuckers have been fairly common in northern and central New Hampshire, but rather locally distributed south of the White Mountains, throughout the present century (Allen 1903, Hoffman 1904, Wright 1911, Forbush 1927, Ridgely 1977). They have increased somewhat during recent decades in parts of central and southern New Hampshire (Faxon and Allen 1888, Allen 1889, Hill 1956, Ridgely 1977, Allison and Allison 1979). They never have been known to nest in the coastal plain or lower Merrimack Valley, but occur there as migrants (Dearborn 1903, Scott 1921, White 1937).

The Atlas map shows widespread distribution in the North Country, White Mountains, Lakes Region, and Western Highlands, and continued absence as breeding birds in southeastern New Hampshire. BBS data indicate a significant decline in the Northeastern states and Canada during 1976–78, attributed to severe winters during those years (Robbins et al. 1986). Sapsuckers are able to recover readily from vagaries of weather, and their status in the state appears secure for the foreseeable future.

Lawrence Kilham & Carol R. Foss

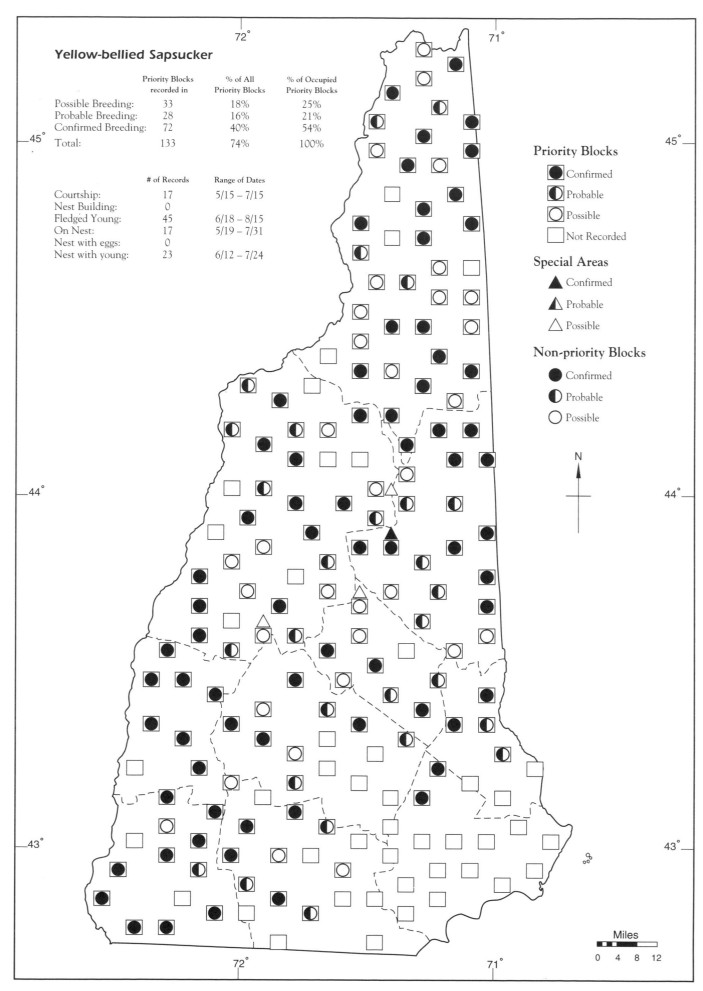

Yellow-bellied Sapsucker

	Priority Blocks recorded in	% of All Priority Blocks	% of Occupied Priority Blocks
Possible Breeding:	33	18%	25%
Probable Breeding:	28	16%	21%
Confirmed Breeding:	72	40%	54%
Total:	133	74%	100%

	# of Records	Range of Dates
Courtship:	17	5/15 – 7/15
Nest Building:	0	
Fledged Young:	45	6/18 – 8/15
On Nest:	17	5/19 – 7/31
Nest with eggs:	0	
Nest with young:	23	6/12 – 7/24

Priority Blocks

● Confirmed
◐ Probable
○ Possible
□ Not Recorded

Special Areas

▲ Confirmed
◮ Probable
△ Possible

Non-priority Blocks

● Confirmed
◐ Probable
○ Possible

N

Miles
0 4 8 12

Downy Woodpecker
Picoides pubescens

New Hampshire's smallest woodpecker is a common year-round resident of open deciduous and mixed woodlands throughout the state, and occurs in villages and suburban yards as well as large forested tracts. Its range includes the continental U.S. except for the Southwest, and much of Canada and Alaska. The Downy Woodpecker is nearly identical in plumage to the larger Hairy Woodpecker, but has black bars on its white outer tail feathers. The Downy's diminutive size and petite bill readily distinguish it from the Hairy. Individual Downies have unique patterns of black and white (and red, in the case of males) on the backs of their heads (Kilham 1983).

Downy Woodpeckers prefer breeding habitat with lower canopy height and smaller stems than Hairy and Pileated woodpeckers and Northern Flickers (Conner and Adkisson 1977). Schroeder (1983) described optimal Downy Woodpecker habitat as forested stands with basal areas of 43.6 to 87.2 sq ft/a (10.1 to 20 sq m/ha) and snags exceeding 6 in (15 cm) dbh at a density of at least 5 a (0.4 ha). Areas lacking adequate snags for nest sites do not provide suitable breeding habitat (Kilham 1974, Schroeder 1983).

Although male and female Downies maintain separate feeding territories during fall and early winter, members of a pair may begin to feed together as early as January (Kilham 1983). Drumming and territorial conflicts begin in February or early March and may continue for 2 weeks or more (Shelley 1932 in Tyler 1939, Kilham 1983). Males drum to advertise their territories and attract females; females drum to communicate with their mates (Kilham 1974, 1983). Brewster (1876b in Tyler 1939) noted that the drumming of Downy Woodpeckers tends to be softer and more drawn out than that of Hairy Woodpeckers, with longer rolls separated by briefer pauses. However, it often is impossible to distinguish the drumming of the 2 species (Kilham 1983). Territorial conflicts involve

a dance in which 2 males (or occasionally 2 females) move about near the ground on tree trunks along a section of their common boundary, jerking their heads and bodies from side to side while opening their wings and fanning their tails (Kilham 1983).

Once pair bonds are established and boundaries settled, a pair seeks a suitable nest site, usually in March. The male and female may find different sites and try to attract the other to their chosen stub by drumming or tapping (Kilham 1983). The nest site may be 8 to 50 ft (2.6 to 16.4 m) from the ground in a branch or a stub (Harrison 1978). It is nearly always in dead wood or wood infected with fungal heart rot (Conner et al. 1976). The opening is likely to be on the underside of a limb or leaning trunk (Conner 1975). With both sexes excavating, the cavity requires 13 to 20 days to complete (Harrison 1978).

After weeks of activity, pairs become relatively quiet in early May as the time of mating approaches. A typical clutch contains 4 or 5 eggs, but rarely may have 3 or 6 to 8 eggs (Tyler 1939). The adults share incubation over a period of 11 or 12 days, with the male spending nights on the nest (Tyler 1939, Kilham 1983). Young Downy Woodpeckers remain in the nest for 20 to 22 days (Harrison 1978). During the nestling period, both adults bring them food, but the male removes the majority of fecal sacs. White (1937) notes young in a Concord nest on 4 June.

When foraging, Downies often begin at the base of a tree and move rapidly up the trunk into the branches, gleaning insects as they go, then drop to the base of another tree and start again (Kilham 1983). They forage more on live than on dead wood, which they use more in winter than in summer (Schroeder 1983; J.A. Jackson, pers. comm.). Males forage more frequently on small branches, while females forage more on trunks and larger limbs (Jackson 1970a). The diet includes beetle larvae, ants, weevils, caterpillars, and sometimes flying insects caught on the wing (Tyler 1939). Downies sometimes extract grubs from stems of large forbs and from goldenrod galls (Tyler 1939, Confer and Paicos 1985). In fall and winter they consume a variety of fruits and seeds, especially those of sumac. Coccid-infested paper birches provide important winter food in some parts of New Hampshire (Kilham 1970).

Fledglings depend on their parents for food for about 3 weeks after leaving the nest and are quite aggressive toward the adults when demanding food (Kilham 1983). Conspicuous and vocal, they provide the easiest means of "confirming" nesting. Fledged young accounted for 60% of the "confirmed" nesting records obtained throughout the Atlas project. The majority (66%) of these records were from July, with 29% from June and 2 records each from May and August. Downy Woodpeckers join foraging flocks of nuthatches, chickadees, creepers, and other small birds during late summer, fall, and winter.

Authors during the late 19th and early 20th centuries considered the Downy Woodpecker common in New Hampshire, but differed over the relative abundance of this species and the Hairy Woodpecker (Coues 1868, Maynard 1871, Dearborn 1898, Allen 1903, Dearborn 1903, Wright 1911) in various locations.

Atlas observers missed this species in only 7 priority blocks, demonstrating its conspicuous occurrence throughout the state. BBS data from 1966 to 1979 suggest a stable population in the Northeast and a significant increase in the continental population (Robbins et al. 1986). Since this woodpecker breeds in suburbs and city parks as well as woodlands, its future in our state appears secure.

Carol R. Foss

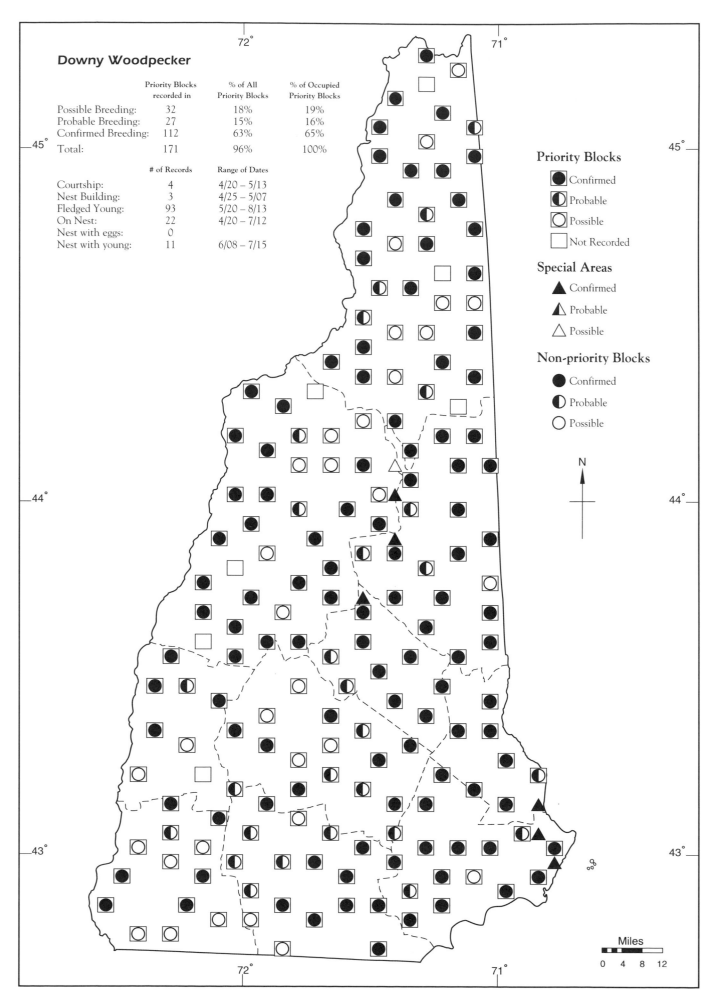

Downy Woodpecker

	Priority Blocks recorded in	% of All Priority Blocks	% of Occupied Priority Blocks
Possible Breeding:	32	18%	19%
Probable Breeding:	27	15%	16%
Confirmed Breeding:	112	63%	65%
Total:	171	96%	100%

	# of Records	Range of Dates
Courtship:	4	4/20 – 5/13
Nest Building:	3	4/25 – 5/07
Fledged Young:	93	5/20 – 8/13
On Nest:	22	4/20 – 7/12
Nest with eggs:	0	
Nest with young:	11	6/08 – 7/15

Priority Blocks
- Confirmed
- Probable
- Possible
- Not Recorded

Special Areas
- Confirmed
- Probable
- Possible

Non-priority Blocks
- Confirmed
- Probable
- Possible

N

Miles
0 4 8 12

Hairy Woodpecker
Picoides villosus

Hairy Woodpeckers are alert and active birds that enliven New Hampshire's mature woodlands the year around, and frequently visit backyard bird feeders and suet bags. The black and white striped Hairy is almost identical to the Downy Woodpecker in plumage, but is larger and has a relatively longer bill. Males of both species have a patch of red on the nape, which the females lack. Also like Downies, juvenile Hairies of both sexes may have red on their crowns (Farrand 1983).

Hairy Woodpeckers typically inhabit mature deciduous or mixed forest, but sometimes nest in isolated trees and in orchards (Bent 1939). They are noisy and excitable birds, quick to respond to the daylight hooting of an owl, or the imitation of one (Elkins, pers. obs.). Their most common call is a sharp "keep," louder and with more of an "e" sound than the Downy's similar call. They also produce a rattle somewhat like that of the Belted Kingfisher (Saunders 1935), and a variety of other calls (Stokes 1979, Kilham 1983).

Although present in New Hampshire throughout the year, Hairy Woodpeckers are to some extent migratory (Forbush 1927). L. O. Shelley observed fall movement in Westmoreland, lasting from late August to late October (Bent 1939), and Forbush (1927) provides evidence for a return migration in spring. Kilham (1983) found both sexes present throughout the winter in Lyme.

Drumming announces the beginning of the breeding cycle in early January. The Hairy's drumming is difficult to distinguish from that of the Downy and some other woodpeckers. Both sexes drum (Kilham 1983). On some winter mornings Hairies fly directly from their roost hole to meet a neighboring pair at a territorial boundary. The males face each other with bills pointed upward as they swing them back and forth like conductors' batons while jerking their bodies and making half-starting motions with their wings. These early morning displays, with occasional clashes, may

continue for an hour or more (Kilham 1969). Hairies have a stronger pair bond and a more lively courtship than Downies. The midwinter courtship includes display flights, copulatory behavior, and early stages of nest cavity excavation (Kilham 1966b). Courtship vocalizations include exuberant "joick, joicks" and "chewi, chewi, chewi" notes.

Both sexes excavate the nest cavity, primarily in late April and early May (Kilham 1983), leaving a pile of fresh chips at the base of the tree (Dearborn 1903). It is usually in a live trunk or branch of a deciduous tree that has begun to rot at the center (Conner et al. 1976; Kilham, pers. obs.), and may be 3 to 55 ft (0.9 to 16.8 m) from the ground (Harrison 1978). Starlings often take over cavities in open situations, although not without a battle (Kilham 1983). Flying or red squirrels may usurp newly excavated cavities in the woods (Kilham 1983).

Copulatory behavior peaks in April, and incubation of the 3 to 6 eggs, most often 4, usually begins in May or early June in our latitude (Bent 1939). Pairs will replace lost clutches, sometimes in the same cavity (Harrison 1978). Both sexes incubate, for 11 to 12 days, with the male on the nest at night (Harrison 1978). Hairies usually are relatively quiet during the incubation period (Kilham 1983).

After the brood hatches, the female forages near the nest within hearing of the noisy young; the male forages farther away and visits the nest less frequently, but brings more food per trip (Kilham 1983). Female Hairy Woodpeckers generally forage by scaling bark and digging out superficial prey, but males, whose bills are longer, dig for larger prey lying deeper in dead or rotting wood (Kilham 1965; Kilham, pers. obs.). Both parents brood the young for 4 to 9 days after hatching (Kilham 1983). The 29 July Atlas date for a nest with young likely represents a renesting attempt.

Young leave the nest after about 4 weeks (Harrison 1978). White (1937) observed young in a nest in Concord on 22 May 1921, which fledged on 3 June. Parents usually divide the fledglings between them until the young become independent after about 6 weeks (Kilham 1983). Vocalizations of fledglings include a variety of "speaks", whinnys, "quares", "queeks", and quavers (Kilham 1983). Family groups are highly visible, and may remain together into mid-August.

Hairy Woodpecker pairs occupy separate territories during the fall and early winter. They commonly excavate cavities in trees for night roosting (Kilham 1983), but sometimes roost outside on tree trunks (Forbush 1927, White 1937).

The Hairy Woodpecker may have expanded its range in New Hampshire's coastal plain during the present century. Allen (1903) considered the breeding range to be confined to the southwestern and northern portions of the state, although Dearborn (1903) found the species nesting around Durham at about that time. Later Goodhue (1922) called this bird a common resident in general, but uncommon in the vicinity of the Seacoast. Forbush (1927) considered the Hairy common in New Hampshire, but uncommon to rare further south in New England.

Atlas results and BBS data indicate that Hairy and Downy woodpeckers have similar distributions and population densities in New Hampshire at the present time. Hairies outnumber Downies on BBS routes in Maine, but are less common than Downies in Massachusetts (Robbins et al. 1986). New Hampshire Atlas workers missed Hairy Woodpeckers in only 2 priority blocks, both of which received relatively low atlasing effort. Hairy Woodpeckers likely will remain common in New Hampshire as long as our state remains well forested.

Kimball C. Elkins & Lawrence Kilham

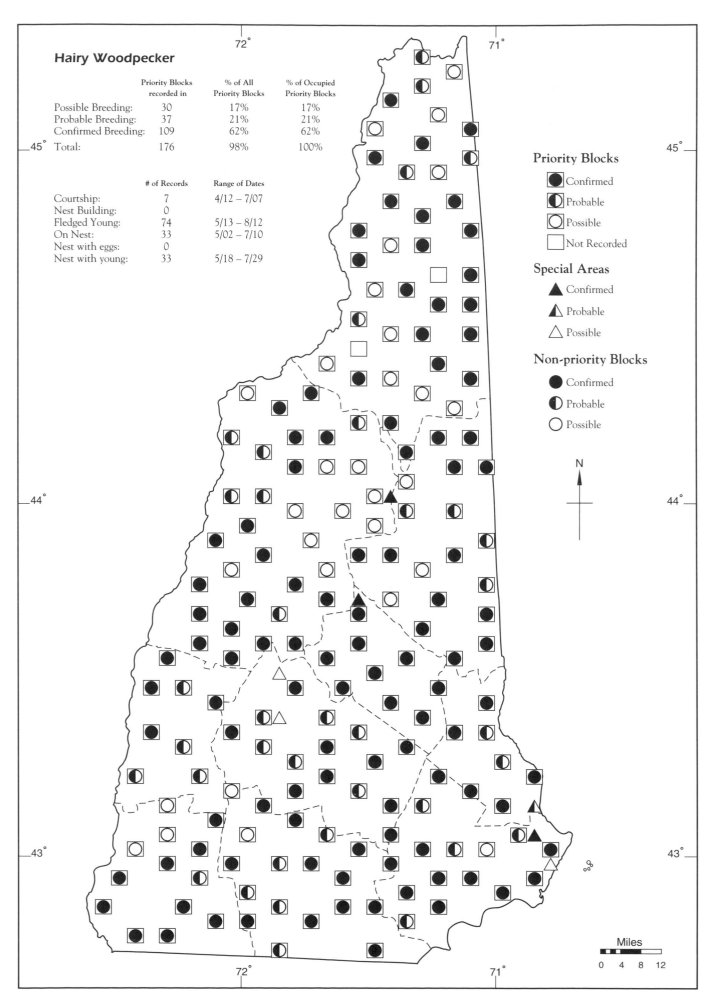

Hairy Woodpecker

	Priority Blocks recorded in	% of All Priority Blocks	% of Occupied Priority Blocks
Possible Breeding:	30	17%	17%
Probable Breeding:	37	21%	21%
Confirmed Breeding:	109	62%	62%
Total:	176	98%	100%

	# of Records	Range of Dates
Courtship:	7	4/12 – 7/07
Nest Building:	0	
Fledged Young:	74	5/13 – 8/12
On Nest:	33	5/02 – 7/10
Nest with eggs:	0	
Nest with young:	33	5/18 – 7/29

Priority Blocks
- ◐ Confirmed
- ◖ Probable
- ○ Possible
- ☐ Not Recorded

Special Areas
- ▲ Confirmed
- ◣ Probable
- △ Possible

Non-priority Blocks
- ● Confirmed
- ◖ Probable
- ○ Possible

N

Miles
0 4 8 12

Three-toed Woodpecker
Picoides tridactylus

The Three-toed Woodpecker, formerly known as Northern Three-toed Woodpecker and American Three-toed Woodpecker, is a rare and sedentary inhabitant of New Hampshire's northern coniferous forests. This species is distinguished from the slightly larger Black-backed Woodpecker by its somewhat browner coloration and a vertical white band marked with uneven, blurry black bars down the center of its back.

This quiet and unsuspicious woodpecker is a year-round resident of the spruce-fir zone of Canada and the northern U.S., and Eurasia. Although locally common in the West, this species is rare in eastern North America (Robbins et al. 1966). In New Hampshire it occurs in the North Country and above 3,000 ft (910 m) in the White Mountains (Forbush 1927). Breeding habitat in this state includes bogs and logged areas with standing dead conifers.

The habits of this species are poorly known in North America. Both sexes excavate a nest hole in a live or dead tree, usually in May (Palmer 1949, Bull 1974, Harrison 1978). The nest tree is most often a spruce, tamarack, balsam, or cedar (Forbush 1927) with a diameter of at least 12 in (31 cm) (Thomas et al. 1979). The nest cavity frequently is excavated in dead wood, and the entrance hole is usually 5 to 12 ft (1.5 to 3.7 m) from the ground, with a beveled lower edge (Harrison 1975, Harrison 1978).

The male and female share incubation of the 4 eggs, which takes about 14 days, and both brood and feed the young, with the male spending nights on the nest (Ruge 1971, Harrison 1975, Harrison 1978). Wright (1911) described adults bringing food to a nest in Jefferson Notch, Thompson and Meserves Purchase, undisturbed by the close proximity of observers. Young feed directly on insects brought in their parents' bills and leave the nest 22 to 26 days after hatching. The chattering of older young in the nest is audible at 100 yd (90 m) (Wright 1911, Forbush 1927). Fledged young stay with their parents for 2 months (Ruge 1975).

Brewster (1938) described the drumming of this species as a long, even roll, similar to that of a Downy Woodpecker. A female Three-toed Woodpecker in Success on 6 July 1986 used variable drumming patterns: one regular but faster at the end, others regular and rapid throughout or irregular in cadence (Foss, pers. obs.). Vocalizations include single notes resembling those of American Robins at dusk and rattles resembling those of Hairy Woodpeckers, but softer (Wright 1911, Brewster 1938). Short (1974) found Three-toed Woodpeckers to be less vocal than Black-backs at a site in the Adirondack Mts., N.Y., and described drumming patterns and vocalizations encountered there.

Black-backed and Three-toed woodpeckers have similar foraging methods and habitats. Both consume larvae of bark- and wood-boring beetles, and both inhabit spruce-fir forests. In the Adirondacks, Short (1974) observed Three-toeds feeding higher in trees and more often in live trees than Black-backs.

Coues (1868) did not list the Three-toed Woodpecker as a breeding species in New England. Chadbourne (1887), however, cites a female and young bird shot in August 1884 below Hermit Lake in Tuckerman's Ravine, Sargents Purchase, and another observed in the Great Gulf Wilderness, Thompson and Meserves Purchase, on 5 July 1886. Brewster found a nest with 2 eggs at Umbagog Lake on 2 June 1897 (Allen 1903). Allen (1903) considered this species more common than the Black-backed Woodpecker in the White Mountains and found it in summer in rich, damp balsam fir forest from about 3,000 ft (910 m) to 4,000 ft (1,220 m). Bolles (1893) found both species in dense spruce forest at the summit of Mt. Passaconaway, Waterville Valley, which he considered to be the southern limit of the Three-toed's range in New Hampshire.

Historical breeding season locations for this species include Jefferson Notch, Thompson & Meserves Purchase; Mt. Starr King, Jefferson; Lancaster; Mt. Adams, Thompson and Meserves Purchase; Tuckerman's Ravine and Great Gulf on Mt. Washington; Mt. Passaconaway, Waterville Valley; the Carter Range, Beans Purchase/Shelburne; and Umbagog Lake, Errol (Allen 1903, Wright 1911, Brewster 1938). J.H. Kennard and L. Kilham (pers. comm.) observed a Three-toed Woodpecker by the Greeley Ponds, Livermore, in the summer of 1927. On 10 July 1980, Quinn (1981) watched adults coming to a nest by the lower pond.

Observers in Pittsburg reported a number of sightings during the 1950s (NHAQ, *passim*), including a female with young in a nest at East Inlet on 29 June 1952 (ASNH 1952) and a new nest hole on 30 May 1954 which contained young on 5 July (ASNH 1954). Breeding season locations during the 1960s and 1970s included the Nancy Pond area, Livermore; Mt. Webster, Harts Location; Kancamagus Pass, Lincoln/Livermore; Mt. Clinton, Beans Grant, and Mt. Washington.

The Atlas produced Three-toed Woodpecker records from a bog in Success; the vicinity of Nancy Pond and another location along the Nancy Pond Trail, Livermore; and the Phillips Brook drainage in Millsfield. Small numbers of these woodpeckers may persist in the White Mountains and the North Country if adequate areas of large spruce and fir remain.

Carol R. Foss

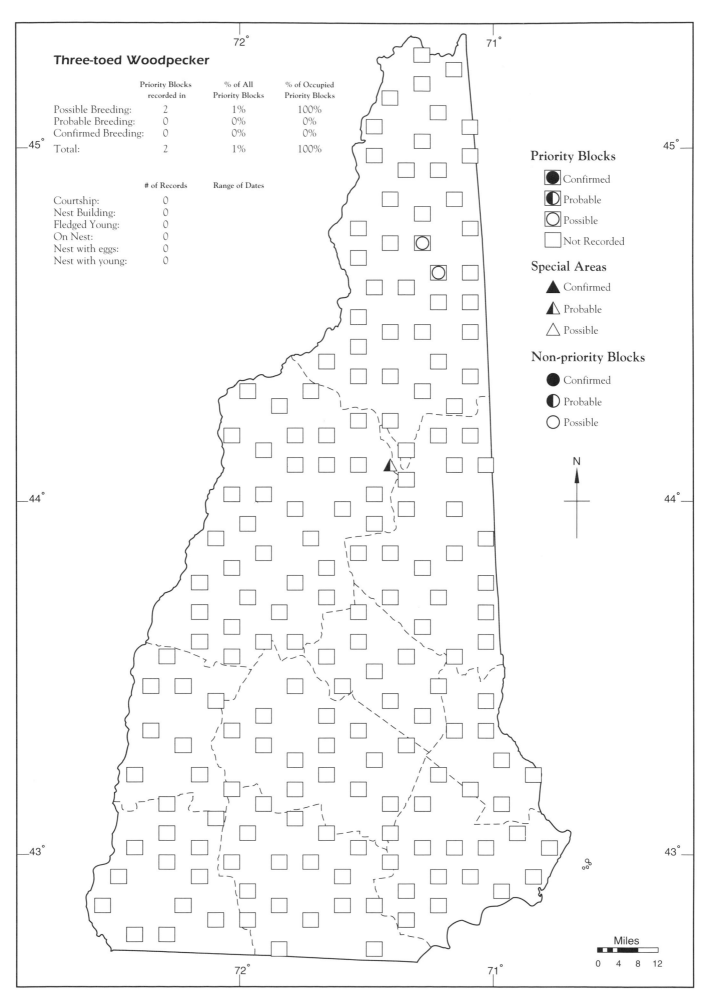

Three-toed Woodpecker

	Priority Blocks recorded in	% of All Priority Blocks	% of Occupied Priority Blocks
Possible Breeding:	2	1%	100%
Probable Breeding:	0	0%	0%
Confirmed Breeding:	0	0%	0%
Total:	2	1%	100%

	# of Records	Range of Dates
Courtship:	0	
Nest Building:	0	
Fledged Young:	0	
On Nest:	0	
Nest with eggs:	0	
Nest with young:	0	

Priority Blocks

● Confirmed
◐ Probable
○ Possible
□ Not Recorded

Special Areas

▲ Confirmed
◮ Probable
△ Possible

Non-priority Blocks

● Confirmed
◑ Probable
○ Possible

N

Miles
0 4 8 12

Black-backed Woodpecker
Picoides arcticus

This boreal forest inhabitant often allows a close approach when birders are fortunate enough to encounter one. Its solid black back distinguishes it from the slightly smaller Three-toed Woodpecker. Like the latter, the male Black-backed has a yellow crown patch, which the female lacks. The range of this nonmigratory species extends across the boreal forests of Canada, reaching south into the United States in western mountains, the Great Lakes region and the northern forests of Maine, New Hampshire, Vermont, and New York.

Black-backs nest in New Hampshire's White Mountains and North Country at elevations up to at least 3,600 ft (1,090 m) (Wright 1911). They often occur in or near logged, burned, swampy, or spruce budworm-infested areas where dead trees are abundant (Kilham 1966a). Spruce-fir stands that have experienced noticeable mortality within 3 to 5 years provide typical breeding habitat in northeastern Vermont (Lisi 1988).

Black-backed Woodpeckers nest primarily in dead stubs or in living spruces or balsam firs with decayed centers, usually at or near the edge of a forest opening. They also may nest in a small (<0.5 a [0.2 ha]) stand of trees remaining in a clearcut, as long as adequate foraging habitat is available nearby (Kilham 1983; Foss, pers. obs.). Several nests in Errol, Cambridge, and Dummer during the 1980s were located at the edge of woods facing busy roads. The nest cavities are atypically low for woodpeckers, usually 2 to 15 ft (0.6 to 4.8 m) above the ground (Harrison 1975, Harrison 1978). Wright (1911) observed nests in the Jefferson area at heights of 18 to 20 ft (5.5 to 6.1 m) in dead spruce trees. A nest in Errol, located 7 ft (2.1 m) up in a dead balsam fir on the edge of Rt. 16, produced young annually from 1977 to 1982, when the tree was cut down (J. Lanier, pers. comm.). The lower edge of the nest hole typically is beveled. The birds sometimes fleck the bark from the trunk for about a foot above and below

the nest, exposing bare wood or inner bark.

Black-backs can be quite conspicuous in April and early May as they establish territories and excavate nest holes (Lisi 1988). As with most woodpeckers, male and female Black-backs share the tasks of nesting (Kilham 1983). Males do most of the excavating, remove most fecal sacs, and sometimes spend nights on the nest (Short 1974). Females make more feeding visits but bring fewer insects at a time than males (Short 1974, Kilham 1983). Both sexes incubate the 2 to 6 eggs for about 2 weeks (Harrison 1975). In northeastern Vermont, incubation begins in mid-May, and the woodpeckers are quite inconspicuous for the duration (Lisi 1988).

Nestlings make almost continuous rattling calls, which are audible at a considerable distance. They sometimes are so aggressive that the adults have difficulty feeding them (Short 1974). Wright (1911) observed nests with young at 3,500–3,600 ft (1,060–1,090 m) on Mt. Starr King, Jefferson, on 7 July 1906, 22 June 1908, and 28 June 1909. Kilham (1983) observed 2 pin-feathered nestlings in Pittsburg on 19 June 1963. Young fledge at 20 to 24 days of age, and may remain in the vicinity of the nest tree with their parents at least through July (Lisi 1988). In Vermont, home ranges encompass at least 150 a (61 ha) and pairs nest at least a mile apart in extensive areas of good habitat (Lisi 1988).

The most common vocalization of these woodpeckers is a repeated "chet," and parent Black-backs sometimes greet each other with a loud "pet-wree-oo" (Kilham 1983). Short (1974) describes additional vocalizations, including a "kyik-ek" call given frequently by a female at the nest. A female Kilham encountered on Mt. Whiteface, Waterville Valley on 26 August 1962 made loud, metallic "tchup" notes.

Although Coues (1868) did not know of these woodpeckers nesting in New England, Samuels (1867) found 2 nests in June 1864 in the Magalloway River valley in Maine, and Brewster (1925) observed them in the vicinity of Umbagog Lake during his field work there before and after the turn of the century. Allen (1903) considered this species to be less common than the Three-toed Woodpecker, and Forbush (1927) described it as a rare resident in northern New Hampshire and the White Mountains. Wright (1911) considered it uncommon in the Jefferson region and knew of nesting pairs in Jefferson Notch, Thompson & Meserves Purchase, and on Mt. Starr King. The widespread logging and fires that occurred in northern New Hampshire between 1870 and 1920 undoubtedly decimated this species along with its habitat. Whittle (1920) encountered a concentration of more than 30 adult and young Black-backed and Three-toed woodpeckers in a small remnant of virgin spruce and fir with many diseased firs near Mt. Pisgah, Clarksville, in October 1917, after much of the spruce and fir in northern New Hampshire had been cut.

New Hampshire's Black-backed Woodpecker population may have increased in recent years as spruce-fir forests have regenerated and matured. Observers have encountered this species regularly in Pittsburg, Clarksville, Stewartstown, Columbia, Colebrook, Errol, Cambridge, and Dummer, and in the White Mountains during the past 3 decades (SRS).

As the Atlas map illustrates, the present breeding range of the Black-backed Woodpecker in New Hampshire encompasses the North Country and the White Mountains. The southernmost "confirmed" nesting is in the Sandwich Range. While this woodpecker is appropriately considered a Special Concern Species in New Hampshire, it appears reasonably secure at the present time.

Lawrence Kilham & Carol R. Foss

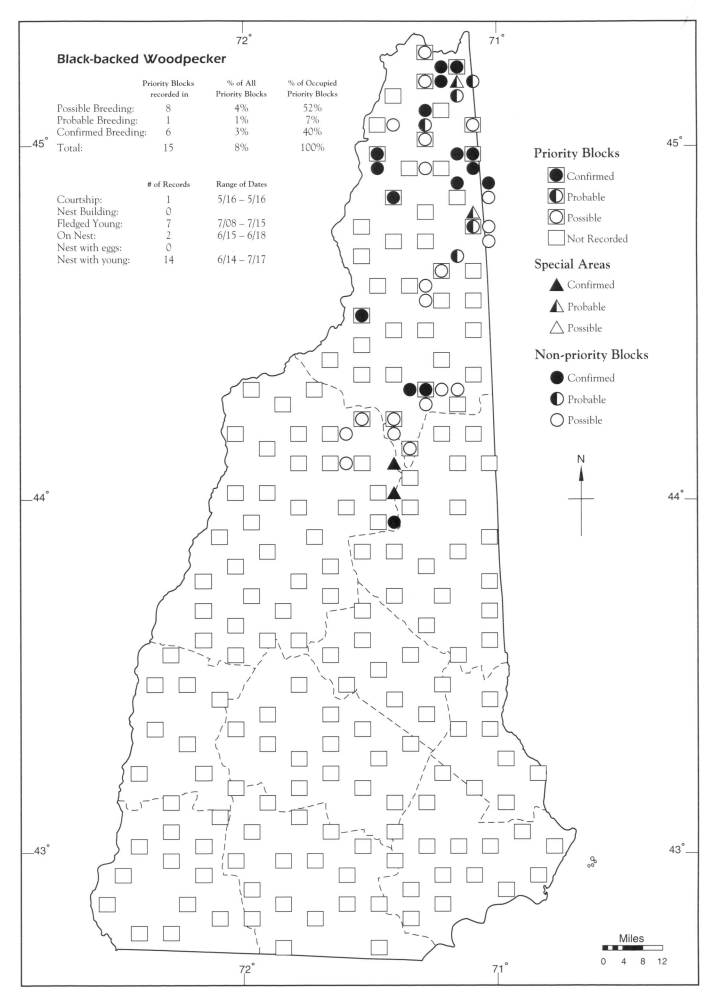

Black-backed Woodpecker

	Priority Blocks recorded in	% of All Priority Blocks	% of Occupied Priority Blocks
Possible Breeding:	8	4%	52%
Probable Breeding:	1	1%	7%
Confirmed Breeding:	6	3%	40%
Total:	15	8%	100%

	# of Records	Range of Dates
Courtship:	1	5/16 – 5/16
Nest Building:	0	
Fledged Young:	7	7/08 – 7/15
On Nest:	2	6/15 – 6/18
Nest with eggs:	0	
Nest with young:	14	6/14 – 7/17

Priority Blocks

- ◕ Confirmed
- ◑ Probable
- ○ Possible
- ☐ Not Recorded

Special Areas

- ▲ Confirmed
- ◤ Probable
- △ Possible

Non-priority Blocks

- ● Confirmed
- ◐ Probable
- ○ Possible

N

Miles
0 4 8 12

Northern Flicker
Colaptes auratus

Our only brown woodpecker spends more time feeding on the ground than in trees. The flicker's loud "WICK-a-WICK-a-WICK" call is a familiar sound in open country. At a distance, flickers are distinctive as large, brownish birds with conspicuous white rumps and a deeply undulating flight pattern. At close range, the large black spots on their tan breasts are visible.

Northern Flickers breed throughout North America except for the extreme Arctic, and winter throughout all but the northernmost United States. During the breeding season, they are common in towns, agricultural areas, and open woodlands throughout New Hampshire, most commonly but not exclusively at elevations below 2,000 ft (610 m) (Allen 1903; T. Richards, unpubl. data). Flickers east of the Rocky Mountains generally are "yellow-shafted," with yellow underwings, and "Yellow-shafted Flicker" is a recent former name. Western "red-shafted flickers" occasionally appear in New Hampshire (Hotchkiss 1967).

The flicker's main food is ants, from eggs to adults. This species also consumes small fruits and berries in late summer and fall and depends on these food sources in the northern portions of its winter range.

Flickers return to New Hampshire in April. Soon after arrival, they begin to drum loudly on dead trees, rain gutters, antennas, or other metal work. Their drumming is rapid and even, with second-long bursts separated by shorter pauses. Males do the most drumming but sometimes a pair performs an alternating drumming duet (Kilham 1983).

Early in the breeding season, flickers perform bill-waving dances by slightly raising their wings, spreading and tilting their tails to display the bright yellow underneath, swinging their bodies from side to side, and jerking their bills up and down in a W- or figure-8-shaped course (Kilham 1959b). The dances may involve 2 males at a territorial boundary or a pair in courtship. As April advances, a male often sits quietly while 2 females call a shrill "we-cup, we-cup" and display facing one another (Kilham, pers. obs.).

Once rivalries are settled, a pair seeks a large tree or stub to excavate. Nest trees are often alive, but always have decayed heartwood. Nest holes are usually 8 to 25 ft (2.4 to 7.6 m) from the ground, but may be as high as 60 to 100 ft (18.3 to 30.5 m) (Harrison 1975, Harrison 1978). The best nesting trees are at least 12 in (30.5 cm) dbh (Thomas et al. 1979). The male does most of the excavating (Kilham 1983). Completion of the nest hole may take 15 to 28 days (Harrison 1978). Unlike most New Hampshire woodpeckers, flickers may nest in an old cavity or an especially large bird box (Kilham 1983).

Nesting attempts in early May frequently fail when starlings force flickers to leave their nearly completed cavity. Flickers, however, are persistent, and after losing 2 nest cavities they will excavate a third. Flicker eggs occasionally appear among those of other cavity-nesting birds, such as Eastern Bluebird, Tree Swallow, House Sparrow, and Pileated Woodpecker (Harrison 1975).

Flicker pairs usually nest singly within a breeding territory. In June and July 1973, however, 3 pairs nested fairly close together at a beaver pond in Lyme (Kilham 1983). Fledging dates indicated that the flickers had staggered their nestings at intervals of about 2 weeks, which may have enabled the 3 pairs to nest in close proximity without serious territorial conflicts.

Once the 6 to 8 eggs are laid, flickers become quiet and incubate for 11 or 12 days. A nest in Concord contained one egg on 20 May, and incubation of 7 eggs was underway on 2 June (White 1937). Both sexes incubate, the male usually doing so at night (Harrison 1978).

Flickers feed their young every 40 to 60 minutes, interlocking bills and regurgitating insects. Males do most of the feeding and removal of fecal sacs. Nestlings put their heads out of entrances at 16 to 21 days, and fledge at 25 to 28 days (Harrison 1978, Kilham 1983). Unfledged young in the Concord area have been in the nest as late as 13 July (White 1937).

After several weeks of tending fledglings, adult flickers may engage in dances, outbursts of drumming, and high, loud "wick-a-wick-a-wick" calls in July (Kilham 1983). Flickers remain in family groups throughout the summer, and migrate south by late October. Flickers sometimes overwinter in New Hampshire's Seacoast area (Dearborn 1903) and occasionally elsewhere in the state. They winter more regularly from Maryland south.

Flickers have been common in New Hampshire for at least the past century (Dearborn 1898, Allen 1903, Dearborn 1903, White 1937, Allison and Allison 1979). The species may have increased in northern New Hampshire after extensive logging there during the late 1800s. Wright (1911) considered it common in "the more open country and thinned woods, but not found in the deep forests" of the Jefferson region.

As the Atlas map suggests, this woodpecker is well distributed throughout the state. Only 8 priority blocks, all in the White Mountains and North Country, lack records for this species. BBS data from 1966 to 1979 suggest a significant recent decrease east of the Mississippi River, which may have resulted in part from severe winters in 1976-77 and 1977-78 (Robbins et al. 1986). The rotting of elms killed by Dutch elm disease, which had allowed a temporary population surge, also may have contributed to the decline (J. A. Jackson, pers. comm.). While future population trends will bear watching, the flicker seems secure in New Hampshire at the present time.

Lawrence Kilham & Carol R. Foss

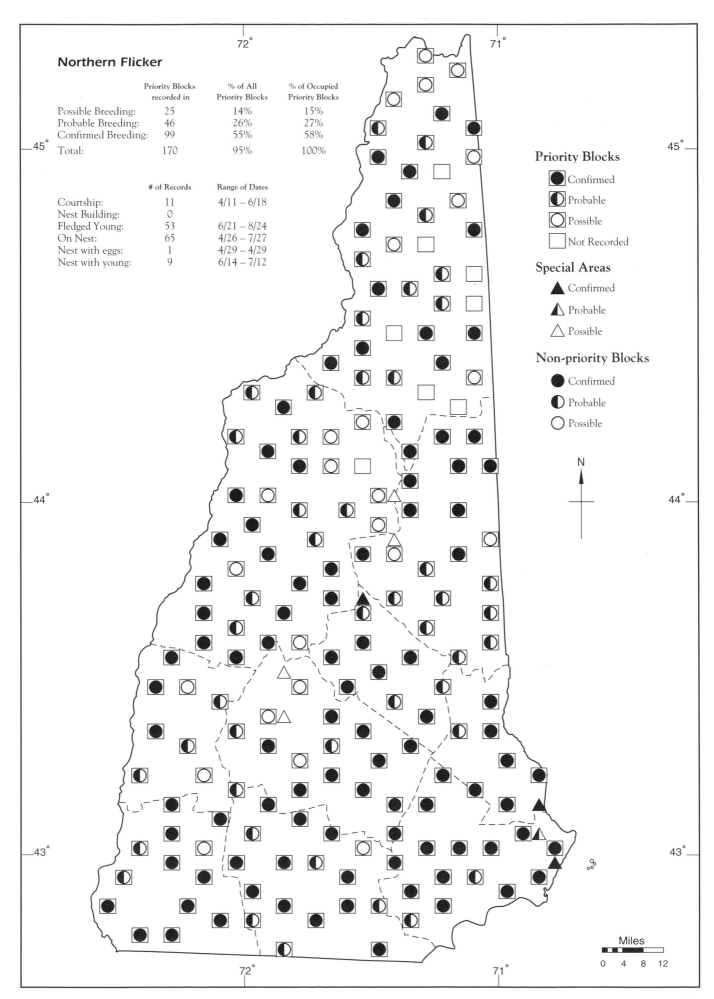

Northern Flicker

	Priority Blocks recorded in	% of All Priority Blocks	% of Occupied Priority Blocks
Possible Breeding:	25	14%	15%
Probable Breeding:	46	26%	27%
Confirmed Breeding:	99	55%	58%
Total:	170	95%	100%

	# of Records	Range of Dates
Courtship:	11	4/11 – 6/18
Nest Building:	0	
Fledged Young:	53	6/21 – 8/24
On Nest:	65	4/26 – 7/27
Nest with eggs:	1	4/29 – 4/29
Nest with young:	9	6/14 – 7/12

Priority Blocks

● Confirmed
◑ Probable
○ Possible
□ Not Recorded

Special Areas

▲ Confirmed
◮ Probable
△ Possible

Non-priority Blocks

● Confirmed
◖ Probable
○ Possible

N

Miles
0 4 8 12

Pileated Woodpecker
Dryocopus pileatus

With its tall red crest, predominantly black plumage, and striking black and white facial pattern, this crow-sized woodpecker seems out of place in northern woodlands. Nonetheless, the "log-cock" is a long-time resident of New Hampshire, residing in extensive tracts of mature deciduous and mixed woods at elevations below 2,000 ft (610 m). This species requires woodlands with a high, closed canopy and large trees with decayed centers for nesting and roosting. The Pileated Woodpecker developed a reputation for shyness during the 1800s, when it was shot as a game bird (Griscom 1929). With legal protection, it has become much more tolerant of human activity.

Foraging Pileateds dig bathtub-shaped holes in tree trunks, leaving substantial piles of chips at the base of the tree. Kilham found a pellet of ant exoskeletons lying on top of one such pile. Typical prey includes carpenter and other ants and wood-boring beetle larvae. In late summer and fall, Pileated Woodpeckers also consume wild fruits and berries, beechnuts, and acorns (Knight 1908 *in* Christy 1939).

Pileated Woodpeckers remain paired throughout the year. Allen (*in* Christy 1939) witnessed a dance of 2 Pileateds on 13 October 1908 on Mt. Monadnock, Jaffrey. The birds hopped up and down on the trunk of a spruce within 5 ft (1.5 m) of the ground, pecking at each others' bills, lifting and partly spreading their wings, and occasionally uttering soft "wahk, wahk, wahks." Members of a pair seldom roost far apart. In late winter, the female often flies to the vicinity of the male's roost for a rendezvous at dawn (Kilham 1976b).

Pileated Woodpeckers begin breeding activity in midwinter. Their distinctive territorial drumming consists of repeated 3-second bursts, which drop in pitch and cadence toward the end and may carry for a mile through snow-covered woods. Territorial conflicts can be spectacular when 2 pairs, with flaming crests raised and the white under their raised wings displayed, meet by a boundary and give shrill "g-waick, g-waick" calls (Kilham 1959e). The Pileated Woodpecker's rattle resembles that of the Northern Flicker, but is faster and less strident. The entire call is slightly lower than the flicker's, and the terminal drop in pitch is diagnostic.

Courtship includes bill-waving dances and "wuck, wuck," or "woick, woick" vocalizations (Kilham, pers. obs.). Both sexes excavate the nest cavity, which is located under the canopy in a dead tree or the dead top of a live tree and often faces east or south. The entrance hole is typically 15 to 70 ft (4.6 to 21.3 m) from the ground at a place where the trunk has a diameter of 15 to 20 in (37.5 to 50 cm). It may be round, but is usually triangular, with the lower margin beveled downward (Christy 1939).

Atlas observers reported no dates for excavation, which in New Hampshire presumably occurs in March and April. When taking turns at excavating, the departing bird may tap rapidly against the side of the hole before flying away. As a cavity nears completion, the pair may enter together (Kilham, pers. obs.).

Nest sites usually are near water in forested valleys or bottomlands (Christy 1939). The Pileated nests predominantly in deciduous trees, but occasionally nests in conifers. A pair often returns to the same vicinity to nest year after year, sometimes to the same tree trunk. Several nest and roost holes may exist within an area of 100 sq yd (84 sq m) (Christy 1939).

Copulation usually takes place on a horizontal limb that may or may not be near the nest. The 4 (occasionally 3) eggs, laid in late April or early May, hatch in 15 or 16 days (Kilham 1979). Both adults incubate and may switch as frequently as every 2 hours during the day. The male incubates and broods at night (J. A. Jackson, pers. comm.). The attending adult may perch in the upper portion of the nest cavity when the eggs are about to hatch and when the young are small, frequently thrusting its head out of the hole (Christy 1939).

Parents feed their young by regurgitation, leaning into the cavity from the entrance rim (Christy 1939). Young come to the entrance for food about 15 days after hatching (Kilham, pers. obs.). White (1937) reported a male feeding young at a nest in Concord during 20–26 June 1936. The young leave the nest after 22 to 26 days (Harrison 1978) and stay with their parents into the fall, sometimes as late as 24 November (Kilham, pers. obs.).

Presumably this species was common prior to European settlement, but decreased to the point of rarity during the 1800s as forests were cleared. Around the turn of the century, it was uncommon to rare in and south of the White Mountains, but more common in the southwestern highlands and the North Country (Faxon and Allen 1888, Allen 1889, Dearborn 1898, Allen 1903, Dearborn 1903, Thayer 1909 *in* Allison and Allison 1979). This woodpecker was essentially absent from Concord during 1865 - 1928. Although more rural and forested towns nearby continued to support nesting pairs, the first nest in Concord for many years was found in 1936 (White 1937).

Pileated Woodpecker populations have expanded during the last several decades, as abandoned farmlands have returned to forest. BBS data from 1966 to 1979 suggest a significant increase in New Hampshire (Robbins et al. 1986). As the Atlas map indicates, these woodpeckers now occur widely throughout New Hampshire, but remain sparsely distributed in the southeastern corner of the state.

Lawrence Kilham & Carol R. Foss

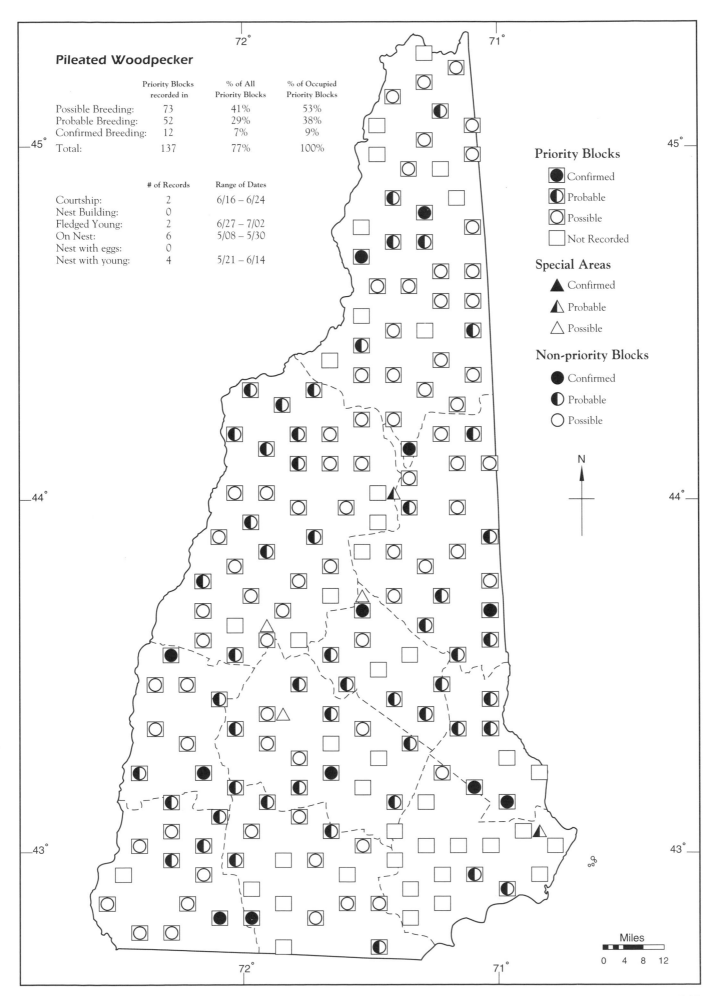

Pileated Woodpecker

	Priority Blocks recorded in	% of All Priority Blocks	% of Occupied Priority Blocks
Possible Breeding:	73	41%	53%
Probable Breeding:	52	29%	38%
Confirmed Breeding:	12	7%	9%
Total:	137	77%	100%

	# of Records	Range of Dates
Courtship:	2	6/16 – 6/24
Nest Building:	0	
Fledged Young:	2	6/27 – 7/02
On Nest:	6	5/08 – 5/30
Nest with eggs:	0	
Nest with young:	4	5/21 – 6/14

Priority Blocks
- ● Confirmed
- ◑ Probable
- ○ Possible
- ☐ Not Recorded

Special Areas
- ▲ Confirmed
- ◪ Probable
- △ Possible

Non-priority Blocks
- ● Confirmed
- ◖ Probable
- ○ Possible

N

Miles
0 4 8 12

143

Olive-sided Flycatcher
Contopus borealis

Conspicuously perched high in a dead or dead-topped tree, the Olive-sided Flycatcher presents an unmistakable profile, even at a distance, with its stocky body, large head, and short neck and tail. At closer range, the brownish olive plumage and dark olive sides contrasting with the central white breast streak become obvious. White tufts on the sides of the rump are diagnostic when visible. The male's distinctive song, a clear whistled "quick-three-beers," carries long distances and commands attention. Both sexes utter high-pitched "pip-pip-pip" calls and "puip-puip-puip" alarm notes.

From treetop vantage points, Olive-sided Flycatchers dart out after passing insects, especially honeybees, flying ants, and parasitic wasps (Beal 1912 *in* Bent 1942). If not feeding young, the adults often return to the same perch after securing prey.

These flycatchers occur most commonly during the breeding season at elevations of 1,500 to 3,000 ft (460 to 910 m), and formerly nested in coastal lowlands (Allen 1903). Typical breeding habitat is open woodland, often near water, where mature conifers are either the chief element or a conspicuous one. Preferably such trees are rather openly spaced and have dead limbs. Cutover forests, bogs, swamps, beaver ponds with water-killed trees, and openings or edges of denser woods provide the primary nesting habitat in New Hampshire. Many Olive-sided Flycatchers in New Hampshire inhabit recent clearcuts or heavily cut areas with standing dead trees (K. C. Elkins, C. R. Foss, pers. comm.).

Migrating north from wintering areas in Central America and western South America, the Olive-sided Flycatcher arrives in New Hampshire during the third week of May, rarely earlier. The male vigorously defends an extensive territory, which includes several acres (Harrison 1975), engaging in intense aerial battles with others of his species until both participants are completely exhausted (Forbush 1927). No informa-tion on territory size is available for New England, but Stewart and Robbins (1958) report territories of 4 to 8 a (1.6 to 3.2 ha) in Maryland.

The nest, also well defended by the male, is a mossy saucer constructed of twigs, rootlets, and *Usnea* lichens, lined with moss and fine rootlets. It is usually placed in a conifer, well out from the trunk on a horizontal branch, 5 to 70 ft (1.5 to 21.3 m) above ground (Harrison 1978). Conceal-ment among needles in a cluster of upright twigs makes the nest difficult to see from below.

The clutch of 3 (rarely 2 or 4) eggs is usually complete before the end of June (Palmer 1949). The female alone incubates for 14 days (Burns 1915), and the brood, which both parents tend, remains in the nest 14 to 16 days (Harrison 1975). There is only a single brood annually, but the female will build a new nest and lay a new clutch if her first and even second nests are destroyed (Harrison 1975).

The height and effective concealment of nests make their discovery difficult; "nest building" and "on nest" observations contributed less than 20% of "confirmed" records. Adults and recently fledged young are, however, noisy and conspicuous. Nearly half of all "confirmed" records resulted from sightings of adults carrying food or fecal sacs, while fledged young provided a third of the confirmations.

These flycatchers sing until late in July, and continue to give the call note until mid to late August, when fall migration begins. Most Olive-sideds leave the state by mid-September, although sightings have occurred as late as 4–5 October in Ossipee (E.E Pratt, USFWS unpubl. data).

Bagg and Eliot (1937) suggest that the Olive-sided Flycatcher, originally a Western species, spread eastward through Canada as far as Cape Breton Island, then down the Appalachians to North Carolina. Most historical references describe the Olive-sided Flycatcher as an uncommon to fairly common summer resident in New Hampshire (Coues 1868, Dearborn 1898, Allen 1903, Forbush 1927, Ridgely 1977). It was considered quite common in the Umbagog Lake and Androscoggin valleys (Coues 1868, Maynard 1871, Allen 1903), but was rare in Franconia (Faxon and Allen 1888, Porter 1903), Manchester (USFWS unpubl. data), Concord (F. B. White 1928–39, unpubl. journals), Durham (Dearborn 1903), and Monadnock (Thayer 1909 *in* Allison and Allison 1979). Forbush (1927) believed the species to be less common in New England than formerly. BBS data from 1966 to 1979 indicate a recent decline in Central New England and in the Spruce-Hardwood Forest of Quebec (Robbins et al. 1986).

The Atlas map indicates that this flycatcher currently has a scattered distribution in the White Mountains, North Country, Western Highlands and Eastern Uplands. It likely always has been more common in the northern part of the state than south of the mountains, and the majority of Atlas records are from the 3 northern counties. While increasing beaver populations in northern New Hampshire will continue to create suitable breeding habitat, future forest practices are likely to play a major role in shaping the Olive-sided Flycatcher's future distribution and status in this state.

Andrea E. Robbins

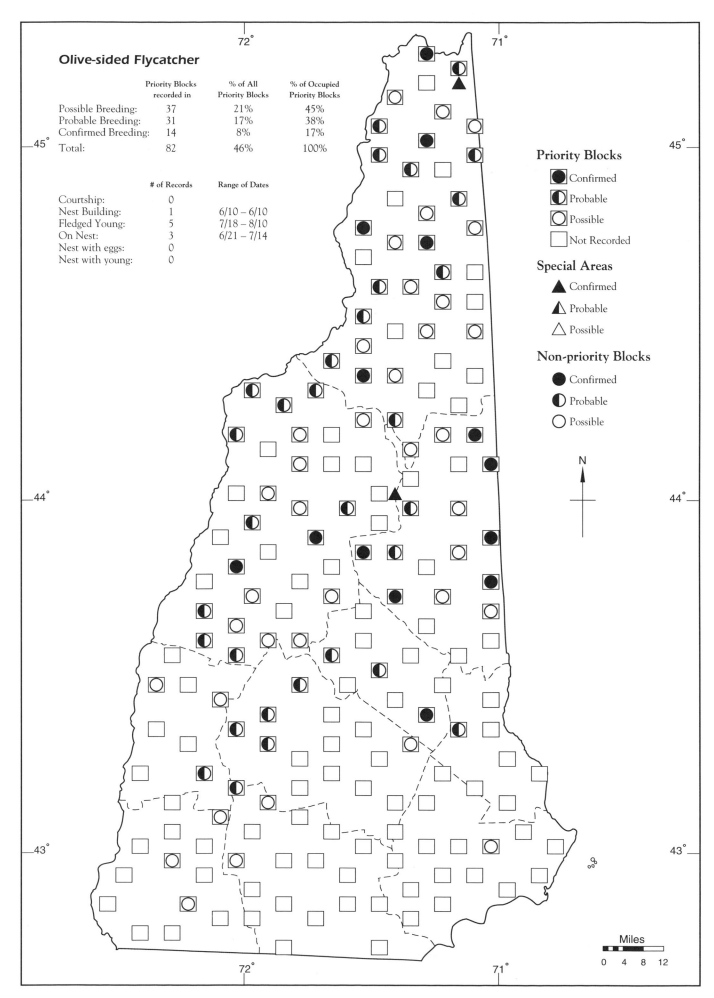

Olive-sided Flycatcher

	Priority Blocks recorded in	% of All Priority Blocks	% of Occupied Priority Blocks
Possible Breeding:	37	21%	45%
Probable Breeding:	31	17%	38%
Confirmed Breeding:	14	8%	17%
Total:	82	46%	100%

	# of Records	Range of Dates
Courtship:	0	
Nest Building:	1	6/10 – 6/10
Fledged Young:	5	7/18 – 8/10
On Nest:	3	6/21 – 7/14
Nest with eggs:	0	
Nest with young:	0	

Priority Blocks
- ● Confirmed
- ◐ Probable
- ○ Possible
- □ Not Recorded

Special Areas
- ▲ Confirmed
- ◮ Probable
- △ Possible

Non-priority Blocks
- ● Confirmed
- ◑ Probable
- ○ Possible

N

Miles
0 4 8 12

145

Eastern Wood-Pewee
Contopus virens

The pewee's slow, deliberate 3-note song signals the return of summer. A common summer resident throughout northern New England, the Eastern Wood-Pewee winters in South America. Typical breeding habitat in New Hampshire includes mature hardwoods, shade trees, and orchards up to elevations of about 2,300 ft (700 m) (Dearborn 1903, Ridgely 1977).

This olive-gray, sparrow-sized flycatcher has 2 conspicuous, dull white wing bars, which readily distinguish it from the Eastern Phoebe. Also unlike the phoebe, this species does not constantly wag its tail when perched. The young of the 2 species are similar, however, and both have 2 buffy wing bars (Forbush 1927). The phoebe's tail-wagging habit is less pronounced in young birds, which may promote confusion between the 2 species (McDermott, pers. obs.). To the practiced eye, the pewee is smaller, with a relatively shorter tail and relatively longer wings. Close observation of behavior and plumage is needed to identify fledglings in the absence of adults.

Pewees may arrive in New Hampshire during the first 2 weeks of May, but their spring migration peaks during 15 – 31 May. Pairs often return each spring to the same group of trees and may even nest in the same spot year after year (Tyler 1942b). Pewees often sit quietly on dead tree limbs. Males are more animated early in the breeding season. Rival males often are combative while establishing territories, hovering, falling, and chasing each other through the branches (Dickey 1942 *in* Tyler 1942b). During courtship the males often fly slowly with vibrating wings (Audubon 1840a *in* Tyler 1942b), give chattering calls suggestive of Ruby-crowned Kinglets, and pursue females in rapid aerial chases (Roberts 1932 *in* Tyler 1942b).

The pewee sings a continuous, 5-note rhythmical song for up to 40 minutes in early mornings before dawn and again in the evenings after sunset. Most often heard, however, is the slow, plaintive, slurred "pee-a-wee" call, often followed by a "pe-eer" which drops in pitch. Pewees may call from dawn to dusk into late August (Tyler 1942b).

Pewees frequent mixed woods without extensive undergrowth, typically at edges of fields or clearings (Bendire 1895 *in* Tyler 1942b). During the gypsy moth infestation of 1981–83, McDermott frequently found pewees on the fringes of affected areas. Nest building occurs most commonly during the first 2 weeks of June. The nest tree usually is deciduous, frequently an oak (Harrison 1975). The female places the nest on a horizontal branch well away from the trunk. She usually builds it within 20 ft (6.1 m) of the ground (Samuels 1870), but it may be at heights of 15 to 65 ft (4.6 to 19.8 m) (Harrison 1975). Dearborn (1903) describes the nest as a "low, lichen-covered structure" that resembles a natural growth on the branch. A nest in Concord was nearly completed on 2 June (White 1937).

The female incubates her 3 eggs, laid during late June or early July, for 12 to 13 days (Tyler 1942b). White (1937) mentions a 7 July food delivery to a sitting bird at a nest in Concord. Both parents tend the young, which fledge after about 16 days (Bendire 1895 *in* Tyler 1942b). Postbreeding dispersal occurs during the last 2 weeks of July. The fall migration extends from early August through October, but most pewees have departed by mid-September.

Some early ornithologists considered the Eastern Wood-Pewee a deep forest species (Samuels 1870, Chapman 1906), although others included more open woods with large trees, shade trees, and orchards in descriptions of its habitat (Dearborn 1898, White 1924). Allen (1903) considered it common in New Hampshire north to the White Mountains, and noted its presence in large elms along village streets. Maynard (1871) and Coues (1868) found it to be less common in northern New Hampshire, particularly in spruce-fir forests and mountainous terrain. The pewee undoubtedly has declined in some areas since the early 1800s, when it was generally considered to be more common than the Eastern Phoebe (Audubon and Wilson *in* Tyler 1942b). Undoubtedly the clearing of the Eastern forests significantly reduced earlier numbers of the species.

The Eastern Wood-Pewee currently occurs throughout New Hampshire. As was the case a century ago, it is most common at lower elevations in the southern part of the state. Atlas observers failed to locate this species in only 5 priority blocks south of the White Mountains, 4 of which are in the Western Highlands. By comparison, 10 priority blocks in the White Mountains and North Country lack records for this species. BBS data suggest an increase in New Hampshire's pewee population during 1966–89, and a higher density of this species in New Hampshire than in Vermont, Maine, Quebec, or New Brunswick. The future of this flycatcher appears secure in our state at the present time.

James McDermott

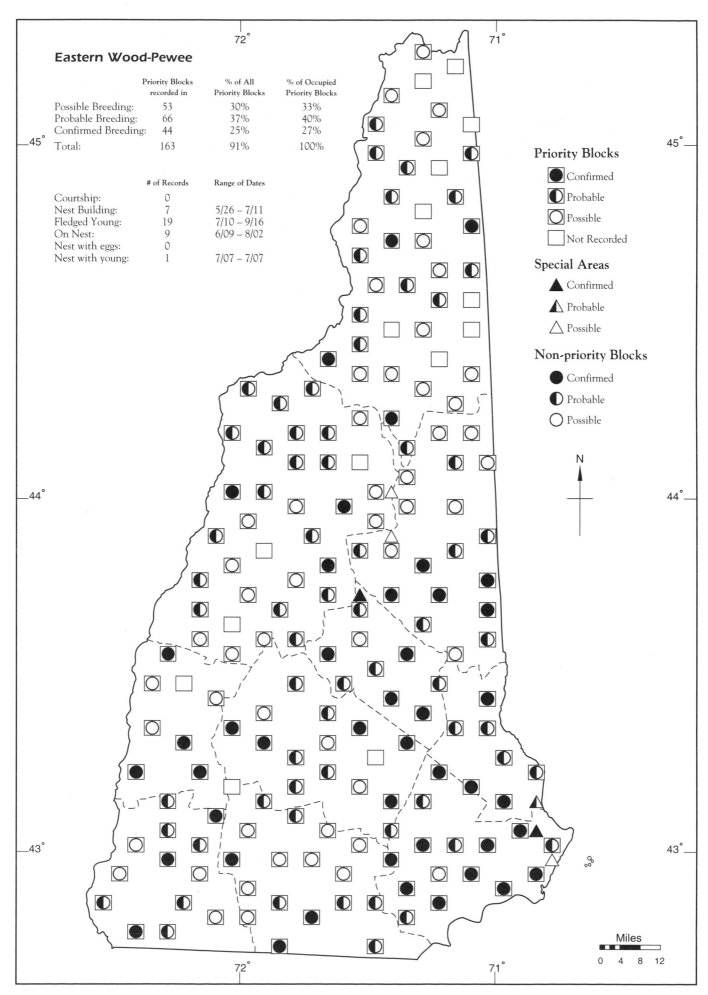

Eastern Wood-Pewee

	Priority Blocks recorded in	% of All Priority Blocks	% of Occupied Priority Blocks
Possible Breeding:	53	30%	33%
Probable Breeding:	66	37%	40%
Confirmed Breeding:	44	25%	27%
Total:	163	91%	100%

	# of Records	Range of Dates
Courtship:	0	
Nest Building:	7	5/26 – 7/11
Fledged Young:	19	7/10 – 9/16
On Nest:	9	6/09 – 8/02
Nest with eggs:	0	
Nest with young:	1	7/07 – 7/07

Priority Blocks

● Confirmed
◑ Probable
○ Possible
□ Not Recorded

Special Areas

▲ Confirmed
◮ Probable
△ Possible

Non-priority Blocks

● Confirmed
◑ Probable
○ Possible

N

Miles
0   4   8   12

Yellow-bellied Flycatcher
Empidonax flaviventris

With its greenish back, yellow throat and belly, and yellowish eye-ring, the Yellow-bellied Flycatcher is the easiest to identify of all the *Empidonax* flycatchers. However, this shy bird may be one of the hardest to see because of its fondness at all seasons for damp, impenetrable, coniferous forests and bogs. Our only ground-nesting flycatcher, the species is uncommon to fairly common in and north of the White Mountains, up to elevations of 4,000 ft (1,220 m), rarely to 5,000 ft (1,520 m) in spruce krummholz (Janeway, pers. obs.; T. Richards, unpubl. data).

The Yellow-bellied Flycatcher arrives in New Hampshire in late May, generally after most other nesting flycatchers (T. Richards, pers. comm.). It is usually silent during migration. The bird's entire body and tail quiver while it sings, usually from a perch 30 to 40 ft (9.1 to 12.2 m) above the ground (Godfrey 1966). Sitting quite still but for the quivering, a singing bird may be difficult to locate (Ridgely 1977). This retiring flycatcher responds to "squeaking", however, and its voice betrays it to those who are willing to search remote, wet habitats where biting insects abound. Its "killick" call note resembles the Least Flycatcher's "chebec," but is more liquid (Janeway, pers. obs.). Its plaintive, whistled question, "pur-wee?" resembles a pewee's song, but is shorter (Terres 1980). Just after sunset this flycatcher sometimes sings a peculiar flight song, in which it alternates "pu-ree" and "killick" repeatedly (Allen 1903, Wright 1911).

The Yellow-bellied Flycatcher nests in high-elevation conifers and northern coniferous wetlands where there is dense sphagnum moss (Harrison 1975). One of the Atlas records of recently fledged young is from a small bog at the top of Kinsman Ridge, Woodstock, where the spruce trees are low and thick (Janeway, pers. obs.). Another Yellow-bellied Flycatcher observation occurred in dense spruce near the wet, marshy overflow area of Mountain Pond, North Conway (J.

Longnecker, pers. comm.).

The well-concealed and camouflaged nest sits in moss on the ground or in exposed roots of fallen trees and is very difficult to observe. Nests in Coos County have been located in a small depression in the mossy side of an overturned stump, and in moss in a depression on the side of a large rock, about 16 in (41 cm) above the ground, "well hidden behind some roots and dead spruce branches, a small blueberry bush, a small balsam fir, some sphagnum moss and fine cranberry bushes" (Dyer and Walkinsaw 1959). The female builds the bulky cup nest of dry mosses and sedges, the outside "faced with beautiful fresh green mosses, thickest about the rim" (Purdie 1878 *in* Bent 1942) and lined with black plant fibers and fine rootlets (Brown *in* Bent 1942).

Ornithologists apparently never have described the courtship behavior of the Yellow-bellied Flycatcher. The usually secretive female calls "pe-wee" repeatedly when disturbed from the nest (Dyer and Walkinsaw 1959). She incubates the clutch of 3 to 5, usually 3 or 4 eggs for 15 days. A nest in Lancaster located "near a low, swampy piece of woods" contained 5 fresh eggs on 14 June 1886 (Spaulding 1887 *in* Allen 1903). Young birds leave the nest about 13 days after hatching (Walkinshaw and Henry 1957b *in* Terres 1980), and there is but one brood a year (Forbush 1927). The Yellow-bellied Flycatcher's diet is primarily insects.

In the late 19th century, the Yellow-bellied Flycatcher was a common summer resident in the White Mountains at elevations from about 3,000 to 4,500 ft (910 to 1,370 m), with an occasional pair found at lower elevations (Chadbourne 1887, Faxon and Allen 1888, Allen 1903). North of the White Mountains it was common at Umbagog Lake, Errol (Maynard 1871). Thayer (*in* Allen 1903) provided the first suggestion of breeding south of the White Mountains, a pair observed "in a certain forest swamp on Mt. Monadnock at about 1400 feet" for several summers in succession. The species occurred during the breeding season in Lempster in June 1955, on Mt. Sunapee, Newbury, in June 1953 and July 1955, and in Dublin in 1958 (T. Richards, unpubl. data). Observers found it in spruce woods on Mt. Kearsarge, Warner/Wilmot in June 1953, 1954, 1972, and 1976 (K. C. Elkins, pers. comm.), but have detected none there since (R. C. Vernon, pers. comm.).

The Atlas map shows no records in southern New Hampshire, and few south of the White Mountains. Additional Atlas effort in the remote priority blocks in Coos County likely would have produced more records and increased the proportion of "confirmations". BBS data from 1966 to 1979 suggest a significant increase of this species east of the Mississippi River (Robbins et al. 1986). The Yellow-bellied Flycatcher's damp and remote haunts are secure from immediate threats, and this diminutive bird will likely greet the intrepid visitor to northern bog and mountain for many years to come.

Elizabeth C. Janeway

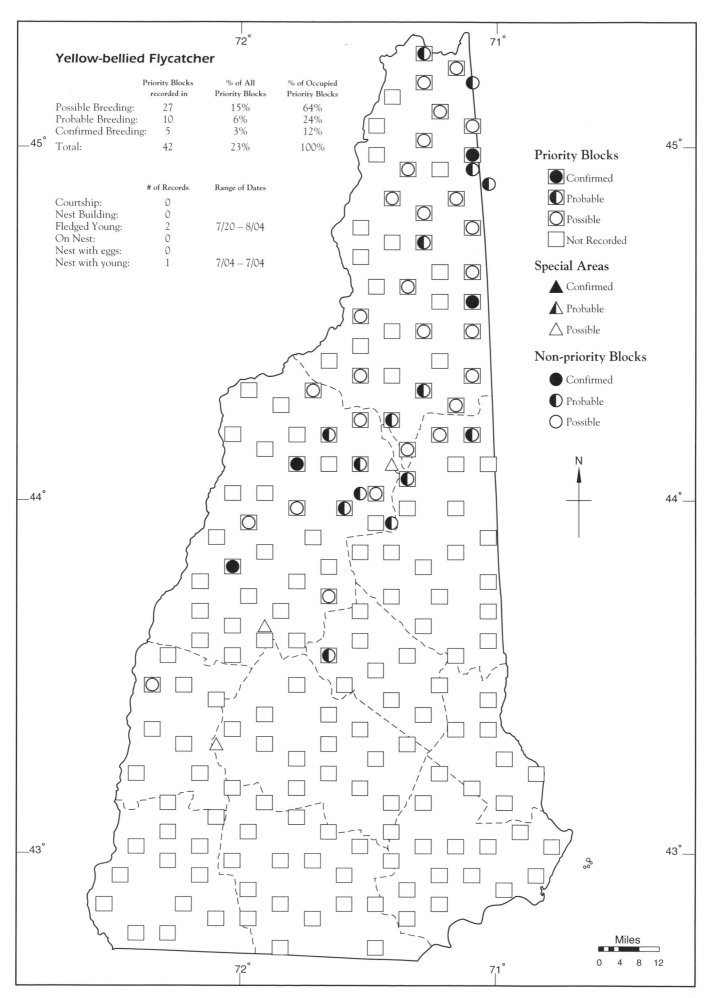

Yellow-bellied Flycatcher

	Priority Blocks recorded in	% of All Priority Blocks	% of Occupied Priority Blocks
Possible Breeding:	27	15%	64%
Probable Breeding:	10	6%	24%
Confirmed Breeding:	5	3%	12%
Total:	42	23%	100%

	# of Records	Range of Dates
Courtship:	0	
Nest Building:	0	
Fledged Young:	2	7/20 – 8/04
On Nest:	0	
Nest with eggs:	0	
Nest with young:	1	7/04 – 7/04

Priority Blocks

● Confirmed
◑ Probable
○ Possible
□ Not Recorded

Special Areas

▲ Confirmed
◤ Probable
△ Possible

Non-priority Blocks

● Confirmed
◐ Probable
○ Possible

N

Miles
0 4 8 12

149

Acadian Flycatcher
Empidonax virescens

The Acadian Flycatcher is among the small, confusingly similar flycatchers often lumped together as "empids" (from the scientific name) by frustrated bird watchers who find identification nearly impossible by sight alone. In summer, however, this bird is readily identifiable by its song, a sharp, explosive "pit-see!" (Peterson 1980), generally delivered from a perch under a dense canopy of beech or other hardwood trees. The Acadian Flycatcher is typically quite inconspicuous and usually perches in deep shade less than 20 ft (6.1 m) from the ground (Christy 1942). Of the 5 *Empidonax* flycatchers which breed in eastern North America, all but the Acadian are regular summer residents in New Hampshire. The occurrence of this species in the state apparently is limited to migratory "overshoots" which occasionally establish breeding territories.

The Acadian Flycatcher breeds primarily in mature deciduous bottomland forests and swamps of the southeastern U. S. Its range barely reaches southern New England, much less New Hampshire. It winters in Central America and northwestern South America. This flycatcher's curious name, despite its absence from the "land of Evangeline," derives from the fact that all 5 Eastern *Empidonax* flycatchers, several of which nest in the Maritime Provinces, were once considered a single species. As knowledge of the group increased, ornithologists eventually separated out the other species, leaving this one with the name (Pearson 1936).

Like most flycatchers, this species is among the last of the migrants to return in spring, and nesting does not occur until June. Christy (1942) notes that males are extremely aggressive and chase warblers, vireos, and tanagers, as well as each other, in defending their nesting territories, which may be only 200 yd (180 m) or less across.

The unique nest is loosely constructed of plant stems and other fibrous material and usually includes hanging streamers of grass, birch bark, or other plant fibers, which may extend 2 ft (0.6 m) below the nest bowl (Harrison 1975). It commonly is suspended on a fork near the end of a lower branch of a large hardwood tree or occasionally, a hemlock (Christy 1942). The nest typically is placed about 10 ft (3 m) above the ground, often over a stream (Pough 1946). The female incubates the clutch of 2 to 4 eggs for 13 or 14 days (Harrison 1975). Both parents feed the young, which remain in the nest for 13 days and continue to depend on their parents for food for about 12 days after fledging (Harrison 1978). This species raises a single brood annually.

Bagg and Eliot (1937) state that the first positively identified specimen from New England was a male collected in Suffield, Conn. in June 1874, that may have been nesting. Another bird and a nest with 3 eggs was taken at Hyde Park, Mass. in 1888. Although records from New Hampshire are scarce, several recent breeding season records on file at ASNH are noteworthy. In 1980, R. Bradley and C. Miles heard and saw an Acadian Flycatcher several times between 28 May and 24 June on a steep wooded slope with many oak trees near Partridge Lake between Lyman and Littleton. On 31 May 1982, Andrews heard one singing in a roadside row of dense ash and maple trees bordering a field with white pines along Route 136, west of New Boston village. The bird sang regularly and appeared to be defending a territory during more than an hour of observation, although no mate was seen. The bird was still present on 10 July, but again no second bird was seen. Remarkably, a bird was singing at the same location on 9 June 1983, but was not heard on brief stops in 1984 and 1985.

S. Williamson (pers. comm.) observed a singing male in Strafford in May 1986. Then, on 10 July 1986, C.R. Foss, B.S. Ridgely and R.S. Ridgely (pers. comm.) observed a female Acadian Flycatcher with a nest containing 3 eggs suspended above a small stream between the lower and middle Hall Ponds, Sandwich. The agitated female flew from perch to perch below the canopy in the mixed hemlock-northern hardwoods forest, usually selecting a deciduous branch. She consistently uttered a loud and emphatic call note, jerking her tail as she called. No male was observed. Thin strands of birch bark dangled from the shallow, loosely constructed nest, which was slung from a fork in a horizontal branch of a beech sapling about 8 ft (2.4 m) over the water and well out from the trunk. T. Richards photographed the nest and eggs on 18 July, with the bird still present. The eggs failed to hatch, and B.S. Ridgely collected the nest on 22 August after the bird had departed. The nest is now in the University of New Hampshire collection.

This species is equally scarce in states adjacent to New Hampshire. It was not recorded in the Vermont Atlas (Laughlin and Kibbe 1985) and was reported from only 4 blocks in Massachusetts, including 2 "confirmed" nestings in the southeastern part of the state and 2 sightings in the Connecticut River valley (Mass. BBA proj., unpubl.). This flycatcher has been extending its breeding range northward into northern New Jersey, southeastern New York, and southern New England (NGS 1983). Although it may continue to expand its range into New England, it is not likely to become a regularly nesting species in New Hampshire in the near future.

Ralph Andrews

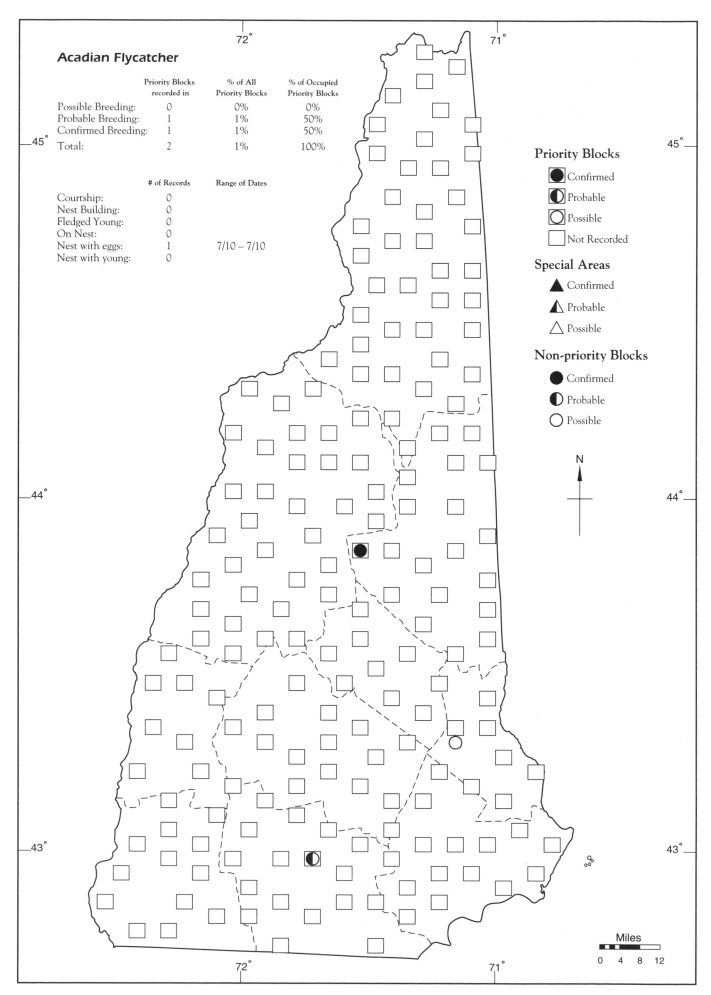

Acadian Flycatcher

	Priority Blocks recorded in	% of All Priority Blocks	% of Occupied Priority Blocks
Possible Breeding:	0	0%	0%
Probable Breeding:	1	1%	50%
Confirmed Breeding:	1	1%	50%
Total:	2	1%	100%

	# of Records	Range of Dates
Courtship:	0	
Nest Building:	0	
Fledged Young:	0	
On Nest:	0	
Nest with eggs:	1	7/10 – 7/10
Nest with young:	0	

Priority Blocks
- Confirmed
- Probable
- Possible
- Not Recorded

Special Areas
- Confirmed
- Probable
- Possible

Non-priority Blocks
- Confirmed
- Probable
- Possible

N

Miles
0 4 8 12

Alder Flycatcher
Empidonax alnorum

When Joseph Hickey (1943) wrote his classic comment more than 50 years ago about birdwatchers being people who like to rise at dawn to sit in bogs, he may have been thinking about the Alder Flycatcher. This locally common but inconspicuous bird resides in some of the most inaccessible habitats imaginable — alder-choked swamps and stream banks, and sometimes bogs — defying attempts to become intimate with the species. Formerly considered a subspecies of the Traill's Flycatcher, this species was distinguished from the closely related and similar Willow Flycatcher in 1973 (AOU 1983), based on a number of characteristics (Stein 1958, 1963). Older literature lists this subspecies as Alder Flycatcher. The name is appropriate, at least in New Hampshire, where Atlas workers invariably included speckled alders in plant lists associated with habitat descriptions for this species. (This was not true for the Willow Flycatcher.)

The Alder Flycatcher frequently nests in close proximity to the Willow, but typically breeds at higher, cooler elevations (up to 2,500 ft [760 m]) and often in wetter areas than its congener. It occupies similar habitats in neighboring states. In Massachusetts almost all Atlas records were from the western half of the state, which resembles northern New England in terrain and climate (Mass. BBA proj., unpubl.). This species occurs virtually throughout New Hampshire, while the Willow Flycatcher is limited almost entirely to the southern half of the state and to lower elevations.

Alder Flycatchers must be identified by their burry "fee-bee'- o" song, since they are virtually indistinguishable from Willow Flycatchers in appearance. Although singing may continue from arrival in late May or early June until well into August, the frequency of singing tapers off markedly during July. Males sing from within the alder canopy or, especially on arrival, from exposed perches in plain view (Wright 1911, Forbush 1927).

The loosely constructed nest is suspended above an upright crotch low in an alder, willow, blackberry, hawthorn, *Viburnum*, spirea, swamp rose, or other shrub. It usually is not more than 4 ft (1.2 m) off the ground and typically is near alders, if not in one. Nests in one study averaged 22 in (0.56 m) above the ground (Harrison 1975). The Willow Flycatcher's nest usually is higher. Strips of plant material frequently hang from the bottom of an Alder Flycatcher's nest, giving it a ragged appearance. This helps to distinguish it from the Willow's neater nest. The discovery of an Alder Flycatcher nest is a real accomplishment. The Atlas project produced 112 Alder Flycatcher records, but only one nest observation!

Given the dearth of observed nests, information on egg dates is scarce. Egg dates from Maine (Bent 1942), Massachusetts (Forbush 1927), and Vermont (Kibbe and Nichols *in* Laughlin and Kibbe 1985) suggest that Alder Flycatcher nests in New Hampshire typically should have eggs in the latter half of June or the first week of July. Allen (1903) found a freshly built nest on the Saco meadows at Intervale (Conway/Bartlett) on 21 June 1899; 4 eggs, laid on the successive 4 days, hatched in 14 days. The female incubates the 3 or 4 eggs for 12 to 14 days. Young remain in the nest for a similar period before fledging. Alders reportedly slip off the nest when disturbed and do not return soon, although they will stay nearby and scold (Bent 1942). Like other *Empidonax*, Alder Flycatchers do not remain long on their breeding grounds, and most are gone by the end of August.

This flycatcher has been somewhat locally distributed in New Hampshire for the last 100 years. Around the turn of the century, it was a summer resident in suitable habitat in Belknap and Merrimack counties and in the vicinity of Durham (Dearborn 1898, 1903). Allen (1903) considered it rather common in valleys of northern New Hampshire, and less common further south. Wright (1911) described it as an abundant summer resident along the Israel River and its tributaries in the Jefferson region. White (1937) knew it only as a rare spring transient in Concord.

BBS data for this species vary widely from year to year, but the median figure appears to be holding steady. Atlas observers considered it numerous, especially in northern and central parts of the state. The Atlas project documented Alder Flycatchers in 82% of priority blocks in Coos County in northern New Hampshire, and in a majority of priority blocks in all other counties except Cheshire and Rockingham, in the state's southwestern and southeastern corners.

Whether increasing numbers of Willow Flycatchers will affect Alder Flycatcher populations remains to be seen. Observers found the 2 species defending adjacent territories in a number of locations, including the New England Forestry Foundation's tract in Center Harbor, the ASNH Thompson Refuge in North Sandwich (B. S. Ridgley, pers. comm.), and a wet meadow beside the Seabrook dog track (Berry, pers. obs.).

Habitat protection probably will be more important to the Alder's success than any interspecific competition, since wetlands often are vulnerable to development pressures. The Alder Flycatcher, clearly less adaptable in habitat than the Willow, may gradually withdraw from areas of the state where wetlands are captured by suburbia. Elsewhere it probably will remain fairly stable as long as wetlands are protected.

Jim Berry

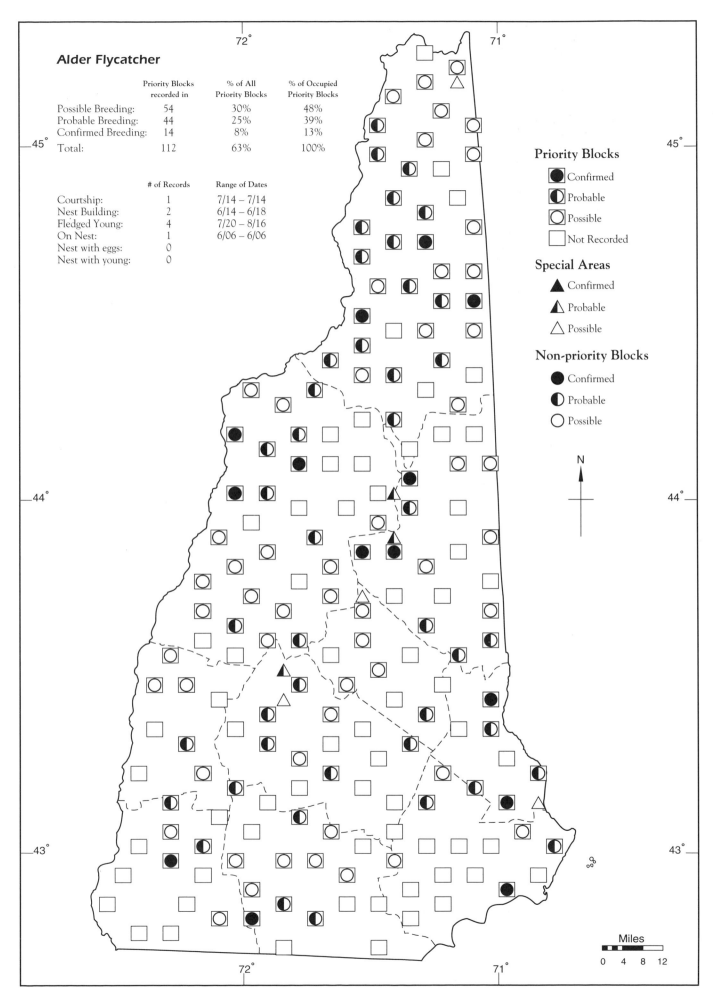

Alder Flycatcher

	Priority Blocks recorded in	% of All Priority Blocks	% of Occupied Priority Blocks
Possible Breeding:	54	30%	48%
Probable Breeding:	44	25%	39%
Confirmed Breeding:	14	8%	13%
Total:	112	63%	100%

	# of Records	Range of Dates
Courtship:	1	7/14 – 7/14
Nest Building:	2	6/14 – 6/18
Fledged Young:	4	7/20 – 8/16
On Nest:	1	6/06 – 6/06
Nest with eggs:	0	
Nest with young:	0	

Priority Blocks

● Confirmed
◐ Probable
○ Possible
□ Not Recorded

Special Areas

▲ Confirmed
◣ Probable
△ Possible

Non-priority Blocks

● Confirmed
◑ Probable
○ Possible

N

Miles
0 4 8 12

Willow Flycatcher
Empidonax traillii

The Willow Flycatcher, as dull-colored and inconspicuous as the closely related Alder Flycatcher, gained recognition as a separate species as recently as 1973, when the AOU separated the Traill's Flycatcher (*Empidonax traillii*) into these 2 species. The separation resulted primarily from observed differences in song and nesting behavior (Stein 1958, Stein 1963). These characteristics may provide reproductive isolating mechanisms where populations of both species coexist. The Willow Flycatcher kept the specific name *E. traillii*, while the Alder received the generic name of its namesake shrub (*E. alnorum*).

In New Hampshire, the Willow Flycatcher generally occurs at lower elevations than the Alder, usually 1,000 ft (300 m) or less. Although they often overlap, the Willow's habitat tends to be drier than that of the Alder and includes brushy upland pastures as well as wetlands. Whereas Atlas observers invariably found Alder Flycatchers associated with speckled alders, they found Willow Flycatchers in dry brushy areas almost as frequently as at alder-edged wetlands (ASRF). This flexibility in habitat occurs throughout the species' range (Harrison 1975, Peterson 1980). The Willow Flycatcher, unlike the Alder, occupies dry shrubby fields and apparently can survive in settled areas which the Alder avoids.

Like the Alder, the Willow Flycatcher is a tropical species that arrives late and departs early. There is a clear difference in vocalizations, especially the song. The Willow's emphatic "fitz'-bew" is separable from the Alder's burry "fee-bee'-o" or "rhee-beer'," which enabled atlasers to make their identifications. As with the Alder, the majority of all Willow songs reported (85%) were heard in June, with a range of 22 May to 17 July. Presumably this bird occasionally may sing into August, as does the Alder.

The nesting schedule, number of eggs (3 or 4), number of broods (one), incubation habits, and territorial behavior are very similar to the Alder's, but nest site selection and nest construction frequently differ between the 2 species. Willow Flycatcher nests are normally higher, ranging from 3.5 to 15 ft (1.1 to 4.6 m), and are located in forks or on horizontal branches (Harrison 1975). Although they also are typically tidier than Alder Flycatcher nests, Willow Flycatcher nests may have plant material dangling from the bottoms, and often have feathers in the rims (Harrison 1975). Shrubs of choice include upland species such as hawthorn. In wetlands, Willow Flycatchers reportedly prefer small willows (Sorrie 1975), though they will use a variety of shrubs, as do Alder Flycatchers (Harrison 1975).

Although the Willow's habitat sometimes is less inhospitable than that of its sibling species, nesting records were few and far between, with a handful of "confirmations" and only 2 nests found. A nest in Seabrook had 2 eggs on 15 June 1985 (Berry, pers. obs.). This is the only New Hampshire egg date available. Berry found a nest with eggs on 4 July 1976 in nearby Ipswich, Mass.

Historical information on the Willow Flycatcher in New Hampshire is lacking because of its recent recognition as a species. The literature for New England is chiefly on the "eastern" race of the former Traill's Flycatcher, which became the Alder Flycatcher when the species was split. The race that became the Willow Flycatcher had a more southern and western distribution. However, Alder and Willow range maps (e.g., Peterson 1980) now show an extensive area of overlap in the northeastern U.S., and the question is whether the Willow has been here all along or is a recent invader. Most sources support the latter hypothesis (Harrison 1975, Sorrie 1975, Nichols *in* Laughlin and Kibbe 1985). The Willow Flycatcher's range appears to be contracting in the West and expanding in the East, where the Willow may be replacing the Alder in some areas (Peterson 1980; B.S. Ridgely, pers. comm.).

Atlas records for this flycatcher are concentrated in the coastal plain, and the species is locally distributed in the rest of southern New Hampshire. The Willow Flycatcher is rare in the northern half of the state, where the Atlas project documented only "possible" breeding records, all at lower elevations. Peterson (1980) shows the northeastern limit of the species' distribution extending southeast from northern Vermont through north central New Hampshire to southwestern Maine. Vermont and New Hampshire Atlas project results conform perfectly with Peterson's map. Several "probable" nestings, which extend about 100 mi (161 km) northeast of Peterson's (1980) mapped range in southwestern Maine, provide additional evidence for the Willow Flycatcher's continuing range expansion (Adamus 1988). These areas of Maine, along with southern New Hampshire, will be ideal locations to study the interactions of Willow and Alder flycatchers in their mutual wetland habitats. Any effects they have on one another's populations should become evident in the coming years and bear close monitoring.

Jim Berry

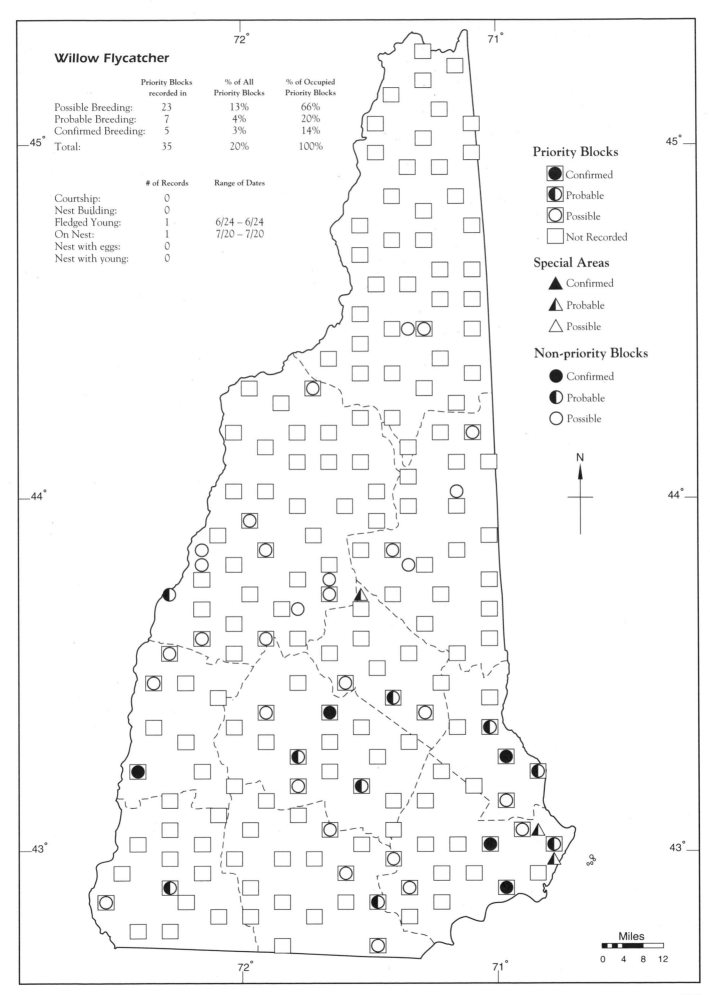

Willow Flycatcher

	Priority Blocks recorded in	% of All Priority Blocks	% of Occupied Priority Blocks
Possible Breeding:	23	13%	66%
Probable Breeding:	7	4%	20%
Confirmed Breeding:	5	3%	14%
Total:	35	20%	100%

	# of Records	Range of Dates
Courtship:	0	
Nest Building:	0	
Fledged Young:	1	6/24 – 6/24
On Nest:	1	7/20 – 7/20
Nest with eggs:	0	
Nest with young:	0	

Priority Blocks

● Confirmed
◐ Probable
○ Possible
□ Not Recorded

Special Areas

▲ Confirmed
◮ Probable
△ Possible

Non-priority Blocks

● Confirmed
◖ Probable
○ Possible

N

Miles
0 4 8 12

Least Flycatcher
Empidonax minimus

Although drab in coloration and small in size, Least Flycatchers can be conspicuous in deciduous woodlands. Their persistent "chebec" resounds throughout the state along roadsides, in old orchards, in wooded borders of beaver ponds and wetlands, and in wooded areas at elevations below 2,000 ft (610 m) throughout the state from early May into July.

Upon arrival in the breeding area, males establish territories, which they advertise actively by flying with stiffly vibrating wings from perch to perch and giving their "chebec" calls. "Stiff-winged" display flights take place mostly in the subcanopy. Sometimes, often at dusk, males perform flight displays above the canopy during which they repeatedly give the "chebec" call (MacQueen 1950; Sherry, unpubl. data). Song activity is greatest at dawn but persists through much of the morning. Heights of 20 singing perches in the Hubbard Brook Experimental Forest, Thornton, averaged 25 ft (7.6 m) (Holmes 1986).

When females arrive, males actively follow them as they search for nest sites, which vary with habitat. Dearborn (1898) and Bent (1942) indicate a decided preference for apple trees, with nests often placed on horizontal branches, seldom at heights greater than 25 ft (7.6 m). Of 85 nests found at Hubbard Brook, heights ranged from 6 to 70 ft (1.8 to 21 m), averaging 35 ft (10.6 m) (Sherry and Holmes, unpubl. data). Most were in sugar maple or yellow birch trees, some in American beech. Usually set in an upright fork where a branch leaves the main trunk, nests occasionally were in forks along horizontal branches.

At Hubbard Brook, most pairs begin laying eggs in the last week of May and complete their 3 or 4 egg clutches by early June (Holmes and Sherry, unpubl. data). Females alone incubate the eggs for 15 or 16 days. Both adults feed nestlings, which fledge in about 14 days (MacQueen 1950). After leaving the nest, fledglings remain together in tight groups, attended by one or both adults. At this time they often are high in the canopy and relatively inconspicuous, although both young and adults make a characteristic "chip" note. The young become independent after 10 to 14 days (MacQueen 1950). Adult Least Flycatchers leave their breeding areas almost immediately thereafter and begin their southward migration in mid to late July, with most immatures migrating about a month later (Hussell 1980). Thus, Least Flycatchers seen in New Hampshire during the fall (White 1924, Ridgely 1977, Allison and Allison 1979) are primarily young of the year.

The distribution of Least Flycatchers throughout their breeding habitat is patchy (Breckenridge 1956, Davis 1959, Sherry 1979, Sherry and Holmes 1985). At Hubbard Brook and other mid-elevation sites in the White Mountains, widely separated aggregates range in size from a few to 50 or 60 territories. Within these "colonies" Least Flycatchers chase each other and even attack other species, especially American Redstarts, which occupy the same strata in the forest and take similar kinds of foods (Sherry 1979). Perhaps because of this interspecific aggression, redstart densities are lower within flycatcher "colonies" than outside. When the flycatchers disappear from a site, redstarts immediately move in (Sherry and Holmes 1988).

Least Flycatchers sometimes forage by sitting on exposed perches in the subcanopy and darting out after flying insects. More frequently, however, they sit and scan nearby vegetation, then fly up, hover momentarily, and snatch prey from a leaf or twig. At Hubbard Brook, this mode of foraging constituted 81% of 993 foraging attempts, compared to only 9.6% for hawking of insects from the air (Robinson and Holmes 1982). In either case, most prey taken are small flies, wasps, beetles, and occasional Lepidoptera larvae (Robinson and Holmes 1982).

Least Flycatchers apparently occurred most frequently in old apple orchards and among shade trees during the late 1800s and early 1900s (Dearborn 1898, 1903, Bent 1942). Allen (1903) noted that they usually occurred in the vicinity of human dwellings during the breeding season and suggested that the introduction of apple trees had influenced the nesting behavior of the species. A habitat shift apparently was underway by the 1930s, when White (1937) found these flycatchers "ubiquitous" in the Concord area, inhabiting dense growth of shrubs and saplings along edges of streams, ponds, fields, and roadsides, as well as orchards. New Hampshire has become increasingly wooded, and now Least Flycatchers seem most abundant in forests, particularly 25 to 60 year old hardwoods with closed overstory and relatively open subcanopy (Breckenridge 1956, Sherry 1979).

During the Atlas project, "confirmed" records were based primarily on observations of adults carrying food or fecal sacs and of fledged young, while most "probable" records were of territorial males. Atlas records for Least Flycatchers are well distributed throughout New Hampshire, but a number of priority blocks with good observer coverage lack records of this species. New Hampshire BBS data also show considerable variation from one route to another. The species' patchy distribution may be related at least in part to forest age. BBS data indicate that the Least Flycatcher has declined in abundance in New Hampshire over the last 10 years, and Holmes et al. (1986) recorded a local decline at Hubbard Brook. This change could reflect a general maturing of New Hampshire's forests and thus a reduction in suitable breeding habitat. Alternatively, events in their tropical wintering grounds or during migration could be affecting abundance. The need for further research on this species is clearly indicated.

Richard T. Holmes & Thomas W. Sherry

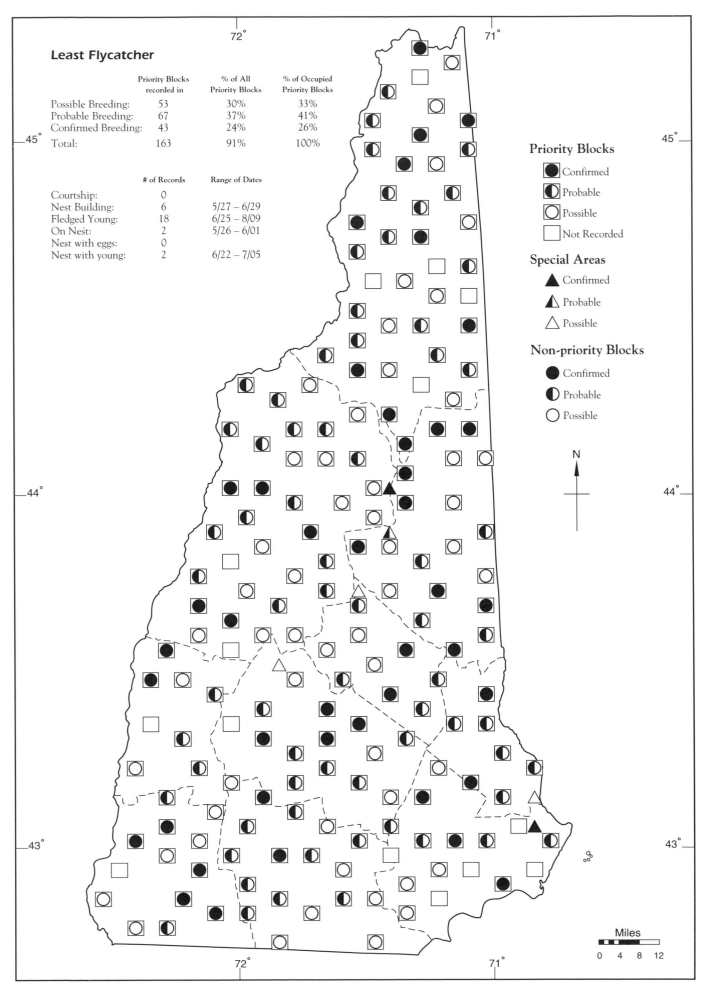

Least Flycatcher

	Priority Blocks recorded in	% of All Priority Blocks	% of Occupied Priority Blocks
Possible Breeding:	53	30%	33%
Probable Breeding:	67	37%	41%
Confirmed Breeding:	43	24%	26%
Total:	163	91%	100%

	# of Records	Range of Dates
Courtship:	0	
Nest Building:	6	5/27 – 6/29
Fledged Young:	18	6/25 – 8/09
On Nest:	2	5/26 – 6/01
Nest with eggs:	0	
Nest with young:	2	6/22 – 7/05

Priority Blocks

- ● Confirmed
- ◑ Probable
- ○ Possible
- □ Not Recorded

Special Areas

- ▲ Confirmed
- ◭ Probable
- △ Possible

Non-priority Blocks

- ● Confirmed
- ◐ Probable
- ○ Possible

N

Miles
0 4 8 12

Eastern Phoebe
Sayornis phoebe

Few nests are easier to find or better known than the moss-covered, mud nest of the common, plainly dressed, tail-wagging Eastern Phoebe. This small gray flycatcher prefers a roof over its nest and builds on porches, in barns, beneath sheltering eaves of houses, sheds and outbuildings, and under bridges. Occasionally, phoebes still nest under cliff overhangs, the curls of riverbanks, or among the roots of fallen trees. The breeding range includes much of the eastern U.S. and extends into northwestern Canada (NGS 1983).

Phoebes arrive in New Hampshire from wintering grounds in Mexico and the Southern states during the last weeks of the maple sugaring season, when the first flying insects appear; 23 March is an early date in Webster for our hardiest flycatcher (Janeway, pers. obs.). Breeding habitat typically includes a forest clearing or more extensive open lands near a pond or stream. Phoebes nest at elevations up to at least 1,600 ft (490 m) (Wright 1911).

The male phoebe sings from the very day of arrival, and it would be difficult to miss his song. Loudly and persistently he calls his name: "Fee-bee? Fee-bee!," with a distinct nasal burr ("Whee-zee!" would be more accurate). This differs considerably from the clear, descending "fee-bee" whistle of the Black-capped Chickadee, with which it is often confused, and the plaintive, whistled "pee-a-wee" of the Eastern Wood-Pewee. During courtship, the male may fly in a circle with tail spread, fluttering his wings, while singing a flight song (Forbush 1927, Murray *in* Tyler 1942c). His early morning song is apt to be an hour or more of ceaseless "phoebes."

The first nest is usually built during the first week of May, but occasionally in late April. It is a sturdy cup of layered mud pellets, neatly covered with fresh green moss and lined with soft grasses. The site is usually near water and 5 to 10 ft (1.5 to 3 m) above the ground or water. Some nests, especially those beneath bridges, are but a foot or 2 above the water, and fledgling phoebes must be able to fly up and out to avoid drowning. Bridge nests tend to foil Brown-headed Cowbirds (Weeks 1984), which frequently parasitize this species (Harrison 1978). The phoebe is an easy bird to "confirm," as its nest site is so predictable. New Hampshire Atlas participants found nests beneath the eaves of an outhouse, on an iron beam supporting a bridge, on top of a light bulb socket 9 ft (2.7 m) above the ground, on a carport beam, atop a porch column, and in barns at varying heights.

Many a homeowner has shared a porch with this bird, which may remain on her nest throughout the comings and goings of her human neighbors. Phoebes grow attached to their chosen nest site, and it is difficult, sometimes impossible, to persuade them to build elsewhere. They occasionally will reuse an old nest (Janeway, pers. obs.).

The female does most of the nest building (Forbush 1927). The job takes 3 to 13 days; up to 3 weeks may then elapse before egg laying (Harrison 1975). She lays 3 to 8, usually 5 white eggs and incubates for 14 to 16 days (Harrison 1978). The young fledge after 15 to 17 days, and both parents tend them for another 2 to 3 weeks (Harrison 1978). Fledglings have greenish backs and buffy wing bars.

Phoebes raise usually 2 and sometimes 3 broods (Forbush 1927). The female may build an entirely new nest for her next brood, or simply add a double-decker to the first one. Smith (1905 *in* Tyler 1942c) reported a nest 5 stories high and 9 in (23 cm) tall, and similar nests are not uncommon today (Janeway, pers. obs.).

Phoebes commonly perch on tree limbs, fence posts, or roof edges, tails twitching up and down, a motion they nearly always make immediately upon landing. This habit makes identification easy. From a prominent perch, phoebes dart out to catch houseflies, mosquitoes, moths, beetles, wasps, bees, and other flying insects, consuming many insect pests (Forbush 1927). They eat dragonflies (Tyler 1942c) and also a few wild fruits, berries, and seeds (Beal 1912 *in* Tyler 1942c).

In September, phoebes young and old appear to be everywhere around country houses, still singing. They linger well into October, long after the Barn Swallows and most other insectivorous migrants have flown south.

Phoebes have been common summer residents in New Hampshire at least since the mid-1800s (Coues 1868, Allen 1903, Dearborn 1903, Wright 1911, White 1924). Their numbers may have increased after the arrival of Europeans, whose structures have provided many new nest sites.

BBS data from 1966 to 1979 suggest that New Hampshire and Vermont support the highest phoebe densities in North America. The severe winter of 1976–77 produced high mortality in the northern portion of their wintering range, and apparently affected phoebe nesting populations from Maryland to northern New England, where the population has been recovering gradually (Robbins et al. 1986).

The phoebe is widely distributed in the southern half of New Hampshire, where the Atlas project produced records for every priority block. The Atlas map shows gaps only in the mountains and North Country, which are heavily forested and sparsely populated.

Phoebe nesting habitat seems permanently secure in New Hampshire. Despite periodic, temporary impacts of severe weather, this common bird likely will likely continue to grace our homes with its presence.

Elizabeth C. Janeway

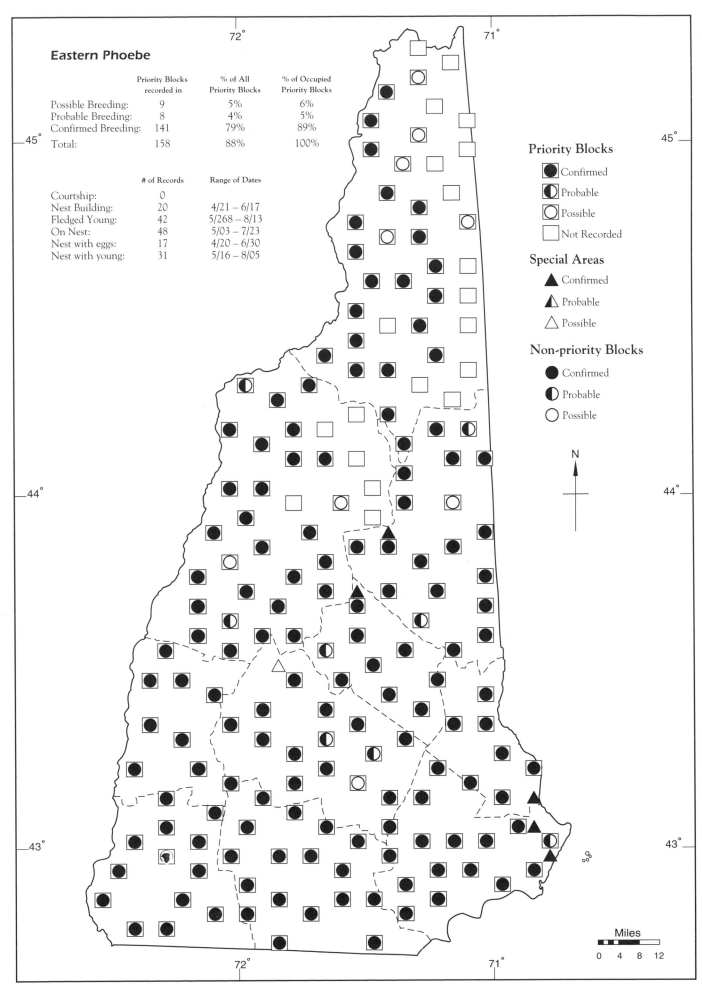

Eastern Phoebe

	Priority Blocks recorded in	% of All Priority Blocks	% of Occupied Priority Blocks
Possible Breeding:	9	5%	6%
Probable Breeding:	8	4%	5%
Confirmed Breeding:	141	79%	89%
Total:	158	88%	100%

	# of Records	Range of Dates
Courtship:	0	
Nest Building:	20	4/21 – 6/17
Fledged Young:	42	5/268 – 8/13
On Nest:	48	5/03 – 7/23
Nest with eggs:	17	4/20 – 6/30
Nest with young:	31	5/16 – 8/05

Priority Blocks

- ◕ Confirmed
- ◑ Probable
- ○ Possible
- ☐ Not Recorded

Special Areas

- ▲ Confirmed
- ◣ Probable
- △ Possible

Non-priority Blocks

- ● Confirmed
- ◑ Probable
- ○ Possible

N

Great Crested Flycatcher
Myiarchus crinitus

The Great Crested Flycatcher's cinnamon-rufous tail, yellow belly, and dark gray breast make it the most colorful of our nesting flycatchers. It is also the largest and, in season, the noisiest. This species most commonly inhabits the edges of forest openings rather than deep woods. It often nested in old orchards when they were common, and it still sometimes nests near human habitations. The Great Crested Flycatcher breeds throughout the eastern U.S. west to North Dakota and Texas and in parts of southern Canada. It winters in southern Florida and from Mexico to northwestern South America.

The first or second week of May is the time to look and listen for the vanguard of arriving Great Crested Flycatchers. These birds, presumably males, are likely to be noisy for a few days, then quiet for a longer period before their calls are conspicuous again. Crested flycatchers return to their large territories year after year, sometimes to the same nest sites and mates (Bent 1942). They are aggressive in defending their nesting territory against squirrels and small birds, as well as competing males, with which they often engage in furious battles (Dickey *in* Bent 1942). In courtship the males give prolonged chase to the females (Dickey *in* Bent 1942).

Unlike our other flycatchers, this species is a cavity nester. Although it uses both natural tree cavities and abandoned holes of the larger woodpeckers, it apparently prefers the former. The heights of nest cavities vary from 3 to at least 75 ft (0.9 to 22.9 m), but average 10 to 20 ft (3 to 6.1 m) (Harrison 1975). This flycatcher sometimes nests in birdhouses, including wood duck boxes, and has used the latter in Hillsboro (R. Sprague, pers. comm.). In such situations the birds crisscross large twigs under the piles of debris that support the nest to reduce the size of the nesting cavity (Forbush 1927).

Nest building, in which both sexes participate, may take as long as 2 weeks (Harrison 1975). The bulky nest is made of "wool, hair, feathers, cornhusks, onion skins, rags, and almost invariably one or more snake skins" (Goodhue 1922). Bolles (1890) found a nest in Tamworth in which a snake skin encircled the single egg like a wreath. S.B. Turner (pers. comm.), however, inspected 10 New Hampshire nests, none of which contained snake skins. The pair sometimes uses onion skins, cellophane, paper, or plastic instead.

There are usually 5 or 6 eggs, sometimes 4 to 8. Incubation, by the female, takes 13 to 15 days. Both parents feed the young, whose peeping is sometimes audible from as far as 50 ft (15.2 m) away (Mousley 1934a). The nestling period is variously reported as 12 to 21 days (Bent 1942).

Like other flycatchers, Great Cresteds feed largely on flying insects; they sometimes bring large butterflies to feed their young (Mousley 1934a). They also glean caterpillars and other insects from foliage and the bark of tree trunks, usually while hovering, and pick up grasshoppers and crickets from the ground (Gabrielson 1915).

After the young fledge, sometime in July, the family roams around the forest together (Roberts 1932). The birds are rather quiet during this period and become increasingly so for the rest of the summer so that one is likely to miss their departure. Probably most go in August and early September, with only stragglers staying later (Elkins, pers. obs.).

Since Great Crested Flycatchers feed within the canopy most of the time, they are more often heard than seen. Their common call is a loud "wheep." Other notes are a soft "whit whit whit" and a rattling "cr-r-r-reep." Allen (1922) and Saunders (1935) have described a song, given at dawn.

The recorded history of the Great Crested Flycatcher in New Hampshire apparently is one of gradual increase. Belknap (*in* Allen 1903) mentioned the species in 1792. Although Maynard (1871) stated that only stragglers went further north than Massachusetts, during the period 1876 to 1909 Brewster (1937) found this bird to be very common at Umbagog Lake, where stub forests furnished exceptionally favorable nesting habitat. Dearborn (1898) called it "tolerably common" but locally distributed in Belknap and Merrimack counties. Thayer (1909 *in* Allison and Allison 1979) found it "very rare" at Dublin in the early 1900s. Allen (1903) considered the species uncommon in New Hampshire. Dearborn (1903) in Durham, and White (1924) in Concord saw the Great Crested Flycatcher only on migration. By 1937, however, the latter reported it as a summer resident (White 1937). It would seem that, at least prior to the 1930s, the Great Crested was only locally a common breeder in our state. BBS data for New Hampshire from 1966 to 1984, show that this bird was at best only moderately common prior to the 1980s, when its numbers increased noticeably.

Despite intense competition for nesting cavities, especially from starlings, these birds are now common breeders in many areas in southern New Hampshire. Only 3 priority blocks south of the White Mountains lack Atlas records. In the mountains and North Country they occur only locally, due to their preference for low elevations and deciduous woodlands. However, the Atlas project produced "confirmed" breeding records even in Pittsburg, our northernmost township.

Vera H. Hebert & Kimball C. Elkins

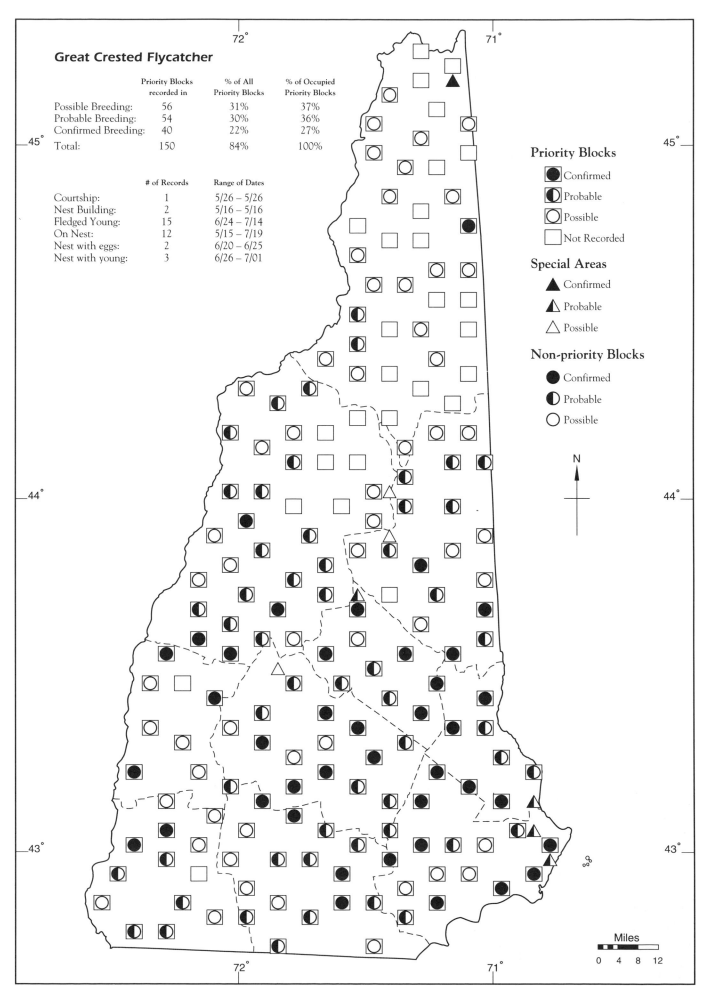

Great Crested Flycatcher

	Priority Blocks recorded in	% of All Priority Blocks	% of Occupied Priority Blocks
Possible Breeding:	56	31%	37%
Probable Breeding:	54	30%	36%
Confirmed Breeding:	40	22%	27%
Total:	150	84%	100%

	# of Records	Range of Dates
Courtship:	1	5/26 – 5/26
Nest Building:	2	5/16 – 5/16
Fledged Young:	15	6/24 – 7/14
On Nest:	12	5/15 – 7/19
Nest with eggs:	2	6/20 – 6/25
Nest with young:	3	6/26 – 7/01

Priority Blocks

- ◑ Confirmed
- ◐ Probable
- ○ Possible
- ☐ Not Recorded

Special Areas

- ▲ Confirmed
- ◣ Probable
- △ Possible

Non-priority Blocks

- ● Confirmed
- ◗ Probable
- ○ Possible

N

Miles
0 4 8 12

Eastern Kingbird
Tyrannus tyrannus

When perched atop a bush, small tree, or snag, the Eastern Kingbird is an unusually striking bird. It makes up for its lack of bright colors with its sharply contrasting dark gray and white plumage, beautifully proportioned form, and typically erect posture. What makes the kingbird remarkable, however, are its aggressiveness and its extraordinary powers of flight, which are best demonstrated in pursuit of insects or other birds or during courtship flights.

In New Hampshire the Eastern Kingbird is a locally common summer resident, especially of lake, pond, and stream edges, wetlands, farms, and other open lands. It is a conspicuous, noisy bird but has a somewhat musical dawn song and a flight song, as well as its usual shrill notes (Tyler 1942a). It ranges up to well over 2,000 ft (610 m) elevation and has occurred during the breeding season as high as 2,800 ft (850 m) at Kancamagus Pass, Lincoln/Livermore (Richards, pers. obs.). The kingbird is most common in eastern North America, but breeds from British Columbia to southern Quebec, south to Oregon in the West and Florida in the East, and winters from Colombia to Argentina (AOU 1983).

Highly gregarious in the tropics in winter and during spring and fall migration (Skutch *in* Tyler 1942a), kingbirds usually arrive unobtrusively in New Hampshire from early to late May, migrating partly by day. Courtship consists of repeated flights by the male, which involve short flights straight up followed by short dips and longer dives, tumbles and even somersaults, with accompanying shrill cries. The small red crown patch and terminal white tail band present in both sexes do not seem to be important in courtship (Tyler 1942a).

The nest, which the female builds, often is exposed to the elements. It commonly is situated well up in an apple or other live tree, low in a swamp shrub, or in a tree, bush, or dead stub overhanging or out in the wa-ter. Occasionally it is built on a man-made structure, such as one found on the cross of a church 100 ft (30.5 m) from the ground in Woodsville (Forbush 1929). It is relatively easy to locate, especially along water courses. Usually shallow and roughly made of twigs, the nest often contains straw, bits of cloth, and feathers.

In the vicinity of Concord, nest construction occurs during the last week of May and the first week of June, and clutches are completed during the second week of June (White 1937). The female incubates her clutch of 3 to 5 eggs for 12 to 16 days (Forbush 1929). The male usually perches near the nest during the female's absences (Morehouse and Brewer 1968). Young remain in the nest for 14 to 17 days (Morehouse and Brewer 1968). Herrick (1905 *in* Tyler 1942a) describes 2 parents making 108 visits during a 4-hour period—feeding their 4 nestlings 91 times, brooding 18 times, and removing fecal sacs 7 times.

Fledged kingbirds tend to perch close together, waiting for their parents to feed them and calling frequently (Tyler 1942a). Adults may continue to feed them for at least 35 days after they leave the nest (Harrison 1978). Kingbirds generally remain in family groups at least into late August (Morehouse and Brewer 1968). As time for migration approaches, families join to form flocks of 12 or more birds, which perch quietly in loose associations (Tyler 1942a). Examples of this behavior include 24 kingbirds perched on fences surrounding a field in Swanzey on 2 September 1959 and 20 seen together mostly perched on wires in Conway on 3 September 1981 (Richards, unpubl. data). Kingbirds leave New Hampshire in August and early September.

Insects comprise about 90% of the kingbird's diet, but seeds and fruits are sometimes included (Beal *in* Tyler 1942a). In pursuing insects, the kingbird often performs remarkable aerobatics, zig-zagging after them at high speed and sometimes flying straight up.

Kingbirds are justly famous for attacking larger birds, especially crows, and often ride on their backs. S. M. Sutcliffe (pers. comm.) observed one alight on the neck of a Red-shouldered Hawk and peck at it, remaining there until after the hawk landed! Dearborn (1903) saw a kingbird pounce upon the back of a cat that had made off with one of the bird's young. On the other hand, other small birds, including Yellow Warblers (Tyler 1942a) and Yellow-bellied Sapsuckers (Brewster 1937), sometimes attack kingbirds.

Before the forests were cleared for agriculture, the kingbird probably was less common in New Hampshire than at the present time. During the last century, however, when there were many more farms and millponds (but few if any beaver ponds), it likely was more common than it is today. Dearborn (1898) wrote that it "belongs to every farm from May 1 to September 1," and Allen (1903) considered it "a characteristic orchard bird." On the other hand, it has undoubtedly benefitted from the return of the beaver in recent decades.

BBS data suggest a significant decline in kingbird numbers from 1966 through 1975, followed by a slight increase from 1976 to 1979. Kingbirds occur at similar densities on BBS routes in New Hampshire, Massachusetts, and Vermont, but at lower densities in Maine, which is more heavily forested (Robbins et al. 1986).

The Atlas map indicates that the kingbird is well distributed throughout virtually all of southern New Hampshire, but occurs rather locally in the mountainous northern part of the state. Since this species readily adapts to many of the habitat changes associated with human activities, its future as a summer resident in New Hampshire seems secure.

Tudor Richards

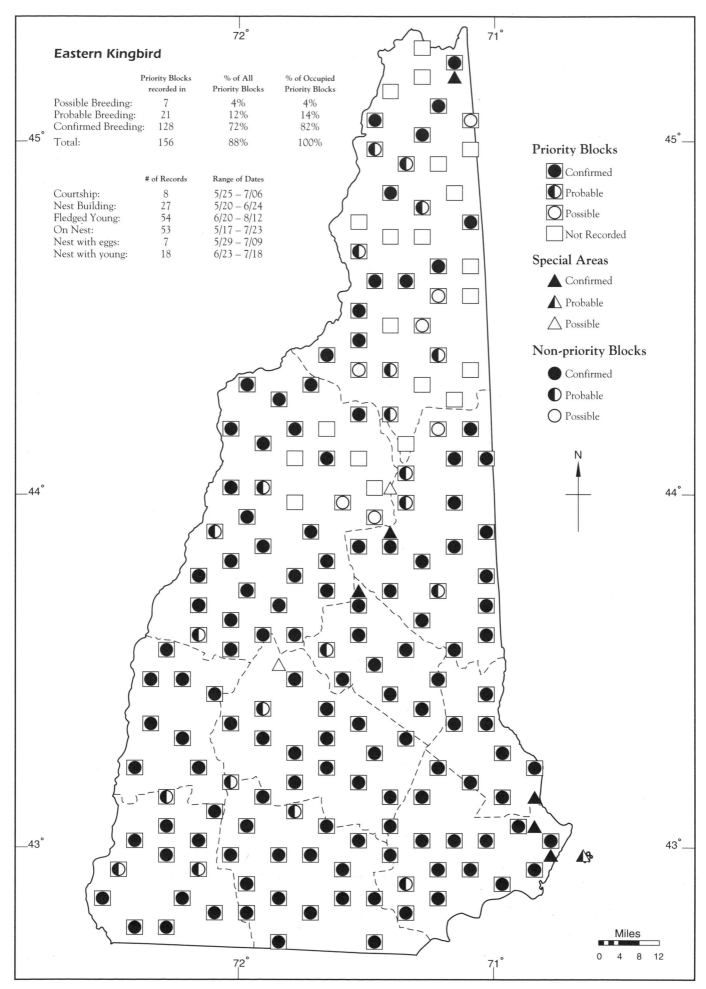

Eastern Kingbird

	Priority Blocks recorded in	% of All Priority Blocks	% of Occupied Priority Blocks
Possible Breeding:	7	4%	4%
Probable Breeding:	21	12%	14%
Confirmed Breeding:	128	72%	82%
Total:	156	88%	100%

	# of Records	Range of Dates
Courtship:	8	5/25 – 7/06
Nest Building:	27	5/20 – 6/24
Fledged Young:	54	6/20 – 8/12
On Nest:	53	5/17 – 7/23
Nest with eggs:	7	5/29 – 7/09
Nest with young:	18	6/23 – 7/18

Priority Blocks

- ◖ Confirmed
- ◐ Probable
- ○ Possible
- ☐ Not Recorded

Special Areas

- ▲ Confirmed
- ◭ Probable
- △ Possible

Non-priority Blocks

- ● Confirmed
- ◐ Probable
- ○ Possible

N

Miles
0 4 8 12

163

Horned Lark

Eremophila alpestris

Most observers in New Hampshire associate Horned Larks with winter along the Coast, where larks occur between October and March, often with Snow Buntings and Lapland Longspurs. This sparrow-sized bird is light brown above and white below with light brown flanks and a black chest band. The forehead, face, and throat are pale yellow. It has black "whiskers," and the adult has short tufts of erectile feathers on each side of the crown — the "horns" for which it was named.

Several subspecies occur in North America. The majority of New Hampshire records likely involve the so-called "Northern" form (*E. a. alpestris*), which winters in the state and breeds in the uplands of Canada and the Arctic tundra. The paler "Prairie" form (*E. a. praticola*) breeds in New Hampshire, having extended and its range eastward from the great prairies of the West after about 1844, as clearing of land for agriculture provided suitable nesting habitat (Palmer 1949, Hurley and Franks 1976).

"Prairie" Horned Larks usually arrive in New Hampshire from mid-February to mid-March (RNEB, *passim*; SRS) and seek extensive open areas with sparse vegetation and some bare ground. Airports, overgrazed pastures, golf courses, and cemeteries are typical breeding locations.

The male performs an elaborate song flight, silently rising from the ground in a series of irregular circles to a height of several hundred feet. He begins to sing at the apex of his ascent, turning in slow circles or hanging motionless in the wind, wings and tail fanned. The song is a mixture of whistles, trills, and high-pitched notes in a seemingly breathless chorus. The male also sings from the ground (Bent 1942).

The nest site is on the ground, usually beside a grass tussock, rock, clod of soil, or piece of wood. Horned Larks sometimes place rabbit droppings, pebbles, or small pieces of peat around the nest (Forbush 1927). This habit may provide protection from wind (Ellison

in Laughlin and Kibbe 1985), hasten snow melt or create an eddy for wind blown snow (C. R. Foss, pers. comm.), or provide a way of "sign-posting" the nest in an otherwise featureless landscape (MacLeod, pers. obs.).

Nest building takes 2 to 4 days (Harrison 1975) and often begins in March when snow is still on the ground. The nest is a loose structure of dry grass, rootlets, and plant stems in a hollow which the female creates in the ground. The cup is lined with finer materials such as feathers, hair, and fur.

The female incubates her 2 to 7, usually 4 eggs for 10 to 14 days (Harrison 1978). She will perform a distraction display if disturbed when the eggs are near hatching, but usually runs from the nest through the grass before taking flight (Forbush 1927). Both parents tend the young, which leave the nest after 9 to 12 days to hide individually in nearby cover. They fly 3 to 5 days later (Harrison 1978). White (1937) reports a nest in Concord on 10 May 1936 with 3 young, which had left the nest 7 days later. Horned Larks occasionally have 2 broods, in which case the male tends the first brood while the female incubates a second clutch (Forbush 1927). The mottled brown juveniles lack facial markings and are easily distinguishable from adults (Farrand 1983).

The first documented nesting of Horned Larks in New England occurred in Vermont in 1889 (Forbush 1927). Horned Larks were nesting in Massachusetts by 1892, and were well distributed there during the early 1900s (Forbush 1927). In New Hampshire, Faxon (1892) suspected nesting in Franconia in 1891, and a nest in Errol contained an egg and 2 newly hatched young on 22 June 1903 (Allen 1903). Torrey (1905) observed a pair at about 6,000 ft (1,830 m) elevation on Mt. Washington during 7 to 17 July 1905, and a nest in a cornfield in Jefferson contained 4 downy young on 20 June 1905 (Wright 1911).

Forbush (1927) indicates that the Horned Lark sometimes was locally common in the White Mountains and North Country, and uncommon or occasional in southern New Hampshire as a nesting species. Breeding was unknown in Belknap and Merrimack counties (Dearborn 1898), and in the vicinity of Durham and the Coast (Dearborn 1903) around the turn of the century. However, observers documented "Prairie" Horned Larks in Boscawen in 1901 and in Concord in 1913 (White 1937). Sightings during 1940–68 (RNEB, *passim*) indicate that the vast majority of Horned Larks in New Hampshire are winter visitors of the Northern subspecies which arrive in October and depart in March. Summer sightings (May through July) suggest nesting of the Prairie subspecies in Concord, Hampton, Hampton Falls, Littleton, Milton, Monroe, Seabrook, and Whitefield.

In contrast to earlier times, when Horned Larks were most common in northern New Hampshire, all Atlas records are from the southeastern part of the state. The 3 "confirmed" breeding records during the Atlas years are from Hampton Beach State Park, Hampton; Boire Airport, Nashua; and Suncook. "Probable" records are from the Concord and Manchester airports. All were in extensive areas of sparse and short mown grass.

The decline of agriculture and resulting reforestation have reduced this species' breeding distribution in New England during the present century. Reported sightings suggest that Horned Larks are less common today as either migrants or breeders in New Hampshire than they were even in the 1960s (RNEB, *passim*; SRS). Airports may provide the only suitable nesting habitat over the long term. The distribution and status of New Hampshire's Horned Lark breeding population bears continued monitoring.

Iain C. MacLeod

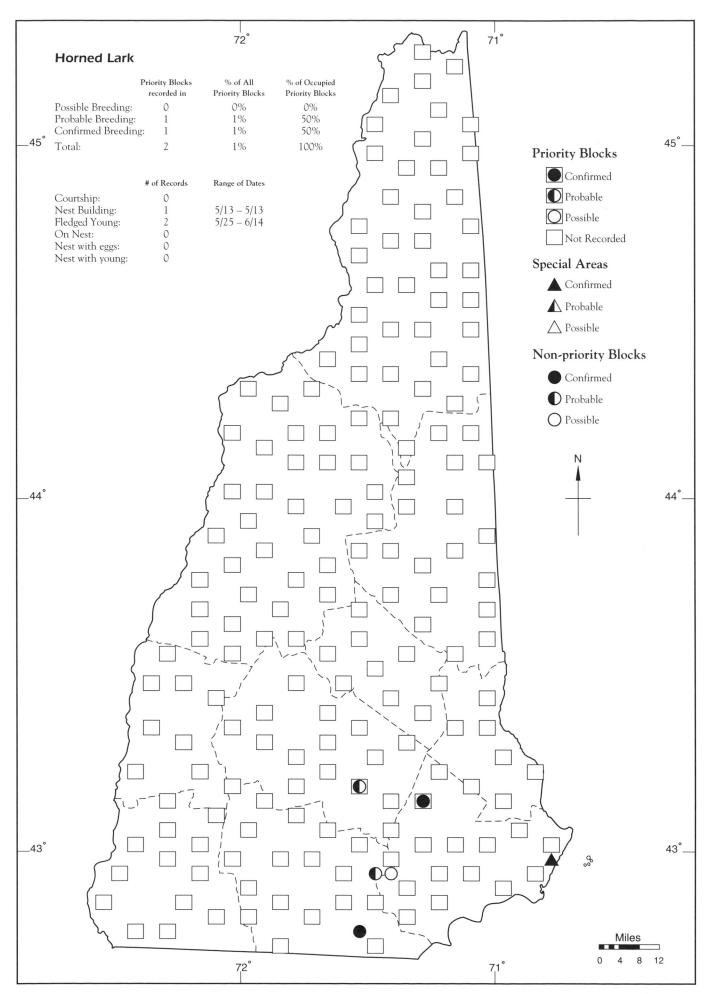

Horned Lark

	Priority Blocks recorded in	% of All Priority Blocks	% of Occupied Priority Blocks
Possible Breeding:	0	0%	0%
Probable Breeding:	1	1%	50%
Confirmed Breeding:	1	1%	50%
Total:	2	1%	100%

	# of Records	Range of Dates
Courtship:	0	
Nest Building:	1	5/13 – 5/13
Fledged Young:	2	5/25 – 6/14
On Nest:	0	
Nest with eggs:	0	
Nest with young:	0	

Priority Blocks

● Confirmed
◐ Probable
○ Possible
□ Not Recorded

Special Areas

▲ Confirmed
◮ Probable
△ Possible

Non-priority Blocks

● Confirmed
◐ Probable
○ Possible

N

Miles
0   4   8   12

Andrew Robbins

Purple Martin
Progne subis

This colonially nesting swallow depends entirely on multicelled nesting boxes in New Hampshire, and the presence of a colony in one's yard is something of a status symbol. This species has an extremely limited breeding distribution in New England, particularly in New Hampshire, where it is considered a Threatened Species. The Purple Martin is sensitive to cold and prolonged rainy weather, and recovers slowly from weather disasters. Competition for nest boxes from introduced House Sparrows and European Starlings, and the decrease of open agricultural lands during the present century, also have contributed to recent population declines.

Martins from the United States and Canada winter in South America east of the Andes, largely in enormous urban roosts south of the equator in Brazil. The Purple Martin is the first subequatorial migrant to arrive in New Hampshire in the spring. "Scouts" reach nesting colonies in late April, often before a dependable supply of flying insects is available to support them.

Although martins prefer the proximity of ponds or rivers, they may establish colonies several kilometers from water bodies. The chief habitat requirements are open land, a dependable supply of flying insects, and a cluster of nesting cavities. Colonies can nest successfully along urban streets, in suburban gardens, or in rural settings, but not in extensive forest or under a solid canopy of trees. Before European settlement, martins nested in tree cavities, on cliffs, or in hollow gourds hung by indigenous people.

Nests are scant and nearly flat, consisting of a few twigs and green leaves, and sometimes a rim of mud. In spite of the early arrival of some males, in northern New England martins do not begin laying their single clutches of 4 to 6 eggs until June (Forbush 1929), perhaps waiting until nearly all members of the colony have arrived. Martins lay most eggs within a single

week, although a few pairs may lay later and continue to feed young after most of the colony has departed. Egg dates in 233 Ontario nests ranged from 21 May to 7 August, with half from 20 to 30 June (Peck and James 1987). Incubation requires 14 to 17 days (Peck and James 1987).

Flocks of Purple Martins gather in nocturnal roosts for several weeks in late July and August, before suddenly departing for their winter home. Martins have used a small roost near Effingham Falls, Effingham for more than 50 years. Most martins have left New Hampshire by the last week in August.

The Purple Martin's diet consists primarily of insects, but includes a few spiders. Bees, wasps, flies, bugs, beetles, butterflies, moths, and dragonflies are important prey items (Beal 1918).

The first dated observation of a Purple Martin in New Hampshire was in Hollis on 28 April 1875 (Fox 1876). Belknap (1792), however, listed this species for New Hampshire under the name of Black Martin. Early accounts (Knight 1897, Clark 1899, Howe and Allen 1901, Forbush 1929) refer to the Purple Martin as locally common in New England, but extensive periods of rainy weather periodically devastated colonies, as in the summers of 1823, 1851, about 1864, 1914, and 1959 (Forbush 1929, Palmer 1949, Hebert 1960b) and especially in June 1903 (Horton 1903). The species has never recovered from the 1903 disaster.

Small colonies have persisted locally, especially in Merrimack and Carroll counties, but even here martins gradually have abandoned nest boxes. An ASNH survey in 1920–21 found active colonies in Antrim (2), Canaan (2), Center Harbor, Enfield, Epsom, Meredith, Northwood (3), Raymond, Strafford (2), Tilton (2), and Barrington. A subsequent survey in 1959–60 found active colonies at only 5 of these sites: Antrim (2), Canaan, Meredith, and Tilton. However, this survey reported additional sites in Danville, Hancock, Hollis, Loudon, Nashua, New London (2), North Hampton, Ossipee, Rindge, Sandwich (2), Springfield, Swanzey, Warner, and Wolfeboro.

Observers have detected Purple Martins on 15 of the state's 22 BBS routes, but regularly on only one. Martins are highly detectable on roadside surveys because most colonies are within hearing of roads, and the birds forage up to a half mile or more from their nest box, calling frequently in flight.

Purple Martins are among the very first diurnal birds to become active in the morning, and their voices carry great distances over treetops in the predawn stillness. Observers almost certainly would have detected martins nesting in a carefully covered Atlas block. The high percentage of "confirmations" reflects the ease with which this species can be "confirmed" once an occupied nest box is located.

The Atlas map documents the location of active colonies and corroborates the previously reported decline. Purple Martin colonies increase in number northeastward from Concord through the Lakes Region and into Maine, corresponding with lower elevations in the state. Atlas records are totally lacking for Grafton, Sullivan, and Cheshire counties in western New Hampshire, where active colonies existed earlier in this century.

The future of the Purple Martin in New Hampshire is uncertain. Because present colonies are few and small, a single incident of prolonged rain just after hatching in June could kill an entire year's production and most of the adults as well. New Hampshire residents can promote the survival and spread of this much-sought species through properly constructed, placed, and monitored martin apartment houses. With human interest and knowledgeable assistance, this largest swallow can continue to grace our skies.

Chandler S. Robbins

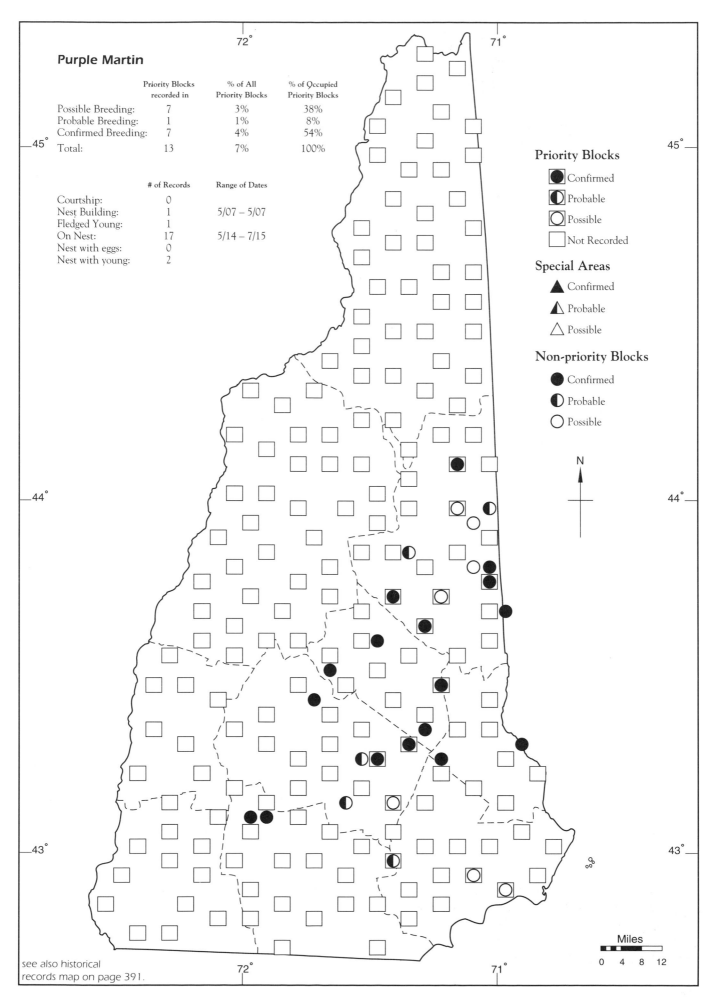

Purple Martin

	Priority Blocks recorded in	% of All Priority Blocks	% of Occupied Priority Blocks
Possible Breeding:	7	3%	38%
Probable Breeding:	1	1%	8%
Confirmed Breeding:	7	4%	54%
Total:	13	7%	100%

	# of Records	Range of Dates
Courtship:	0	
Nest Building:	1	5/07 – 5/07
Fledged Young:	1	
On Nest:	17	5/14 – 7/15
Nest with eggs:	0	
Nest with young:	2	

Priority Blocks

- ◕ Confirmed
- ◑ Probable
- ○ Possible
- ☐ Not Recorded

Special Areas

- ▲ Confirmed
- ◤ Probable
- △ Possible

Non-priority Blocks

- ● Confirmed
- ◖ Probable
- ○ Possible

N

see also historical records map on page 391.

167

Tree Swallow
Tachycineta bicolor

Around country homes, Tree Swallows are a common and welcome sight. These graceful and hardy birds nest in holes in tree stubs standing in or near still water and also in birdhouses throughout nearly all of New Hampshire. They apparently even have nested in structures on the top of Cannon Mtn. at an elevation of more than 4,000 ft (1,220 m) (T. Richards, unpubl. data). Although they compete successfully for birdhouses with Eastern Bluebirds and House Wrens, House Sparrows in turn may chase them away. Furious battles are a common sight.

Males are milk white below and brilliant metallic blue-green above, with a dark cap pulled down over the eyes. A white spot on their rear flanks shows in flight. The tails are slightly forked. Females, juveniles, and first summer males are duller and more brownish.

The hardiest of our swallows, Tree Swallows follow rivers during migration (Tyler 1942d) and are the first swallows to arrive, in late March or early April. Rivers provide the earliest source of flying insects, but Tree Swallows often arrive before insects are available and must depend on berries and seeds for food (Tyler 1942d). Along the coast, migrating Tree Swallows eat bayberries (Forbush 1929). In a spring storm, they crowd together for warmth in a tree cavity or birdhouse (Forbush 1929), or disappear, presumably making a strategic southward retreat (Tyler 1942d). During cold or stormy weather in May, hundreds of Tree Swallows often circle low over New Hampshire lakes, where insects presumably are more numerous than elsewhere (K. C. Elkins, pers. obs.). Large flocks of migrating Tree Swallows first gather in New Hampshire marshes in early spring, but disperse after a few weeks, leaving a few pairs to nest in wooded swamps, open woods, and fields near water. Where there are many dead trees in water, the swallows are semigregarious, nesting close to one another.

Tree Swallows eat many insect pests such as beetles, flies, and mosquitoes. In a desperate attempt to control biting insects, a lumberyard in the White Mountains put up about 50 swallow boxes. Tree Swallows occupied every box, and the men worked in comfort (S.B. Turner, pers. comm.).

Quick and agile in flight, Tree Swallows glide, dip, and flutter over water and pastures, hunting insects. Tail-chasing males, sometimes grappling in midair, are a common sight early in the breeding season.

The Tree Swallow's song is a twittering "silip," given repeatedly in flight or from a perch. The male courts the female in acrobatic aerial pursuit, wings at or below the horizontal (Allen *in* Tyler 1942d). He also performs flutter-flight around the nest site when the female is present, then alights and bows while approaching her (Stokes 1979).

In New Hampshire, nest building occurs primarily in May (NHBBA data). Tree Swallows prefer to nest in birdhouses when they are available, and otherwise nest in old woodpecker holes (Tyler 1942d). This is an easy bird to "confirm" as it is readily observed entering a nest box or tree cavity. Pairs compete intensely for nest sites.

The female spends from a few days to 2 weeks building the nest (Harrison 1975), an untidy mass of grasses and straw stuffed into a tree cavity or nest box and lined with feathers, usually white ones. After laying 4 to 6 white eggs, she incubates for 13 to 16 days. The male brings food to her on the nest. The young fledge 16 to 24 days later, and are distinctive with brown backs and the shadow of a breast band. Normally, a pair produces a single brood annually. Some females, largely yearlings, which have distinctly browner backs and wings, nest relatively late in the season (Turner and Rose 1989). After fledging, usually in late June or early July, young Tree Swallows remain near the nest area for a while. They are common over fields and ponds until August, when they disperse (Tyler 1942d).

This is the last of our swallows to fly south in autumn (Forbush 1929). Thousands once roosted in coastal marshes in August (Forbush 1929). Tree Swallows winter from central America north to the United States near the Gulf Coast, where enormous flocks flow over wetlands for many minutes at a time (Janeway, pers. obs.).

The Tree, or "white-bellied" Swallow appears to have been a common but somewhat local summer resident of New Hampshire for a long time (Coues 1868, Allen 1903, Scott 1921, White 1924, Forbush 1929). BBS data suggest a significant increase in Tree Swallow numbers in the Northeastern states during 1966–79, and show the greatest abundances for this species in central New England and the Adirondack Mtns., with the highest state and provincial means in Vermont, New Hampshire, Maine, and New Brunswick (Robbins et al. 1986).

Atlas records for Tree Swallows are lacking from only 9 priority blocks, all in the White Mountains and North Country, where mountainous terrain, extensive forests, and low beaver populations contribute to a relative scarcity of suitable habitat. Increased availability of nest boxes and a wealth of beaver ponds provide ample nesting habitat in southern New Hampshire. This species is likely to remain common in the state for the foreseeable future.

Elizabeth C. Janeway

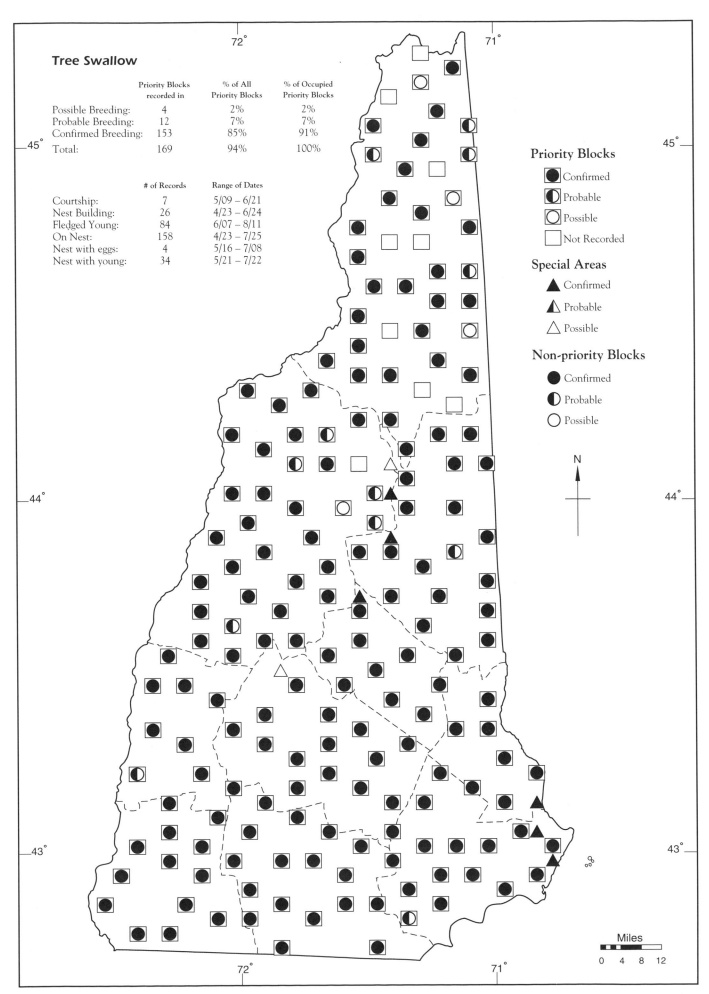

Tree Swallow

	Priority Blocks recorded in	% of All Priority Blocks	% of Occupied Priority Blocks
Possible Breeding:	4	2%	2%
Probable Breeding:	12	7%	7%
Confirmed Breeding:	153	85%	91%
Total:	169	94%	100%

	# of Records	Range of Dates
Courtship:	7	5/09 – 6/21
Nest Building:	26	4/23 – 6/24
Fledged Young:	84	6/07 – 8/11
On Nest:	158	4/23 – 7/25
Nest with eggs:	4	5/16 – 7/08
Nest with young:	34	5/21 – 7/22

Priority Blocks

● Confirmed
◐ Probable
○ Possible
□ Not Recorded

Special Areas

▲ Confirmed
◮ Probable
△ Possible

Non-priority Blocks

● Confirmed
◐ Probable
○ Possible

N

Miles
0 4 8 12

169

Northern Rough-winged Swallow
Stelgidopteryx serripennis

This drab and unobtrusive swallow is known to few except ornithologists and birdwatchers. It resembles the Bank Swallow in appearance, but is slightly larger, and has a brownish gray throat without a breast band and lighter brown upperparts. Its flight is steady and gliding, in contrast to the bouncing, erratic flight of the Bank Swallow. The common calls of the 2 species are somewhat similar, but the Northern Rough-wing's "brrrtt" is lower and harsher (Armistead *in* Farrand 1983). These swallows often occur together, and both commonly nest in sand or gravel banks. Northern Rough-winged Swallows breed from southern Canada south to southern Mexico, and winter north to the extreme southern U.S.

The name "rough-winged" describes peculiar serrations on the outer primary of each wing. These feathers have barbs that are stiffened and free of barbules at the tip, hooked in the males, nearly straight in the females. Their function is unknown.

In New Hampshire the first Northern Rough-winged Swallows seldom arrive before mid-April. They start nesting in May, raise a single brood, and leave for the south early. Although most depart before the end of July, a few occasionally linger through August. During the breeding season they are widely but thinly distributed, primarily in river valleys. They commonly occur near water and, like all swallows, forage over fields, wetlands, and open water.

Northern Rough-wings nest primarily in burrows in riverbanks or gravel pits, but they are adaptable and make use of a great variety of nest sites (Lunk 1962). In New Hampshire they often use drain pipes under bridges; these nests frequently must be washed away during heavy rains. When nesting in sand or gravel banks, these birds commonly use abandoned burrows of Belted Kingfishers and Bank Swallows. Although Northern Rough-wings usually excavate their own burrows in some areas (Weydemeyer 1933, Dingle 1942),

Lunk (1962) examined nearly 100 of their nests in Michigan without finding any in a burrow that the swallows had excavated. He found that they would readily accept artificial nest tubes, which he inserted in sand banks.

Northern Rough-wings do not breed in colonies like Bank Swallows, but 2 or more pairs may nest under the same bridge, or several pairs may occupy a single large gravel bank. Solitary pairs are common. When people approach the nesting locality, the birds often will alight on utility wires or other convenient perches and wait quietly for the intruders to leave.

In courtship the male spreads his long, white undertail coverts so that they show conspicuously on either side of the brown tail (Grinnell and Storer 1924 *in* Bent 1942). The female builds the bulky nest of rootlets, weeds, leaves, and grasses and incubates the clutch of 4 to 8 white eggs for 16 days, unassisted by her mate. Atlas observers noted Northern Rough-wings entering probable nesting holes as early as 7 May and as late as 4 August. Observers have found eggs in Vermont from 18 May to 10 July (Norse *in* Laughlin and Kibbe 1985).

Both parents feed the young, which leave the nest at ages ranging from 18 to 21 days (Lunk 1962). There were young in a nest in Andover on 21 June 1961 (Elkins, pers. obs.), and adults were bringing food to young in a nest near New Boston on 10 July 1982 (R. Andrews, pers. comm.). Fledged young were perching on utility wires in Kensington on 12 July 1983 (G.W. Gavutis, pers. comm.). The young are dependent on their parents for a short time after leaving the nest. Family groups quickly depart from the nesting locality (G.W. Gavutis, pers. comm.).

Northern Rough-winged Swallows were unknown in New Hampshire prior to the present century. They spread into the state from the south in the early 1900s. The first documented nesting in Massachusetts occurred in North Adams in 1895 (May 1929). Records of breeding "at or near Hanover" in 1905 and 1906 (Goodhue 1922) may refer to a pair which nested in Norwich, Vermont, in 1905 (May 1929). A nest found in Boscawen on 3 July 1909 (May 1929) therefore may represent the first breeding record for New Hampshire. Northern Rough-wings "settled for the summer" in Tilton in 1913, and several pairs were present there in 1914 (Goodhue 1922). They nested in Ashland in 1917, in Manchester in 1923, and in Snowville, Eaton, in 1925 (May 1929). The species continued to extend its range and reached Pittsburg, the northernmost township, at least as early as 1953 (Halberg *in* Wallace 1953). BBS data provide evidence that the northward expansion is continuing, and show significant increases in the Eastern and Central regions and for the continent as a whole (Robbins et al. 1986).

The Atlas map shows this swallow to be widely distributed but local south of the White Mountains, except in the Western Highlands and the Connecticut Valley, where it appears to be rare. The Northern Rough-wing is absent from the White Mountains, except around the edges, but has penetrated the North Country, though it is still rare there. It is present in the Ammonoosuc, Johns, and Israel river valleys in northern New Hampshire, but was not found in the Androscoggin River valley. The gravel banks and highway bridges where the species usually nests are most frequent in and near river valleys. Thus, it is not surprising that a very large proportion of the blocks with records for this swallow include or are close to rivers. There is no obvious explanation for the lack of records in the Connecticut Valley, however.

Kimball C. Elkins

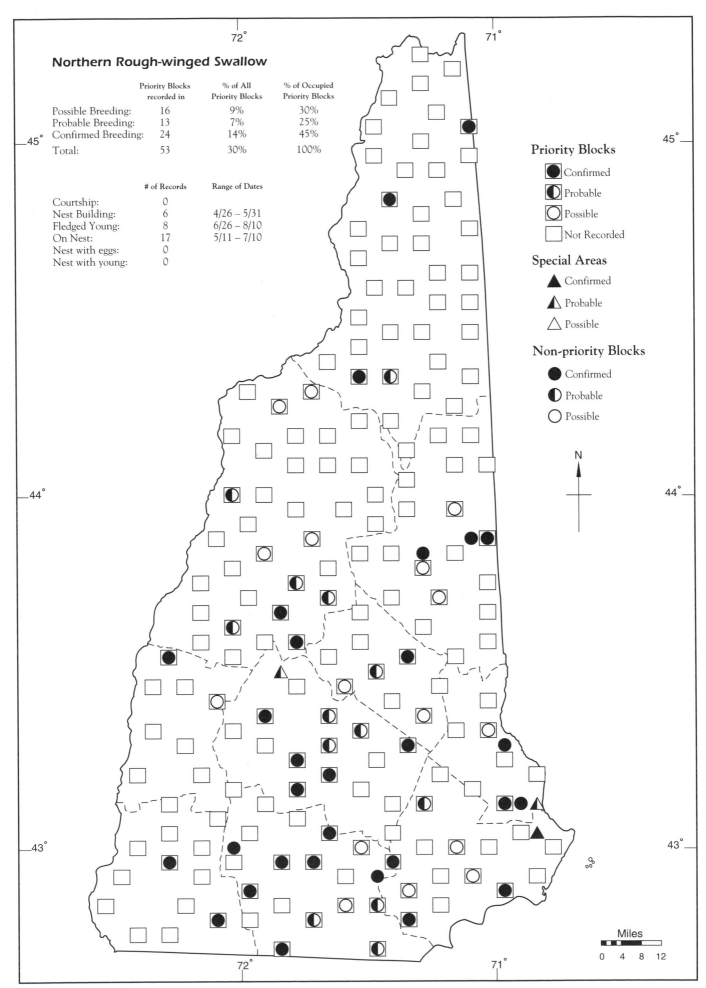

Northern Rough-winged Swallow

	Priority Blocks recorded in	% of All Priority Blocks	% of Occupied Priority Blocks
Possible Breeding:	16	9%	30%
Probable Breeding:	13	7%	25%
Confirmed Breeding:	24	14%	45%
Total:	53	30%	100%

	# of Records	Range of Dates
Courtship:	0	
Nest Building:	6	4/26 – 5/31
Fledged Young:	8	6/26 – 8/10
On Nest:	17	5/11 – 7/10
Nest with eggs:	0	
Nest with young:	0	

Priority Blocks
- Confirmed
- Probable
- Possible
- Not Recorded

Special Areas
- Confirmed
- Probable
- Possible

Non-priority Blocks
- Confirmed
- Probable
- Possible

N

Miles
0   4   8   12

Bank Swallow
Riparia riparia

The Bank Swallow is our smallest and most gregarious swallow, well known for its tight clusters of nest burrows excavated in vertical banks of rivers and commercial gravel pits. A buzzy, gritty voice and well-defined breast band help distinguish the Bank Swallow from the longer winged Northern Rough-winged Swallow, with its brownish wash over throat and breast. Bank Swallows occur throughout the Northern Hemisphere. In New Hampshire they breed throughout the state, nesting at elevations up to 2,000 ft (610 m) in the White Mountains (T. Richards, unpubl. data). North American populations winter in South America (Ehrlich et al. 1988).

Migrating flocks of Bank Swallows arrive in New Hampshire in late April or early May (Gross 1942a, SRS). Upon arrival at breeding sites they spend much of their time feeding and may sleep in the previous year's burrows (Forbush 1929). Opportunistic feeders on many kinds of flying insects, they often forage over water, especially in early spring, flying erratically with shallow, rapid wing beats. Emlen and DeJong (1975) report extensive feeding territories covering 12 to 20 sq mi (30 to 50 sq km), which could overlap several Atlas priority blocks.

Courtship and burrow excavation begin within 2 weeks of arrival (Stoner 1936, Gross 1942a). Courtship usually occurs during early stages of excavation and may involve an in-flight exchange of feathers (Ehrlich et al. 1988). Although these swallows sometimes renovate old burrows, erosion often necessitates new ones. Both sexes, using bills and feet, excavate the burrows into banks of sand or clay, using their wings to help eject material (Stoner 1936). Burrows are usually near the top of a bank and may be less than 6 in (15 cm) apart, sometimes resulting in the coalescence of 2 burrows to form a common chamber (Gross 1942a). Competition during excavation is intense, especially in large colonies. Conflicts begin at burrow entrances and then continue as aerial fights, sometimes ending with combatants tumbling to the ground (Hoogland and Sherman 1976). Colonies of 2, 15, 50, and 110 pairs have been reported in New Hampshire (Scott 1921, Ridgely 1977, Allison and Allison 1979). Colonies may reach several hundred pairs (Petersen 1955).

The nest, which consists of grass, rootlets, twigs, and sometimes horsehair or sheep wool, is constructed in an enlarged chamber at the end of the burrow (Stoner 1936). New Hampshire nest-building dates range from the first week of May to late June. An average clutch includes 5 eggs, although 2 to 8 egg clutches are known (Hjertaas et al. 1988). Both sexes incubate for a total of about 15 days, beginning a few days before the clutch is complete (Petersen 1955, Harrison 1975).

Bank Swallows add an inner lining of feathers to the nest after the onset of incubation (Stoner 1936). Feather fights, sometimes involving more than 100 birds, may erupt after other swallows detect a parent carrying a feather toward its nest burrow (Hoogland and Sherman 1976).

Observations in New Hampshire show an extended peak of occupied nests throughout June which account for most "confirmed" breeding records. Stoner (1936) reported that a few Bank Swallows raise second broods. However a more recent study of marked birds in 54 colonies showed the presence of late nesters, but no clear evidence of second broods (Hoogland and Sherman 1976). The presence of inactive burrows within colonies requires careful observation to determine colony size.

The nestling period lasts 20 to 23 days (Petersen 1955, Hjertaas et al. 1988). Many chicks may starve during extended periods of cold wet weather (Stoner 1936). Chicks develop unique signature calls at the age of 15 to 17 days (Beecher et al. 1981b). Young swallows begin to make short flights from their nest burrows 18 days after hatching (Beecher et al. 1981a). Fledglings form mixed family assemblages (creches) on powerlines and in other areas away from the colony. Offspring recognition enables parents to feed their own young in creches and in the air, as well as at the nest burrow entrance. On 10 July 1990, a flock of 35 Bank Swallows foraged on the lee side of Stinson Mtn., Rumney, where adults fed juveniles on the wing (Wicklow, pers. obs.).

Most Bank Swallows leave their colonies to gather in flocks in mid-July (Allen 1903). Migration begins in late July and continues into August. Bank Swallow sightings are rare after the first week of September (Forbush 1929).

Mobbing swallows fly in a circular pattern around potential predators, occasionally hovering over the intruder's head. House Sparrows elict a mobbing response and sometimes successfully evict Bank Swallows to use their nest burrows (Hoogland and Sherman 1976). In July 1986, M.J. Murray (pers. comm.) observed a red fox preying on Bank Swallows in a large colony along the Israel River, Lancaster. Other predators include Common Crows, American Kestrels, minks, weasels, and skunks (Forbush 1929, Stoner 1936, Freer 1979).

Bank Swallows have been locally abundant summer residents of New Hampshire at least since the mid-1800s (Samuels 1867, Dearborn 1898, Allen 1903, Dearborn 1903, Wright 1911, White 1937). They are widely distributed in the state, but limited to areas where suitable banks exist for nesting. Dearborn (1903) knew of no colonies in the Durham area, where sand banks are generally lacking.

Atlas workers found this species in 53% of all priority blocks, but in only 42% of those in the mountainous 3 northern counties. There are no "confirmed" breeding records for the Seacoast region.

BBS data from 1966 to 1990 indicate a decline in New Hampshire Bank Swallow numbers (J.R. Sauer, unpubl. data), possibly due to the closing and grading of gravel pits and landfills. Although availability of nesting habitat in such areas is subject to change, riparian habitats are likely to provide ample nest sites for the future.

Barry J. Wicklow

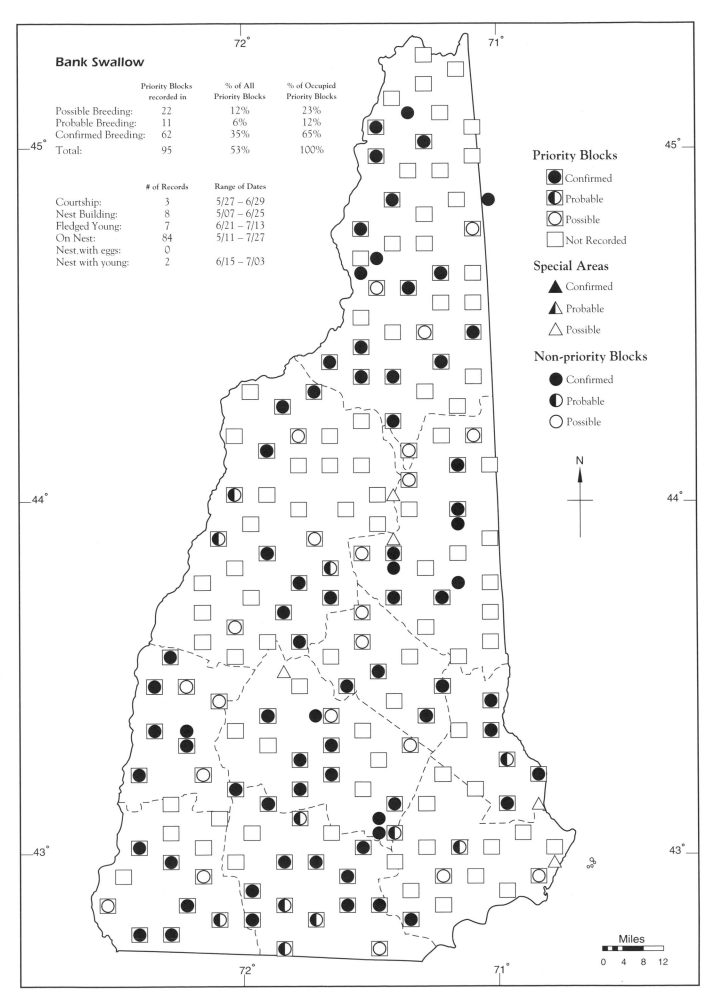

Bank Swallow

	Priority Blocks recorded in	% of All Priority Blocks	% of Occupied Priority Blocks
Possible Breeding:	22	12%	23%
Probable Breeding:	11	6%	12%
Confirmed Breeding:	62	35%	65%
Total:	95	53%	100%

	# of Records	Range of Dates
Courtship:	3	5/27 – 6/29
Nest Building:	8	5/07 – 6/25
Fledged Young:	7	6/21 – 7/13
On Nest:	84	5/11 – 7/27
Nest with eggs:	0	
Nest with young:	2	6/15 – 7/03

Priority Blocks

● Confirmed
◑ Probable
○ Possible
□ Not Recorded

Special Areas

▲ Confirmed
◮ Probable
△ Possible

Non-priority Blocks

● Confirmed
◐ Probable
○ Possible

N

Miles
0 4 8 12

Cliff Swallow
Hirundo pyrrhonota

These rather quiet swallows are readily distinguished by their buffy rumps, pale foreheads, dark throats, and square tails. Juveniles are duller, with pale throats. Their song and call notes are husky (Saunders 1935). Their steady flight is usually higher than the swooping, gliding flight of Barn Swallows, with which they often occur (Samuel 1971). Cliff Swallows feed on flying insects, often high in the sky and sometimes as far as 4 mi (6.4 km) from their nests. They forage over open land and water, avoiding wooded areas (Emlen 1954).

Cliff Swallows, like a number of their relatives, are named for the location in which they place their nests. Nests on cliffs are rare in eastern North America, however, and may be unknown in New Hampshire. Here, the majority of these birds nest under the eaves of buildings, hence their local name "eave swallows." They also nest under the roofs of porches, under bridges, and sometimes inside barns or other buildings, where the nest usually is placed nearer the entrance than most Barn Swallow nests (Samuel 1971). A large colony once nested on a dam in Errol (Brewster 1938). Other nest locations are common, but all have a vertical surface beneath a protruding overhang and a clearance below of at least 8 ft (2.4 m) if over land, 3 ft (0.9 m) if over water (Emlen 1954).

The first Cliff Swallows often arrive in late April but the majority come in May. Nesting activities begin soon after arrival. Much twittering accompanies an aerial courtship (Terres 1980), but pair formation is completed at the nest site, which the male selects. He at first repels but later accepts the female as she repeatedly returns (Emlen 1954).

Pairs congregate at the edges of puddles, where they sit in groups with quivering wings picking up "gobs" of mud. They roll the mud into pellets in their mouths before flying to the nest sites (Samuel 1971). The pair works together at building the gourd-shaped nest, which, in exposed situations, has a projecting tube for an entrance (Gross 1942b). The nest is lined with grass or leaves and often feathers. Nest construction takes a week or 2 (Harrison 1975). In New Hampshire it most often occurs in late May or early June, but dry weather may delay nest building, owing to the need for mud. Construction observed in July or August is probably for a second brood or to replace a lost nest.

Both sexes incubate the 3 to 6 eggs for about 15 days (Harrison 1975), and tend the young, which fly at 23 days and may return to the nest for 2 or 3 days after fledging (Harrison 1978). Sometimes there are 2 broods.

Cliff Swallows often perch on utility wires in late July and early August. Many migrate at about this time; the remainder go in late August and September.

Cliff Swallows probably nested in eastern North America before Europeans arrived (Coues 1868, Forbush 1929), but in few and widely scattered colonies where suitable cliffs occurred near open foraging areas. Allen (1903) mentions a report of Cliff Swallows from the White Mountains in 1816, which may be the first New Hampshire record. Cliff Swallows were nesting at the Crawford's in Crawford's Purchase in 1818 (Boott *in* Nuttall 1903), presumably under eaves. They were known from Maine much earlier, and there are reports of eave nesting there as early as 1800 (Palmer 1949). Eave nesting enabled rapid population increases and range expansion. Cliff Swallows appeared in Jaffrey in 1838 (Gross 1942b), and Coues (1868) considered them abundant summer residents of New England as early as 1868. In 1871 they were common everywhere in Coos County (Maynard 1871).

Forbush (1929) indicates that House Sparrows, introduced in New England in the 1850s, subsequently drove nearly all the Cliff Swallows in southern New England into Maine. No severe decline took place in New Hampshire. Cliff Swallows were common in Holderness in 1885 and 1886 and in Franconia in 1886 and 1887 (Faxon and Allen 1888). In the 1890s they were increasing in Belknap and Merrimack counties (Dearborn 1898). A decade or so later they were common in Jefferson (Wright 1911) and fairly common in Dublin (Thayer 1909 *in* Allison and Allison 1979). Goodhue (1922) considered them "more plenty" in Merrimack County than 30 years previous.

Although House Sparrows have usurped some Cliff Swallow nests in New Hampshire (Allison and Allison 1979), the swallow's decline during the past 50 years or so is probably mainly due to the decline of agriculture. Fewer open areas and fewer unpainted barns with livestock combine to limit suitable breeding habitat. During cold, wet summers many swallows may starve. For these and perhaps other reasons, colonies of 50 to 75 pairs of Cliff Swallows, their nests occupying the entire length of a barn, now are seldom seen.

BBS data from 1966 to 1985 show higher Cliff Swallow numbers north of the White Mountains than farther south. In the North Country they were numerous in 1966, relatively scarce during the next 4 years, common again from 1971 to 1975, then again rather scarce from 1976 to 1985. During this entire period relatively few were recorded south of the mountains.

Atlas data indicate a widespread distribution in New Hampshire, with substantial gaps in the White Mountains and the southeastern corner of the state. This species now occurs largely in small colonies and isolated pairs, often nesting on buildings other than barns (Elkins, pers. obs.). Although this swallow seems likely to persist in New Hampshire for the foreseeable future, its population in the state bears watching in the years to come.

Vera H. Hebert & Kimball C. Elkins

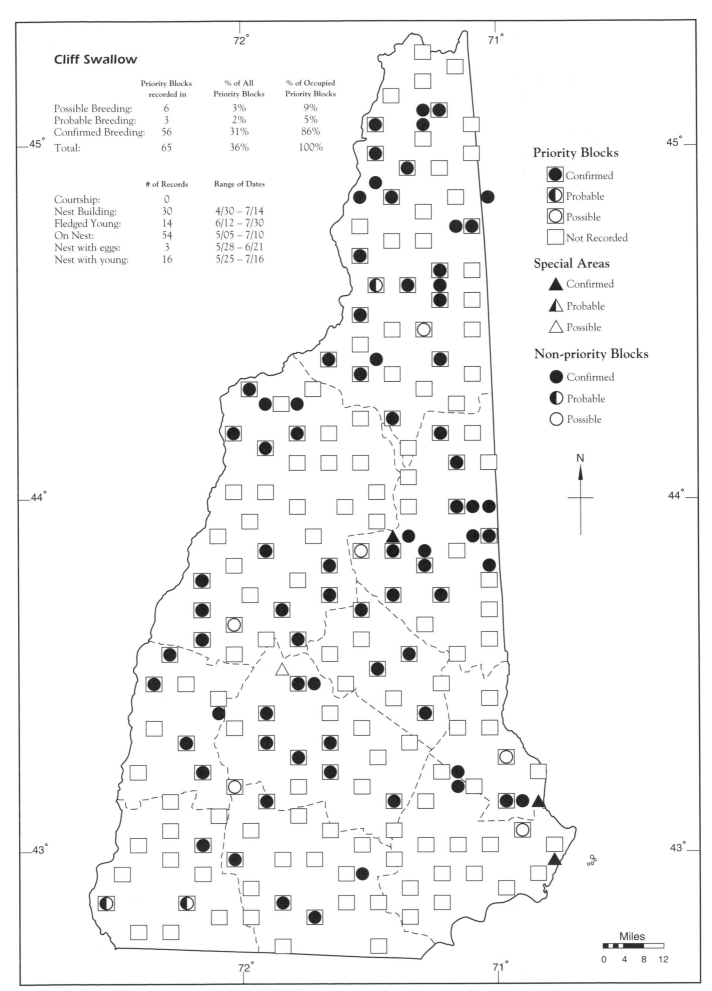

Cliff Swallow

	Priority Blocks recorded in	% of All Priority Blocks	% of Occupied Priority Blocks
Possible Breeding:	6	3%	9%
Probable Breeding:	3	2%	5%
Confirmed Breeding:	56	31%	86%
Total:	65	36%	100%

	# of Records	Range of Dates
Courtship:	0	
Nest Building:	30	4/30 – 7/14
Fledged Young:	14	6/12 – 7/30
On Nest:	54	5/05 – 7/10
Nest with eggs:	3	5/28 – 6/21
Nest with young:	16	5/25 – 7/16

Priority Blocks
- ● Confirmed
- ◐ Probable
- ○ Possible
- □ Not Recorded

Special Areas
- ▲ Confirmed
- ◥ Probable
- △ Possible

Non-priority Blocks
- ● Confirmed
- ◗ Probable
- ○ Possible

N

Miles
0 4 8 12

Barn Swallow
Hirundo rustica

The graceful Barn Swallow, whose deeply forked, white-spotted tail distinguishes it from our other swallows, is as much a part of New Hampshire farms as cows in their pastures. This species, which has a worldwide distribution, nests throughout our state, from the Seacoast to above 4,000 ft (1,220 m). A pair observed in the tramway shed on Cannon Mtn., Franconia, at 4,000 ft (1,220 m) elevation on 8 July 1972 apparently was nesting there (T. Richards, unpubl. data). The highest elevation at which Barn Swallows nest regularly in New Hampshire may be at the base of the Mt. Washington railroad in Thompson and Meserves Purchase at about 2,700 ft (820 m) (T. Richards, unpubl. data).

These highly sociable, steel-blue swallows, with chestnut-brown throats and foreheads and buffy underparts, arrive here in late April or, more usually, early May, with the hatching of black flies. Adults return to their nest sites and, if available, to their mates of the previous year (Shields 1984). Year-old swallows return in spring to a site which they visited during exploratory flights of 3.8 to 23 mi (6 to 37 km) from the nest before fall migration (Shields 1984).

From predawn well into the gathering dark of warm summer evenings, Barn Swallows constantly forage for insects in the air or skim water surfaces, where large frogs and fishes have been known to capture them (Forbush 1929). Lacking melodious song, Barn Swallows twitter incessantly and utter gutteral clicks and churring sounds near their nests.

Barn Swallows will dive to attack cats, but tolerate human activity about the barns in which they nest. These swallows plaster their mud nests, reinforced with straw and lined with grass and feathers, onto rough boards or beams. Unlike Cliff Swallows' nests, theirs are always open at the tops, and are inside, rather than outside buildings.

While there may be dozens of active nests in a large barn, 6 to 8 nests is a more usual number for one location. Barn Swallows raise 2, and rarely 3, broods each year, laying clutches of 4 or 5 eggs from mid-May through mid-July. White (1937) cites complete clutches in Concord as early as 18 May. Both sexes incubate for a period of 13 to 17 days, and nestlings fledge in 18 to 23 days (Davis 1937 *in* Terres 1980). Other Barn Swallows, including young from previous broods as well as additional adults, may assist a pair in feeding their nestlings (Myers and Waller 1977). Young swallows have paler plumage and shorter tails than adults.

In haying season, Barn Swallows swoop and dive closely behind cutter and rake, capturing insects. They also follow farm animals, dogs, and humans moving through tall grass. Courting, eating, and drinking on the wing, they pack insects into their gullets to regurgitate to their nestlings as pellets (Forbush 1929). One pair of Barn Swallows, flying an estimated 600 mi (960 km) per day while feeding, will consume thousands of insects within a range of 0.5 mi (0.8 km) from the nest (Bull and Farrand 1977, DeGraaf et al. 1980) — with far more finesse than an electric bug zapper.

Barn Swallows gathering together before the fall migration are a familiar sight from mid-July through August, entire families lining up and jostling for position on a wire outside their barn. A few may remain into September, and often a lone parent will stay behind to care for the nestlings of a late brood. The last individuals depart by mid-September (Dearborn 1903, White 1937).

Barn Swallows may have graced New Hampshire skies for centuries before European settlers arrived and built barns. Then the swallows nested in rocky crevices and mountain caves, on cliffs by lakes and rivers, and in hollow trees (Forbush 1929). Since colonial days, they have entirely altered their nesting behavior by adopting man-made dwellings and have nearly or entirely abandoned natural sites. When New Hampshire was all forested, this probably was not a common swallow. However, clearing for agriculture and construction of barns greatly increased suitable habitat, and the species was common to abundant in the late 1800s and early 1900s (Dearborn 1898, 1903, White 1937).

Slowly, however, old, swallow-accessible barns have been disappearing from the countryside. In many cases the scrappy House Sparrow is invading those that remain. Modern barns, tightly constructed with an eye for sanitation, are not as welcoming to the Barn Swallow. Whether this species will again adopt nesting sites in natural shelters is for a future Atlas project to discover.

The Barn Swallow is an easy bird to "confirm," for its nests are highly visible. The relatively few priority blocks lacking records, nearly all in the White Mountains or North Country, are likely to be heavily forested or to lack suitable buildings for nests. BBS data for this species fluctuate widely from year to year (Robbins et al. 1986). The future outlook for New Hampshire's Barn Swallows, at present common but becoming more local, depends upon the availability of suitable structures and the swallow's ability to adapt to decreasing availability of human-built nesting sites.

Elizabeth C. Janeway

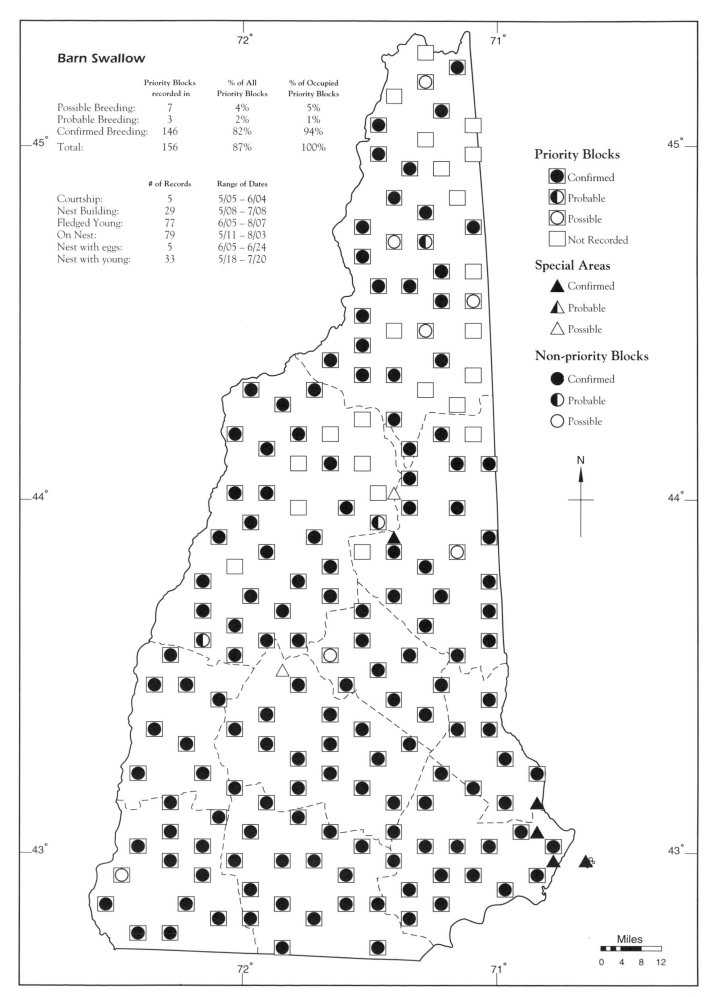

Barn Swallow

	Priority Blocks recorded in	% of All Priority Blocks	% of Occupied Priority Blocks
Possible Breeding:	7	4%	5%
Probable Breeding:	3	2%	1%
Confirmed Breeding:	146	82%	94%
Total:	156	87%	100%

	# of Records	Range of Dates
Courtship:	5	5/05 – 6/04
Nest Building:	29	5/08 – 7/08
Fledged Young:	77	6/05 – 8/07
On Nest:	79	5/11 – 8/03
Nest with eggs:	5	6/05 – 6/24
Nest with young:	33	5/18 – 7/20

Priority Blocks

- Confirmed
- Probable
- Possible
- Not Recorded

Special Areas

- Confirmed
- Probable
- Possible

Non-priority Blocks

- Confirmed
- Probable
- Possible

N

Miles
0 4 8 12

Gray Jay
Perisoreus canadensis

The Gray Jay's bold inquisitiveness earned this bird a reputation among lumberjacks and trappers of old. Names such as "camp robber," "grease bird," and "venison hawk" reveal this species' propensity for stealing food and its willingness to eat almost anything. Its extensive variety of vocalizations and slow, gliding flight as it silently floats from perch to perch are reminiscent of its more familiar blue cousin, but the Gray Jay is readily distinguished by its gray plumage and dark crown.

The Gray Jay is distributed across northern North America from Alaska to Newfoundland, and south into northern California, Colorado, New York, New England, and Nova Scotia. Considered rare in New Hampshire, the Gray Jay resides in the coniferous forests and bogs of the North Country and at elevations above 2,500 ft (760 m) in the White Mountains (T. Richards, unpubl. data). This species is not given to long distance migration. Seasonal movements are generally restricted to wanderings within the breeding range or travels to lower elevations (Ridgely 1977, DeGraaf et al. 1980). Occasional winter sightings have occurred in southern parts of the state (White 1924, Richards 1958).

Contrasting with their usual outgoing nature, Gray Jays become reclusive during the breeding season, which begins in February and March when snow still covers their remote habitat. The well-hidden nest typically is located high in a conifer close to the trunk or in an upright crotch 6 to 11 ft (1.8 to 3.6 m) above the ground, but may be as low as 4 ft (1.2 m) or as high as 30 ft (9.1 m) (Harrison 1975, Goodwin 1976). Male and female together carefully construct the nest from twigs, bark strips, and dry mosses and thickly line it with feathers, fur, cocoons, or similar soft materials, which provide good insulation. Courtship displays at the nest may include wing flutters, neck pecking, token feeding, and soft mewing vocalizations (Lawrence 1961). There are 2 to 5 eggs, usually laid in March (Forbush 1927, Bent 1946).

The female begins incubating with the first egg laid and continues alone through the 16 to 18 day incubation period (Goodwin 1976). Young remain in the nest approximately 15 days (Bent 1946). Both adults feed the nestlings, but the male contributes more to this effort initially (Goodwin 1976). Adults may carry food to the nest in their gular pouches, or may regurgitate food from the crop (C.R. Smith, pers. comm.). The sooty gray fledglings, which are noisy and conspicous in midsummer, provide the easiest way to "confirm" nesting, and accounted for all Atlas "confirmations". Despite their early start, Gray Jays do not raise a second brood.

Gray Jays have extremely varied diets, which include insects, berries, conifer seeds, and fungi. Scavenging leads them to carrion, and scraps from mammalian carcasses may be an important food source in late winter (Goodwin 1976). During the breeding season, this species also preys on eggs and fledglings of sparrows, warblers, and thrushes (Ouellet 1970). While the "camp robber's" visits to human establishments often result in offerings of bread or crackers, an informal study showed that these jays prefer a serving of baked beans and cheese (Goodwin 1976).

Food storage is characteristic of the crow family, and Gray Jays exhibit this trait to the extreme. Their uniquely developed salivary glands, largest of any jay, are used to form saliva-coated boli (Dow 1965). They diligently cache these morsels in crevices and among conifer needles, helping to sustain both adults and young in early spring before other food sources become available.

Gray Jays may travel in small groups, especially during the nonbreeding season, they have a repertoire of displays that establish a hierarchy, possibly enabling a group to feed together (Geist 1968 in Goodwin 1976).

Early records suggest that the "Canada Jay" once was only a winter visitor to New Hampshire (Audubon in Samuels 1867, Coues 1868). Maynard (1871) cites specimens taken in June 1870 at Umbagog Lake, and states "May breed, but this is south of its usual summer range." However, Samuels (1867) considered it a year-round resident in northern New England, and Chadbourne (1887) documented summer sightings in the Presidential Range, "though nowhere plenty." By the early 1900s this species was considered a permanent resident in northern New Hampshire and the White Mountains, where it was common at elevations of 3,000 to 4,000 ft (910 to 1,220 m) (Allen 1903, Wright 1911, ASNH 1920, Forbush 1927). Allen (1903) mentions reports of nesting on Mt. Washington and the Carter-Moriah range, and Wright (1911) notes sightings of families in Jefferson Notch, Thompson and Meserves Purchase. This may reflect more thorough knowledge of northern bird distribution rather than a change in breeding status.

Summer sightings have continued within the Gray Jay's established range in the White Mountains and North Country since the 1950s (Dyer and Walkinshaw 1959, SRS). This species may have undergone a recent population decline in northern New Hampshire (T. Richards, pers. comm.), and New Hampshire biologists recommended it as a Special Concern Species in 1986 (Smith and Choate 1985).

The Atlas project focused special effort on the Gray Jay, soliciting information on sighting locations outside priority blocks. The resulting map shows the expected mountain and northern distribution, with an apparent concentration in northeastern Coos County.

Diane Evans

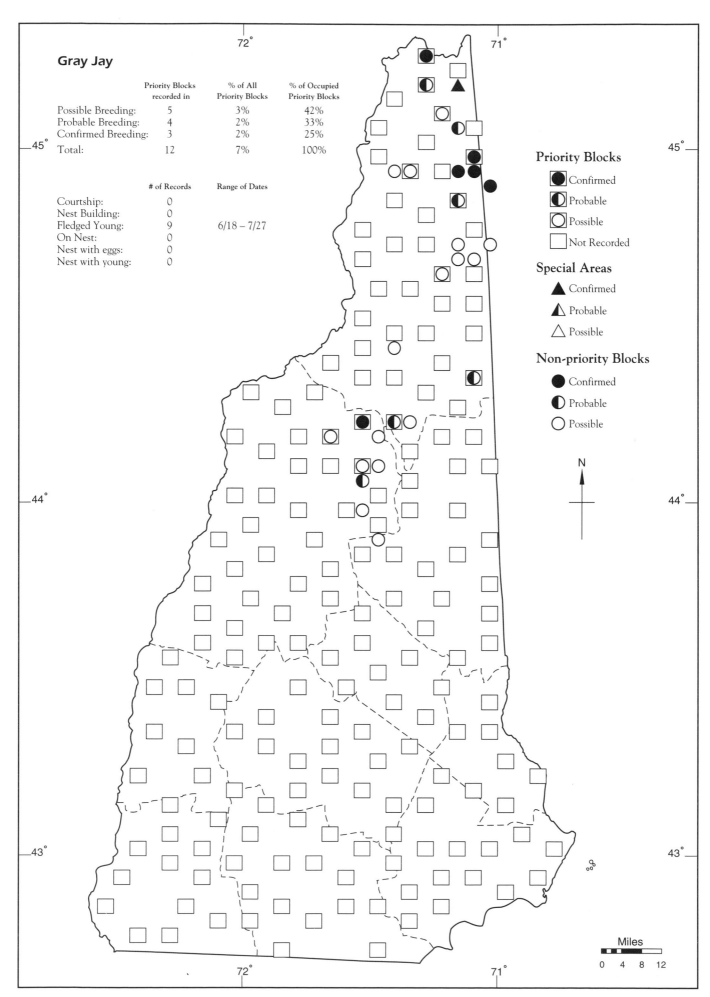

Gray Jay

	Priority Blocks recorded in	% of All Priority Blocks	% of Occupied Priority Blocks
Possible Breeding:	5	3%	42%
Probable Breeding:	4	2%	33%
Confirmed Breeding:	3	2%	25%
Total:	12	7%	100%

	# of Records	Range of Dates
Courtship:	0	
Nest Building:	0	
Fledged Young:	9	6/18 – 7/27
On Nest:	0	
Nest with eggs:	0	
Nest with young:	0	

Priority Blocks

● Confirmed
◐ Probable
○ Possible
□ Not Recorded

Special Areas

▲ Confirmed
◭ Probable
△ Possible

Non-priority Blocks

● Confirmed
◑ Probable
○ Possible

N

Miles
0 4 8 12

179

Blue Jay
Cyanocitta cristata

The Blue Jay is one of the most brightly colored of New Hampshire's birds and is one of the easiest to identify, with its unique blue and white plumage. Field marks for flying birds include steady, level flight with rather slow wing beats. A crest and some black and white markings are visible on perched birds.

Blue Jays conspicuously announce the presence of intruders or predators with a raucous uproar in the woods. A screaming group of jays may swoop repeatedly at a hawk or owl, coyote, fox, cat, or snake. Their common call is described as "jay, jay" or "thief! thief!" and is easily recognized. However, jays have a variety of other notes, including a musical 2-syllable bell-like note and a low guttural rattle. Blue Jays sometimes mimic the calls of raptors, especially Red-shouldered and Broad-winged hawks, and occasionally those of songbirds.

Some Blue Jays are permanent residents in New Hampshire, but migrating flocks pass through the state as well. Most Blue Jays nest at elevations below 1,500 ft (460 m), but some occur in mountainous areas at elevations up to at 3,000 ft (915 m) and occasionally higher (Allen 1903; T. Richards, unpubl. data). Blue Jays once resided primarily in forests, but they have adapted to the encroachment of human populations and now nest in many habitats, including residential neighborhoods of cities and suburbs (Hoffman 1904, Eaton 1914, Terres 1980). The usual nesting habitat is coniferous or mixed woods, but they also nest in deciduous woods.

While Blue Jays exhibit little territorial behavior, they perform a number of distinct courtship displays (Stokes and Stokes 1989). The most conspicuous such behavior involves courtship flocks of 3 to 10 birds which form in late winter and early spring, and presumably include previously unmated males and a single female. They roam as a group during the morning hours, calling noisily in flight. When perched, usually in treetops, they engage in bobbing displays and vocalize with rattles, "whee-delees," and "toolools." Once paired, Blue Jays become quiet and secretive for the remainder of the breeding season. Males of established pairs feed their mates, who often give a "kueu" call as the males approach with food.

Nest building takes place from mid-March through April. The nest is usually well concealed in a conifer, especially a white pine or hemlock, but sometimes in a hardwood tree (Harrison 1975). Both sexes build the bulky nest, which is made of twigs and lined with rootlets, grass, or other soft material. The nest is located in a crotch of a tree, and may be 5 to 50 ft (1.5 to 15 m) above the ground, but often is at a height of 10 to 25 ft (3 to 7.6 m) (Harrison 1975). White (1934) observed 3 nests in Concord which were 5 to 15 ft (1.5 to 4.5 m) above ground in small pines, and contained eggs on 8, 11, and 13 May, respectively.

The 3 to 6, usually 4 or 5 eggs hatch after an incubation period of 16 to 18 days (Harrison 1978). Both parents care for their single brood and defend them vigorously, screaming, diving, and even pecking at intruders (Tyler 1946). Young fledge at 17 to 21 days of age. They begin to forage for themselves about 3 weeks later, although the adults continue to feed them for some time thereafter (Harrison 1978). The juvenal plumage resembles that of adults, but the tail and crest are shorter, and the back is grayer (Forbush 1927). Families may remain together into September.

Blue Jays are omnivorous. About one-quarter of the diet is animal matter and three-quarters vegetable matter. The animal matter includes some insects, such as beetles, grasshoppers, and caterpillars; young birds and eggs; and occasionally small vertebrates including fish, frogs, and salamanders. Vegetable matter includes beechnuts, acorns, corn, a variety of smaller seeds, and some wild fruits (Beal 1897 *in* Tyler 1946). Blue Jays sometimes harvest acorns by plucking them from twigs while hovering in the air (Brewster 1937 *in* Tyler 1946), but usually retrieve them from the ground.

Blue Jays store some food for winter use in forks of tree branches, bark crevices, or in the ground. Beechnuts and acorns are important sources of food in winter, and those stored in the ground may germinate, thus aiding in seed dispersal. In years when the mast crop is poor, greater numbers of Blue Jays migrate south in September to find other sources of food. In recent years back yard bird feeders have supplied a significant amount of winter food, enabling some Blue Jays to overwinter even when little or no mast is available. Resident Blue Jays also undertake irregular movements in fall and winter from regions of food scarcity to regions where food is more plentiful. Large migrating flocks observed in late May probably are heading further north.

Historical accounts suggest no particular long term trends in New Hampshire's Blue Jay population. Samuels (1867) noted that the species was more common in southern than in northern New England. Authors earlier in the present century described the Blue Jay as generally distributed in the state (Allen 1903), "common" in the Durham area (Dearborn 1903), and present "in moderate numbers" in the vicinity of Jefferson (Wright 1911). BBS data from 1966 to 1979 suggest a slight but significant decrease in Blue Jay abundance in the Eastern region (Robbins et al. 1986).

The Atlas map demonstrates that this colorful resident remains common throughout the state. The only Atlas priority block lacking a Blue Jay record is remote and at high elevation. This adaptable species is likely to have a secure future in New Hampshire.

Frederic L. Steele

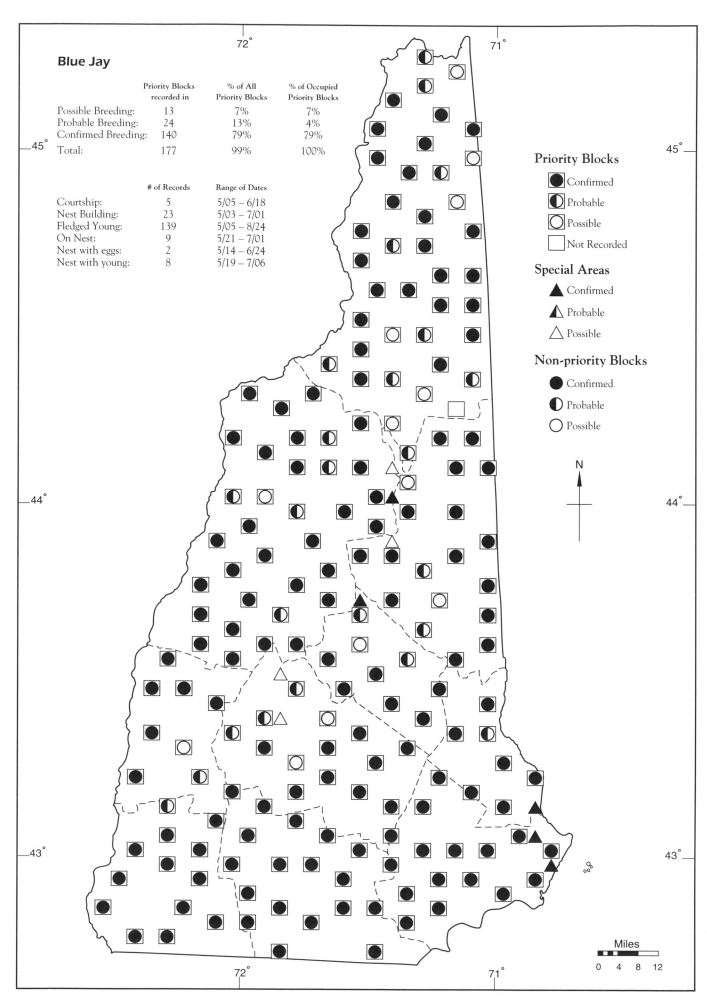

Blue Jay

	Priority Blocks recorded in	% of All Priority Blocks	% of Occupied Priority Blocks
Possible Breeding:	13	7%	7%
Probable Breeding:	24	13%	4%
Confirmed Breeding:	140	79%	79%
Total:	177	99%	100%

	# of Records	Range of Dates
Courtship:	5	5/05 – 6/18
Nest Building:	23	5/03 – 7/01
Fledged Young:	139	5/05 – 8/24
On Nest:	9	5/21 – 7/01
Nest with eggs:	2	5/14 – 6/24
Nest with young:	8	5/19 – 7/06

Priority Blocks
- ◐ Confirmed
- ◑ Probable
- ○ Possible
- ☐ Not Recorded

Special Areas
- ▲ Confirmed
- ◣ Probable
- △ Possible

Non-priority Blocks
- ● Confirmed
- ◖ Probable
- ○ Possible

N

Miles
0 4 8 12

American Crow

Corvus brachyrhynchos

The American Crow, long persecuted for its fondness for agricultural crops, has perhaps the highest intelligence and most complex social organization of any native bird. The crow was completely unprotected in New Hampshire until 1978, when provisions under the Migratory Bird Treaty Act established the first crow hunting season and protected the crow for the remainder of the year. Found throughout southern Canada and the continental United States, crows are year-round residents in New Hampshire. Their occurrence is more local in winter, depending largely on food availability. Migrating crows pass through New Hampshire in October and return in March.

Crows prefer habitat which includes agricultural lands or urban areas, where they forage, adjacent to forested lands, where they nest and roost (Bull 1974). They are among the relatively few native birds that commonly occur in the hearts of New Hampshire's larger cities.

The crow's characteristic "caw," large size, and completely black coloration, including plumage, bill, and feet, readily distinguish it from other New Hampshire species, except for the Common Raven and the Fish Crow. The American Crow has a smaller bill than its larger relative, the raven, and its distinctly fan-shaped tail in flight contrasts with the raven's wedge-shaped tail. Unlike ravens, crows cannot soar, but can glide for short distances. Typically gregarious, except during the breeding season, crows frequently harass ravens, hawks, owls, and eagles.

American Crows are capable of a great variety of sounds. Chamberlain and Cornwell (1971) documented and described the environmental and behavioral context for 23 vocalizations. The young crows' "cah" can be confused with the calls of the Fish Crow, which occurs locally in southeastern New Hampshire, but the "caw" of an adult is fairly distinctive. While some calls of the raven are similar, its croaks are not.

American Crows live in cooperative groups and are intensely territorial (Kilham 1984a, Chamberlain-Auger et al. 1990). Kilham (1985b) observed groups of crows in both Florida and New Hampshire which contained 7 or 8 birds, including 2 or 3 yearlings, 2 or 3 nonbreeding adults, and the breeding pair. In a 5-year study of American Crows on Cape Cod, Mass., Chamberlain-Auger et al. (1990) also confirmed cooperative breeding in groups of up to 10 birds, composed of the breeding pair and offspring one to several years old. The offspring remained on the natal territories and actively assisted the breeding pair in nest building, incubation, brooding, and feeding the young. L. Kilham (pers. comm.) has observed 2 groups of crows in Lyme which have maintained a territorial boundary for 5 years.

Where American Crows are permanent residents, they actively defend their territories throughout the year (Kilham 1985a, Chamberlain-Auger et al. 1990). Territories on Cape Cod ranged in size from 23 to 257 a (9.4 to 104 ha) with a mean size of 104 a (42 ha). During the coldest winter months crows from the observed breeding groups left their territories toward dusk, joined other crows in a common roost for the night, and then returned to their territories at dawn (Chamberlain-Auger et al. 1990).

Courtship in American Crows begins in late winter and initially involves chases and fights among members of the group. Later on, the breeding pair engages in head-to-head bobbing displays and rattle-calls (Goodwin 1976). Copulation generally takes place on the nest (Kilham 1984b). Crows do not breed until they are 2 years old.

Crows in New Hampshire carry sticks for nest building in March and April. Nesting occupies most of May and June. The nest often is high in a white pine or oak and is difficult to observe. All members of the group, yearlings as well as adult helpers, cooperate in building the nest, feeding the female while she incubates for 18 or 19 days, and feeding the nestlings, which fledge in 36 to 41 days (Kilham 1984a). Young crows are relatively quiet as nestlings, but once fledged, their begging calls carry for a considerable distance. This accounts for the high proportion (87.5%) of fledgling observations among Atlas "confirmations" for this species.

The diet includes 25% animal matter (large insects and larvae, spiders, frogs, bird eggs and young, and carrion, including roadkills) and 75% vegetable matter (chiefly corn but also other grains, wild fruits and seeds, and cultivated vegetables and fruits) (Gross 1946). Crows forage primarily on the ground in flocks and small groups, with one or more birds on sentry duty to warn of any imminent danger.

The Atlas map shows that the American Crow is widespread in the southern half of New Hampshire, and more locally distributed further north. Only 3 priority blocks south of the White Mountains lack records for American Crows. Crow records are lacking for a larger percentage of blocks in the White Mountains and North Country, where high elevations and extensive forests reduce the availability of suitable habitat.

The status of this species has changed little since Dearborn (1898) wrote that "Crows are too numerous and too notorious to deserve more than passing mention." BBS data indicate a slight increase in New Hampshire and Northeastern crow populations during 1966–79 (Robbins et al. 1986). Increasing numbers of roadkilled mammals on new roads with higher speed limits may be compensating for losses of foraging habitat on dwindling agricultural lands. Despite generations of persecution, which has made them extremely wary and usually difficult to observe closely, crows likely will continue to be common New Hampshire residents.

Harold P. Nevers

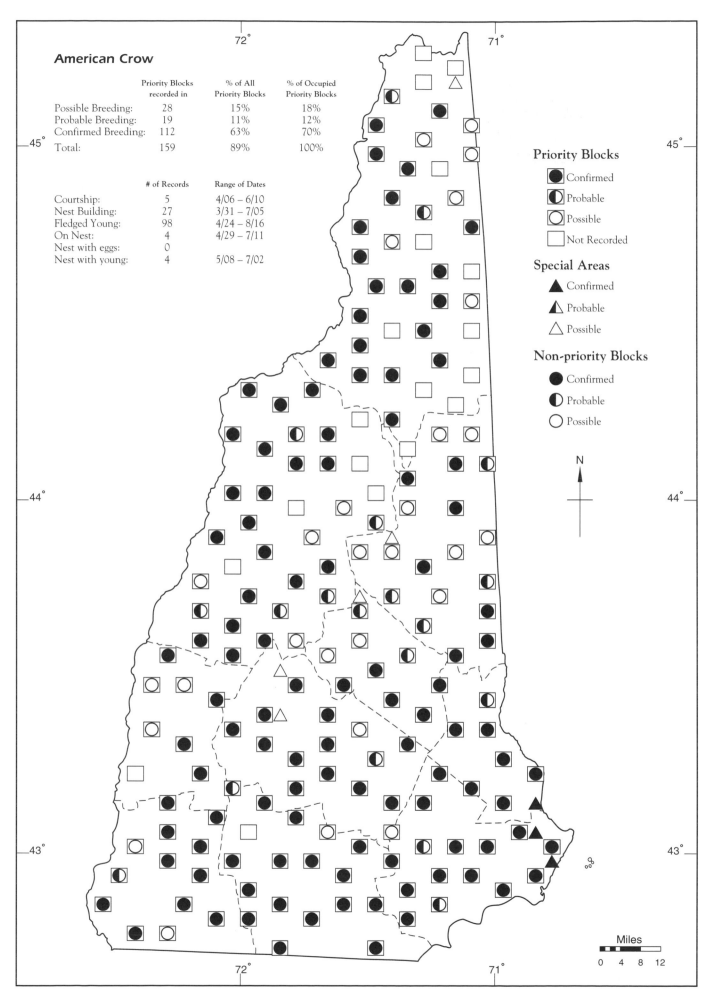

American Crow

	Priority Blocks recorded in	% of All Priority Blocks	% of Occupied Priority Blocks
Possible Breeding:	28	15%	18%
Probable Breeding:	19	11%	12%
Confirmed Breeding:	112	63%	70%
Total:	159	89%	100%

	# of Records	Range of Dates
Courtship:	5	4/06 – 6/10
Nest Building:	27	3/31 – 7/05
Fledged Young:	98	4/24 – 8/16
On Nest:	4	4/29 – 7/11
Nest with eggs:	0	
Nest with young:	4	5/08 – 7/02

Priority Blocks
- Confirmed
- Probable
- Possible
- Not Recorded

Special Areas
- Confirmed
- Probable
- Possible

Non-priority Blocks
- Confirmed
- Probable
- Possible

Miles
0 4 8 12

Fish Crow
Corvus ossifragus

Scavenging over a brackish water mud flat at low tide, a hovering Fish Crow utters a short nasal "cah-r," and quickly descends to devour a stranded mud crab. The call, almost identical to that of a young American Crow, is useful for identification only before young American Crows begin to call in mid-May (Forbush *in* Allen 1909). At other seasons, Fish Crows easily can be misidentified.

To the knowledgeable eye the all-black Fish Crow has a thinner bill and more pointed wings than the common American Crow. It also has a weaker, shorter, nasal call, somewhat hoarse and staccato (Bent 1946). To most of us, however, the 2 species are virtually indistinguishable. The sexes are identical in size and plumage.

At the extreme northern edge of its range here, the Fish Crow is a rare New Hampshire resident found along coastal beaches, marshes, and estuaries and occasionally inland along ponds, lakes, and rivers. Seldom seen singly, the Fish Crow is more gregarious at all seasons than the American Crow (Bent 1946).

Fish Crows fly faster than American Crows with fewer wing flaps, sail more, and often hover on rapidly beating wings as they search for floating food. Fish Crows sometimes drink while skimming the water and may catch small minnows near the surface with their feet (Wilson 1832 *in* Bent 1946). Like other members of the crow family, Fish Crows are omnivorous with a major appetite for insects, seeds, wild fruit and berries, aquatic organisms, bird eggs, and carrion found on tidal flats, beaches, and stream banks.

Although they are not regularly migratory (Bent 1946), New Hampshire Fish Crows probably move to more temperate climates during the winter. Fish Crows apparently return to Durham in mid to late March. First sightings of the year occurred on 25 March 1982, 27 March 1989, and 16 March 1990 (M. Davis, pers. comm.). Some Fish Crows have wintered at a dump in

Massachusetts, south of Boston (K. C. Elkins, pers. comm.).

Courtship, as described in Bent (1946), begins during the first 2 weeks of April with the birds becoming especially animated. Two males often bicker over a single female in tall trees. After leaning back against boughs with their wings half unfolded and their beaks opened in a seemingly defensive attitude, they glide away through stream-bank treetops and out over more open lands.

Fish Crow pairs nest singly, or more often, in loose colonies of 2 to 4 pairs, with each pair nesting in a different tree. The nest may be 20 to 80 ft (6.1 to 24.4 m) from the ground, most frequently near the top of a conifer tree, commonly a pine (Forbush 1927). The nest tree is often beside a stream bank or other waterway. The nest consists of dead sticks and twigs lined with fibrous bark, pine needles, hair, grass, and similar materials (Harrison 1975, Goodwin 1976). Fish Crows were carrying nesting material in Durham on 1 May 1989 and 16 June 1982 (M. Davis, pers. comm.).

Both members of the pair help build the nest and probably share incubation duties (Harrison 1975). The 3 to 5 eggs (Forbush 1927, Bent 1946), are smaller than, but otherwise virtually identical to those of the American Crow (Harrison 1975). They hatch in 16 to 18 days, and the young fledge 21 days later (Bent 1946). M. Davis (pers. comm.) observed a Fish Crow feeding a fledgling on a roof in downtown Durham on 10 June 1989. Fish Crows produce only one brood each year (Bent 1946), but in cases of nest failure a pair may nest again, often using the same nest.

Historical records of Fish Crows in New Hampshire are few. Bent (1946) considered the species' northern limit to be southern Massachusetts, where it was rare and local. Forbush (1927) reported no New Hampshire records, but Scott (1921) indicated that Fish Crows occasionally occurred near saltwater in the Durham area in spring and summer. More recent New Hampshire Fish Crow records include 24 observations of one to 6 individuals in Kingston in April and May during 1971–78, and one bird heard and seen at Lake Massabesic, Manchester on 26 May and 14 June 1980 (SRS).

Apparently the first documented Fish Crow nesting in New Hampshire occurred on the University of New Hampshire campus in Durham. Fish Crows had been observed on campus annually since at least 1977 (D. Miller, pers. comm.), and M. Davis (pers. comm.) "confirmed" breeding activity in 1982. Sightings occurred at various locations at the northern end of campus on 10 days during 25 March – 18 June 1982. The nest was located in a white pine behind Kendall Hall, with 2 crows present, on 18 June 1982. The outcome of the nest is unknown.

Additional Atlas period records include a pair on the Salmon Falls River, Dover, on 5 June 1983; one or 2 birds in the Hooksett/Manchester area throughout the summer of 1983; and single birds in Kingston on 15 April 1984, along the Merrimack River in Concord on and before 14 May 1983, and in Portsmouth on 18 May 1983.

The Fish Crow has expanded its range elsewhere in the Northeast as evidenced by New York Atlas data (Andrle and Carroll 1988) and the Massachusetts Atlas map (Mass. BBA proj., unpubl.), which shows considerable breeding activity in the vicinity of Boston and the south shore. The first presumed breeding in the Connecticut River valley took place in Springfield, Mass., in 1986 (Veit and Petersen 1992). Neither the Maine nor Vermont atlas projects produced Fish Crow records. The few New Hampshire records probably accurately reflect the Fish Crow's rare to uncommon status in the state.

Harold P. Nevers

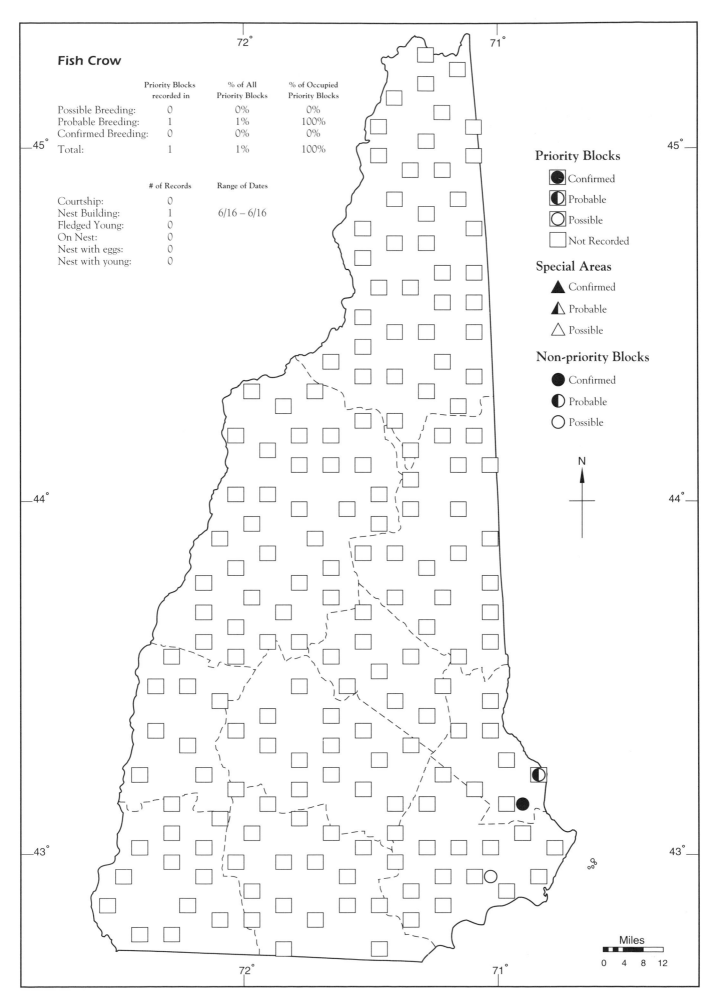

Fish Crow

	Priority Blocks recorded in	% of All Priority Blocks	% of Occupied Priority Blocks
Possible Breeding:	0	0%	0%
Probable Breeding:	1	1%	100%
Confirmed Breeding:	0	0%	0%
Total:	1	1%	100%

	# of Records	Range of Dates
Courtship:	0	
Nest Building:	1	6/16 – 6/16
Fledged Young:	0	
On Nest:	0	
Nest with eggs:	0	
Nest with young:	0	

Priority Blocks

◑ Confirmed
◑ Probable
◯ Possible
▢ Not Recorded

Special Areas

▲ Confirmed
◮ Probable
△ Possible

Non-priority Blocks

● Confirmed
◑ Probable
◯ Possible

N

Miles
0 4 8 12

Common Raven
Corvus corax

The raucous croaking, playful soaring, and distinctive shape of the raven leave no doubt as to its identity. Ravens are distinguishable from crows by their vocalizations, larger size, and longer, wedge-shaped tails. They sometimes indulge in aerobatics, such as closing their wings, dropping through the air, and doing a half roll before continuing in normal flight. They often soar and circle high like buteos.

The Common Raven is circumboreal and mainly north temperate to Arctic in distribution. In eastern North America the southern limit of the contiguous range stretches from New England inland to the Great Lakes states, with a disjunct population in the Appalachians from Pennsylvania to northern Georgia. In the west, the range extends south to Nicaragua (Bent 1946, NGS 1983). The raven is a year-round resident of New Hampshire, where it typically nests in mountainous and other heavily forested terrain. Ravens begin to establish a pair bond with metallic "glock-uk, glock-uk" and "kok, kok, kok" vocalizations in late summer. Beginning in October, pairs fly wing tip to wing tip over their territories. Although ravens typically nest on cliffs, they also nest in tall pine trees with full crowns (Harlow 1922). Peregrine Falcons and ravens nest successfully as neighbors on some New Hampshire cliffs.

Most reported New Hampshire nests are on ledges, including nearly all nests that Atlas observers located. A tree nest that was active and successful during 1985 and 1986 is located in a 75 ft (22.9 m) white pine on a wooded slope on the shore of Lake Winnepauket, Webster.

Nest building or rebuilding occurs in March, with egg laying in April. The incubation period, during which the male feeds the female, lasts for about 21 days, and young remain in the nest about 41 days after hatching (Stiehl 1985). Young ravens are noisy both before and after fledging in late May, and can be heard for considerable distances. Fledglings flutter their wings on the approach of a parent, which may deliver food by regurgitation, placing its bill inside that of a juvenile, or by laying the food on the ground. The juveniles are playful in picking up objects and chasing each other about.

Ravens are omnivorous, congregating at garbage dumps throughout their range, and eating berries in season. They feed largely on carrion, but also consume eggs and nestlings of smaller birds. Coyotes and ravens have a close symbiotic relationship (Ryden 1979). The wide-ranging ravens probably aid coyotes in locating carcasses and depend on coyotes to tear open the tough hides of large mammals. Ravens will rob crows, pursuing them in the air until they drop their food and performing spectacular dives to retrieve morsels (Kilham 1985c).

Apparently Common Ravens largely disappeared from New Hampshire before the present century. Samuels (1867) knew of none nesting in New England. Coues (1868) regarded them as residents of northern sections, and Maynard (1871) considered them common in Chatham. Brewster (1937) suggests that they may have been more common in the Umbagog Lake region in the early 1800s than during the 1880s, when he encountered them there only twice. However, Bent (1946) considered records from Sutton in December 1878 and Warner in February 1879 to be "outside the normal range," and Allen (1903) considered them only accidental visitors to the state. Wright (1911) fails to mention them in his ornithology of the Jefferson region, and Bagg and Eliot (1937) knew of no ravens nesting in New Hampshire or Vermont. Bent (1946) considered the raven "uncommon or rare over most of its range in the U.S.," but population increase and range extension were evident in Maine in 1949 and 1950 (Palmer 1949, Cruickshank 1950, Taber 1950). Sightings in New Hampshire began to increase during the next decade. Observers documented 20 records for 1950–59, mostly from northern locations and fall and winter months (RNEB, *passim*), and Richards (1958) described the raven as "very rare, but now possibly a permanent resident in extreme north." From 1956 on they occurred regularly in spring at Pittsburg (McDade 1963), but sightings did not increase substantially until the mid-1960s (RNEB, *passim*).

Observers found the first New Hampshire nest documented in this century in 1976 on a cliff in Wentworth, after suspecting nesting for 6 to 7 years; 5 eggs were present on 4 April and 3 fully feathered young were subsequently observed (SRS). A pair also nested in Marlow in that year (SRS). A cliff nest in Alstead contained 4 nearly fledged young on 21 May 1977 (SRS). Less than a decade later, the Atlas generated a remarkable number of "confirmations" and documented a distribution which includes much of the Western Highlands and some of the Merrimack Valley and Eastern Uplands, in addition to most of the North Country, White Mountains, and Lakes Region. The species now nests as far south as Chesterfield, in the Connecticut River valley, and as far east as Deerfield, a few miles from the coastal plain.

BBS data from 1966 to 1979 documented a significant increase for the Eastern region (Robbins et al. 1986). Whether or not New Hampshire's raven population has reached its peak remains to be seen. Future population trends of this intriguing and adaptable species will be interesting to observe.

Lawrence Kilham & Carol R. Foss

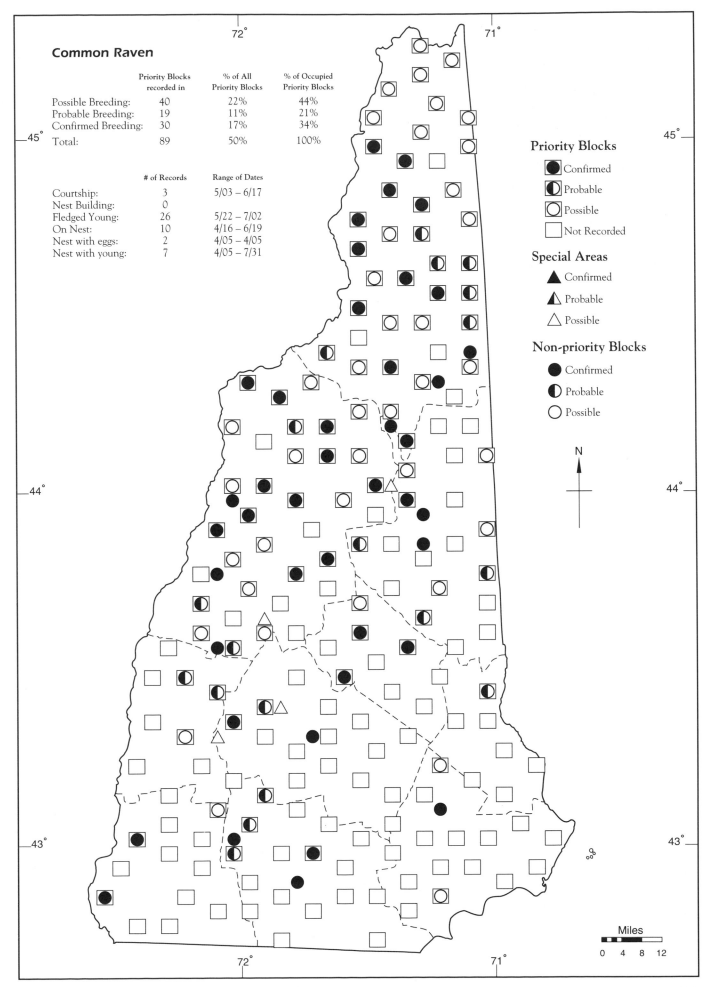

Common Raven

	Priority Blocks recorded in	% of All Priority Blocks	% of Occupied Priority Blocks
Possible Breeding:	40	22%	44%
Probable Breeding:	19	11%	21%
Confirmed Breeding:	30	17%	34%
Total:	89	50%	100%

	# of Records	Range of Dates
Courtship:	3	5/03 – 6/17
Nest Building:	0	
Fledged Young:	26	5/22 – 7/02
On Nest:	10	4/16 – 6/19
Nest with eggs:	2	4/05 – 4/05
Nest with young:	7	4/05 – 7/31

Priority Blocks
- ● Confirmed
- ◐ Probable
- ○ Possible
- □ Not Recorded

Special Areas
- ▲ Confirmed
- ◤ Probable
- △ Possible

Non-priority Blocks
- ● Confirmed
- ◑ Probable
- ○ Possible

N

Miles
0 4 8 12

Black-capped Chickadee
Parus atricapillus

The acrobatic Black-capped Chickadee is familiar to nearly everyone in the Northeast who feeds birds or walks in the woods at any season. Small, but hardy, intelligent and energetic, the chickadee keeps us company throughout the coldest winters and comes readily to a "squeak" or imitation of its call. Abundant and unafraid of humans, it is easily recognized by its trim black cap and bib and distinctive call.

Throughout the year, one can hear the familiar "chick-a-dee-dee-dee." On bright winter days, occasionally in mid-January and increasingly in March and April, the chickadee sings a pure, high, easily imitated "fee-bee" whistle. Both sexes sing this song, the male louder and more frequently (Odum 1941). Additional winter calls are "seee," a rich chortle, high "tsips," and other delicate, high, bell-like notes. A rapid "dee-dee-dee-dee" in a lower key is typical of both chickadees and titmice.

Common throughout New Hampshire, Black-capped Chickadees inhabit mixed woods and especially conifers. They breed at elevations up to 3,000 ft (910 m), where they may occur with the brown-capped Boreal Chickadees. Outside the breeding season they have been recorded at almost 4,500 ft (1,370 m) in the White Mountains, and in winter at close to 4,000 ft (1,220 m) (T. Richards, unpubl. data).

Black-capped Chickadees breed in a variety of habitats in suburbs and woodlands (Odum 1941). Pairs separate from winter flocks in March and rigorously defend breeding territories of 8 to 17 a (3 to 7 ha) until July. They mob predators, especially during the breeding season, but continue this behavior even in freezing winter weather (Shedd 1985).

In courtship the female quivers her wings and hops in front of the male. He may ignore her (Odum 1941) or may touch her beak with his (Ficken et al. 1978).

Chickadees usually to nest in snags with firm outer shells and decayed interiors in which they excavate their holes. In New Hampshire, birch, aspen, and pin cherry may provide ideal nest sites. They also may use natural cavities, or cavities made by other birds. In many areas chickadees must compete with the scrappy House Sparrows for nesting cavities and sometimes use nest boxes. Nest cavities usually are situated 4 to 10 ft (1.2 to 3.0 m) above the ground (Harrison 1975). Pairs carry wood chips away from the nest holes (Janeway, pers. obs.) and line nests with mosses, plant and animal fibers, and cocoons (Terres 1980). In East Washington, a chickadee struggled to fit a large white feather into its tree hole (Janeway, pers. obs.).

A chickadee becomes secretive when nesting and may try to frighten intruders from its nest with an "explosive hiss" (Terres 1980). Between early May and early June (Bent 1946) the female lays 5 to 8 eggs, which she incubates for 11 to 13 days (Odum 1942, Brewer 1961). The male feeds his mate on the nest (Odum 1942, Brewer 1961). Both parents feed their young for the 16 days they remain in the nest and for about 10 days thereafter, when the young conspicuously beg for food (Brewer 1961). Young chickadees disperse widely from their home area (Odum 1941). From August to February, highly structured, social flocks defend nonbreeding territories of about 20 to 55 a (8 to 22 ha) (Odum 1942). The home range may depend upon food supply (Brewer 1961).

Black-capped Chickadees are engaging visitors at feeders. They prefer sunflower seeds, cracking them with their short bills on nearby perches. They often cache food in crevices. They forage energetically in trees, sometimes clinging upside down, hunting in bark crevices for insect eggs and larvae, spiders, and ants. Like flycatchers, they can catch insects in the air. They also forage for conifer and other tree seeds, bayberries, and wild fruit (Bent 1946).

Although one often encounters both large and small groups made up exclusively of chickadees, these birds often forage with other species. In mixed groups chickadees usually are the most numerous, and generally behave differently from their companions. Nuthatches move head first down tree trunks, while creepers spiral upwards, and kinglets hover and flutter among branches, often near the ground (Janeway, pers. obs.). Chickadees forage at all tree heights, but tend to stay high in the branches and move steadily with a slow and flitting flight, calling to each other. In the fall, migrating warblers frequently join flocks of chickadees, which may guide the migrants to local food sources (Forbush 1929).

Over the years local chickadee populations have fluctuated with the cutting and regeneration of forests, but with no apparent long-term change in status. The Black-capped Chickadee has been a common bird in New Hampshire throughout this century. Allen (1903) considered it common throughout most of the state, but rare above 3,000 ft (910 m). Dearborn (1903) found it common all year near Durham, and Wright (1911) found it common up to and above 3,000 ft (910 m) in the Jefferson region.

BBS data from 1966 to 1979 indicate an increase in Black-capped Chickadee numbers in the Northeast, and especially high counts in several New England states, including New Hampshire (Robbins et al. 1986). The Atlas map illustrates this species' ubiquitous distribution in the state, with records for every priority block, and "confirmed" breeding in all but a few.

Elizabeth C. Janeway

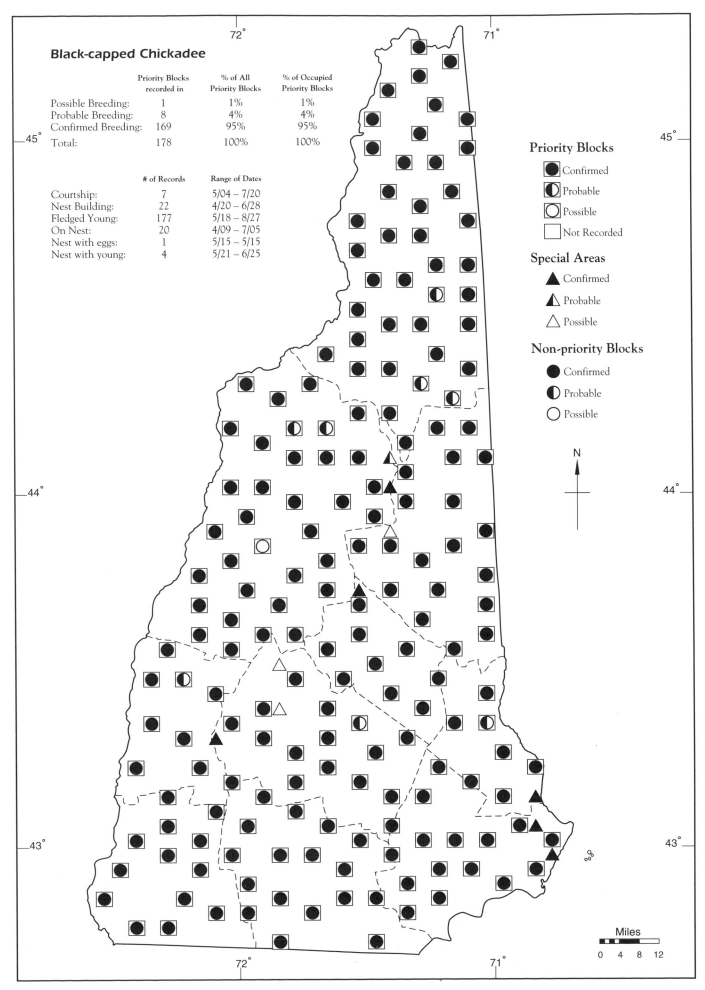

Black-capped Chickadee

	Priority Blocks recorded in	% of All Priority Blocks	% of Occupied Priority Blocks
Possible Breeding:	1	1%	1%
Probable Breeding:	8	4%	4%
Confirmed Breeding:	169	95%	95%
Total:	178	100%	100%

	# of Records	Range of Dates
Courtship:	7	5/04 – 7/20
Nest Building:	22	4/20 – 6/28
Fledged Young:	177	5/18 – 8/27
On Nest:	20	4/09 – 7/05
Nest with eggs:	1	5/15 – 5/15
Nest with young:	4	5/21 – 6/25

Priority Blocks

- ◐ Confirmed
- ◑ Probable
- ○ Possible
- ☐ Not Recorded

Special Areas

- ▲ Confirmed
- ◣ Probable
- △ Possible

Non-priority Blocks

- ◐ Confirmed
- ◑ Probable
- ○ Possible

N

Miles
0 4 8 12

189

Boreal Chickadee
Parus hudsonicus

A hike along any forested, high-elevation trail in the White Mountains affords a good chance of encountering one or more of these brown-capped northern sprites. The Boreal Chickadee, formerly known as the "Brown-capped Chickadee," also occurs locally at lower elevations, mostly between 1,000 and 2,000 ft (300 to 610 m), in North Country black spruce and tamarack bogs and adjacent spruce-fir flats (Richards 1967). Though tame and curious, it frequents dense, mature spruce and fir and is less easily observed than the more familiar Black-capped Chickadee. It is most often noticed by its distinctive nasal, drawling call.

In New Hampshire the Boreal Chickadee's breeding range extends northward from the southern fringe of the White Mountains. These chickadees are widespread and fairly common permanent residents in spruce-fir forests on upper slopes of the White Mountains from 2,500 to 3,000 ft (760 to 910 m) to tree line at approximately 4,800 ft (1,460 m). Northern New England and New York comprise the southernmost limit of the species' breeding distribution in eastern North America, although Bent (1946) reported breeding season occurrences in Massachusetts and Pennsylvania.

From late fall to early spring, Boreal Chickadees wander in small flocks, which sometimes include other species. They occasionally visit the southern half of the state in winter, often frequenting spruces with Black-capped Chickadees. Pair formation begins while the birds are still in winter flocks, with pairs separating from the flock in late April or early May (McLaren 1975). A pair establishes a territory after 2 to 3 weeks, and the female begins to beg food from the male. He continues to feed her until the eggs hatch, 4 to 5 weeks later. Males defend territories with vocalizations and chases, sometimes into early July. Territory size exceeded 12.4 a (5 ha) in spruce-fir forests in Ontario (McLaren 1975).

Like its black-capped cousin, the Boreal Chickadee is a cavity nester. Trees commonly used include spruce, birch, and cedar (Harrison 1975). Nest site selection seems to depend more on heartwood softness and exterior firmness than on tree species (McLaren 1975). A pair may inspect and partially excavate several cavities before choosing a nest site 1 to 12 ft (0.3 to 3.7 m) from the ground (McLaren 1975). They sometimes use natural tree cavities or old woodpecker holes. Boreal Chickadees apparently do not nest in the same tree in successive years (McLaren 1975).

Boreal Chickadee nests are difficult to find (Harrison 1975). The cavity entrance is most often on the side but is sometimes at the open top of a stub. The female lines the cavity with feathers, fur, plant down, bark strips, and moss (Harrison 1975, DeGraaf et al. 1980). Vermont Atlas observers reported nest building as early as 9 May (Oatman *in* Laughlin and Kibbe 1985).

The female lays 4 to 9, usually 6 or 7 eggs in late May, June, or occasionally early July, and incubates for 11 to 16 days. Harrison (1975) found both adults very tame during incubation at a nest in Maine. Both parents feed the young, which fledge after about 18 days. The adults feed them with decreasing frequency for about 2 weeks, after which they do not occur regularly in the nesting territory (McLaren 1975).

Foraging Boreal Chickadees search conifer trunks, branches, and twigs for tiny moths, beetles, and other insects, many of which are injurious to trees (Bent 1946). Gage et al. (1970 *in* Cadman et al. 1987) observed high densities of Boreal Chickadees during spruce budworm outbreaks.

Adults carrying food or fecal sacs, and recently fledged young produced all 11 Atlas "confirmations", nearly all of which occurred from the third week of June through the third week of July. Because Boreal Chickadees tend to stay out of sight, "pishing" or "squeaking" can aid observation or confirmation.

Allen (1903) considered the "Hudsonian Chickadee" rather common in northern New Hampshire and at elevations from 3,000 to 4,500 ft (910 to 1,370 m) in the White Mountains. Wright (1911) listed this species among several whose numbers had declined in the Jefferson region due to logging and fires. This likely was true throughout the White Mountains during the late 1800s and early 1900s.. Some recovery presumably has occurred since regeneration of spruce-fir forests during the past 60 years. Widespread "salvage cutting" during the most recent spruce budworm outbreak has reduced available habitat in the northernmost part of the state.

The Atlas map shows the breeding range of the Boreal Chickadee extending from the southern White Mountains (Sandwich Range) northward, corresponding with the species' preference for northern coniferous forests. In the White Mountains, Atlas observers found Boreal Chickadees in isolated lowland areas of suitable habitat and in ridgetop spruce-fir forests up to 4,400 ft (1,340 m) elevation. North of the mountains, most occurred at elevations between 1,000 and 2,000 ft (300 to 610 m). Apparently, this chickadee does not breed in the relatively small and isolated spruce-fir tracts on mountains south of the White Mountains. The southernmost "confirmed" record was in Waterville Valley. All blocks with Boreal Chickadee records experience killing frosts later than 21 May, and have a normal mean July temperature of less than 68° F (18° C).

The future distribution and abundance of this species at lower elevations in northern New Hampshire will depend on management practices in spruce-fir forests and the availability of mature stands of sufficient size to support breeding pairs. A decreasing population trend in this region, especially in Quebec and New Brunswick (Robbins et al. 1986) signals a need to monitor this species in the coming years.

Steve Smith

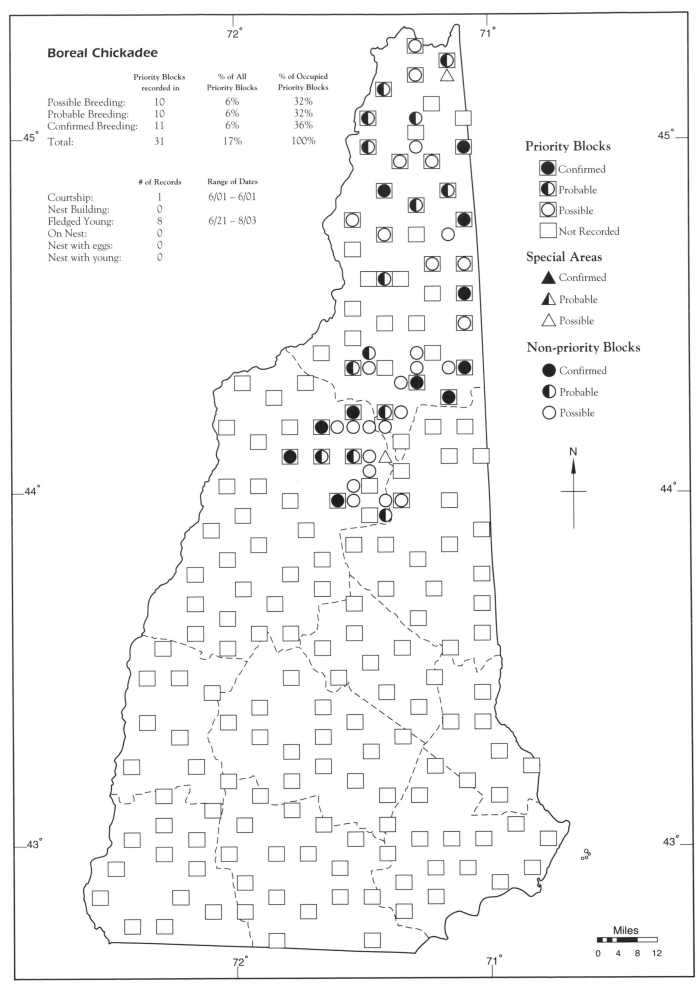

Boreal Chickadee

	Priority Blocks recorded in	% of All Priority Blocks	% of Occupied Priority Blocks
Possible Breeding:	10	6%	32%
Probable Breeding:	10	6%	32%
Confirmed Breeding:	11	6%	36%
Total:	31	17%	100%

	# of Records	Range of Dates
Courtship:	1	6/01 – 6/01
Nest Building:	0	
Fledged Young:	8	6/21 – 8/03
On Nest:	0	
Nest with eggs:	0	
Nest with young:	0	

Priority Blocks

● Confirmed
◐ Probable
○ Possible
☐ Not Recorded

Special Areas

▲ Confirmed
◥ Probable
△ Possible

Non-priority Blocks

● Confirmed
◐ Probable
○ Possible

N

Miles
0 4 8 12

Tufted Titmouse
Parus bicolor

The loud, clearly whistled "peter-peter-peter" of the Tufted Titmouse has become a commonly heard call in or near open deciduous woods and wooded residential areas in southern New Hampshire during the last 30 years. The Tufted Titmouse is our only small gray bird with a crest and is one of New Hampshire's newest year-round residents. This pert songbird is a common visitor to bird feeders near woodlands up to elevations of 1,000 ft (300 m). A resident of the eastern U.S. from Florida and the Gulf north to New England, west to Lake Erie, Illinois, Iowa, and Nebraska, the titmouse is increasing and spreading in the Northeast.

The Tufted Titmouse is larger than the closely related Black-capped Chickadee. Both sexes have identical plumage, gray above and white below with rusty brown flank feathers. Both sexes sing, although the female is less vocal (Brackbill 1970).

Pair bonds, which appear to be permanent (Gillespie 1930, Harrison 1975) can form at any season, and pairs separate from winter flocks by February to prepare for nesting (Brackbill 1970). Both sexes use a "high-see" call during courtship and mate feeding, a "tseep" call for short distance communications, and a variety of other whistled and rasping calls, some of which resemble those of chickadees (Stokes and Stokes 1983). A good imitation of their "peter-peter-peter" song usually brings them into view, especially in spring.

Titmice typically nest in mixed woods in a natural cavity or abandoned woodpecker hole 1 to 90 ft (0.3 to 27.4 m) above ground (Harrison 1975, Harrison 1978). They occasionally nest in hollow pipes, fence posts (Laskey 1957), and bluebird houses (Nevers, pers. obs.). The nest is built with bark strips, dead leaves, moss, and grass, and lined with hair, fur, bits of string and cloth, and sometimes snakeskin (Harrison 1978). Females sometimes pull hair from live squirrels, woodchucks, and even people (Harrison 1975).

Egg laying occurs from April to late May in New Hampshire. The female incubates her 4 to 8, usually 5 or 6 eggs for 12 to 14 days (Harrison 1975). The male calls the incubating female from the nest to feed her. Young remain in the nest for 15 to 18 days before fledging (Laskey 1957, Harrison 1978), and both parents feed them. From fall to early spring titmice travel in loose bands and often visit feeding stations with Black-capped Chickadees and White-breasted Nuthatches.

Tufted Titmice forage by probing and gleaning along branches, tree trunks, leaf surfaces, and the ground for insects, seeds, and fruit. Foods include insects, various berries, sumac, alder and poison ivy seeds, and acorns and beechnuts (Terres 1980).

Forbush (1929) reported that titmice were rare or casual visitors to New England and "doubtfully recorded" in New Hampshire. Richards (1958) considered them accidental in the state and cites the first state records as sightings in Wilton and Claremont in the fall of 1957. Doherty reported 9 titmice during 9–18 January 1958 in Franklin (Hebert 1958c), and observers occasionally reported titmice during the succeeding years. The first Tufted Titmouse documented in Dublin was in 1971 (Allison and Allison 1979). Ridgely (1977) reported the species as a casual visitor most likely to occur during October–December in the Squam Lakes region.

The New Hampshire records coincide with an "invasion" of cardinals and titmice northward in the Connecticut Valley, eastern Massachusetts, and Rhode Island during the fall of 1957 (Kricher 1981). Boyd (1962) reported only 4 titmouse records in Massachusetts prior to 1929, and a range extension commencing around 1940. They reached Vermont and Maine in 1957, and 1958 marked the first Massachusetts nesting record.

A winter Cardinal-Tufted Titmouse Survey, which ASNH initiated in 1967, recorded 4 titmice the first year, 62 in 1970, 442 in 1975, 880 in 1980, 1,097 in 1985, and 1,318 in 1986. Hillsborough, Merrimack, and Rockingham counties accounted for 87% of sightings during the 1986 survey. Boyd (1962) theorized that the titmouse's northward range extension was due in large part to warmer winters during the current century and to the proliferation of well-supplied bird feeders.

The first documented New Hampshire nestings occurred in 1973, when pairs raised 3 or 4 young in Merrimack and 6 young in Londonderry (Hebert 1973). The Atlas recorded Tufted Titmice in 67 priority blocks, mainly from the Merrimack Valley to the coast and north along the Maine boundary to Wakefield. Titmice were sparsely represented in the Lakes Region and southern portions of the Western Highlands, and absent from priority blocks north of the White Mountains. They breed widely throughout Massachusetts, but are absent from forested areas at higher elevations (Veit and Petersen 1993). Titmice occur at low elevations in southern Vermont and north along the Connecticut River (Nichols *in* Laughlin and Kibbe 1985).

The Atlas map indicates that the range of the Tufted Titmouse in New Hampshire still is limited essentially to the southern half of the state. The Atlas project produced titmouse records for all priority blocks below 500 ft (150 m), but only 4 blocks above 1,000 ft (300 m) elevation. The only Tufted Titmouse observed north of the White Mountains was calling on 2 August 1983 at the gate keeper's camp, at 1,280 ft (390 m) elevation, in Second College Grant. Future range expansion in New Hampshire is likely to occur primarily south of the White Mountains, but may extend to the North Country valleys of the Connecticut, Ammonoosuc, and Androscoggin rivers.

Harold P. Nevers

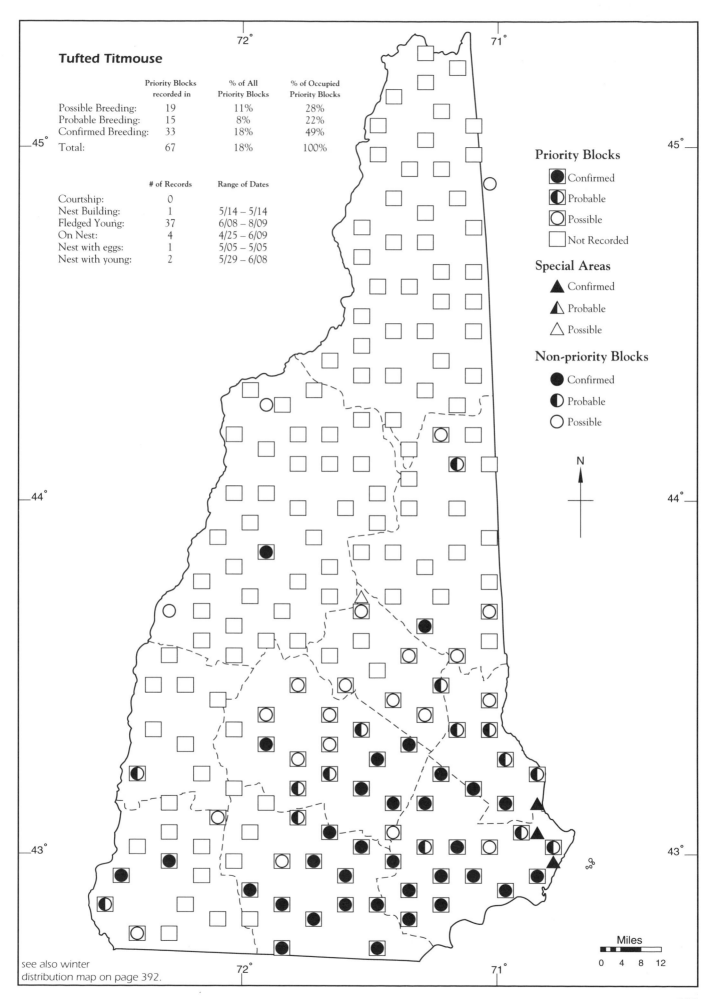

Tufted Titmouse

	Priority Blocks recorded in	% of All Priority Blocks	% of Occupied Priority Blocks
Possible Breeding:	19	11%	28%
Probable Breeding:	15	8%	22%
Confirmed Breeding:	33	18%	49%
Total:	67	18%	100%

	# of Records	Range of Dates
Courtship:	0	
Nest Building:	1	5/14 – 5/14
Fledged Young:	37	6/08 – 8/09
On Nest:	4	4/25 – 6/09
Nest with eggs:	1	5/05 – 5/05
Nest with young:	2	5/29 – 6/08

Priority Blocks

● Confirmed
◐ Probable
○ Possible
□ Not Recorded

Special Areas

▲ Confirmed
◣ Probable
△ Possible

Non-priority Blocks

● Confirmed
◐ Probable
○ Possible

N

see also winter
distribution map on page 392.

Miles
0 4 8 12

Red-breasted Nuthatch

Sitta canadensis

Twittering softly as they forage on trunks and branches of coniferous trees, Red-breasted Nuthatches are conspicuous inhabitants of coniferous and mixed woods. Their distinctive shape, with stubby tails and frequently upturned necks, and their habit of coming down tree trunks head first immediately identify them as nuthatches. Rusty breast and a black eye-line distinguish these birds from the larger White-breasted Nuthatches. Red-breasteds occur throughout New Hampshire from the Seacoast region to elevations of 3,000 to 3,500 ft (910 to 1,068 m) and occasionally higher, and are more common in the northern part of the state.

Some Red-breasted Nuthatches remain paired throughout the year. Songs of unmated males provide the first signs of breeding behavior in spring and serve to establish territories and to court females (Stanwood *in* Tyler 1948b, Kilham 1973). The courtship song consists of 2 to 6 plaintive nasal "waa-aa, ans" in a series, repeated 12 to 16 times per minute (Kilham 1973). Courtship songs of the White-breasted Nuthatch are similar, but are distinguishable to experienced observers.

During April and May a male Red-breasted Nuthatch courts his mate by bringing her insects. She may crouch with wings quivering and bill pointed upward, begging with whistled "purp" notes. He too may quiver his wings as he feeds her bill tip to bill tip (Kilham 1973).

Red-breasted Nuthatches usually excavate their nest hole in a well-decayed hardwood or conifer stub (Tyler 1948b, Kilham 1973). Occasionally they may nest in a natural cavity, an old woodpecker hole, or even a nest box (Tyler 1948b). The female selects the site and does the initial excavating. Nests may be at heights of 5 to 40 ft (2 to 12 m) (Harrison 1978). The Atlas project produced only 6 records of nest building, 3 of which were in May. The earliest, 8 April, was from

the Dover area. During late stages of excavation and continuing into the nesting period, Red-breasted Nuthatches collect pitch droplets from softwoods and dab them around the nest entrance. On at least one occasion the pitch barricade has fatally entrapped a member of the nuthatch pair (Kilham 1972a). As the hole nears completion, the male initiates high speed chases of his mate which sometimes precede mating (Wellman 1933 *in* Tyler 1948b, Kilham 1973).

The female nuthatch lines the cavity with soft materials and lays 4 to 7, usually 5 or 6 eggs (Tyler 1948b). The male brings food throughout the 12-day incubation period and feeds her at the entrance hole (Burns 1921a). Both adults tend the young, which fledge 18 to 21 days after hatching (Stanwood *in* Tyler 1948b).

Ornithologists generally believe this species to be single brooded, but an aviary pair in Lyme hatched a second brood in July after successfully fledging an initial brood (Kilham 1973). In light of this, the 9 July nest-building record from the Atlas project is intriguing, but may represent a renesting attempt after previous failure.

After fledging, Red-breasted Nuthatches remain in conspicuous family groups. The Atlas project produced 85 records of fledged young, representing 62 priority blocks (73% of priority blocks with "confirmed" records) and 5 Special Areas. The earliest fledgling record, 28 May, came from the Peterborough area. Of the 85 records, 62% are from July. Families roam through the forest for much of the summer, moving like tiny, winged acrobats in the tops of conifers and sometimes flying out to hawk insects from the air. Their diet includes conifer seeds and insect eggs, larvae, and adults. In August and September, Red-breasted Nuthatches often join in mixed flocks with chickadees, titmice, and warblers.

Although typically these nuthatches are year-round residents of New Hampshire, they will leave the northern forests in winter if the cone crop is poor. At such times, back yard feeders may sustain them in populated areas of the state. In years of extreme food scarcity, large flocks of these tiny birds move south in search of food (Tyler 1948b, Bock and Lepthien 1972).

The Red-breasted Nuthatch likely retreated from much of its original range in New Hampshire as lands were cleared for agriculture during the 1700s and early 1800s. Around the turn of the present century, they were absent from the Durham area in summer, but abundant in winter (Dearborn 1903), and the majority of birds wintering in Belknap and Merrimack counties moved further north to nest (Dearborn 1898). Allen (1903) considered them common in the spruce-fir forests of northern New Hampshire and indicated that they nested regularly in the Western Highlands but only sporadically in the southern part of the state. As forests, with a significant component of white pine, invaded abandoned farms and grew to maturity, the Red-breasted Nuthatch regained considerable habitat in central and southern New Hampshire.

The Atlas map shows a distribution which reflects the high percentage of forested land in New Hampshire and the broad occurrence of conifers throughout the state. The Red-breasted Nuthatch is uncommon at elevations below 1,000 ft (305 m) and rare below 500 ft (150 m) (T. Richards, unpubl. data), which may explain the gaps in the Connecticut and Merrimack river valleys. BBS data from 1966 to 1979 indicate no significant trend for the Red-breasted Nuthatch and show higher densities for this species in Maine and New Hampshire than for other Northeastern states (Robbins et al. 1986). The future of this pert sprite of the softwoods seems secure.

Carol R. Foss

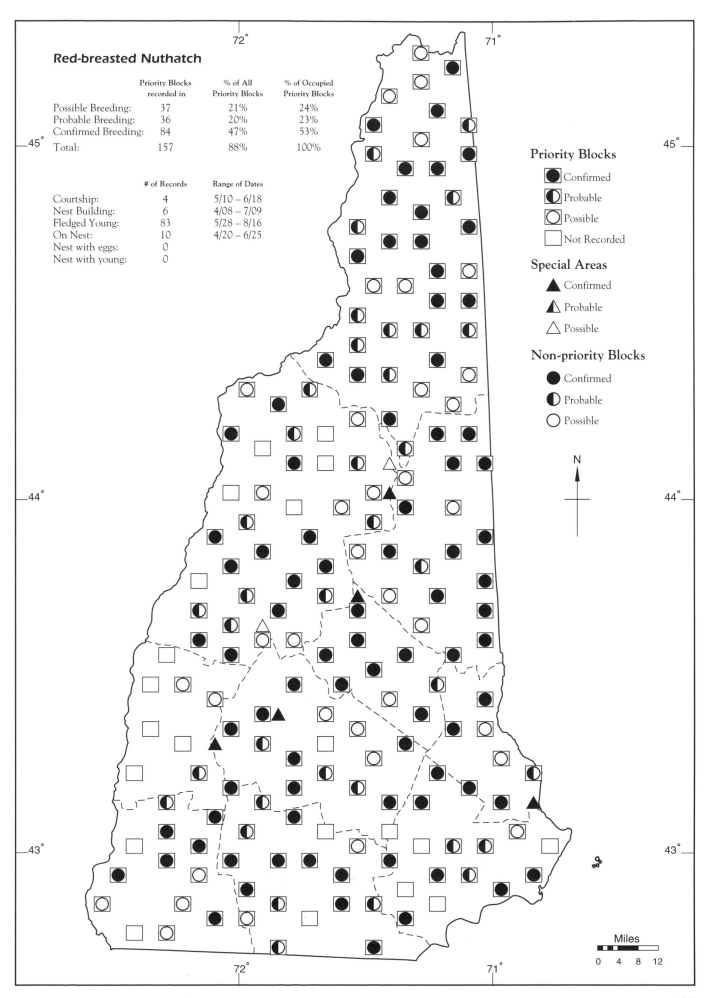

Red-breasted Nuthatch

	Priority Blocks recorded in	% of All Priority Blocks	% of Occupied Priority Blocks
Possible Breeding:	37	21%	24%
Probable Breeding:	36	20%	23%
Confirmed Breeding:	84	47%	53%
Total:	157	88%	100%

	# of Records	Range of Dates
Courtship:	4	5/10 – 6/18
Nest Building:	6	4/08 – 7/09
Fledged Young:	83	5/28 – 8/16
On Nest:	10	4/20 – 6/25
Nest with eggs:	0	
Nest with young:	0	

Priority Blocks

● Confirmed
◐ Probable
○ Possible
□ Not Recorded

Special Areas

▲ Confirmed
◮ Probable
△ Possible

Non-priority Blocks

● Confirmed
◖ Probable
○ Possible

N

Miles
0 4 8 12

195

White-breasted Nuthatch

Sitta carolinensis

Pausing to peer about as they move headfirst down the trunks of trees, these plump acrobats enliven the woods with their nasal notes and lively antics. White-breasted Nuthatches are common year-round residents of mature deciduous and mixed woods throughout New Hampshire, occurring at elevations up to 2,500 ft (760 m) (T. Richards, unpubl. data). They are gray above and white below, with distinctive black caps. The well-known "yank, yank, yank" of these agile birds resembles the busy signal of an old-fashioned telephone.

These nuthatches reside in a variety of habitats, from extensive deciduous and mixed forests to villages and residential neighborhoods with numerous deciduous trees. Their breeding range covers most of the continental United States and extends north into southern Canada and south to southern Mexico (Tyler 1948c). Oak, beech, and hickory trees provide important food sources, and may be important in determining local distribution and abundance (Ellison *in* Laughlin and Kibbe 1985, Ridgely 1988).

White-breasted Nuthatches remain paired throughout the year, and maintain year-round territories of about 37 a (15 ha) (Kilham 1981). Breeding behavior may begin in early January. Kilham (1972b) studied this species extensively in Lyme and provides the following information about courtship. The male sings a series of "wurp" notes from a high, exposed perch in the first half hour after emerging from his roost hole on winter mornings from January into early March. The female subsequently joins him, and the 2 may forage together for several hours, maintaining contact with soft "hit-tuck" notes, and occasionally pausing for additional courtship songs. In February, the male may instigate wild pursuit flights, chasing his mate in a rapidly twisting path around and through the trees. Courtship feeding also begins in February and continues into May. Copulations follow an intricate dance, in which the male presents the back of his head while moving about near the female.

Rather than excavating their own nest holes, White-breasted Nuthatches use natural cavities or old woodpecker holes located 15 to 50 ft (4.6 to 15.2 m) above the ground (Harrison 1975). Typical nest sites are in large trees, with a minimum dbh of 12 in (30 cm) (Thomas et al. 1979). Occasionally they use other sites, such as birdhouses, and a pair once nested in a hole at the end of a barn's ridgepole (Dearborn 1903).

After the pair has selected a suitable cavity, the female lines the bottom with shreds of bark, grasses, rootlets, twigs, and fur. During the nest-building period and until the young fledge, White-breasted Nuthatches may sweep areas of the tree trunk and limbs in the vicinity of the nest, often with an insect, some fur, or a fragment of plant material in their bills (Kilham 1968).

The male brings the female food as she incubates the 5 to 10, usually 8 eggs for about 12 days, and broods the newly hatched young (Harrison 1975). Both parents feed older nestlings, which leave the cavity 24 to 26 days after hatching, usually in mid to late June (L. Kilham, pers. comm.). The playful, curious young depend on their parents for about 2 weeks after fledging (Harrison 1978). Family groups are readily detectable during this period and produced the vast majority of "confirmed" breeding records. Nuthatches remain in family groups during July and August, providing an extended opportunity for "confirmations".

These nuthatches forage for insects and spiders and their eggs in bark crevices of tree trunks and large limbs, and gather nuts, acorns, large seeds, and various berries and small fruits (Forbush 1929). They visit feeding stations for sunflower seeds and suet, often caching tidbits in nearby crevices.

In winter White-breasted Nuthatches often travel in mixed flocks with Black-capped Chickadees, Downy Woodpeckers, and Brown Creepers. They roost in a variety of cavities, including those of Downy Woodpeckers (Kilham 1971b). Northern populations may range widely during the winter months in search of food, sometimes occupying areas in which they are not known to breed (Forbush 1929).

The status and abundance of this species in New Hampshire appears to have changed somewhat during the present century. Ornithologists of the early 1900s considered the White-breasted Nuthatch an uncommon breeding resident in much of the state and found it more common in winter than in summer (Dearborn 1898, 1903, Allen 1903, Wright 1911, White 1924, Forbush 1929).

As the Atlas map indicates, this nuthatch is now ubiquitous in southern New Hampshire. The Atlas project documented the White-breasted Nuthatch in every priority block in the 9 southern counties, and in about half of the Coos County priority blocks. BBS data from 1966 to 1979 indicate that in the Eastern region, the breeding abundance of this species in New Hampshire is exceeded only in Massachusetts and Connecticut, and suggest significant population increases for Eastern and Central North America (Robbins et al. 1986).

Reforestation following the decline of agriculture may be a key factor in this species' increase in southern New Hampshire. Recent increases in the hardwood component of North Country forests could explain the expansion further north. The recent proliferation of bird feeders in suburbs and villages also may have played a role by reducing reliance on natural food sources. In any event, this spry and energetic neighbor seems likely to thrive in New Hampshire back yards and woodlands for many years to come.

Carol R. Foss

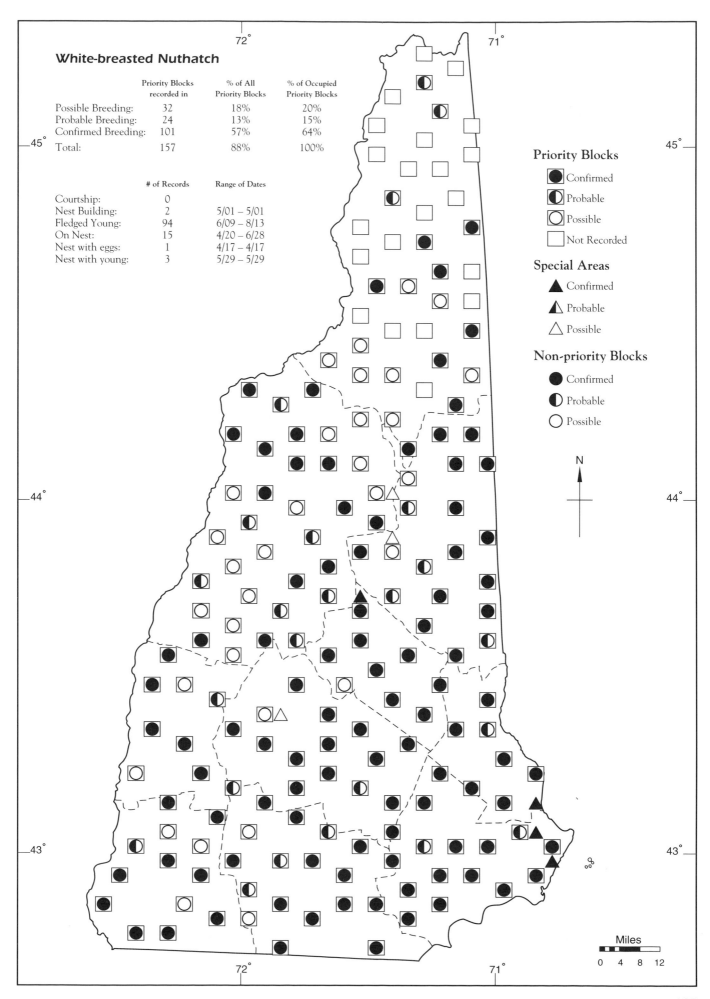

White-breasted Nuthatch

	Priority Blocks recorded in	% of All Priority Blocks	% of Occupied Priority Blocks
Possible Breeding:	32	18%	20%
Probable Breeding:	24	13%	15%
Confirmed Breeding:	101	57%	64%
Total:	157	88%	100%

	# of Records	Range of Dates
Courtship:	0	
Nest Building:	2	5/01 – 5/01
Fledged Young:	94	6/09 – 8/13
On Nest:	15	4/20 – 6/28
Nest with eggs:	1	4/17 – 4/17
Nest with young:	3	5/29 – 5/29

Priority Blocks

● Confirmed
◐ Probable
○ Possible
□ Not Recorded

Special Areas

▲ Confirmed
◣ Probable
△ Possible

Non-priority Blocks

● Confirmed
◑ Probable
○ Possible

N

Miles
0 4 8 12

197

AER

Brown Creeper
Certhia americana

The well-camouflaged Brown Creeper, a fluid curve from slender bill to long, bracing tail, is a small, tree-spiraling climber that is easily overlooked. Circumpolar and the only member of its family in North America, the creeper is widely distributed throughout New Hampshire as a breeding bird, migrant, and winter resident. It inhabits wooded swamps or mature woodlands near water, nesting at elevations up to 4,100 ft (1,250 m) (Allen 1903; T. Richards, unpubl. data).

Creepers climb head first up the trunk of a tree, shifting from side to side as they search for insects and insect eggs, then fly down to the foot of another tree to start up again. Groups of creepers are noticeable as they probe bark crevices or the undersides of branches, often in the company of chickadees, nuthatches, and kinglets. They follow "a certain beat, each circuit requiring an hour or two" (White 1924). Brown Creepers "freeze" to escape predators, remaining motionless and nearly invisible for 15 minutes or more (Janeway, pers. obs.).

In late March the creeper's high tinkling song is an early sign of spring. The short, silvery waterfall of 4 to 6 notes, so high that some people cannot hear it, is repeated frequently from a vertical perch in the top of a tree (Davis 1978). The call note is a quiet "tsee."

In all seasons, both sexes resemble gray-brown mice, blending into mottled bark with their white-speckled backs. The clear white underparts are conspicuous during courtship flights. During these vigorous displays of aerial agility, a male creeper twists in and out among the trees and tightly around tree trunks at great speed (Tyler 1948a). In another display, the members of a pair closely pursue one another in a series of spiraling flights up a tree trunk (Hunt 1907 in Tyler 1948a).

Brown Creeper nests are as unique as their song. Brewster (1879) documented the preferred nest site of this species, under strips of loose bark on standing dead trees, near Umbagog Lake, Errol, in 1879. Ornitholo-

gists previously had assumed that creepers nested in old woodpecker or knot holes, which they do only when lacking loose-barked trees. Nest tree size and the length of sheltering bark strips vary widely (Davis 1978).

Beginning in April, the male helps the female collect nesting material. He feeds her while she is building the crescent-shaped cup of twigs, grass, bark strips, moss, fern down, cobwebs, feathers, and fine fibers (Forbush 1929). Nests are usually 3 to 15 ft (0.9 to 4.6 m) above ground or water level (Harrison 1975). A nest discovered on a dead maple in the Bradford Bog, Bradford, on 19 June 1985 was at eye level from a canoe, and fitted the curve of the tree trunk (Janeway, pers. obs.). Creepers used a nest in Hopkinton for 3 years in a row (S. Gallagher, pers. comm.).

The female incubates the 5 or 6 eggs for 2 weeks, usually in May or June. J. McDermott (pers. comm.) observed a nest in Raymond on 5 July 1985 about 20 ft (6 m) high in a dead white pine and noted that, "The bird does not fly directly to the opening but lands 2 to 3 feet below it and works its way up, making a small call when approaching the opening." A sitting female sticks close to her nest when people approach.

Both parents care for the young. Davis (1978) observed that they carry fecal sacs "away from the nests to trees where, with one quick movement of the bill, each sac was slapped on the bark where it stuck." Young remain in the nest for about 2 weeks. One nest Atlas observers found was 5 ft (1.5 m) from the ground under loose bark of a dead elm in Weare, and held young on 8 June 1985 (C.R. Foss and D. Stavros, NHBBA data).

Fledglings are very active and noisy from late June until mid-August, calling with high notes (Janeway, pers. obs.). Nearly all Atlas confirmations were from fledged young or parents feeding them. At night, fledglings roost together in a tight circle, their heads hidden in the center and shoulder plumage fluffed out (Davis 1978). Creepers appear to stay in family groups for several weeks, and perhaps longer. Janeway observed a group of 5 calling and following each other from tree to tree in a wooded swamp in Sandwich on 30 January 1986.

The Brown Creeper's range in New Hampshire apparently has expanded during the last 50 years. In the early 1900s this species nested primarily in thick coniferous woods of northern New Hampshire (Allen 1903, Forbush 1929). The creeper occurred as a migrant and winter resident in the southeastern (Dearborn 1903) and central (Dearborn 1898, White 1924, White 1937) parts of the state, and primarily as a migrant in the southwest, where it sometimes nested on Mt. Monadnock, Jaffrey (Thayer 1909 in Allison and Allison 1979).

As the Atlas map illustrates, the Brown Creeper is now well distributed throughout the state. Many of the blocks lacking records may support the species, which is most vocal in early spring, and is relatively inconspicuous by the time migrants arrive to nest. BBS data from 1966 to 1985 suggest a population decline in New Hampshire; however, Brown Creepers are relatively quiet during June, when Breeding Bird Surveys take place. As long as the state remains well forested and supports an abundance of suitable dead trees with loose bark, the future of the Brown Creeper seems secure.

Elizabeth C. Janeway & Sally M. Sutcliffe

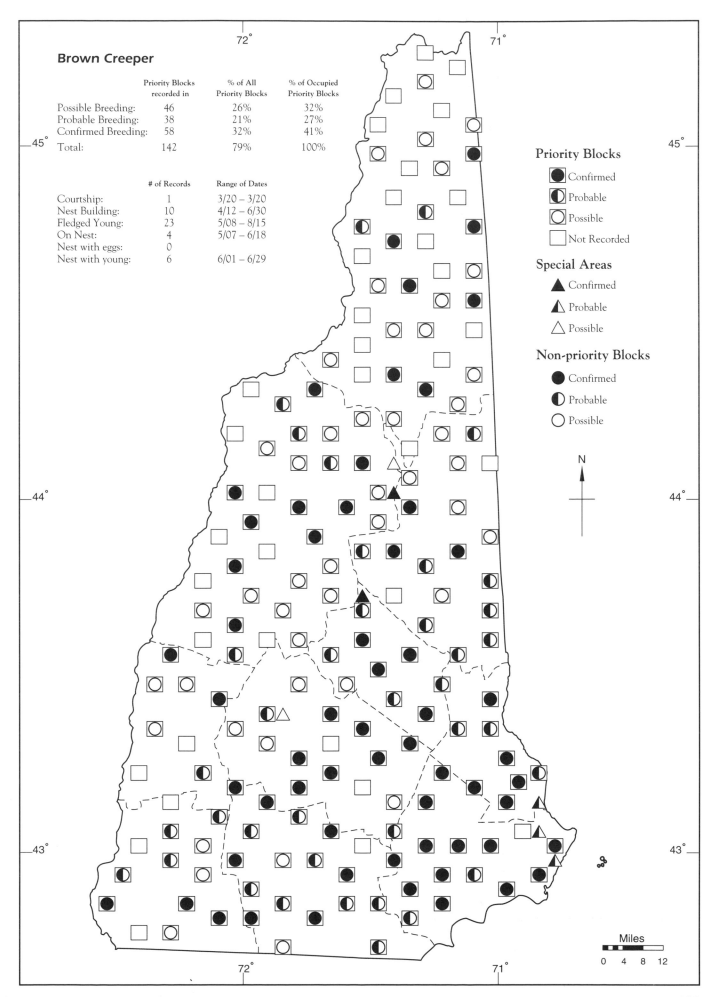

Brown Creeper

	Priority Blocks recorded in	% of All Priority Blocks	% of Occupied Priority Blocks
Possible Breeding:	46	26%	32%
Probable Breeding:	38	21%	27%
Confirmed Breeding:	58	32%	41%
Total:	142	79%	100%

	# of Records	Range of Dates
Courtship:	1	3/20 – 3/20
Nest Building:	10	4/12 – 6/30
Fledged Young:	23	5/08 – 8/15
On Nest:	4	5/07 – 6/18
Nest with eggs:	0	
Nest with young:	6	6/01 – 6/29

Priority Blocks

◐ Confirmed
◑ Probable
○ Possible
□ Not Recorded

Special Areas

▲ Confirmed
◣ Probable
△ Possible

Non-priority Blocks

● Confirmed
◐ Probable
○ Possible

N

Miles
0 4 8 12

House Wren

Troglodytes aedon

The House Wren is a familiar bird to New Hampshire residents who have nest boxes in their gardens. The loud, lively, bubbling song calls attention to the male immediately upon his arrival from the Southern states during the first week of May. The slender bill and rather long, barred, cocked-up tail distinguish this species from other tiny brown songbirds. This busy little mite is not at all timid or secretive and may sing right on top of its nest box.

This is primarily a bird of gardens, hedgerows, and wood margins, with dense undergrowth. Its food, usually obtained within 30 ft (9 m) of the ground, is typically 100% animal matter, especially crickets, beetles, grasshoppers, and spiders (USFWS, unpubl. data). It nests in cavities. Nest boxes provide the most common nest sites, and are best placed 4 to 8 ft (1.2 to 2.4 m) up on fence posts or tree trunks in suitable nesting habitat. The House Wren also will nest in pipes, outbuildings, clothespin bags, old woodpecker holes, and natural cavities. In Ontario, tree cavities most frequently used were in birches, elms, white cedar, and apple (Peck and James 1987).

The House Wren seems to be obsessed with stuffing multiple nest boxes with sticks and often will prevent other cavity nesting songbirds from successfully nesting within what it considers its own domain. It even punctures nearby eggs of its own or other species (Belle-Isles and Picman 1986). The stick nests are lined with grass, hair, and feathers. Because this bird builds dummy nests, observers cannot assume that a bird carrying nesting material is about to enter its nest; additional evidence such as "food for young" is necessary. Nests are placed from 4.5 to 60 ft (1.4 to 18 m) above ground. Nest building occurs in mid-May and again in early July since pairs normally raise 2 broods.

There are usually 6 or 7 eggs in the first brood, often one fewer in the second. The most common New Hampshire Atlas "confirmations" were "on nest".

However, information on dates of eggs and young is scanty. Incubation averages 13 days, and the young remain in the nest about 15 days.

Singing continues into July. Thereafter the monotonous scolding of adults and young betrays their presence until departure in mid-September. House Wrens in a banded population in Cleveland, Ohio, changed mates between successive broods in the same season (Baldwin 1921).

The early history of the House Wren in New Hampshire is enshrouded in mystery. The first published reports (Maynard 1871, Minot 1876, Faxon and Allen 1888, Clark 1899) came from the northern part of the state, and W. Cooke of the U.S. Biological Survey rejected them as probably Winter Wrens. Allen (1903) finally clarified the status and range of this wren as, "Uncommon summer resident of the Transition valleys in the southern and central parts of the state . . . rare north of Lake Winnepesaukee."

House Wrens in New England declined from about 1875 to 1883, after the introduction of House Sparrows from Europe, and their status changed to rare and local (Forbush 1929). Dearborn (1903) called this species "certainly less common in the state now than they were fifty years ago." He found it very scarce and irregular in the Durham area even as a migrant, and knew of no local nesting.

The House Wren has expanded its range in New Hampshire during the past century. Wright (1911) found 10 to 16 singing males in a slash area in Jefferson, the first indication that this species was locally common in the White Mountains region. Not until 1917 and especially 1918 did the House Wren return to former nesting sites in Massachusetts and southern Maine. White (1924) found his first nest in the Concord area in 1921 and made an unprecedented count of 6 pairs in Concord in 1935 (White 1937). This species is documented from Westmoreland, Ossipee, Manchester, Sanbornton, and Hanover during 1925–39 (USFWS, unpubl. data).

By 1977 the House Wren was locally fairly common in the Squam Lakes area (Ridgely 1977). BBS data indicate that House Wren populations increased in New Hampshire from 1966 to 1975, declined to a low point in 1978 (presumably as a result of the hard winter of 1977–78 in the southeastern states), then gradually increased again (Robbins et al. 1986). This species has been recorded on all but one far northern New Hampshire BBS route, but is least common and not regular in northern Coos County. It is most abundant in southeastern New Hampshire. The Atlas project occurred during a time of high populations.

Atlas workers found the House Wren most widely distributed south of the White Mountains. Only 4 priority blocks in the 7 southern counties lack Atlas records for the species. Although widely distributed in central New Hampshire, it still is not common there. This wren remains very local in the heavily forested mountains and the Northern Highlands. In the Ossipee Lake quadrangle, observers found a few pairs in most of the villages, but failed to locate any in the forested hills and isolated farmsteads. The future outlook for this species in New Hampshire is favorable in the light of moderating climate, suburban expansion, and an increasing number of nest boxes.

Chandler S. Robbins

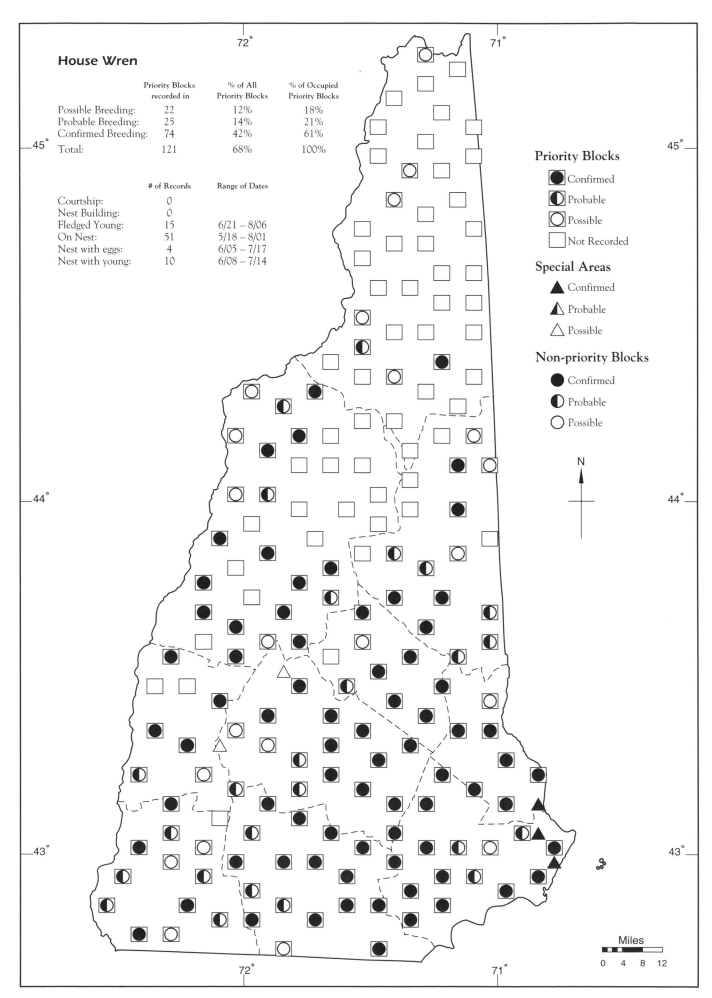

House Wren

	Priority Blocks recorded in	% of All Priority Blocks	% of Occupied Priority Blocks
Possible Breeding:	22	12%	18%
Probable Breeding:	25	14%	21%
Confirmed Breeding:	74	42%	61%
Total:	121	68%	100%

	# of Records	Range of Dates
Courtship:	0	
Nest Building:	0	
Fledged Young:	15	6/21 – 8/06
On Nest:	51	5/18 – 8/01
Nest with eggs:	4	6/05 – 7/17
Nest with young:	10	6/08 – 7/14

Priority Blocks

- ◑ Confirmed
- ◐ Probable
- ○ Possible
- ☐ Not Recorded

Special Areas

- ▲ Confirmed
- ◭ Probable
- △ Possible

Non-priority Blocks

- ● Confirmed
- ◐ Probable
- ○ Possible

N

Miles
0 4 8 12

Winter Wren

Troglodytes troglodytes

Perched on some projecting point, this tiny brown songster delivers its 7- to 10-second series of high-pitched trills with a volume and complexity which belie its size. Unless its song or its "tic-tic" call reveals its location, the Winter Wren can be a difficult species to see. Shy and secretive, it skulks among the underbrush, spending most of its time near the ground. Low cover of various types, including slash and fallen trees, provide typical nesting and feeding sites. Preferred habitat is damp coniferous and mixed woodlands near water.

Winter Wrens nest throughout the state where suitable habitat is present, from the lowlands to the limits of tree growth in the mountains. They are common along streams in the White Mountains, and a few occur among the scrub at 4,500 ft (1,370 m), where the mossy ground is saturated (Wright 1911). There also are records from 5,000 ft (1,520 m) elevation near Lakes of the Clouds, Sargents Purchase (E.G. Loomis, unpubl. data). Sabo (1980) found Winter Wren densities of 4–14 pairs/0.4 sq mi (1 sq km) and territories of about 3 a (1.2 ha) in subalpine habitat on Mt. Moosilauke, Benton.

A few Winter Wrens overwinter in New Hampshire, but most migrate to wintering areas in the Southern states. Returning Winter Wrens typically arrive in New Hampshire throughout the month of April. The male appears first and, after establishing his territory, usually by early May, builds a number of unlined nests composed of moss, grasses, fine twigs, and rootlets. These are most often placed in well-hidden cavities in the upturned roots of fallen trees. Hollow stumps, old woodpecker holes, mossy hummocks, and crevices among rocks or fallen trees also provide nest sites. Occasionally, the male suspends a round mass of twigs and moss with a small side opening from a branch of a coniferous tree up to 10 ft (3 m) above ground (Forbush 1929). He often mates with several females in succes-

sion. Each female chooses a nest, most often one near the ground, and lines it with feathers or fur. She incubates the clutch of 4 to 7 eggs for 14 to 17 days (Harrison 1978). Both parents feed the young, the male helping with his successive broods.

The nests are difficult to find, and Atlas workers discovered only 5, accounting for only 12% of confirmations. With young in the nest, the cryptically plumaged adults are exceedingly wary and perhaps even more difficult than usual to see; fecal sac and food carrying supplied only 21% of the "confirmed" breeding records. The fledged young, which leave the nest at 15 to 20 days of age (Harrison 1978), become noticeable in late June, and are quite noisy. Family groups of parents and recently fledged young are most conspicuous when moving around and foraging. Winter Wrens forage primarily on fallen logs and the forest floor (Sabo 1980), and feed almost entirely on insects, especially beetles, bugs, caterpillars, and small hymenopterans (Bent 1948). Sightings of fledged young accounted for 61% of the breeding "confirmations" for New Hampshire. Brewster (1898 *in* Griscom 1938) saw a brood "scarce able to fly" in the Umbagog Lake area as late as 31 August, and notes 2 vocalizations apparently unique to the young, a "fine, wiry tre-e-e" and a soft "chirr up." Fall migration occurs mainly during October, and sightings later than 5 November are quite rare (White 1924).

Historically, this species was common in the White Mountains and northern New Hampshire (Samuels 1870, Maynard 1871, Minot 1876, Chadbourne 1887, Faxon and Allen 1888, Minot 1895, Allen 1902, Forbush 1929) and uncommon and local in the central and southern parts of the state (Dearborn 1898; Allen 1909; White 1924; Forbush 1929; Shelley, unpubl. data; Weaver, unpubl. data; Thayer 1902; Thayer 1909 *in* Allison and Allison 1979). Dearborn (1898) knew it primarily as a transient in Belknap and Merrimack counties and observed it in the area only once during the breeding season. White (1924) had no evidence of nesting in the vicinity of Concord.

The Winter Wren has extended its range southward in New Hampshire during the last 50 years, aided no doubt by reversion of abandoned agricultural lands to forest. This expansion is evident in Belknap and Merrimack counties, where 16 priority blocks have records for the species, 4 of them "confirmed."

As the Atlas map illustrates, the Winter Wren continues to be well distributed in the White Mountains and North Country of New Hampshire. Only one priority block in Coos County lacks an Atlas record. It is fairly common in the central and southwestern highlands, but remains scarce as a breeder in southeastern New Hampshire and along the southern half of the Connecticut River valley.

A noticeable decline in New Hampshire's breeding population of Winter Wrens became evident after the severe winters of 1976–78, during which prolonged freezing temperatures occurred throughout wintering grounds in the southeastern U.S. (Robbins et al. 1986). Populations have since rebounded, and BBS data from 1966 to 1990 show an insignificant positive trend in New Hampshire (J.R. Sauer, pers. comm.). The Winter Wren is likely to remain a common resident in the extensive suitable habitat of northern New Hampshire, and may expand its range further southeastward in the coming years.

Andrea E. Robbins

Atlas of Breeding Birds in New Hampshire

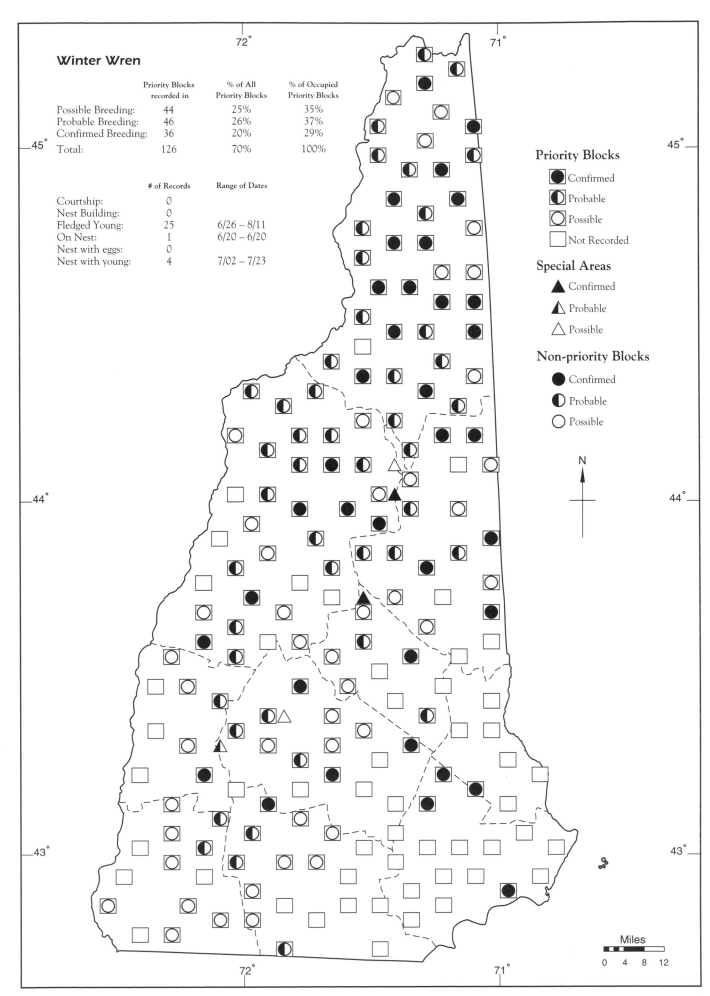

Winter Wren

	Priority Blocks recorded in	% of All Priority Blocks	% of Occupied Priority Blocks
Possible Breeding:	44	25%	35%
Probable Breeding:	46	26%	37%
Confirmed Breeding:	36	20%	29%
Total:	126	70%	100%

	# of Records	Range of Dates
Courtship:	0	
Nest Building:	0	
Fledged Young:	25	6/26 – 8/11
On Nest:	1	6/20 – 6/20
Nest with eggs:	0	
Nest with young:	4	7/02 – 7/23

Priority Blocks

● Confirmed
◑ Probable
○ Possible
□ Not Recorded

Special Areas

▲ Confirmed
◮ Probable
△ Possible

Non-priority Blocks

● Confirmed
◑ Probable
○ Possible

N

Miles
0 4 8 12

Sedge Wren
Cistothorus platensis

This secretive inhabitant of wet grass and sedge meadows is more easily heard than seen. The male repeatedly sings a "tsip-tsip-trrrrrrrrup" (Farrand 1983) up to 12 times a minute throughout the breeding season, which lasts from May until September (Walkinshaw 1935). Distinguishing characteristics of the Sedge Wren (formerly called Short-billed Marsh Wren) are its small size and typical wren profile, a streaked crown and back, an indistinct whitish eyebrow, and buffy underparts. The similar and closely related Marsh Wren has a distinct white eye-line, unstreaked crown, and distinctly different song. Habitats of the 2 species also differ. The Sedge Wren nests in wet meadows with dense sedges and grasses, whereas the Marsh Wren occurs in marshes with coarser vegetation such as cattails, reeds, and sometimes buttonbush, and usually with deeper water.

There have been only 14 breeding season reports of Sedge Wrens in New Hampshire since 1963, and in only 2 of these years were more than 2 reported (SRS). This wren was added to New Hampshire's list of Endangered Species in 1987.

Typical Sedge Wren habitat is the higher ground around the edges of a marsh or a wet meadow with a brook winding through it. If standing water is present, it typically is shallow (Walkinshaw 1935; K. C. Elkins, pers. comm.). Sedge Wrens arrive in the state during the latter part of May and sometimes linger well into September or perhaps later (Walkinshaw 1935, Elkins 1982).

The male builds numerous nests, which are used for nesting, roosting, and possibly as decoys for predators (Burns 1982). Burns (1982) found that the 12 males he was studying built an average of 9 nests each. Nests are located in dense vegetation 2 to 3 ft (0.6 to 0.9 m) above the ground or water (Harrison 1975). In an Iowa study, nests were in marsh vegetation dominated by river bulrush or reed canary grass (Crawford 1977); in

a Minnesota study they were located in tussock sedge, water sedge, and hard-stem bulrush (Burns 1982). These and a number of similar plant species occur in New England wetlands (Tiner 1988). The nest is a globular structure with a small entrance hole on one side, made of interwoven sedges and grasses. The female chooses the one in which she will lay eggs, and lines it with finer grasses, feathers, fur, or other cottony material (Walkinshaw 1935).

Polygyny is common in the Sedge Wren and may reach levels of 30 to 50% (Burns 1982). Crawford (1977) reported polygyny levels of 19% in Iowa, where secondary females began nesting later, laid smaller clutches, and fledged fewer young than primary females. In Minnesota some females, including both primary females and mates of monogamous males, were double brooded, but secondary females always had one brood (Burns 1982).

The incubation period is approximately 14 days and begins before the clutch of 4 to 10 eggs is complete (Forbush 1929, Mousley 1934b, Crawford 1977, Burns 1982). Egg dates in the Northeast range from late May through July (Forbush 1929, Bull 1974). The female incubates the eggs and does almost all the feeding of the nestlings while the male continues to advertise his territory (Burns 1982). The young fledge 11 to 16 days after hatching (Crawford 1977).

The Sedge Wren appears to be an extremely mobile and opportunistic breeder. It may be common in a given area one year and then almost completely absent in the same area during subsequent years. Both males and females have been known to appear and disappear suddenly within a single breeding season, and arrival times may vary substantially from one season to the next (Burns 1982). This may explain why observers have first noticed the birds on some territories as late as the last week in July.

Sedge Wrens sing from the tops of low bushes, weeds, or grass stalks, but are shy and usually avoid close approach. When not singing, they are almost certain to escape detection unless the observer tramps through wet vegetation and happens to flush one. If flushed, Sedge Wrens make a short flight and drop back into the grass. They are reluctant to flush again (Forbush 1929). These wrens are especially active in early morning and at dusk and often sing at night (Forbush 1929).

The Sedge Wren was historically a rare and local summer resident of New Hampshire (Forbush 1929), and most authors considered it to be rare in or absent from their areas (Coues 1868, Dearborn 1903, Goodhue 1877 *in* Elkins 1961, Thayer 1909 *in* Allison and Allison 1979). White (1924), however, considered this wren numerous around Concord. T. Richards (unpubl. data) documented the species from all sections of the state between 1947 and 1961, but considered it rare and local. BBS data from 1966 to 1979 suggest a decline in the Northeastern states, among other areas, including Wisconsin, where the species was recorded on 63 of 70 routes (Robbins et al. 1986). Reasons for the decline are unknown, but may relate to widespread losses of fresh-water wetlands and wet meadows.

Even though the Atlas project resulted in more birders in the field than perhaps ever before, they produced reports of the Sedge Wren from only 4 localities in the state. The Vermont Atlas indicates that the Sedge Wren also is a rare species in Vermont (Kibbe *in* Laughlin and Kibbe 1985). Although the Vermont Atlas project "confirmed" breeding, the New Hampshire Atlas project documented this wren as only a "probable" breeder. While this species always has been rare and local in the Northeast, it has become significantly more so in recent years, and its future in the region is uncertain.

Thomas H. Arter

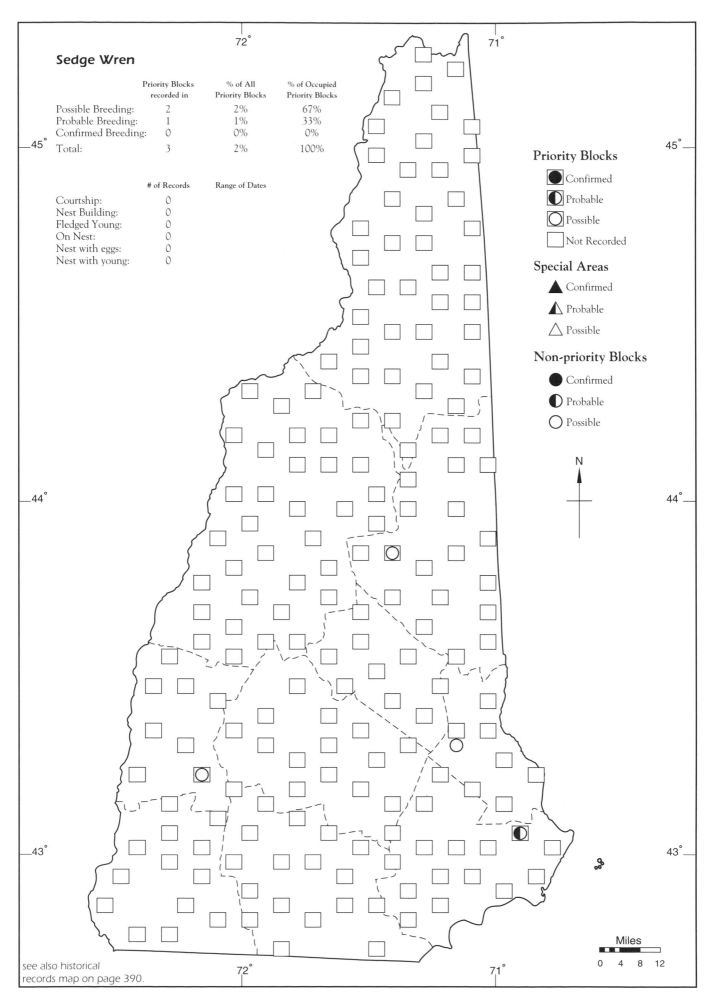

Sedge Wren

	Priority Blocks recorded in	% of All Priority Blocks	% of Occupied Priority Blocks
Possible Breeding:	2	2%	67%
Probable Breeding:	1	1%	33%
Confirmed Breeding:	0	0%	0%
Total:	3	2%	100%

	# of Records	Range of Dates
Courtship:	0	
Nest Building:	0	
Fledged Young:	0	
On Nest:	0	
Nest with eggs:	0	
Nest with young:	0	

Priority Blocks
- Confirmed
- Probable
- Possible
- Not Recorded

Special Areas
- Confirmed
- Probable
- Possible

Non-priority Blocks
- Confirmed
- Probable
- Possible

N

Miles
0 4 8 12

see also historical records map on page 390.

205

Marsh Wren
Cistothorus palustris

Like many marsh inhabitants, the Marsh Wren (formerly Long-billed Marsh Wren) is often heard before it is seen. The bubbling and gurgling notes of its song can serve to alert one not only to the species' presence, but even to the existence of a previously unknown marsh. Like most other wrens, the Marsh Wren is an incessant singer. The Marsh Wren differs from our other wetland wren, the Sedge Wren, in having a solid rusty cap and prominent white line over the eye. The Sedge Wren has a streaked crown and obscure, buffy eye-line.

Arriving in this state in early to mid-May, Marsh Wrens immediately search out their favorite haunts: coastal salt and brackish marshes, or inland cattail or mixed marsh with cattails present. Narrow-leaved species of cattails seem to be preferred over broad-leaved ones (Welter 1935), and the presence of some open water also seems to be important. Sedge Wrens, on the other hand, prefer moist meadows with sedges, grasses, and scattered shrubs.

These wrens can occur in small marshes of 2 to 3 a (0.8 to 1.2 ha) (Kibbe *in* Laughlin and Kibbe 1985), or be absent entirely from marshes of major proportions. Where marsh conditions are suitable, however, typically more than one pair occurs. Various authors (Welter 1935, Kale 1965, Verner 1965 *in* DeGraaf and Rudis 1986) report territories ranging from 72 to 4,300 sq yd (60 to 3,595 sq m).

Males sing constantly, defending their territories against intruders. Even in full song, they are often difficult to see. At other times they will sing while perched conspicuously, or even while in fluttery flight above their territories. Flight songs are common early in the breeding season, but become less so later on (K. C. Elkins, pers. comm.).

The male begins building oblong dummy or "cock" nests shortly after arrival, and continues to do so throughout much of the summer. One male may con-struct anywhere from a few to a few dozen such nests (Welter 1935). These false nests look real but lack linings, and sometimes entrances. They serve to confuse predators and provide polygynous males with many places from which to sing to attract females. The female alone often builds the actual nest, over a period of 5 to 8 days (Harrison 1975). The nest is a sphere of shredded plant material lashed to standing cattails, reeds, or shrubs, usually at a height of 1 to 3 ft (0.3 to 0.9 m) above water (Bent 1948). Sometimes the female merely lines one of the male's nests, then lays her 3 to 6 eggs (Harrison 1975). She alone incubates for 12 to 14 days (Harrison 1978) and also tends to most of the feeding of nestlings. Typical food consists of ants, grasshoppers, caterpillars, flies, mosquitoes, snails, and small crustaceans.

The males continue to defend their territories throughout the nesting period, and even go out of their way to destroy the eggs of conspecifics and other species, including Red-winged Blackbirds and Least Bitterns (Bent 1948). Chicks fledge at 13 to 15 days (Harrison 1978). It is uncertain, though possible, that Marsh Wrens raise 2 broods in New Hampshire. They raise as many as 3 broods in southerly parts of their breeding range, which extends from the southern coasts of the United States to the Northern states and southern Canada. Leaving for wintering grounds in the mid-Atlantic and Southern states, most Marsh Wrens depart by the end of September (Kibbe *in* Laughlin and Kibbe 1985).

Early ornithologists indicated that this species did not occur regularly anywhere north of Massachusetts (Samuels 1870, Minot 1895, Allen 1909, Forbush 1929). Palmer (1949) states in reference to Maine, that "in view of the fact that this wren now breeds in a number of localities that were familiar to ornithologists in former years and where it was not found by them, it seems safe to conclude that the establishment of this species as a regular breeder has occurred since about 1920." This statement probably is appropriate for New Hampshire as well. An early nest record is from Manchester in 1925 (USFWS, unpubl. data). Marsh Wrens apparently became quite common in suitable marsh habitats between the late 1940s and late 1960s (T. Richards, pers. comm.). Dozens of locations, from Nashua to Errol and Hinsdale to Hampton, formerly supported these wrens. For some unknown reason, however, sightings have decreased substantially over the past 20 years. BBS data for this species are insufficient for analysis of trends.

Atlas observers located Marsh Wrens in only 7 priority blocks, one Special Area, and 4 other locations, all in the southern half of the state. Since the Atlas period, observers have found these wrens in northern New Hampshire at Harpers Meadow, Errol, and Pontook Reservoir, Dummer (SRS).

The New York and Ontario atlases cite habitat loss due to draining and filling of wetlands as possible reasons for declines (Cadman et al. 1987, Andrle and Carroll 1988), but these do not apply at many formerly occupied New Hampshire sites. Because these wrens are quite conspicuous when vocalizing, it seems unlikely that atlasers missed them in marshes where they were present. It is possible, however, that some were present in marshes that were not searched. This species bears watching in the coming years.

George C. Robbins

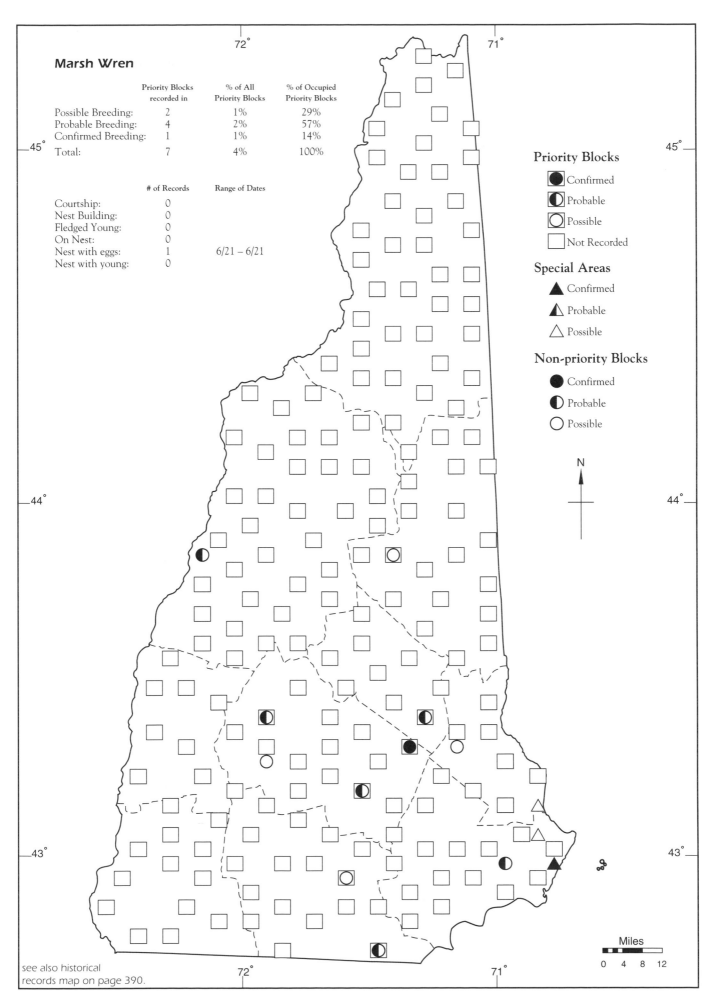

Marsh Wren

	Priority Blocks recorded in	% of All Priority Blocks	% of Occupied Priority Blocks
Possible Breeding:	2	1%	29%
Probable Breeding:	4	2%	57%
Confirmed Breeding:	1	1%	14%
Total:	7	4%	100%

	# of Records	Range of Dates
Courtship:	0	
Nest Building:	0	
Fledged Young:	0	
On Nest:	0	
Nest with eggs:	1	6/21 – 6/21
Nest with young:	0	

Priority Blocks
- ● Confirmed
- ◑ Probable
- ○ Possible
- ☐ Not Recorded

Special Areas
- ▲ Confirmed
- ◮ Probable
- △ Possible

Non-priority Blocks
- ● Confirmed
- ◑ Probable
- ○ Possible

N

see also historical records map on page 390.

Miles
0 4 8 12

Golden-crowned Kinglet

Regulus satrapa

The diminutive "gold-crest," with its quiet, high-pitched song, is easily overlooked in the dense spruce-fir habitat where it is locally common (Forbush 1929). This kinglet breeds in northern and southwestern New Hampshire, occurring in the mountains at elevations from 1,000 to 4,000 ft (300 to 1,220 m) and occasionally even higher (Allen 1903; T. Richards, unpubl. data). Both sexes are olive above and buffy below. The orange center of the male's crown often is concealed unless he is agitated or displaying (Bent 1949). While feeding, these kinglets frequent the ends of branches, hovering briefly while searching for spiders, beetles, flies, moths, and caterpillars (McAtee 1926 in Bent 1949). All kinglets flick their wings as they move about in the foliage (Forbush 1929, Farrand 1983).

Although most Golden-crowned Kinglets winter south of New England, variable numbers overwinter in New Hampshire, frequenting evergreen woods and birches (Dearborn 1903, Bent 1949). Migrants return in April and may occur anywhere there are trees and shrubs (Bent 1949). They reach their breeding grounds in New Hampshire in April and early May.

Golden-crowned Kinglets sing a high, lisping "zee zee zee" or "tsee-tsee" similar to the song of Brown Creepers, followed by a chickadeelike chatter (Bent 1949, Ridgely 1977). The call, given year round, is a sharp and rapidly repeated "see see see" which resembles similar notes of both chickadees and Brown Creepers (Hoffman 1904).

Golden-crowned Kinglets breed in a wide range of coniferous and mixed habitats, including bogs, swamps, high and low elevation spruce-fir forests, and conifer plantations (Andrle in Andrle and Carroll 1988). Although they also occur in pines, hemlocks, cedars, tamaracks, and firs, these kinglets are especially associated with spruces (Bent 1949). Sabo (1980) found Golden-crowned Kinglets most abundant in old spruce forests in subalpine areas of the White Mountains,

where they maintained territories of 1.5 a (0.6 ha). These kinglets occurred at a density of 60 pairs/0.4 sq mi (1 sq km) in a virgin spruce grove at Nancy Pond, Livermore (Sabo 1980).

Both Golden-crowned and Ruby-crowned kinglet nests typically are placed 6 to 60 ft (1.8 to 18.3 m) above ground near the end of a branch of a coniferous tree, most often a spruce; the nests of the 2 kinglets cannot be distinguished reliably (Harrison 1975, Harrison 1978). Durfee (in Bent 1949) found 8 nests an average of 14 ft (4.2 m) above the ground in "pasture spruces" in Lancaster, and another at a height of 46 ft (124 m) in a large spruce in a hardwood stand. The female builds the deep, pendant nest in 9 or more days, weaving the supporting horizontal branches into its constricted rim. The nest consists of mosses and lichens and is lined with fine rootlets, strips of inner bark, and feathers which arch over the eggs with quills pointing downward (Harrison 1975).

Egg laying occurs in late May or early June, and the clutch consists of 5 to 10, commonly 8 or 9 eggs (Bent 1949, Harrison 1975). The nest is so small that the eggs typically form 2 layers (Bent 1949). The incubation period is unknown, but begins before the clutch is complete, and these kinglets may raise 2 broods in a year (Harrison 1975). Maynard (1871) noted that Golden-crowned Kinglets lay around the first of June in the Umbagog area, and Minot (1877 in Bent 1949) found 6 young in a nest in the White Mountains on 16 July 1875. In Maine, families often are foraging together in spruce and hemlock woods by 20 June (Stanwood in Bent 1949). Observers have documented fledglings in New Hampshire from 22 June through mid-August; most records, however, are from 22 June to 22 July.

Families begin to move from nesting areas in mid-August, and these kinglets become more noticeable as they leave the deep woods for more open terrain. They may frequent orchards during fall migration, which peaks in October (Samuels 1870). The constant chatter of chickadees may signal the presence of migrating kinglets.

The Golden-crowned Kinglet's distribution in New Hampshire has changed little during historic times. It always has been a common summer resident from the White Mountains north, and locally distributed to the south (Samuels 1870, Maynard 1871, Allen 1903, Forbush 1929). Dearborn (1898) noted that this kinglet occasionally spent the summer in central New Hampshire, and found a nest containing young in Alton on 26 July 1889. It also has nested regularly at higher elevations in the vicinity of Andover (K. C. Elkins, pers. comm.). An uncommon nester in the Squam Lakes region (Ridgely 1977), it nests fairly commonly at higher elevations in the Monadnock region, where spruce-fir forests occur (Allison and Allison 1979).

Golden-crowned Kinglet populations apparently are subject to considerable fluctuations resulting from severe weather on their wintering grounds (Sabo 1980, Robbins et al. 1986). Sabo (1980) observed a 56% decrease in Golden-crowned Kinglet numbers on study areas in the White Mountains between the 1976 and 1977 breeding seasons and an additional but lesser reduction the following year. BBS data show a sharp peak in the Eastern population in 1979, followed by a distinct drop the following year (Robbins et al. 1986).

The Atlas project documented this species as well distributed in and north of the White Mountains and locally distributed in the Western Highlands. Essentially all records are from elevations above 1,000 ft (300 m), with a good representation from above 2,000 ft (610 m). This kinglet is noticeably more widespread in New Hampshire than the Ruby-crowned Kinglet, for which there are no "confirmations" in the southern counties.

James McDermott

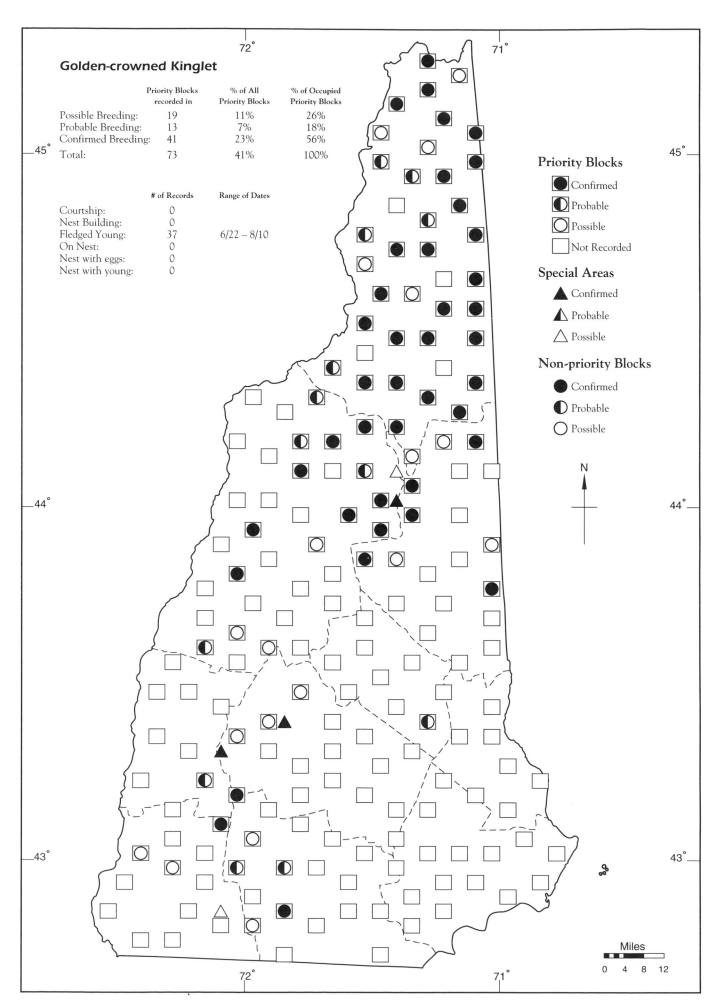

Golden-crowned Kinglet

	Priority Blocks recorded in	% of All Priority Blocks	% of Occupied Priority Blocks
Possible Breeding:	19	11%	26%
Probable Breeding:	13	7%	18%
Confirmed Breeding:	41	23%	56%
Total:	73	41%	100%

	# of Records	Range of Dates
Courtship:	0	
Nest Building:	0	
Fledged Young:	37	6/22 – 8/10
On Nest:	0	
Nest with eggs:	0	
Nest with young:	0	

Priority Blocks
- Confirmed
- Probable
- Possible
- Not Recorded

Special Areas
- Confirmed
- Probable
- Possible

Non-priority Blocks
- Confirmed
- Probable
- Possible

N

Miles
0 4 8 12

Ruby-crowned Kinglet
Regulus calendula

The delightfully musical Ruby-crowned Kinglet recently extended its nesting range southward into northern New Hampshire, where it is now a fairly common, local summer resident. Both sexes of this tiny bird are olive-gray above and grayish white below, with 2 prominent white wing bars and nearly complete white eye-rings. The male often sings its loud, rollicking song in spring migration and, when excited, raises its usually hidden, bright red crown patch.

The Ruby-crowned Kinglet breeds from northwestern Alaska to Labrador, south to central British Columbia and northern New England, and winters from Maryland to Guatemala (AOU 1957). In New Hampshire the Ruby-crowned Kinglet breeds fairly commonly from the White Mountains northward and apparently rarely in the southwest highlands. Its favorite habitats are dense northern conifer stands in bogs and flats, and on mountain slopes at elevations from 1,000 ft (300 m) to timberline at about 4,500 ft (1,370 m) (Richards, unpubl. data). The Golden-crowned Kinglet has a similar range in New Hampshire, but breeds locally in the southern part of the state and nests at lower elevations in the White Mountains.

Ruby-crowns are common migrants in New Hampshire and usually begin arriving in mid-April, reaching their northern breeding grounds between early and late May. Once on territory they sing persistently more or less throughout the day during much of the breeding season (Richards, unpubl. data). Rival males follow each other around, heads bent forward to display their ruby crowns, tails spread, and body feathers fluffed out, while uttering their rasping call notes (Burroughs *in* Bent 1949).

The well-concealed nest, attached to pendant twigs of a conifer 2 to 100 ft (0.6 to 30.5 m) from the ground, usually is placed in thick foliage at the end of a branch, most often in a spruce. Made of plant materials, especially green mosses, with a lining of small feathers, it is roughly globular and often pensile (Bent 1949). The deep cup conceals the 7 to 9 eggs; incubation takes about 12 days (Bent 1949, Harrison 1975).

The male sings loudly near the nest and becomes extremely agitated when an intruder approaches (Harrington *in* Bent 1949). Both parents feed the young, but the female removes the fecal sacs (Soper 1920 *in* Bent 1949). The age at fledging is not yet documented, but the young probably remain in the nest for about 12 days (Bent 1949). Juveniles closely resemble adult females.

Almost constantly flicking their wings, Ruby-crowns actively search the branches of trees and shrubs for insects, but also eat some seeds and berries (Bent 1949). Often associating with Golden-crowned Kinglets, chickadees, and warblers, they generally start south in late September and October. Some may remain in New Hampshire until at least late December (CBC data).

Before 1915 the Ruby-crowned Kinglet was not known to breed in New England except in Maine, where it was considered rare (Allen 1909, Forbush 1929). Comey (1904) documented an individual seen in the Squam Range, Holderness on 15 July 1903. The first known breeding records in New England south of Maine are from western Massachusetts in 1915, 1920, and 1932 (Bagg and Eliot 1937), but there were no summer records from Massachusetts for many years thereafter.

Although Brewster never found Ruby-crowned Kinglets in summer during his many visits to the Umbagog Lake region during 1871–1909, on 15 June 1932 Perry found a singing male on the Maine side of the lake (Griscom 1938), and W. Taber (unpubl. data) observed one in Errol on 30 May 1940. Breeding may have occurred near Lost River, Woodstock, in 1937 (N.H. Nature Camp 1938); near Mt. Chocorua, Albany, in 1938; in Errol in 1940 (W. Taber, unpubl. data); and in Ossipee in 1945 (Wade 1947). Richards established the first New Hampshire breeding record when, after finding a male singing in an old field spruce in Rumney on 18 June 1947, he observed parents feeding young there on 13 July (RNEB). Scattered records continued in 1948 and 1949, and on 25 May 1950 Richards found Ruby-crowns "fairly common in softwood swamps" in Pittsburg, with some still present during 15–16 July (RNEB). Hebert (1958a) recorded 44 there during 7–8 June, 1958. The first breeding season records from southern New Hampshire were of singing males at Mt. Kearsarge, Warner/Wilmot on 6–10 June 1974 and 18 June 1975 (K. C. Elkins, unpubl. data).

Singing males at about 3,800 ft (1,160 m) on Mt. Moosilauke, Benton, on 19 May 1957, and at the same elevation on Mt. Washington on 12 June 1960, apparently provide the first potential high-elevation breeding records (Richards, unpubl. data). The species continued to increase in the mountains, and on 6 July 1972, 10 singing males were observed above 3,000 ft (910 m) on the Carter Range, Beans Purchase/Shelburne, 2 of which were above 4,500 ft (1,370 m) (Richards, unpubl. data).

The Atlas map shows fairly wide distribution of the Ruby-crown from the White Mountains north, but few records further south. The southernmost "confirmed" record is from Piermont Mtn., Piermont. The Massachusetts Atlas project (unpubl. data) produced one "confirmed" breeding record in the northwest corner of the state, and 3 of Vermont's 7 "confirmations" were from high elevations in the southern part of the state (Laughlin and Kibbe 1985). The relatively recent southward expansion is remarkable in view of the many more cases of "southern birds" moving north. This species seems likely to maintain its status as a summer resident in northern New Hampshire and the White Mountains.

Tudor Richards

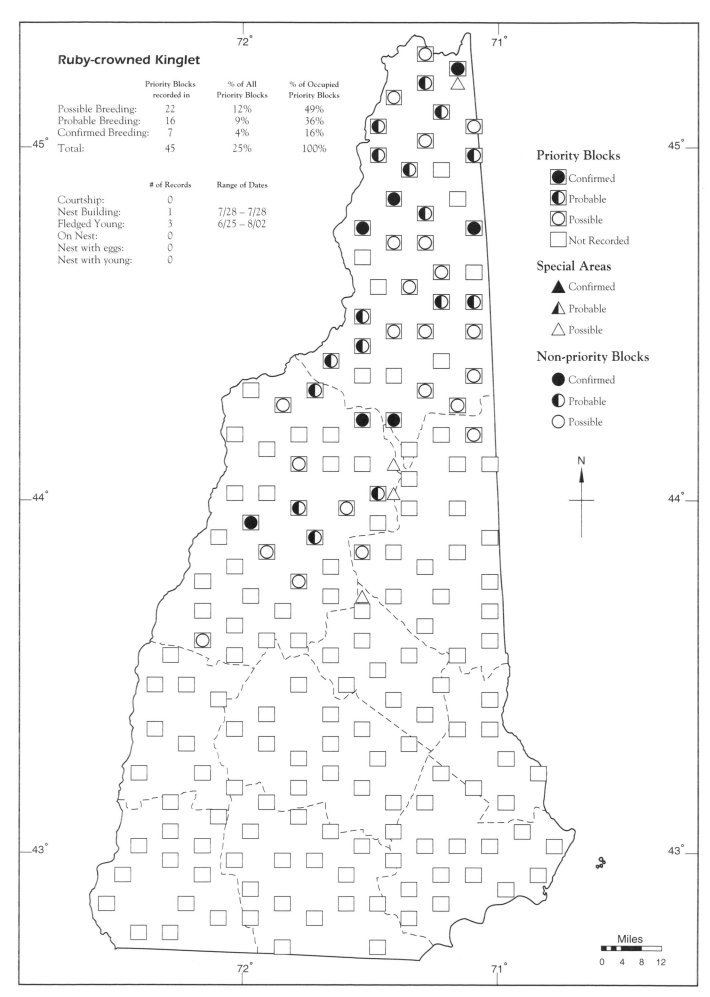

Ruby-crowned Kinglet

	Priority Blocks recorded in	% of All Priority Blocks	% of Occupied Priority Blocks
Possible Breeding:	22	12%	49%
Probable Breeding:	16	9%	36%
Confirmed Breeding:	7	4%	16%
Total:	45	25%	100%

	# of Records	Range of Dates
Courtship:	0	
Nest Building:	1	7/28 – 7/28
Fledged Young:	3	6/25 – 8/02
On Nest:	0	
Nest with eggs:	0	
Nest with young:	0	

Priority Blocks
- ● Confirmed
- ◐ Probable
- ○ Possible
- ▢ Not Recorded

Special Areas
- ▲ Confirmed
- ◣ Probable
- △ Possible

Non-priority Blocks
- ● Confirmed
- ◐ Probable
- ○ Possible

N

Miles
0 4 8 12

Blue-gray Gnatcatcher
Polioptila caerulea

The nasal, complaining, insectlike "zreee" call of the Blue-gray Gnatcatcher is the most common clue to locating these tiny birds, which recently have extended their range northward into New Hampshire. The faint, melodious song is seldom heard. With their long white-bordered, black tails in almost constant motion, gnatcatchers suggest "miniature mockingbirds" (Peterson 1980) and may flick their tails like a wren, bob them like a Palm Warbler, or even wag them like a dog.

Spring migration may bring early gnatcatchers to New Hampshire from Central America and the Gulf States during the last week of April, but most arrive during May (RNEB, *passim*; SRS). Males defend their territories with posturing and a soft song of 4 to 8 short phrases (Root 1969).

In courtship, the male sings an elaborate, whispered song, perches near the female in an upright posture, and leads her to inspect potential nest sites (Root 1969). On 5 June 1983, a male in Somersworth lured his mate from a utility wire to follow him in short, intricate courtship flights by flitting, then hovering in front of her (Turner, pers. obs.).

In the southern U.S., Blue-gray Gnatcatchers nest in a variety of habitats, but here in the north they tend to nest near water (Weston 1949). Atlas observers found nests near swamps, a pond, a brook, and the Merrimack River. Gnatcatchers nest in many tree species, usually on a horizontal limb 1 to 2 in (2.5 to 5 cm) in diameter or in a fork (Weston 1949). Nest heights range from 3 to 80 ft (0.9 to 24.4 m) (Harrison 1978). Atlas observers discovered 6 nests at estimated heights of 30 to 60 ft (9.1 to 18.3 m); 2 were in white birch, one in red pine, and 3 in red maple (Turner, pers. obs;, P. Meyette, pers. comm.).

Gnatcatchers gather material from up to 250 ft (76 m) from the nest site (Root 1969). Some pairs tear apart an almost completed nest, using its components to rebuild at another site (Maslowski 1983). Pairs also will dismantle their original nest after successfully fledging a first brood and incorporate the material into a new nest for a second brood (Weston 1949, Root 1969). During the Atlas project, a pair removed the material from a nest site in Exeter to an unknown location.

Both sexes build the deep, neat cup of plant down and fibers, grasses, and hair, bound with spider or caterpillar webs and covered with lichens (Harrison 1975, Harrison 1978). On 10 May 1981, 2 pairs were carrying willow catkin fuzz at Bog Pond, Campton (S. G. and W. Fogelman, pers. comm.). The nest resembles that of the Ruby-throated Hummingbird, but is about 1 in (2.5 cm) larger; hummingbird eggs are dull white, while gnatcatcher eggs are pale bluish and wreathed with speckles at the larger end.

The female lays 3 to 6, usually 4 or 5 eggs in the tight quarters of the 2 to 2.5 in (5 to 6.3 cm) nest (Harrison 1975). Although the male stops singing when incubation begins, the pair continues to use the call note (Root 1969). Both sexes incubate for 13 to 15 days. The noisy young remain in the nest for 12 or 13 days. The adults carry fecal sacs at least 30 ft (9.1 m) from the nest before dropping them (Root 1969). Brown-headed Cowbirds commonly parasitize gnatcatchers (Terres 1980).

Gnatcatchers are active birds, flitting about the leaves in an intense search for insects. They usually gather food within about 200 ft (70 m) of the nest (Root 1969) and fly directly to the nest with food. Both adults feed the fledglings for up to 19 days after they leave the nest (Harrison 1978).

When a predator approaches, gnatcatchers fly silently from the nest before harassing the intruder. Nestlings crouch in the nest in the face of danger; fledglings scatter (Root 1969). On 24 July 1982 in Portsmouth, an adult made several passes at a hawk when it landed in a tree, while fledglings flew from limb to limb, apparently trying to hide (M. Turner, pers. comm.).

Atlas records of incubation on 10 May, nest building on 24 June, a nest with young on 18 July, and fledged young on 24 July suggest that this species may raise 2 broods in New Hampshire. Fall migration occurs by mid-August.

Forbush (1929) described the Blue-gray Gnatcatcher as a "casual visitor and probable summer resident" in New England, "doubtfully recorded" in Vermont and New Hampshire. Most early authors made no mention of the Blue-gray Gnatcatcher in New Hampshire, but Allen (1903) includes a possible sighting in Manchester on 10 May 1900. Early records included 3 May sightings from the late 1940s in Dunbarton, Exeter, and Sandwich, and 6 more from the 1950s in Chesham (Harrisville), Monroe, and New Hampton (RNEB, NHAQ, *passim*). The 1960s brought annual sightings and the first documented nesting, near Squam Lake in 1965 (Ridgely 1977). In 1970 J. R. Kellogg (*in* Hebert 1970) reported 2 pairs with young in Holderness. Continued range expansion produced an increase in both number and distribution of sightings (NHAQ, *passim*). In 1976, observers found a nest with young in Weare, a nest with a sitting bird in Hancock, and a singing male on 2 visits to Campton Bog, Campton (Hebert 1976).

The Blue-gray Gnatcatcher has nested as far north as Ossipee, but has not been "confirmed" breeding north of the White Mountains. However, one was calling on a BBS route in Milan in 1980, and a pair was in Monroe near the Connecticut River on 5 and 6 May 1981 (E. Emery, pers. comm.). Atlas field work "confirmed" the first nest in the Seacoast area, where gnatcatchers have occurred regularly in spring and fall since the late 1960s.

BBS data from 1966 to 1979 reflect a northward expansion of the range (Robbins et al. 1986), but BBS observers still encounter gnatcatchers infrequently in New Hampshire. The Atlas map illustrates a sparse but widely scattered distribution south of the White Mountains. Since apparently suitable habitat is widely available, continued range expansion and population increase in New Hampshire seem likely in the coming years.

Sandra B. Turner

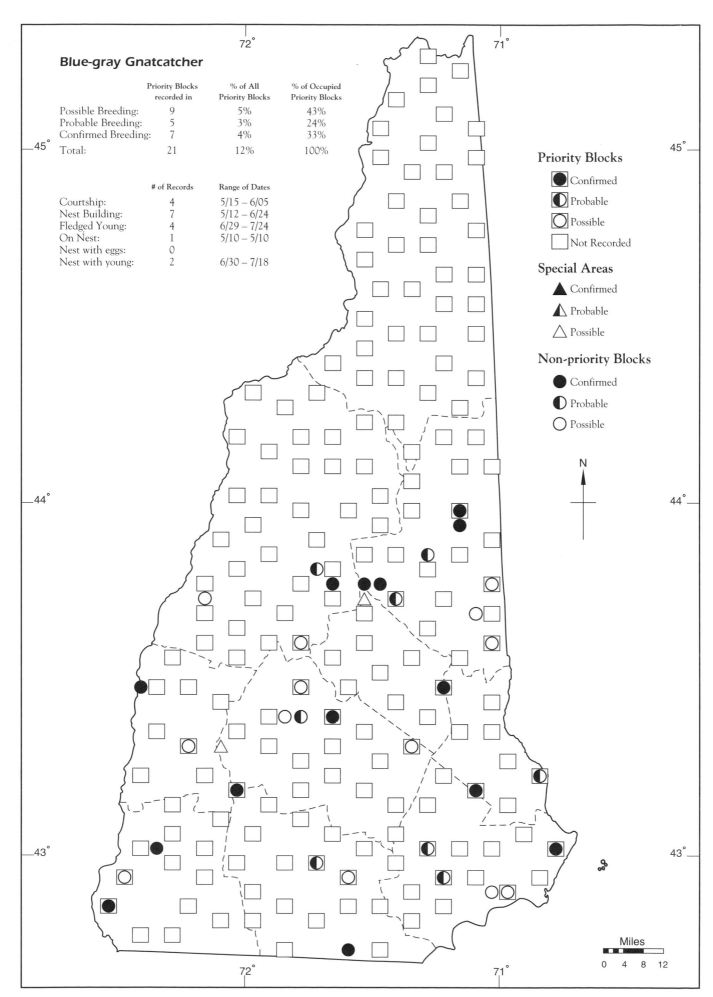

Blue-gray Gnatcatcher

	Priority Blocks recorded in	% of All Priority Blocks	% of Occupied Priority Blocks
Possible Breeding:	9	5%	43%
Probable Breeding:	5	3%	24%
Confirmed Breeding:	7	4%	33%
Total:	21	12%	100%

	# of Records	Range of Dates
Courtship:	4	5/15 – 6/05
Nest Building:	7	5/12 – 6/24
Fledged Young:	4	6/29 – 7/24
On Nest:	1	5/10 – 5/10
Nest with eggs:	0	
Nest with young:	2	6/30 – 7/18

Priority Blocks

● Confirmed
◐ Probable
○ Possible
□ Not Recorded

Special Areas

▲ Confirmed
◢ Probable
△ Possible

Non-priority Blocks

● Confirmed
◐ Probable
○ Possible

N

Eastern Bluebird
Sialia sialis

The male of this once familiar but now uncommon songbird is easily recognized by its bright blue back, dull red breast, and white belly. The female is more gray than blue, but has blue wings and tail. A young bird has a speckled breast and gray upperparts but shows traces of blue. When perched, the bluebird's round-shouldered or hunched posture is diagnostic. This species breeds in eastern North America from southern Canada south into Central America, and winters regularly from New York and Connecticut south. A few sometimes winter in New Hampshire, but most arrive here in March and April (rarely in late February).

Bluebirds are cavity nesters and use nest boxes as well as natural tree cavities and woodpecker holes. They breed in open or semiopen country with low or sparse vegetation and scattered trees. Rural dooryards often provide favorable habitat, as do pastures, field borders, unsprayed orchards, golf courses, and woodland clearings. Bluebirds also nest in beaver flowages (Elkins, pers. obs.) and forest clearcuts (Conner and Adkisson 1974). During the breeding season bluebirds forage for insects and other small invertebrates by flying to the ground from low branches, bushes, fence posts, or utility wires.

Bluebirds sing on arrival, or soon after. Both sexes give the low-pitched soft and melodious song (Zeleny 1978), which plays a large part in courtship, as does wing quivering (Hamilton 1943). The male brings food to the female and searches for a suitable nesting cavity, which the female must accept to complete pair formation (Zeleny 1978).

Bluebirds compete for nesting cavities with Tree Swallows, House Sparrows, and starlings. Bluebirds usually can defend a cavity against swallows, or a pair (but not a flock) of House Sparrows, but starlings are too big and strong for them. Bluebirds can, however, use cavities with entrances only 1.5 in (3.8 cm) in diameter, which are too small for starlings. The female builds the nest, which is loosely made of grasses and weed stalks (Harrison 1975), and incubates the 4 or 5 egg clutch for 13 or 14 days, rarely more or less (Zeleny 1978). There are usually 2 broods, sometimes 3. Song ceases with the beginning of incubation (Saunders 1935), but resumes when a new nesting begins.

Both parents feed the nestlings, which fledge in 15 to 18 days (Harrison 1978). They both feed the fledglings for 7 to 10 days, then the male continues for 10 to 14 days longer (Zeleny 1978), while the female may nest again. Young from the first brood sometimes help tend later young, especially if one parent has died (Zeleny 1978).

In the fall bluebirds wander around open country in small flocks of one or more families, commonly perching on utility wires. They often enter nest boxes at this time, and frequently utter a musical but melancholy sounding call: "far-a-way, far-a-way" (Wright 1911) or "farewell, farewell" (White 1937). Migration extends from September through October, sometimes into early November.

A century ago bluebirds were common summer residents in New Hampshire except in mountainous and heavily forested regions (Allen 1903), and in some areas of dense human population where introduced House Sparrows had driven them out (Dearborn 1903). They remained common in rural areas until the 1950s (Wright 1911, Forbush 1929, White 1937, Hill 1965, Thayer 1909 *in* Allison and Allison 1979), although periodically suffering losses owing to severe weather. They recovered quickly from substantial losses during spring migration in 1895 and the winter of 1940 (Allen 1903, Brewster 1906, Palmer 1949).

Bluebirds recovered slowly from heavy losses in the south in 1958 (Hill 1965) for a variety of reasons. Urban growth and reforestation have reduced favorable nesting habitat, and replacement of wooden fence posts with metal posts, removal of dead trees and branches, and pruning of shade and orchard trees have eliminated many nest sites. Pesticide use and increased raccoon populations also have contributed. In some areas competition with House Sparrows and starlings has increased. A serious decline in the quantity of wild fruit, the bluebirds' chief winter food, also has occurred over much of their winter range (Zeleny 1978).

Recent increases in the availability of nest boxes, including "bluebird trails" of many well-spaced nest boxes in suitable habitat have been favorable to bluebirds. One such trail in the Rumney area fledged 103 young in 1988 (G. Kent, pers. comm.). Recently there has been evidence of increased bluebird numbers in New Hampshire (Ridgely 1988, C.R. Foss, pers. comm.).

As the Atlas map illustrates, bluebirds still breed over the length and breadth of New Hampshire. They are well distributed over the southern half of the state, but are somewhat local in the Western Highlands and some densely populated areas of the southeastern counties. They are very local in the North Country and absent from the heart of the White Mountains. The Eastern Bluebird may never again be as common in New Hampshire as it was a century ago, but if people provide suitable nest boxes with some protection from predators and competitors, this colorful bird again may become fairly common in rural areas.

Kimball C. Elkins

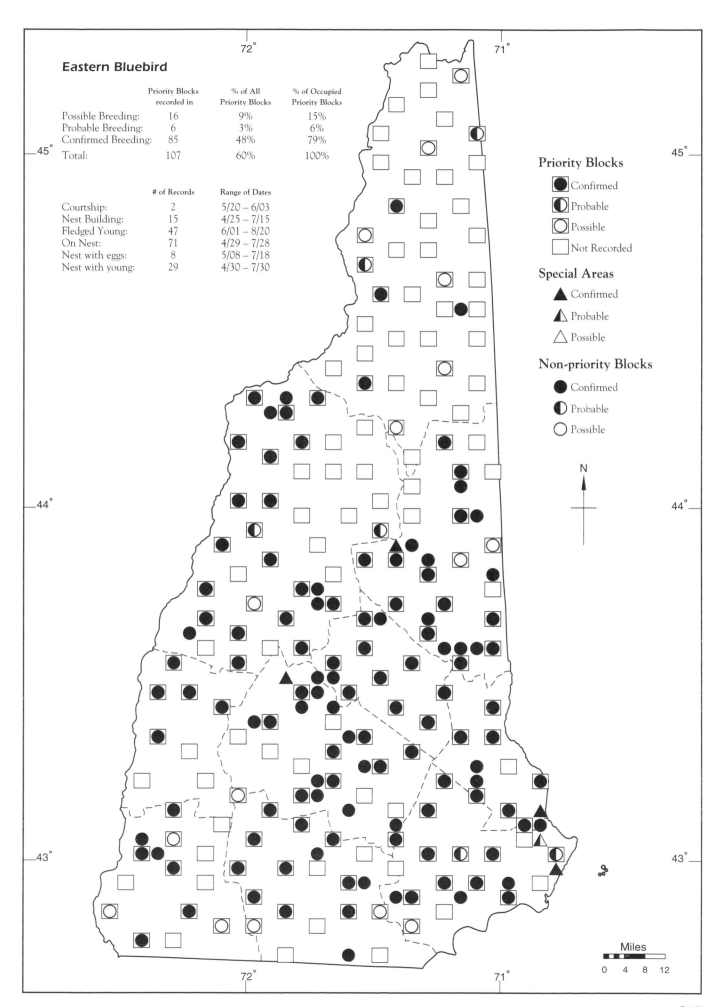

Eastern Bluebird

	Priority Blocks recorded in	% of All Priority Blocks	% of Occupied Priority Blocks
Possible Breeding:	16	9%	15%
Probable Breeding:	6	3%	6%
Confirmed Breeding:	85	48%	79%
Total:	107	60%	100%

	# of Records	Range of Dates
Courtship:	2	5/20 – 6/03
Nest Building:	15	4/25 – 7/15
Fledged Young:	47	6/01 – 8/20
On Nest:	71	4/29 – 7/28
Nest with eggs:	8	5/08 – 7/18
Nest with young:	29	4/30 – 7/30

Priority Blocks

● Confirmed
◑ Probable
○ Possible
□ Not Recorded

Special Areas

▲ Confirmed
◣ Probable
△ Possible

Non-priority Blocks

● Confirmed
◐ Probable
○ Possible

N

Miles
0   4   8   12

Veery
Catharus fuscescens

Noted more for its ethereal voice than its appearance, the Veery has less distinct breast spots and eyerings than do the Wood, Swainson's, or Hermit thrushes. The upper parts are rusty and the sides of the throat and breast are buffy. It commonly breeds in moist woods at low elevations throughout the state.

The Veery dwells in deciduous or coniferous woods at elevations below about 2,000 ft (670 m) (Ridgely 1977; T. Richards, unpubl. data). It is difficult to see in summer because it is shy and chooses woods with a fairly thick understory of ferns or shrubs (Harding 1925, Dilger 1956a). Paszkowski (1984) found that the Hermit Thrush occupies similar habitat in Wisconsin, but prefers an understory of young trees and favors edges of forest openings more than the Veery. The Wood Thrush also selects similar habitat, but prefers mature woodlands and often occurs relatively close to houses and along outer edges of woodlands. Morse (1971) found that in 2 areas in Maine, Wood Thrushes generally occupy drier habitats than Veeries, and Hermit Thrushes drier still. In northern New Hampshire Swainson's Thrushes sometimes occur in the same areas as Veeries.

Veeries arrive in New Hampshire during the first and second weeks in May. Although they occasionally sing during migration, after arriving on the breeding grounds they are quiet until late May. From then until late July they frequently sing and call. After June, however, they sing primarily in the early morning and late evening hours and are among the last birds to stop singing in the evening.

The song consists of 3 to 5 descending spirals of vibrant, flutelike notes, "per-VEER, Veer, veer, veer," which can sound ethereal from a distance. Each downslurred "veer" is lower pitched and slightly fainter than the preceding. Whereas Wood Thrushes sing from perches in or near the tops of trees, Veeries sing from perches at heights of 6 to 25 ft (1.8 to 7.6 m) from the ground (Bertin 1977). A distinctive call is quite loud and consists of a rather variable downslurred, whistled "few," which can be quite harsh. Males in adjacent territories often "few" at each other rather than uttering their songs. They also call after arriving on the breeding grounds before they begin to sing.

The Veery generally builds its nest on or near the ground in thick undergrowth during late May or June. The bulky structure consists of plant materials. Where the ground is wet, a thick layer of leaves on the bottom keeps the eggs dry and makes the entire nest quite large, up to 10 in (25 cm) in diameter (Bent 1949, Harrison 1975). By contrast the nest of the somewhat larger Wood Thrush is only about half this size (Harrison 1975). The Hermit Thrush also nests on the ground but since its habitat is somewhat different, there seems to be little competition for nest sites (Harrison 1975).

The female incubates the 3 to 5, commonly 4 eggs for 11 or 12 days (Harrison 1975). Most Atlas records of nests with eggs were from June, with one each from May and July. White (1937) notes a nest found in Concord with 4 unincubated eggs on 30 May 1926, and another with eggs hatching on 28 June 1936. Both parents feed the young, which fledge after 2 weeks (Dilger 1956a). Veeries migrate south in August and September to wintering areas from Central America to Brazil.

Like other woodland thrushes, Veeries forage mostly on or near the ground. The average foraging height at the Hubbard Brook Experimental Forest, Thornton, is 2 ft (0.6 m), somewhat higher than that of the Wood Thrush but lower than that of the Hermit Thrush (Dilger 1956a, Holmes et al. 1979). While foraging on the ground, Veeries probe with their bills, turning over dead leaves and snapping up bits of food. They often fly from the ground to low perches and then back to the ground again to snap up additional morsels (Bent 1949). The food consists of some vegetable matter and small invertebrates such as beetles, ants, and spiders.

The Veery has been common in southern New Hampshire since at least the middle of the last century (Samuels 1867, Coues 1868, Dearborn 1898, White 1924, Forbush 1929). Samuels (1867) indicates that the Veery was absent from northernmost New Hampshire in the mid-1800s. Available literature (Samuels 1867, Dearborn 1898, Allen 1903, Wright 1911, Forbush 1929, White 1937) suggests that the distribution, relative abundance, and habitat use patterns of Veeries and Wood, Hermit, and Swainson's thrushes in New Hampshire have been rather dynamic over the course of the past 150 years. The role of interspecific competition in these changes is unclear.

As the Atlas map shows, the Veery presently is well distributed throughout the state. Of the 6 priority blocks lacking Veery records, most lack suitable habitat. The northern blocks are all or nearly all above 2,000 ft (610 m). The species was probably missed in the Croydon block, where Atlas effort was minimal and limited to a single year. The Coastal block, in Hampton, includes very little woodland.

Robert C. Vernon

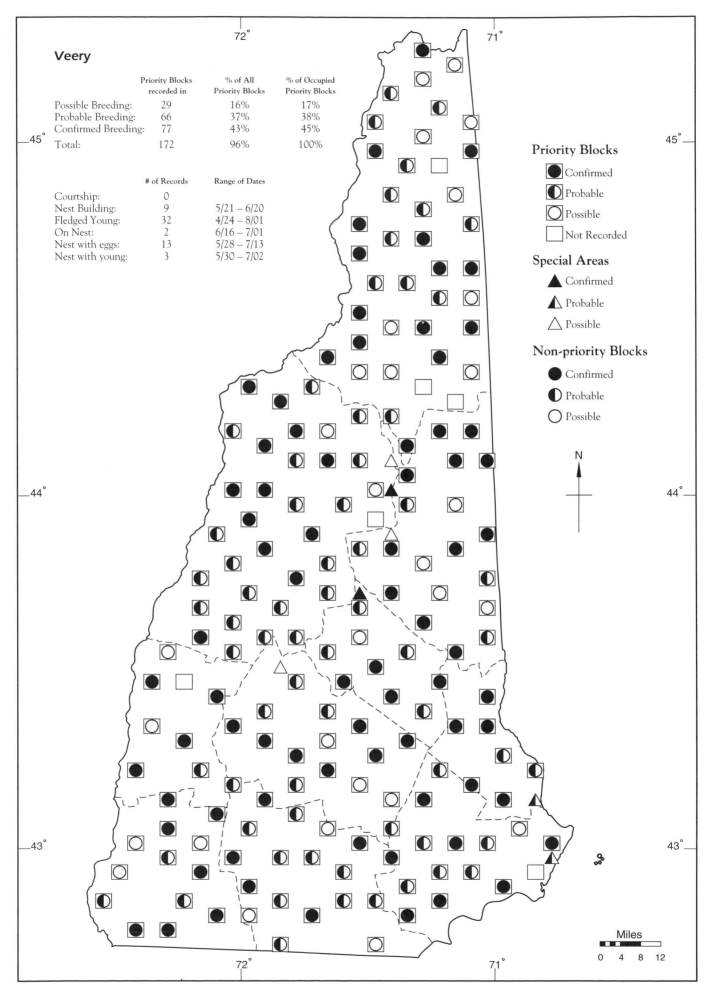

Veery

	Priority Blocks recorded in	% of All Priority Blocks	% of Occupied Priority Blocks
Possible Breeding:	29	16%	17%
Probable Breeding:	66	37%	38%
Confirmed Breeding:	77	43%	45%
Total:	172	96%	100%

	# of Records	Range of Dates
Courtship:	0	
Nest Building:	9	5/21 – 6/20
Fledged Young:	32	4/24 – 8/01
On Nest:	2	6/16 – 7/01
Nest with eggs:	13	5/28 – 7/13
Nest with young:	3	5/30 – 7/02

Priority Blocks

- ● Confirmed
- ◐ Probable
- ○ Possible
- □ Not Recorded

Special Areas

- ▲ Confirmed
- ◢ Probable
- △ Possible

Non-priority Blocks

- ● Confirmed
- ◐ Probable
- ○ Possible

N

Miles
0 4 8 12

Gray-cheeked Thrush

Catharus minimus

In New Hampshire, the Gray-cheeked Thrush is a little known denizen of the White Mountain region, where it is a common to abundant breeding species in the zone of stunted balsam fir, red and black spruce, and paper birch just below timberline. In migration it is wary, silent, and seemingly rare. The breeding range extends from northeastern Siberia to northern Quebec on the north and from northeastern British Columbia to northern New England on the south. The wintering range includes Hispaniola's mountains and parts of Venezuela (AOU 1957). Birds nesting in the Northeast have been considered a separate and slightly smaller subspecies, once called "Bicknell's Thrush," which E. P. Bicknell "discovered" in the Catskills in 1881 (Wallace *in* Bent 1949). Recent studies suggest that the Bicknell's thrush may be a distinct species (Ouellet 1991, Seutin 1991).

Both subspecies occur in 2 color forms, one with an olive-brown head, back, and tail and the other with slightly grayer coloration. The grayish cheeks, less prominent eye-ring, thin, Veery-like song, and "beer" call note distinguish this species from the Swainson's Thrush. Both sexes have a bright yellow basal portion of the mandible during the breeding season (W. C. Dilger, pers. comm.).

Dilger (1956a) provides a detailed description of the breeding habitat. Richards (unpubl. data) found the Gray-cheek to be most common at elevations of 3,500 to 4,500 ft (1,070 to 1,370 m) in the White Mountains during the 1940s–80s, and obtained very few records below 2,500 ft (760 m) or above 5,000 ft (1,520 m). The lowest breeding season elevation for Gray-cheeked Thrush in New Hampshire is from about 1,900 ft (580 m) in Dixville Notch, Dixville(Richards, unpubl. data).

Gray-cheeked Thrushes arrive in New Hampshire in late May. They may go directly to the mountains, as a record of 2 or 3 at 4,200 to 4,500 ft (1,280 to 1,370 m) on Mt. Lafayette, Franconia on 24 May 1953 suggests (Richards, unpubl. data). W. Faxon found them returning to Mt. Moosilauke, Benton during 25–30 May (Allen 1903).

Wallace (1939) made a detailed nesting study of the Northeastern subspecies on Mt. Mansfield, Vermont during the summers of 1933, 1935, and 1936 and compiled migration records from specimens taken in various parts of New England. Most of the following information comes from his account *in* Bent (1949).

Soon after arrival on their breeding grounds in late May or early June, males sing while making evening courtship flights over their territories, sometimes in pursuit of their mates. Females also sing, especially when on the nest. Dilger (1956b) described vocalizations and territorial behaviors.

Nest building on Mt. Mansfield began in early June. Nests were composed of twigs and much moss, lined with partially decomposed organic debris. The majority of more than 30 nests were in evergreens 3 to 12 ft (0.9 to 3.7 m) from the ground. The females laid 3 or 4 eggs, beginning 9 June, and incubated alone for 13 to 14 days.

Both parents feed insects to the newly hatched young. Adults also feed almost entirely on insects, though in late summer they eat some berries. The young usually leave the nest at 11 to 13 days, after acquiring their buffy-brown, much bespeckled, short-tailed juvenal plumage. Gray-cheeked Thrushes on Mt. Mansfield were quiet in late summer but became more active in September, calling loudly and singing briefly. Migration records for Massachusetts date from 18 September to early October (Griscom and Snyder 1955), presumably the time Gray-cheeks leave New Hampshire.

Torrey (1885) heard Gray-cheeked Thrushes singing along the Crawford Path in the Presidential Range in June 1882, which constituted New Hampshire's first breeding season record. Brewster (1883) collected specimens on Mt. Washington later that summer. By 1900 the species was known to breed more or less throughout the White Mountains proper, on Mt. Mansfield in Vermont, and on Mt. Greylock in western Massachusetts (Torrey 1892, Allen 1903).

Apparently the first summer records for New Hampshire's North Country were from Dixville Notch, where several were singing on 11 July 1951, and from above Third Connecticut Lake, Pittsburg on 28 June 1952 (Richards, unpubl. data). Meanwhile, in southern New Hampshire, K. C. Elkins (pers. comm.) heard one near the 2,900 ft (880 m) summit of Mt. Kearsarge, Warner/Wilmot on 15 July 1950, where he had failed to find any during 1936–49. He found a nest with eggs there on 22 June 1957. The species was regularly present in summer during 1950–77, but has not been found there since. Richards (unpubl. data) found this thrush on Mt. Monadnock, Jaffrey on 2 July 1951; on Mt. Sunapee, Newbury, on 16 June 1953; and on Mt. Cardigan, Orange/Alexandria, on 29 June 1970. In recent years the Gray-cheeked Thrush appears to have declined in numbers and disappeared from Kearsarge, Monadnock, Sunapee, and Dixville Notch. The Atlas map shows the breeding range of the Gray-cheeked Thrush as almost entirely restricted to the White Mountains proper, with outlying "possibles" very thinly distributed north almost to Canada and southwest to Mt. Cardigan. The range is almost certainly more continuous in the many 3,000 to 3,700 ft (910 to 1,130 m) northern peaks, many of which lack trails and are relatively inaccessible.

Tudor Richards

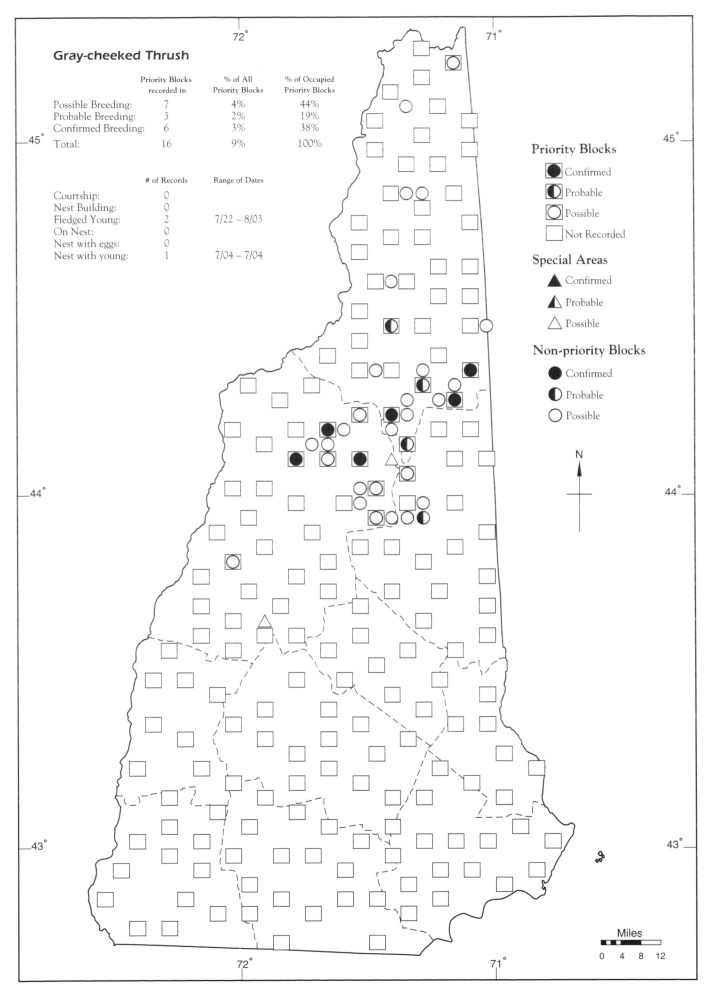

Gray-cheeked Thrush

	Priority Blocks recorded in	% of All Priority Blocks	% of Occupied Priority Blocks
Possible Breeding:	7	4%	44%
Probable Breeding:	3	2%	19%
Confirmed Breeding:	6	3%	38%
Total:	16	9%	100%

	# of Records	Range of Dates
Courtship:	0	
Nest Building:	0	
Fledged Young:	2	7/22 – 8/03
On Nest:	0	
Nest with eggs:	0	
Nest with young:	1	7/04 – 7/04

Priority Blocks

Confirmed
Probable
Possible
Not Recorded

Special Areas

Confirmed
Probable
Possible

Non-priority Blocks

Confirmed
Probable
Possible

N

Miles
0 4 8 12

219

Swainson's Thrush

Catharus ustulatus

The Swainson's Thrush may be distinguished from the Gray-cheeked Thrush by the buffy eye-ring and the buffy wash on its cheeks and spotted white breast, and from the other woodland thrushes by the absence of reddish or tawny tones on its olive-brown upperparts. The older name, Olive-backed Thrush, was appropriate for our Eastern birds. This thrush is very common in and north of the White Mountains, and breeds locally further south, chiefly at higher elevations. The first spring migrants seldom arrive before the second week in May. Most pass through New Hampshire in late May, and often many are still migrating in early June. Fall migration occurs mainly in September, but extends well into October.

Usual breeding habitat is spruce-fir forests, but this thrush also nests in mixed woods and mostly deciduous forests. The conspicuous nest usually is constructed on horizontal branches close to a tree trunk and only a few feet above the ground (Bent 1949), where it is susceptible to predators (Stanwood 1913). The nest site often is in a dense growth of small trees (Bent 1949). Nest materials are variable, and may consist largely of grasses, twigs, or mosses (Bent 1949). Mud may be a conspicuous element (Stanwood 1913). The only New Hampshire Atlas nest-building record is for 3 June, but there is a Vermont record for 21 May (Kibbe *in* Laughlin and Kibbe 1985). Egg dates in Maine range from 29 May to 24 July (Bent 1949). The female incubates for 10 to 13 days, and both parents feed the young, which stay in the nest for 10 to 12 days (Stanwood 1913). Little is known of their habits between fledging and fall migration.

Swainson's Thrushes seldom sing on migration, but on their breeding grounds they are loud and persistent singers, hence easy to locate. The song resembles that of the Hermit Thrush in tone, and the Veery's in form, but rises rather than falls in pitch. The most common call note is a soft whistled "whit." Migrants passing overhead at night utter a sharp "queep."

In New Hampshire's mountain forests the Swainson's Thrush rarely breeds below 1,000 ft (300 m) elevation or above 4,500 ft (1,370 m), and is most abundant between 1,500 ft (460 m) and 3,500 ft (1,070 m) (T. Richards, pers. comm.). At lower elevations its range overlaps with those of the Wood Thrush and Veery and more widely with that of the Hermit Thrush. Above about 2,500 ft (760 m), it overlaps with that of the Gray-cheeked Thrush.

The ability of the Swainson's Thrush to coexist with these closely related species apparently is due in part to different habitat preferences and in part to variations in behavior. The Wood Thrush and the Veery are mainly birds of deciduous woods; Swainson's prefers conifers. The Swainson's Thrush is largely an arboreal forager and is adept at flycatching, whereas the other species (except the Veery) are mainly ground feeders (Dilger 1956a, Noon 1981). There is some evidence that the Hermit Thrush is dominant over the Swainson's (Morse 1972).

The Swainson's Thrush once may have been rather scarce even in much of northern New Hampshire, for Samuels (1867) wrote that he had been unable to find it south of the latitude of Umbagog Lake, and that even there it was uncommon. Allen did not include it in his list of birds observed in Franconia and Bethlehem in August 1874, but by 1886 it was locally common in Franconia (Faxon and Allen 1888). At the beginning of the present century Allen (1903) considered the Swainson's Thrush common in the White Mountains and northward, but rare and local further south, as at Bridgewater, the "Ossipee Hills," and Nubanusit Lake, Hancock/Nelson. Still later it was common on Mt. Monadnock, Jaffrey; Mt. Sunapee, Newbury; and Mt. Kearsarge, Warner/Wilmot (Thayer 1909 *in* Allison and Allison 1979; T. Richards, pers. comm.; Elkins, pers. obs.), and locally only moderately uncommon in the Western Highlands (Elkins, pers. obs.).

BBS data from New Hampshire provide evidence for a rather substantial recent decline of the Swainson's Thrush. During 1966–75, New Hampshire BBS observers recorded an average of 34 per year, but only 22.5 during 1976–84. An even greater apparent decline has occurred in northern Merrimack County, notably on Mt. Kearsarge, beginning in the 1960s or earlier, and continuing to the 1980s. In a morning spent on Kearsarge prior to 1962, one often heard 10 or more Swainson's Thrushes; after 1962 never more than 4; and since 1980 often none at all (Elkins, pers. obs.; R.C. Vernon, pers. comm.). Records from Mt. Monadnock and Mt. Sunapee in the 1950s and 1960s also suggest the beginnings of a decline (T. Richards, pers. comm.).

The present distribution of the Swainson's Thrush as shown on the Atlas map resembles that described by Allen (1903), but provides no evidence of breeding in Bridgewater or on the Ossipee Mountains. Mt. Monadnock provided the only "confirmed" record south of the White Mountain foothills. Nearly all records are from blocks including elevations above 1,000 ft (300 m). The Swainson's Thrush still may be common in the White Mountains, where both Richards (pers. comm.) and Ridgely (1988) consider it the most commonly heard bird next to the Blackpoll Warbler from 2,000 to 3,000 ft (610 to 1,070 m) elevation. The population may have shifted northwards and upwards in elevation, perhaps in response to climate changes or to competition with the Hermit Thrush.

Kimball C. Elkins

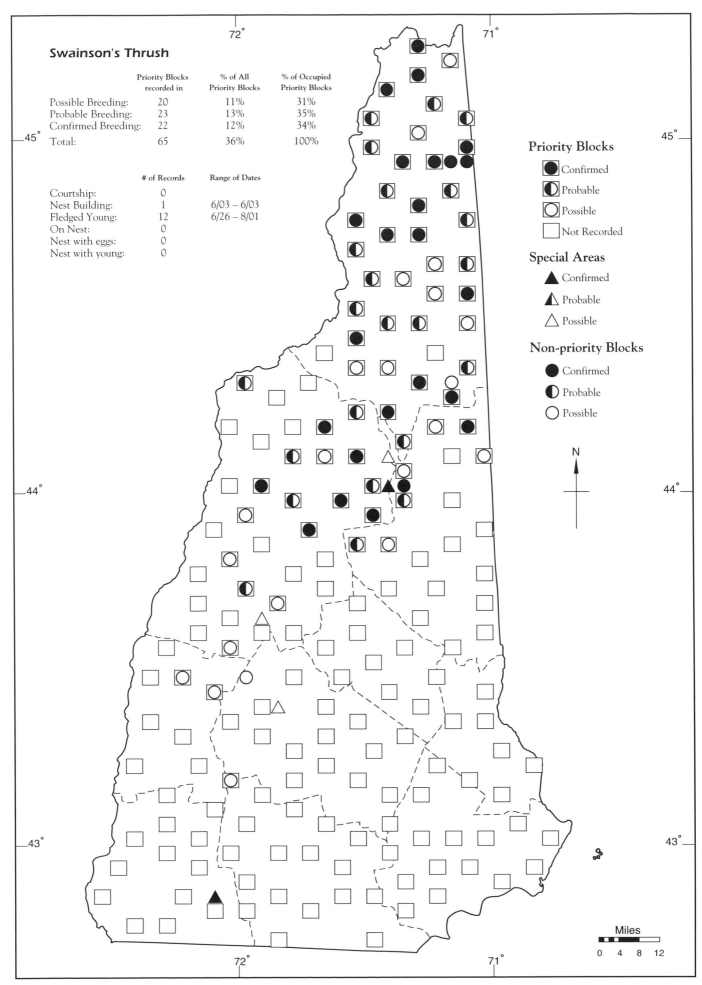

Swainson's Thrush

	Priority Blocks recorded in	% of All Priority Blocks	% of Occupied Priority Blocks
Possible Breeding:	20	11%	31%
Probable Breeding:	23	13%	35%
Confirmed Breeding:	22	12%	34%
Total:	65	36%	100%

	# of Records	Range of Dates
Courtship:	0	
Nest Building:	1	6/03 – 6/03
Fledged Young:	12	6/26 – 8/01
On Nest:	0	
Nest with eggs:	0	
Nest with young:	0	

Priority Blocks
- Confirmed
- Probable
- Possible
- Not Recorded

Special Areas
- Confirmed
- Probable
- Possible

Non-priority Blocks
- Confirmed
- Probable
- Possible

N

Miles
0 4 8 12

221

Hermit Thrush
Catharus guttatus

The ethereal song of the Hermit Thrush, filtering through the trees at dusk, provides a satisfying ending to a pleasant summer day. This species is sometimes called the "American nightingale" because of its superb singing. The Hermit Thrush is slightly smaller than our other woodland thrushes and is more boldly spotted on the undersides than is the Veery. Its rufous tail and rump contrast with its brownish olive back and head. After alighting, it quickly raises then slowly lowers its tail.

These fairly common thrushes favor woods with some conifers and occur up to 4,000 ft (1,220 m) elevation (T. Richards, pers. comm.), somewhat higher than Veeries go and lower than the highest Swainson's Thrushes. Hermit Thrush habitat overlaps somewhat with that of Veeries, but Veeries generally prefer wetter and more deciduous woodlands (K. C. Elkins, pers. comm.). For nesting habitat Hermit Thrushes favor edge situations such as fire lanes, utility corridors, the edges of burned or cutover areas, and the borders of bogs, whereas Swainson's Thrushes tend more to forest interiors (Dilger 1956a).

Both Hermits and Veeries forage in the understory and midstory. Hermit Thrushes forage somewhat more on the ground and in young saplings, whereas Veeries favor low shrubs (Paszkowski 1984). Food includes insects, spiders, and some fruit, especially in the fall (Forbush 1929).

Hermit Thrushes arrive in New Hampshire in April and begin breeding in May. Males advertise their territories with a beautiful song, each phrase of which starts with a single, clear, flutelike note on a higher pitch than the preceding one. A rapid jumble of notes of different pitches completes the phrase. Veeries and Swainson's Thrushes also have thin, ethereal voices but their individual notes run more rapidly together than the notes of the Hermit Thrush. The Wood Thrush's song is fuller and more robinlike in quality.

Call notes include a nasal "mew" and a staccato "chuck" similar to a blackbird's. The "mew" often announces the Hermit's presence in early spring before males begin singing. Gross (1949) describes still other notes.

The female alone builds the compact nest, which usually is on the ground in a natural depression of a knoll or hummock, well hidden under a small conifer or ferns (Gross 1949). Occasionally the nest is in a tree 2 to 5 ft (0.6 to 1.5 m) above ground, and Forbush (1929) mentions 2 nests under the eaves of porches, one in Holderness in 1919 and one at Lake Winnipesaukee in 1925. The nest consists of twigs, strips of bark, dried grass, and ferns with a lining of pine needles, plant fibers, or rootlets (Gross 1949). The female lays 3 to 6 eggs from mid-May to mid-June and incubates for about 2 weeks. The male feeds the incubating female. She is very wary and leaves the nest at the first sign of intrusion (Harrison 1975).

During incubation, the male sings frequently and guards his territory against intruders. He often chooses a sentinel post on the tip of a small, dead stub or the lower branch of a large pine about 40 ft (12.2 m) from the nesting site (Gross 1949). In some areas, singing may end in mid-July (Allen 1903) but elsewhere a second song period begins in late July and lasts until about the middle of August (Thayer 1909 *in* Allison and Allison 1979).

Both parents feed the young, which leave the nest in another 2 weeks. Pairs may raise a second, and possibly a third brood. Nest building was underway in a Sunapee priority block on 15 July 1985. White (1937) reports extreme egg dates of 12 May and 19 July in Concord. Eggs can be found into August. F. H. Allen (*in* Gross 1949) reported 3 eggs on 1 August 1883 in Bridgewater, and Wright (1911) observed a nest on Boy Mtn., Jefferson, which contained 3 eggs on 16 August 1906.

Like the robin and bluebird, the Hermit Thrush is quite hardy. It winters as far north as Massachusetts (Forbush 1929) and occasionally in New Hampshire (SRS). Most, however, leave in October or November.

Hermit Thrushes long have been at least fairly common in most of New Hampshire (Dearborn 1898, Allen 1903, Dearborn 1903, Thayer 1909 *in* Allison and Allison 1979). Maynard (1871), however, considered them "not very common" in Coos County and in Oxford County, Maine. Their numbers fluctuate considerably from year to year. Surveys of breeding birds conducted in June or early July on 8 survey routes in the New London area during 1980–88 ranged from 4 to 18 (mean = 9.2) (Vernon, unpubl. data). BBS data from New Hampshire follow a similar pattern of fluctuation. Robbins et al. (1986) attribute the periodic declines in part to severe winters, since the wintering range extends as far north as southern New England. Habitat changes favoring the Wood Thrush, which has increased substantially in numbers and expanded its range northward since the 1930s, also may be involved (T. Richards, K. C. Elkins, pers. comm.). Before the 1950s, the Hermit Thrush and Veery were the most common woodland thrushes in northern Merrimack County. Subsequently the Wood Thrush has become much more common there than the Hermit Thrush (K. C. Elkins, pers. comm.).

The Atlas map indicates that the Hermit Thrush is well distributed throughout most of New Hampshire but is somewhat local along the Connecticut and Merrimack river valleys and is absent from much of the Coastal Lowlands. The single North Country priority block lacking a record likely reflects limited Atlas field efforts rather than absence of the species.

Robert C. Vernon

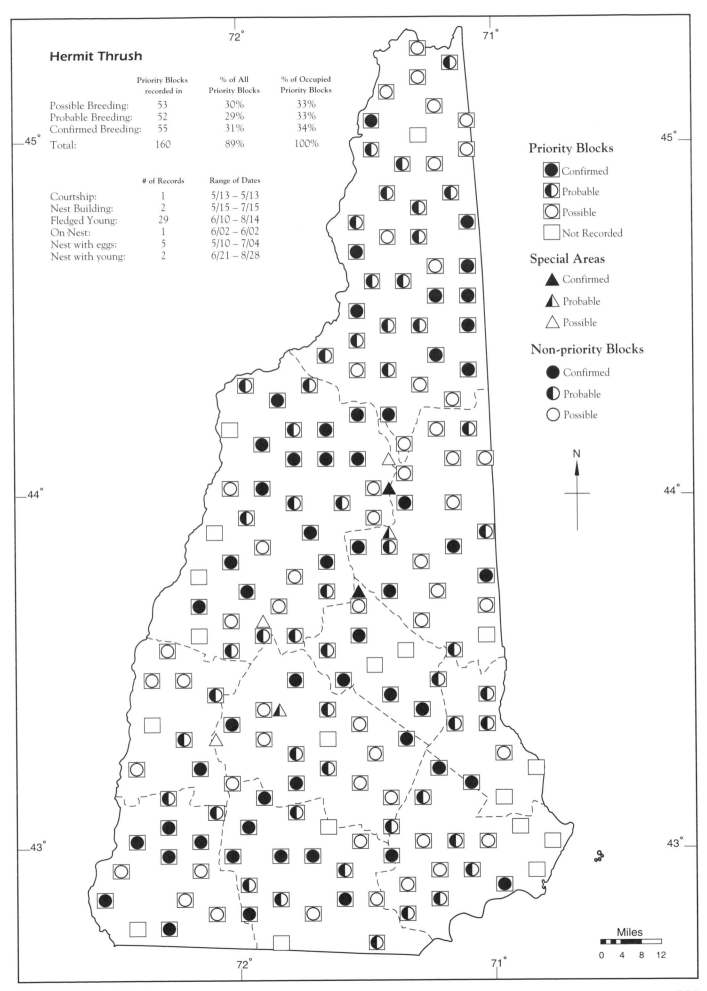

Hermit Thrush

	Priority Blocks recorded in	% of All Priority Blocks	% of Occupied Priority Blocks
Possible Breeding:	53	30%	33%
Probable Breeding:	52	29%	33%
Confirmed Breeding:	55	31%	34%
Total:	160	89%	100%

	# of Records	Range of Dates
Courtship:	1	5/13 – 5/13
Nest Building:	2	5/15 – 7/15
Fledged Young:	29	6/10 – 8/14
On Nest:	1	6/02 – 6/02
Nest with eggs:	5	5/10 – 7/04
Nest with young:	2	6/21 – 8/28

Priority Blocks

- Confirmed
- Probable
- Possible
- Not Recorded

Special Areas

- Confirmed
- Probable
- Possible

Non-priority Blocks

- Confirmed
- Probable
- Possible

Miles
0 4 8 12

Wood Thrush
Hylocichla mustelina

The Wood Thrush is the largest of our spotted-breasted thrushes, and can be recognized by its reddish brown head, strongly and thickly spotted breast, and melodious song. It is one of our finest songsters. The song consists of a series of different musical phrases of 3 to 5 notes, separated by short pauses (Saunders 1935), and may continue for several minutes or longer. The common call notes are rather harsh: a sharp "pit-pit-pit" and a low "tut-tut" which sometimes blend together, and a liquid "quirt."

The first Wood Thrushes arrive early in May, rarely in late April. These are males that immediately start singing on their territories. The females soon follow. Their courtship features rapidly repeated chase flights around a circle of about 30 ft (9.2 m) diameter (Weaver 1949).

The Wood Thrush nests in deciduous or mixed woods, usually in moist locations where there is an undergrowth of shrubs or saplings. It is partial to mature forests (Bertin 1977), but prefers edge situations to forest interiors (Dilger 1956a). BBC data indicate higher densities in northern hardwoods than in oak-hardwoods in New Hampshire. This species is most common at elevations below 2,000 ft (610 m) (T. Richards, unpubl. data). It sometimes nests close to houses. The female builds the nest, in the fork of a sapling or shrub, or saddled on a horizontal branch (Weaver 1949). The nest may be 6 to 50 ft (1.8 to 15.2 m) above the ground, but is usually rather low (Weaver 1949). It consists of grass or weed stalks, dead leaves, and mud or leaf mold and is lined with rootlets. Many nests contain pieces of paper or other white material (Weaver 1939).

The female incubates the 3 or 4 eggs for 12 to 14 days, and both parents feed the young during the 12–13 day nestling period (Harrison 1978). After the young have fledged, the parents divide the brood between them (Brackbill 1958). The young begin to for-age for themselves about 10 days after fledging (Harrison 1978). Two broods are the rule in much of the species' range, but it is not known if this is common in New Hampshire. Wood Thrushes are unobtrusive after they stop singing, usually about the end of July. Some regularly stay into October, occasionally until late in the month.

Prior to 1894 the Wood Thrush was almost unknown in New Hampshire. In that year 2 singing males were observed "near Mt. Moosilauke," Benton, and observers found the species in Dublin in 1895 (Allen 1903) and in Franconia in 1899 (Wright 1911). In 1900 the birds were reported to be common around Manchester (Elkins 1957) and were recorded for the first time in Concord (White 1937) and Franklin (Allen 1903). Dearborn (1898) mentioned a single report, from Franklin, for Belknap and Merrimack counties, and Dearborn (1903) reported a single sighting, from Hampton, in the Seacoast area. Wright (1911) reported singing males at a number of locations in the Jefferson region, beginning in 1902. Severe winters in 1893, 1895, and 1899 in the Southern states greatly reduced the Hermit Thrush population in New England (Griscom 1949), which may have enabled the Wood Thrush to expand into former Hermit territories (Bagg and Eliot 1937). The Hermit Thrush population quickly recovered, and there is some evidence of a temporary decline in numbers of Wood Thrushes, at least locally (Wright 1911, White 1937). Goodhue (1922) considered them rare except in the Merrimack Valley north of Manchester. Their population expanded slowly in the 1920s and 1930s, and rapidly in the 1940s and later (Elkins, unpubl. data), following heavy Hermit Thrush mortality in the winter of 1940 (Griscom 1949). BBS data suggest that Wood Thrushes reached peak numbers in the state in the 1970s, and have declined slightly since then.

The expansion of the Wood Thrush into New Hampshire coincided with, and perhaps contributed to a severe decline in Hermit Thrush populations, but has impinged less, if at all, on the Veery. Wood Thrushes are dominant over both Hermit Thrushes and Veeries, and sometimes take over territories formerly occupied by those species (Morse 1971). Habitats of the 3 species overlap but are not identical. Veeries will use wetter areas than Wood Thrushes, and Hermits will occupy drier sites than are acceptable to Wood Thrushes, enabling all 3 species to nest in the same forest (Dilger 1956a, Morse 1971). Both Wood and Hermit thrushes are primarily ground foragers, but Veeries get much of their food low in trees, or by fly-catching maneuvers (Dilger 1956a). Competition is thus likely to be more intense between Wood and Hermit thrushes than between Wood Thrushes and Veeries where their habitats overlap.

Wood Thrushes now occur throughout New Hampshire south of the mountains, and only one southern priority block lacks an Atlas record. In the White Mountains they are rare above 2,000 ft (610 m) (T. Richards, unpubl. data), hence were not found in some high elevation priority blocks. In the North Country they were present in a majority of priority blocks despite being near the present northern limit of their breeding range and in an area of relatively high elevation. While coniferous forests once dominated New Hampshire's North Country, widespread clearcutting has favored hardwood regeneration, which may have enhanced the Wood Thrush's expansion into this region.

Kimball C. Elkins

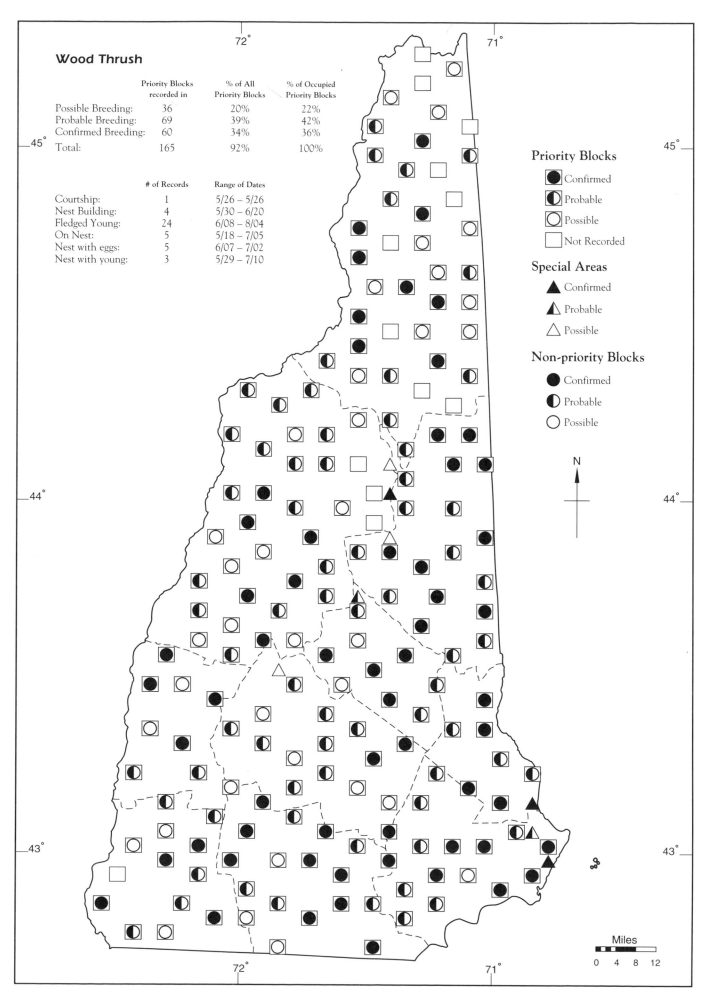

Wood Thrush

	Priority Blocks recorded in	% of All Priority Blocks	% of Occupied Priority Blocks
Possible Breeding:	36	20%	22%
Probable Breeding:	69	39%	42%
Confirmed Breeding:	60	34%	36%
Total:	165	92%	100%

	# of Records	Range of Dates
Courtship:	1	5/26 – 5/26
Nest Building:	4	5/30 – 6/20
Fledged Young:	24	6/08 – 8/04
On Nest:	5	5/18 – 7/05
Nest with eggs:	5	6/07 – 7/02
Nest with young:	3	5/29 – 7/10

Priority Blocks

◐ Confirmed
◑ Probable
○ Possible
□ Not Recorded

Special Areas

▲ Confirmed
◣ Probable
△ Possible

Non-priority Blocks

● Confirmed
◗ Probable
○ Possible

N

Miles
0 4 8 12

American Robin
Turdus migratorius

Few birds are more familiar than the American Robin, our largest and most adaptable thrush. This open land and forest edge species occupies a wide diversity of habitats from suburban back yards to clearings in boreal forests. With grayish brown upperparts and brick red underparts, the "robin red breast" is among the first birds children learn to recognize. Common at elevations up to 2,500 ft (760 m) (Ridgely 1977), it occurs and may nest at 5,000 ft (1,520 m) (Richards, unpubl. data).

Robins breed throughout North America and winter from the northern U.S. south through Mexico to Guatemala (Terres 1980). While most of New Hampshire's breeding population migrates south in the fall, individuals overwinter in all but the northernmost regions of the state. Spring arrival begins in March and extends through April. During migration conspicuous flocks forage on lawns and fields, retreating to the shelter of conifers during cold or stormy weather.

The cheerful, caroling song, beginning in the predawn twilight, signals the start of the breeding season. Overwintering birds may sing on warm days as early as mid-February (Dearborn 1903). Males may winter further north than females (Hoffman 1904), and rapidly develop into breeding condition after mid-March as they begin to establish and defend territories (Kemper and Taylor 1981).

During courtship the male may strut with tail spread, wings shaking, and throat inflated; several courting males may chase a single female (Ehrlich et al. 1988). Young (1955) also reports symbolic feeding and bill-gaping behavior. The female, sometimes with help from the male, builds the nest of mud and grass on a framework of twigs and coarse grass. Construction takes an average of 7 days (Young 1955). Observers have reported late April nest-building dates for New Hampshire (Dearborn 1903, White 1924) but most nest building occurs in May and extends through mid-July.

Nearly 60% of Atlas records for nest building are from May.

Robins usually nest in conifers, but may use deciduous trees as the season progresses. Nests are most likely to be in branches just below the layer with the largest volume of foliage (Savard and Falls 1981). Nests also may be in shrubs, on buildings and cliffs, and even on the ground (Forbush 1929, Knupp et al. 1977, Ehrlich et al. 1988). Nest heights average 13.8 ft (4.2 m) in conifers, and 22.6 ft (6.9 m) in deciduous trees (Knupp et al. 1977).

Clutches usually include 4 eggs, sometimes 3 or 5. Clutches of more than 5 may result from 2 females sharing a nest (Howard 1967). A shared nest in Orford yielded a clutch of 8 eggs (Forbush 1929). The female incubates for 11 to 14 days (Harrison 1978). Robins usually remove cowbird eggs laid in their nests (Howard 1967).

Nest mortality results primarily from predators including ravens, crows, Blue Jays, wrens, Common Grackles, red squirrels, chipmunks, and snakes (Knupp et al. 1977). Robins mob predators during the breeding season, using wing flicking, tail wagging, clucks, pipes, rattles, and screams, as well as direct attacks to the head and neck (Shedd 1982, McLean et al. 1986). A robin in Barrington defended its nest and 4 eggs from a 33 in (84 cm) milk snake with piping calls and unusual bill snapping. The snake kept the robin at bay with occasional feigned strikes. The robin's defense not only was unsuccessful, but appeared to attract a second, 43 in (109 cm) milk snake to the nest (Wicklow, pers. obs.).

Nestlings fledge 14 to 16 days after hatching (Harrison 1978) and remain dependent on their parents for 2 weeks thereafter. The male cares for the first brood while the female begins a second. Observations of fledglings account for most "confirmed" Atlas breeding records in New Hampshire. Of 99 records of fledglings, 29% were from the last 2 weeks of June and 25% were from the first 2 weeks of July. The latest fledgling record, 23 August, was from the Mt. Washington quadrangle. Juvenal plumage features the dark breast spots characteristic of thrushes.

Juveniles join adult males in communal night roosts, often in "some low wooded swamp" (Hoffman 1904), that enlarge as fall migration approaches. New Hampshire departure dates extend from October to early December (White 1924, Ridgely 1977).

Robins feed on a broad range of invertebrates, such as earthworms and insects (mostly beetles and moths), and a wide variety of fruits, which make up 90% of their fall and winter diet (Wheelwright 1986). Robins hunt by sight. Newly mowed lawns enhance their success by allowing easy movement and exposing vulnerable prey (Eiserer 1980). Thus, residential development has contributed to population expansion.

Robins have been common in New England throughout this century (Allen 1903, Forbush 1929). They once were hunted in communal winter roosts, then sold at market (Forbush 1929). DDT caused high local mortalities during the 1950s (Hickey and Hunt 1960), but populations have since returned to pre-DDT levels (Beaver 1980). BBS data from 1966 to 1979 show "strong and significant recovery across the continent" (Robbins et al. 1986).

Atlas field workers found robins in all but one priority block and "confirmed" breeding in all but 7. This species is likely to enjoy a long and secure future in New Hampshire.

Barry J. Wicklow

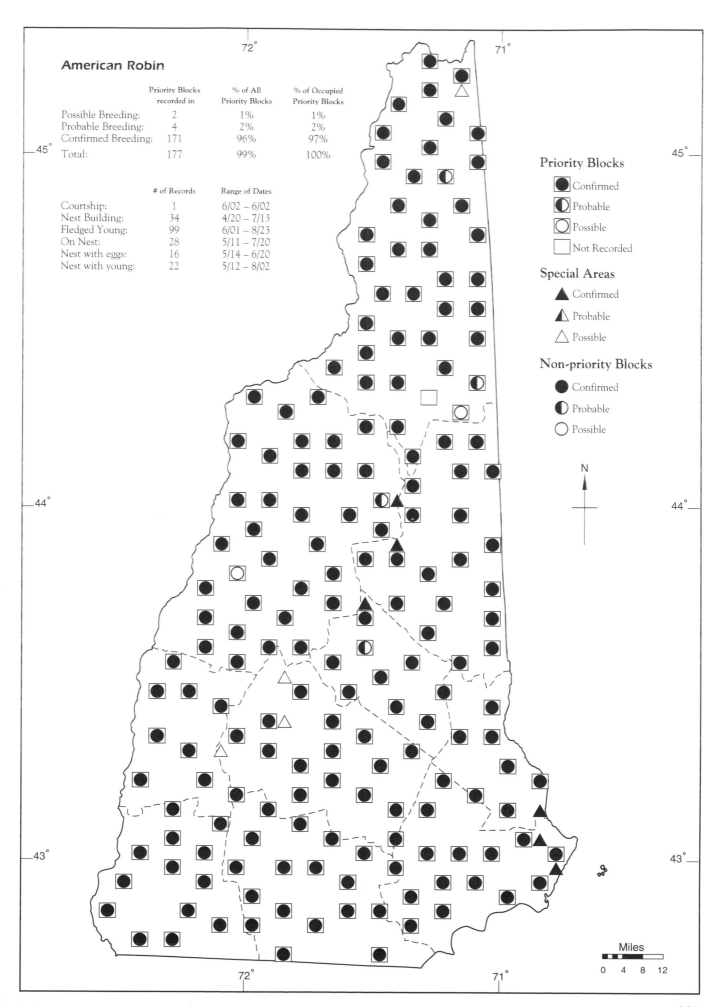

American Robin

	Priority Blocks recorded in	% of All Priority Blocks	% of Occupied Priority Blocks
Possible Breeding:	2	1%	1%
Probable Breeding:	4	2%	2%
Confirmed Breeding:	171	96%	97%
Total:	177	99%	100%

	# of Records	Range of Dates
Courtship:	1	6/02 – 6/02
Nest Building:	34	4/20 – 7/13
Fledged Young:	99	6/01 – 8/23
On Nest:	28	5/11 – 7/20
Nest with eggs:	16	5/14 – 6/20
Nest with young:	22	5/12 – 8/02

Priority Blocks

- ◐ Confirmed
- ◑ Probable
- ○ Possible
- ☐ Not Recorded

Special Areas

- ▲ Confirmed
- ◮ Probable
- △ Possible

Non-priority Blocks

- ● Confirmed
- ◗ Probable
- ○ Possible

N

Miles
0 4 8 12

Gray Catbird
Dumetella carolinensis

Although known to many as a garden species, the somber Gray Catbird is most at home in dense shrub swamps where insects flourish and native fruits are abundant in season. The generic name *Dumetella* means "little thicket," and the English name reflects the resemblance of the catbird's common agitation call to the "meow" of the household cat.

The catbird is plain gray except for its black cap and rufous undertail coverts. It nests throughout the state at low elevations. Its squeaky song is varied and includes some imitations, as do the songs of its close relatives, the thrashers and mockingbirds. Unlike its relatives, the catbird does not repeat each phrase or usually sing from conspicuous perches. Whittle (1923b) watched a female repeat its mate's song as a whisper song while she was sitting on her nest in Peterborough. Scott (1921) reported midnight singing in southern New Hampshire, but nocturnal singing is less frequent than with the mockingbird.

Catbirds winter primarily in the southeastern states, with smaller numbers in Mexico, Central America, and the Greater Antilles. Migrants reach New Hampshire at night in the first third of May. Males arrive first, and adults typically return to the previous year's nesting territories. Courtship begins immediately on arrival of the females. It includes many short chases by the males while they give brief fragments of song (Stokes 1979).

Moist thickets along streams or wood margins are ideal habitat for nesting catbirds, but these birds also use shrubbery in human settlements. Nickell (1965) studied catbird nest locations, mostly in Michigan, and found that branching patterns of gray dogwood, tartarian honeysuckle, and hawthorns were especially favorable for catbird nests, with 40% of 3,939 nests in these species. Gray Catbirds build twig nests lined with dark rootlets. The compact basket is smaller than the similar Brown Thrasher nest (Nickell 1965). Nests average about 5.2 ft (1.6 m) above ground or water.

The catbird lays 3 to 5 unmarked bluish green eggs. It typically attempts 2 broods each season, so the varied, squeaky song is heard from early May until the molt begins in late July or early August. In Michigan, Nickell (1965) found that nest construction averaged 5.1 days. Females laid their first eggs after 2.1 days, and typically laid eggs before 9 a.m. Incubation averaged 13.4 days after laying of the last egg. Most young hatched in the afternoon, spent an average of 11.3 days in the nest, and left the nest in late afternoon. Most Atlas records of nest building were from the last week of May and the first week of June, but there was a very early 2 May date in Hillsboro. Egg dates for 18 New Hampshire nests range from 11 May to 30 July with the peak 50% from 26 May to 7 June. The catbird is common and conspicuous, builds its nest at about eye level, and has a comparatively long nesting season. Both adults and young respond vigorously to "squeaking" sounds. Breeding was thus easy to "confirm."

Both parents feed the nestlings, bringing food 2 to 4 times per hour (Johnson and Best 1982). Ants, beetles, caterpillars, and grasshoppers form the bulk of the catbird's diet in spring and early summer. By autumn, fleshy fruits dominate its choice more than in any other native bird; blackberries and cherries head the list (Martin et al. 1951).

Only stragglers remain after the end of September, but there are occasional November and December records from the southern half of the state (Oliver 1902; Blanchard 1904; NHAQ, *passim*). Apparently the catbird rarely if ever successfully overwinters here.

Belknap (1792) first reported the catbird from New Hampshire. Observers near the close of the 19th century reported its status as common at various localities in the Winnipesaukee Lowlands (Faxon and Allen 1888, Allen 1889, Comey 1904), but uncommon to rare along the fringes of the White Mountains in Bethlehem (Minot 1876), Franconia (Porter 1903), Jefferson (Wright 1911), and Kearsarge (Bartlett/Conway) (Porter and Porter 1904). Allen (1903) considered the species rather common in the Transition areas up to the outskirts of the White Mountains and reported a few pairs annually in the river bottom at Intervale (Bartlett/Conway), rarely up the slopes to 500 to 600 ft (150 to 180 m), as well as in the lower country north of the mountains. T. Richards (unpubl. data) observed this species above 2,000 ft (600 m) at Long Pond, Benton, on 8 July 1966.

BBS data do not indicate any change in Gray Catbird abundance during 1966–79. This species undoubtedly is more common along roadsides than in more heavily forested tracts. There is no indication that the Northern Mockingbird's invasion of New Hampshire has affected catbird populations.

Atlas data confirm the catbird's widespread distribution south of the White Mountains and document its presence in much of northern New Hampshire, where suitable habitat occurs at elevations below 1,500 ft (460 m). The Gray Catbird adapts well to the human environment and even ejects cowbird eggs. It should long remain a common nesting species at low and medium elevations, except in densely populated urban areas.

Chandler S. Robbins

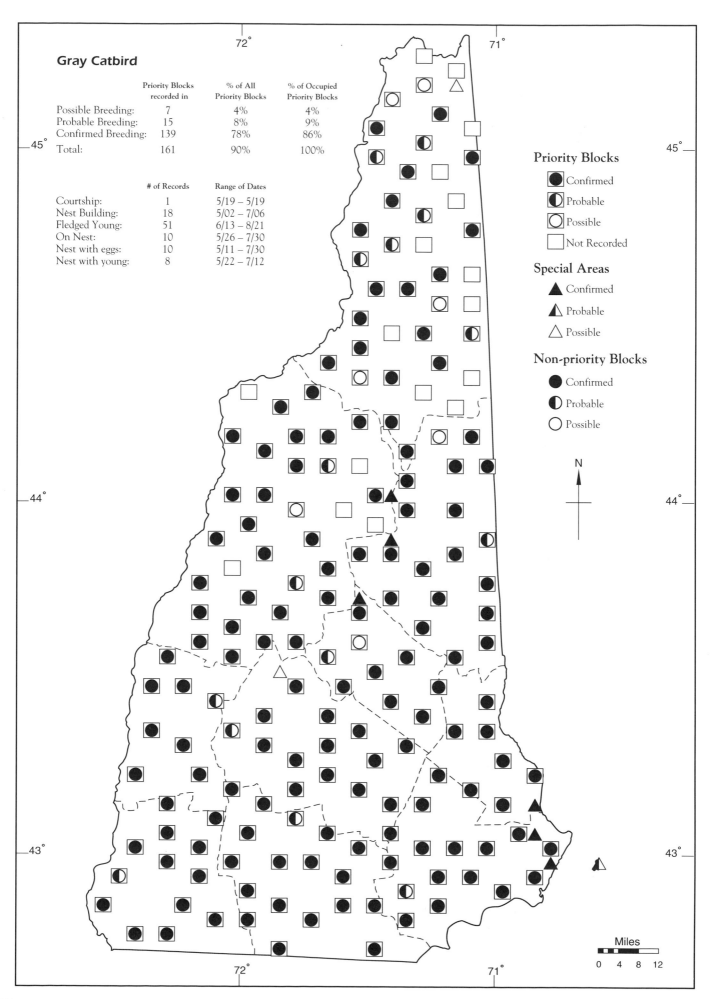

Gray Catbird

	Priority Blocks recorded in	% of All Priority Blocks	% of Occupied Priority Blocks
Possible Breeding:	7	4%	4%
Probable Breeding:	15	8%	9%
Confirmed Breeding:	139	78%	86%
Total:	161	90%	100%

	# of Records	Range of Dates
Courtship:	1	5/19 – 5/19
Nest Building:	18	5/02 – 7/06
Fledged Young:	51	6/13 – 8/21
On Nest:	10	5/26 – 7/30
Nest with eggs:	10	5/11 – 7/30
Nest with young:	8	5/22 – 7/12

Priority Blocks
- ◐ Confirmed
- ◑ Probable
- ○ Possible
- ☐ Not Recorded

Special Areas
- ▲ Confirmed
- ◤ Probable
- △ Possible

Non-priority Blocks
- ● Confirmed
- ◖ Probable
- ○ Possible

N

Miles
0 4 8 12

Northern Mockingbird
Mimus polyglottos

This accomplished imitator, whose Latin name means "many tongued mimic," is a recent arrival on the New England scene. Of southern origin, it was known for 2 centuries as just Mockingbird. A slim, gray, robin-sized bird, it displays large white wing patches and white outer tail feathers in flight. Mockingbirds are most common in villages and even cities, but some occur in rural environments.

In spring, the mockingbird will imitate an amazing number of avian species in rapid succession, by day or night. It imitates primarily songbirds, but also will utter calls of flickers and other woodpeckers, shorebirds such as Killdeer and yellowlegs, and even Saw-whet Owls, which Robbins has heard only at dawn and dusk. In 1985 a White-eyed Vireo visited Durham for 2 days; a resident mockingbird fooled many birders thereafter by its excellent imitation (M. Davis, pers. comm.).

A courting male carries nesting material to potential nest sites on his territory. When a female joins him, she chooses the nest site and assists with construction (Laskey 1962). Mockingbirds are very aggressive around the nest, and some individuals monopolize feeding stations. Mockingbirds perform a unique "dance" in territorial defense throughout the year. Facing each other on the ground, they repeatedly hop into the air.

The bulky nests of twigs generally are placed 3 to 16.5 ft (1 to 5 m) up in a shrub or tree (Laskey 1962). Early nests (late April and May) often are in evergreens, especially ornamental spruces near extensive lawns. Mockingbirds typically raise 2 broods, but may attempt more (Laskey 1962). Incubation takes 11 to 13 days (Peck and James 1987). The female incubates the 3 to 5 eggs and broods the young alone. Both parents feed the young, which usually leave the nest at 12 days of age (Laskey 1962). Atlas dates for adults with food or fecal sacs and for fledged young are representative of the breeding season in New Hampshire. Once inde-

pendent, young mockingbirds explore the neighborhood for feeding areas and potential winter territories. They frequently engage in wing-flashing, especially when encountering an unfamiliar situation (Laskey 1962).

Insects, especially beetles, ants, wasps, and grasshoppers, are mockingbirds' chief fare in spring and summer. In fall and winter, native fruits comprise more than half the diet (Martin et al. 1951).

Mockingbirds are quiet in late summer, then engage in a burst of song during autumn. In winter their chief vocalization is a diagnostic loud "chuck," often heard at dawn. Cats or other threats also trigger this call.

Originally a denizen of the deep South, mockingbirds have expanded their range northward during this century, becoming common in the Washington/Baltimore area during 1905–08 (Stewart and Robbins 1958) and in New York State during 1951–70 (Bull 1974). Many early New England strays were discovered in fall or winter, keeping warm on tops of chimneys and subsisting on suet, wild berries, and fruit and bread at bird feeders. The first New Hampshire records were from Hampton on 24 August 1900 (Dearborn 1903), Milford on 7 November 1904 (Wright 1921), and Manchester, 5–6 November 1916 (Varick 1917). Early summer records include birds in Manchester on 16 June 1922 (USFWS data) and 25 May 1927 (Weaver 1941). A bird in Bedford in March and April 1928 may have been the state's first winter survivor (USFWS data).

Early records (pre-1960) were primarily from low elevations in the southern counties. During the 1960s mockingbirds spread through the Coastal Lowlands and lower Merrimack Valley, with scattered records north to the base of the White Mountains and 2 records at low elevations north of the Presidentials.

The first confirmed nestings for New Hampshire were a nest with 4 eggs found in Durham on 7 June 1957 by T. Richards (pers. comm.), and a pair with young at the nest in Durham on 5 July 1959 (RNEB 1959). New Hampshire BBS data show a gradual increase from a single bird in 1967 to a high of 43 in 1987, when observers found the mockingbird on 14 of the state's 23 BBS routes. Only the House Finch and Tufted Titmouse exceeded the average annual increase of 13.3% during 1966–79 (Robbins et al. 1986).

By the close of the Atlas period, observers had found mockingbirds in all but 2 priority blocks east of the Merrimack River, and in all but 9 priority blocks in the 5 southeastern counties. Occurrence is spotty in the southwest and increasingly so to the north, but the statewide occurrence in 46% of the priority blocks is very impressive. The only records in and north of the White Mountains are in the vicinity of Dummer, Milan, Gorham, and Carroll. Nearly all Atlas records were from elevations below 1,000 ft (300 m), and most were below 500 ft (150 m). The great majority of records were from blocks with an average summer rainfall less than 11 in (28 cm) and a growing season of at least 110 days.

Much of the mockingbird's northward expansion likely results from widespread planting of multiflora roses, which provide both shelter and a dependable winter food supply. This species likely will continue to increase in abundance in the settled areas of New Hampshire.

Chandler S. Robbins

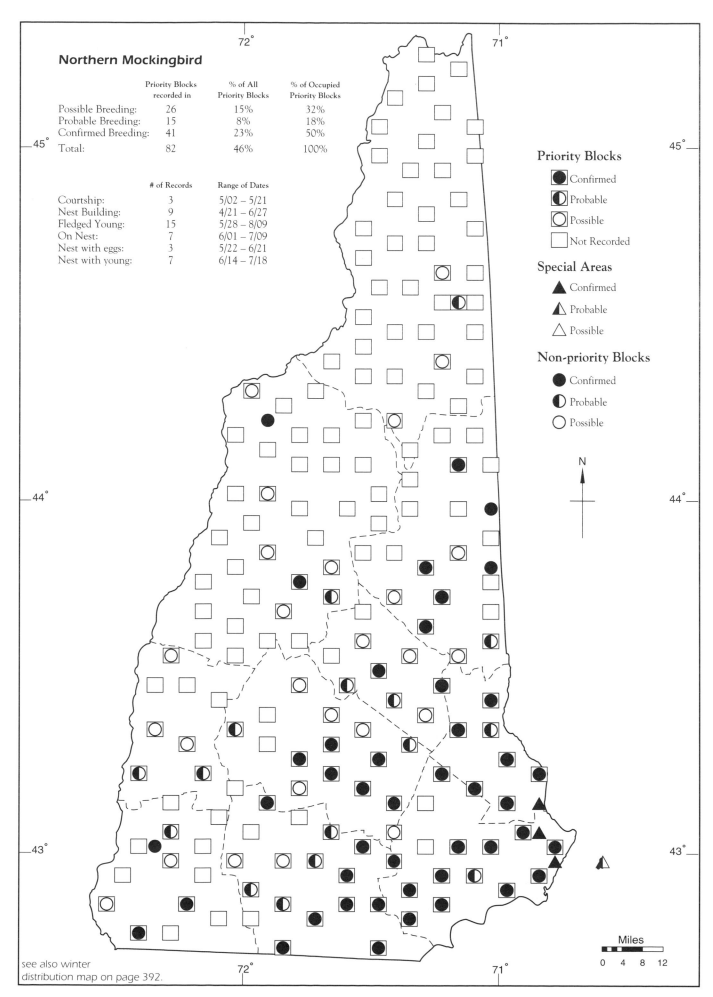

Northern Mockingbird

	Priority Blocks recorded in	% of All Priority Blocks	% of Occupied Priority Blocks
Possible Breeding:	26	15%	32%
Probable Breeding:	15	8%	18%
Confirmed Breeding:	41	23%	50%
Total:	82	46%	100%

	# of Records	Range of Dates
Courtship:	3	5/02 – 5/21
Nest Building:	9	4/21 – 6/27
Fledged Young:	15	5/28 – 8/09
On Nest:	7	6/01 – 7/09
Nest with eggs:	3	5/22 – 6/21
Nest with young:	7	6/14 – 7/18

Priority Blocks
- ◑ Confirmed
- ◐ Probable
- ○ Possible
- ☐ Not Recorded

Special Areas
- ▲ Confirmed
- ◮ Probable
- △ Possible

Non-priority Blocks
- ● Confirmed
- ◑ Probable
- ○ Possible

N

see also winter distribution map on page 392.

Miles
0 4 8 12

Brown Thrasher

Toxostoma rufum

This yellow-eyed, long-tailed road-runner of country lanes in southern New Hampshire announces its presence from a treetop in May and early June. The Brown Thrasher is a "mimic thrush," and was called Fox-coloured Thrush (Catesby 1731), Brown Thrush, Sandy Mocker, and Song Thrush (Minot 1895) in earlier centuries.

The Brown Thrasher usually arrives from the Southern states in late April, but occasionally by mid-April (Allen 1903; L. C. Rising, pers. comm.). Its loud song differs from that of the Northern Mockingbird in repeating each phrase twice in succession rather than many times. In New England the song period typically corresponds with spring planting, and country people once rendered the song of the "planting bird" as "drop it, drop it, cover it, cover it, I'll pull it up, I'll pull it up" (Forbush 1929). This species occasionally includes imitations of the notes of other birds in its song (Forbush 1929). After a few weeks of vigorous singing, the Brown Thrasher becomes less vocal and is more often seen than heard.

While the closely related Gray Catbird favors moist thickets, the Brown Thrasher prefers drier hedgerows and wood margins. It is especially common in sandy areas and in scrubby growth at elevations below 1,000 ft (300 m) and occurs in human-altered habitat in suburbia and around summer cottages, along roadsides and railroad tracks, and in recently logged areas. About 6 pairs were present in the vicinity of an active gravel pit in Rochester during the 1985 breeding season (S.B. Turner, pers. comm.).

The thrasher conceals its bulky twig nest in bushes, vines, and small trees, generally about 3 to 6 ft (0.9 to 1.8 m), rarely above 12 ft (3.7 m), from the ground. Peck and James (1987) reported that 161 of 648 Ontario nests were on the ground. Thorn bushes are preferred sites. Scott (1921) noted that 60% of nests found in the Durham area were in barberry bushes,

10% in hawthorn, and the rest in wild apples, young cedars, or junipers. Nest material includes leaves, strips of cedar or grapevine bark, rootlets, and hairs. The male and female complete nest construction in 5 to 7 days (Harrison 1975). The 3 to 5 grayish or greenish white eggs are thickly spotted with small brown dots, in contrast to the unmarked eggs of the Gray Catbird. The Brown Thrasher is the largest songbird which cowbirds parasitize (Harrison 1975). Both sexes incubate, usually for 12 to 13 days, but occasionally for 11 or 14 days (Harrison 1975).

Adults vigorously defend their eggs. Single broods are typical in New Hampshire, but Peck and James (1987) report second broods in Ontario. Both parents tend the young, which remain in the nest for 12 to 14 days (Harrison 1978). When thrashers raise a second brood, the male tends the fledglings while the female nests again (Harrison 1978), sometimes with a different mate (Harrison 1975).

Insects, obtained largely by scratching in leaves on the ground, form the major part of the diet during the breeding season. Wild fruits are important during late summer and fall. Most fall departures are in September, but several records of October sightings exist, including one at Errol on 14 October 1947 (T. Richards, unpubl. data). Thickets provide important habitat for this species during migration (Forbush 1929).

Thrashers were known to early settlers (Belknap 1792, Little 1870), but the earliest specific records are for Hollis on 9 May 1874 and 7 May 1875 and 1876 (Fox 1876). Brewster (*in* Minot 1895), called the Brown Thrasher a common summer resident in southern New England, but local north of Massachusetts in cultivated areas. Allen (1903) knew the Brown Thrasher as a not uncommon summer resident of southeastern New Hampshire, and Scott (1921) considered thrashers more common around Durham than elsewhere in the state. The species occurred in small numbers along valleys in the White Mountains (Allen 1903), but only as a rare spring and summer visitor in the Jefferson region (Wright 1911). It was fairly common on the sandy Ossipee plain (Allen 1903), where it remains fairly common today.

High-elevation records include one seen at the Crawford House, Carroll 1,900 ft (580 m) elevation in July 1905 (Marble 1907 *in* Wright 1911); a singing bird by Hermit Lake, Tuckerman's Ravine, Mt. Washington, at about 3,800 ft (1,160 m), 10 May 1970; and a pair at Kancamagus Pass, Lincoln/Livermore, 2,850 ft (870 m), 8 July 1975 (T. Richards, unpubl. data).

BBS data indicate a sharp decline in New Hampshire during 1966–87. Part of this decline probably reflects local losses of suitable scrubby habitat along roadsides. This thrasher has occurred on every New Hampshire BBS route, annually on most routes in the southern part of the state.

The Atlas map illustrates the wide distribution of Brown Thrashers in southern New Hampshire, and their more local occurrence in and north of the mountains. They occur sparingly up to 1,700 ft (520 m) in northern brushy deciduous habitats, but are absent from higher elevations. Thrashers were found in 10 of 22 priority and nonpriority blocks visited in the Ossipee Lake quadrangle, but in only 3 of 15 blocks visited in the adjacent, more mountainous Mt. Chocorua quadrangle. Just across the Maine line, in the Brownfield and Kezar Falls quadrangles, they occurred in 8 of 12 low-lying 3 mi (5 km) blocks (Robbins, unpubl. data), suggesting that elevation and heavy forest growth rather than latitude limit the breeding range of the Brown Thrasher in New Hampshire.

Chandler S. Robbins

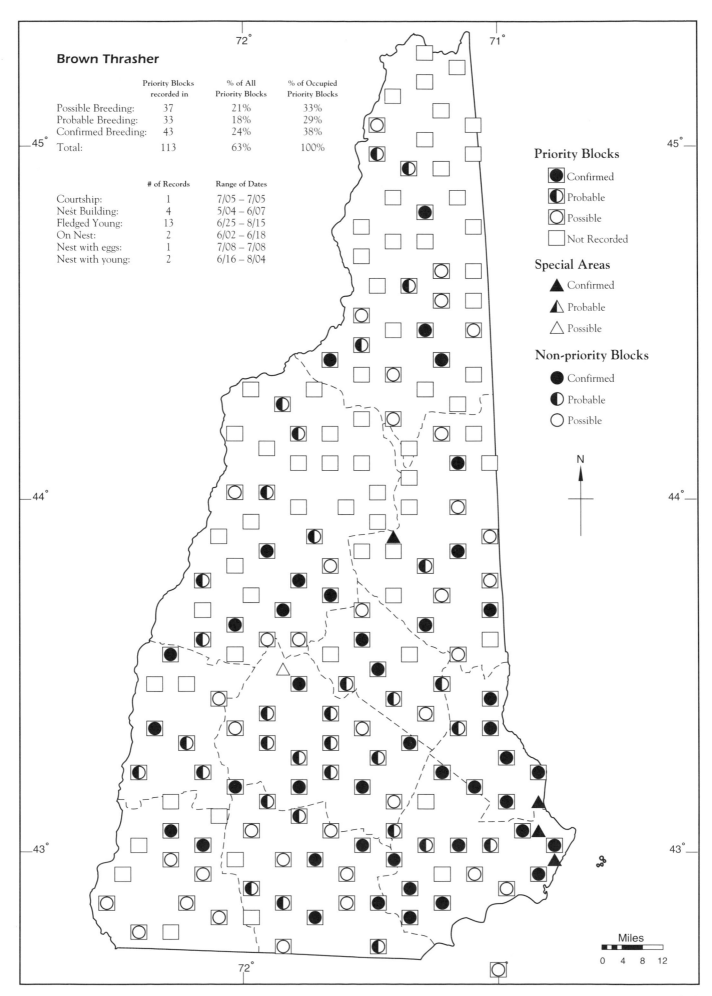

Brown Thrasher

	Priority Blocks recorded in	% of All Priority Blocks	% of Occupied Priority Blocks
Possible Breeding:	37	21%	33%
Probable Breeding:	33	18%	29%
Confirmed Breeding:	43	24%	38%
Total:	113	63%	100%

	# of Records	Range of Dates
Courtship:	1	7/05 – 7/05
Nest Building:	4	5/04 – 6/07
Fledged Young:	13	6/25 – 8/15
On Nest:	2	6/02 – 6/18
Nest with eggs:	1	7/08 – 7/08
Nest with young:	2	6/16 – 8/04

Priority Blocks

- ◐ Confirmed
- ◑ Probable
- ○ Possible
- ☐ Not Recorded

Special Areas

- ▲ Confirmed
- ◪ Probable
- △ Possible

Non-priority Blocks

- ● Confirmed
- ◑ Probable
- ○ Possible

N

Miles
0 4 8 12

Cedar Waxwing
Bombycilla cedrorum

The high pitched "Seeee" calls of Cedar Waxwings immediately announce the presence of one of New Hampshire's most common breeding birds. "Cedar birds" are highly visible even during the breeding season, when they travel in gregarious flocks to and from feeding areas. Both sexes have sleek, silky tan plumage, with black masks, conspicuous crests, pale yellow bellies, white undertail coverts and yellow bands at the ends of squared tails. Cedar Waxwings are named for the small, scarlet, waxlike drops on the tips of their secondary wing feathers and their fondness for red cedar fruits.

Cedar Waxwings occur in New Hampshire throughout the year but are most common from May to October. Their seasonal movements and migrations are irregular and appear to be related to the abundance or scarcity of berries or other fruits, which comprise 80% of their diet (DeGraaf and Rudis 1986). Waxwings frequently utilize open deciduous and coniferous woodlands, apple orchards, and shrubby fields near water.

Cedar Waxwings mature sexually within one year and nest from June to September, during the peak abundance of wild fruits. Allen (1903) noted their nesting in mid-July in valleys of the White Mountains. Courtship, which may begin in migrating flocks and continues up until incubation, consists of repeated side-hopping, passing of a berry or flower petal between mates, and rapid circular chases between the pair (Tyler 1950c).

The pair determine the nest site although the female seems to be more active in site selection (Palmer 1949). The nest is located in a forked branch well out from the trunk of a deciduous or coniferous tree or shrub, 4 to 50 ft (1.2 to 15.2 m) above the ground (Harrison 1975). Waxwings often establish small territories in which mating and nesting occur, but a number of pairs may nest within a relatively small area (Tyler 1950c). The pair jointly build the nest in about

6 days (Putnam 1949). The nest consists of twigs, dry grasses, weed stems, lichens, pine needles, and wool and is lined with fine grasses and old caterpillar nest webbing. Of 2 nests found in Goffstown in June 1985, one was 40 ft (12.2 m) up in a white pine tree and another was 10 ft (3 m) from the ground in a clump of speckled alders covered with grapevines (C. R. Foss, NHBBA data). Cedar Waxwings sometimes appropriate nesting materials from other bird nests (Mountjoy and Robertson 1988).

Waxwings are seldom alone except when the female is on the nest, and even then the male is usually nearby on a conspicuous "sentinel" perch. He brings fruit to the female while she incubates her 3 to 6 eggs for 12 to 14 days (Crouch 1936, Putnam 1949). At hatching the male begins to bring insects to the nest, and both parents feed the young. Insects constitute much of the nestlings' diet for about 3 days, after which they begin to eat fruit (Putnam 1949). The young fledge in 14 to 18 days and usually depend on their parents for at least another week. The fledglings' persistent food begging facilitates "confirmation" of successful breeding.

About 9 days after the young hatch a pair may reinitiate courtship and begin to construct a second nest. The female lays the eggs of a second brood before or soon after the first young fledge. This enables the pair to raise 2 broods in 65 days (Putnam 1949). The Atlas project's 66-day range of nest building dates (23 May to 27 July, 43 records) and 79 day range of fledged young dates (18 June to 30 August, 51 records) suggest double brooding here. Immature birds usually lack the waxy droplets, and before molting in September or October have streaked underparts and grayer plumage than adults (Terres 1980). Flocks of juveniles are common until the end of August, and large groups occur from late September to early October prior to fall dispersal from nesting areas (Bagg and Eliot 1937, Putnam 1949).

Waxwings feed on fresh and dried fruits, sap from maple trees, tree flower petals, and a wide variety of insects (Tyler 1950c). Waxwings typically forage by hawking, fly catching from waterside trees, gleaning insects from leaf surfaces, and plucking fruit from branches. Flocks feeding in trees constantly utter high-pitched calls and may gorge themselves until they can hardly fly. Sometimes they become drunk on overripe fruit (Terres 1980).

Despite changes in New Hampshire land use patterns during the past 150 years, Cedar Waxwings have remained common summer residents (Dearborn 1898, Allen 1903, Abbott 1906, White 1924, Ridgely 1977, Allison and Allison 1979). As the Atlas map indicates, the Cedar Waxwing continues to be widespread throughout New Hampshire. Additional field work likely would have detected the species in the single priority block that lacks a record. BBS data from 1966 to 1979 indicate an increase in the Eastern region and in the Northeastern states; New Hampshire's mean number of birds per route (9.5) was the highest of all the Eastern states and provinces (Robbins et al. 1986). The future of the Cedar Waxwing in New Hampshire appears positive, as land use changes, forestry practices, and wildlife plantings foster continual establishment of berry patches and fruit-bearing trees and shrubs.

Harold P. Nevers

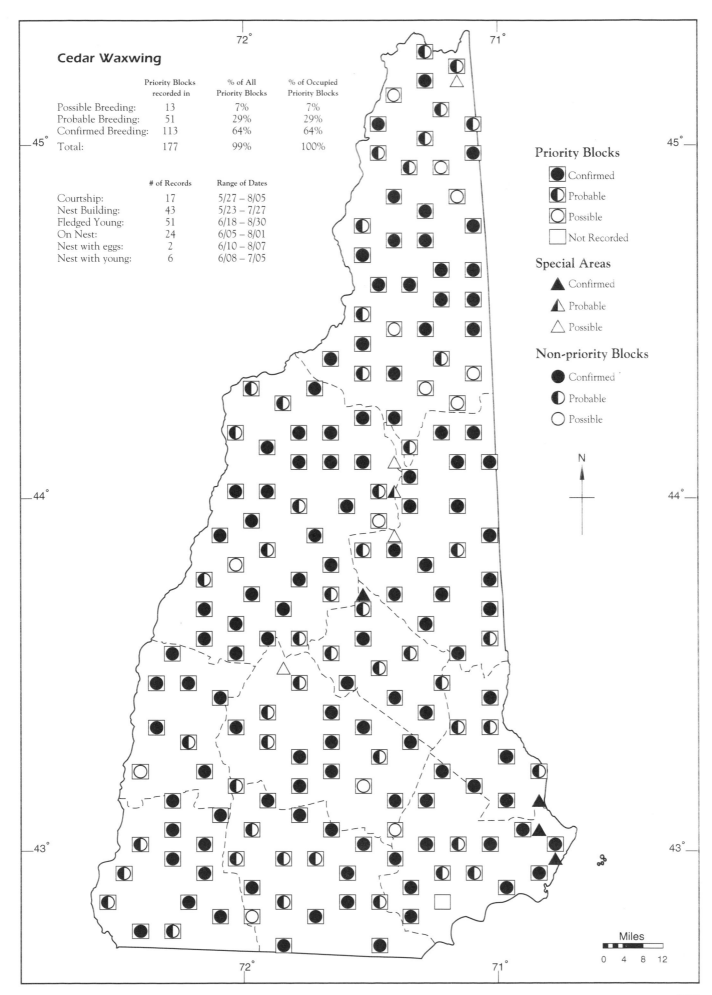

Cedar Waxwing

	Priority Blocks recorded in	% of All Priority Blocks	% of Occupied Priority Blocks
Possible Breeding:	13	7%	7%
Probable Breeding:	51	29%	29%
Confirmed Breeding:	113	64%	64%
Total:	177	99%	100%

	# of Records	Range of Dates
Courtship:	17	5/27 – 8/05
Nest Building:	43	5/23 – 7/27
Fledged Young:	51	6/18 – 8/30
On Nest:	24	6/05 – 8/01
Nest with eggs:	2	6/10 – 8/07
Nest with young:	6	6/08 – 7/05

Priority Blocks

- ● Confirmed
- ◑ Probable
- ○ Possible
- ▢ Not Recorded

Special Areas

- ▲ Confirmed
- ◮ Probable
- △ Possible

Non-priority Blocks

- ● Confirmed
- ◗ Probable
- ○ Possible

N

Miles
0 4 8 12

European Starling
Sturnus vulgaris

Noisy flocks of this introduced species are common in both rural and urban areas. The starling may be our most unloved bird, but that has been no deterrent in one of the most remarkable success stories of avian colonization in North America. Arising from a few score birds released in New York City's Central Park in 1890–91, the North American population of about 200,000,000 is still growing (Feare 1984). This species occurs from the Atlantic Coast to the Pacific and from sub-arctic Canada to tropical Mexico. It commonly nests in human settlements and has benefited from human modification of the environment. Although this bird often is called the common starling or just starling, the correct name is European Starling, which separates it from other species of its large Old World family.

Starlings are widespread and abundant throughout most of New Hampshire, but locally distributed in the extensively wooded northern part of the state and the White Mountains. In summer they disperse throughout cities, suburbs, and rural areas with croplands and pastures. Those remaining in winter are largely restricted to urban areas. Many migrate out of New Hampshire to winter further south, and are among the earliest migrants to return in spring.

Starlings are vocal throughout the year, but are quieter from late summer through the winter than during the breeding season. Winter flocks break up early in spring, and males seek suitable nesting cavities, which they advertise to potential mates with a variety of whistles, squeals, and imitations of other birds. Starlings are not particular about the cavity in which they place their nests and will use a wide range of sites, old woodpecker holes, natural tree cavities, birdhouses, and crevices in man-made structures such as buildings, bridges, street lights, and even abandoned automobiles (Bent 1950).

Because these aggressive birds select nest sites before most native cavity-nesting species have returned, biologists attribute declines of some species, such as the Eastern Bluebird and Great Crested Flycatcher, in part to the starlings' monopoly of good cavities. A pair of starlings can fill a large duck box with leaves, grass, scraps of paper, and various other trash in a few hours, burying a clutch of duck eggs. Starlings sometimes harass excavating flickers until they abandon their cavity, which the starlings then take over (Bent 1950).

Starling nests are unkempt and often filthy with the droppings of young birds. A pair may use the same nest site for successive broods and even for several years. Both parents incubate the 4 or 5 pale bluish eggs for 12 to 14 days. The young leave the nest after 2 or 3 weeks (Bent 1950). A pair may raise 2, and sometimes 3 broods annually (Pough 1946). Dates for egg laying in New Hampshire are scarce since the nests are in concealed locations. Observers have reported nest building as early as 6 April, and recently fledged young as early as 29 May.

Both parents feed the nestlings, primarily on insects, most of which they capture on the ground. Hungry fledglings often follow parents as they probe for grubs of Japanese beetles on lawns. Occasionally they feed on cherries and other fruits. Fledged young are conspicuous and highly vocal.

The dusky-colored juveniles gather in large flocks after fledging, eventually joined by adults and often by various species of blackbirds. Flying starlings can be distinguished from blackbirds by their short tails, triangular silhouettes, and swift, direct flight. These flocks converge at enormous, noisy night roosts in dense trees or tall marsh grasses. In winter, New Hampshire starlings may roost under bridges or on building ledges.

The starling's establishment in North America is generally attributed to the introductions at Central Park. However, many previous introduction attempts occurred during the 1870s and 1880s, apparently under the misguided impression that the starling would control insect pests. In New England, 100 released near Springfield, Mass. in 1897 apparently left or died, as none were evident there again until 1907 (Pearson 1936). Forbush (1927) noted that some had been released in Worcester, Mass. in 1884.

By 1910 this bird nested throughout Long Island and most of New Jersey and Connecticut and had extended its range into Rhode Island and southern Massachusetts (Bent 1950). Between 1916 and 1920 it reached Maine, New Hampshire, and Vermont. Scott (1921) noted that it was becoming fairly common in southern New Hampshire, while White (1924) noted that a small colony had been established on Clinton Street in Concord for "some years" and that starlings also occurred in other parts of the town.

Although the European Starling population in North America seems to be constantly increasing, BBS data indicate a slight decline in the eastern U.S. during 1966–79, attributed to heavy mortality during the severe winters of 1976–77 and 1977–78 (Robbins et al. 1986).

Atlas observers found breeding starlings in all but 32 priority blocks (18%). Nearly all blocks lacking records were in the White Mountains and North Country, but a few (3) were in extensively wooded areas of central and southern New Hampshire. The starling likely will increase in numbers and expand its distribution in the state as more woodlands are converted to suburban lawns and buildings.

Ralph Andrews

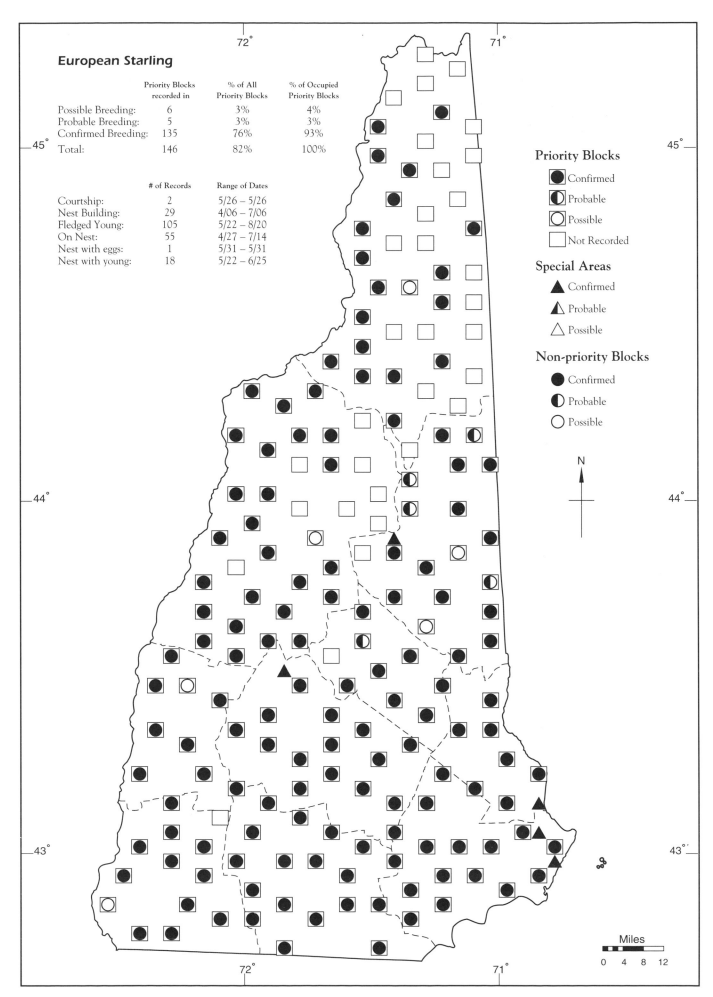

European Starling

	Priority Blocks recorded in	% of All Priority Blocks	% of Occupied Priority Blocks
Possible Breeding:	6	3%	4%
Probable Breeding:	5	3%	3%
Confirmed Breeding:	135	76%	93%
Total:	146	82%	100%

	# of Records	Range of Dates
Courtship:	2	5/26 – 5/26
Nest Building:	29	4/06 – 7/06
Fledged Young:	105	5/22 – 8/20
On Nest:	55	4/27 – 7/14
Nest with eggs:	1	5/31 – 5/31
Nest with young:	18	5/22 – 6/25

Priority Blocks

- ● Confirmed
- ◑ Probable
- ○ Possible
- ▢ Not Recorded

Special Areas

- ▲ Confirmed
- ◤ Probable
- △ Possible

Non-priority Blocks

- ● Confirmed
- ◐ Probable
- ○ Possible

N

Miles
0 4 8 12

White-eyed Vireo
Vireo griseus

This denizen of moist thickets has been expanding its range northeastward in recent decades, and now may nest occasionally in southeastern New Hampshire after an absence of many years. The White-eyed Vireo nests in dense, shrubby habitats throughout the eastern U.S. from southeastern Nebraska south to central Texas and east to Massachusetts and Florida. Its wintering range extends south along the Atlantic Coast from central North Carolina, and along the Gulf Coast to Panama (Farrand 1983). The White-eyed Vireo resembles the Solitary and Yellow-throated vireos with 2 white wing bars and yellowish sides, but is distinguished from them by a combination of yellow lores and eye-rings with a white throat and, at close range, by its white eye.

White-eyed Vireos arrive in New Hampshire in May (RNEB, passim; SRS). Potential breeding habitat includes swampy streamside thickets, overgrown fields with shrubby vegetation, bramble patches, and damp, brushy tangles (Bent 1950, Harrison 1975, Meade in Andrle and Carroll 1988).

These vireos spend most of their time in low vegetation, typically out of sight. Fortunately, the males sing loudly and persistently. Colorful paraphrases of the song include "who are you, eh?," "pick-up-the-beer-check" (Borror 1987), "gingerbeer, —quick," and "chick'ty-beaver, —lim'ber, stick" (Ridgway 1889 in Bent 1950). Each male has 10 to 17 song types and repeats one 12 to 118 times before switching to another (Borror 1987). White-eyed Vireos sometimes include fragments from the songs of other species within their songs, or mimic various calls or notes (Forbush 1929, Adkisson and Conner 1978, McNair and Forster 1983). Bradley (1980) provides a detailed analysis of song behavior. Calls include short ticks, harsh mews, and loud whistles (Farrand 1983). White-eyed Vireos utter a harsh, rasping chatter in response to intruding vireos, potential predators, and "pishing" humans (Bradley 1980).

Male White-eyed Vireos are highly territorial where habitat patches are large enough to accommodate multiple pairs. They devote considerable time and energy to singing from the perimeters of their territories and defending against intruding males (Bradley 1980). Singing continues from arrival into August, providing ample opportunity to locate breeding pairs. Measured territories range in size from 0.33 a (0.13 ha) (Brewer 1955 in DeGraaf and Rudis 1986) to 6.5 a (2.6 ha) (Fitch 1950 in DeGraaf and Rudis 1986). Torrey (1885 in Bent 1950) observed a male in courtship who puffed out his feathers and spread his tail, while uttering yips and catbirdlike snarls.

Both sexes build the deep-cupped nest, which is typically well concealed and suspended from forked twigs of a shrub or small tree 1 to 25 ft (0.3 to 7.6 m), but usually less than 8 ft (2.4 m) from the ground (Harrison 1975, Harrison 1978). The nest is distinctively cone-shaped, and has an outer covering of leaves, bark flakes, and wasp nest fragments (Harrison 1978).

Both adults incubate the 3 to 5 eggs for 12 to 16 days (Bent 1950, Harrison 1978). One eastern Massachusetts nest held a single egg on 26 May 1912, and another held 4 fresh eggs on 6 June 1908 (Bent 1950). The nestling period is estimated at 11 days (Bradley 1980). Fledglings often follow the male about his territory, sometimes assisting in its defense, and occasionally begging for food (Bradley 1980). Young males may begin to sing within 2 weeks of fledging and may establish and defend territories after dispersing in late summer. Butterflies and moths and their caterpillars are the mainstays of the White-eyed Vireo diet, which also includes other insects, spiders, snails, and berries (Bent 1950).

The White-eyed Vireo apparently nested formerly in New Hampshire. The first reference is B. Stolworthy's record of a nest in Franklin prior to 1898 (Dearborn 1898). Allen (1903) cited F.W. Batchelder's reports of nesting at 2 sites in Manchester in and prior to 1899, and W.E. Cram's reports of sightings in Hampton Falls. White-eyed Vireos were fairly common in the vicinity of Cambridge, Mass. before the turn of the century but subsequently became scarce and probably disappeared from New Hampshire about the same time (Bent 1950).

The next New Hampshire record is of an accidental visitor in the Monadnock region on 7 May 1955 (Hill 1956). Sightings increased in the next few decades, with 17 spring and 8 fall records during 1964–80, mostly from the Seacoast area (SRS). Spring dates range from 3 May to 7 June; fall dates range from 5 September to 16 November.

BBS data document a continuing northeastward range extension in southern New England, and significant population increases in the Eastern region (Robbins et al. 1986). Atlas data include 4 White-eyed Vireo records from 2 priority blocks in the Seacoast area in late May and early June. These birds likely were migratory overshoots, but some may have nested. With spring sightings most frequent along the coast, where moist thickets are abundant, and confirmed nesting in nearby Massachusetts, the White-eyed Vireo is likely to nest in Rockingham County in the near future, if it has not done so already.

Carol R. Foss

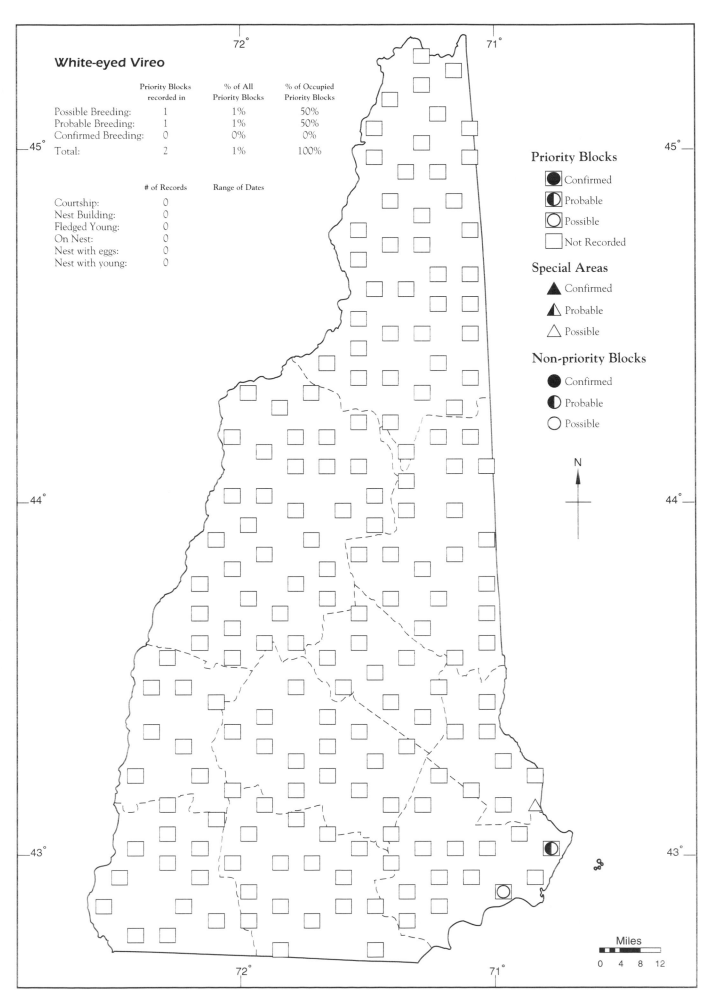

White-eyed Vireo

	Priority Blocks recorded in	% of All Priority Blocks	% of Occupied Priority Blocks
Possible Breeding:	1	1%	50%
Probable Breeding:	1	1%	50%
Confirmed Breeding:	0	0%	0%
Total:	2	1%	100%

	# of Records	Range of Dates
Courtship:	0	
Nest Building:	0	
Fledged Young:	0	
On Nest:	0	
Nest with eggs:	0	
Nest with young:	0	

Priority Blocks
- ◐ Confirmed
- ◑ Probable
- ○ Possible
- ☐ Not Recorded

Special Areas
- ▲ Confirmed
- ◢ Probable
- △ Possible

Non-priority Blocks
- ● Confirmed
- ◐ Probable
- ○ Possible

N

Miles
0 4 8 12

Solitary Vireo
Vireo solitarius

This vireo with a loud, melodious song is the first of its family to arrive in the spring, the last to depart in the fall, and the one most partial to conifers. It was formerly known as the Blue-headed Vireo, although its head is actually bluish gray. This feature, together with its white throat and spectacles and its yellowish sides, makes the Solitary easy to distinguish from our other common vireos. The Solitary Vireo breeds across Canada, in New England and the Great Lakes states; also south in the eastern mountains to Georgia, and in the western mountains to the highlands of Mexico, Guatemala, and El Salvador. It winters from South Carolina to southern California southward through Central America.

The first Solitary Vireos to appear in spring usually arrive by the last week in April, occasionally earlier. In southern New Hampshire most migrant individuals have gone north by 20 May. The spring migration often coincides with the hatching of tent caterpillars, and these birds feast on the small larvae (Bagg and Eliot 1937). In autumn Solitary Vireos stay until the second or third week of October, stragglers sometimes into November.

The song of the Solitary Vireo resembles those of the Red-eyed and Philadelphia vireos in being continued for long periods, with phrases separated by pauses, but it is more varied and musical. It is also louder, and the notes are more deliberate with longer pauses between them, in this respect resembling the song of the Yellow-throated Vireo. Sometimes the Solitary sings a continuous warbled song. An observer approaching a nest or young may hear the scolding note, which is a loud, musical chatter.

These vireos commonly inhabit mixed hardwood and hemlock forests, but they also nest in white pine groves and in woods of spruce and fir, especially if intermixed with hardwoods. Their nesting territories are larger than those of other vireos, except the Yellow-throated. Pairs seldom nest close to each other, hence the name "Solitary." In the White Mountains, Solitary Vireo territories studied averaged 12.5 a (5.1 ha) and were often narrow and long, up to nearly 3,000 ft (915 m) along streams (Sabo 1980). These birds breed in limited numbers above 3,000 ft (910 m) elevation—higher than any other vireos—but are most common in the 1,000 to 2,500 ft (300 to 760 m) range (T. Richards, unpubl. data).

Townsend (1920) and James (1973) described the courtship of the Solitary Vireo, in which the male, singing repeatedly with many variations, conspicuously fluffs his yellow flank feathers and bobs and bows to the female. Both sexes collect material for the nest, but the female constructs most of it. The nest, like that of other vireos, is suspended by its upper rim from the fork of a twig, usually less than 20 ft (6.1 m) above the ground (Harrison 1975). Goodhue (1922) examined many nests, most of them presumably in southern New Hampshire, of which "all but a few" were in hemlocks; the others were in pines or small firs. Nests are often in deciduous trees (Bent 1950). Both parents incubate the 3 to 5, usually 4 eggs. The male often sings while incubating (Bent 1950). Incubation lasts 13 or 14 days, the nestling period is about 2 weeks, and parents may feed young for a month or more after fledging occurs (James 1973, Peck and James 1987). Adults sing infrequently or not at all while caring for growing young, but thereafter sing until early August, and intermittently into October (Saunders 1935).

Solitary Vireo numbers have fluctuated in New Hampshire over the years, and various observers have called this summer resident common, uncommon, or even rare or absent at different times and places (Dearborn 1898, Allen 1903, Dearborn 1903, White 1937, Ridgely 1977, Allison and Allison 1979). Although its range encompasses the entire state, it always has been more common in the north than in the south, and in uplands than in lowlands. Allen (1903) considered it rare as a nesting species in the southeastern lowlands, and it still is today. Severe winters in the southern U. S., such as occurred in 1895 (Griscom and Snyder 1955), and harsh weather after their arrival in New Hampshire, as during the spring freeze of 1899 (Allen 1903) and the May snowstorms in 1940 (RNEB 1940, 1941) and 1963 (Bradley and Hebert 1963), may reduce the population for several years.

BBS data from 1966 to 1979 indicate a statistically significant population increase in New Hampshire and throughout the Northeastern states (Robbins et al. 1986). The New Hampshire data indicate rather low numbers from 1966 to 1970, an increase from 1971 to 1979, and another decline during the early 1980s. Low numbers during 1966–70 might have resulted from losses suffered during a May snowstorm in 1963. The increase during 1971–79 then would constitute normal recovery.

Atlas field work indicates that in New Hampshire Solitary Vireos continue to be primarily upland birds. They were found in almost all priority blocks that are entirely or mostly above 1,000 ft (300 m), in roughly two-thirds of the blocks at 500 to 1,000 ft (150 to 300 m), and in less than half of the blocks at 200 to 500 ft (60 to 150 m) elevation. Only one of 8 priority blocks below 200 ft (60 m) has an Atlas record for the species. They are common in the White Mountains and North Country, and only 5 priority blocks in the northern 3 counties lack Solitary Vireo records. The species is reasonably well distributed in south central and southwestern New Hampshire, but rare in the Coastal Lowlands.

Kimball C. Elkins & Vera W. Hebert

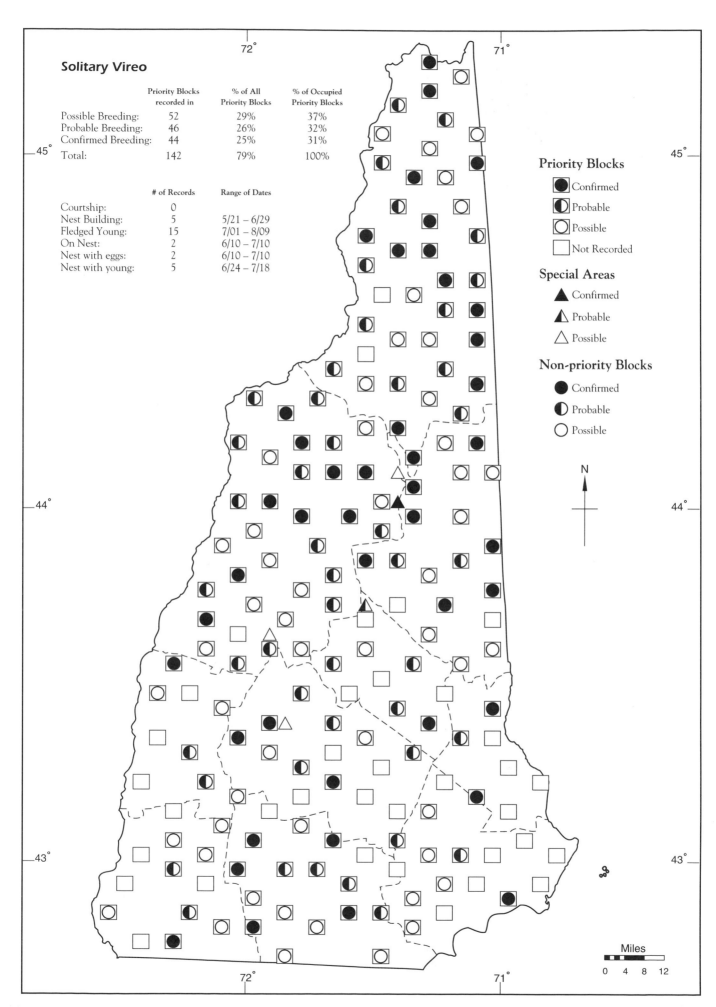

Solitary Vireo

	Priority Blocks recorded in	% of All Priority Blocks	% of Occupied Priority Blocks
Possible Breeding:	52	29%	37%
Probable Breeding:	46	26%	32%
Confirmed Breeding:	44	25%	31%
Total:	142	79%	100%

	# of Records	Range of Dates
Courtship:	0	
Nest Building:	5	5/21 – 6/29
Fledged Young:	15	7/01 – 8/09
On Nest:	2	6/10 – 7/10
Nest with eggs:	2	6/10 – 7/10
Nest with young:	5	6/24 – 7/18

Priority Blocks
- ◐ Confirmed
- ◑ Probable
- ○ Possible
- ☐ Not Recorded

Special Areas
- ▲ Confirmed
- ◭ Probable
- △ Possible

Non-priority Blocks
- ● Confirmed
- ◑ Probable
- ○ Possible

N

Miles
0 4 8 12

Yellow-throated Vireo
Vireo flavifrons

In spite of its bright yellow breast, the Yellow-throated Vireo is much more often heard than seen. Its loud song of slow, hoarse, slurred phrases is distinctive but unfamiliar to many, and can be confused with those of the Scarlet Tanager and Solitary Vireo. Preferred habitat is extensive tracts of lowland hardwood forest along a stream or lake, but some nesting territories occur along forest edge or in village shade trees near extensive forest (James 1979). The Yellow-throated Vireo generally arrives from Central America in mid-May, but occasionally appears earlier.

The male arrives first, in full song, typically returning to the previous summer's territory. Because he initially patrols a large nesting territory before mating, he sings for only a minute or 2 from one tall tree before flying to a distant perch high in another tree. Once mated, he sings much less, and may be silent for more than 30 minutes at a time while incubating (James 1984). As a result, a bird found on one trip may be missed easily on a subsequent visit, and will appear on an Atlas map as only a "possible" nester. Song ceases during the molt in August, but resumes briefly just before departure in September.

This vireo raises a single brood, often high in an oak tree. The pensile nest, suspended from the fork of a horizontal branch, is formed from strips of thin bark and grasses, decorated with lichens, and held together with caterpillar silk (Davie 1898). Scott (1921) found nests in the Durham area to be almost always in willow trees. In Ontario, these vireos prefer to nest in large mature deciduous trees, especially maples, poplars, oaks, and elms (Peck and James 1987). Most nests observed were in the crown or outer branches, but some were located 2 to 4 ft (0.6 to 1.2 m) from the trunk. Heights of 78 nests in Ontario ranged from 4 to 80 ft (1.2 to 24.3 m), with half in the 24 to 44 ft (7.3 to 13.5 m) range.

The 3 to 5 eggs hatch in 12 to 14 days. The young fledge in another 2 weeks (Bent 1950). The diet consists primarily of insects, largely butterflies and moths, but includes some wild fruits in late summer and autumn.

Few New Hampshire nest records exist. Atlas observers documented a nest with eggs near Squam Lake on 1 July 1984, and young in a nest at West Nottingham during 12–23 June 1985 (M.J. Murray, pers. comm.). The 3 Atlas records of adults carrying food or fecal sacs (2 June to 29 July) coincide with the expected period for dependent young.

Goodhue (1877) provided the earliest published reference for this species in New Hampshire and considered this vireo a rather common summer resident in the vicinity of Webster. Allen (1889) found it "not common" at Bridgewater during 12 July – 4 September 1883. Field records from several locations in the Lakes Region and White Mountains during 1885–87 do not include this species (Chadbourne 1887, Faxon and Allen 1888, Allen 1889). Farmer (1895) provided the first documented nest record for the state from Amoskeag, Manchester, on 14 June 1894 (Allen 1909).

Allen (1903) considered the Yellow-throated Vireo an uncommon to locally common summer resident in Transition valleys in southern New Hampshire, and rarer farther north. He knew of no record north of Lake Winnipesaukee. Torrey (1900) reported the only 19th century record north of the White Mountains, a male singing in Franconia on 3 June 1899. The only historical breeding record north of Haverhill is that of a bird carrying nesting material in Lancaster in 1900 (Wright 1911).

Pre-Atlas project distribution in the 20th century differed little from the above description. Scott (1921) stated that the Yellow-throated Vireo was fairly common in Durham in certain years, but was absent in others. This vireo gradually became scarcer in the state during the 1950s (Richards 1956), but increased in the Andover area after 1965 (K. C. Elkins, pers. comm.). Some former habitats, such as orchards and shade trees along village streets, still lack the breeding populations of past years.

The Atlas project documented for the first time that Yellow-throated Vireos are widely distributed from the Massachusetts border north to the base of the White Mountains and are not restricted to the score of towns from which nearly all previous records had come. Observers have recorded this vireo on 12 of the 15 BBS routes south of the White Mountains, and on 4 of the 7 routes in or north of the mountains. Atlas data include "possible" records from Jackson, Errol, and a cluster of 5 priority blocks in the Littleton area. Yellow-throated Vireos have occurred at elevations of 1,240 ft (380 m) at Morey Pond, Andover (K. C. Elkins, pers. comm.), 1,000 ft (305 m) in Harts Location, and 1,300 ft (396 m) near Stinson Lake, Rumney (T. Richards, pers. comm.).

BBS data suggest an average annual increase of 1.6% in New Hampshire during 1966–87. However, this species should be monitored, especially here at the northern edge of its breeding range. It may become increasingly threatened by loss of streamside and lakeshore habitat, fragmentation of extensive low elevation deciduous forests, and loss of tropical forest wintering habitat.

Chandler S. Robbins

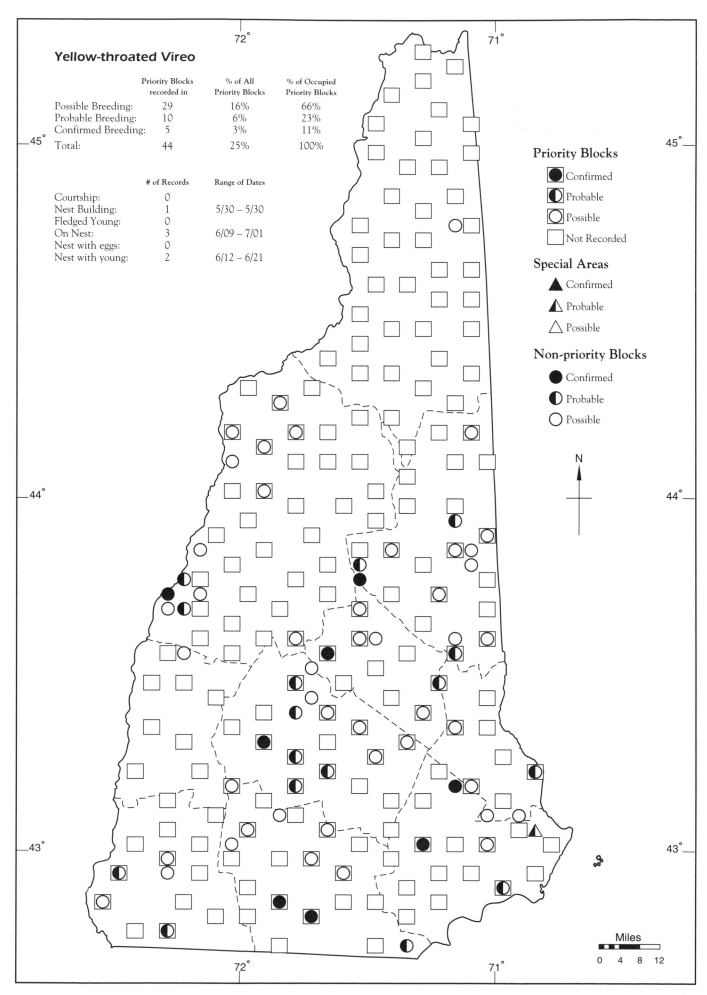

Yellow-throated Vireo

	Priority Blocks recorded in	% of All Priority Blocks	% of Occupied Priority Blocks
Possible Breeding:	29	16%	66%
Probable Breeding:	10	6%	23%
Confirmed Breeding:	5	3%	11%
Total:	44	25%	100%

	# of Records	Range of Dates
Courtship:	0	
Nest Building:	1	5/30 – 5/30
Fledged Young:	0	
On Nest:	3	6/09 – 7/01
Nest with eggs:	0	
Nest with young:	2	6/12 – 6/21

Priority Blocks
- ● Confirmed
- ◐ Probable
- ○ Possible
- □ Not Recorded

Special Areas
- ▲ Confirmed
- ◭ Probable
- △ Possible

Non-priority Blocks
- ● Confirmed
- ◐ Probable
- ○ Possible

N

Miles
0 4 8 12

Warbling Vireo
Vireo gilvus

The Warbling Vireo is plain and unobtrusive to the eye. Its grayish olive upperparts and white underparts blend with the dense foliage in which it lives. Those whose ears are attuned to bird song, however, find it a conspicuous inhabitant of shade trees in many New Hampshire villages during the summer months. Tall, well-spaced deciduous trees along village streets, streams, ponds, and country roads, in cemeteries, and around farmhouses provide this vireo with favorable nesting environments. Its preferred habitat differs from that of the Red-eyed Vireo in having more widely spaced trees, less undergrowth, and less dense shade (James 1976).

Although the Yellow-throated Vireo has broadly overlapping habitat requirements, little if any territorial competition occurs between the 2 species. Warbling Vireos forage mainly on leaves, while Yellow-throated Vireos forage primarily on branches and twigs (James 1976). Warbling Vireos forage high in deciduous trees, moving deliberately within the canopy in search of moths, caterpillars, beetles, pupae, and insect eggs. They also catch flying insects on the wing, and, rarely, catch grasshoppers and locusts from the ground (Forbush 1929).

Warbling Vireos usually arrive shortly after the trees have begun to leaf out, in early or mid-May. They sing incessantly from May to early August, and often again in September. They sometimes sing on the wing (Tyler 1950a), and often sing on the nest. This habit may enable a patient observer to find even a well-concealed nest; more than half of Atlas "confirmations" involved finding a nest. The Warbling Vireo's long, unhurried, rambling warble is quite different from the songs of other vireos. It often ends with an upward inflection, as if the bird were asking a question. The scanty information on courtship indicates that the male spreads his wings and tail and struts around the female (Dunham 1964).

The nests of Warbling Vireos usually are well hidden in the foliage of deciduous trees, especially elms, maples, willows, and poplars. Although Audubon (1967) and Harrison (1975) state that both sexes participate in nest building, other authors indicate that only the female builds (Goodhue 1922, Harrison 1978, Howes-Jones 1985). The nest usually is placed higher than those of other vireos at 15 to 60 ft (4.6 to 18.3 m), and well out from the trunk (Tyler 1950a, Harrison 1975). Like other vireo nests, it is suspended from the fork of a twig. The well-rounded cup is made of shreds of bark and various plant fibers but, unlike other vireos' nests, includes little birch bark (Harrison 1975).

The usual clutch is 4 eggs. Both parents incubate for 12 days, and both feed the young, which stay in the nest for about 12 days (Howes-Jones 1985). The fledged young are distinctively pale, with light brown backs, yellow-washed breast and flanks, and hoary heads (Tyler 1950a). Both adults and young have a sneezelike note which suggests garden shears clipping in the distance (Tyler 1950a). These vireos inconspicuously depart southward in August and September.

This vireo is unlikely ever to have been more than locally common in New Hampshire. Maynard (1871) thought the White Mountains formed the northern limit of its range. Allen (1903) considered this species rare from the mountain valleys north, and an uncommon summer resident in the lowlands south of the mountains. Dearborn (1898) regarded it as common in Merrimack and Belknap counties, and noted that it was less common near the coast than inland (Dearborn 1903). Thayer (1909 *in* Allison and Allison 1979) reported that it was rare in Dublin but common in Keene. Wright (1911) found it rare in Jefferson but common in Lancaster. Observers in Massachusetts noted a pronounced decline of this species in the 2 decades prior to 1930 (Bagg and Eliot 1937, Griscom 1949). In southern New Hampshire, however, Scott (1921) observed a great increase in the few years prior to about 1920. White (1937), on the other hand, stated that its numbers were very low around Concord during 1917–27, and attributed the decline, at least in part, to the spraying of shade trees.

Beginning in the 1930s, Warbling Vireo populations gradually increased (Bagg and Eliot 1937, White 1937, Griscom 1949), but Dutch elm disease and the pesticides used against it must have affected the species in many New Hampshire localities, as was the case in New York (Bull 1974). Although this vireo is a common victim of the Brown-headed Cowbird, which has increased greatly in New Hampshire in the last half century, it is not clear that cowbird parasitism has had any substantially harmful effect. New Hampshire BBS data from 1966 to 1984 show a modest increase of Warbling Vireos beginning about 1979.

This vireo is still locally common in its restricted habitat in lowland areas south of the White Mountains, where the Atlas project produced records for the majority of priority blocks. The species' absence in some lowland priority blocks and rather local occurrence in the Western Highlands probably is due to scarcity of suitable habitat. T. Richards (pers. comm.) has not found the Warbling Vireo above 1,000 ft (300 m) in the mountains. In the North Country, where most valleys and villages are above 1,000 ft (300 m), it now occurs sparingly even as far north as Pittsburg. This may indicate a recent range extension, perhaps encouraged by forest practices which have favored hardwoods.

Vera H. Hebert & Kimball C. Elkins

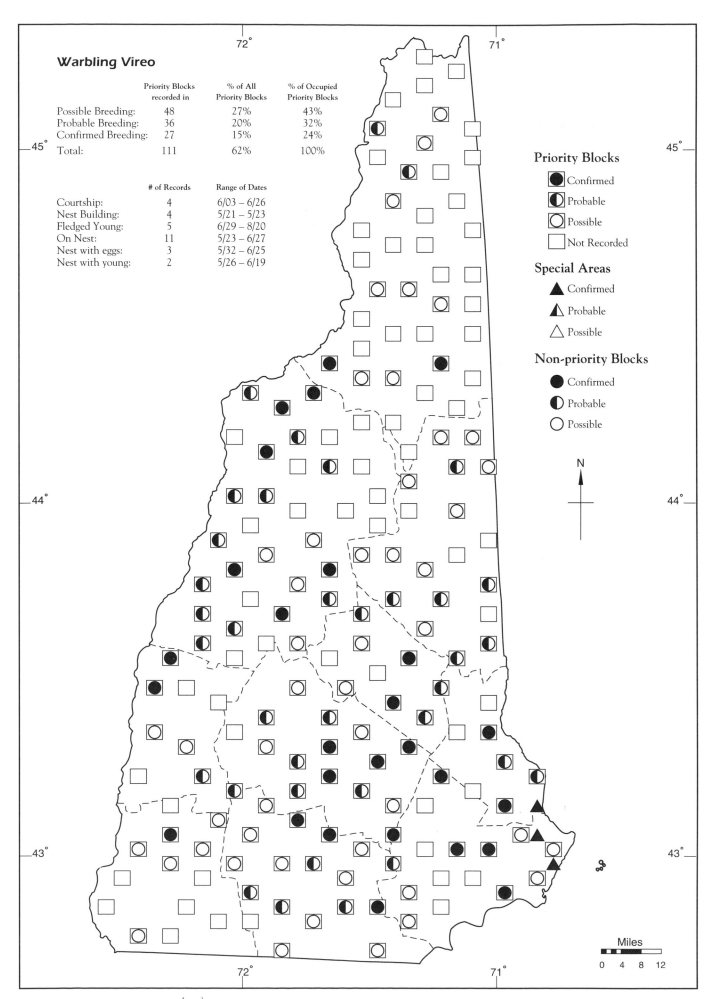

Warbling Vireo

	Priority Blocks recorded in	% of All Priority Blocks	% of Occupied Priority Blocks
Possible Breeding:	48	27%	43%
Probable Breeding:	36	20%	32%
Confirmed Breeding:	27	15%	24%
Total:	111	62%	100%

	# of Records	Range of Dates
Courtship:	4	6/03 – 6/26
Nest Building:	4	5/21 – 5/23
Fledged Young:	5	6/29 – 8/20
On Nest:	11	5/23 – 6/27
Nest with eggs:	3	5/32 – 6/25
Nest with young:	2	5/26 – 6/19

Priority Blocks
- ● Confirmed
- ◑ Probable
- ○ Possible
- ☐ Not Recorded

Special Areas
- ▲ Confirmed
- ◮ Probable
- △ Possible

Non-priority Blocks
- ● Confirmed
- ◐ Probable
- ○ Possible

N

Miles
0 4 8 12

245

Philadelphia Vireo
Vireo philadelphicus

The Philadelphia Vireo is smaller and more active than our other vireos and is the only one with both yellowish underparts and no wing bars. Because it looks somewhat like a Warbling Vireo and sounds like a Red-eyed Vireo, the Philadelphia is easily overlooked. Olive gray above, this vireo has a dark line through the eye and an indistinct, whitish eyebrow. The otherwise similar Tennessee Warbler has a much thinner bill and, like the Red-eyed and Warbling vireos, lacks the Philadelphia's extensive yellow coloring on the undersides in the breeding season.

This vireo was first described in 1851. The original specimen was collected in September 1842 near Philadelphia, and the species thus acquired the name of a location well south of its breeding range. The Philadelphia Vireo breeds in Canada and in the extreme northeastern U.S., where it is uncommon. It is rare in New Hampshire, breeding in the northern part of the state. Breeding habitat includes woodland edges, young deciduous growth, willow and alder thickets, and other deciduous trees along streams, rivers, and lakeshores (Brewster 1880, Pough 1946, Harrison 1978). In Ontario this vireo is frequently associated with trembling aspen (James *in* Cadman et al. 1987).

Brewster (1880) found that Philadelphia Vireos arrived in the Umbagog Lake area in late May with the last flight of warblers. There they frequented the tops and upper branches of young deciduous trees in clearings and burned-over areas, preferring cherries and gray birches. The birds arrived singly, began full singing around 10 June, and paired up subsequently. These findings differ from those of Barlow and Rice (1977) in Ontario, where Philadelphia Vireos arrive earlier than Red-eyed Vireos and pair immediately. The males are in full song in June, but frequency of singing diminishes rapidly around July first (Dwight 1897 *in* Bent 1965).

The male's typical song consists of a series of 2- or 3- syllable, liquid phrases usually repeated about half as frequently as those of the Red-eyed Vireo. The songs of the 2 species are very similar, but the Philadelphia's is generally slower, thinner, and less variable. The male Red-eyed Vireo does not discriminate between the territorial songs of the 2 species (Rice 1978a); observers should not rely solely on song to identify the Philadelphia Vireo. There are no reports of interbreeding. Each species responds aggressively to the other's song, and they occupy mutually exclusive, but sometimes partially overlapping territories (Barlow and Power 1970, Rice 1978b). The Philadelphia also gives a distinctive "ehhh" call, and a "bubble" song which resembles a call of the Yellow-throated Vireo (Barlow and Rice 1977). Lewis (1921 *in* Bent 1965) described songs of the female, some of which differ from those of the male.

Some authors report that both sexes help in nest building (Bent 1965, Harrison 1975), but Barlow and Rice (1977) found that females alone built the 43 nests they observed. The nest resembles those of other vireos and hangs from a horizontal fork in a tree or shrub 10 to 40 ft (3 to 12 m) above ground (Harrison 1975). It is made of strips of birch bark, weed stems, spider webs, *Usnea* lichens, and grasses. A nest at East Inlet, Pittsburg, was slung between 2 branches of a speckled alder, 11 ft (3.4 m) above the ground (Dyer and Walkinsaw 1959). It was made of cottony materials and decorated with wide strips of yellow birch bark.

The Philadelphia Vireo lays 3 to 5, usually 4 eggs in June. Unlike Red-eyed Vireos, both male and female Philadelphias share incubation (Barlow and Rice 1977). The male sings on the nest (Harrison 1975), and the incubating female allows close approach by humans (L. H. Walkinshaw, unpubl. data). The incubation period is about 14 days, and another 2 weeks pass before the young leave the nest (Bent 1965, Harrison 1978). Eggs in the nest at East Inlet hatched on 23 and 24 June 1959 (Walkinshaw 1960).

The Philadelphia Vireo forages more actively than other vireos, often hovering or gleaning insects from leaves. Occasionally it leaps into the air and snaps up a flying insect, or hangs upside down while picking insects from a cluster of leaves (Lewis 1921 *in* Bent 1965, Ridgely 1977). The diet consists almost exclusively of insects, especially caterpillars and beetles, and includes flies, bugs, bees, and ants (Bent 1965). Southward migration occurs during late August and September, at which time the species occurs throughout the state.

The Philadelphia Vireo always has been rare in New Hampshire. Brewster (1880) found the species breeding in the vicinity of Umbagog Lake and at Dixville Notch, Dixville, in the 1870s, and Hoffman (*in* Allen 1903) provided a breeding season record for Dixville Notch in 1903. Observers also found it in Franconia in June and July 1887 (Faxon and Allen 1888) and June 1889 (Torrey 1890). A pair at Chocorua on 5 June 1900 may have been late migrants (Allen 1903). In the Jefferson region, Wright (1911) knew the species only from fall migration. More recently, T. Richards (unpubl. data) documented Philadelphia Vireos at elevations of 1,500 to 3,000 ft (455 to 910 m) in the White Mountains on visits from 1946 to 1986.

Atlas data suggest that this vireo may be somewhat more widespread than previously recognized in the White Mountains and North Country. The birch and aspen stands that follow clearcuts in much of northern New Hampshire may have expanded available breeding habitat for this species.

Robert C. Vernon

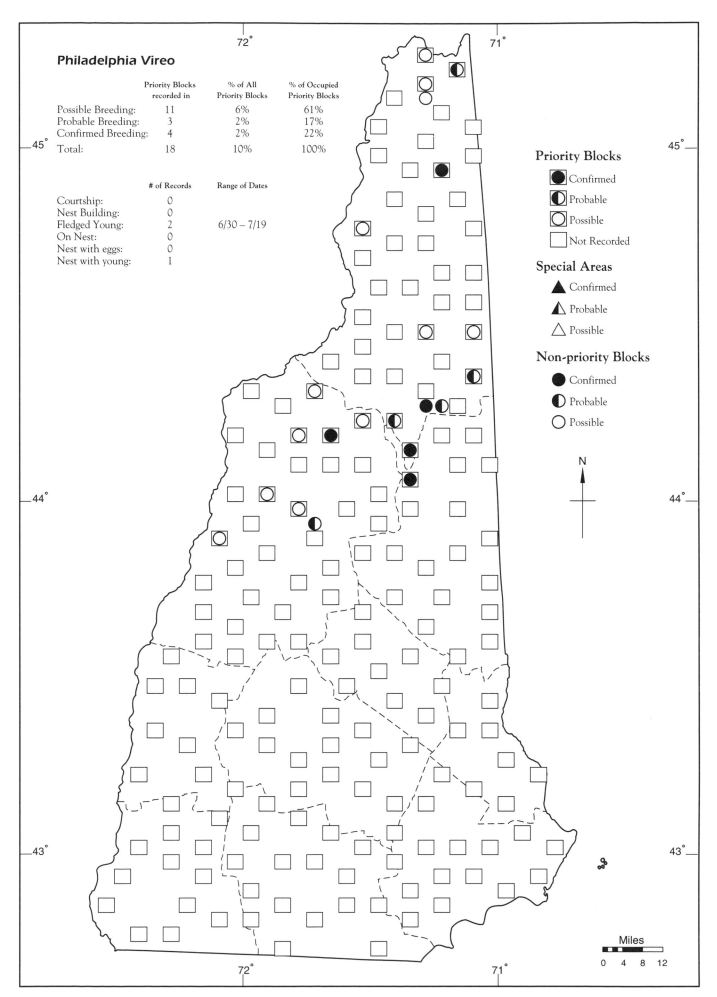

Philadelphia Vireo

	Priority Blocks recorded in	% of All Priority Blocks	% of Occupied Priority Blocks
Possible Breeding:	11	6%	61%
Probable Breeding:	3	2%	17%
Confirmed Breeding:	4	2%	22%
Total:	18	10%	100%

	# of Records	Range of Dates
Courtship:	0	
Nest Building:	0	
Fledged Young:	2	6/30 – 7/19
On Nest:	0	
Nest with eggs:	0	
Nest with young:	1	

Priority Blocks
- ● Confirmed
- ◐ Probable
- ○ Possible
- ☐ Not Recorded

Special Areas
- ▲ Confirmed
- ◣ Probable
- △ Possible

Non-priority Blocks
- ● Confirmed
- ◐ Probable
- ○ Possible

N

Miles
0 4 8 12

Red-eyed Vireo
Vireo olivaceus

The Red-eyed Vireo is New Hampshire's most wide-spread, abundant, and vociferous songbird. Its plumage blends well with deciduous leaves in the middle and upper canopy, where it moves slowly, hunting insects, or sits motionless on its nest. It can be a difficult bird to see, but is easily heard. This vireo's short, robinlike phrases pour forth from dawn to dusk, and sometimes at night, from May until August. In the hottest hours of midday when most birds are silent, the "preacher bird" seems to ask and answer its own incessant questions. The male sings even while eating.

New Hampshire BBS routes produce the highest Red-eyed Vireo counts of all the states and provinces in North America (Robbins et al. 1986). Typical territories average 1.7 a (0.7 ha) (Harrison 1975), although nests may be found close together. There are no New Hampshire nesting records of this species on the Isles of Shoals nor above 3,000 ft (910 m), but T. Richards (unpubl. data) has observed 17 individuals, mostly singing males, at 2,500 to 3,000 ft (760 to 910 m) in the White Mountains. Wintering in the vast Amazon Basin, the Red-eyed Vireo arrives in New Hampshire in mid-May and departs by the latter half of September.

This vireo is olive-green above, grayish white below, with a gray cap and no wing bars. The sexes are similar; immatures are slightly browner, with brown eyes. Although sometimes confused with Philadelphia (similar song) and Warbling (similar plumage) vireos, only the Red-eyed Vireo has a black-bordered white stripe above its eyes. Philadelphia and Red-eyed vireos are extremely difficult to distinguish by song alone.

Courtship includes vigorous chases through the high, leafy canopy. The male also performs a curious display in front of the female, swaying his upper body with fanned tail, fluffed body feathers, and sleeked head feathers, while warbling continuously. The female may react aggressively and resist his advances while building the nest, but as it nears completion she takes greater notice of his courtship and holds out her wings and quivers, often with raised tail, while calling "tchet, tchet, tchet" (Lawrence 1953).

We may become so used to the Red-eyed's continuous song, timed from 40 to 80 songs a minute (Peterson 1947, Tyler 1950b) that after a while we no longer hear it. During one 10-hour summer day, a Red-eyed Vireo sang 22,197 times (de Kiriline 1954). When her mate stops singing, the incubating female becomes restless and leaves the nest to feed (Lawrence 1953). The male does not sing during his late summer molt, but will sing again on quiet August days. The "nasal, whining 'chway'" (Peterson 1947) is a commonly heard call note and can help atlasers locate young vireos begging food from their parents.

Red-eyed Vireos nest in deciduous or mixed woodlands, orchards, or suburban shade trees. They require a leafy canopy for foraging and some sapling growth in which to nest (Lawrence 1953, Williamson 1971). The female chooses the site and builds the nest, which is suspended from a fork or between 2 twigs and a branch and always close to dense foliage (Lawrence 1953). The nest is usually 5 to 10 ft (1.5 to 3 m) from the ground, but may be at heights of up to 60 ft (18.3 m) (Lawrence 1953, Harrison 1978). Nest materials may include birch or other bark, especially long, narrow strips of grapevine, paper from a hornet nest, or even newspaper, fine grasses, and spider webs (Tyler 1950b, Harrison 1975). The hanging nest is not hard to find. Although it may remain in place for 2 or 3 years, the pair does not reuse it (Forbush 1929). A nest in a cutover area in Charlestown, observed on 24 June 1986, was securely suspended 25 ft (7.6 m) up in a fork, 5 ft (1.5 m) out on a horizontal branch of a black birch sapling (Janeway, pers. obs.).

Red-eyed Vireos may attack other birds that come close to their nest trees, even those as large as the Pileated Woodpecker (Zirrer *in* Tyler 1950b). The female incubates the 3 or 4 eggs for 12 to 14 days, and sometimes raises 2 broods (Lawrence 1953). In some areas cowbirds heavily parasitize this species (Scott 1921, Harrison 1975), but Lawrence (1953) found no parasitism among the Red-eyeds she studied. Both parents feed the young, which fledge in 10 or 11 days and remain vociferously dependent on their parents for 3 to 4 more weeks (Lawrence 1953). They disperse widely in late summer.

The Red-eyed Vireo gleans insects from the foliage, working mainly in the outer edges of the middle and upper canopy (DeGraaf and Rudis 1986). It often forages in the understory, usually by hovering (James 1976). The diet includes hairy caterpillars such as gypsy moth and tent caterpillars, a variety of other insects, land snails, and berries (Forbush 1929, Tyler 1950b).

For decades this species has been an extremely abundant summer resident and migrant in New Hampshire (Allen 1903, Forbush 1929). More Red-eyed Vireo habitat exists in New Hampshire today than in the 1800s, when farms and open fields covered much of the state. BBS data suggest an increasing population in the Eastern region during 1966–79 (Robbins et al. 1986). The Atlas map illustrates this vireo's currently widespread distribution in the state, with only one priority block lacking a record for the species. Given the Red-eyed Vireo's diversity in nesting habitat and food requirements, it probably will remain abundant here for the foreseeable future.

Elizabeth C. Janeway

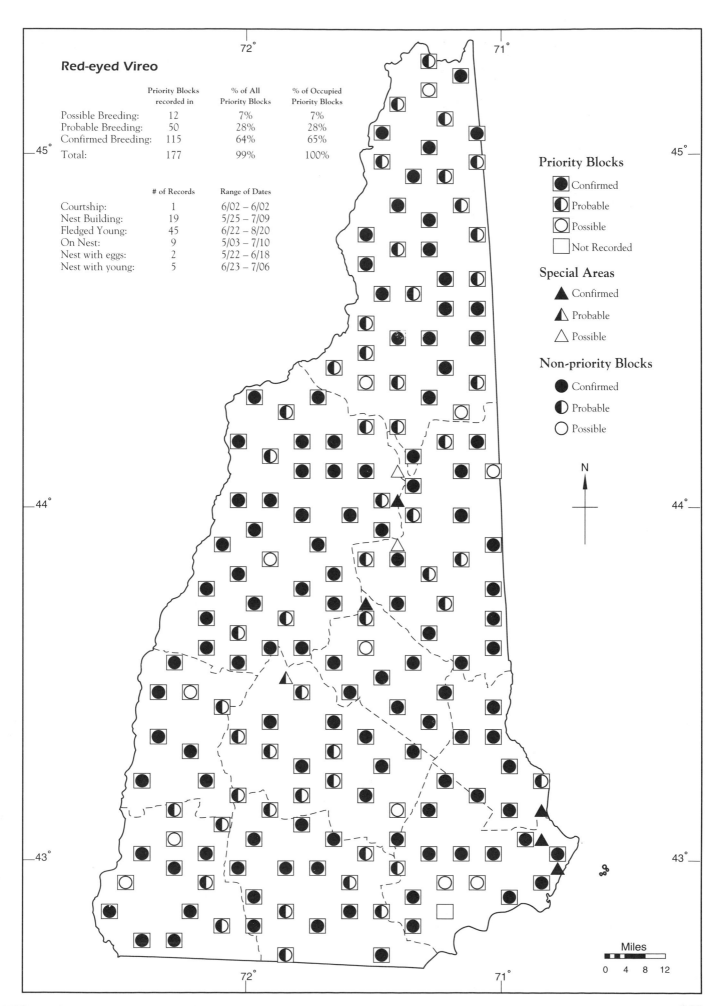

Red-eyed Vireo

	Priority Blocks recorded in	% of All Priority Blocks	% of Occupied Priority Blocks
Possible Breeding:	12	7%	7%
Probable Breeding:	50	28%	28%
Confirmed Breeding:	115	64%	65%
Total:	177	99%	100%

	# of Records	Range of Dates
Courtship:	1	6/02 – 6/02
Nest Building:	19	5/25 – 7/09
Fledged Young:	45	6/22 – 8/20
On Nest:	9	5/03 – 7/10
Nest with eggs:	2	5/22 – 6/18
Nest with young:	5	6/23 – 7/06

Priority Blocks
- Confirmed
- Probable
- Possible
- Not Recorded

Special Areas
- Confirmed
- Probable
- Possible

Non-priority Blocks
- Confirmed
- Probable
- Possible

N

Miles
0 4 8 12

Blue-winged Warbler
Vermivora pinus

Despite its brilliant yellow plumage, the Blue-winged Warbler is an unobtrusive forager that moves deliberately like a vireo while gleaning insects from twigs and leaves. The Blue-wing is a relative newcomer to New Hampshire, having become established here since 1950. Overgrown pastures, wrested from New Hampshire's heavily forested landscape during the last century but now reverting to woodland, provide perfect habitat for the northeasterly expansion of this warbler's range. The Blue-wing prefers drier and less recently abandoned pastures than the closely related Golden-winged Warbler.

The mostly yellow Blue-winged Warbler has slaty blue-gray wings with 2 white wing bars, and a distinctive black eye-line. This warbler interbreeds with the closely related Golden-winged Warbler to produce 2 distinctive hybrids, the "Brewster's" and "Lawrence's" warblers. The Brewster's has several plumage variations but generally has the white underparts of the Golden-winged Warbler and always has the narrow eye-line. The Lawrence's also shows plumage variations, with generally yellow underparts and black face and throat patches (NGS 1983). These hybrids are the most studied of any hybrid birds in the wild (Reilly 1979). The frequency of hybridization is a low 5 to 10%, and the hybrids are fertile (Gill 1980). Both the more common Brewster's Warbler and the rare Lawrence's Warbler occur in New Hampshire. Blue-winged, Golden-winged and Brewster's warblers occur regularly at East Foss Farm, Durham (M. Davis, pers. comm.). In 1986 singing males of both species and both hybrids were present in a quarter acre area in South Hampton (G. W. Gavutis, pers. comm.).

The Blue-winged Warbler arrives on New Hampshire breeding grounds in early May from wintering grounds in Central America. An insectlike "beeee-buzz" song is often the first indication of Blue-wing presence. The male sings from an open, high perch during courtship (Terres 1980), but seldom sings once the nest is built and incubation begins (Murray and Gill 1976). The similar song of the Golden-wing is longer, but songs of both species are variable. Because the hybrids may sing either song and a Blue-wing may give the Golden-wing song, only a sighting provides positive identification.

Gill (1985) found that Golden-winged Warblers in northern New York state prefer fields with few trees and shrubs, while Blue-winged Warblers will accept older fields, hedgerows, and swamp edges also. All areas in New Hampshire that have supported Golden-wings now report Blue-wings, and Blue-wings now occur in many areas that had no previous reports of Golden-wings.

Ficken and Ficken (1968b) report Blue-wing territories of less than 1 a (0.4 ha) in New York. Observations of a New Hampshire colony in Dover indicate territories of slightly less than an acre each (Turner, pers. obs.). The arrival of Blue-wings has been cited as causing Golden-wing declines, but evidence is contradictory (Confer 1992).

Courtship displays of Blue-winged and Golden-winged warblers are similar, and pair-bond formation is rapid. Interactions include "bill dueling," soliciting, "moth flight," and a female approaching a singing male, who subsequently chases her (Ficken and Ficken 1968a, Murray and Gill 1976).

The female builds a deep, bulky nest, usually on the ground in concealing vegetation, often a goldenrod clump (Harrison 1984). Made of grasses, dead leaves, and strips of bark, it is well camouflaged (S.R. Mirick, pers. comm.). Nonetheless, this species is highly vulnerable to nest predation and Brown-headed Cowbird parasitism (Harrison 1984). The single clutch consists of 4 to 7 eggs, usually 5. Like many ground nesters, the female sits closely, and incubates her eggs for 10 or 11 days (Harrison 1978). One breeding "confirmation" occurred when a female flew from tall grass at the base of an aspen with a fecal sac which she dropped about 25 ft (7.6 m) away (Turner, pers. obs.).

A population of Blue-winged Warblers in Dover in 1985 seems to support the possibility that more males than females exist in the breeding population. Bachelors sometimes help feed nestlings of an established pair, moving on to another brood when the first brood fledges (Short 1964). The young leave the nest at 8 to 10 days (Harrison 1978).

The first New Hampshire records of the Blue-winged Warbler came from Wilton on 21–22 May 1955, Concord on 13 May 1956, Hancock on 24 May 1958, and Kensington on 17 May 1959 (RNEB and NHAQ, *passim*). Scattered spring and occasional late summer records continued and increased during the 1960s. Early breeding season records include individuals in Hollis in 1966 and in Kensington and Newfields in 1967. Consistent spring observations in Kensington, beginning in 1959, suggest that the state's first nesting attempts may have occurred there. Observers reported a Blue-wing paired with a Lawrence's Warbler there in 1972 (Hebert 1972).

This species' population increase and range expansion continued during the 6 years of Atlas field work, culminating in 1985 with a singing male as far north as Tilton and at least 5 singing males on a power-line right-of-way in Dover, where none were reported before 1984 (Turner, pers. obs.). The majority of observations occur in the coastal plain, but Blue-wings occur as far west as the Merrimack Valley. If current trends continue, the Blue-winged Warbler will continue to expand in range and numbers in New Hampshire as it has in other northern states from Minnesota east (Bull 1974, Confer and Knapp 1979, Gill 1980, Clark *in* Laughlin and Kibbe 1985, Robbins et al. 1986).

Sandra B. Turner

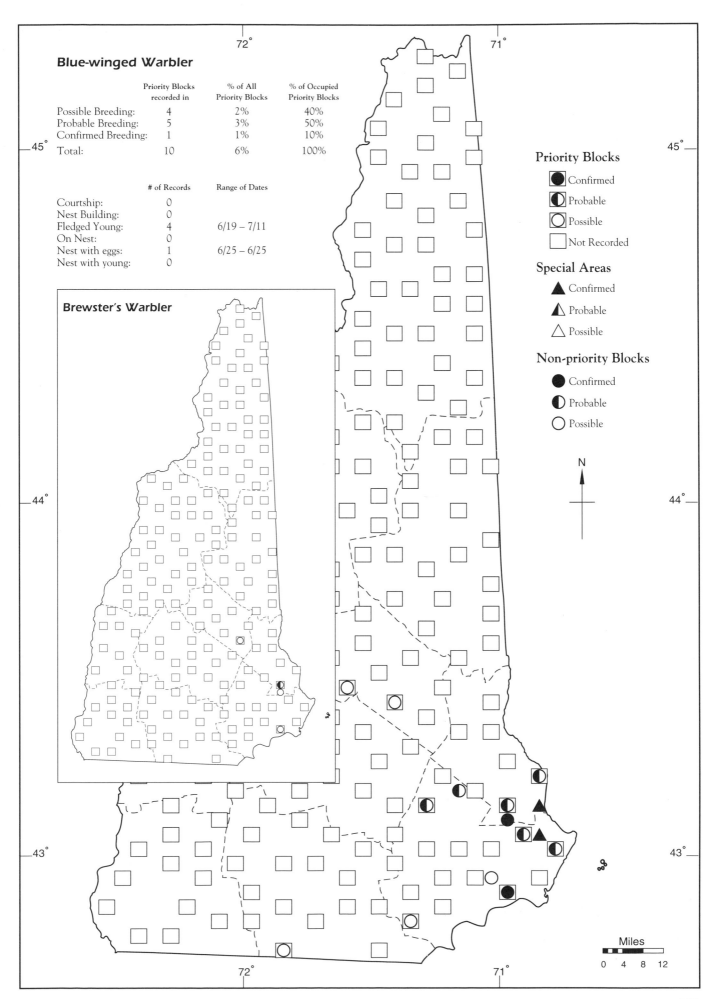

Blue-winged Warbler

	Priority Blocks recorded in	% of All Priority Blocks	% of Occupied Priority Blocks
Possible Breeding:	4	2%	40%
Probable Breeding:	5	3%	50%
Confirmed Breeding:	1	1%	10%
Total:	10	6%	100%

	# of Records	Range of Dates
Courtship:	0	
Nest Building:	0	
Fledged Young:	4	6/19 – 7/11
On Nest:	0	
Nest with eggs:	1	6/25 – 6/25
Nest with young:	0	

Brewster's Warbler

Priority Blocks
- ◑ Confirmed
- ◑ Probable
- ○ Possible
- □ Not Recorded

Special Areas
- ▲ Confirmed
- ◭ Probable
- △ Possible

Non-priority Blocks
- ● Confirmed
- ◑ Probable
- ○ Possible

N

Miles
0 4 8 12

Golden-winged Warbler
Vermivora chrysoptera

The colorful and distinctive Golden-winged War-bler is one of our rarest breeding birds. Its seemingly strong adaptation to early successional habitat (Con-fer and Knapp 1979) may be contributing to its demise as the acreage of overgrown farmland dwindles. The USFWS listed the Golden-winged Warbler as a Migra-tory Nongame Bird of Management Concern in 1987. The species' rather restricted breeding range extends from eastern Minnesota to southern Vermont and New Hampshire, and south along the Appalachian Mts. to northern Georgia (Peterson 1980). This warbler win-ters from Central America south to Columbia and Venezuela (Harrison 1984).

The male Golden-wing arrives in New Hampshire about mid-May and quickly establishes a territory by persistently singing his monotonous buzzy "bee-bz-bz-bz" song from prominent perches. Typical breeding habitat includes a combination of dry uplands and marshes or bogs (Confer 1992), often a moist, brushy meadow adjacent to deciduous woods (Green *in* Forbush 1929).

The nest usually is located near the edge of an open-ing within the shade of neighboring trees. It is built on the ground and generally is supported by a base of dead leaves and weed stalks. Harrison (1975) observed con-struction of a nest which was completed in 5 days. In Massachusetts, the 4 to 6 eggs usually are laid in late May and early June. The incubation period lasts 10 to 12 days (Peck and James 1987, Ehrlich et al. 1988). Both parents tend the young, which leave the nest at 10 days of age (Harrison 1978). Young Golden-wings have a characteristic call note which persists well af-ter fledging (Tyler 1953a).

"Pishing" readily attracts and agitates these warblers during the nesting season (Gavutis, pers. obs.). How-ever, Golden-wings can be very unobtrusive once the males cease their persistent singing in mid-June (Tyler 1953a). They become increasingly quiet and difficult to find in July and August and usually migrate by early September.

The Golden-winged Warbler readily interbreeds with the closely related Blue-winged Warbler, yielding the rare and colorful "Brewster's" and "Lawrence's" hybrids. During 2 different breeding seasons in the late 1970s and early 1980s, Gavutis observed a territorial male Golden-winged War-bler in Kensington replaced first by a Brewster's or Lawrence's hybrid and then by a male Blue-winged Warbler, all within a week. At another site in South Hampton, males of both species and both hybrids were actively singing along a small stream in a recently clear-cut area of about 0.25 a (0.10 ha) on 14 May 1986 and were all present on 31 May 1986 (D. Abbott and Gavutis, pers. obs.). One hybrid used a typical Blue-wing call, which emphasizes the need for visual verification. Subsequent visits yielded only Golden-wings, one of which was carrying food on 14 June.

In Durham, S. R. Mirick (ASRF) observed an agitated male Golden-wing carrying food on 27 June and fledged young in the same area on 28 June 1984. This site, which consistently has supported Golden-winged and/ or Blue-winged warblers in recent years, is an abandonded field with scat-tered Atlantic white cedars, common junipers, barberry bushes, apple trees, and other small trees and shrubs.

Most naturalists have considered the Golden-wing a rare resident in southeastern New Hampshire and accidental elsewhere in the state (Coues 1868, Richards 1958, Thayer 1909 *in* Allison and Allison 1979). W. E. Cram collected an early specimen at Hampton Falls in May 1887 (Allen 1903), and Dearborn (1903) collected another in Durham on 24 May 1898.

Both Blue-winged and Golden-winged warblers have experienced a northward and eastward expansion during this century (Harrison 1984). Scott (1921) reported it as rare and not nesting in New Hampshire despite nesting nearby in north central Massachusetts and in eastern Vermont near the Connecticut River. White (1937) provides records for Concord from late May and early June 1902, and 15 May 1934. Records from 1939 to 1957 include individuals in Andover, Exeter, Hampstead, Hampton Falls, Hanover, Manchester, and Seabrook in spring or late summer (RNEB, *passim*). K. C. Elkins (pers. comm.) observed an individual in Warner on 4 June 1964. Several sites supported territorial males in the Exeter/ Kensington area beginning about 1958 and continuing during the 1970s and 1980s (RNEB, *passim*; S. Clements, K. C. Elkins, S. Kilgore, pers. comm.).

New Hampshire breeding season observations of the Golden-wing dur-ing 1963–79 were primarily on the coastal plain (ASNH data), and New Hampshire Atlas data follow a similar pattern. The Maine Breeding Bird Atlas project produced only one Golden-wing record, in South Berwick (Adamus 1988).

Since Blue-winged Warblers first became more common here approxi-mately 30 years ago, there have been strong indications that they have been replacing Golden-wings (SRS). In Connecticut, Gill (1980) reported that the Golden-wing usually disappears from an area within 50 years af-ter the blue-wing's arrival. However, Confer (1992) points out that the de-cline of the Golden-wing is correlated both with the arrival of the blue-wing and with the loss of habitat as succession proceeds from shrublands to forest, and that the evidence for the "relative importance of these two factors is sometimes contradictory." The Golden-winged Warbler currently is surviving at a few sites in southeastern New Hampshire. Small clear-cuts along streams may be one management option for this rare and declining species.

George W. Gavutis, Jr.

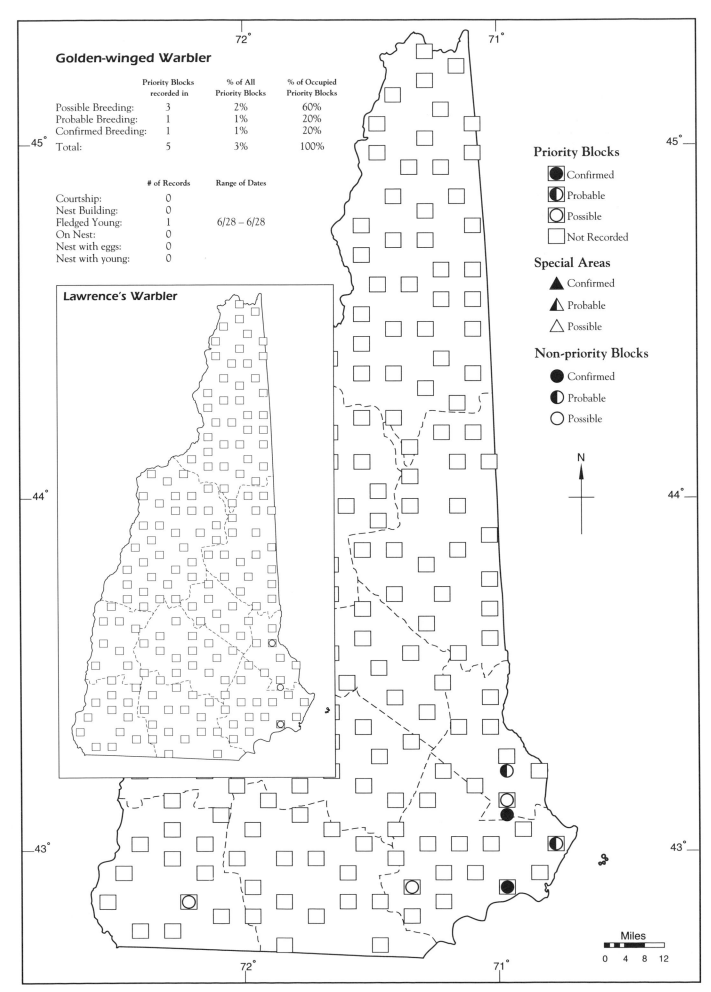

Golden-winged Warbler

	Priority Blocks recorded in	% of All Priority Blocks	% of Occupied Priority Blocks
Possible Breeding:	3	2%	60%
Probable Breeding:	1	1%	20%
Confirmed Breeding:	1	1%	20%
Total:	5	3%	100%

	# of Records	Range of Dates
Courtship:	0	
Nest Building:	0	
Fledged Young:	1	6/28 – 6/28
On Nest:	0	
Nest with eggs:	0	
Nest with young:	0	

Lawrence's Warbler

Priority Blocks
- ◑ Confirmed
- ◑ Probable
- ◯ Possible
- ☐ Not Recorded

Special Areas
- ▲ Confirmed
- ◤ Probable
- △ Possible

Non-priority Blocks
- ● Confirmed
- ◐ Probable
- ○ Possible

N

Miles
0 4 8 12

Tennessee Warbler
Vermivora peregrina

The greenish and white Tennessee Warbler resembles a vireo except for its thinner bill and generally quicker movements. Only because the species was first discovered in Tennessee, as a migrant, does it carry that name. This bird breeds across Canada and the very northern fringe of the U.S., and winters from southern Mexico to Colombia and Venezuela (AOU 1957). In New Hampshire it sometimes is a common to abundant migrant, at least in autumn, but is an irregular, local and uncommon to rare summer resident in the northern part of the state. It may be entirely absent in some summers and even for periods of years.

Like the Cape May and Bay-breasted warblers, this species is a spruce budworm specialist, and its local abundance is directly related to the population status of this northern forest insect (Kendeigh 1947, Erskine 1977, Morse 1989). Northern tamarack swamps at elevations of 1,000 to 2,000 ft (300 to 610 m) are the usual habitat in the Granite State, but this warbler also uses spruce-fir forests up to elevations of more than 4,000 ft (1,220 m) and sometimes mixed stands of conifers and hardwoods (Richards, pers. obs.).

Tennessee Warblers arrive in New Hampshire between mid-May and early June. Persistent singing may be the main courtship performance, and males may sing on their breeding grounds until mid-August (Palmer 1949). The loud staccato song is a lengthy, accelerating and somewhat musical chipping, usually with 3 distinct sections. Bent (1953) suggests that colonial nesting may occur. Six males singing in tamaracks in Wentworth's Location on 6 July 1955 (Richards, unpubl. data) may support this theory.

Knight (in Palmer 1949) found nests in Maine on mossy hummocks among alders in a boggy area, constructed mostly of grass. In Nova Scotia nests are in open woodlands, pastures, or clearings, but are well concealed (Tufts 1986). In Maine the Tennessee Warbler may nest promptly after arriving, as indicated by

Knight's records (in Palmer 1949) of 5 eggs advanced in incubation on 4 June 1895 and nestlings on 10 and 15 June. Eggs number 4 to 7 (Bent 1953), and the female alone incubates. Incubation and nestling periods probably are similar to the 11 or 12 days of the closely related Nashville Warbler (Harrison 1978). Both parents feed the young.

These dexterous warblers consume large numbers of small insects, gleaning them from the outermost foliage of the canopy. They favor caterpillars, flies, beetles, plant lice, and spiders. They also eat some berries, and puncture grapes for drinks (King in Griscom 1938).

Singing males sometimes appear in early July in New Hampshire well south of their usual summer range (SRS). Apparently the first relatively recent record was one at New Ipswich on 8 July 1960 (Wellman in Hebert 1960a). Other scattered records followed in some of the succeeding years. In July 1981 unprecedented numbers of singing males occurred in southern and central New Hampshire (Quinn 1982), including 3 to 5 which sang incessantly from apparent territories in the Philbrick-Cricenti Bog, New London, during 14–22 July (Vernon in Quinn 1982). Observers also reported Tennessee Warblers during July in Wolfeboro, Sandwich, and Albany. Perhaps significantly, no females were among these July records. Oatman (in Laughlin and Kibbe 1985) notes that singing males south of or even within the breeding range may be unmated, and that Tennessee Warblers may begin to move south from Vermont breeding sites in mid-July. Thus, the breeding status of this species is difficult to deduce from July records. During fall migration, which generally extends from early August to about 20 September in New Hampshire, this species often associates with other warblers, vireos, chickadees, and other birds.

New Hampshire's Tennessee Warbler breeding population has experienced considerable fluctuations, with increases generally related to periodic spruce budworm outbreaks. Brewster (in Griscom 1938) commented that during the last century the Tennessee Warbler was common during some of his earlier visits to Umbagog Lake and absent during his later ones. Perry (in Griscom 1938) found the warbler at Umbagog during 1932–33, but not in 1936. It was present again in 1955. BBS data show an increase east of the Mississippi River in the period 1966–79 during a budworm outbreak (Robbins et al. 1986). Similar irregularities seem to have occurred in northern New Hampshire in recent years. An overall increase may have occurred during the last century (Griscom 1949, Bent 1953), though Palmer (1949) suggests that the increase in Maine records "probably is due to a greater number of trained observers."

New Hampshire's first high-elevation breeding season record for the Tennesee Warbler seems to be of 3 or 4 singing males in Oakes Gulf, Mt. Washington, at about 4,000 ft (1,220 m), on 18–20 July 1946 (Richards, pers. obs.). Others include individuals near Carter Notch, Beans Purchase, in July 1946; at Lonesome Lake, Lincoln, during 3–4 July 1962; near Mt. Jackson, Beans Grant, on 13 July 1966; and 2 in the Great Gulf, Thompson and Merserves Purchase, on 8 July 1967 (Richards, unpubl. data). There are also some more recent high-elevation records.

The Atlas map shows an expected concentration of records in far northern New Hampshire and a few in the White Mountains and the Western Highlands south to Mt. Sunapee, Newbury. During "good" Tennessee Warbler years the distribution could well be wider. The range of this species tends to fluctuate even where habitat conditions appear to be favorable. Wide fluctuations thus are not surprising near the southern limit of its range.

Tudor Richards

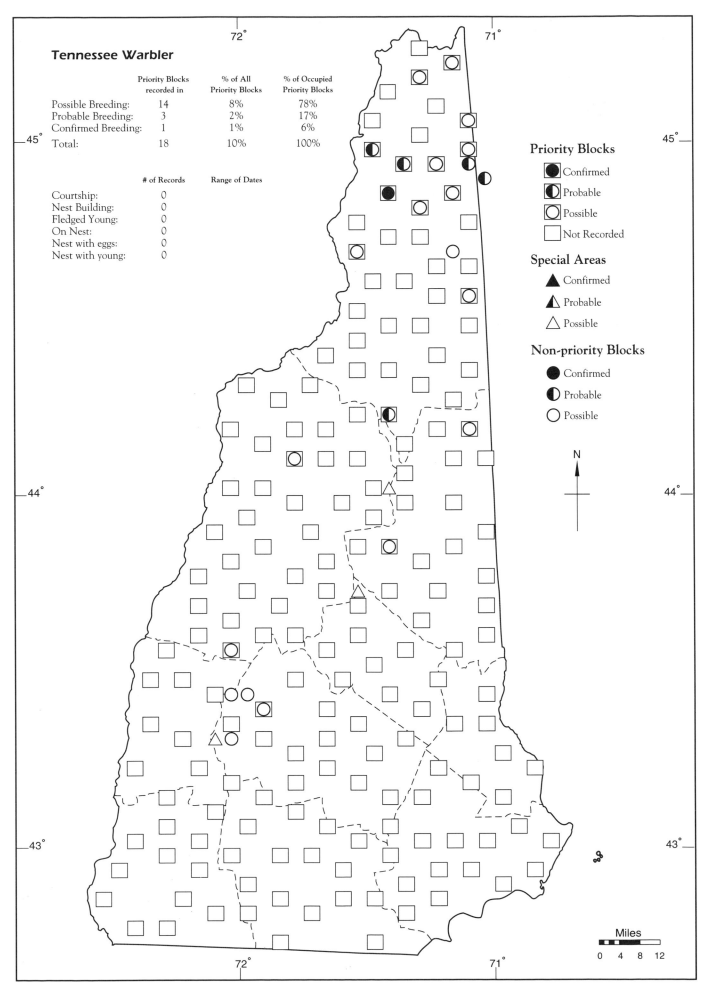

Tennessee Warbler

	Priority Blocks recorded in	% of All Priority Blocks	% of Occupied Priority Blocks
Possible Breeding:	14	8%	78%
Probable Breeding:	3	2%	17%
Confirmed Breeding:	1	1%	6%
Total:	18	10%	100%

	# of Records	Range of Dates
Courtship:	0	
Nest Building:	0	
Fledged Young:	0	
On Nest:	0	
Nest with eggs:	0	
Nest with young:	0	

Priority Blocks
- ● Confirmed
- ◑ Probable
- ○ Possible
- ☐ Not Recorded

Special Areas
- ▲ Confirmed
- ◤ Probable
- △ Possible

Non-priority Blocks
- ● Confirmed
- ◑ Probable
- ○ Possible

N

Miles
0 4 8 12

Nashville Warbler
Vermivora ruficapilla

The small, sprightly Nashville Warbler is a widely distributed and fairly common inhabitant of young, brushy, regenerating forests, spruce bogs, and forest edges. An active forager in shrubs and low trees, the Nashville is identified by its gray head, bright yellow underparts, olive-green back, conspicuous eye-ring, and lack of wing bars. Its scientific name, which means "red-haired," refers to the male's (usually concealed) chestnut crown and is more fitting than its common name, as the Nashville's breeding range extends no farther south than West Virginia (Hall 1983).

Most Nashvilles arrive in New Hampshire during mid-May, though some may appear as early as 1 May. During migration they are widespread and occur in tall treetops as well as lower growth (Pough 1949). They breed at elevations from near sea level to timberline in the White Mountains, where they are common in subalpine forests from 2,600 to 4,500 ft (790 to 1,370 m) (Allen 1903, Wright 1911, Sabo 1980).

The Nashville's distinctive 2-part song consists of a series of 2-note phrases followed by a lower trill. The song resembles that of the Tennessee Warbler, but the latter is normally a staccato 3-part song, faster at the end but not dropping in pitch. The Nashville also may give a flight song in late summer (Chapman 1907). The male usually sings from the tops of small trees that are 15 to 30 ft (4.6 to 9.2 m) tall (Kendeigh 1945a, Pough 1949). His territory may range from about 0.5 a (0.2 ha) (Lawrence 1948) to 2.7 a (1.1 ha) (Sabo 1980). Males may silently chase other birds for short distances in territorial defense (Kendeigh 1945a). The song period extends until the middle of July in the White Mountains (Wright 1911). Atlas records suggest a sharp decline in song after 10 July, with the latest record on 22 July.

The well-hidden nest is on the ground in a mossy or grassy depression or hummock, or at the base of a shrub or stump. In Michigan, Roth (1977) found Nashville nests in open areas with well-developed herbaceous ground cover and tall balsam fir nearby. The female builds the small, neat cup of grasses, leaves, moss, and roots lined with fine grasses, pine needles, hair, and rootlets in 7 to 9 days (Harrison 1975).

The female lays 3 to 5 eggs in late May or June, and incubates for 11 or 12 days. Locating nests is nearly impossible unless one follows a female with nesting material or flushes her during incubation (Forbush and May 1939, Harrison 1975). The female sits closely during incubation while the male sings from nearby treetops (Forbush and May 1939). The male may feed the incubating female (Roth 1977). If disturbed on the nest, the female may put on a distraction display (Lawrence 1948), which several atlasers observed in late June and early July.

Both parents feed the young, which stay in the nest for 10 or 11 days (Forbush 1929). Most Atlas "confirmations" were of adults carrying food or fecal sacs (mostly during mid-June to mid-July) and recently fledged young (concentrated in mid-July). When the young can fly well, the family forages together (Forbush and May 1939). Southward migration begins in late August. Most Nashvilles have departed by the third week of September, though a few remain into early October.

Until the mid-1800s, the Nashville was considered a rare breeding species in New England (Bent 1953). Before widespread settlement, it probably was restricted to forest edges around burns, beaver meadows, and bogs (Kibbe *in* Laughlin and Kibbe 1985). When clearing and cultivation decreased in the late 1800s, forest regeneration on abandoned agricultural land created extensive habitat for the Nashville, which became fairly common in much of New England by the turn of the century. Even so, its distribution was irregular and its numbers seemed to fluctuate (Bent 1953).

During the late 1800s and early 1900s in New Hampshire, this species was variously described as common in Franconia and Gorham but uncommon at Umbagog Lake (Maynard 1871), "very common" near Squam Lake (Faxon and Allen 1888), "rather scarce" in the Lakes Region (Dearborn 1898), an abundant breeder in the Monadnock region, nesting nearly to the 3,165 ft (965 m) summit of Mt. Monadnock, Jaffrey (Thayer *in* Chapman 1907), a common summer resident in the White Mountains (Wright 1911) and the Durham area (Scott 1921), and fairly common, though variable, around Concord (White 1924, 1937). Allen (1903) noted it as a "rather common" summer resident throughout most of the state.

Atlas observers found Nashvilles throughout New Hampshire, though they appear to be most widespread in the Western Highlands, the Eastern Uplands, and the North Country. The existence of records in every priority block in Coos County, where many blocks received minimal Atlas effort, attests to their conspicuous presence there. The apparent absence of Nashvilles in parts of the Lakes Region, White Mountains, and southern New Hampshire may reflect a lack of suitable habitat in areas of extensive mature forest and in thickly settled areas.

It seems certain that the Nashville has benefited from widespread forest regeneration over the past hundred years, but unlike the Chestnut-sided Warbler, it never became truly abundant throughout the state. As second-growth forests mature and shade out low, brushy cover, the Nashville Warbler may become less common (Pough 1949, Bull and Farrand 1977). Patterns of forest regeneration and succession will strongly influence the future of the Nashville Warbler in New Hampshire.

Steve Smith

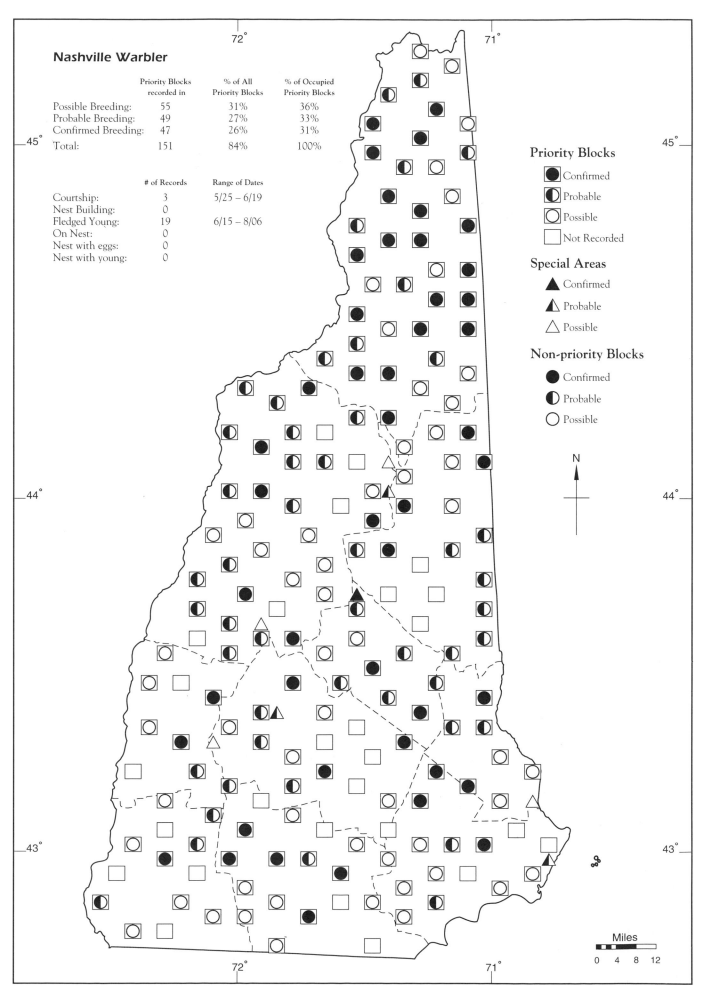

Nashville Warbler

	Priority Blocks recorded in	% of All Priority Blocks	% of Occupied Priority Blocks
Possible Breeding:	55	31%	36%
Probable Breeding:	49	27%	33%
Confirmed Breeding:	47	26%	31%
Total:	151	84%	100%

	# of Records	Range of Dates
Courtship:	3	5/25 – 6/19
Nest Building:	0	
Fledged Young:	19	6/15 – 8/06
On Nest:	0	
Nest with eggs:	0	
Nest with young:	0	

Priority Blocks
- Confirmed
- Probable
- Possible
- Not Recorded

Special Areas
- Confirmed
- Probable
- Possible

Non-priority Blocks
- Confirmed
- Probable
- Possible

N

Miles
0   4   8   12

Northern Parula
Parula americana

The diminutive Northern Parula occurs most often in openings in damp coniferous forests where bearded lichen, the favorite nesting material, grows in abundance. The buzzy, ascending song often announces the presence of this warbler, which is blue-gray above with a greenish yellow patch on the back, and yellow on the underparts. The male is distinguished by a chestnut and black band across the breast. The sedate and deliberate Northern Parula methodically examines tree limbs and trunks and often hangs like a chickadee or creeps like a nuthatch. Parulas are fairly common in northern New Hampshire, but are very uncommon and local in the southern part of the state. In the mountains they are restricted to valleys and lower slopes, occurring up to about 2,500 ft (760 m) in elevation (Allen 1903; T. Richards, unpubl. data).

In New Hampshire, the Northern Parula's typical nesting habitat is coniferous forest at the edge of a wetland, stream, or pond where trees are festooned with lichens. This warbler usually nests around openings or at the edge of the forest and seldom occurs in deep woods (Graber and Graber 1951, Morse 1967b). Occasionally the Northern Parula nests in other habitats. Bent (1953) reported frequent nesting in old orchards with extensive lichen growth. Allen (1903) noted that the Northern Parula occurred in forests with little bearded lichen, and Scott (1921) found that the species favored hardwood swamps in southern New Hampshire and carried lichen a long distance from coniferous woods to the nest site.

Northern Parulas begin to arrive in New Hampshire in late April or early May. They may occur almost anywhere during migration but favor deciduous trees. Males sing persistently during spring migration. Morse (1967b) designated 2 distinct song types, a single ascending, buzzy trill with an abrupt and emphatic final note, and a series of buzzy notes ending with a shorter and less emphatic rising trill. The regular song period

extends through late July; the latest Atlas record of a singing male was 22 July. Wright (1911) noted intermittent singing through August and even into September.

The Northern Parula's unique nest, which the female builds in late May or early June, is usually located in a 2 to 12 in (5 to 30 cm) long hollowed-out clump of bearded lichen (Bent 1953), hanging from a branch 6 to 100 ft (1.8 to 30.5 m) above the ground. It is sparingly lined with fine grasses, bark strips, plant down, hair, or finely shredded mosses, and may have either a side or a top entrance. From the ground the nest resembles a tennis ball held in the bottom of the pendant clump of lichen (Harrison 1975).

Where bearded lichen is unavailable, Northern Parula nests are quite variable (Harrison 1975). They may be built in bunches of leaves, hanging clusters of twigs, or even in the debris left in tree branches by spring floods. Completed nests are well concealed and rarely found, a fact underscored by the lack of "on nest" and "nest with young" records from the Atlas project.

The Northern Parula typically lays 4 or 5 eggs between late May and early July. The female incubates, unassisted, for 12 to 14 days. When disturbed at the nest, she may become quite agitated and engage in bill-wiping or a distraction display (Graber and Graber 1951). Conversely, some observers have reported the Northern Parula to be quite fearless and tame around the nest.

Both parents feed the young, which reportedly remain in the nest for 11 days (DeGraaf et al. 1980). Bull (1974) recorded nestling dates from 5 June to 24 July in New York. The 5 New Hampshire Atlas records of adults carrying food range from mid-June to late July. Three reports of fledglings include 2 in mid-July and one in early August. Most Northern Parulas depart for the south between late August and mid-September, though some individuals may linger into the first week of October (K. C. Elkins, pers. comm.).

Historical information suggests that the Northern Parula may have been more common 60 to 100 years ago than it is today. Early ornithologists considered it common in the White Mountains and North Country into the early part of this century (Coues 1868, Minot 1876, Wright 1911), and locally common in southeastern New Hampshire, including the Durham area and a Barrington swamp (Dearborn 1903, Scott 1921).

The Atlas map shows the Northern Parula to be fairly widespread in coniferous forests from the White Mountains north, but uncommon and local farther south. Of the 75 blocks in which the species was recorded, 53 are north of a line across the southern fringe of the White Mountains. The Northern Parula was found in about 75% of Northern Highlands blocks and 40% of White Mountains blocks. There were scattered records in the Lakes Region and the middle Western Highlands, but only a handful of sightings in the southern quarter of the state.

Some observers report that Northern Parula numbers seem to be decreasing throughout the Northeast, possibly because bearded lichen is especially sensitive to air pollution and is disappearing from much of the parula's breeding range (Ridgely 1977, Peterson 1980, Kibbe *in* Laughlin and Kibbe 1985). However, BBS data from 1966 to 1979 suggest that a strong population increase began in the Eastern region in the early 1970s (Robbins et al. 1986). Population trends of the Northern Parula deserve careful monitoring in the years ahead.

Steve Smith

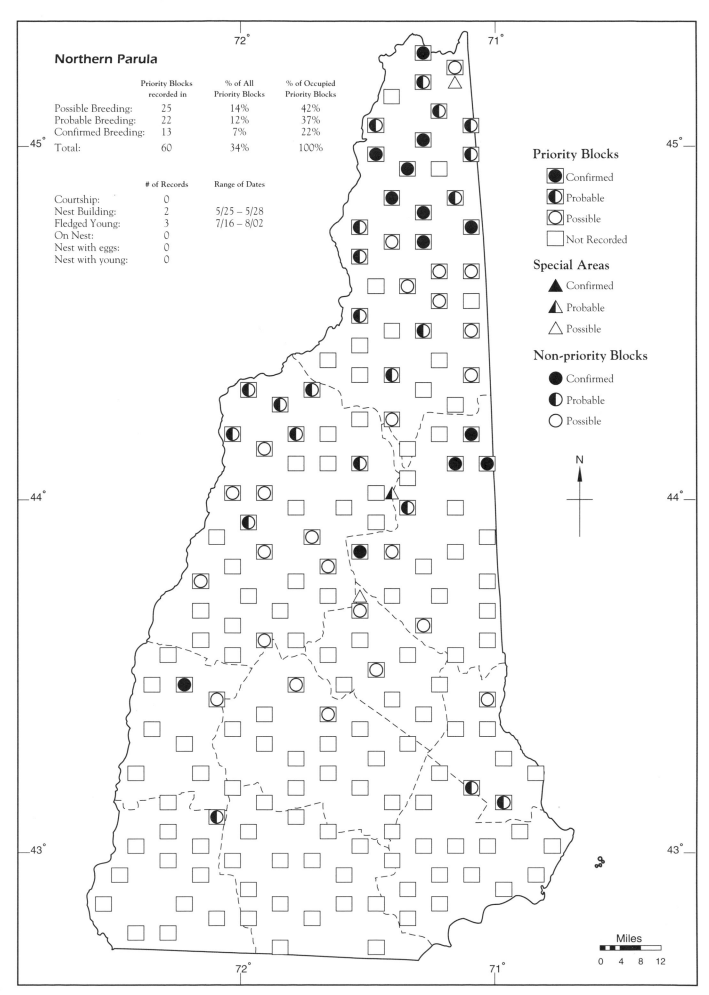

Northern Parula

	Priority Blocks recorded in	% of All Priority Blocks	% of Occupied Priority Blocks
Possible Breeding:	25	14%	42%
Probable Breeding:	22	12%	37%
Confirmed Breeding:	13	7%	22%
Total:	60	34%	100%

	# of Records	Range of Dates
Courtship:	0	
Nest Building:	2	5/25 – 5/28
Fledged Young:	3	7/16 – 8/02
On Nest:	0	
Nest with eggs:	0	
Nest with young:	0	

Priority Blocks

● Confirmed
◐ Probable
○ Possible
☐ Not Recorded

Special Areas

▲ Confirmed
◮ Probable
△ Possible

Non-priority Blocks

● Confirmed
◑ Probable
○ Possible

N

Miles
0 4 8 12

Yellow Warbler
Dendroica petechia

The Yellow Warbler is one of the best-known breeding birds of yard and garden, where its flashy yellow plumage enlivens shrubbery, and hedges. Also found in shrubby wetlands, orchards, and roadside thickets, this warbler is common and widespread throughout most of the state, usually at elevations below 1,000 ft (300 m). It occurs in New Hampshire from mid-May to mid-September, although fall migration begins in July. The Yellow Warbler usually is easy to observe. The adult male is bright yellow, with chestnut streaking on breast, sides, and flanks. The female is duller and lacks chestnut streaking. This species has the widest breeding range of all wood warblers and nests from the Atlantic to the Pacific and from the Barren Grounds in Canada to Mexico and the Gulf states (Terres 1980).

Yellow Warblers breed from mid-May to early July in the northern regions of their range (Goossen and Sealy 1982, Peck and James 1987). In ideal habitat, they may nest in colonies. Territories may be as small as 0.4 a (0.1 ha) (Harrison 1975), and density of breeding pairs may reach 8 pairs/a (0.4 ha)(Goossen and Sealy 1982).

Males arrive on the breeding grounds before females. Their singing increases when females arrive, and courtship begins quickly (Harrison 1984). The variable song is a sweet, rapid "tsee tsee tsee tsee titiwee" or "weet weet weet weet tsee tsee" (Peterson 1980), often phrased as "sweet sweet sweet I'm so sweet."

The female, working mostly alone, completes the neat, strong nest in 3 to 5 days (Harrison 1984). The nest is usually in an upright fork or crotch of a shrub. Nest height averages 3 to 6 ft (0.9 to 1.8 m) above ground, but in trees may be 40 to 60 ft (12.1 to 18.3 m) (Terres 1980). Nest materials include plant down, grasses, wool, fur, lichens, and mosses, which are bound with spider silk or tent caterpillar webbing. Plant down, hairs, and fine grasses line the nest (Bent 1953, Terres 1980).

The female lays a single egg daily until the clutch is completed with 3 to 6, usually 4 or 5 eggs (Harrison 1975, Goossen and Sealy 1982). The female incubates for 11 or 12 days (Clark and Robertson 1981). Both parents tend the young, but the female does most of the brooding while the male does most of the feeding of nestlings (Harrison 1978, Biermann and Sealy 1982). Because they are relatively tolerant of human activity and inhabit open areas, often near houses, Yellow Warblers were easier to "confirm" than most warblers. Although the light-colored nests often are conspicuous, adults with food or fecal sacs provided the majority of Atlas "confirmations."

Nestlings fledge at 9 to 12 days (Terres 1980). White (1937) observed a nest in Concord which was completed by 18 May, and contained 5 eggs on 26 May. Young had hatched by 6 June and had fledged by 17 June. Wright (1911) found one or 2-day-old nestlings in Jefferson on 23 June 1905. Yellow Warblers rarely attempt second broods (Clark and Robertson 1981, Goossen and Sealy 1982). Southward migration may begin as soon as the young are independent, and most local birds leave by August.

Brown-headed Cowbirds parasitize Yellow Warbler nests in almost every province of Canada and every state in the United States (Friedmann 1963). Studies in Ontario and Manitoba reported parasitism rates of 25% to 41% (Clark and Robertson 1981, Goossen and Sealy 1982, Peck and James 1987). Clark and Robertson (1981) found that the effect of cowbird parasitism on Yellow Warbler nesting success depends on the number of warbler eggs removed, the stage of nesting when the cowbird egg is laid, and the warbler's response to the cowbird egg. Burying the eggs under a new nest floor and laying a new clutch or deserting the nest increase the Yellow Warbler's nesting success.

Yellow Warblers forage for insects by gleaning from foliage and bark, hawking, and hover gleaning (Busby and Sealy 1979). Midges, mosquitoes, and larval inchworms are their chief prey (Busby and Sealy 1979, Biermann and Sealy 1982). They also eat cankerworms, gypsy moth and brown-tail moth larvae, beetles, borers, weevils, small moths, aphids, grasshoppers, and spiders (Terres 1980).

The Yellow Warbler was considered an abundant summer resident in at least parts of New Hampshire in the late 1800s (Samuels 1867, Dearborn 1898). Allen (1903) described the Yellow Warbler as a "not uncommon summer resident" in valleys of southern and western New Hampshire, local north of Lake Winnipesaukee, and rare or absent in the White Mountain valleys and north. However, Faxon and Allen (1888) documented the species at Franconia and Bethlehem in 1874. Wright (1911) found it "not uncommon" at Lancaster, in the Connecticut River valley, but rare at the lowest elevations in the nearby mountain township of Jefferson. BBS data from 1966 to 1979 suggest a slight population increase in the northeastern U.S. (Robbins et al. 1986).

Atlas observers found Yellow Warblers in all southern New Hampshire priority blocks east of the Merrimack River, but missed them in 7 priority blocks in the Western Highlands and in a few others south of the White Mountains, most of which were above 1,000 ft (300 m) elevation. A scarcity of suitable habitat in the White Mountains and North Country may account for their absence in many northern priority blocks. Atlas observers may have missed Yellow Warblers in some blocks because they stop singing early in the breeding season, but the pattern of scarcity in the heavily wooded northern blocks resembles that in Vermont and Maine (Laughlin and Kibbe 1985, Adamus 1988).

Susan Absalom Staats

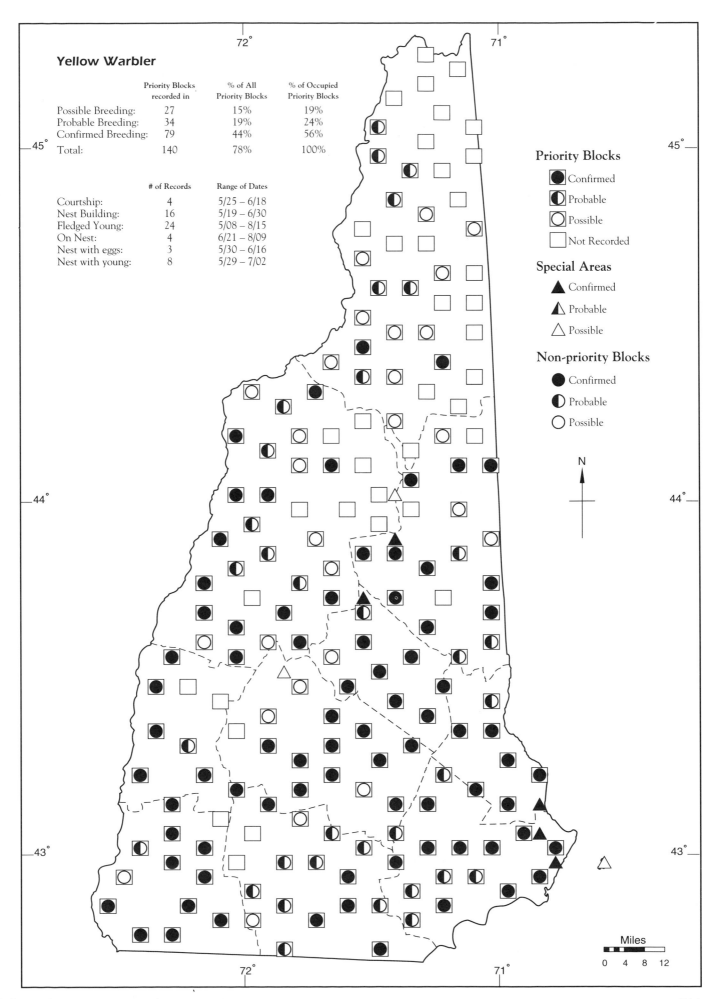

Yellow Warbler

	Priority Blocks recorded in	% of All Priority Blocks	% of Occupied Priority Blocks
Possible Breeding:	27	15%	19%
Probable Breeding:	34	19%	24%
Confirmed Breeding:	79	44%	56%
Total:	140	78%	100%

	# of Records	Range of Dates
Courtship:	4	5/25 – 6/18
Nest Building:	16	5/19 – 6/30
Fledged Young:	24	5/08 – 8/15
On Nest:	4	6/21 – 8/09
Nest with eggs:	3	5/30 – 6/16
Nest with young:	8	5/29 – 7/02

Priority Blocks

- ● Confirmed
- ◐ Probable
- ○ Possible
- ☐ Not Recorded

Special Areas

- ▲ Confirmed
- ◢ Probable
- △ Possible

Non-priority Blocks

- ● Confirmed
- ◑ Probable
- ○ Possible

N

Miles
0 4 8 12

Chestnut-sided Warbler
Dendroica pensylvanica

One of the most typical summer sounds of brushy abandoned fields and young deciduous woodlands is the cheerful "please please pleased to meet you" song of this colorful warbler. Easily identified by its unique combination of yellow crown and white underparts bordered by chestnut stripes, the Chestnut-sided Warbler favors sunny, open places and forages—sometimes fly catching and fluttering—in shrubs and lower branches of trees (Bent 1953).

Ideal nesting habitat for this species develops during the early stages of deciduous forest regeneration after clearcutting and on abandoned farmland. The Chestnut-sided Warbler is an abundant and widespread breeder across New Hampshire, from near sea level to about 2,000 to 2,500 feet (610 to 760 m) in the White Mountains (Allen 1903, Wright 1911, Ridgely 1977).

The male arrives first in spring, usually during the first or second week of May. He immediately sets up a territory of 1.2 to 2.5 a (0.5 to 1.0 ha), which expands into a larger, but less vigorously defended "home range" later in the breeding season (Kendeigh 1945a). The more familiar of the species' 2 songs has a strongly accented ending and typically is used to advertise territory and attract a female (Ficken and Ficken 1965). Early in the season, the male may sing 5 or 6 times per minute at any time of day from any of several song posts on his territory, and neighboring males may compete in song or engage in chasing (Kendeigh 1945a). Courtship displays, brief and infrequently observed, include the male diving at the female or displaying with tail feathers spread, wings extended, and crown erect (Kendeigh 1945a).

The female, accompanied by the male, locates a nest site, often outside the male's original territory (Kendeigh 1945a). The female builds the nest in about 5 days, concealing it in the fork of a small bush, sapling, or vine, usually 1 to 4 ft (0.3 to 1.2 m) above the ground (Peck and James 1987). The thin-walled struc-

ture is made from bark strips, grasses, shredded stems, and plant down, and is lined with fine grasses and hair (Harrison 1975).

Atlas data suggest that nest building is concentrated in late May and early June, though White (1924) found a completed nest in Concord on 18 May with the first egg laid on 20 May. The female begins her clutch of 3 to 5, typically 4 eggs one to 5 days after finishing the nest. Atlas data apparently provide the first published egg dates for Chestnut-sided Warblers in New Hampshire, which ranged from 13 to 20 June. The female incubates for 10 to 13 days (Harrison 1975, Harrison 1978). This warbler frequently is a victim of the parasitic Brown-headed Cowbird (Bent 1953, Friedmann 1963).

The nestling period lasts 10 to 12 days. Both adults are quite attentive and actively search for food for the young (Burns 1921b, Kendeigh 1945a, Sawyer 1947, Griscom and Sprunt 1957). Adults carrying fecal sacs or food accounted for about half of New Hampshire Atlas "confirmations." The female may engage in a distraction display when an intruder approaches within 13 ft (4 m) of the nest (McConnell 1981), and adults may vigorously defend a nest with young (Bent 1953).

The Chestnut-sided sings a different and quite variable song later in the season (Pough 1949). Song frequency decreases as incubation and raising of young proceed (Kendeigh 1945a, Lawrence 1948). Atlas observers documented few singing males after the first week of July.

Lawrence (1948) found young begging for food 28 days after leaving the nest, explaining the ease of "confirmation" with FF and FL codes. Though a few recently fledged young were recorded in June and August, most were observed during July. Tate (1970) considered late nesting reports from a Michigan study to be renesting attempts, and second broods are unlikely. Southward migration starts by mid-August. Most Chestnut-sideds have departed by mid-September, though some stragglers may be present until the end of the month.

Atlas results illustrate this species' status as one of New Hampshire's most widespread warblers. Of the 5 priority blocks which lack Chestnut-sided Warbler records, 4 were heavily forested White Mountain and North Country blocks at high elevations. BBS data from 1966 to 1979 show an average of 14.7 Chestnut-sided Warblers per route in New Hampshire, more than in any other state or province (Robbins et al. 1986).

In contrast to its present-day abundance, the Chestnut-sided Warbler was virtually unknown here 150 years ago. Early ornithologists, including Audubon, Wilson, and Nuttall, rarely saw the species, but it had begun to increase in New England by the middle of the 19th century (Bent 1953). Ever since the late 1800s it has been considered a common summer resident in most areas of New Hampshire (Coues 1868, Dearborn 1898, 1903, Allen 1903, Wright 1911, White 1937, Ridgely 1977, Allison and Allison 1979).

More dramatically than perhaps any other species, this warbler has benefited from disturbances such as logging, fire, and abandonment of farmland. Although some observers have noted periodic fluctuations in abundance (Allen 1903; E.E. Pratt, unpubl. data; J. McDermott, pers. comm.), the outlook for this species in New Hampshire should be favorable as long as human land uses produce early stages of hardwood regeneration.

Sally M. Sutcliffe & Steve Smith

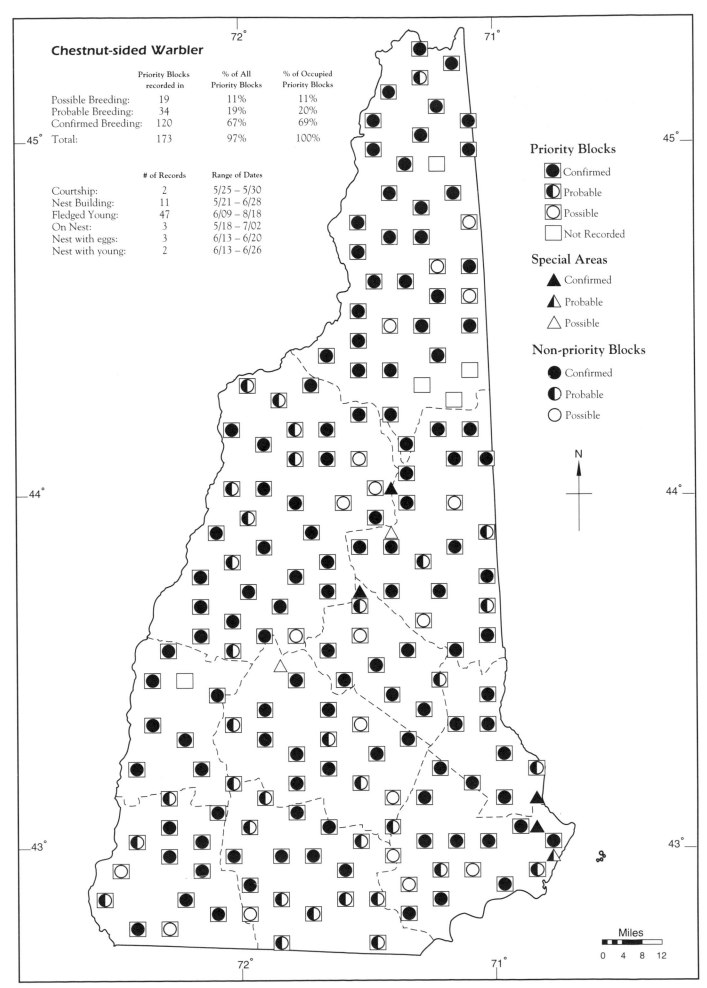

Chestnut-sided Warbler

	Priority Blocks recorded in	% of All Priority Blocks	% of Occupied Priority Blocks
Possible Breeding:	19	11%	11%
Probable Breeding:	34	19%	20%
Confirmed Breeding:	120	67%	69%
Total:	173	97%	100%

	# of Records	Range of Dates
Courtship:	2	5/25 – 5/30
Nest Building:	11	5/21 – 6/28
Fledged Young:	47	6/09 – 8/18
On Nest:	3	5/18 – 7/02
Nest with eggs:	3	6/13 – 6/20
Nest with young:	2	6/13 – 6/26

Priority Blocks
- ◑ Confirmed
- ◐ Probable
- ○ Possible
- ☐ Not Recorded

Special Areas
- ▲ Confirmed
- ◣ Probable
- △ Possible

Non-priority Blocks
- ● Confirmed
- ◑ Probable
- ○ Possible

Miles
0 4 8 12

Magnolia Warbler
Dendroica magnolia

The Magnolia Warbler's flashy black and yellow plumage, habitual wing drooping and tail spreading, and emphatic song enliven northern coniferous forests during the summer months. In northern New Hampshire and at higher elevations farther south, this animated warbler is common in open stands of young conifers, primarily spruce and fir. Elsewhere in the state it is uncommon and local, nesting in patches of spruce or hemlocks or even in small pines in recently abandoned fields or pastures. This warbler breeds from coastal lowlands to above 4,000 ft (1,220 m) in the White Mountains. Sabo (1980) described a range in the White Mountains from 820 ft (250 m) in the Pemigewasset River valley to 4,600+ ft (1,400+ m) in krummholtz on Mt. Moosilauke, Benton. This species is a common migrant throughout New Hampshire in May, sometimes in impressive numbers. Fall migration extends from late August into October.

The breeding season begins in late May. Territorial males are easily detected by their short but energetic and variable song. Singing often continues into late July. The latest Atlas record of a singing male was from 22 July. Moore (1904 *in* Bent 1953) observed prenesting behavior which included fierce battles between rival males and plumage displays of males to females.

Territory size may range from 1.8 to 3.3 a (0.7 to 1.3 ha), depending on forest type (Stenger 1959 *in* DeGraaf et al. 1980). Sabo (1980) reported a density of 30 pairs/0.4 sq mi (1 sq km) in White Mountain subalpine forest, with a mean territory size of 1.8 a (0.7 ha). In study plots where Black-throated Green Warblers occurred, they aggressively displaced Magnolia Warblers (Sabo 1980).

The nest is well concealed on a horizontal branch, usually 1 to 15 ft (0.3 to 4.6 m) above the ground (Harrison 1975), often in a small conifer. The female does most of the building, but the male helps gather material (Forbush 1929). The loosely built nest is made of twigs and plant stems, with a characteristic lining of black rootlets (Harrison 1975).

Egg dates for 39 Magnolia Warbler clutches collected in Lancaster and elsewhere in the North Country during 1879–1906 range from 31 May to 21 June (mus. coll.). Forbush (1929) includes New Hampshire egg dates of 24 May to 20 June. Clutch size is 3 to 6, typically 4. The female incubates alone for about 12 days. The young fledge in another 10 days, and the adults feed them for up to 25 days after fledging (Bent 1953). The Magnolia Warbler forages in the lower levels of trees, gleaning insects from twigs, leaves, and bark. Males in a Maine spruce forest foraged somewhat higher (and closer to singing areas) than females, who foraged closer to the nest (Morse 1968). Following fledging of the young, Magnolia Warblers in Maine increased their foraging in deciduous trees (Morse 1967a).

This species is relatively fearless and often is observed at close range. Though it tends to keep to the interior of a tree, the Magnolia may be drawn out by "pishing" or by the alarm call of another bird, such as the "chink" of the White-throated Sparrow. It becomes quite agitated if disturbed near its nest or young, and may engage in a distraction display.

Both parents bring food to the young, and may feed nestlings every 5 to 10 minutes (Bent 1953). Adults with food or fecal sacs provided 60% of "confirmed" Atlas records, spread rather evenly from 22 June through 29 July. Recently fledged young are quite evident as they call constantly for food. Adults may feed young for up to 25 days after they leave the nest (Bent 1953).

Historical records suggest that the Magnolia Warbler long has been a common breeding bird in the White Mountains. Marble (1907) called it "probably the most common" warbler breeding in the woods around Crawford House at the top of Crawford Notch, Harts Location. Most early authors considered the mountains to be the southern limit of the species' breeding range in New Hampshire (Maynard 1871, Bolles 1893, Scott 1921, White 1924). However, Dearborn (1898) found it breeding "sparingly" in Belknap and Merrimack counties. Allen (1903) found it common in the White Mountains and breeding in small numbers, in spruce only, around Mt. Monadnock, Jaffrey, and locally elsewhere in southern and western New Hampshire.

The Magnolia Warbler's current distribution is closely correlated with that of its favored coniferous habitat. Atlas workers found it in every priority block in the Northern Highlands and White Mountains, in a majority of Western Highlands blocks, and in about half of the blocks in the Lakes Region. Most observations occurred at elevations above 1,000 ft (300 m).

Atlas data provide a number of records, including 2 "confirmations," in southeastern New Hampshire. This apparent range expansion, and a similar trend in Vermont may result from the reversion of farmland to forest during the early and mid-1900s (Kibbe *in* Laughlin and Kibbe 1985). Since New Hampshire is now largely forested and logging will continue to provide regenerating stands, the Magnolia Warbler should remain a common species in New Hampshire for many years.

Steve Smith

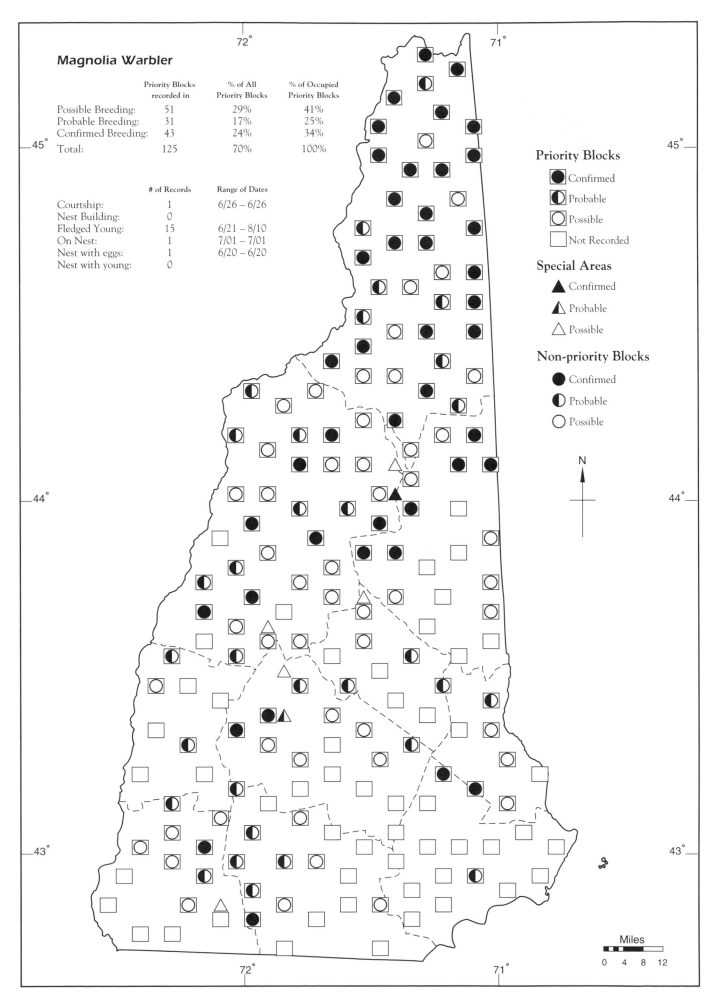

Magnolia Warbler

	Priority Blocks recorded in	% of All Priority Blocks	% of Occupied Priority Blocks
Possible Breeding:	51	29%	41%
Probable Breeding:	31	17%	25%
Confirmed Breeding:	43	24%	34%
Total:	125	70%	100%

	# of Records	Range of Dates
Courtship:	1	6/26 – 6/26
Nest Building:	0	
Fledged Young:	15	6/21 – 8/10
On Nest:	1	7/01 – 7/01
Nest with eggs:	1	6/20 – 6/20
Nest with young:	0	

Priority Blocks
- ◑ Confirmed
- ◑ Probable
- ○ Possible
- ☐ Not Recorded

Special Areas
- ▲ Confirmed
- ◮ Probable
- △ Possible

Non-priority Blocks
- ● Confirmed
- ◖ Probable
- ○ Possible

N

Miles
0 4 8 12

Cape May Warbler
Dendroica tigrina

With bright chestnut cheek patches and tiger-striped underparts, the male Cape May Warbler is a handsome inhabitant of coniferous forest stands in the north woods, where it emits a quiet, lisping song from the tops of spruces and firs. Females are duller and lack the chestnut cheek patches. Cape Mays prefer moderately open coniferous forest with mature spruces, but occasionally inhabit dense spruce forests with tall spires jutting from the canopy (Gunn *in* Griscom and Sprunt 1957).

Cape Mays pass through southern New Hampshire during May en route to breeding grounds in the White Mountains and farther north, where they arrive in mid-May to early June. During fall migration, which begins in August and extends through September (RNEB, *passim*), these birds may visit shrubbery, woods, and thickets (Forbush 1929).

The weak song consists of 5 or 6 monotonous, high-pitched "zee" or "zeet" phrases, often repeated without pauses (Allen *in* Bent 1953, Harrison 1984). A less common version is sung at a quicker tempo with phrases of 2 or 3 syllables (Gunn *in* Griscom and Sprunt 1957). With less than half the volume of the Tennessee Warbler's song, the Cape May's is sharper and more penetrating than the similar songs of Bay-breasted, Blackburnian, and Black-and-white warblers (Bond 1937, Brewster 1938 *in* Bent 1953).

Cape May Warblers begin courtship and nest building soon after reaching breeding areas. Bond (1937) reported that these birds arrive in coastal Maine in late May, and observed a female building a nest on 2 June. He noted a characteristic courtship display, where the male "flies with rigid wings just above the female when she works on the nest." Cape Mays can be aggressive, attacking and chasing each other, and males chase their mates during nest building (Merriam 1917).

The Cape May Warbler builds a relatively large nest, usually 30 to 60 ft (9.1 to 18.3 m) from the ground in a dense clump of needles in a spire top of spruce or fir. Invisible from the ground, the nest is composed predominantly of sphagnum moss and thickly lined with hair and feathers (Gunn *in* Griscom and Sprunt 1957, Harrison 1984). The female does not fly directly to her nest, but lands lower in the tree and climbs up from branch to branch near the trunk. When leaving, she dives toward the ground, then swoops up and disappears (Harrison 1984). The male often is visible while he sings near the top of a large conifer, but is difficult to find when inactive, even when on an exposed perch (Gunn *in* Griscom and Sprunt 1957).

Bent (1953) reported egg dates in Maine as 6 to 15 June, and dates for New Hampshire probably are similar. With the largest clutch of any wood warbler, Cape Mays may lay 4 to 9 eggs (Harrison 1984). Large clutches are more common during spruce budworm outbreaks. The incubation period and age at fledging are unknown (Terres 1980).

Spruce budworm outbreaks provide an abundant food source for Cape Mays and other warblers. Consequently, populations of Cape May Warblers may increase rapidly in infested areas (Gunn *in* Griscom and Sprunt 1957, Harrison 1984). Even when budworms are plentiful the warblers take only a small part of the budworm population; budworms may not provide a complete diet for these birds (Morse 1978). Cape Mays also eat beetles, crickets, dragonflies, flies, ants, wasps, small bees, daddy-longlegs, and spiders. They primarily glean insects from peripheral vegetation near the tops of trees, and occasionally hawk flying insects. They also puncture grapes for juice and take sap from sapsucker holes (Terres 1980).

Prior to 1900, Cape Mays typically were "extremely rare summer residents" in New England (Coues 1868). Maynard (1871) found them breeding at Umbagog Lake, and Brewster (1925) found them common there in one or more years. Cape Mays seemed to be somewhat less rare about 1909 (Forbush 1929), but Wright (1911) knew them only as migrants in the Jefferson region. A large migration passed through southern New Hampshire in May 1917 (Scott 1921, White 1924). Since 1950 they have been rare and irregular breeders in the White Mountains, and uncommon to common in the North Country. In fall migration they have been numerous in some years and absent in others (K.C. Elkins, pers. comm.). RNEB (*passim*) includes records from scattered northern locations, including Albany, Errol, Franconia, Lincoln, Pittsburg, and Whitefield, in 1953, 1954, 1959, and 1964–67.

The Atlas map suggests that Cape May Warblers may be somewhat more common in the North Country than in the White Mountains. Atlas workers probably missed some breeding activity due to this warbler's inconspicuous behavior and the arduous access to its nesting habitat, especially in the mountains. Thus, these warblers may be more common than the Atlas data indicate, at least in some years. Atlas data may suggest population fluctuations during 1981–86, with 11 of the 31 records produced in 1982 and 7 in 1984. This pattern coincides with a budworm outbreak in parts of northern New Hampshire during the early 1980s.

While softwood harvest patterns and spruce budworm population cycles will affect its annual abundance and distribution, this colorful warbler is likely to remain an uncommon and irregular nesting species in the mature spruce-fir forests of northern New Hampshire.

Susan Absalom Staats

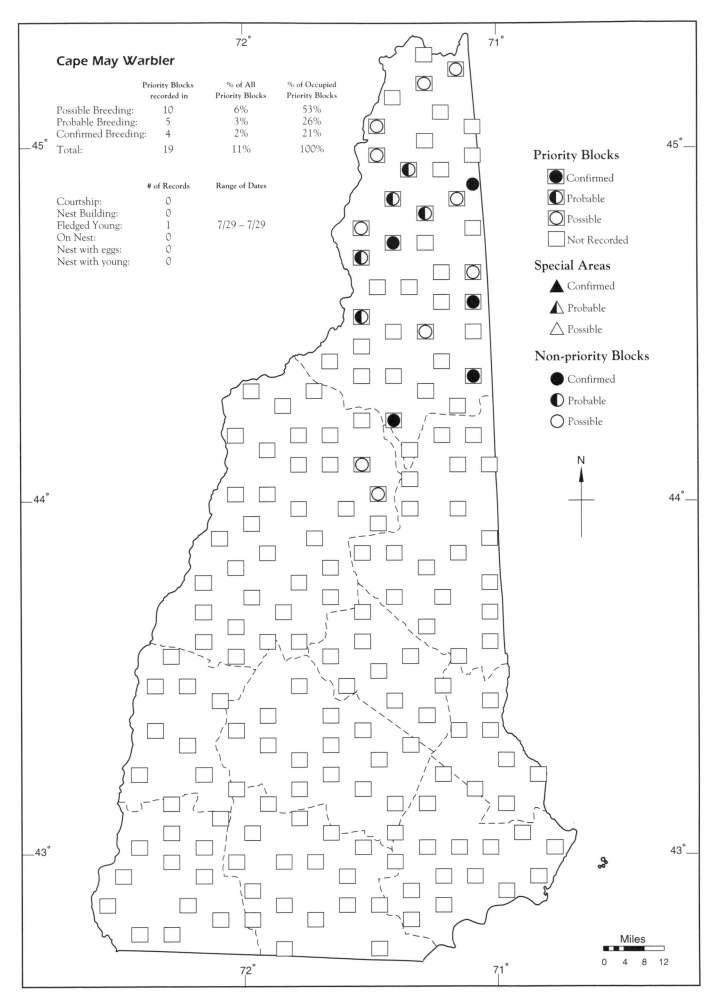

Cape May Warbler

	Priority Blocks recorded in	% of All Priority Blocks	% of Occupied Priority Blocks
Possible Breeding:	10	6%	53%
Probable Breeding:	5	3%	26%
Confirmed Breeding:	4	2%	21%
Total:	19	11%	100%

	# of Records	Range of Dates
Courtship:	0	
Nest Building:	0	
Fledged Young:	1	7/29 – 7/29
On Nest:	0	
Nest with eggs:	0	
Nest with young:	0	

Priority Blocks
- ● Confirmed
- ◐ Probable
- ○ Possible
- ☐ Not Recorded

Special Areas
- ▲ Confirmed
- ◪ Probable
- △ Possible

Non-priority Blocks
- ● Confirmed
- ◑ Probable
- ○ Possible

N

Miles
0   4   8   12

Black-throated Blue Warbler
Dendroica caerulescens

The Black-throated Blue Warbler is a common denizen of deep woods, occurring mainly in extensive stands of mature northern hardwood forests at elevations below 3,000 ft (910 m), chiefly in north, central, and southwestern New Hampshire. It occurs locally in deciduous and mixed coniferous stands in southern portions of the state, apparently avoiding the coastal plain. Black-throated Blues return from Caribbean wintering areas during the first 2 weeks of May, with males appearing shortly before females. They reside in breeding areas throughout the summer, and some occur here as late as mid-October.

This species requires dense shrubbery under a more or less continuous overstory of tall trees. Mountain laurel, striped maple, hobblebush, and extensive patches of yew are characteristic of Black-throated Blue habitat in New Hampshire (Harding 1931, Bent 1953).

Male Black-throated Blues defend relatively large territories of approximately 5 a (2 ha) that are evenly dispersed through deciduous forest habitat (Sherry and Holmes 1985). Their typical song is a slow, buzzy "zur-zur-zur-zee," with the last syllable slurred upward. The dull-colored female builds the nest, usually in a shrub or small sapling within 3.3 ft (1 m) of the ground. The average height of 182 nests found in or near the Hubbard Brook Experimental Forest, Thornton, was 18 in (45 cm) (Holmes, Sherry, and N.L. Rodenhouse, unpubl. data). Of these 182 nests, 51% were in hobblebush, 21% in beech saplings, 9% in sugar maple saplings, and the remainder in red spruce, balsam fir, striped and mountain maple, and other shrub layer vegetation. S. Gonzalez (pers. comm.) found a nest on an old stump near Indian Head, Lincoln.

The nest usually is situated in a major crotch, often where a dead branch is leaning against the nest shrub or sapling (Holmes, Sherry, and N.L. Rodenhouse, unpubl. data). The female builds while the male remains nearby, often singing softly above her (Holmes et al. 1992). The nest is constructed of thin strips of bark, usually yellow birch, and is lined with fine black rootlets or mammal hair (Harding 1931).

Clutch size for the Black-throated Blue Warbler at Hubbard Brook,, ranges from 2 to 5 (mean 3.8–0.4) (Holmes et al. 1992). Bent (1953) cites New Hampshire egg dates from 3 to 22 June, with half from 10 to 15 June. Laying of first clutches at Hubbard Brook peaks during 21 to 31 May and of second clutches during 21 to 30 June (Holmes et al. 1992). During incubation, the female spends 75% of the daylight hours on the nest, the remainder in foraging (Black 1975). The latter is intensive and occurs in bouts of 6 to 17 minutes, after which she returns to incubate for 20 to 50 minutes before departing to feed again (Black 1975). When disturbed from the nest, the female may give a distraction display (S.B. Turner, pers. comm.). Hatching usually occurs on the 12th day of incubation. The male does not incubate but assists with about 25 to 30% of food deliveries to the nestlings, although this assistance is quite variable among males (Nice 1930, Black 1975). Most "confirmed" records were based on observations of adults carrying food or fecal sacs. Following fledging, the pair often divides the brood, with each parent attending one or 2 young (Black 1975). Studies at Hubbard Brook found up to 50% of females successfully fledging second broods and one female that fledged 3 broods (Holmes et al. 1992).

This species is the only common warbler in New Hampshire that feeds extensively in the shrub and subcanopy strata of deciduous forests. In searching for food, a Black-throated Blue Warbler first scans the undersides of leaves and the surfaces of branches and trunks from a short distance away and then flies up to snatch a caterpillar, moth, cranefly, or other small insect (Robinson and Holmes 1982). This differs from the foraging methods of most other *Dendroica* warblers, which usually glean prey from surfaces.

The Black-throated Blue Warbler no doubt decreased in overall abundance in New Hampshire when the virgin forests were cleared for agriculture. Faxon and Allen (1888) found it rare in the vicinity of Squam Lake in 1885 and 1886, but common in Bethlehem in 1874 and in Franconia in 1974, 1976, and 1877. Dearborn (1898) considered it one of the "less common" warblers in Merrimack and Belknap counties, but knew it to occur during the breeding season in Sanbornton and New Hampton. Allen (1903) considered it common in the northern forests. This warbler has increased in southern New Hampshire in recent decades as abandoned farmland has reverted to woods. White (1937) observed a pair carrying food near Turkey Pond, Concord on 23 and 30 June 1935. It had become fairly common in the Squam Lakes region by the 1970s (Ridgely 1977).

As the Atlas map illustrates, the Black-throated Blue Warbler at the present time is distributed widely throughout the state, except in the southeast. Only 5 priority blocks in the 3 northern counties lack records, and there are relatively few gaps in central New Hampshire. The Black-throated Blue was found in nearly all priority blocks in the southwestern corner of the state, perhaps owing to the presence of mountain laurel, which offers good nesting habitat.

Richard T. Holmes & Thomas W. Sherry

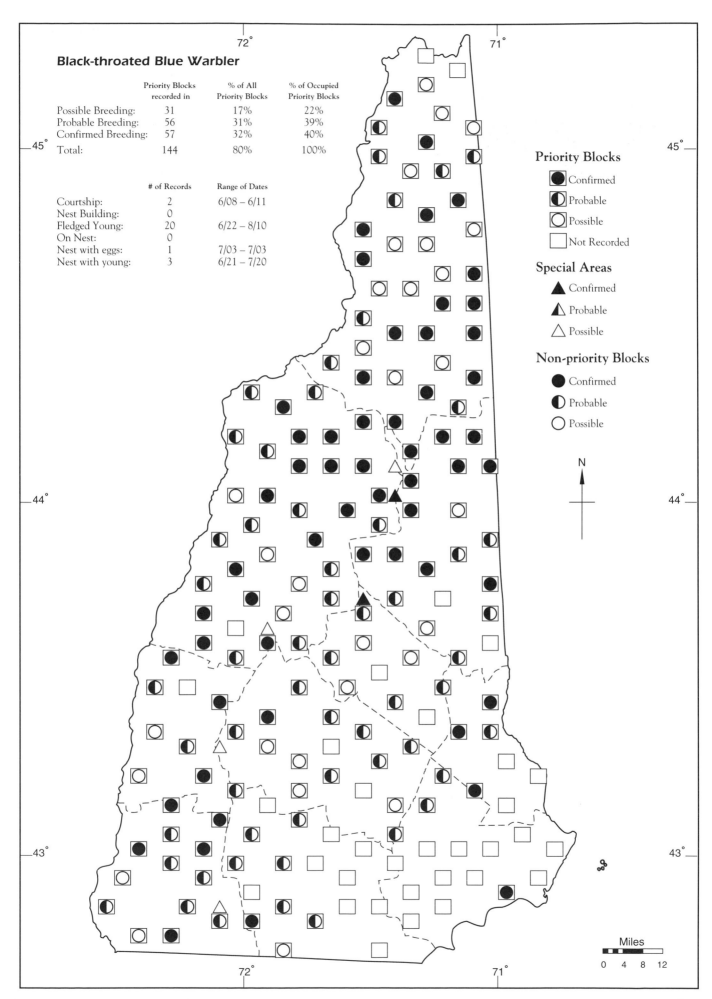

Black-throated Blue Warbler

	Priority Blocks recorded in	% of All Priority Blocks	% of Occupied Priority Blocks
Possible Breeding:	31	17%	22%
Probable Breeding:	56	31%	39%
Confirmed Breeding:	57	32%	40%
Total:	144	80%	100%

	# of Records	Range of Dates
Courtship:	2	6/08 – 6/11
Nest Building:	0	
Fledged Young:	20	6/22 – 8/10
On Nest:	0	
Nest with eggs:	1	7/03 – 7/03
Nest with young:	3	6/21 – 7/20

Priority Blocks
- ◕ Confirmed
- ◑ Probable
- ○ Possible
- ☐ Not Recorded

Special Areas
- ▲ Confirmed
- ◤ Probable
- △ Possible

Non-priority Blocks
- ● Confirmed
- ◗ Probable
- ○ Possible

N

Miles
0 4 8 12

Yellow-rumped Warbler
Dendroica coronata

Whether darting forth for an insect, foraging in shrubbery for berries, or gleaning caterpillars from leaves and branches, this colorful warbler is hard to overlook. The Yellow-rumped Warbler, which includes the former Eastern "Myrtle" and Western "Audubon's" warblers, also has been known as the "Yellow-crowned Wood Warbler" and as the "Golden-crowned Fly-catcher". These names fit the species well, as adults in breeding plumage have bright yellow patches on the crown, rump, and sides of the breast. Unlike the Western "Audubon's" race, the Eastern form has a white throat. The Yellow-rumped, probably one of our best known warblers, occurs throughout New Hampshire.

This warbler breeds from the Arctic treeline south to New England and eastern Pennsylvania. The western breeding range, at higher elevations, extends as far south as Mexico. The winter range includes the Atlantic Coast as far north as New England (NGS 1983). The Yellow-rumped Warbler is most common in coniferous forests, especially at higher elevations, but also inhabits mixed woods. While the species is common in New Hampshire at elevations between 1,000 and 5,000 ft (300 and 1,520 m), it occasionally nests at both higher and lower elevations (T. Richards, unpubl. data).

Yellow-rumps are among the first warblers to arrive in New Hampshire in spring. They migrate through New England in steady waves from mid-April through May, males preceding the females. Their pleasant "sleigh-bell" trill of jingling notes is characteristic throughout the migration (Forbush 1929, Ridgely 1977), and their rising "check" or "sweet" call seems to come from all directions.

Arriving on their New Hampshire breeding grounds by late April to mid-May, they begin territorial and courtship activities. Males sing and display by fluffing out their plumage, raising their wings, and erecting their crown feathers (Forbush 1929). One seldom en-

counters a solitary pair, for if present, they usually are common. Morse (1976) documented breeding season densities of 30 to 39 pairs/100 a (40 ha) in spruce forests in Maine.

Nest building usually occurs during the last 2 weeks of May and requires 6 to 10 days (Knight *in* Forbush 1929). Small coniferous trees such as spruce and cedar are favored nest trees in the Northeast (Maynard 1871, Tufts 1907 and Knight 1908 *in* Bent 1953). Nest sites often are in a thicket of evergreens bordering an opening (Knight 1908 *in* Bent 1953). The nest, made of small twigs and lined with feathers (often of Ruffed Grouse), usually is on a horizontal branch away from the trunk (Harrington *in* Bent 1953, Harrison 1975), but also may be situated among twigs or foliage, in a fork, or saddling a branch (Harrison 1978). Nest heights may range from 4 to 50 ft (1 to 15 m), but average around 20 ft (6 m)(Harrison 1975). Yellow-rumps work the shafts of feathers lining the nest into its sides in such a way that the tops arch over and conceal the eggs when the female is off the nest.

The female incubates the clutch of 4 or 5 eggs for 12 or 13 days (Knight 1908 *in* Bent 1953). New Hampshire egg dates range from 26 May to 12 June. The young fledge about 2 weeks after hatching (Forbush 1929). Most Atlas fledgling records are from the 6 weeks from mid-June through July.

During the breeding season these warblers feed primarily on spiders, flies, beetles, ants, aphids, and caterpillars. Berries, including those of poison ivy, red cedar, and bayberry, comprise about 17% of the diet in early spring and fall (Martin et al. 1951). This warbler's former name derived from its fondness for "waxmyrtle" berries during spring migration along the Atlantic Coast (Forbush 1929).

Fall migration begins in early September, but this large and hardy warbler is among the last warblers to leave. The southerly flow continues through mid-November, with a major peak during the first 2 weeks of October. The Yellow-rumped Warbler occasionally overwinters in New Hampshire, especially near the Coast where bayberries provide a reliable food supply.

The Yellow-rump apparently has extended its breeding range southward in New Hampshire during the present century. Maynard (1871) considered this a strictly northern species which rarely nested south of the White Mountains, and Dearborn (1898) did not know it to nest in Belknap or Merrimack counties. Chapman (1907) described the distribution as extending south to southern Maine and the mountains of New Hampshire and Vermont. Whether it was a northern species before European settlement or had retreated north as lands were cleared for farming is not clear.

In the early 1900s the Yellow-rumped Warbler was common in the Monadnock region, nesting as low in elevation as Dublin (Thayer 1909 *in* Allison and Allison 1979). By the 1920s it was an uncommon summer resident around Concord (White 1924) but still occurred only as a migrant in the Durham area (Scott 1921). Forbush (1929) considered it most common in northern New Hampshire and at higher elevations, and described it as "uncommon, local, rare, or absent in summer in low and coastal lands" in the southern part of the state.

As the Atlas map illustrates, this warbler now nests throughout New Hampshire except for the immediate vicinity of the Coast. Occurrence is rather scattered below 500 ft (150 m) elevation, and most records are from elevations above 1,000 ft (303 m). BBS data from 1966 to 1979 indicate consistent increases for this species in northern New England (Robbins et al. 1986). Reforestation undoubtedly has contributed to both the population increase and the range expansion or recolonization. This warbler should continue to prosper in the years ahead.

James McDermott

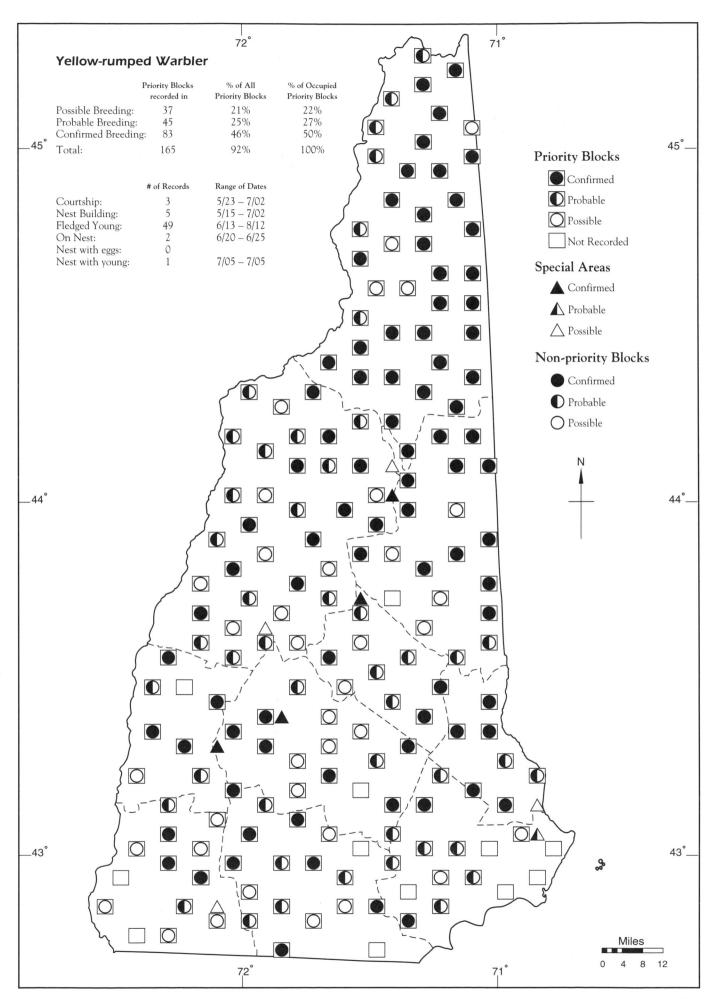

Yellow-rumped Warbler

	Priority Blocks recorded in	% of All Priority Blocks	% of Occupied Priority Blocks
Possible Breeding:	37	21%	22%
Probable Breeding:	45	25%	27%
Confirmed Breeding:	83	46%	50%
Total:	165	92%	100%

	# of Records	Range of Dates
Courtship:	3	5/23 – 7/02
Nest Building:	5	5/15 – 7/02
Fledged Young:	49	6/13 – 8/12
On Nest:	2	6/20 – 6/25
Nest with eggs:	0	
Nest with young:	1	7/05 – 7/05

Priority Blocks
- ◕ Confirmed
- ◑ Probable
- ○ Possible
- ☐ Not Recorded

Special Areas
- ▲ Confirmed
- ◢ Probable
- △ Possible

Non-priority Blocks
- ● Confirmed
- ◗ Probable
- ○ Possible

N

Miles
0 4 8 12

Black-throated Green Warbler
Dendroica virens

Blending with the verdant woods of spring and summer, the Black-throated Green Warbler is more often heard than seen. During the breeding season, the colorful male is distinctive with bright olive green back, black throat and upper breast, and contrasting yellow sides of the head and neck. The female is similar, but duller.

Although their population densities are highest in conifers, these active warblers also inhabit mixed woods (Morse 1967a), breeding in pine, spruce-fir, birch-beech-maple, and spruce-fir-deciduous forests throughout New Hampshire (Collins 1983). They occur as locally common breeders up to 3,000 ft (910 m) elevation (Ridgely 1977).

Black-throated Green Warblers are early migrants, arriving in southern New Hampshire from late April on. Dearborn (1903) heard them singing when "snow was still in the woods, and the leaves were still in bud." During migration, they often consort with Black-capped Chickadees and Black-and-white and Yellow-rumped warblers. Fall migration takes place during September (White 1924).

Black-throated Greens are noted for their 2 unique, buzzy songs. The more familiar is a lazy "zee zee zee zoo zee." Males whistle this song from below treetop level while foraging or establishing territories early in the season. The second song, a "zoo zee zoo zoo zee," is mostly territorial and resounds from treetops (Morse 1967a), where singing males occasionally linger on exposed perches. The male also uses the second song as a whisper song near the nest (Pitelka 1940).

Throughout the nesting period, breeding males are aggressive toward intruding males, chasing trespassers to territory boundaries. Pitelka (1940) watched a nesting pair attack other passerines that approached a Michigan nest. Males on adjacent territories sometimes sing competitively (Kendeigh 1945a). In mixed woods in New York, Kendeigh (1945a) found territory sizes

ranging from 0.6 to 2.5 a (0.2 to 1.0 ha) and averaging 1.6 a (0.6 ha).

Black-throated Greens occupy territories by early June, and nests may even be underway at this time (Bent 1953). The well-concealed nests are generally built in dense foliage on a horizontal limb or fork; 6 of 12 Ontario nests were 3 to 12 ft (0.9 to 3.7 m) from the trunk (Peck and James 1987). These birds usually nest in conifers, but occasionally nest in maples, birches, and other hardwoods (Harrison 1975). Females do most of the construction, shaping the deep, compact nests in about 4 days (Pitelka 1940, Harrison 1975). Bark, twigs, and mosses commonly compose the outsides. Hair, fur, and feathers line the insides. Curly strips of paper birch on the outside sometimes reveal a nest's position in dense vegetation. Mean height of 9 nests in the Hubbard Brook Experimental Forest, Thornton, was 37.1 ft (11.3 m) (Holmes 1986).

Peck and James (1987) reported 13 of 27 Ontario egg dates from 13 to 29 June. The female incubates the 4 or 5 eggs for 12 days (Pitelka 1940). These birds are frequent victims of nest parasitism by Brown-headed Cowbirds (Peck and James 1987). Young leave the nest 8 to 10 days after hatching, and the adults remain protective. The male continues to sing, and both adults may distract intruders by fluttering wings and dragging fanned tails (Pitelka 1940). Renesting, while not documented, is likely. Bent (1953) recorded nesting dates in mid-July, and Peck and James (1987) cite an egg date of 9 August in Ontario.

Robinson and Holmes (1982) concluded that Black-throated Green Warblers at Hubbard Brook forage predominantly by gleaning small and cryptic prey such as caterpillars and leafhoppers. Stomachs of 10 New England and Ontario birds contained 100% animal material, primarily Lepidoptera and spiders (USFWS, unpubl. data). In the northern hardwoods forest at Hubbard Brook, female Black-throated Green Warblers forage primarily on yellow birch trees, while males forage about equally on yellow birches and sugar maples (Holmes 1986).

The overall status of the Black-throated Green Warbler in New Hampshire has changed little since the time of the state's first bird records. Early ornithologists found it common in many areas (Coues 1868, Goodhue 1877, Faxon and Allen 1888, Allen 1889, Dearborn 1898, Allen 1903, Wright 1911, White 1924, Thayer 1909 in Allison and Allison 1979). BBS data from 1966 to 1979 indicate a general increase in the Northeast (Robbins et al. 1986). However, Ridgely (1988) suggests a recent decline in the Squam Lakes region.

BBS data from 1966 to 1979 show the highest densities of Black-throated Green Warblers in Maine and parts of Canada. Average numbers of birds per route were 7.4 in Nova Scotia, 5.1 in Maine, and 4.8 in New Brunswick. Densities in central New England were lower, with 1.6 birds per route in New Hampshire and 1.1 in Vermont (Robbins et al. 1986).

Black-throated Green Warblers presently are well distributed and solidly represented in New Hampshire, perhaps reflecting this species' ability to breed in a variety of habitats. Atlas data indicate that these warblers are nearly ubiquitous in northern New Hampshire and the Western Highlands, but somewhat locally distributed in the south central and southeastern parts of the state. Of the 23 priority blocks lacking Atlas records, only one is from northern New Hampshire, and more than half are from Hillsborough and Rockingham counties. The relative concentration of blocks lacking records in the lower Merrimack Valley may reflect habitat loss because of expanding human settlement and/or higher rates of cowbird parasitism than in more extensively forested areas. The relatively small number of "confirmed" breeders undoubtedly reflects the species' camouflaged nests and secretive nesting behavior.

Susan Absalom Staats

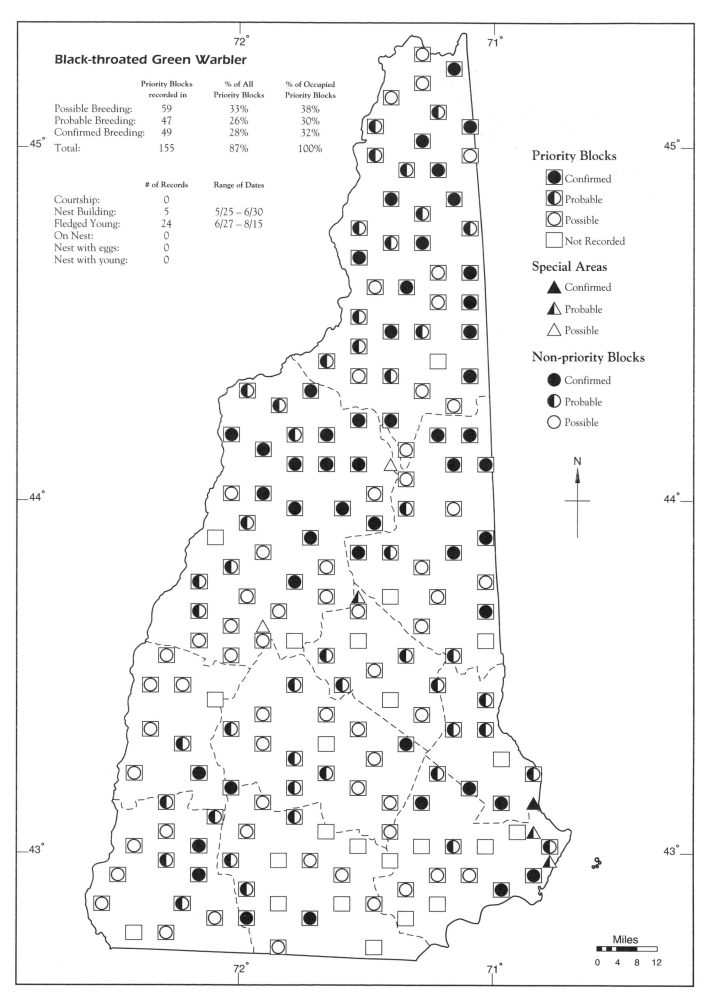

Black-throated Green Warbler

	Priority Blocks recorded in	% of All Priority Blocks	% of Occupied Priority Blocks
Possible Breeding:	59	33%	38%
Probable Breeding:	47	26%	30%
Confirmed Breeding:	49	28%	32%
Total:	155	87%	100%

	# of Records	Range of Dates
Courtship:	0	
Nest Building:	5	5/25 – 6/30
Fledged Young:	24	6/27 – 8/15
On Nest:	0	
Nest with eggs:	0	
Nest with young:	0	

Priority Blocks

- ● Confirmed
- ◐ Probable
- ○ Possible
- □ Not Recorded

Special Areas

- ▲ Confirmed
- ◮ Probable
- △ Possible

Non-priority Blocks

- ● Confirmed
- ◐ Probable
- ○ Possible

Miles
0 4 8 12

Blackburnian Warbler

Dendroica fusca

One encounters the male Blackburnian Warbler poised at the top of the tallest evergreens, its fiery throat ignited by the morning sun. This attractive species is locally common in New Hampshire. Its orange (male) or yellow (female and young) facial pattern and black and white striped back are distinctive in all plumages.

The Blackburnian Warbler inhabits evergreen and mixed woods, occurring at elevations up to 3,000 ft (910 m) (Allen 1903, Forbush 1929, Thayer 1907 *in* Bent 1953). On Mt. Monadnock, Jaffrey, Thayer (1907 *in* Bent 1953) found it, along with Black-throated Blue, Northern Parula, and Canada warblers, to be a common summer resident in the heaviest timber. Knight (1908 *in* Bent 1953) notes that in suitable habitat, the Blackburnian Warbler may form small, loose colonies and may be quite common within a specific area.

Although the first "torch-birds" (Blanchan 1898) arrive in New Hampshire during the first 2 weeks of May, peak migration occurs during the last 2 weeks of that month. Blackburnians typically feed by gleaning insects from the foliage of upper branches, usually foraging from 39 to 63 ft (11.8 to 19.2 m) above ground (Holmes et al. 1979), but early spring arrivals will eat berries in cold weather (Forbush 1929). At the Hubbard Brook Experimental Forest, Thornton, these warblers forage primarily on yellow birch trees, using conifers, beeches, and sugar maples to a considerably lesser extent (Holmes 1986).

Once on territory, males frequently sing during mornings from the tops of tall conifers. Holmes (1986) observed males singing from perches with a mean height of 44.7 ft (13.4 m) at Hubbard Brook. Their variable song is characteristically very high with a trailing note rising beyond human hearing (Ellison *in* Laughlin and Kibbe 1985). Allen (1910 *in* Bent 1953) describes one version as "serwee' serwee' serwee' serwee' serwip" with an emphasis on the "wip."

The female builds the nest, working mostly during mornings, and may complete it in 3 days (Forbush 1929). It is generally placed near the top of a coniferous tree on a horizontal limb well away from the trunk (Harrison 1975). Nest trees include spruces, fir, pines, cedars, tamarack, and especially hemlock (Bent 1953). Nests are commonly 30 to 40 ft (9.1 to 12.2 m), above the ground, but may be from 5 ft (1.5 m) to 84 ft (26 m) (Scott 1921, Bent 1953, Harrison 1984). Mean height of 3 nests found at Hubbard Brook was 23.9 ft (7.3 m) above the ground (Holmes 1986). A nest loosely woven of hemlock twigs, rootlets, pine needles, and *Usnea* fragments, and thinly lined with horse hair was located 60 ft (18 m) above ground and 7 ft (2 m) out on a hemlock limb in southern New Hampshire. It contained 5 eggs on 8 June 1890, but a pair completed a nest in the same tree on 15 June 1891 (Bowles 1895). The female incubates her 4 or 5 eggs for 11 to 13 days, during June to early July (Harrison 1975, Godfrey 1979).

Their treetop habits and densely wooded habitats make Blackburnian Warblers difficult to "confirm." Breeding adults most often are "confirmed" while carrying food. The male brings food to the female during incubation; both parents feed the young. Fledged young first appear at the beginning of July and are evident through the end of the month. White (1937) observed a female attending young on 14 July 1922 in Concord.

One of the earliest warblers to stop singing, this bird is often silent by mid-July in southern New Hampshire and by late July in the north. Locating this species is very difficult after that time. The southward migration begins in mid-August, with peak movement occurring in the first 2 weeks of September (NHAQ, *passim*). Few are reported from New Hampshire in October.

Historical accounts suggest that the Blackburnian Warbler has been at least locally common as a summer resident in northern New Hampshire and scarcer in the southern part of the state since at least the late 19th century. Samuels (1870) considered it rare in New England, but Maynard (1871) found it common in Coos County, and Wright (1911) found it the most abundant species in a 50 a (20 ha) woodland at Jefferson Highlands, Jefferson, where 10 to 12 pairs were present annually. Dearborn (1898) considered the Blackburnian an uncommon but regularly nesting species in Belknap and Merrimack counties and White (1937) knew it to nest occasionally in Concord. Dearborn (1903) knew of no nesting records in the Durham area, but Fox (*in* Allen 1903) knew it to nest in Hollis, near the Massachusetts border. Scott (1921) believed that the species was increasing in southern New Hampshire, a trend that may be continuing. BBS data from 1966 to 1979 indicate an increase in the Northeastern states during this period (Robbins et al. 1986). Recent BBS data (1966–1990) show a significant and substantial increase in Maine, and insignificant minor decreases in Vermont and New Hampshire (J.R. Sauer, unpubl. data).

Atlas records are concentrated in the northern 3 counties, where only 5 priority blocks lack records. Records are more sporadic in southeastern New Hampshire, including about half of the priority blocks in the Eastern Uplands, Merrimack Valley, and Coastal Lowlands. Atlas observers found this species in almost all priority blocks with elevations above 600 ft (180 m), but only about half of those at lower elevations.

James McDermott

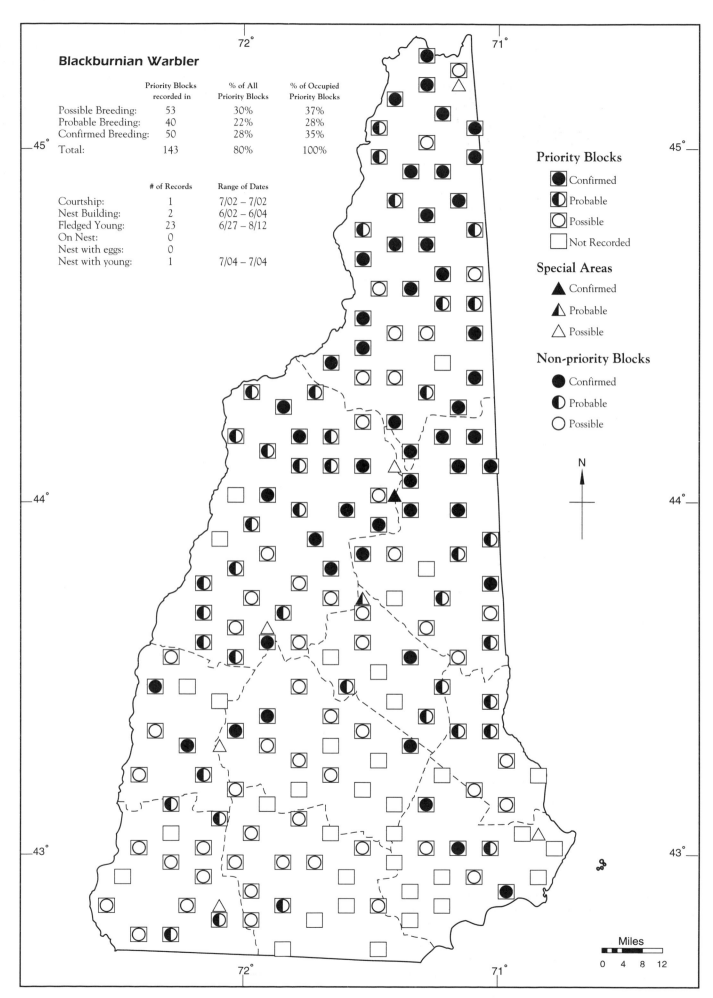

Blackburnian Warbler

	Priority Blocks recorded in	% of All Priority Blocks	% of Occupied Priority Blocks
Possible Breeding:	53	30%	37%
Probable Breeding:	40	22%	28%
Confirmed Breeding:	50	28%	35%
Total:	143	80%	100%

	# of Records	Range of Dates
Courtship:	1	7/02 – 7/02
Nest Building:	2	6/02 – 6/04
Fledged Young:	23	6/27 – 8/12
On Nest:	0	
Nest with eggs:	0	
Nest with young:	1	7/04 – 7/04

Priority Blocks
- ● Confirmed
- ◑ Probable
- ○ Possible
- □ Not Recorded

Special Areas
- ▲ Confirmed
- ◮ Probable
- △ Possible

Non-priority Blocks
- ● Confirmed
- ◑ Probable
- ○ Possible

Miles
0 4 8 12

Andrea Robbins

Pine Warbler
Dendroica pinus

The breeding distribution of this well-named species correlates closely with the range of pine forests in the eastern U.S. This hardy warbler is one of New England's earliest migrants, generally arriving from the southeastern states in mid to late April, but in exceptionally early springs during the first week of the month, when snow may still cover the forest floor. Individuals occasionally overwinter at bird feeders. The Pine Warbler is recognized by its yellow breast and throat, broad white wing bars, and unstreaked back. Its musical trill, which resembles the song of a junco, is a familiar sound from high in lofty pines.

Pine Warblers nest in white, red, and pitch pines, but seem to prefer pitch pines where all 3 species occur together in New Hampshire. The compact nests are on horizontal pine branches, generally concealed by a cluster of pine needles, and contain 3 to 5, usually 4 eggs. Nests consist of strips of bark, pine needles, bits of leaves, and caterpillar or spider silk with feather, hair, or fern down linings. Because of the great height at which they are typically built, Pine Warbler nests are rarely found. New Hampshire nest heights are not available, but published extremes are 8 ft (2.4 m) and 135 ft (41.2 m) (Wayne 1910). Excluding these extremes, heights of 19 nests averaged 36 ft (11 m), with the majority between 30 and 50 ft (9.1 to 15.2 m) (Bagg and Eliot 1937, Robbins 1950, Graber et al. 1983, Peck and James 1987).

Atlasers "confirmed" this species by observing nest-building activity, food or fecal sac carrying, and fledged young, but located no nests. Eighteen Massachusetts egg dates range from 22 May to 28 June, with 10 of them during 23 to 31 May (Bent 1953). The incubation and nestling periods for the Pine Warbler apparently are unknown. The female incubates, possibly with assistance from the male, and probably for about 12 or 13 days (Harrison 1975). Both parents tend the young (Harrison 1978, Harrison 1984).

These warblers use many foraging techniques, including climbing along trunks and branches, searching clusters of pine needles, sallying for flying insects, and walking on the ground. Roberts (1963) observed Pine Warblers flushing moths by shaking pine needles when alighting near the tips of branches and by singing a quick phrase of song immediately on alighting.

After singing ceases at the end of July, Pine Warblers may leave the pines to feed in deciduous trees and orchards, flocking with other warblers, Chipping Sparrows, Eastern Bluebirds, and other species. Although many Pine Warblers linger into early September, very few remain in New Hampshire after mid-month.

Some early observers (Belknap 1792, Fox 1876, Farmer 1892) did not report the Pine Warbler in southern New Hampshire. Little (1870), however, reported the "Pine-creeping Warbler" as common in Warren, and the first New Hampshire specimen was shot in Bridgewater on 21 August 1883 (Allen 1889). Allen (1903) thoroughly researched its distribution and called it uncommon locally in Transition valleys and lowlands, and fairly common in the extensive pitch pines of the Ossipee plain. He reported that R. Hoffmann had found small numbers summering up the Connecticut River as far as Cornish and that a few followed the Saco valley as far north as Conway and Intervale (Bartlett/Conway) to an elevation of about 500 ft (150 m). Wright (1911) knew of a pair in a grove of white pines in Jefferson in 1889 and 1900, but they disappeared when the pines were cut in 1901. A pair then occurred in a similar grove in Whitefield, but left when that grove was felled. Brewster (*in* Griscom 1938) found the species in Shelburne, and T. Richards (pers. comm.) observed it there on 11 June 1975.

Pine Warblers are widespread throughout southern New Hampshire. BBS data document their occurrence on all but one of the 14 routes south of the mountains, and on 4 routes in the White Mountains, but not on any of the 4 northernmost routes. Numbers in New Hampshire vary greatly from year to year. Fluctuations can result from mortality during prolonged cold weather on their wintering range or shortly after their return to the nesting grounds, if their food is scarce. BBS data indicate a significant increase in Pine Warblers in New Hampshire during 1966-87.

The Atlas map generally corroborates BBS data and shows the Pine Warbler occurring generally throughout the eastern half of the state north to the base of the mountains, and more locally in the western half, with very few records in the Connecticut River valley. Robbins found the Pine Warbler in 17 of 22 priority and nonpriority blocks in the Ossipee Lake quadrangle at the base of the White Mountains, but in only 5 of 15 blocks in the more mountainous Mt. Chocorua quadrangle immediately to the west. This illustrates how the mountains limit the Pine Warbler's range and distribution. The highest elevation record was 1,230 ft (375 m).

Though the breeding distribution of the Pine Warbler is spotty, both the total breeding range and the wintering range are extensive. The future outlook for this species in New Hampshire is bright, since pine habitats are widespread south of the mountains.

Chandler S. Robbins

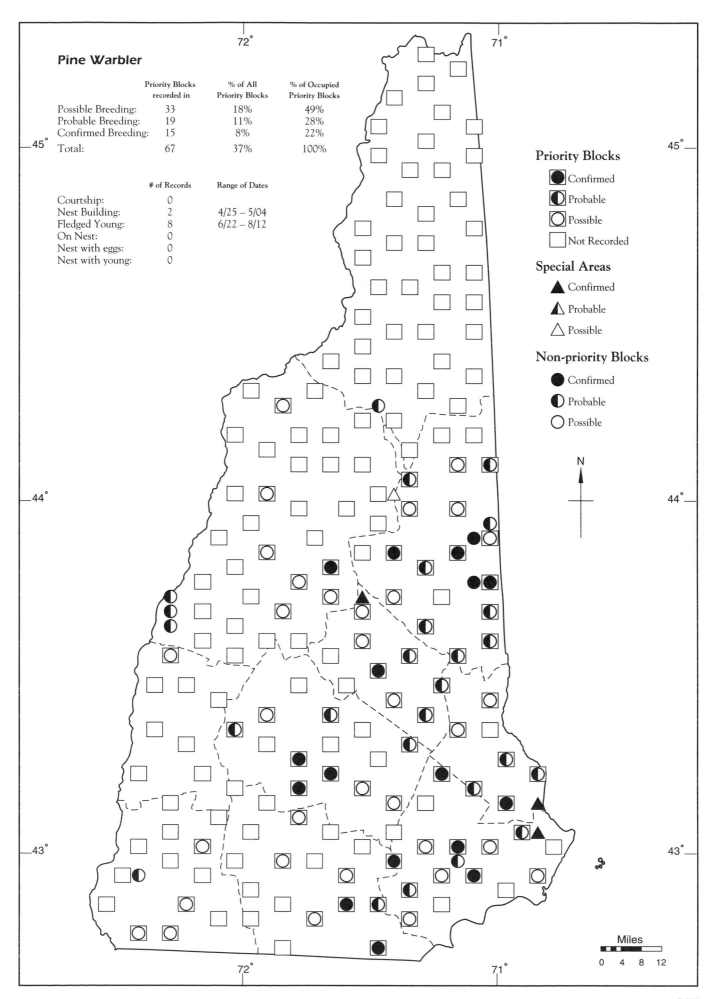

Pine Warbler

	Priority Blocks recorded in	% of All Priority Blocks	% of Occupied Priority Blocks
Possible Breeding:	33	18%	49%
Probable Breeding:	19	11%	28%
Confirmed Breeding:	15	8%	22%
Total:	67	37%	100%

	# of Records	Range of Dates
Courtship:	0	
Nest Building:	2	4/25 – 5/04
Fledged Young:	8	6/22 – 8/12
On Nest:	0	
Nest with eggs:	0	
Nest with young:	0	

Priority Blocks

- ◑ Confirmed
- ◐ Probable
- ○ Possible
- ☐ Not Recorded

Special Areas

- ▲ Confirmed
- ◭ Probable
- △ Possible

Non-priority Blocks

- ● Confirmed
- ◐ Probable
- ○ Possible

N

Miles
0 4 8 12

Prairie Warbler
Dendroica discolor

Buzzy notes ascending the chromatic scale are the trademark of this tiny warbler. The Prairie Warbler is olive-green above and bright yellow below, with black streaks along the flanks. The male has a distinctive black and yellow face pattern which the female lacks. Habitat includes brushy abandoned fields and cutover forests, overgrown gravel pits, and maintained brushy habitats such as power-line and railroad rights-of-way. This warbler is easy to spot as it darts among shrubs and small saplings, flicking its tail as it forages in low branches. Most arrivals are in mid-May, singing ceases in mid-July, and departures occur in August.

The Prairie Warbler is rare in most of New Hampshire because it is at the very northern limit of its breeding range. Although fairly common in suitable habitat in coastal Rockingham and Strafford counties and parts of Merrimack County, the Prairie Warbler is increasingly local as one moves inland.

The following information is from Nolan's (1978) monograph on the behavior of this species in Indiana. Adult males defend a territory that averages 4.3 a (1.7 ha), from which they glean moth and butterfly larvae, beetles, and weevils. They typically sing from the upper part of the tallest tree in the territory. Indiana nests consisted of an outer shell of plant fibers bound with spider webs; a padding made from downy broom-sedge seeds, feathers, or fur; and an inner lining of fine plant material, feathers, or fur. Nearly half of more than 550 nests in Indiana were in upright forks. Half of the others were on one or more twigs against the trunk of a small tree. Of 608 Indiana nests, 77% were within 9.8 ft (3 m) of the ground, with late season nests tending to be higher than early ones. Females laid 3 to 5 eggs, generally 4 in the first clutch and 3 or 4 in a second. Incubation required 10.5 to 15.4 days (mean of 12), and normal fledging age was 9 or 10 days. More than half of Nolan's nests were in young American elms, with sugar maple a second choice (9%), but 18 of 22

Ontario nests (Peck and James 1987) were in low juniper shrubs.

Neither New Hampshire nor Vermont atlas observers found an active Prairie Warbler nest. Food or fecal sac observations and fledged young provided breeding "confirmations" in New Hampshire. Adults carrying food to nestlings fly directly to their nest (Nolan 1978). Occurrence of second broods in New Hampshire is questionable.

Samuels (1867) considered Massachusetts the northern range limit for the Prairie Warbler. Brewster seldom found it more than 15 mi (24 km) from tidewater in eastern Massachusetts, although it was very numerous in portions of Connecticut and Rhode Island, especially near the coast (Minot 1895). Allen (1903) and others have questioned reports (Minot 1875) of eggs near Mt. Washington and a nest in Bethlehem. Allen (1903) cites a male taken in the company of half-grown young in Hollis on 28 June 1884, single birds taken there on 23 August and 4 September 1876, and a small colony in Manchester. Other early authors indicate that the Prairie Warbler was uncommon in Grafton County (Sherman 1889) and quite common in northern Hillsborough County (Farmer 1892). Colonies occurred on the Bedford plains and on the plains near Rock Rimmon, Manchester, in June 1901 (Batchelder 1902). Allen (1903) questioned a report of 2 nests and an egg collected about 1880 in Northfield (Herrick 1883), which was north of any site known at that time. Northfield, however, is well within the species' present range.

Prairie Warblers have occurred on all southern New Hampshire BBS routes, except Gilmanton and the 4 routes in counties bordering the Connecticut River. BBS data include no records in or north of the mountains. Although BBS data during 1966–79 indicate a population decline in the eastern U. S. (Robbins et al. 1986), data from 1966 to 1989 indicate no significant change in New Hampshire numbers.

The Prairie Warbler has spread north in New Hampshire in recent decades along major north-south power-line corridors (T. Richards, K. C. Elkins, pers. comm.). Atlas "confirmations" in Andover and Franklin were along power-lines, and T. Richards (pers. comm.) has found the species on a power-line corridor in Alexandria.

The Atlas map shows a peculiar distribution, including nearly all priority blocks in Rockingham and Strafford counties. There were only 2 records in the vicinity of the Connecticut valley, although the Vermont Atlas documented the species in 9 blocks on the Vermont side of the river, where colonies occurred in 2 locations (Laughlin and Kibbe 1985). The Ossipee plain yielded no Prairie Warblers during the Atlas period, although they occurred just across the Maine line in Fryeburg in 1984 and 1985 (J. O'Brien, pers. comm.), farther north than any New Hampshire records. The northernmost New Hampshire record was from the Holderness area.

As land in New Hampshire is used more intensively, the habitat type on which this species depends is likely to become scarcer. Utility corridors can provide a continuing stronghold, but cowbirds present an increasing menace. Although Friedmann (1929) found only 10 known instances of parasitism, more recent parasitism rates range from 27 to 33% (Walkinshaw 1959, Nolan 1978, Peck and James 1987). Thus, the outlook for this species in New Hampshire is one of guarded optimism.

Chandler S. Robbins

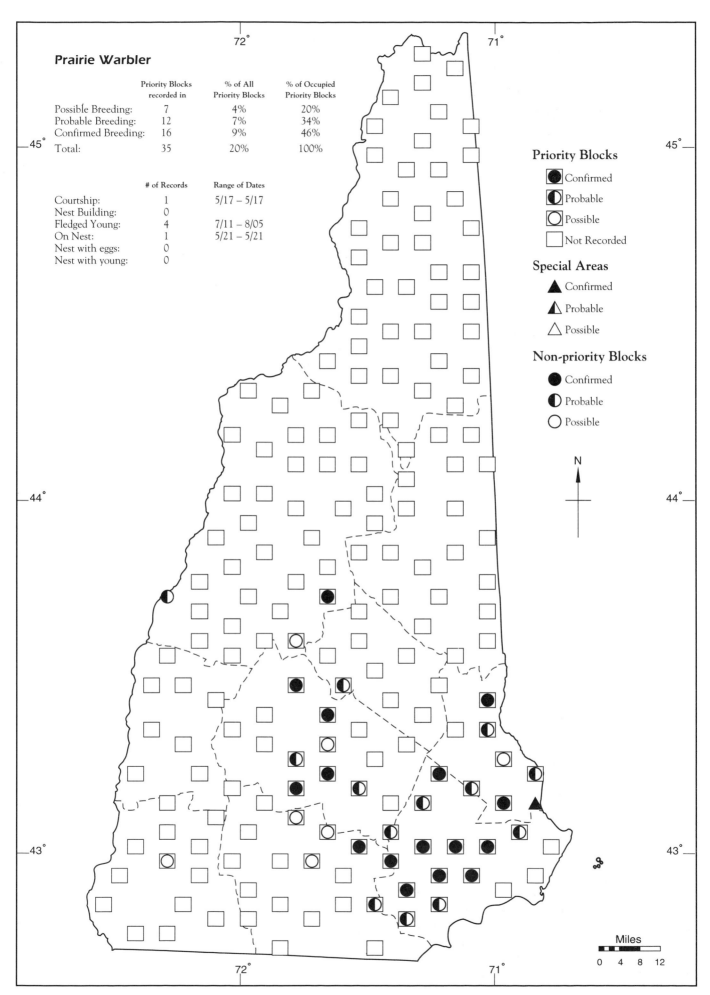

Prairie Warbler

	Priority Blocks recorded in	% of All Priority Blocks	% of Occupied Priority Blocks
Possible Breeding:	7	4%	20%
Probable Breeding:	12	7%	34%
Confirmed Breeding:	16	9%	46%
Total:	35	20%	100%

	# of Records	Range of Dates
Courtship:	1	5/17 – 5/17
Nest Building:	0	
Fledged Young:	4	7/11 – 8/05
On Nest:	1	5/21 – 5/21
Nest with eggs:	0	
Nest with young:	0	

Priority Blocks

- Confirmed
- Probable
- Possible
- Not Recorded

Special Areas

- Confirmed
- Probable
- Possible

Non-priority Blocks

- Confirmed
- Probable
- Possible

N

Miles
0   4   8   12

Bay-breasted Warbler

Dendroica castanea

The Bay-breasted Warbler is a handsome but inconspicuous denizen of the northern coniferous forest. Despite its beautiful chestnut plumage, this relatively large warbler is easily overlooked. In New Hampshire, where it reaches the southern limit of its breeding range, this warbler breeds fairly commonly at elevations up to 4,000 ft (1,220 m) in coniferous and mixed forests from the White Mountains north. Like Tennessee Warblers, Bay-breasteds occasionally may linger and possibly breed south of their normal range (Oatman *in* Laughlin and Kibbe 1985). However, singing males in such locations often are unpaired.

The Bay-breasted Warbler arrives in New Hampshire during the last 2 weeks of May, and migration may continue into early June. Like several other northern warblers, it prefers small forest openings, particularly the edges of clearings, bogs, and ponds. It favors vigorous, mature conifers with thick lower branches (MacArthur 1958). In Harts Location, it occurs both in boggy, semiopen spruce-fir at 1,600 ft (490 m) and in old-growth spruce-fir forest at 3,000 ft (910 m) (S.D. Smith, pers. comm.). Sabo (1980) reported Bay-breasted Warblers in White Mountain subalpine forests with a mean canopy height of 37 ft (11.3 m). He documented a territory size of 3.7 a (1.5 ha) and an average density of 2 pairs/0.4 sq mi (1 sq km) in subalpine forest on Mt. Moosilauke, Benton, and 14 pairs/0.4 sq mi (1 sq km) in a virgin spruce grove near Nancy Pond, Lincoln.

The breeding season starts in late May or early June. The male's high-pitched trill is easily confused with those of the Cape May, Blackpoll, and Blackburnian warblers, which share spruce-fir habitat. The song period peaks during the first 2 weeks of June (D. Welsh, pers. comm.), but extends into late July and sometimes early August (Wright 1911). A Bay-breasted Warbler may sing continuously from the same perch for as long as 15 minutes (Oberholser 1957 *in* Reilly 1979), but

may be invisible from the ground. The female, accompanied by the male, gathers material and builds the bulky, loosely woven nest on a horizontal limb of a spruce, fir, hemlock, or other tree, usually 5 to 20 ft (1.5 to 6.1 m) but sometimes up to 50 ft (15.2 m) above the ground and usually 5 to 10 ft (1.5 to 3 m) out from the trunk (Harrison 1975).

Bent (1953) recorded egg dates from 12 to 28 June in New Hampshire. The clutch includes 3 to 7, commonly 4 or 5 eggs (Harrison 1978). The male feeds his mate on the nest during the 12 or 13 day incubation period and stands guard nearby in her absence (Harrison 1975). The female is quite fearless at the nest, but may perform a distraction display if an intruder approaches too closely. Both parents feed the young, which remain in the nest 11 or 12 days. Mendall (1937) found both adults and one young together near the nest site 8 days after the young had fledged. This species departs south during mid-August to mid-September, generally before the Blackpoll Warbler, with which it is easily confused in the fall.

Populations of this species and the rarer Cape May Warbler respond to periodic spruce budworm outbreaks (MacArthur 1958). Both lay considerably larger clutches during years of high budworm populations (MacArthur 1958). During the years between budworm outbreaks, Bay-breasted Warbler numbers decline locally, and the species may disappear from some areas.

Both Bay-breasted and Cape May warblers tend to favor red spruces for foraging (Morse 1978). The Bay-breasted forages primarily among interior branches in the middle sections of conifers, while the Cape May forages mainly in treetops among the outer tips of the branches. The Bay-breasted Warbler often feeds in the same tree for long periods of time (MacArthur 1958), moving from branch to branch in hops and short flights.

Historical information on this species reflects its periodic fluctuations in numbers. Maynard (1871) considered this species the most abundant warbler at Umbagog Lake and reported several nests there. Wright (1911) described the Bay-breasted as a "not uncommon summer resident" in the Jefferson region, noting few records before 1905, a subsequent increase through 1909 possibly related to a budworm outbreak, and greatly diminished numbers in 1911 (MacArthur 1958). T. Richards (pers. comm.) found the Bay-breasted Warbler to be the most common bird in virgin spruce forest at East Inlet, Pittsburg on 8 July 1953. RNEB (*passim*) includes New Hampshire records from every year from 1949 to 1960 and for 1965–67, primarily from Pittsburg.

There are 3 records of apparent breeding south of the Bay-breasted Warbler's normal range in New Hampshire. Allison and Allison (1979) reported possible nesting on Mt. Monadnock, Jaffrey; Bent (1953) found a nest on the shore of Squam Lake in 1930; and K. C. Elkins (pers. comm.) found Bay-breasted Warblers in a spruce forest on a northeast ridge of Mt. Kearsarge, in Salisbury, at an elevation of 1,200 to 1,300 ft (370 to 400 m) each summer from 1936 to 1940. Following extensive logging in the early 1940s, the birds apparently did not return.

The Atlas project documented nesting only in the White Mountains and the North Country, although there was one "possible" breeding record from the Peterborough area. Other than population fluctuations related to spruce budworm outbreaks, the continued availability of mature spruce-fir forest will be the most important factor determining the Bay-breasted Warbler's future in New Hampshire.

Ralph Andrews

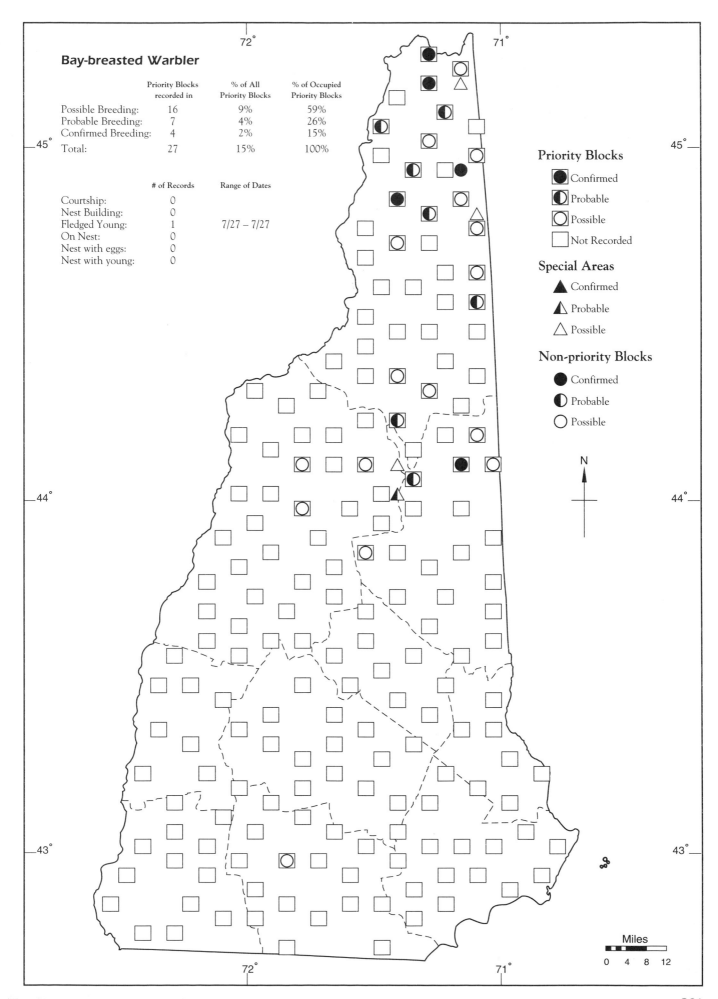

Bay-breasted Warbler

	Priority Blocks recorded in	% of All Priority Blocks	% of Occupied Priority Blocks
Possible Breeding:	16	9%	59%
Probable Breeding:	7	4%	26%
Confirmed Breeding:	4	2%	15%
Total:	27	15%	100%

	# of Records	Range of Dates
Courtship:	0	
Nest Building:	0	
Fledged Young:	1	7/27 – 7/27
On Nest:	0	
Nest with eggs:	0	
Nest with young:	0	

Priority Blocks

- ◐ Confirmed
- ◑ Probable
- ○ Possible
- ☐ Not Recorded

Special Areas

- ▲ Confirmed
- ◣ Probable
- △ Possible

Non-priority Blocks

- ● Confirmed
- ◐ Probable
- ○ Possible

N

Miles
0   4   8   12

Blackpoll Warbler
Dendroica striata

The handsome black and white striped male Blackpoll is distinguished from the Black-and-white Warbler by its solid black cap and white cheeks. In New Hampshire this warbler is a common to abundant migrant and an abundant summer resident in spruce-fir forests above 2,500 ft (760 m), from the White Mountains northward. Its favorite nesting haunts are just below timberline, between 4,000 and 4,500 ft (1,220 and 1,370 m), and dominated by balsam fir, with lesser amounts of red and black spruce and heart-leaved paper birch. It rarely breeds below 1,500 ft (460 m).

The Blackpoll Warbler breeds from north central Alaska to northern Labrador in the north, and from British Columbia to central New England in the south. Its winter range, reached by an extraordinary, partially oceanic migration route, extends from northern South America to Brazil and Chile (Gross 1953a, AOU 1957).

Individuals make an annual round trip of 2,500 to 5,000 mi (4,000 to 8,000 km) between breeding and wintering grounds (Gross 1953a), one of the longest migratory journeys of all the world's small land birds.

The Blackpoll Warbler arrives in New Hampshire from mid-May to early June. An early record is of a singing male on 10 May 1953, at about 3,000 ft (910 m) on Mt. Whiteface, Waterville Valley, in the Sandwich Range (Richards, unpubl. data).

Blackpoll populations in the White Mountains tend to increase with increasing elevation from about 1,460 ft (450 m) to treeline (Morse 1979; Sabo 1980; Richards, unpubl. data). Richards (unpubl. data) obtained about 450 possible breeding records of Blackpoll Warblers during numerous hikes in the White Mountains from 1946 to 1986. Of these, 13% occurred below 2,500 ft (760 m), 16 to 19% in each 500 ft (152 m) interval from 2,500 ft (760 m) to 4,000 ft (1,220), 27% between 4,000 and 4,500 ft (1,220 and 1,370 m), and 8% above 4,500 ft (1,370 m). This warbler outnumbers all other bird species in the krummholz zone of the White Mountains.

The high-pitched, insectlike song is loudest in the middle. It most commonly sounds like a fast "zip-zip-zip-zip-zip-zip-zip," but may be a trill. Males sing mostly from the tops of trees, which become gradually more stunted from about 3,500 ft (1,070 m) to timberline. The species seems to have no special courtship display. Territories often are close together, and densities may be about 154 pairs/0.4 sq mi (1 sq km)(Sabo 1980).

The well-concealed, bulky nest is often against the trunk of a small conifer, 2 to 10 ft (0.6 to 3 m) above the ground, and supported by one or 2 horizontal branches (Harrison 1975). The female does most of the building, using twigs, bark, sprays of spruce, grasses, mosses, and lichens, with a characteristic lining of feathers. The Yellow-rumped Warbler, a common species in the Blackpoll's range, builds a similar nest, which is less bulky and not built against a tree trunk (Harrison 1975).

The female incubates her 4 or 5 eggs for at least 11 days, and may begin before the clutch is complete. The male feeds the female on the nest, helping the careful observer to find it (Harrison 1975). Of 18 New Hampshire egg dates, 11 were from 16 June to 16 July, and 7 were from 20 to 28 June (Gross 1953a). Both parents feed the young during their 11-day nestling period. Blackpolls consume a great variety of insects, as well as some seeds and berries (Forbush 1929, Gross 1953a). Spruce budworm and other larvae that feed inside conifer buds and needles are important food sources (Eliason 1986). Blackpolls forage primarily by foliage gleaning, but may hover near vegetation or hawk flying insects (Gross 1953a).

Some Blackpoll Warblers start south in August, but their migration generally peaks in mid-September. On 15 September 1900, Allen (1903) heard a local Blackpoll singing and observed a flight of several hundred warblers, three-quarters of them Blackpolls, passing north through Carter Notch, Beans Purchase. Blackpolls continue migrating through New Hampshire until mid-October.

Allen (1903) called the Blackpoll Warbler a common summer resident of the upper Canadian zone which is 2,000 ft (610 m) and above on north slopes, 3,000 ft (910 m) and above on south slopes. Wright (1911) considered it abundant in summer on coniferous slopes in the Jefferson region. Brewster (*in* Griscom 1938) found it only a migrant in the Umbagog area, though it undoubtedly nested in Dixville Notch, Dixville. Breeding season records suggest possible nesting in the past on Mt. Kearsarge, Warner/ Wilmot; and Mt. Sunapee, Newbury (Richards, unpubl. data); and Mt. Monadnock, Jaffrey (Richards *in* Baldwin 1970).

Blackpoll Warbler populations no doubt have fluctuated considerably as a result of spruce budworm outbreaks, hurricanes, forest fires, and extensive logging. Blackpolls also must contend with the perils of migration and, in recent decades, widespread use of pesticides, both on breeding and on wintering grounds, where habitat loss also may be a serious factor. Populations may have declined appreciably in recent decades. BBS routes in New England do not include the primary range of Blackpolls, so they provide insufficient data for analyzing population trends.

The Atlas map shows a fairly continuous distribution in the White Mountains and scattered records from the more isolated mountains further north. More thorough coverage of high elevations north of the White Mountains almost certainly would have yielded additional records. The southernmost "confirmed" record is from Mt. Cube, Orford. Records in southwestern New Hampshire are associated with a few higher peaks, including Mt. Kearsage; Grantham Mtn., Grantham; Cardigan Mtn., Orange; Moose Mountain, Hanover; and Pack Monadnock Mtn., Peterborough.

Tudor Richards

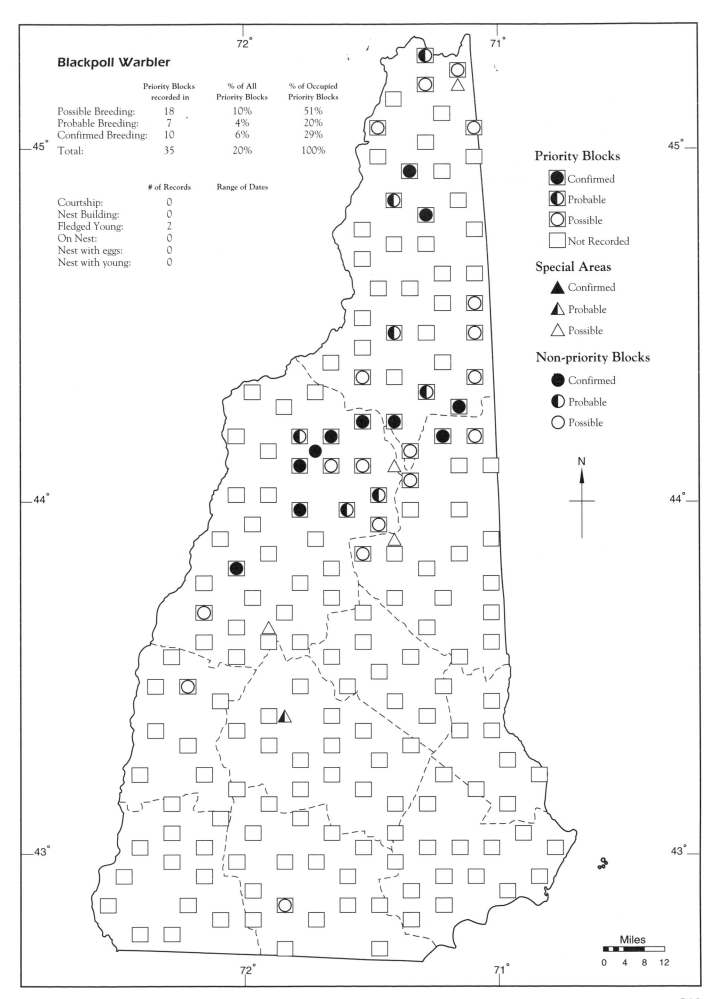

Blackpoll Warbler

	Priority Blocks recorded in	% of All Priority Blocks	% of Occupied Priority Blocks
Possible Breeding:	18	10%	51%
Probable Breeding:	7	4%	20%
Confirmed Breeding:	10	6%	29%
Total:	35	20%	100%

	# of Records	Range of Dates
Courtship:	0	
Nest Building:	0	
Fledged Young:	2	
On Nest:	0	
Nest with eggs:	0	
Nest with young:	0	

Priority Blocks

◐ Confirmed
◑ Probable
○ Possible
☐ Not Recorded

Special Areas

▲ Confirmed
◢ Probable
△ Possible

Non-priority Blocks

● Confirmed
◐ Probable
○ Possible

N

283

Black-and-white Warbler
Mniotilta varia

The Black-and-white Warbler is unique among North American wood warblers because it forages by creeping along the trunks of trees like a nuthatch or Brown Creeper. It even has been called the Black-and-white Creeper, although it is not closely related to the creepers. In appearance it resembles the Blackpoll Warbler, but has a striped head rather than a solid black cap. Nesting habitat and feeding behavior of the 2 species are distinctly different. The female Black-and-white resembles the boldly striped male, but has fewer black streaks.

The Black-and-white Warbler nests throughout the hardwood forests of eastern North America, with a definite preference for damp deciduous or mixed woodlands (Pough 1946, Godfrey 1966). Forbush (1929) and Harrison (1975) note a preference for hillsides and ravines in some areas. It generally avoids predominantly coniferous areas, but sometimes nests in pine woods. This warbler is scarce or absent at elevations above 2,000 ft (610 m) in New Hampshire (Ridgely 1977). Most Black-and-white Warblers winter in the West Indies, Mexico, Central America, or northern South America, but a few go no farther than Florida or southern Texas (Peterson 1980).

Although this warbler's food consists of insects and other invertebrates, its habit of feeding on eggs and larvae in bark crevices frees it from the need to feed in the leafy canopy. Not surprisingly, therefore, it is one of the earliest warblers to return in spring. The first arrivals reach southern New Hampshire by the end of April. Males arrive shortly before the females and establish territories from which they repeat their thin, wiry song almost endlessly until well into the nesting period. In New Hampshire, nesting gets underway in mid-May.

The female builds a nest that is carefully concealed among leaves on the ground and often at the base of a tree. She alone incubates the 4 or 5 speckled eggs for

11 or 12 days (Harrison 1978). Cowbirds often parasitize the nest (Peck and James 1987). The young leave the nest after another 10 to 12 days (Harrison 1975). Both parents share the feeding of young. They raise only a single brood, but a pair is likely to renest if a predator destroys its initial attempt (Pough 1946). Departure for the wintering grounds begins by early August, and most birds have departed by late September (Elkins 1982).

People seldom find the well-concealed nests, and Atlas observers discovered only 2 in priority blocks. Andrews found a nest with 4 eggs in late May 1979 beside a moss-covered log near Nashua after nearly stepping on an incubating adult. He discovered another nest with young at the base of a clump of gray birches on 16 June 1984 in the Thompson Sanctuary, Sandwich. Nearly all "confirmed" records were based on observations of fledged young or of adults carrying food for young.

Population declines in some parts of the Black-and-white Warbler's breeding range have followed fragmentation of extensive woodlands into small, scattered woodlots (Whitcomb 1977). The clearing of New Hampshire's forests during the 1800s may have had a similar impact. The subsequent reversion of pastures to woods in much of the state during the last 100 years presumably has favored this species, which readily accepts cutover and regenerating woodlands.

At the turn of the century, the Black-and-white Warbler was considered a common to abundant summer bird in Durham (Dearborn 1903), Concord (White 1924), and Belknap and Merrimack counties (Dearborn 1898). Maynard (1871) found it "not common" in Coos County, where woodlands were predominantly spruce-fir. Hardwoods have intruded vigorously into better-drained lowland sites in much of the North Country following clearcutting of spruce and fir (Marchand 1987), which probably accounts for the northward range expansion in New Hampshire during this century.

The Atlas data show that the Black-and-white Warbler is a widely distributed nesting species in New Hampshire. Only 9 priority blocks lack records, and all but 2 of these were in the White Mountains or North Country.

BBS data from 1966 to 1979 show New Hampshire to be in the area of highest density for this species (Robbins et al. 1986). BBS data from 1966 to 1987 suggest that populations in New Hampshire were stable during that period. Although this species is in no apparent jeopardy here, growing urbanization in the southern part of the state will reduce numbers of nesting pairs. As a ground nester, this warbler is vulnerable to predation and disturbance by humans and pets, even in unaltered habitat. The drastic, extensive clearing of deciduous broadleaf woodlands in the Middle American tropics where the Black-and-white Warbler winters also may affect this species adversely (Rappole et al. 1983). However, it should be less sensitive to such clearing than most other warblers because it has an extensive winter range in the tropics and occurs in many habitats there, including citrus groves, cacao, and shade coffee (C. S. Robbins, pers. comm.).

Ralph Andrews

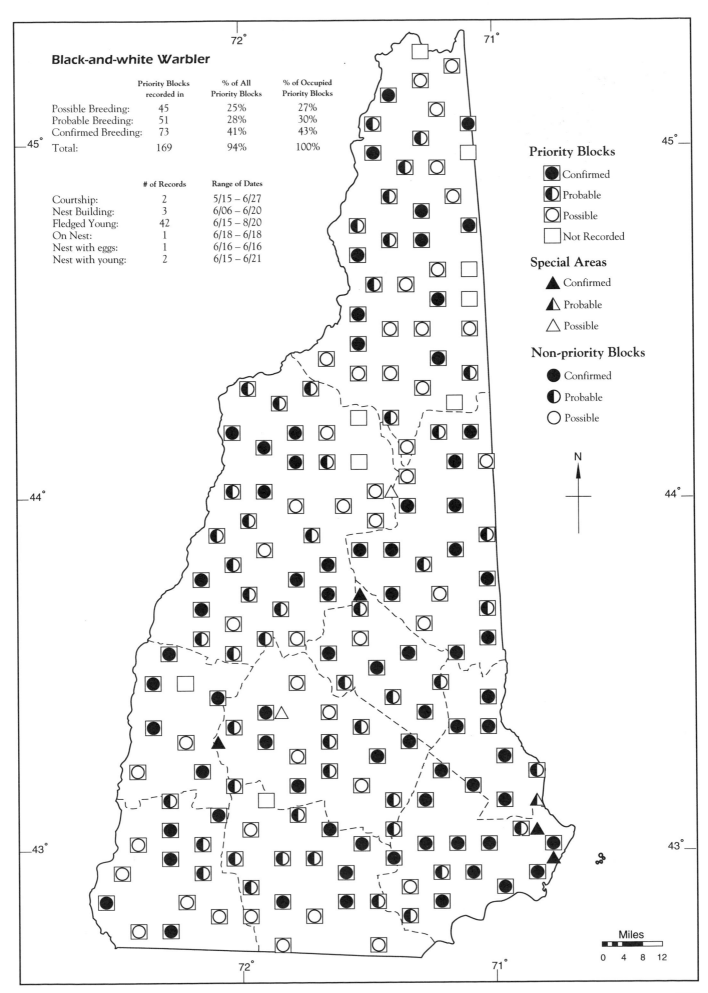

Black-and-white Warbler

	Priority Blocks recorded in	% of All Priority Blocks	% of Occupied Priority Blocks
Possible Breeding:	45	25%	27%
Probable Breeding:	51	28%	30%
Confirmed Breeding:	73	41%	43%
Total:	169	94%	100%

	# of Records	Range of Dates
Courtship:	2	5/15 – 6/27
Nest Building:	3	6/06 – 6/20
Fledged Young:	42	6/15 – 8/20
On Nest:	1	6/18 – 6/18
Nest with eggs:	1	6/16 – 6/16
Nest with young:	2	6/15 – 6/21

Priority Blocks

◑ Confirmed
◐ Probable
○ Possible
□ Not Recorded

Special Areas

▲ Confirmed
◤ Probable
△ Possible

Non-priority Blocks

● Confirmed
◐ Probable
○ Possible

N

American Redstart
Setophaga ruticilla

Flying acrobatically after evasive insects, then pirouetting through woodland foliage with tails fanned, American Redstarts resemble colorful butterflies with their orange and black or yellow and gray plumage, depending on age and sex. Redstarts are broadly distributed, breeding from Canada and Alaska south into Louisiana and Texas. They are abundant in moist woodlands and thickets throughout New Hampshire, especially in northern hardwood forests, and breed from near sea level to above 3,000 ft (910 m) in the White Mountains (Sabo 1980).

Redstarts typically return in early to mid-May from wintering in the Caribbean islands, Central America, and northern South America. Two-year and older males return first, usually between 5 and 10 May, followed in one to 2 weeks by females and yearling males. The latter closely resemble the females, but show their true identity with song, and almost invariably have small patches of black feathers on their breasts, necks, heads, and faces.

Redstarts vigorously defend territories using a variety of stereotyped postures and behaviors (Ficken 1962, Ficken 1963a, Ickes and Ficken 1970). Males often resolve territorial boundary disputes with repeated "circle chases," in which one flies towards, and circles less than 3.3 ft (1 m) in front of another, which then pursues and circles just in front of the first. During courtship males often display to females by bowing, fluffing their feathers, or spreading their tails, and then may glide away with wings spread.

Males initially sing one "accented" song type repeatedly, and after courting gradually switch to a repertoire of up to 8 unaccented song types, whose primary function may be to repel neighboring males (Lemon et al. 1985, MacNally and Lemon 1985, Kroodsma 1989). Older males may court and mate with late-arriving females on secondary territories often far from the primary one (Secunda and Sherry 1991; Sherry, unpubl. data).

The female constructs the nest, usually by the last week of May for early nests, or by early June (Sherry and Holmes, unpubl. data). A pair in Concord in 1937 constructed a nest during 21 – 26 May (White 1937). The female firmly attaches the compact, open-cup nest to a vertical crotch, usually the main trunk of a small tree or sapling.

Redstarts often nest in understory shrubs and saplings (Scott 1921, Peters 1953, Morris and Lemon 1988). Sherry and Holmes (unpubl. data) observed more than 400 redstart nests in the WMNF between 1981 and 1990, and found that redstarts nested in most shrub and tree species present, but avoided conifers and white ash. Nest heights ranged from less than 3.3 ft (1 m) to more than 98 ft (30 m), with a mode of 6.6 to 13 ft (2 to 4 m) and median of 20 to 25 ft (6 to 7 m).

Although redstarts may attempt to rear only one brood in a season, they will renest up to 3 times when nests are lost. Clutch size declines from 4 (occasionally 5) eggs in late May and early June to 3 (occasionally 1 or 2) eggs in July (Sherry and Holmes, unpubl. data). The female incubates for 11 or 12 days and broods nestlings until they fledge 8 or 9 days after hatching. Both adults share the feeding of nestlings about equally (Sturm 1945; Sherry and Holmes, unpubl. data), and divide the brood after the young have fledged (Boxall 1983). Little is known about postfledging behavior, but some redstarts leave breeding areas in August, and the rest depart by late September (Peters 1953).

Weather and nest predators are important factors in nest failures in the White Mountains (Sherry and Holmes 1992). Nest predators include squirrels, chipmunks, raccoons, and Blue Jays (Sherry and Holmes, unpubl. data). Both parents try to distract predators away from eggs, nestlings, or fledglings, by fluttering away and displaying spread tails with quivering, outstretched wings (Skutch in Peters 1953; Ficken 1963a; Sherry, pers. obs.).

American Redstarts feed primarily on small, agile jumping and flying insects such as leafhoppers and plant hoppers and small moths and flies, but also take larger insects such as caterpillars, beetles, and wasps (Robinson and Holmes 1982; Sherry 1985 and unpubl. data). Redstarts forage actively at all heights within vegetation, with frequent hops and perch-change flights, tumbling chases after evasive insects, hovering flights at leaf tips and along tree trunks, gleans of prey from foliage and twig surfaces, and conspicuous fanning of tails in some seasons—presumably to flush cryptic prey (Robinson and Holmes 1984; Sherry, unpubl. data).

The status of redstarts in New Hampshire has changed little during the last century. Early authors considered the species common to abundant at a variety of locations throughout the state (Allen 1889, Dearborn 1898, Allen 1903, Dearborn 1903, White 1937, Thayer 1909 in Allison and Allison 1979). Faxon found redstarts abundant in Franconia during 11 – 21 June 1886 and 4 June – 1 August 1887, but Allen had considered them uncommon in Franconia and Bethlehem during July and August 1874 (Faxon and Allen 1888).

BBS data from 1966 to 1979 indicate a population increase in the Northeastern states; during this period the species' highest densities occurred in New Hampshire, Maine, New Brunswick, and Nova Scotia (Robbins et al. 1986). Poor nesting success apparently caused a population decline during the mid-1980s (Sherry and Holmes 1992). Atlas observers recorded redstarts in every priority block except 2: Nashua, which may lack sufficiently large forest patches (see Sherry and Holmes 1992), and Corbin Park, Croydon, where Atlas effort was minimal.

Thomas W. Sherry & Richard T. Holmes

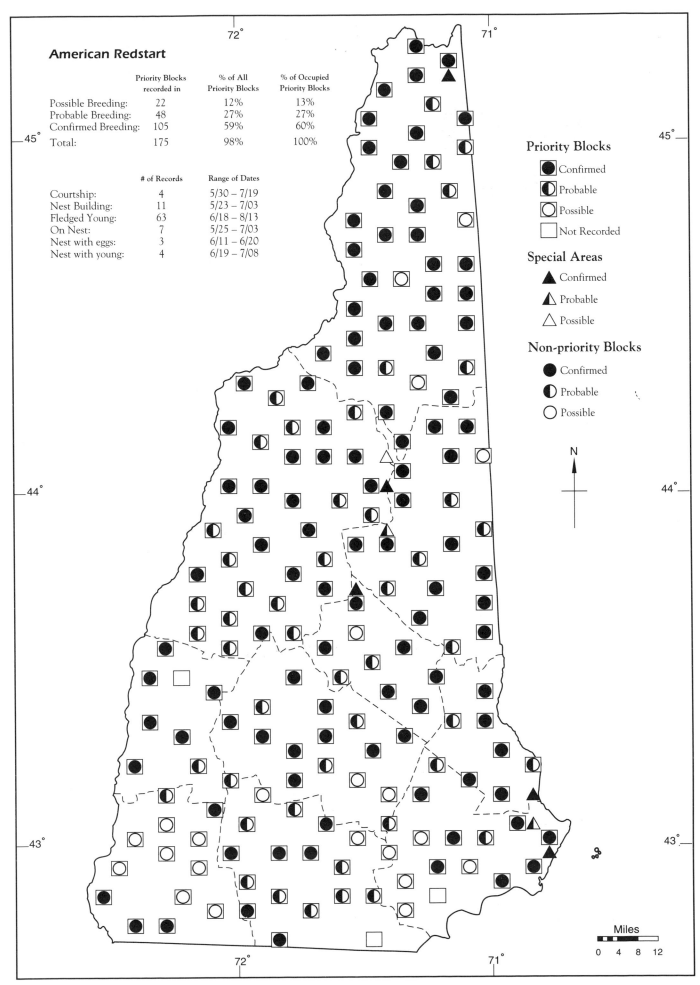

American Redstart

	Priority Blocks recorded in	% of All Priority Blocks	% of Occupied Priority Blocks
Possible Breeding:	22	12%	13%
Probable Breeding:	48	27%	27%
Confirmed Breeding:	105	59%	60%
Total:	175	98%	100%

	# of Records	Range of Dates
Courtship:	4	5/30 – 7/19
Nest Building:	11	5/23 – 7/03
Fledged Young:	63	6/18 – 8/13
On Nest:	7	5/25 – 7/03
Nest with eggs:	3	6/11 – 6/20
Nest with young:	4	6/19 – 7/08

Priority Blocks

- Confirmed
- Probable
- Possible
- Not Recorded

Special Areas

- Confirmed
- Probable
- Possible

Non-priority Blocks

- Confirmed
- Probable
- Possible

N

Miles
0 4 8 12

Worm-eating Warbler
Helmitheros vermivorus

The Worm-eating Warbler resembles the Ovenbird in behavior and appearance, but has unmarked buffy underparts and unmistakable black and buff stripes on the head. This poorly named warbler is no more partial to "worms" (i.e., inchworms) than others in its family (Ridgely 1977). Bent (1953) suggests that "hillside warbler" might be a more appropriate name. Long considered an occasional migratory overshoot in New Hampshire, this species has no breeding records north of western Massachusetts, and there are few New Hampshire sight records. A lone territorial male was present in South Hampton for 2 breeding seasons during the New Hampshire Atlas project. The species occurs irregularly during spring migration in southern Maine.

The Worm-eating Warbler's preferred habitat reportedly is extensive medium-aged deciduous woods with sapling and shrub understory, often (but not always) on a steep, cool, and moist slope or ravine uphill from a swamp tangle, stream, or river (Bent 1953, Todd 1940 *in* Bent 1953, Ridgely 1977). The South Hampton site generally fits this description, but includes quite a few white pines and has very little steep terrain. The area contains numerous American chestnut sprouts and saplings, dense fern ground cover, and several overgrown logging roads. This warbler apparently requires extensive areas of contiguous forest, and does not nest in small isolated woodlots (C. S. Robbins, pers. comm.).

Worm-eating Warblers sing from the time of their arrival until the end of June or early July on breeding areas south of New Hampshire (Bicknell 1884 *in* Bent 1953). The song resembles that of a Chipping Sparrow, but is higher pitched and more rapid, buzzy, and insectlike (Ridgely 1977). The South Hampton male sang several times on 1 June 1985 while in full flight, and continued its song, bill vibrating and open, after alighting on its next perch (Gavutis and J. Berry, pers.

obs.). Burroughs (*in* Forbush 1929) noted a flight song performed near sunset.

The nest usually is in a hollow in the ground, in and under a layer of dry, dead leaves, and is often beside a rock, log, or the base of a tree or shrub (Forbush 1929, Bull 1974). Forbush (1929) indicated egg dates from 25 May to 19 June in Connecticut. Bull (1974) lists New York egg dates of 24 May to 18 June; nestlings 6 June to 15 July; and fledglings 16 June to 29 July. The female sits very closely during incubation of the 4 or 5 eggs, and adults are very protective of the young (Bent 1953). Burns (1905 *in* Bent 1953) reported an incubation period of 13 days.

Bent (1953) and Forbush (1929) described the Worm-eating Warbler as shy and secretive, and Peterson (1980) stated that this species is "...heard more often than seen." Although Farrand (1988) stated that this warbler "...spends most of the time on the ground quietly searching," the South Hampton bird never walked on the ground during several hours of observation (Gavutis, pers. obs.). In 50 years of observing the species, C.S. Robbins (pers. comm.) has rarely seen individuals on the ground, except to approach the nest. New Hampshire observations have involved males foraging in the canopy and understory and singing from dead limbs and other prominent perches.

Forbush (1929) mentioned 3 reports of fall sightings in New Hampshire, but these are highly questionable. A singing male in Center Sandwich from 25 June through 1 July 1976 may be the first reliable record for the state.

The Worm-eating Warbler met the criteria for a "probable" nester during the Atlas period with observations of a territorial male singing and foraging in South Hampton in June and July 1985 and in late May and early June 1986. Since no female ever was observed, breeding is unlikely to have occurred.

The South Hampton male was first seen on 1 June 1985, 1.25 mi (2.0 km) from the Massachusetts line; then noted on 8 June, 22 June, and 4 July 0.25 mi (0.4 km) south; and finally on 14 July, another 0.5 mi (0.8 km) south, only 0.5 mi (0.8 km) from the Massachusetts line. This bird usually sang from a 30 to 60 ft (9 to 18 m) canopy of deciduous trees, but during one hot midday, he preened and occasionally sang in a supracanopy white pine of about 80 ft (24 m). He chased a female Blackburnian Warbler that was feeding young, and then stayed in her vicinity for at least 15 minutes. The male was last located 10 days later singing in mixed woods 0.5 mi (0.8 km) farther downhill near a large swamp, in company with a female Blackburnian Warbler and her fledged but still dependent brood.

The Worm-eating Warbler has been extending its range northward in recent years, and substantial populations now exist in Connecticut and southern New York. Griscom and Snyder (1955) mentioned one certain and one possible nesting record for Massachusetts, where "confirmed" nestings occurred at 6 locations during 1974–79 (Mass. BBA proj., unpubl.). The species continues to be a rare and local breeder there (Veit and Petersen 1993). Although none of the Massachusetts breeding pairs are near the New Hampshire border, it seems very possible that the Worm-eating Warbler could nest in southern New Hampshire, at least occasionally, in the near future.

George W. Gavutis, Jr.

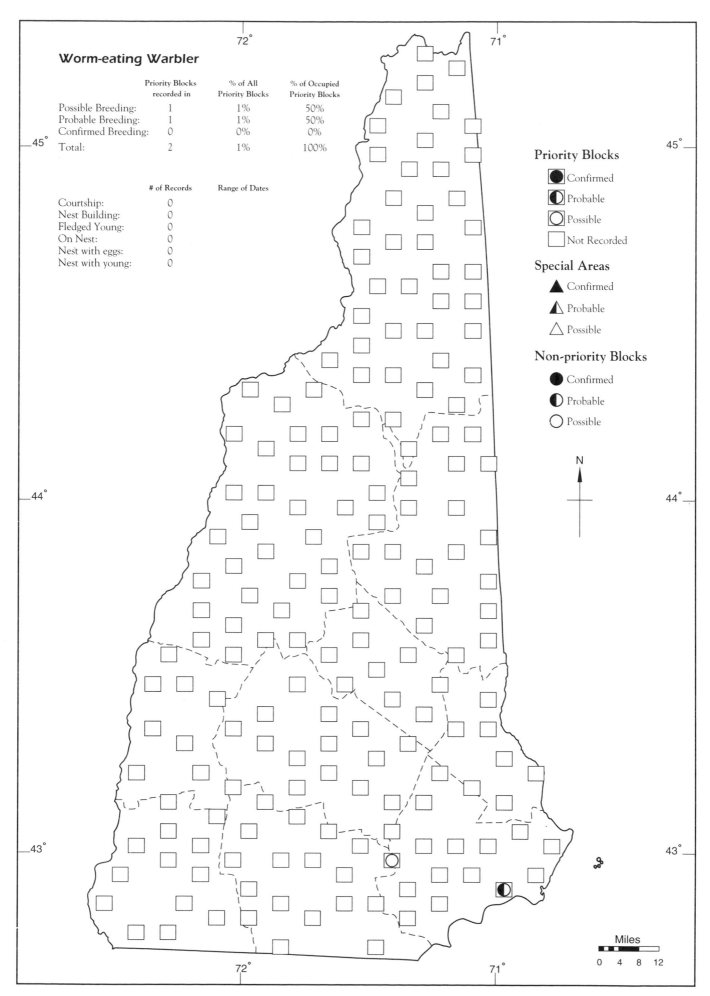

Worm-eating Warbler

	Priority Blocks recorded in	% of All Priority Blocks	% of Occupied Priority Blocks
Possible Breeding:	1	1%	50%
Probable Breeding:	1	1%	50%
Confirmed Breeding:	0	0%	0%
Total:	2	1%	100%

	# of Records	Range of Dates
Courtship:	0	
Nest Building:	0	
Fledged Young:	0	
On Nest:	0	
Nest with eggs:	0	
Nest with young:	0	

Priority Blocks

● Confirmed
◑ Probable
○ Possible
□ Not Recorded

Special Areas

▲ Confirmed
◤ Probable
△ Possible

Non-priority Blocks

● Confirmed
◑ Probable
○ Possible

N

Miles
0   4   8   12

Ovenbird

Ovenbird

Seiurus aurocapillus

The diminutive Ovenbird calls its mighty "tea-cher, Tea-Cher, TEA-CHER, Tea" from New Hampshire's southern lowlands to the North Country. The song is more familiar than the bird itself. This species sometimes is mistaken for a thrush with its boldly spotted and streaked white breast, plain brownish upperparts, and russet stripe on its crown. The white eye-ring gives it a perpetually alert look as it walks among the leaf litter, raising and dropping its tail.

Ovenbirds breed throughout most of New Hampshire, occurring to elevations of 2,500 to 2,800 ft (760 to 850 m) (Ridgely 1977). They arrive in the state during the first or second week of May and depart by mid-September (Elkins 1982).

The Ovenbird usually sings from low, dead branches of trees and from the ground (Kendeigh 1945b). A "flight song" consists of a long rich warble and includes some "teacher" phrases. It is sung more frequently towards the end of the breeding season and often at dusk or even into the night (Gunn *in* Griscom and Sprunt 1979). Lein (1981) describes Ovenbird singing behavior in detail.

The female builds her nest among leaf debris in open, usually deciduous or mixed woods. Ovenbirds apparently require dead leaves from broad-leaved trees for nest building; the presence of breeding pairs in coniferous forests may depend on the proximity of at least a few deciduous trees or shrubs (Kendeigh 1945b). In conifer stands this species often nests along hiking trails where a break in the canopy allows broad-leaved shrubs to thrive.

Ovenbird territories in Ontario, Can., ranged in size from 0.8 to 4.3 a (0.3 to 1.7 ha), depending on the character of vegetation and the availability of food (Stenger and Falls 1959). A New Jersey study of forest fragments found Ovenbirds in a minimum area of 9.9 a (4 ha) (Galli et al. 1976), but a mixed forest fragment of only 3 a (1.2 ha) in East Rochester, supported a

breeding pair during 1980–86 (Turner, pers. obs.).

When there is no natural depression in the ground at a chosen nest site, the female Ovenbird forms a hollow with her body (Harrison 1978). If disturbed while building the nest or during the early egg-laying period, she generally will abandon the site (Griscom and Sprunt 1979). The delicately built nest has the form of an old-fashioned Dutch oven, hence the species' common name. The unique dome of grasses and leaves is well camouflaged from above; the entrance is on the side.

Egg laying typically occurs in late May or early June. The female Ovenbird incubates her clutch of 3 to 6 eggs, usually 4 or 5 (Harrison 1975), for 11 to 14 days (Harrison 1978). Of the 8 Atlas records for nests with eggs, 4 were in late May and 3 in June. A late nest with eggs discovered on 3 July 1982 in Peterborough may have been a second nesting after the first had failed. K. C. Elkins (unpubl. data) observed nestlings in Andover on 28 June 1947 and 21 June 1949. D. W. Crumb (CLO Nest Rec. Prog. 1970) observed a clutch of 4 eggs in Surry on 6 July 1970; on 11 July there were 4 young, but a predator had killed them all by 19 July — a common occurrence among ground nesters. Occasionally Ovenbirds are double brooded (Hann 1937). Atlasers found an adult still feeding young on 14 August 1984 near Mt. Osceola, Livermore/Lincoln, which may have been a second brood. Ovenbirds are very common hosts for Brown-headed Cowbirds (Friedmann 1929).

An incubating Ovenbird typically remains on her nest until the very last minute when a predator or human intruder threatens. The female may perform a "broken wing" distraction display if danger is imminent (Forbush and May 1939). However, 2 intensely alert Ovenbirds watched motionless from separate trees when Turner stopped near their nest, which was hidden beneath ferns and trillium leaves beside a trail in Beans Purchase and contained 3 partially feathered young.

Ovenbirds usually feed on the ground, picking from the leaf litter (Stenger 1958). The diet includes a wide variety of insects and other invertebrates. Beetles, slugs, and insect larvae constitute the primary food items for nestlings (Stenger 1958).

The young leave the nest after 8 to 10 days, following a parent and begging with a "jingling" call. The adults divide the brood, and the female leaves the male's territory with her following of young (Zack and Falls 1975). The young are independent about 30 days after hatching (Stenger and Falls 1959).

The Ovenbird was a common and well-known breeding bird in New Hampshire a century ago (Samuels 1867, 1883, Dearborn 1898, Allen 1903, Hoffmann 1904). Allen (1903) considered it most abundant in the "rich, shady woods of mixed growth" in the White Mountains at elevations below 3,000 ft (910 m), and 8 to 10 pairs occupied a 50 a (20 ha) woodland at Jefferson Highland in the early 1900s (Wright 1911).

Because Ovenbirds are ground nesters, housing developments and the accompanying influx of household pets can have a detrimental effect on local populations. Forest fragmentation significantly reduces habitat for Ovenbirds, which prefer to nest in the interior of forested tracts and avoid or occur at reduced densities around the peripheries of forest fragments (MacClintock et al. 1977). Despite habitat losses, BBS data from 1966 to 1979 suggest a population increase for Ovenbirds east of the Mississippi River, and show New Hampshire to be within the area of North America's highest Ovenbird abundance (Robbins et al. 1986). The 3 Atlas priority blocks lacking Ovenbird records are relatively inaccessible and received minimal Atlas effort.

Sandra B. Turner

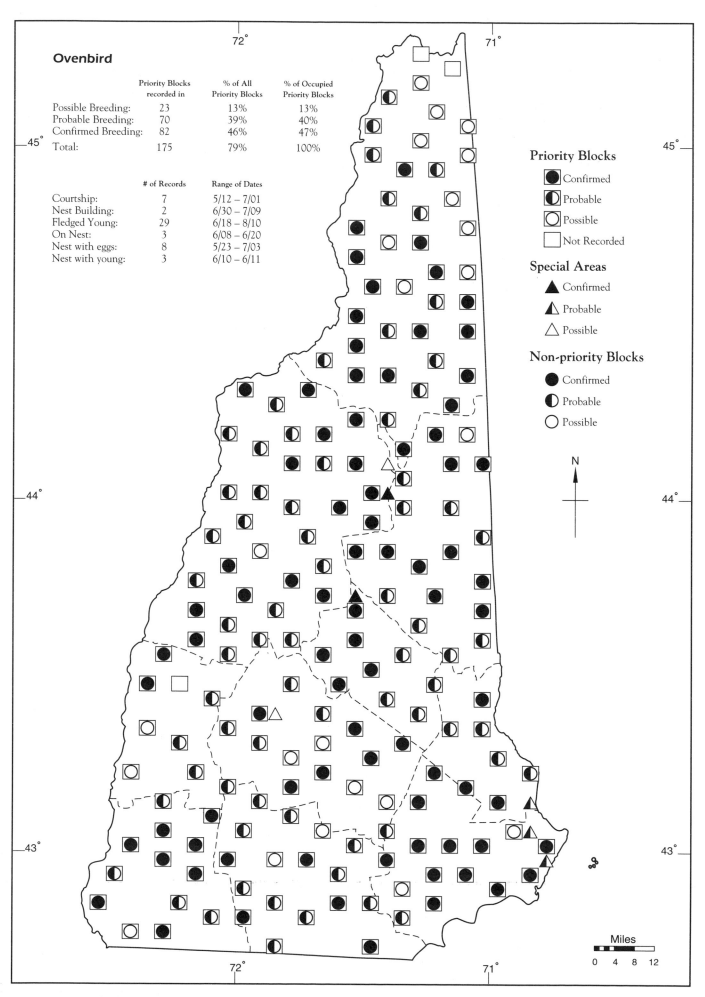

Ovenbird

	Priority Blocks recorded in	% of All Priority Blocks	% of Occupied Priority Blocks
Possible Breeding:	23	13%	13%
Probable Breeding:	70	39%	40%
Confirmed Breeding:	82	46%	47%
Total:	175	79%	100%

	# of Records	Range of Dates
Courtship:	7	5/12 – 7/01
Nest Building:	2	6/30 – 7/09
Fledged Young:	29	6/18 – 8/10
On Nest:	3	6/08 – 6/20
Nest with eggs:	8	5/23 – 7/03
Nest with young:	3	6/10 – 6/11

Priority Blocks
- Confirmed
- Probable
- Possible
- Not Recorded

Special Areas
- Confirmed
- Probable
- Possible

Non-priority Blocks
- Confirmed
- Probable
- Possible

N

Miles
0 4 8 12

Northern Waterthrush
Seiurus noveboracensis

The 2 waterthrushes are large warblers that look like miniature thrushes and act much like Spotted Sandpipers. Both species typically forage on the ground, walking along water margins and constantly "teetering." The northern species, formerly known as Small-billed Waterthrush and, still earlier, as Water Wagtail, is the more common in New Hampshire. It may be distinguished from the Louisiana Waterthrush by its cream-colored underparts, usually tinged with yellow, its yellowish superciliary stripe, and its song.

The Northern Waterthrush breeds across Canada and the northern U.S. to Alaska, and in the mountains south to West Virginia and Maryland. This bird nests throughout New Hampshire in suitable habitat up to elevations of about 2,800 ft (850 m) (Ridgely 1988), occurring most commonly below 2,500 ft (760 m), and rarely above 3,000 ft (910 m) (T. Richards, unpubl. data). It resides in wooded swamps and bogs and in wet woods bordering ponds and streams. The Northern Waterthrush is less partial to rushing streams than the Louisiana. Either species also may occur where brooks meander through swamps or have been dammed by beavers. Diptera larvae, especially Chironomids, comprise a large part of the diet, which also includes a wide variety of other aquatic insect larvae, small snails, and crustaceans (Craig 1987).

Male Northern Waterthrushes return first in spring from wintering areas that stretch from southern Florida and Texas to northern South America. They arrive in New Hampshire toward the end of April or in early May; females arrive a week or so later. Males commonly sing from perches on horizontal limbs about two-thirds of the way up the trees (Eaton 1957). Their loud, ringing songs attract attention, but the birds often are hard to see. The song is liquid and musical, usually with the first notes highest, and in New Hampshire usually ends with 3 or more notes that sound like "chew, chew, chew."

Nesting begins in May. A typical nest site is among the upturned roots of a fallen tree, usually directly above a pool of water filling the hollow formerly occupied by the roots. Other nest locations are crevices in decayed stumps, fern clumps, and stream banks.

The nest often consists largely of moss and is lined with fine rootlets, grass, or hair. The clutch includes up to 5, usually 4 eggs (Peck and James 1987). Two nests at Umbagog Lake, Errol, contained eggs on 30 May (Palmer 1949); at Squam Lake one held 4 eggs on 16 June, and another was not quite finished on 18 June (Bent 1953). Incubation, by the female, takes 12 to 14 days (Forbush 1929, Eaton 1957). Both parents feed the young, which remain in the nest for at least 9 days (Kendeigh 1945a, Eaton 1957). Full-grown young were following parents on 9 June in Lancaster (Chapman 1907), and White (1937) reported recently fledged young in Concord on 13 July 1933.

The Northern Waterthrush sings infrequently in New Hampshire after early July, but there is a revival of song toward the end of the month. These birds may depart from nesting territories by the end of June (Harrison 1984). Southward migration is protracted, beginning in early July in some years (Whittle 1923a, Harrison 1984) and continuing into October.

Once uncommon to rare as breeding birds *in* southern New Hampshire (Scott 1921, Goodhue 1922, Thayer 1909 in Allison and Allison 1979), Northern Waterthrushes increased during the mid-twentieth century. Reforestation of swampy lowlands may be responsible for the increase, also noted in Massachusetts (Griscom and Snyder 1955). Louisiana Waterthrushes, which have increased and are extending their range in New Hampshire, may interact aggressively with Northern Waterthrushes where they occur together. Observers have reported Louisianas chasing Northern Waterthrushes in Andover in 1954 (Elkins, pers. obs.) and in New Hampton in July 1952 (Brainard 1953). Louisianas have replaced Northern Waterthrushes at 2 other locations in Andover, both wet woodlands with brooks running through them (Elkins, pers. obs.). In western Pennsylvania Todd (1940) noted that Louisianas were supplanting Northerns in some areas, but in Connecticut Craig (1984, 1987) observed the 2 species coexisting in overlapping territories without interspecific aggression.

In New Hampshire the Northern Waterthrush is more common in the north than the south, and in highlands than lowlands. The Northern Waterthrush was scarce in the Coastal Lowlands and the lower valleys of the Connecticut and Merrimack rivers, but occurred in two-thirds of North Country priority blocks. Northern Waterthrush records are lacking in 6 priority blocks just east of the southern Merrimack River valley. This area is thickly settled, and all but one of these blocks also lacked the Louisiana.

BBS data suggest an overall stable population in New Hampshire during 1966–87, with an increase during 1966–84 and a slight decrease beginning in 1985. Future trends will bear watching, especially in southern New Hampshire where increasing development may reduce habitat availability.

Kimball C. Elkins

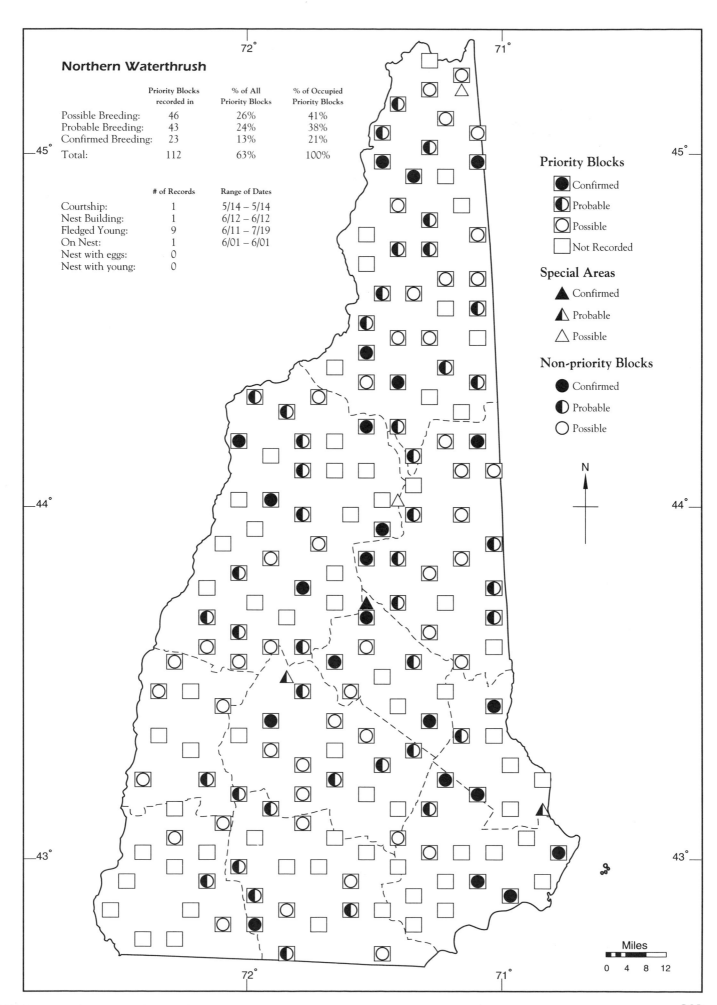

Northern Waterthrush

	Priority Blocks recorded in	% of All Priority Blocks	% of Occupied Priority Blocks
Possible Breeding:	46	26%	41%
Probable Breeding:	43	24%	38%
Confirmed Breeding:	23	13%	21%
Total:	112	63%	100%

	# of Records	Range of Dates
Courtship:	1	5/14 – 5/14
Nest Building:	1	6/12 – 6/12
Fledged Young:	9	6/11 – 7/19
On Nest:	1	6/01 – 6/01
Nest with eggs:	0	
Nest with young:	0	

Priority Blocks

● Confirmed
◐ Probable
○ Possible
□ Not Recorded

Special Areas

▲ Confirmed
◣ Probable
△ Possible

Non-priority Blocks

● Confirmed
◐ Probable
○ Possible

N

Louisiana Waterthrush
Seiurus motacilla

New Hampshire had no nesting bird associated primarily with running brooks until the Louisiana Waterthrush arrived in our state during the present century. It has become established as a widespread, though somewhat uncommon breeder in southern New Hampshire, and is making explorations into the North Country. The Louisiana Waterthrush has whiter underparts and a more conspicuous and whiter line above the eye than the Northern Waterthrush. The once-proposed name "brook-bird" (Bagg and Eliot 1937) is appropriate.

The Louisiana Waterthrush sings very loudly. Its distinctive song is higher pitched and more musical than that of the Northern Waterthrush, and the song includes 3 to 6 long notes followed by a series of short, rolling, rapid, emphatic notes, which generally fall in pitch toward the end (Saunders 1935). It carries easily above the roar of a rapid brook.

Louisiana Waterthrushes are among the earliest warblers to arrive in spring. In New Hampshire the first males appear during the second week or more typically the third week in April, when freezing weather and even snowstorms are not unusual. Females arrive about a week later. Eaton (1958) found that severe spring weather in Ithaca, N.Y., inhibited singing but did not cause mortality. Caddisfly larvae comprise a large part of the diet, which also includes various other aquatic insects, small snails, leeches, and crustaceans (Eaton 1958, Craig 1984, 1987).

Typical habitat is a wooded valley or hillside near a rapid stream, but these birds also nest where quiet brooks meander through wooded swamps and at beaver ponds. Territories typically are long and narrow, following a stream. Nests in glens near Cayuga Lake, N.Y., were usually located about midway along approximately 0.25 mi (0.4 km) long territories (Eaton 1958).

The following summary of breeding biology is mainly from Eaton's (1958) life history study. Males sing loudly and persistently from their arrival on territories until they have found mates, but once paired, rarely sing again before incubation starts, when songs are softer and less frequent. Both sexes build the nest, which commonly is in a crevice in the bank of a stream, under an overhanging stream bank, under exposed tree roots, or concealed among the upturned roots of fallen trees. It is made mainly of wet, dead leaves with linings of grass, rootlets, plant stems, and hair (Harrison 1975). A path of dead leaves often leads to the nest.

The female incubates the 4 to 6 eggs for 12 to 14 days. A nest in Pawtuckaway State Park, Nottingham, contained 5 eggs on 9 June 1985 (D.J. Abbott and D.N. Finch, NHBBA data). Both sexes feed the young, which leave the nest when 10 days old and depend on their parents for almost another month. Adults carried food to concealed nestlings on 31 May 1970 in Andover (Elkins, pers. obs.) and on 4 June 1984 in Barrington (M.J. Murray, NHBBA data).

Observations in New Hampton indicate that in late July Louisiana Waterthrushes may move at least 0.5 mi (0.8 km) from their breeding locations, even visiting shade trees on village streets. At this season males may be quite aggressive, especially toward Northern Waterthrushes, and often sing highly variable songs which usually are shorter than the full spring song (Brainard 1953).

The first report of a Louisiana Waterthrush in New Hampshire is of one in Dublin on 19 August 1901 (Thayer 1902). Forbush (1929) cited records from Jaffrey on 29 May 1920 and 30 May 1923. Abbott (1942) first confirmed breeding with a nest containing 4 fresh eggs on 27 May 1941 in Harrisville. The well-hidden nest was in a cavity under upturned roots in a boggy area of about 1.5 a (0.6 ha) along a sluggish stream, with many trees uprooted by the 1938 hurricane. Abbott found a pair in another bog in Dublin the same year. Later in the 1940s and early 1950s observers reported the species from Baboosic Brook near Manchester (T. Richards, pers. comm.), New Hampton and Sandwich (ASNH 1950b), and Nottingham, Winchester, and Walpole (RNEB, *passim*). MacArthur (RNEB 1949) observed an adult feeding fledged young in Chesterfield on 9 June 1949.

By 1956 the Louisiana Waterthrush's known range extended to Sandwich in the northeast, Exeter in the southeast, and Hanover in the northwest. By 1970 it occurred in many new localities south of the White Mountains and occasionally penetrated into the mountains and beyond, including Woodstock, Dalton, Albany, Conway, Jefferson, and Pinkhams Grant (NHAQ, *passim*).

New Hampshire's Louisiana Waterthrush population still may be expanding, but BBS data from 10 routes indicate a decline in New Hampshire during 1966–87. The current distribution is widespread but local in all physiographic regions south of the White Mountains. The Atlas data suggest that Louisiana Waterthrushes are most common at elevations of 500 to 1,000 ft (150 to 300 m). The one Atlas record north of the mountains was of an adult feeding a fledgling in the Second College Grant on 3 July 1982.

Kimball C. Elkins

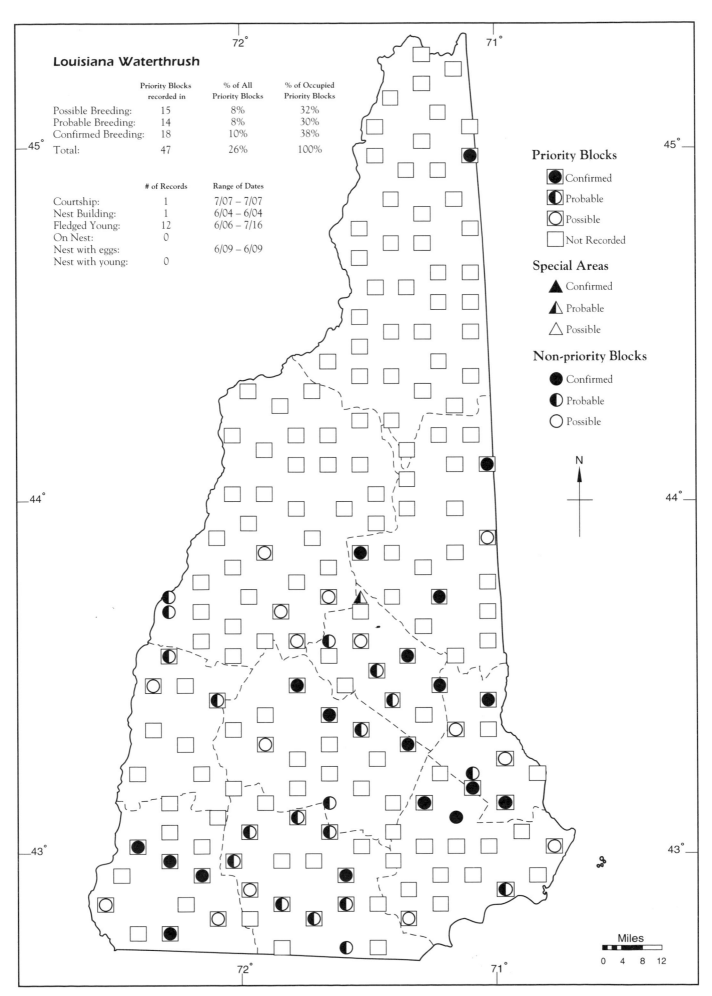

Louisiana Waterthrush

	Priority Blocks recorded in	% of All Priority Blocks	% of Occupied Priority Blocks
Possible Breeding:	15	8%	32%
Probable Breeding:	14	8%	30%
Confirmed Breeding:	18	10%	38%
Total:	47	26%	100%

	# of Records	Range of Dates
Courtship:	1	7/07 – 7/07
Nest Building:	1	6/04 – 6/04
Fledged Young:	12	6/06 – 7/16
On Nest:	0	
Nest with eggs:		6/09 – 6/09
Nest with young:	0	

Priority Blocks
- ◕ Confirmed
- ◑ Probable
- ○ Possible
- □ Not Recorded

Special Areas
- ▲ Confirmed
- ◢ Probable
- △ Possible

Non-priority Blocks
- ● Confirmed
- ◖ Probable
- ○ Possible

N

Miles
0   4   8   12

Mourning Warbler
Oporornis philadelphia

The Mourning Warbler, a so-called "ground war-bler," may be recognized by its gray head, olive-green upperparts, and yellow belly. The male in breeding plumage has a black patch on his gray breast—hence the name "mourning." This species is a fairly common breeding bird north of the White Mountains, uncom-mon in the mountains, and rather rare farther south, where it occurs primarily at higher elevations.

Mourning Warblers are birds of dense thickets. Most spring migrants arrive in late May and early June, when leaves are well developed. They depart early in the fall, sometimes before the end of July (Bent 1953), but mainly in August and the first half of September, when foliage is still dense. Thus they are difficult birds to observe in migration.

For nesting, Mourning Warblers are partial to re-cently burned or cutover woodlands that have grown up to dense tangles of raspberry or blackberry bushes, stump sprouts, and shrubs. They also nest along edges of wooded swamps in patches of jewelweed or nettles (Bent 1953) and in roadside tangles (Harrison 1975). Any canopy present must be at least partially open, and there must be "both herb and shrub cover on the ground" (Cox 1960). Prime nesting habitat is likely to be temporary, so many of these birds must relocate their nesting areas every few years. Hence local num-bers may fluctuate considerably.

Biologists apparently know little about pair forma-tion and courtship among Mourning Warblers. Both male and female defend the nesting territory, which averages a little less than 2 a (0.8 ha) (Cox 1960). One New Hampshire pair had a foraging area of about 1.5 a (0.6 ha) (Wallace 1949b). Chestnut-sided Warblers and Common Yellowthroats frequently occur in the same areas, and their territories sometimes overlap with those of Mourning Warblers (Cox 1960).

The Mourning Warbler places its rather bulky nest of leaves, grasses, plant stalks, bark strips, roots, and hair on or near the ground, concealed in dense vegetation (Harrison 1975). In cutover areas the nest often is in a clump of sprouts or stems (Cox 1960). The female incubates the clutch of 3 to 5 eggs for about 12 days. In ap-proaching, she walks quietly to the nest after landing 30 to 50 ft (9.1 to 15.2 m) away (Harrison 1975). At the approach of an intruder, she scur-ries away like a mouse and does not take wing until 20 ft (6.1 m) or more from the nest. The male feeds the female both at and away from the nest (Cox 1960). Both parents feed the young, which leave the nest when they are 7 to 9 days old, but are unable to fly for another week or so (Harrison 1978). The family remains in the nesting territory for about 3 weeks after the young fledge. The adults may put on a "broken-wing" display if an in-truder approaches their fledged young (Cox 1960).

The Mourning Warbler's distinctive and variable song is loud, with a rich, throaty quality. There are usually 2 parts, with the second part lower in pitch than the first, "charee, charee, charee to to" (Saunders 1935) or "kiss me Charlie, Charlie, Charlie" (Bent 1953). The male may sing while concealed in the underbrush or from a high perch overhead (Cox 1960). His flight song is longer than the territorial song, and "contains several charee notes, usually at the beginning, and several groups of rapid twitters" (Saunders *in* Bent 1953). Singing continues until at least mid-July, and may be revived briefly in August (Saunders *in* Bent 1953). The common alarm note is a rather harsh chip, suggesting those of the Common Yellowthroat and Indigo Bunting (Elkins, pers. obs.).

Mourning Warblers long have been uncommon to locally common summer residents from the White Mountains northward (Maynard 1871, Allen 1903). More recently observers have found them breeding rarely south of the mountains, in the Squam Lakes region (Ridgely 1977) and in New Hampton (Hebert, pers. obs.), where several pairs nested in 1951 (ASNH 1952). Still further south, Elkins observed Mourning Warblers during the nesting season in northern Merrimack County almost annually during 1938–53. In Sullivan County, T. Richards observed a juvenile on Mt. Sunapee, Newbury on 17 July 1954 (ASNH 1954), and 2 pairs oc-curred in Grantham in the summer of 1978 (Hebert 1978). There are also breeding season records from Plainfield (Hebert 1960a), New London, and Walpole (Hebert 1974).

New Hampshire BBS data suggest a fluctuating Mourning Warbler population, with no records in some years. In 1983 and 1984, large num-bers of Mourning Warblers occcupied the dense low growth that followed extensive salvaging of spruce budworm-infested firs in the North Country. These numbers began to decline by 1985 (Hebert, pers. obs.).

Most "confirmed" and "probable" Atlas records were from elevations between 1,000 and 2,000 feet (300 and 610 m). This agrees well with T. Richards' (unpubl. data) altitudinal records for the White Mountains. The Atlas project produced Mourning Warbler records for most North Coun-try priority blocks, but only scattered blocks in the White Mountains. The southernmost "confirmed" nesting was on Tucker Mtn., Hill, and the southernmost "probable" nesting was on Bly Hill, Newbury. A "possible" breeding record in Hillsboro on 10 July suggests nesting.

Mourning Warblers are much more widely distributed in Vermont than in New Hampshire (Laughlin and Kibbe 1985). They also breed in the uplands of northwestern Massachusetts (Griscom and Snyder 1955, Veit and Petersen 1993). Elevations in most of southern New Hampshire may be too low for Mourning Warblers, but they may some day nest in the Monadnock region.

Vera H. Hebert & Kimball C. Elkins

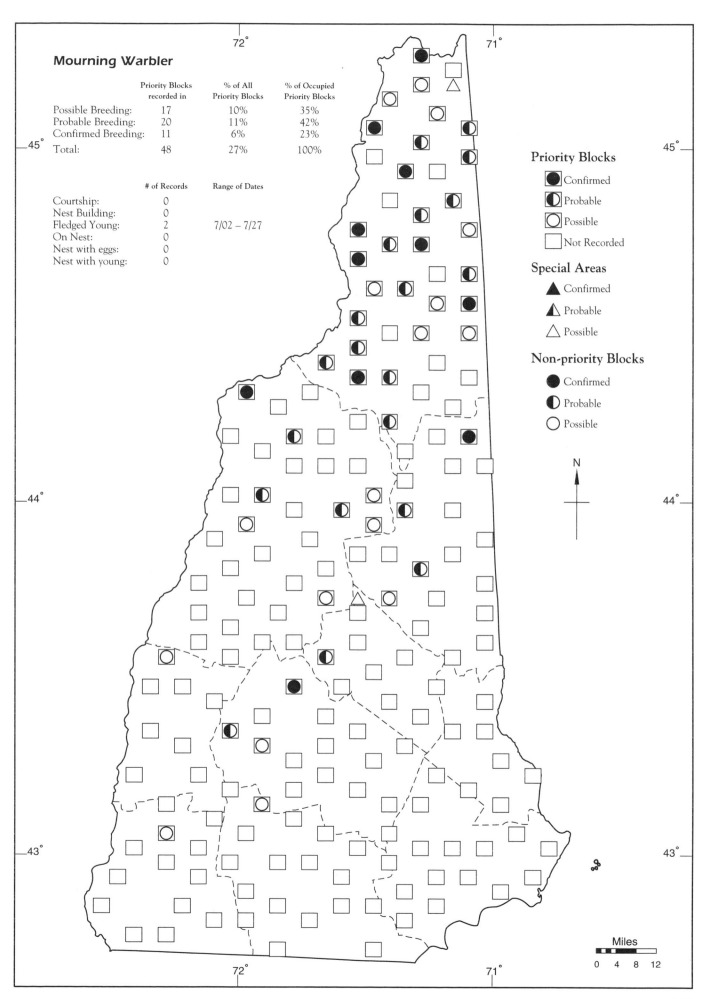

Mourning Warbler

	Priority Blocks recorded in	% of All Priority Blocks	% of Occupied Priority Blocks
Possible Breeding:	17	10%	35%
Probable Breeding:	20	11%	42%
Confirmed Breeding:	11	6%	23%
Total:	48	27%	100%

	# of Records	Range of Dates
Courtship:	0	
Nest Building:	0	
Fledged Young:	2	7/02 – 7/27
On Nest:	0	
Nest with eggs:	0	
Nest with young:	0	

Priority Blocks

● Confirmed
◐ Probable
○ Possible
□ Not Recorded

Special Areas

▲ Confirmed
◤ Probable
△ Possible

Non-priority Blocks

● Confirmed
◖ Probable
○ Possible

N

Miles
0 4 8 12

Common Yellowthroat
Geothlypis trichas

The Common Yellowthroat is one of the most widespread and abundant of the North American wood warblers (Bent 1953, Harrison 1975, Terres 1980). The black-masked male with his incessant "witchity-witchity-witchity" song and his less brightly colored mate are familiar summer inhabitants of a wide variety of shrubby habitats. This warbler frequents low and often wet areas with dense vegetation, and is particularly common in or near fresh or saltwater marshes, bogs, beaver meadows, and overgrown pastures. It also occurs in the undergrowth of open woods, including logged areas and in dry, shrubby areas such as the burned-over tops' of several mountains in New Hampshire.

The yellowthroat varies in appearance across its wide nesting range, which extends from Newfoundland to Alaska and south to Mexico, and has been separated into many subspecies (AOU 1957). Early accounts commonly referred only to the well-known Eastern race, which was called the Maryland Yellowthroat (Coues 1868, Maynard 1871, Dearborn 1898, White 1924) and known locally as the "Ground Warbler" (Pearson 1936).

Males usually return to New Hampshire in the first 2 weeks of May and establish territories that they defend by vigorous and persistent singing. Females return about a week later and select mates. Occasionally the exuberant males perform flight songs during which they rise up to 15 or 20 ft (4.6 to 6.1 m) above the vegetation, uttering long jumbled series of notes, then silently flutter back to the ground near the females.

The female builds the nest, which is bulky and large for a small bird, and placed on or close to the ground in dense vegetation (Harrison 1975). The female incubates the 4 or 5 eggs, which hatch after about 12 days (Gross 1953b). Egg dates for Maine and Massachusetts range from late May to mid-June (Forbush 1929). Atlas egg dates for New Hampshire extend to early July. Young commonly leave the nest after 8 or 9 days, be-

fore they are capable of sustained flight (Stewart 1953), and their parents continue to feed them. The adults' distinctive scolding notes provide a useful clue for atlasers. Unlike most New Hampshire warblers, Common Yellowthroats often are double brooded and may attempt a third nesting if one of the initial 2 fail (Ellison *in* Laughlin and Kibbe 1985). Cowbirds frequently parasitize their nests (Hofslund 1957).

Yellowthroats forage for insects and spiders on the ground and in low shrubs (Gross 1953b). Insect prey includes beetles, grubs, flies, ants, aphids, leafhoppers, caddisflies, damselflies, and numerous butterflies and moths. Yellowthroats are highly efficient foragers on caterpillars, and consume large numbers during cankerworm and gypsy moth outbreaks (Forbes 1883 and Forbush 1907 *in* Gross 1953b).

Yellowthroats begin to migrate south by the end of August and most have left New Hampshire by mid-October. Occasionally, individuals attempt to overwinter in marshes near the Coast, and CBC data include coastal records in late December. This species is not hardy, however, and is unlikely to survive most New England winters.

Most historical accounts of New Hampshire birds state that this species was common (Coues 1868, Little 1870, Goodhue 1877, Allen 1889, Worthen 1891, Dearborn 1898, White 1924), but Maynard (1871) noted it was "not very common at Umbagog in June." Despite the yellowthroat's long widespread occurrence, local abundance undoubtedly has fluctuated with habitat changes over the last 300 years. In the northern part of the state, where extensive coniferous forests once limited suitable habitats to bogs, beaver meadows, and streamsides, it now inhabits many areas where logging has created extensive openings. Elsewhere in the state, it may have reached its greatest abundance during the period when extensive areas were cleared for farms and pastures. Next to the Song Sparrow, it is the most abundant songbird on Appledore Island and presumably reaches a similar status on the New Hampshire Isles of Shoals (Borror 1980).

The Atlas project produced yellowthroat records for all but 3 priority blocks. More intensive coverage of those, which were extensively wooded blocks and at relatively high elevations, might have yielded the species in small pockets of suitable habitat. This is one of the easiest warblers to "confirm," as evidenced by breeding "confirmatins" in 83% of the priority blocks. Most "confirmations" involved adults carrying food, closely followed by sightings of fledged young. The Vermont Atlas project found the Common Yellowthroat in every priority block, and "confirmed" breeding in 96% of priority blocks, including one on Jay Peak at 3,600 ft (1,100 m) elevation (Ellison *in* Laughlin and Kibbe 1985). BBS data from 1966 to 1979 show a very slight but significant upward trend for this species in the Eastern region and across the continent, with the greatest densities in New Hampshire and adjacent parts of central New England (Robbins et al. 1986). BBS data suggest no significant trend for New Hampshire during 1966–87.

In recent decades, urbanization in southern New Hampshire and draining and filling of wetlands have eliminated considerable nesting habitat. However, if remaining wetlands and streamsides are protected, this adaptable species will continue to flourish in the state.

Ralph Andrews

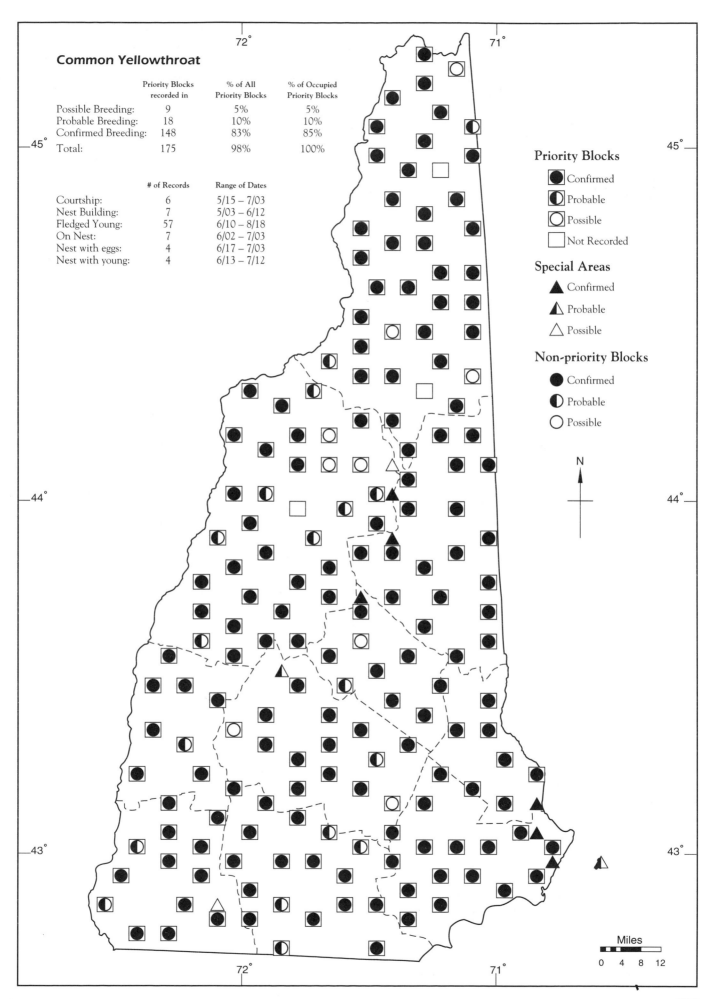

Common Yellowthroat

	Priority Blocks recorded in	% of All Priority Blocks	% of Occupied Priority Blocks
Possible Breeding:	9	5%	5%
Probable Breeding:	18	10%	10%
Confirmed Breeding:	148	83%	85%
Total:	175	98%	100%

	# of Records	Range of Dates
Courtship:	6	5/15 – 7/03
Nest Building:	7	5/03 – 6/12
Fledged Young:	57	6/10 – 8/18
On Nest:	7	6/02 – 7/03
Nest with eggs:	4	6/17 – 7/03
Nest with young:	4	6/13 – 7/12

Priority Blocks
- Confirmed
- Probable
- Possible
- Not Recorded

Special Areas
- Confirmed
- Probable
- Possible

Non-priority Blocks
- Confirmed
- Probable
- Possible

N

Miles
0 4 8 12

Wilson's Warbler
Wilsonia pusilla

Bright yellow and olive with a trim black cap, the Wilson's Warbler is dainty, lively, and nervous. It is an active feeder, noted especially for its aerial "flycatching." In fact, the Wilson's "strong rictal bristles" at the base of a "relatively broad bill" are characteristics more typical of flycatchers than warblers (Rappole and Warner 1980). What little is known of its diet suggests that it is almost exclusively insectivorous (Tyler 1953b).

The breeding range of the Wilson's Warbler corresponds almost exactly with the boreal zone (Godfrey 1979), extending north to tree line in Canada and south to northeastern Vermont, northern New Hampshire, and much of Maine (Forbush 1929, Tyler 1953b, AOU 1983). It is better known in New Hampshire as a migrant, during mid-May to early June and mid-August into early October (Elkins 1982). The winter range extends from southern Louisiana and Texas to Panama (Harrison 1984).

Named for the father of American ornithology, Alexander Wilson, who first described it, this warbler also has been called (Wilson's) Black-capped Warbler, Black-capped Yellow Warbler, and Black-capped Flycatching Warbler in recognition of its most prominent field mark. Contrary to pictures in field guides, most females have dark caps, which can be as glossy black as the adult male's, although they are usually less extensive and sometimes obscured (Forbush 1929, Harrison 1984, Stallcup 1985).

The song is the best clue to this bird's presence. Somewhat similar to that of the Nashville Warbler, the Wilson's song is drier, consisting of staccato single notes instead of paired syllables. The second part, when present, provides a short, speeded-up ending that drops off in pitch and volume compared to the Nashville's longer, even-pitched trill. Peterson (1980) renders the typical song as a rapid "chi chi chi chi chi chet chet."

Nesting in sphagnum-lined alder swales at the edges of tamarack swamps and bogs, these warblers hide their bulky nests in sphagnum moss or grass at the bases of shrubs such as alder, willow, or sapling tamarack. Nests consist of grass, fine stems, moss, and dead leaves and are lined with fine grasses (Harrison 1951, Tyler 1953b, Harrison 1984).

In June, the females lay single clutches of 4 or sometimes 5 eggs (Forbush 1929, Palmer 1949). Incubation lasts 10 to 12 days, and fledging takes about the same length of time. Males do not incubate or brood, but both parents are attentive and remarkably bold at the nest, making confirmation easy (Harrison 1951, Tyler 1953b, Harrison 1984).

The Wilson's Warbler never has been a common breeder in this state, nor has it ever been recorded nesting outside of Coos County. The southernmost records are for Jefferson and Lancaster (Wright 1911). Brewster, in all his summers in the Umbagog Lake area, found only one possible nester (Griscom 1938). Historical and recent sources list Wilson's Warbler as a rare and local breeder in the northern part of the state (Wright 1911, Forbush 1929, Richards 1958, Elkins 1982) and adjacent areas of Maine (Maynard 1871, Palmer 1949).

The patchy and sometimes ephemeral nature of alder thickets implies a patchy and changing distribution of Wilson's Warblers within their range. Not surprisingly, pairs may concentrate into "colonies" in areas of ideal habitat. Clearing of low elevation forest probably benefits Wilson's Warblers by providing shrubby deciduous growth. On one logged and burned site in Jefferson, the number of territorial males increased to a peak 7 years after burning (Wright 1911). The upland edges of wetlands and beaver ponds are more likely long-term breeding sites, however, and even most of these are unoccupied in northern New Hampshire.

During the Atlas project, there were only 2 "confirmed" nestings in the state. Cohn-Haft (ASRF) documented the first on 30 June 1982 in Second College Grant, approximately 25 mi (40 km) east of Vermont's sole "confirmation" (Laughlin and Kibbe 1985). Two birds sang and one carried caterpillars for nestlings at the New Hampshire site, an extensive alder thicket on a sphagnum mat at the outlet of a marsh. A second "confirmation" occurred at East Inlet, Pittsburg, on 22 May 1986. Here R. Suomala (ASRF) observed the female carrying nesting material in an alder swale while the male called attentively nearby.

The scattered distribution of Atlas records suggests that a more intensive search throughout Coos County might turn up local concentrations, most likely in the more extensive areas of suitable habitat near the Connecticut Lakes (Halberg and Halberg 1956) and Umbagog Lake. Nevertheless, at the edge of its range this warbler is unlikely to occupy all the habitat available. We can expect the Wilson's Warbler to remain a rare and local breeder in New Hampshire north of the White Mountains.

Mario Cohn-Haft

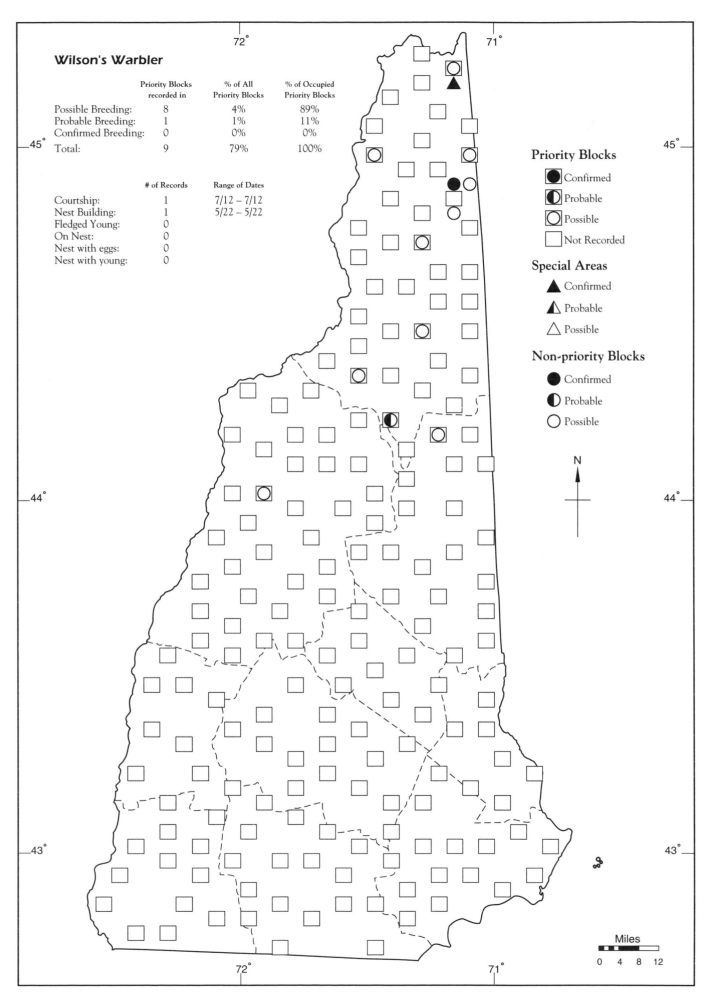

Wilson's Warbler

	Priority Blocks recorded in	% of All Priority Blocks	% of Occupied Priority Blocks
Possible Breeding:	8	4%	89%
Probable Breeding:	1	1%	11%
Confirmed Breeding:	0	0%	0%
Total:	9	79%	100%

	# of Records	Range of Dates
Courtship:	1	7/12 – 7/12
Nest Building:	1	5/22 – 5/22
Fledged Young:	0	
On Nest:	0	
Nest with eggs:	0	
Nest with young:	0	

Priority Blocks
- ◕ Confirmed
- ◐ Probable
- ◯ Possible
- ▢ Not Recorded

Special Areas
- ▲ Confirmed
- ◣ Probable
- △ Possible

Non-priority Blocks
- ● Confirmed
- ◑ Probable
- ○ Possible

N

Miles
0 4 8 12

Canada Warbler
Wilsonia canadensis

This active, low-foraging warbler is common and well distributed throughout much of New Hampshire in cool, moist habitats with luxuriant deciduous undergrowth. It occurs in deciduous, coniferous, and mixed forests; wooded swamps and bogs; streamside thickets; brushy ravines; and cutover areas. The species is easily distinguished by its yellow breast with black "necklace," yellow "spectacles," and gray back, but it is often difficult to observe. The Canada Warbler's broad altitudinal range extends from coastal lowlands up to about 3,500 feet (1,070 m) in the White Mountains. Its range is limited at higher elevations by a lack of deciduous undergrowth (Sabo 1980).

The Canada Warbler is a late migrant. Most individuals arrive in New Hampshire during the last 2 weeks of May. As the breeding season gets underway in early June, territorial males are conspicuous by their loud and persistent singing. Sabo (1980) found a population density of 24 pairs/0.4 sq mi (1 sq km) in subalpine forest on Mt. Moosilauke. Benton, with an average territory size of 1.7 a (0.7 ha). Kendeigh (1945a) reported a territory size of 0.6 a (0.2 ha) before nesting and 2 to 3 a (0.8 to 1.2 ha) after nesting began. Canadas may defend this larger territory with scolding notes and silent chasing (Kendeigh 1945a). Though Canadas favor dense shrubbery, they are inquisitive birds and readily respond to "pishing" or "squeaking."

The variable but distinctive song consists of a rapid, jumbled series of notes and phrases beginning with a low "chip" and concluding with a distinctive, rising 3-note phrase. A male may repeat it as often as 6 times per minute when advertising for a mate; frequency of song decreases after he has found one (Kendeigh 1945a). Song perches were 2 to 32 ft (0.6 to 9.8 m) above ground in a New York hemlock-beech forest (Kendeigh 1945b). The initial song period extends through the second or third week of July. After a short, songless interval during the molt, the Canada resumes singing in late July or August (Wright 1911, Saunders *in* Bent 1953) .

The Canada Warbler nests on or near the ground, usually near a pond, stream, or small wet area. The well-hidden nest may be located atop a mossy log, stump, or hummock, in a bank cavity, amidst upturned tree roots, or in a clump of ferns. Audubon (1967) twice found a nest placed in the fork of a small bush.

The Vermont and New Hampshire atlases produced virtually no egg dates, but Ellison (*in* Laughlin and Kibbe 1985) estimated a range between the first week of June and the first week of July. Egg dates in New York range from 31 May to 30 June (Bull 1974). Clutch size is 3 to 5, typically 4, and one brood is raised per year. Little is known about incubation and nestling periods of this species; Harrison (1975) estimated an incubation period of 12 days.

Canada Warblers become agitated and vocal when disturbed near the nest or young, engaging in wing flapping, bill wiping, and alarm calls (Ellison *in* Laughlin and Kibbe 1985). When an intruder approaches the nest, the Canada will drop to the ground and perform a distraction display. New Hampshire Atlas records of distraction displays occurred during 30 June to 13 July.

The Canada Warbler normally forages from ground level up to about 6 ft (1.8 m). Although this warbler obtains most of its food by leaf and twig gleaning, it is particularly adept at fly catching and for many years was known as the Canada Flycatcher (Bent 1953). Both sexes carry food for the young, and adults carrying fecal sac or food provided most Atlas confirmations. Observers found most recently fledged young during the last week of July. Fall migration through New Hampshire begins in early August and usually ends by mid-September.

Available records indicate that the Canada Warbler was a fairly common breeder in much of New Hampshire in the late 1800s and early 1900s, much as it is today. Maynard (1871) found it common at Umbagog Lake, and Coues (1868) noted that many Canadas nested in New England, some as far south as Massachusetts. Minot (1876) found this warbler quite common in the "cooler woods" of the White Mountains, and it was a fairly common summer resident in the Monadnock region during the early 1900s (Thayer 1909 *in* Allison and Allison 1979). It apparently occurred locally in central New Hampshire (Dearborn 1898, Allen 1903), but only as a migrant in the Durham area (Dearborn 1903, Scott 1921). White (1937) considered it a rare summer resident in Concord, and noted a pair with young near Big Turkey Pond on 29 July 1926.

The Atlas map shows several "confirmation" in southeastern New Hampshire, suggesting that this warbler's breeding range may have expanded into the Coastal Lowlands during the 20th century. Atlas data document the Canada Warbler in all Northern Highlands blocks and in all but one White Mountains block. Most records were at elevations above 1,000 ft (300 m), including one at 3,400 ft (1,040 m) near the summit of Mt. Resolution, Sargents Purchase (Smith, pers. obs.). Previous high elevation records in the White Mountains range from 3,360 ft (1,020 m) (Allen 1903) to above 3,800 ft (1,154 m) (T. Richards, unpubl. data). The Canada also is widespread in southeastern New Hampshire, and was found in 8 of 9 blocks in the Coastal Lowlands. The distribution appears spottier in the south central and southwestern parts of the state, the Lakes Region, and especially the Merrimack Valley, where it was recorded in only 5 of 14 priority blocks.

Steve Smith

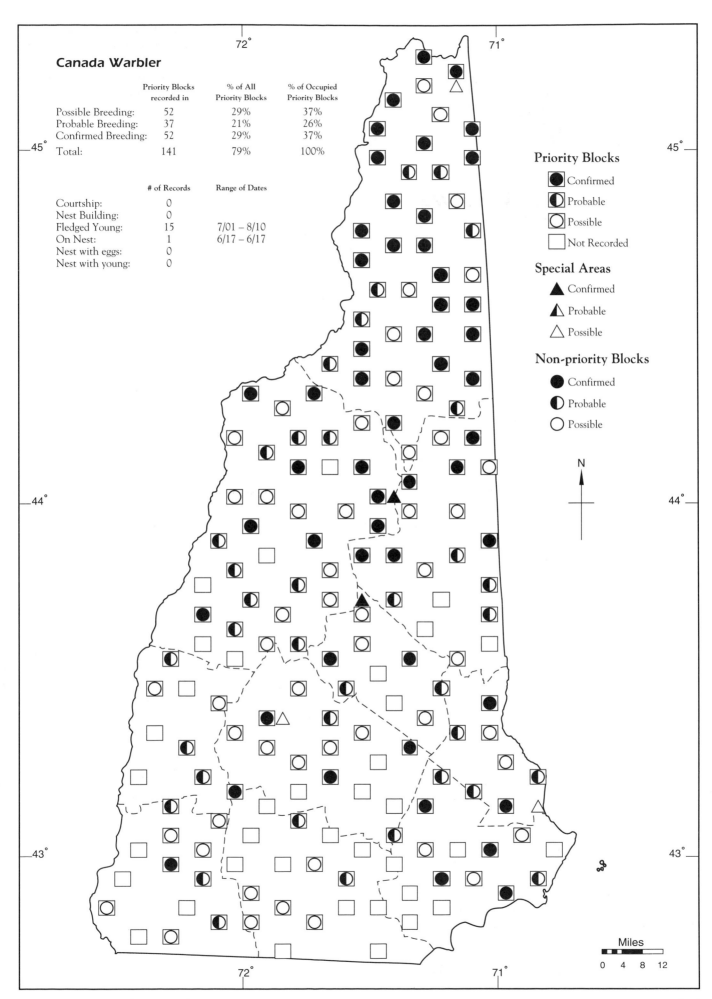

Canada Warbler

	Priority Blocks recorded in	% of All Priority Blocks	% of Occupied Priority Blocks
Possible Breeding:	52	29%	37%
Probable Breeding:	37	21%	26%
Confirmed Breeding:	52	29%	37%
Total:	141	79%	100%

	# of Records	Range of Dates
Courtship:	0	
Nest Building:	0	
Fledged Young:	15	7/01 – 8/10
On Nest:	1	6/17 – 6/17
Nest with eggs:	0	
Nest with young:	0	

Priority Blocks

● Confirmed
◑ Probable
○ Possible
□ Not Recorded

Special Areas

▲ Confirmed
◮ Probable
△ Possible

Non-priority Blocks

● Confirmed
◐ Probable
○ Possible

N

Miles
0   4   8   12

Scarlet Tanager
Piranga olivacea

The flashy male Scarlet Tanager is a master at hiding in treetops while he carols his resounding song over the woods. A glimpse of this concealed songster is well worth the patient effort.

Primarily inhabitants of mature deciduous woods, Scarlet Tanagers also occur in mixed woodlands, roadside shade trees, orchards, and groves. They prefer oak woods, and combinations of oak, pine, and hickory (Harrison 1975, DeGraaf et al. 1980). They usually reach their upper limit at 2,200 ft (670 m) in the White Mountains (Wright 1911), but T. Richards (unpubl. data) has one summer record from above 3,000 ft (910 m). Most Scarlet Tanagers arrive in New Hampshire in May and depart in September, but a few may remain into October (Wright 1911, Elkins 1982) and rarely November (T. Richards, unpubl. data).

Scarlet Tanager plumage differs with age, sex, and time of year. In breeding plumage, an adult male is bright red with glossy black wings and tail. In contrast, a breeding female is camouflaged by a dull light yellow breast, greenish back, and brownish gray wings and tail. A juvenile tanager resembles the female. Beginning as early as mid-July and continuing into August and September, a postnuptial molt gradually replaces the male's scarlet plumage with blotches of yellowish olive until the red disappears completely. Most first year males have brownish wings and retain some yellowish green areas among the red plumage.

Male Scarlet Tanagers begin singing on arrival and continue into mid-July (Allen 1903, White 1937). The song resembles a hoarse robin's, but has continuous phrases and is not slurred, unlike the hoarse song of a Yellow-throated Vireo. A distinctive 2-syllable call, "keep-back," is also diagnostic. Typical song perches are high in the canopy, and may be dead or otherwise exposed limbs, often at the treetop.

The female builds a flimsy nest, usually positioned well out on a horizontal limb of a tree at heights of 8 to 75 ft (2.4 to 22.9 m) (DeGraaf et al. 1980). Constructed of twigs and rootlets and lined with weed stems and grasses, the nest is so shallow that eggs may be visible from the ground. The female incubates the clutch of 3 to 5, usually 4 eggs for 13 or 14 days (Harrison 1978), raising only one brood each year. Both parents feed the young (Forbush 1929), which remain in the nest for about 15 days (Harrison 1978). White (1937) found young just out of the nest in Concord on 24 June. Observations of fledged young and of adults feeding young comprised the majority of Atlas "confirmations."

Tanagers glean insects such as caterpillars, moths, and beetles from twigs and leaves at the outer tips of limbs and dead branches. Females often skulk about in the understory, while males usually remain in the canopy (White 1937). During the gypsy moth infestation of 1980 to 1983, tanagers seemed to be more abundant and more easily observed than in other years (J. McDermott, pers. comm.). F. H. Mosher observed 2 Scarlet Tanagers consume an average of 35 newly hatched gyspy moth caterpillars per minute for 18 minutes in May 1898 (Forbush 1929).

During excessively rainy or cold weather in spring, tanagers may feed on the ground, concentrating on insects washed from trees and shrubs (Tyler 1958b, Zumeta and Holmes 1978). Such conditions occurred here in 1900 (Dearborn 1903) and in late May 1974, when many species of insectivorous birds appeared on lawns, fields, and roadsides, especially in the Connecticut and Pemigewasset/Merrimack river valleys. Tanagers, already weak from migration, were especially affected because of their strong dependence on large insect prey, and many died. These factors contributed to decreased breeding success in 1974 and to low tanager densities in 1975 and 1976 (Zumeta and Holmes 1978, Robbins et al. 1986). Tanager populations subsequently rebounded to approximately their previous densities (Holmes et al. 1986, Robbins et al. 1986).

Ornithologists of the 19th and early 20th centuries considered the Scarlet Tanager a fairly common summer resident in New Hampshire (Coues 1868, Maynard 1871, Dearborn 1898, Allen 1903, Dearborn 1903, Forbush 1929). Wright (1911) found it "not uncommon" at lower elevations as far north as Jefferson and Randolph. Allen (1903) considered this bird rare north of the White Mountains, where it is relatively uncommon today. Hardwood regeneration in clearcuts of many former spruce-fir and mixed stands may have enabled the Scarlet Tanager to increase somewhat in northern New Hampshire in recent years.

Presently, tanagers are common in appropriate habitat throughout most of the state. BBS data from 1966 to 1979 suggest higher abundance in New Hampshire than in Vermont or Maine (Robbins et al. 1986). Atlasers missed this species in only 12 priority blocks. All but 2 of these were in northern New Hampshire. Additional field effort in the 2 southern blocks likely would have produced tanagers.

Scarlet Tanagers are most likely to occur in forests of at least 25 a (10 ha) (Galli et al. 1976), and may occur at low density in woodlands fragmented by dense human populations and development. While increasing development in southeastern New Hampshire undoubtedly has affected local tanager populations, the Atlas map indicates that overall distribution in this area has not suffered to date. BBS data from 1966 to 1990 suggest a long-term stable population trend for Scarlet Tanagers in New Hampshire, and the future of this colorful songbird appears secure.

Susan Absalom Staats

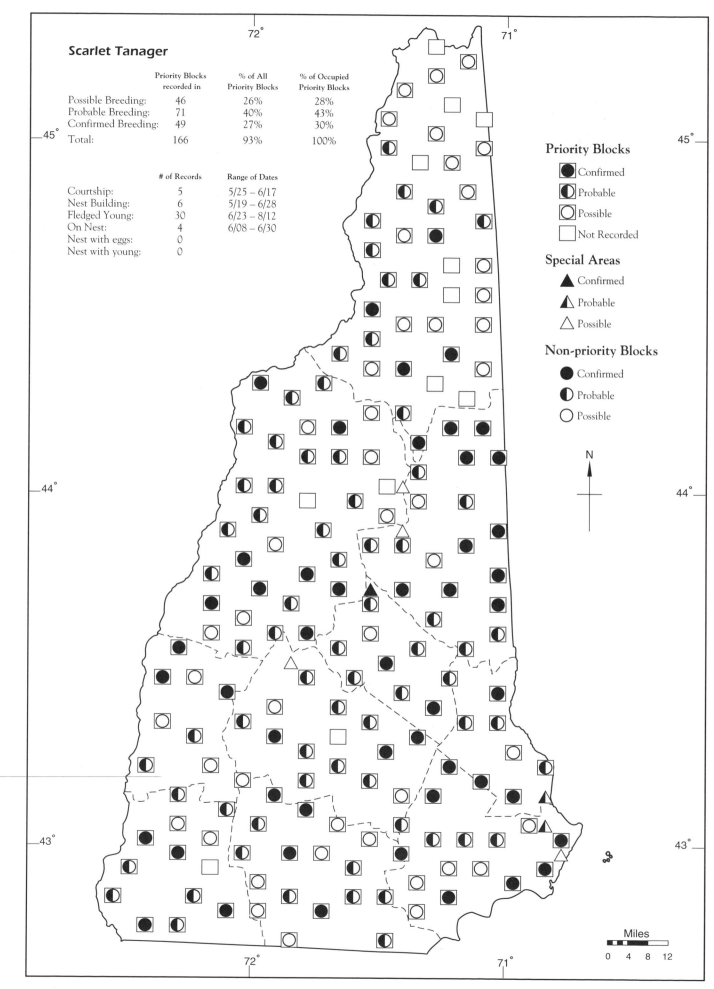

Scarlet Tanager

	Priority Blocks recorded in	% of All Priority Blocks	% of Occupied Priority Blocks
Possible Breeding:	46	26%	28%
Probable Breeding:	71	40%	43%
Confirmed Breeding:	49	27%	30%
Total:	166	93%	100%

	# of Records	Range of Dates
Courtship:	5	5/25 – 6/17
Nest Building:	6	5/19 – 6/28
Fledged Young:	30	6/23 – 8/12
On Nest:	4	6/08 – 6/30
Nest with eggs:	0	
Nest with young:	0	

Priority Blocks

- ● Confirmed
- ◐ Probable
- ○ Possible
- □ Not Recorded

Special Areas

- ▲ Confirmed
- ◤ Probable
- △ Possible

Non-priority Blocks

- ● Confirmed
- ◑ Probable
- ○ Possible

N

Miles
0 4 8 12

Northern Cardinal
Cardinalis cardinalis

This songful bird with bright red plumage, pointed crest, and large, cone-shaped bill is a recent immigrant from the south, where it is called "redbird." It has been extending its range northward and first occurred regularly in New Hampshire in the late 1950s. It is now a fairly common, local, year-round resident of villages, farms, and especially suburbia south of the White Mountains and is a familiar bird at many bird feeders. While some individuals may wander considerable distances outside of the breeding season, the cardinal is not a true migrant.

The Eastern subspecies, *R. cardinalis cardinalis*, now ranges from New Brunswick west to South Dakota and south to the Gulf Coast (Bent 1968). The male is the only mostly red, prominently crested, black-faced North American bird. The female is mostly brown. Both sexes sing, the female almost as well as the male (Bent 1968). The frequently performed song is highly variable, but generally consists of a series of loud, musical whistles often accelerating into almost a trill.

Mated pairs may sing alternately or even in unison in courtship, which also may involve males chasing females. Courting males stretch their necks and sway while singing, fight each other, and swoop around the area. A male also may alight slightly above a female on the same branch and, with crest, neck, and body extended, sidestep down to the female while singing rapidly (Shaver and Roberts *in* Bent 1968).

Most nests are in tangles of vines or thickets or in dense shrubbery, generally 4 to 5 ft (1.2 to 1.5 m) from the ground (Bent 1968). They are bowl shaped, and may be compactly built and well lined, or flimsy and without much lining. Materials include stems, twigs, bark, vines, and rootlets, with leaves or paper interwoven (Laskey 1944 *in* Bent 1968). Nest building in New Hampshire may occur any time from the end of April through June.

The clutch is 2 to 5, usually 3 or 4 eggs. Recent egg dates range from 13 May (Hopkinton) to 17 July (near Portsmouth). The Hopkinton eggs hatched on 24 May, the same day the male was killed by a car, leaving the female to feed the young, which left the nest 10 days later on 3 June (Richards, pers. obs.).

This showy bird is extremely secretive while nesting and was "confirmed" in only 17 of the 55 priority blocks where it was recorded. Observations of fledglings provided the majority of "confirmations." Juveniles resemble adult females but are barely distinguishable from their parents after a complete molt in August.

About 70% of the cardinal's natural food consists of fruits and seeds. The remaining 30% includes insects, spiders, centipedes, snails, slugs, and small bivalves (McAtee 1908 *in* Bent 1968). Nestlings are fed almost entirely on insects. Now, especially in winter, cardinals feed extensively on bird seed at feeders.

Traditionally a southern bird, the cardinal was a casual visitor north of the Ohio River a century ago. By 1910 it had reached Ontario and the lower Hudson River valley (Bent 1968). Cardinals were still rare in New England during the late 1920s, and many early records were believed to be of escaped caged birds (Forbush 1929, Palmer 1949).

The first cardinal reports in New Hampshire were of single birds in December 1931 in Woodsville (Bath), in April 1949 in Monroe, and in May 1956 in Walpole (Richards 1958). The big change began in 1957, when a cardinal invasion of southern New England extended into Vermont and New Hampshire (Hebert 1958b). Records included birds in Tilton, Meriden (Plainfield), Keene, Moultonborough, Claremont, Haverhill, and Intervale (Bartlett/Conway), and a possible record from Pittsburg (Hebert 1957, Hebert 1958b). Several additional records occurred that winter and the following spring (ASNH 1958a, 1958b). A high proportion of the early records were from the Connecticut River valley. During the next several years the cardinal continued to increase in numbers and extend its range in New Hampshire. A pair produced 2 to 4 young in Hanover in 1960, confirming breeding in the state for the first time (Haile *in* Brainard 1960).

A second and greater surge occurred in 1961, with cardinals appearing in 7 of New Hampshire's 10 counties, reaching southeastern New Hampshire (NHAQ, 1961–62, *passim*) and Colebrook, in Coos County (Howard 1968). Another apparent surge occurred in the fall and winter of 1966–67 (SRS). Annual Cardinal-Tufted Titmouse surveys begun in February 1967 reflect a definite increase in cardinal numbers, from 57 in 1967 to a peak of 1,250 in 1983. Since then numbers have leveled off, as has the number of survey participants (CTM data, 1967–86).

The cardinal's range expansion into New Hampshire began along the Connecticut and Merrimack valleys and spread east to the Seacoast after several years. It has resulted, at least in part, from the development of backyard habitats favorable for breeding and winter survival.

The Atlas and winter survey maps show that the cardinal now has a fairly wide distribution over much of southern New Hampshire, having extended its range somewhat further north in the river valleys. The scattered distribution in the southwest highlands and the north suggest that extensive forests, higher elevations, and colder temperatures may be important limiting factors.

Tudor Richards

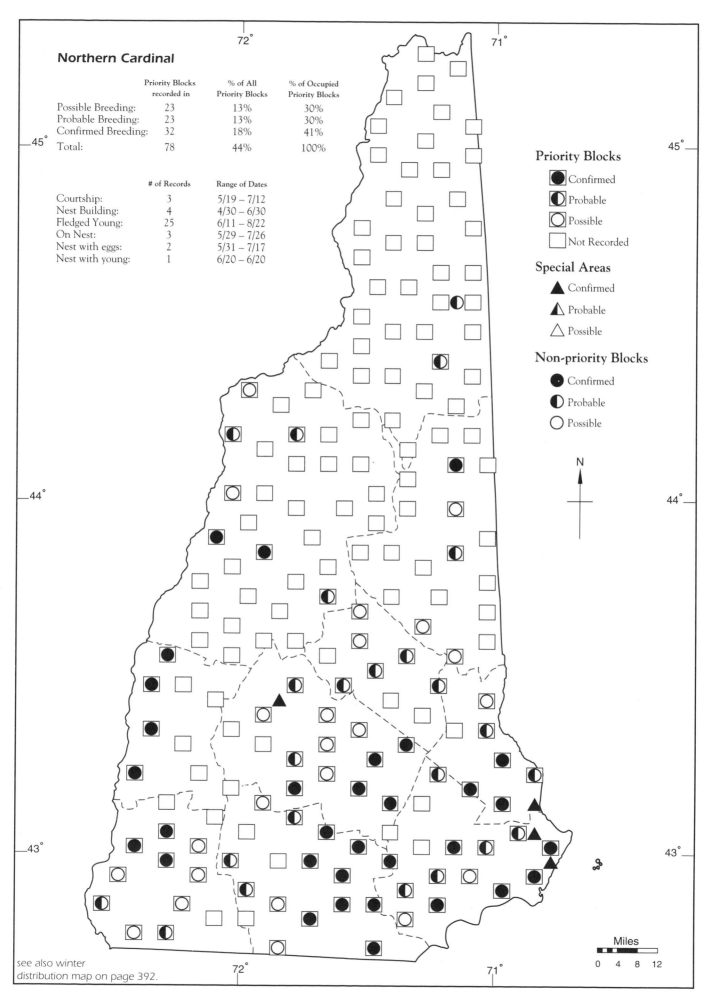

Northern Cardinal

	Priority Blocks recorded in	% of All Priority Blocks	% of Occupied Priority Blocks
Possible Breeding:	23	13%	30%
Probable Breeding:	23	13%	30%
Confirmed Breeding:	32	18%	41%
Total:	78	44%	100%

	# of Records	Range of Dates
Courtship:	3	5/19 – 7/12
Nest Building:	4	4/30 – 6/30
Fledged Young:	25	6/11 – 8/22
On Nest:	3	5/29 – 7/26
Nest with eggs:	2	5/31 – 7/17
Nest with young:	1	6/20 – 6/20

Priority Blocks
- ◑ Confirmed
- ◐ Probable
- ○ Possible
- ☐ Not Recorded

Special Areas
- ▲ Confirmed
- ◣ Probable
- △ Possible

Non-priority Blocks
- ◉ Confirmed
- ◐ Probable
- ○ Possible

N

see also winter distribution map on page 392.

Rose-breasted Grosbeak
Pheucticus ludovicianus

The male Rose-breasted Grosbeak, with its striking black and white plumage and brilliant rose bib, is a relatively conspicuous bird, especially in spring, when it is actively singing, courting, and chasing. The female, however, with its streaked, finchlike plumage, is more cryptic and easily overlooked. The Rose-breasted Grosbeak occurs most frequently in young deciduous woodlands throughout the state, but also inhabits mixed deciduous-coniferous forests and wooded suburbs, mostly below 2,500 ft (760 m) (Ridgely 1977; T. Richards, unpubl. data).

Grosbeaks arrive in New Hampshire as early as the last week of April but more typically in the first 2 weeks of May. Most depart between mid-August and mid-September, with occasional individuals remaining into October and rarely November.

Upon arrival in spring, male grosbeaks move conspicuously about their territories, singing their loud, musical songs, often while in flight. The Rose-breasted Grosbeak's song is robinlike, but more melodious, and less raspy than that of a Scarlet Tanager. Singing occurs mainly in the subcanopy, but birds move frequently into the high canopy and down into the shrub layer. Mean height of singing perches observed at the Hubbard Brook Experimental Forest, Thornton, was 39.4 ft (12.0 m) (Holmes 1986). Chases, involving 2 or 3 males and often a female, occur frequently (Dunham 1966). It is not clear whether these are primarily territorial battles or disputes over the female. The latter may be the case, since when the female is present and even during nest building and egg laying, the male closely follows her as if he were guarding a precious resource (Holmes and Sherry, pers. obs.). Both sexes give a distinctive, short and squeaky call note.

Nesting begins in mid-May. Nest building at Hubbard Brook occurs from about 18 to 25 May. Nests are usually in forks of trees, often along the distal portions of horizontal and drooping branches, but occa-

sionally in crotches along the main trunk. At Hubbard Brook, nests have been located about equally in yellow birch, sugar maple, and American beech, the 3 dominant tree species, at heights averaging 49.2 (15.0 m) (Holmes 1986 and unpubl. data). Elsewhere, the species may nest in a variety of trees, including hemlock, apple, pear, willow, and ironwood (Bent 1968). Nest heights in these species are often low, usually between 6.6 and 13.1 ft (2 and 4 m) (Bent 1968).

The nest is made of relatively coarse twigs and lined with finer strips of bark and rootlike material. The female does most of the building, while the male associates with her closely and sometimes assists (Bent 1968). The male also shares in incubation and occasionally sings while sitting on the nest (Bent 1968). Clutch size ranges from 3 to 5 eggs. The incubation period is about 12 to 14 days (Bent 1968). White (1937) observed a nest in Concord with a complete clutch on 26 May, and barely fledged young there on 2 July. Multiple broods apparently do not occur (Forbush 1929; Bent 1968; Holmes, pers. obs.). Fledged young and adult birds carrying food or fecal sacs are easy to observe, as the relatively high percentage of "confirmed" Atlas records attests.

Grosbeaks feed extensively on insects, which they glean from nearby foliage or snatch as they fly by (Robinson and Holmes 1982). They occasionally sally out and catch flying insects or fly after insects they have flushed from foliage. At Hubbard Brook, grosbeaks forage primarily at middle heights in the forest (Holmes 1986), but some foraging occurs at nearly all levels, even occasionally on the ground (Holmes, pers. obs.). In forested areas, they feed extensively on caterpillars, beetles, and some bees and wasps (Robinson and Holmes 1982). They also take small butterflies and moths, crickets, grasshoppers, spiders, and in mid and late summer a variety of fruits and seeds (Bent 1968). They once were famous for feeding on potato beetles (Hoffman 1904).

In precolonial times the Rose-breasted Grosbeak probably occurred throughout the state in and along shrubby margins of deciduous forests. As land was cleared in the early 1800s, the grosbeak population may have declined accordingly. Samuels (1867) considered the species generally distributed but nowhere common, and Maynard (1871) didn't include it in his ornithology of Coos (N.H.) and Oxford (Me.) counties.

This species was rather locally distributed in northern New England around the turn of the century (Dearborn 1903, Hoffmann 1904). It was fairly common in orchards and village shade trees in Exeter, but apparently did not breed in nearby Durham (Dearborn 1903). Most authors considered it uncommon (Dearborn 1898, Allen 1903, Dearborn 1903), but Wright (1911) found it not uncommon on lower mountains and in "devastated forests" at elevations up to about 2,200 ft (670 m) in the Jefferson region. Frequent records of this species in orchards and shrubby areas during the late 1800s and 1900s (see Bent 1968) probably reflect the lack of extensive forests. Hoffman (1904) stated, "Of late years it has shown a preference for villages, and even for city streets, if well-shaded; it also occurs in orchards, but apparently its natural habitat is a growth of young trees or saplings, particularly in low ground."

Forest regeneration in New Hampshire during the last 50 to 75 years has increased habitat for Rose-breasted Grosbeaks. BBS data document a significant increase in this species in New Hampshire and throughout the Eastern region between 1966 and 1979 (Robbins et al. 1986). Today, this grosbeak nests throughout the state, as the Atlas map attests. Only 4 priority blocks lack Atlas records, all of which are at higher elevations of the White Mountains.

Richard T. Holmes & Thomas W. Sherry

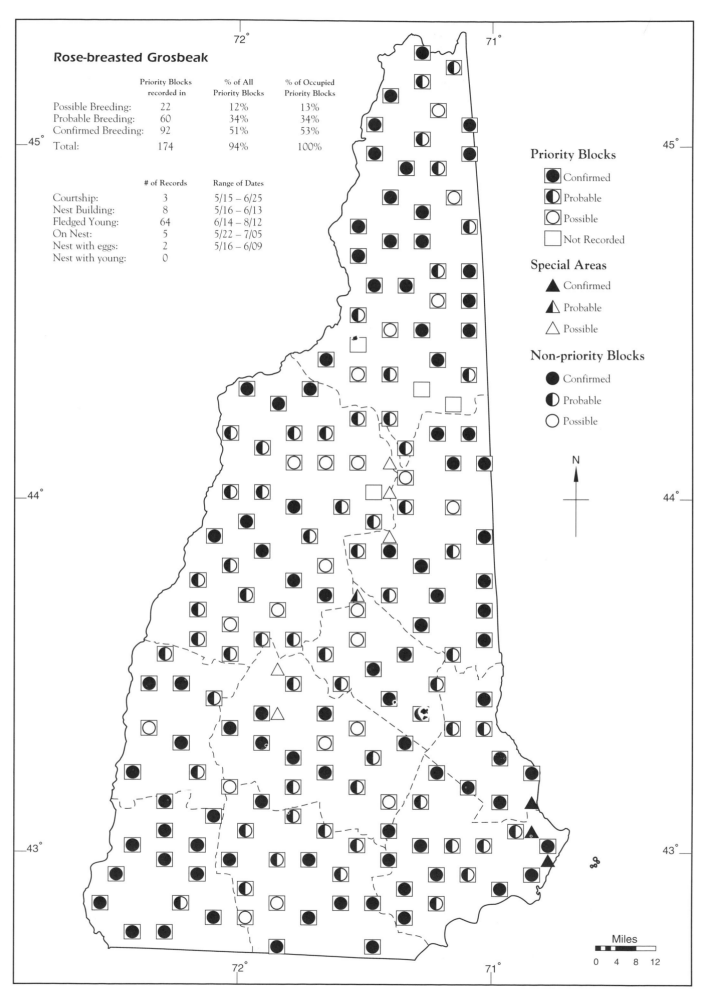

Rose-breasted Grosbeak

	Priority Blocks recorded in	% of All Priority Blocks	% of Occupied Priority Blocks
Possible Breeding:	22	12%	13%
Probable Breeding:	60	34%	34%
Confirmed Breeding:	92	51%	53%
Total:	174	94%	100%

	# of Records	Range of Dates
Courtship:	3	5/15 – 6/25
Nest Building:	8	5/16 – 6/13
Fledged Young:	64	6/14 – 8/12
On Nest:	5	5/22 – 7/05
Nest with eggs:	2	5/16 – 6/09
Nest with young:	0	

Priority Blocks

- ● Confirmed
- ◑ Probable
- ○ Possible
- □ Not Recorded

Special Areas

- ▲ Confirmed
- ◮ Probable
- △ Possible

Non-priority Blocks

- ● Confirmed
- ◐ Probable
- ○ Possible

N

Miles
0 4 8 12

Indigo Bunting
Passerina cyanea

The male Indigo Bunting in breeding plumage is a spectacular ultramarine blue, although in the shade, or against the sky, he may appear black or sometimes grayish blue. In stark contrast, the female is a nondescript yellowish brown. She spends much of her time skulking through the underbrush, twitching her tail from side to side and sputtering all the while. This small finch resides throughout New Hampshire in brushy fields reverting to woodlands, power-line rights-of-way, and cutover areas. Although most common below 1,500 ft (460 m) elevation (Forbush 1929), it has occurred above 2,500 ft (760 m) in the White Mountains (T. Richards, pers. comm.).

The majority of male Indigo Buntings do not reach New Hampshire until late May, and females arrive later still. In some years, however, numbers of these birds appear in New England as early as mid-April. This occurs most commonly in exposed coastal areas such as Cape Cod, but there have been a number of April and early May records recently in New Hampshire, usually of males coming to bird feeders. The earliest known occurrence is 10 April in Concord (Taber and Johnston 1968). The commonly accepted explanation is that these early birds have gotten caught in storms moving up the Atlantic Coast. Tufts (1986), however, has questioned this theory since Indigo Buntings occur regularly in Nova Scotia in April and May, often in fairly large numbers, but are not known to breed in the province.

The male is territorial and vigorously defends his breeding area with song and pursuit of intruding males (Taber and Johnston 1968). The Indigo Bunting often sings from the tops of rather tall trees. The presence of trees or other high perches probably is a habitat requirement. He is a persistent singer, vocalizing during the hottest summer days, often well into August. The high-pitched and strident song usually features paired notes, with each pair on a higher or lower pitch from the preceding pair. Ridgely (1977) described a typical version as "zwee-zwee, rit-rit, reet-reet, say-o," but there is much variation, each individual bird having its own pattern of notes (Borror 1961).

Indigo Buntings build their nests rather low in bushes and briars, usually 2 to 12 ft (0.6 to 3.7 m) above the ground (Harrison 1975). Often nests are in tangles of bushes with thorns such as blackberry, raspberry, or wild rose (Taber and Johnston 1968). This may discourage some predators, as well as Atlas observers, who failed to find even one nest with eggs or young during the 6 years of field work. The female selects the location and builds the nest of twigs, coarse grass, weeds, and a few leaves, lining it with fine grass and sometimes hair, snakeskin, or feathers (Forbush 1929, Harrison 1975). Sometimes she will rebuild an old nest and use it for several years (Forbush 1929).

The female does most of the incubation of the 2 to 6 eggs, which takes 12 or 13 days. She also feeds the nestlings. The young leave the nest at 9 to 13 days and the male may then feed them, "possibly while female renests" (Harrison 1978). There are sometimes 2 broods; second broods have been suspected but not documented in New Hampshire.

Once nesting is over, Indigo Buntings frequent cornfields, especially ones near woodland edges or with trees nearby. Their strong sputtering call notes then reveal their whereabouts. Molting takes place at this time, and the males become a somber brown resembling the females and young. Most Indigo Buntings leave for the south in late August and September, but often a few linger into early October. Allison and Allison (1979) recorded a late date of 6 November.

Indigo Buntings were numerous over much of New Hampshire 100 years ago. Allen (1889) considered the species "very common" in Bridgewater in 1883, and "very abundant" in Moultonborough in 1885. Faxon and Allen (1888) regarded it as "very abundant" in Holderness in 1885 and 1886, and "abundant" even as far north as Franconia in 1886 and 1887. Later compilers of local bird lists more often used the terms "fairly common" or "uncommon" to describe its status (Dearborn 1898, 1903, Ridgely 1977, Allison and Allison 1979). This suggests a decline in numbers, which is confirmed by evidence from elsewhere in New England (Griscom 1949). In Massachusetts their numbers decreased between 1890 and 1930, but shortly afterwards began to increase once again (Griscom and Snyder 1955). Palmer (1949) noted a roughly comparable decline and subsequent increase in Maine.

There is evidence that in recent years Indigo Buntings have increased throughout their breeding range (Robbins et al. 1966). New Hampshire BBS data during 1966–84 show that these birds were moderately common here until 1975, when a pronounced and continuing increase in their numbers began. One can see from the Atlas map that Indigo Buntings are widespread south of the White Mountains and in the northern Connecticut River valley, but in the mountains themselves occur locally, chiefly in the valleys. In the North Country east of the Connecticut Valley they probably always have been scarce, but Indigo Buntings have been observed as far north as Pittsburg on several occasions.

Vera H. Hebert & Kimball C. Elkins

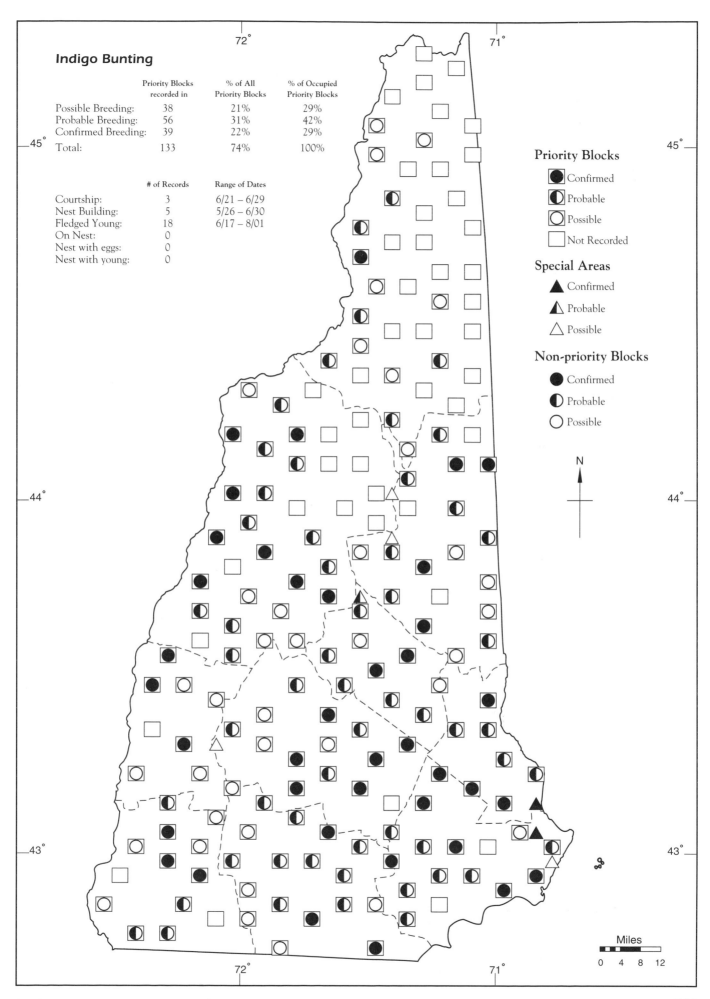

Indigo Bunting

	Priority Blocks recorded in	% of All Priority Blocks	% of Occupied Priority Blocks
Possible Breeding:	38	21%	29%
Probable Breeding:	56	31%	42%
Confirmed Breeding:	39	22%	29%
Total:	133	74%	100%

	# of Records	Range of Dates
Courtship:	3	6/21 – 6/29
Nest Building:	5	5/26 – 6/30
Fledged Young:	18	6/17 – 8/01
On Nest:	0	
Nest with eggs:	0	
Nest with young:	0	

Priority Blocks
- Confirmed
- Probable
- Possible
- Not Recorded

Special Areas
- Confirmed
- Probable
- Possible

Non-priority Blocks
- Confirmed
- Probable
- Possible

N

Miles
0   4   8   12

Rufous-sided Towhee

Pipilo erythrophthalmus

From tangled thickets and scrubby trees, the handsome Rufous-sided Towhee sends forth a cheerful command to "drink your tea!" Towhees usually forage near the ground, where they scuffle noisily in dead leaves and undergrowth in search of seeds and insects, but they routinely sing from the tops of trees, occasionally tall ones. This species approaches the northern limit of its range in northern New Hampshire, and occurs most commonly in the southern half of the state. The towhee breeds throughout much of the forested continental U.S. and extreme southern Canada, south to Guatemala. The Eastern population winters primarily from New Jersey south, but individuals sometimes overwinter further north.

The towhee's warm colors and distinctive shape are easily recognizable. Slightly smaller and slimmer than a robin, which it somewhat resembles, the towhee flashes white outer feathers on its long, rounded tail as it flies or scratches for food. Adult towhees have rusty sides and white bellies; the male's head, throat, and breast are black, and the female's are brown. Immature towhees are dull brown with streaked underparts.

The breeding season begins when the male arrives, a few days ahead of the female, generally from 20 April to 10 May (T. Richards, unpubl. data). Breeding habitat includes pine barrens, brushy areas of old pastures, power-line corridors, road edges, cutover areas, woods, clearings, and abandoned gravel pits. The male establishes his territory by chasing intruders and by singing his loud, ventriloquistic song from a conspicuous perch. He also sings a quiet, musical "whisper song" (Forbush 1929) and often displays his flashy plumage. He chases the female and carries and drops nesting materials, and may sing from a perch above her. He sometimes guards the nest when the female is away, by sitting on the rim (J. Greenlaw, pers. comm.). Both sexes loudly call "chewink!"

The female builds a bulky nest in 2 to 5 days, usu-ally on the ground but occasionally in vines, trees, or bushes from 1 to 5 ft (0.3 to 1.5 m) or rarely 10 to 18 ft (3.0 to 5.5 m) from the ground (Terres 1980). The well-hidden nest consists of grass, roots, twigs, bark strips, and leaves, with a lining of hair or grass (Harrison 1975, Terres 1980). The female incubates her 2 to 6, usually 3 or 4 eggs for 12 or 13 days (Heil *in* Forbush 1929, Terres 1980). Brown-headed Cowbirds often lay their eggs in towhee nests (Harrison 1975). Well camouflaged, the female sits until almost stepped on before leaving the nest and often attempts to lure away intruders with a broken-wing act (Forbush 1929). The male may leave the nest by running off along the ground like a mammal, only more slowly (K.C. Elkins, J. Greenlaw, pers. comm.).

Both parents care for the young for 10 to 12 days in the nest and for about a month after they fledge (Forbush 1929). The male may deliver food to a brooding female, which she then feeds to the young (J. Greenlaw, pers. comm.). The pair usually remains together to raise a second brood in or near the original territory (Harrison 1975). Fall migration occurs primarily during September, but some birds may linger into early November. Individuals occasionally overwinter in New Hampshire (SRS).

Early accounts indicate that during the early years of this century towhees were common in suitable habitat in the central and southern parts of the state, as well as in the lowlands north of Lake Winnipesaukee, where they occurred in bear oak and pitch pine on the Ossipee sand barrens and in the Saco valley (Goodhue 1877, Allen 1903). Scott (1921) considered this species very common in pastures and thickets of young pines and junipers in southern New Hampshire. The towhee was rare in the White Mountains, where Wright (1911) found it an "accidental visitant" in Jefferson. Apparently it did not occur north of the mountains.

During the mid-1900s, the species was common throughout much of southern New Hampshire as abandoned fields and pastures were growing up to shrubs (K.C. Elkins, pers. comm.). Local populations documented 15 to 25 years ago included 13 possible breeding birds on Mt. Monadnock, Jaffrey, on 17 June 1962 and 14 along the Saco River in Conway on 14 June 1972 (T. Richards, unpubl. data). However, BBS data from 1966 to 1979 document a significant decrease in towhee numbers in much of the East, including all the New England states, beginning in the early 1970s (Robbins et al. 1986).

The towhee still occurs in brushy lowland areas and on mountaintops, especially burned-over mountains such as Monadnock, Jaffrey; Cardigan, Orange/Alexandria; and Baldface, Beans Purchase/Chatham at elevations up to 3,000 ft (909 m). The Atlas lacks records for few blocks south of the White Mountains; all but one of these are in the Western Highlands or Connecticut River valley. The towhee's distribution in the North Country clearly illustrates the valley separating the Presidential and Pilot ranges. The only record further north is from the Hall Stream valley in Pittsburg.

As abandoned fields and brushy clearings in New Hampshire grow to forest, or are converted to lawns, the towhee will find less and less of the dense cover it requires for nesting habitat and may become largely restricted to maintained shrubby habitats along power-lines and other utility rights-of-way.

Elizabeth C. Janeway

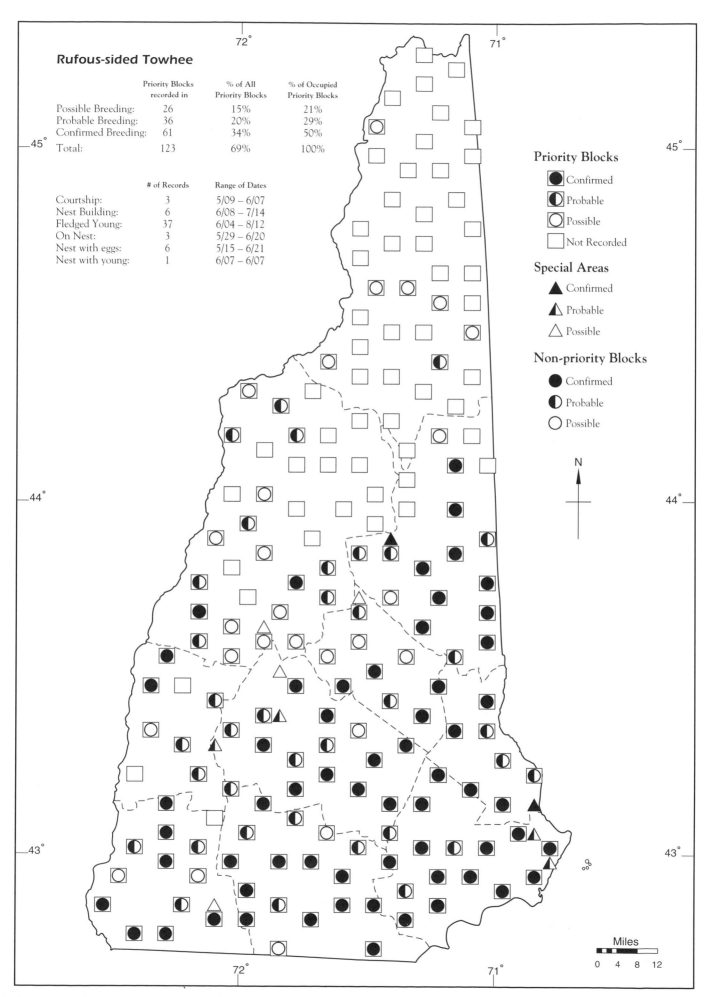

Rufous-sided Towhee

	Priority Blocks recorded in	% of All Priority Blocks	% of Occupied Priority Blocks
Possible Breeding:	26	15%	21%
Probable Breeding:	36	20%	29%
Confirmed Breeding:	61	34%	50%
Total:	123	69%	100%

	# of Records	Range of Dates
Courtship:	3	5/09 – 6/07
Nest Building:	6	6/08 – 7/14
Fledged Young:	37	6/04 – 8/12
On Nest:	3	5/29 – 6/20
Nest with eggs:	6	5/15 – 6/21
Nest with young:	1	6/07 – 6/07

Priority Blocks

- ◐ Confirmed
- ◑ Probable
- ○ Possible
- ☐ Not Recorded

Special Areas

- ▲ Confirmed
- ◪ Probable
- △ Possible

Non-priority Blocks

- ● Confirmed
- ◑ Probable
- ○ Possible

N

Miles
0 4 8 12

Chipping Sparrow
Spizella passerina

This pert, rufous-capped sparrow is locally common to abundant in our state at elevations up to 2,000 ft (610 m) and has been recorded up to 2,600 ft (790 m) (Richards *in* Hebert 1962). Preferred habitat includes residential areas, agricultural lands, open mixed woodlands, and forest openings and edges (Stull 1968). Named for its song, a simple trill on one pitch that may be fast or slow, the Chipping Sparrow is easily recognized by its small size, gray underparts, white wing bars, rufous cap, white eyebrow, and black line through the eye (Farrand 1983). Nearly everyone is familiar with this relatively tame species, which feeds in back yards and often nests in ornamental shrubbery.

Chipping Sparrows begin arriving in New Hampshire by mid-April with peak migrations near the end of the month. Pairs return to their previous nesting areas (Kennard 1963), where males quickly establish territories and defend them by singing (Forbush 1929) and chasing away invading males. The courting male gives short bursts of song from a prominent perch and makes quick flights to the female as she collects grasses and weed stalks. The female solicits copulation by crouching with her head and tail slightly raised and wings vibrating rapidly, and uttering a rapid "see-see-see-see-see" call (Bradley 1940 and Walkinshaw 1944 *in* Stull 1968).

The Chipping Sparrow nests at low to moderate heights in a variety of trees, shrubs, and vines, often in a conifer, and occasionally on the ground. A. Robinson (SRS) found a nest in a garden pea patch in Lebanon in 1976, and B. Hedin (SRS) observed a pair nesting in a red maple in Hancock in 1977.

Nest building occurs during the third week of May in southern New Hampshire and about a week later in northern sections. The female builds the nest over 3 or 4 days, primarily during mornings, using dead grasses, weed stalks, rootlets' and a lining of fine grasses and hair (Walkinshaw 1944 *in* Stull 1968, Stull 1968). The

Chipping Sparrow's affinity for using horse hair in its nest has given rise to the name "hair-bird" (Blanchan 1898, Scott 1921). The female begins the clutch of 3 to 5, usually 4 eggs upon completing the nest, laying one egg a day early in the morning (Samuels 1870, Stull 1968). White (1937) cites egg dates from 13 May to 15 June in Concord. The Brown-headed Cowbird frequently parasitizes this species (Forbush 1929, Friedmann 1963, Stull 1968).

The male brings food to the female during the 11 to 14 day incubation period, uttering a series of low chips as he approaches the nest. The female often leaves the nest to eat what he has brought (Stull 1968). Chipping Sparrows eat predominantly grass and weed seeds, but during the breeding season their diet shifts to a great variety of insects (Martin et al. 1961). The young spend 10 to 14 days in the nest before fledging. A clutch of 4 eggs in Conway hatched on 14 June and the young left the nest on 25 June (CLO Nest Rec. Prog.). The male may provide most of the food during the first few days after hatching, with increasing help from the female as the nestlings get older (Walkinshaw 1944, Stull 1968). Chipping Sparrows often produce a second brood (Harrison 1975). In New Hampshire this may occur in the latter part of June and early July. A pair in Jefferson fledged their first brood on 24 June 1904, and the female had constructed a new nest 2 days later (Wright 1911).

Young Chipping Sparrows seen with adults in early July have finely streaked underparts and are easily identified as young of the year. Immatures in fall and winter have unstreaked underparts and distinctive gray rumps (Farrand 1983). As the families begin dispersing into local fields, they mingle with other species in loose flocks of variable size. At this time they become very skittish and difficult to observe (White 1924).

In the fall, migration is more drawn out than in the spring, occurring primarily from the first of September through mid-October. Occasional stragglers remain into November and December but few, if any, overwinter in New Hampshire.

This sparrow is well represented throughout the state, and Atlas observers recorded the species in 89% of priority blocks. Records are spotty at elevations above 2,000 ft (610 m). Many Atlas "confirmations" resulted from observations of adults carrying food or fecal sacs and of fledglings. Atlas data suggest that first broods fledge during mid to late June and fledging of later broods continues through July and into early August.

Maynard (1871), Dearborn (1898), Scott (1921), White (1924), Ridgely (1977), and Allison and Allison (1979) consistently recorded the Chipping Sparrow as a common to abundant summer resident in New Hampshire. Although this species declined sharply in some areas after the turn of the century (Miller 1933, Price 1935, and Griscom 1949 all *in* Stull 1968), it has continued to be abundant in suitable habitat. BBS data during 1966–79 indicate a slight decline in the Eastern region (Robbins et al. 1986). BBS data for 1966 to 1986 indicate no significant trend.

The Atlas map illustrates the Chipping Sparrow's nearly ubiquitous distribution in southern New Hampshire, where additional effort likely would have located the species in the few priority blocks lacking records. This species is somewhat more local in the White Mountains and North Country, where high elevations and extensive forests limit suitable habitat. Habitat loss due to the decline of agriculture may have been a factor in local declines. However, this species appears secure and stable in New Hampshire at the present time.

James McDermott

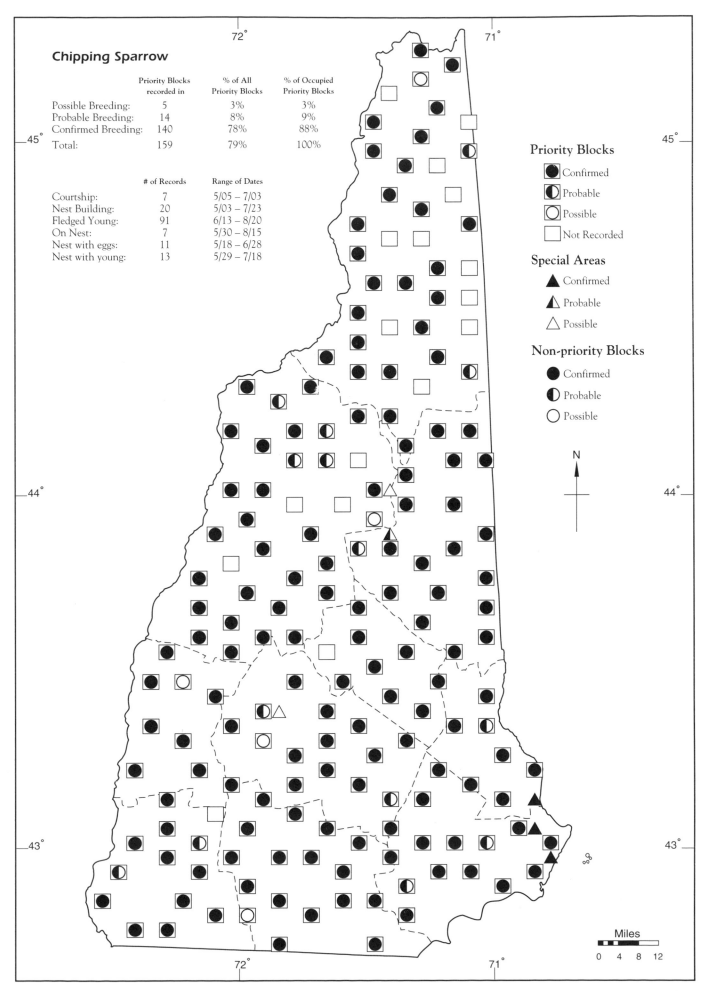

Chipping Sparrow

	Priority Blocks recorded in	% of All Priority Blocks	% of Occupied Priority Blocks
Possible Breeding:	5	3%	3%
Probable Breeding:	14	8%	9%
Confirmed Breeding:	140	78%	88%
Total:	159	79%	100%

	# of Records	Range of Dates
Courtship:	7	5/05 – 7/03
Nest Building:	20	5/03 – 7/23
Fledged Young:	91	6/13 – 8/20
On Nest:	7	5/30 – 8/15
Nest with eggs:	11	5/18 – 6/28
Nest with young:	13	5/29 – 7/18

Priority Blocks

- ◕ Confirmed
- ◑ Probable
- ○ Possible
- □ Not Recorded

Special Areas

- ▲ Confirmed
- ◢ Probable
- △ Possible

Non-priority Blocks

- ● Confirmed
- ◖ Probable
- ○ Possible

N

Miles
0   4   8   12

Field Sparrow

Spizella pusilla

Do not look for the Field Sparrow in open fields. This once common bird, whose loud, plaintive song has the rhythm of a bouncing ping-pong ball, lives in brushy pastures, mostly south of the White Mountains. Old names, "bush sparrow" and "huckleberry bird," are fitting. No longer common in New Hampshire, the Field Sparrow rarely occurs at elevations above 1,500 ft (460 m) (Allen 1903; T. Richards, pers. comm.).

Field Sparrows migrate at night in small flocks, usually with other sparrows, but arrive on breeding grounds singly or a few at a time (Walkinshaw 1968). Returning to New Hampshire from late March to late April, they seek old pastures with berry bushes, young pines, and thorny thickets for nesting. Stump fields, power-line corridors, and overgrown gravel pits also provide suitable habitat.

The male Field Sparrow arrives first. He flies from one shrub or low tree to another, singing from each. The song, which may rise or fall in pitch, is a series of sweet, whistled notes ("tew, tew, tew") that start slowly and speed up, trilling quietly at the end, and seem ventriloqual when heard from a distance (Janeway, pers. obs.). Males sing less often once paired (Walkinshaw 1968). Both sexes utter various calls, commonly including a short "tsip!"

The male chases other male Field Sparrows for several days until the 2 to 6 a (0.8 to 2.4 ha) initial territory shrinks as he compromises with his neighbors (Walkinshaw 1968). When a female arrives one to 3 weeks after the male, he flies at her as if to chase her away. She may dive under a bush and refuse to leave while he repeats his inhospitable behavior. After he accepts her, the pair trills and chips during mating. Pairs feed and roost together, and the male keeps extremely busy guarding his mate and keeping her from wandering off with other males (Walkinshaw 1968).

The female builds her first nest of the season in about 4 or 5 days, working usually in the morning on the cup of leaves and grass lined with hair and rootlets (Walkinshaw 1968, Harrison 1978). The male often accompanies his mate on flights to gather nest materials, usually within 60 yd (55 m) of the nest site. Always wary of cowbirds, the sparrows stop nest building and pretend to be feeding whenever one comes into view (Walkinshaw 1968).

Early nests are on or near the ground, but later nests, which require 2 or 3 days to build, are usually low in a shrub, often in thorny vegetation (Walkinshaw 1968; Best 1977; Evans 1978; K. C. Elkins, pers. comm.). A nest under construction on 8 June 1985 in Weare was 1 ft (30 cm) from the ground in a blackberry bush in a dry, sandy, overgrown field (C. R. Foss and D. Stavros, NHBBA data).

Heavy rain and snow may destroy early nests, and nest predation by accipiters, Blue Jays, Common Grackles, and House Wrens is not uncommon. The female may build up to 7 nests in one season, raising 2 or sometimes 3 broods (Forbush 1929, Walkinshaw 1968). White (1937) noted a late nest with eggs found on 21 July in Concord. The female incubates the 3 to 5 eggs for 10 to 17, usually 11 days (Harrison 1978), while her mate sings nearby and brings her insect larvae. She sometimes leaves the nest to feed with her mate, but spends most of the time incubating. After the eggs hatch, she broods the young birds for 6 more days.

Both parents feed the young and remove fecal sacs. Young leave the nest when 7 or 8 days old but remain nearby, practicing short flights. The female builds a new nest and begins a second family while her mate cares for the first brood of fledglings, which are independent at 26 to 34 days old (Walkinshaw 1968).

After the last young have fledged, Field Sparrows disperse to weedy fields and gardens where they forage on the ground for seeds and insects (Forbush 1929). Adams and Brewer (1981) provide evidence that young Field Sparrows investigate potential breeding habitat at this time and select the breeding area to which they will return the following spring. Flocks gather in September and roost together in bushes, usually leaving by mid-October.

Intensive sheep farming may have limited local populations of Field Sparrows in the 1800s (E. Miller, pers. comm.). Goodhue (1877), however, considered them common in the vicinity of Webster. Field Sparrows were not uncommon in the Randolph/Jefferson area in 1889, but apparently disappeared for a time and subsequently returned to the area in 1907 (Wright 1911). Brewster (*in* Griscom 1938) recorded the Field Sparrow near Umbagog Lake for the first time in June 1909. As farmers abandoned fields and pastures after the turn of the century, abundant habitat became available, and Field Sparrows were common in brushy hillside pastures in southern and central New Hampshire and in the lowlands of Franconia and the Saco valley (Allen 1903, Dearborn 1903, Scott 1921, White 1937).

Field Sparrows have declined in New Hampshire since the turn of the century, probably due to changes in available nesting habitat. BBS data from 1966 to 1979 indicate a significant decrease throughout New England (Robbins et al. 1986). The Atlas map indicates that they still are widely distributed in the southern half of the state, but scarce north of the White Mountains, where they occur mainly in lowlands. As old field habitat in southern New Hampshire reverts to forest or becomes developed, power-line corridors may become the primary strongholds for Field Sparrows in the state.

Elizabeth C. Janeway

Atlas of Breeding Birds in New Hampshire

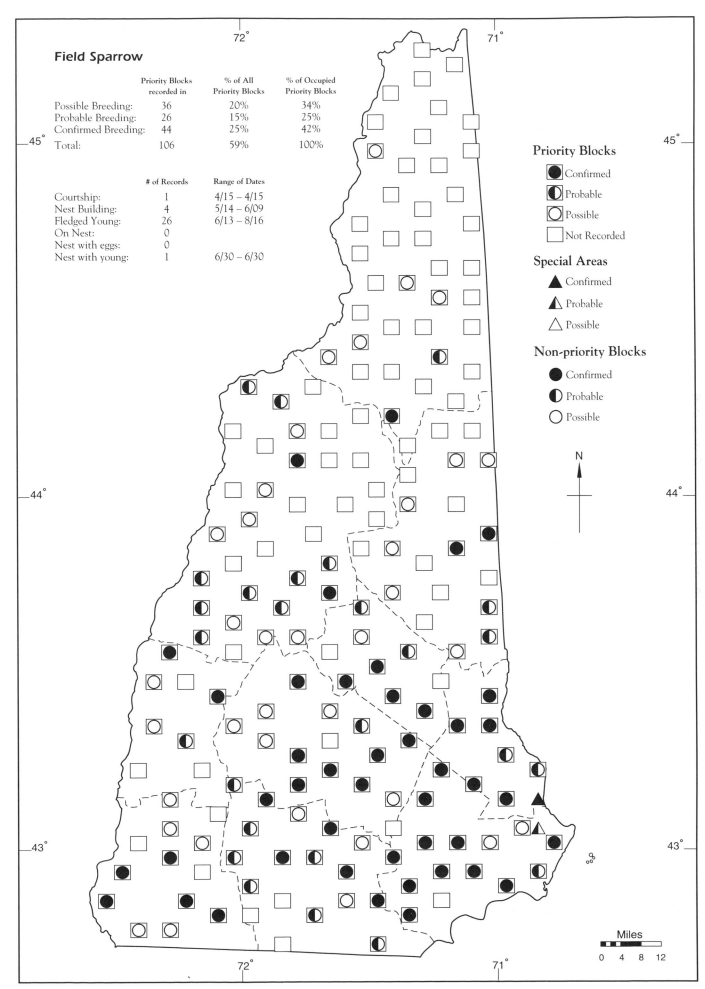

Field Sparrow

	Priority Blocks recorded in	% of All Priority Blocks	% of Occupied Priority Blocks
Possible Breeding:	36	20%	34%
Probable Breeding:	26	15%	25%
Confirmed Breeding:	44	25%	42%
Total:	106	59%	100%

	# of Records	Range of Dates
Courtship:	1	4/15 – 4/15
Nest Building:	4	5/14 – 6/09
Fledged Young:	26	6/13 – 8/16
On Nest:	0	
Nest with eggs:	0	
Nest with young:	1	6/30 – 6/30

Priority Blocks
- ● Confirmed
- ◐ Probable
- ○ Possible
- ☐ Not Recorded

Special Areas
- ▲ Confirmed
- ◣ Probable
- △ Possible

Non-priority Blocks
- ● Confirmed
- ◗ Probable
- ○ Possible

Miles
0 4 8 12

Vesper Sparrow
Pooecetes gramineus

The Vesper Sparrow is a persistent singer and a field dweller. Considered common to abundant throughout New England a century ago (Coues 1868, Goodhue 1877, Dearborn 1898), the Vesper Sparrow's population has dwindled until today its song is unfamiliar to many. When visible, white outer tail feathers that flash in flight distinguish this sparrow from all its relatives (Janeway, pers. obs.). The sexes are similar and resemble Song Sparrows, but overall they are grayer. They have a distinctive reddish brown patch on the shoulder, hence the old name "bay-winged bunting," but it is not easy to see.

Vesper Sparrows generally arrive in early April, or occasionally in late March, when there may be snow still on the ground. The breeding season extends from late April into mid-August (Berger 1968). Forbush (1929) documented a nest with eggs on 15 April in Massachusetts, and Berger (1968) provides a 2 May egg date for Quebec.

Vesper Sparrows inhabit dry, grassy bottomlands and hillside pastures at elevations up to 1,500 ft (460 m) (Allen 1903; T. Richards, pers. comm.). They nest in hayfields, cornfields, and open pastures with sparse grass and sometimes lowbush blueberry (Forbush 1929, Berger 1968). They frequent areas with exposed soil, where they take frequent dust baths. Nesting territories often are adjacent to woods. Fences, utility wires, rocks, forbs, shrubs, and trees provide singing perches. These birds occupy rather large territories, which ranged from 1.2 to 1.8 a (0.5 to 0.7 ha) in an uncultivated field in Michigan (Evans *in* Berger 1968). In Henniker, 4 singing males, spaced well apart, remained in large cornfields by the Contoocook River during the 1985 breeding season (Janeway, pers. obs.).

The male Vesper Sparrow sings throughout the day. The song consists of 2 long, sweet, whistled notes, 2 higher notes, and a descending trill (Terres 1980; Janeway, pers. obs.), which are quieter and more plain-tive than the notes of the Song Sparrow. The Vesper Sparrow sometimes sings at night, and especially on calm evenings after a rain (Terres 1980). The alarm note is a "chip," as opposed to the Song Sparrow's "chenk" (Forbush 1929). A courting male walks or runs before or after the female with wings raised and spread and tail widely spread (Forbush 1929).

The female builds her loosely structured nest of dry grass and rootlets (Forbush 1929, Harrison 1978) on the ground near bare patches of soil, in low vegetation, or beside a tussock of grass, a large plant, or even a clump of earth (Berger 1968). Occasionally a nest is sunk into a small depression (Forbush 1929). There are 2 or 3 broods each year, and the male may feed the first brood while his mate begins her second nest (Berger 1968). White (1937) noted a nest with eggs on 5 July and fledged young from another nest on 30 July in the vicinity of Concord.

The female incubates her clutch of 3 to 5 eggs for 12 or 13 days, with occasional help from the male. The parents eat the empty egg shells after the young have hatched. Young remain in the nest for 7 to 14 days, and both adults tend them (Berger 1968). The Vesper Sparrow often feigns injury if an intruder approaches the nest too closely. Observers have documented broken-wing acts in Andover on 28 May 1967 (K. C. Elkins, pers. comm.) and in Warner on 3 July 1985 (R. C. Vernon, pers. comm.). The young hide quietly after leaving the nest and are extremely difficult to find unless they are being fed (Berger 1968). Parent birds continue to feed fledglings for 30 to 35 days (Berger 1968).

During September Vesper Sparrows gather in small flocks in fields before migrating. Wright (1911) observed a group of 35 in Jefferson on 26 September 1908. They are relatively late migrants, sometimes lingering into mid-November (Berger 1968), although most depart during October.

Early ornithologists considered Vesper Sparrows common in New Hampshire (Dearborn 1898, 1903, Allen 1903, Forbush 1929, Thayer *in* Allison and Allison 1979). This species was reportedly more common than any other sparrow when farming was at its peak (Goodhue 1877). The decline of agriculture and subsequent reforestation have significantly reduced available habitat.

The Vesper Sparrow appears to have left the relatively few remaining dry upland areas in New Hampshire, and today nests only locally on farmland along rivers and at airports. Its population has been declining here since before the 1960s (K. C. Elkins, pers. comm.). BBS data from 1966 to 1979 indicate that the Vesper Sparrow is decreasing throughout much of its range, and document a statistically significant decrease in New Hampshire (Robbins et al. 1986). Atlas data document this sparrow's now scattered distribution and uncommon occurrence in the state, with records for only 19 priority and 15 nonpriority blocks.

The practice of cutting hayfields more frequently than in the past may affect nesting success in some areas (Robbins et al. 1986). Pesticide use on cornfields and other agricultural lands where it nests also may affect this species. Whatever the cause, the Vesper Sparrow has disappeared from many areas, even those that still appear to offer suitable habitat. It is considered a Special Concern Species in New Hampshire.

Elizabeth C. Janeway

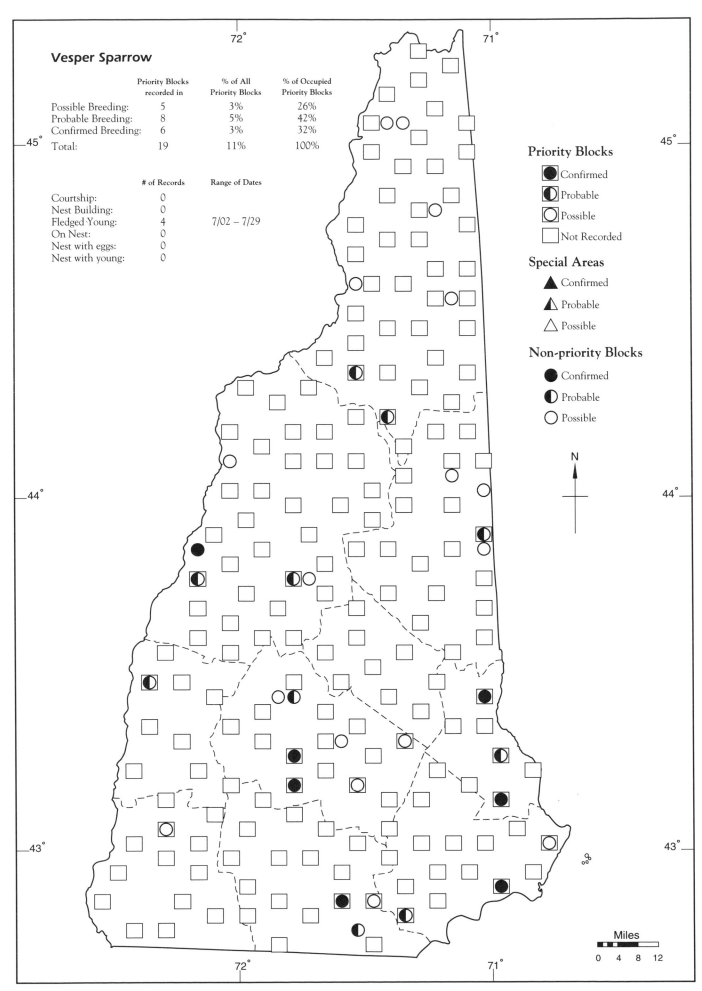

Vesper Sparrow

	Priority Blocks recorded in	% of All Priority Blocks	% of Occupied Priority Blocks
Possible Breeding:	5	3%	26%
Probable Breeding:	8	5%	42%
Confirmed Breeding:	6	3%	32%
Total:	19	11%	100%

	# of Records	Range of Dates
Courtship:	0	
Nest Building:	0	
Fledged·Young:	4	7/02 – 7/29
On Nest:	0	
Nest with eggs:	0	
Nest with young:	0	

Priority Blocks
- ◐ Confirmed
- ◑ Probable
- ○ Possible
- □ Not Recorded

Special Areas
- ▲ Confirmed
- ◮ Probable
- △ Possible

Non-priority Blocks
- ● Confirmed
- ◖ Probable
- ○ Possible

N

Miles
0 4 8 12

Savannah Sparrow
Passerculus sandwichensis

The furtive, ground-inhabiting Savannah Sparrow nests both in New Hampshire and in the high Arctic, ranging over most of North America from the Arctic Circle to Guatemala. Requiring low but dense cover, it breeds in a wide variety of habitats where grasses, sedges, or other short vegetation provide the primary ground cover. Its haunts include sand dunes and salt marshes, meadows, hayfields, and alpine tundra. In July 1878, Allen (1903) discovered a male Savannah Sparrow singing on top of Mt. Washington, at an elevation of 6,288 ft (1,905 m)! This sparrow may be more common than supposed, as it is easily overlooked. In New Hampshire, the Savannah Sparrow has declined as fields have returned to forests, but is still fairly common in suitable habitat at elevations up to 2,500 ft (760 m) (T. Richards, unpubl. data).

Foraging on the ground, this sparrow eats many grass and weed seeds and a wide variety of insects (Baird 1968). The Savannah Sparrow hops while feeding and may scratch on the ground like a towhee (Baird 1968). When disturbed, it usually scurries through the grass before taking off in a brief and erratic flight (Terres 1980). This sparrow's most diagnostic feature is a yellowish line over the eye. The lack of white outer tail feathers separates it from the Vesper Sparrow. The Song Sparrow lacks yellow on its grayer head and has a longer, rounded tail.

Savannah Sparrows generally return to New Hampshire in early to mid-April (Dearborn 1898, White 1924, Ridgely 1977), but individuals may arrive in the latter half of March (Phinney *in* Hebert 1967, Kidder *in* Abbott 1976). Males arrive first (Forbush 1929) and sing persistently as they establish territories (Welsh 1975). They often use low trees and shrubs to define the boundaries of their relatively small territories, which usually decrease in size as the nesting season progresses (Welsh 1975).

The male Savannah Sparrow sings his quiet, unmusical song from exposed perches (Weins 1969) or from the ground. He sings into July, but rarely on migration (Hoffman 1904 *in* Baird 1968). The song is insectlike and distinctly buzzy. A common song pattern in New Hampshire begins with "tip-tip-tip," followed by 2 trills, a rising "seeee" and a falling "saaaay" (Janeway, pers. obs.). In courtship, which occurs in New Hampshire from mid-May to late June, the male sings and vibrates his wings on or just above the ground. Both sexes engage in a mouselike "creeping action" (Baird 1968, Townsend 1920 *in* Baird 1968).

The female builds her nest on the ground in dense cover, usually in a slight hollow under overhanging vegetation. The cup of coarse grasses is lined with rootlets and hair (Harrison 1975, Harrison 1978). Her work takes 4 or 5 days to complete (Welsh 1975). The female alone incubates the 3 to 6 eggs, but both male and female feed the young (Harrison 1975, Welsh 1975, Harrison 1978). The male often sits on the ground near the nest (Welsh 1975). White (1937) observed one nest in Concord which hatched on 1 June 1937, and another which contained recently hatched young on 10 June 1934. Young remain in the nest for 9 to 14 days (Baird 1968, Welsh 1975). A nest at Penacook (Concord) contained young on 15 June 1985 (NHBBA data).

A Savannah Sparrow sometimes feigns injury when it is disturbed near the nest, or may threaten an intruder with open bill and raised wings (Baird 1968). If predation is high, a pair may be able to raise only one brood in a season after replacing destroyed nests (Dixon 1978). Otherwise, a female may raise a second brood, laying the new eggs within 2 weeks after the fledging of her first family. Fledglings may attempt flight as early as 3 days after leaving the nest (Welsh 1975). Observers have noted fledglings as late as 29 July in Hillsboro (NHBBA data).

After dispersing from nesting areas, groups of Savannah Sparrows, presumably families, forage in fields, running well hidden on the ground, but becoming less shy and more visible in August and September (Forbush 1929). This is not, however, a flocking species (Terres 1980), and Savannah Sparrows depart south in small groups during October (Dearborn 1898). Some winter regularly along the New Hampshire coast (CBC data).

The Savannah Sparrow was a common summer resident in New Hampshire during the late 1800s and early 1900s (Dearborn 1898, Allen 1903, Wright 1911, White 1924). Dearborn (1903) reported it in marshes along the Piscataqua River and on Coastal sand dunes during the breeding season.

The Atlas map shows a very local distribution for the Savannah Sparrow in New Hampshire. Records are somewhat concentrated in Coos, Merrimack, and Strafford counties, where extensive farmlands remain, and are more sparsely distributed elsewhere in the state.

BBS data indicate that this species is much more common in the northern part of its range and suggest a stable population in North America during 1966 to 1979 (Robbins et al. 1986). This species is still locally common in New Hampshire, but has become less widely distributed as open land has grown over with shrubs and trees or been developed. This trend is likely to continue in the foreseeable future.

Elizabeth C. Janeway

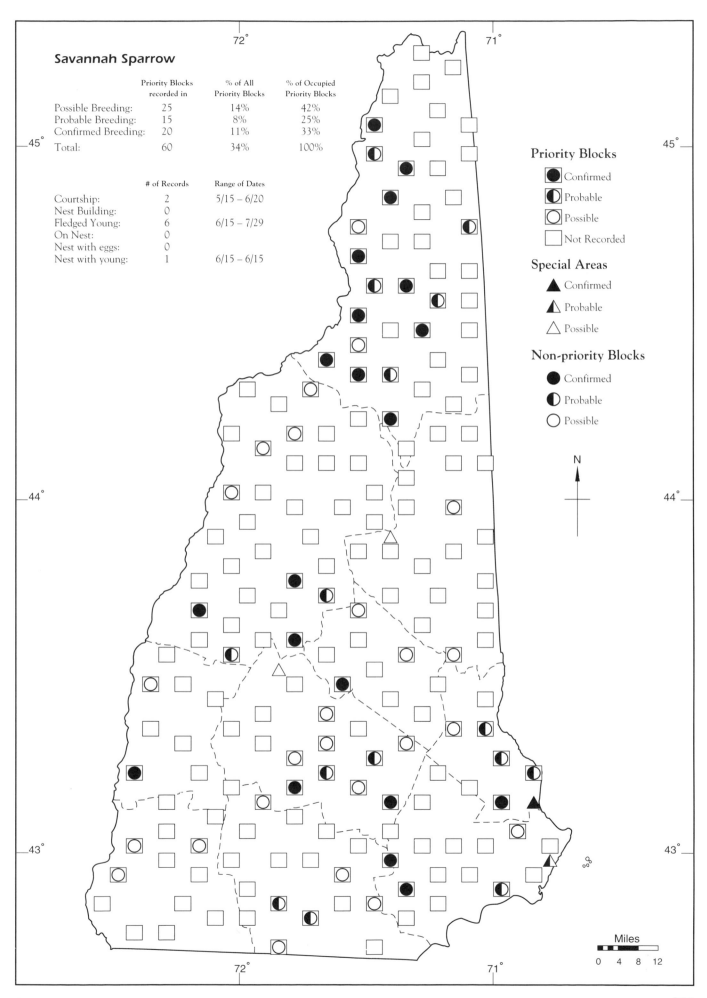

Savannah Sparrow

	Priority Blocks recorded in	% of All Priority Blocks	% of Occupied Priority Blocks
Possible Breeding:	25	14%	42%
Probable Breeding:	15	8%	25%
Confirmed Breeding:	20	11%	33%
Total:	60	34%	100%

	# of Records	Range of Dates
Courtship:	2	5/15 – 6/20
Nest Building:	0	
Fledged Young:	6	6/15 – 7/29
On Nest:	0	
Nest with eggs:	0	
Nest with young:	1	6/15 – 6/15

Priority Blocks
- ● Confirmed
- ◐ Probable
- ○ Possible
- □ Not Recorded

Special Areas
- ▲ Confirmed
- ◭ Probable
- △ Possible

Non-priority Blocks
- ● Confirmed
- ◐ Probable
- ○ Possible

N

Miles
0   4   8   12

Grasshopper Sparrow
Ammodramus savannarum

This furtive inhabitant of dry, weedy fields is well named, for it has a weak, buzzy insectlike song. It moves under a grassy canopy like a mouse and flushes reluctantly, fluttering for only a short distance before dropping back into the grass. Its staple diet consists of insects.

The small, short-tailed, flat-headed Grasshopper Sparrow differs from other grassland sparrows by having an unstriped buffy breast (Peterson 1980). A yellow spot at the bend of the wing, visible at close range, inspired the local name "yellow-winged sparrow" used around the turn of the century (Dearborn 1898). The juvenile is less buffy, with a streaked breast.

The Grasshopper Sparrow reaches the northern edge of its breeding range in central New Hampshire and southern Maine (Peterson 1980). This species has experienced a chronic noncyclic decline throughout much of its former range, as evidenced by BBS data from 1966 to 1979 (Robbins et al. 1986) and its inclusion on the *American Birds* Blue List (Tate 1981). It is considered a Species of Concern in New Hampshire.

Grasshopper Sparrows probably return to New Hampshire from wintering areas in the southern states between mid-April and mid-May and depart by mid-October (Hoffman 1904, Scott 1921), but records are scarce. They prefer low, weedy fields but also occupy fallow croplands and tall grassy meadows where Savannah Sparrows, Bobolinks, and meadowlarks occur. As abandoned farmlands revert to tall shrubs, Grasshopper Sparrows disappear.

The male utters his buzzy song from milkweed stalks or other tall stems. He sometimes uses a rock, fence wire, or shrub as a song perch, but the site is almost always near the ground, and his ventriloquial song makes the singing bird difficult to locate. Occasionally, particularly at twilight, the male may pour forth a more ecstatic song of buzzy trills (Blaisdell 1934). The female has a weaker song (Smith 1959).

Several pairs of Grasshopper Sparrows may nest close together in suitable habitat (Pearson 1936). The well-hidden nest usually is built in a depression on the ground and consists of dried grasses, often arched over to improve concealment (Pough 1946). The female builds the nest, and both sexes share incubation (Smith 1968). Adults approach and leave the nest by a runway under the grass (Pearson 1936). The 4 or 5 eggs hatch in 11 or 12 days, and young may leave the nest before they are able to fly (Harrison 1978). The species commonly raises 2 broods (Smith 1968). Mowing operations may disrupt initial nesting attempts before young fledge, but the season is amply long to permit renesting.

Blaisdell (1934) provides what may be the first New Hampshire nesting record for this species. He initially heard a bird on a high grassy drumlin north of Goffstown on 15 June 1933. On 16 July, with mowing machines already in the field, he observed the pair carrying food, but they refused to approach the nest until he had hidden nearby. He eventually found the nest, with 5 young, at the base of a Queen Anne's lace. Rain delayed the mowing, and on 30 July he saw the adults feeding a fledgling.

On 5 July 1986, Andrews located a pair of Grasshopper Sparrows carrying insect larvae in a weedy abandoned hayfield destined to become part of the Derry Industrial Park in Derry, where a singing male or pair had been observed in each of the previous 2 years. Eventually, an adult dropped into the grass and emerged without food. A search of the area located an empty nest, and a recently fledged young flushed a few feet away. This was the only nesting "confirmed" during the Atlas project.

The Grasshopper Sparrow always has been considered a rare and local summer resident in New Hampshire (Dearborn 1898, Allen 1903, Dearborn 1903, Forbush 1929, White 1924, 1937, Richards 1958, Goodhue 1877 *in* Elkins 1961). Bagg and Eliot (1937) noted that it was locally abundant in the central valley of the Connecticut River at least as far north as Walpole, and it occurred in Hanover during the early 1940s (RNEB, *passim*). Two "small, loose colonies" nested in fields along Parade Road, Meredith, in 1953 (Ridgely 1977). The northernmost records are from Lincoln and Jefferson (RNEB, *passim*).

The low, weedy grasslands which once surrounded New Hampshire's airports provided excellent habitat for this species. In 1968, observers reported a total of 46 Grasshopper Sparrows at 7 sites in New Hampshire, including 25 at Grenier Airport, Manchester, and 12 at Boire Airport, Nashua. In recent years, development has eliminated most suitable habitat at these sites, and the birds have disappeared from both locations. At least 3 pairs were present in late May and June 1982 at the Kessler Farm in Nashua. However, development began the following year, and buildings now fill the site.

The Atlas map reflects the current scarcity of the Grasshopper Sparrow in New Hamsphire, with records for only 2 priority blocks, 6 nonpriority blocks, and one Special Area. The Massachusetts BBA (unpubl.) reported Grasshopper Sparrows from 42 blocks, primarily on Cape Cod and the islands, but also in the Connecticut and Merrimack river valleys. The Vermont Atlas cites only 10 records, primarily from the Connecticut River valley and the Champlain Lowlands (Ellison *in* Laughlin and Kibbe 1985), and the Maine Atlas produced a single record (Adamus 1988). Future prospects for this species in northern New England appear dim.

Ralph Andrews

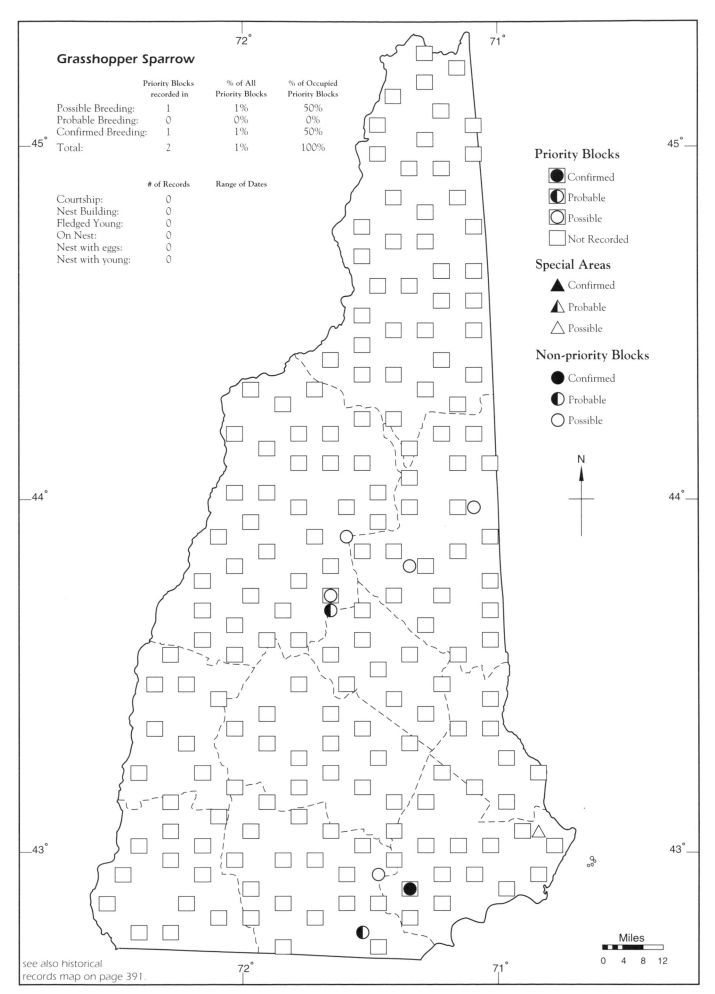

Grasshopper Sparrow

	Priority Blocks recorded in	% of All Priority Blocks	% of Occupied Priority Blocks
Possible Breeding:	1	1%	50%
Probable Breeding:	0	0%	0%
Confirmed Breeding:	1	1%	50%
Total:	2	1%	100%

	# of Records	Range of Dates
Courtship:	0	
Nest Building:	0	
Fledged Young:	0	
On Nest:	0	
Nest with eggs:	0	
Nest with young:	0	

Priority Blocks

● Confirmed
◑ Probable
○ Possible
□ Not Recorded

Special Areas

▲ Confirmed
◤ Probable
△ Possible

Non-priority Blocks

● Confirmed
◑ Probable
○ Possible

N

see also historical
records map on page 391.

Miles
0   4   8   12

Sharp-tailed Sparrow
Ammodramus caudacutus

Sharp-tailed Sparrows are secretive but locally common inhabitants of some of our larger coastal salt marshes. These "mouselike" birds are very reluctant to fly and, after a short, choppy flight, quickly drop back into cover. Seaside and Sharp-tailed sparrows are closely related and occasionally hybridize (Hill 1968). The Seaside Sparrow is larger, darker, and grayer than the Sharp-tail, which is distinguished by its yellow-orange face surrounding a gray cheek patch.

Sharp-tails favor the drier, short-grass portions of a salt marsh except where Seaside Sparrows are rare or absent, but both inhabit the taller and wetter *Spartina alterniflora* marsh in late summer (Hill 1968). Although most New Hampshire Sharp-tails favor *S. patens* marsh, a few share *S. alterniflora* with the relatively scarce Seaside Sparrows (Gavutis, pers. obs.).

Most Sharp-tails probably arrive in New Hampshire in late May and early June when cordgrass growth reaches 6 in (15 cm), and depart in September or October following the first frosts. Hill (1968) listed 22 May as the earliest arrival date and 22 October as his latest departure date for "New Hampton, N.H." (presumably North Hampton or Hampton). A few birds linger in Massachusetts until December (CBC data).

The song consists of a series of variable, relatively faint, high-pitched trills, sometimes preceded by almost inaudible chips. Sharp-tailed Sparrows may sing from atop grass clumps, or in flight. They often sing in flight, wings quivering, at heights up to 20 ft (6.1 m) above the ground. Brewster (*in* Hill 1968) reported that the Sharp-tail rarely sings from the same perch twice. Adults in the Hampton marshes gave "chip" alarm calls with food in their bills (Gavutis, pers. obs.)

Male Sharp-tails occupy but do not defend home ranges of about 4 a (1.6 ha) (Hill 1968). Nests are usually well concealed, 2 to 3 in (5 to 7.5 cm) above ground. Located just above the normal high tide line, many Sharp-tailed Sparrow nests are lost to coastal storms.

A typical Sharp-tailed Sparrow clutch in New England is 4 or 5 eggs, which are noticeably smaller and more finely marked than those of the Seaside Sparrow. The female alone builds the nest and incubates for 11 or 12 days (J. S. Greenlaw, pers. comm.). Gavutis found a Sharp-tail nest containing 4 eggs near the Hampton tern colony on 21 June 1987. It was in *S. patens* at the edge of short *S. alterniflora* approximately 6 in (15 cm) above marsh level.

Young are fully feathered and leave the nest in 10 days. The female then feeds them for another 20 days (Hill 1968; J. S. Greenlaw, pers. comm.). Brewster (*in* Hill 1968) reported that Sharp-tails feeding young fly feebly with feet and legs dangling like a rail's. Hill (1968) reported that they are most active in early morning and late afternoon.

Their food is 80 to 90% animal matter, which they glean primarily from *S. patens* adjacent to salt ponds and ditches (Hill 1968), sometimes from *S. alterniflora* along channels (E. Miller, pers. comm.) and from exposed mud. Sharp-tails rarely hop while foraging, but generally run and walk. They frequently stretch their heads and necks above the vegetation to look around (Hill 1968). "Pishing" from a canoe along a creek shore can provide good looks at Sharp-tails (C.R. Foss, pers. comm.). Sharp-tailed Sparrows will flutter up from the grass ahead of an intruder and hover a bit before dropping back into the grass (Gavutis, pers. obs.).

In the northern part of their range, Sharp-tailed Sparrows are quite local, although abundant in spots, and occur in scattered colonies 0.5 to 1 mi (0.8 to 1.6 km) apart (*in* Hill 1968). Farther south, they are abundant and widespread. Unlike the Seaside Sparrow, the Sharp-tailed Sparrow has a long and well-recorded history on New Hampshire's coastal marshes. Brewster collected a specimen in Rye on 20 August 1869 (Allen 1903), and Dwight (1887) states that they nested as far north as Portsmouth. Dearborn (1903) considered this species "abundant at Hampton during the summer and as late as the 14th of October."

As the Atlas map shows, these sparrows continue to occur at several locations along the New Hampshire coast. The Hampton salt marshes are still a stronghold for Sharp-tailed Sparrows, especially north of the causeway to Hampton Beach (Rt. 51) where approximately 500 a (202 ha) of lush and somewhat brackish marsh supported an estimated 200 to 300 nests during the 1985 breeding season (Gavutis, pers. obs.). Sharp-tails also are common in the brackish marshes north of Depot Road, Hampton Falls. A few birds occurred in small colonies in sparser cover near the brackish upland edge of a better drained but more saline marsh north of the causeway to Seabrook Beach (Rt. 286).

A colony on Great Bay in Newmarket included 4 to 6 birds, which probably were nesting in 1985 (S.R. Mirick, pers. comm.). Several relatively small salt or brackish marshes in Rye yielded only Savannah Sparrows in 1985 (J. Berry and Gavutis, pers. obs.).

This species occurs in some intensively ditched salt marshes, but is most common where numerous shallow ponds (pannes) remain and tidal influence is somewhat restricted. Apparently, restricted tidal fluctuations caused by road and railroad crossings and freshwater influence may be providing the most favorable conditions for Sharp-tails in New Hampshire.

George W. Gavutis, Jr.

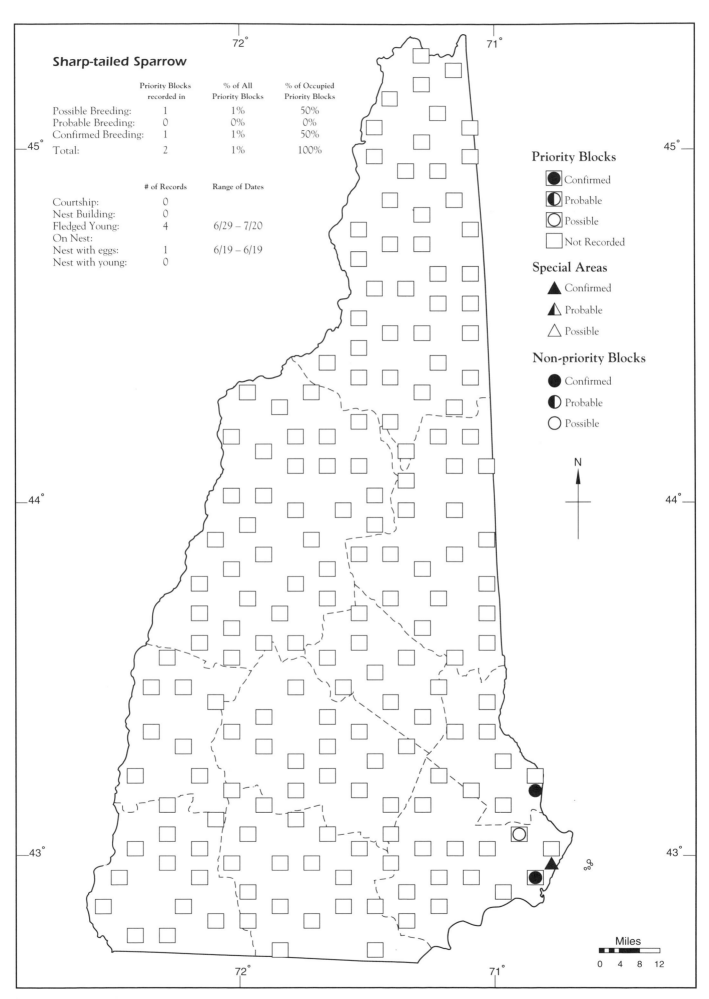

Sharp-tailed Sparrow

	Priority Blocks recorded in	% of All Priority Blocks	% of Occupied Priority Blocks
Possible Breeding:	1	1%	50%
Probable Breeding:	0	0%	0%
Confirmed Breeding:	1	1%	50%
Total:	2	1%	100%

	# of Records	Range of Dates
Courtship:	0	
Nest Building:	0	
Fledged Young:	4	6/29 – 7/20
On Nest:		
Nest with eggs:	1	6/19 – 6/19
Nest with young:	0	

Priority Blocks

- ◐ Confirmed
- ◑ Probable
- ○ Possible
- ☐ Not Recorded

Special Areas

- ▲ Confirmed
- ◣ Probable
- △ Possible

Non-priority Blocks

- ● Confirmed
- ◐ Probable
- ○ Possible

N

Miles
0 4 8 12

Seaside Sparrow
Ammodramus maritimus

The relatively large, gray-brown Seaside Sparrow inhabits the tall cordgrass banks and mud flats of tidal creeks and ditches and is the most maritime of our "land" birds (Woolfenden 1968). Its long bill, dark coloration, habitat preferences, and running habits are reminiscent of rails, and it wades like a sandpiper. This species is noticeably grayer than the browner and more common Sharp-tailed Sparrow which shares its salt-marsh habitat. The Seaside Sparrow is generally more approachable than other "marsh" sparrows, but it, too, can scurry like a mouse through dense grass. Suitable breeding habitat requires the presence of dense clumps of persistent salt-marsh grasses for nesting and relatively open areas for foraging (Greenlaw 1983).

New Hampshire is near the northern edge of this sparrow's range, and sightings in southern Maine are rare. Gavutis discovered a small colony in the Hampton salt marsh on 23 July 1985. This first "confirmed" breeding record in New Hampshire may represent the northernmost breeding record of the species. This sparrow most likely returns to New Hampshire in mid-May and departs again by late September. There are a few winter records only 3.5 mi (5.8 km) south of New Hampshire at Newburyport, Mass.

Seaside Sparrows eat about 80% animal matter in summer (Woolfenden 1968). They are equally adapted to climbing in dense grasses and running rapidly across mud flats, where they forage for small marine animals along the tidal creeks of salt meadows (Bull and Farrand 1977). Merriam (1983) found that Seaside Sparrows in an unaltered salt marsh obtained more food from vegetated areas than those in ditched marshes.

The primary song consists of several short and harsh introductory chips followed by a trill. Males sing most frequently before the females arrive, as they establish their territories (Woolfenden 1968, Post and Greenlaw 1975). During territorial disputes, males engage in bob-bing and wing-raising displays (Post and Greenlaw 1975). They also indulge in song flight, in which a male flutters upward and sings near the top of the ascent. Post and Greenlaw (1975) describe a number of additional vocalizations. The New Hampshire males sang from perches in the tallest cordgrass during July (Gavutis, pers. obs.).

Woolfenden's (1968) observations suggest that Seaside Sparrows nest in lower, wetter parts of the marsh than Sharp-tailed Sparrows, just above the summer high tide line in black rush or *Spartina alterniflora*. In the Hampton marshes, however, the 2 species occurred side by side in a very wet, poorly drained area of salt marsh with extensive stands of lush, tall *S. alterniflora*, along a series of old, partially blocked tidal ditches and creeks. There were extensive areas of mud flats and trapped water along the creek, much hummocky decomposing marsh, large shallow salt ponds (pannes), and extensive windrows of dead cordgrass in the area. Woolfenden (1968) indicated that densities of up to one pair/acre (0.4 ha) sometimes occurred in New Jersey. The New Hampshire colony of 6 to 8 pairs may approach this density (Gavutis, pers. obs.).

The female lays 4 or 5 eggs in June or July, and does all the incubating. The male's alarm note brings her off the nest, and they both "chip" at an intruder. When she leaves to feed, he sometimes goes too, and they may return together. Young leave their nest by the tenth day but don't fly for several more days. Gavutis (ASRF) observed adults feeding a light golden brown fledgling which had flown out of tall *S. alterniflora* onto a mat of thatch on a mud flat. Only one brood is likely this far north (Woolfenden 1968).

The history of this species on the New Hampshire coast is not entirely clear. Forbush (1929) considered it to be probably accidental in New Hampshire and only a rare coastal visitor in adjacent Essex County, Mass. Woolfenden (1968) listed the species as breeding only as far north as Plum Island in Newbury and Newburyport, Essex County, Mass. Scott (1921), however, described the Seaside Sparrow as only slightly less common in New Hampshire than the Sharp-tailed Sparrow, and Coues (1868) claimed to have found it abundant here. The only recent pre-Atlas record for the species is from Hampton on 20 July 1968 (RNEB, *passim*).

Atlas coverage for this species may have been inadequate, and further survey effort would be very worthwhile. E. W. Phinney (pers. comm.) reported a single territorial male on a tidal creek 980 ft (300 m) west of Rye Harbor, Rye, during the summer of 1984 or 1985, which suggests the possibility of additional occupied sites.

Woolfenden (1968) cites salt-marsh drainage and development as serious threats to this species. Post and Greenlaw (1975) found that density of breeding pairs in unaltered salt marshes was significantly higher 61.3/a 24.8/2.5 a (1 ha) than in ditched salt marshes 1.0/2.5 a (1 ha). Merriam (1983) documented a greater total value of food brought to nestlings in unaltered salt marshes than to those in ditched marshes.

The small Hampton colony occupies an uncommon habitat type in New Hampshire which is highly susceptible to alteration. Even natural factors such as severe weather or tidal flushing of clogged channels could alter the small colony's habitat. Efforts to prevent adverse human impacts on this unique area should be undertaken immediately. Other marshes on the New Hampshire coast need to be carefully searched for this species and apparently suitable habitats protected.

George W. Gavutis, Jr.

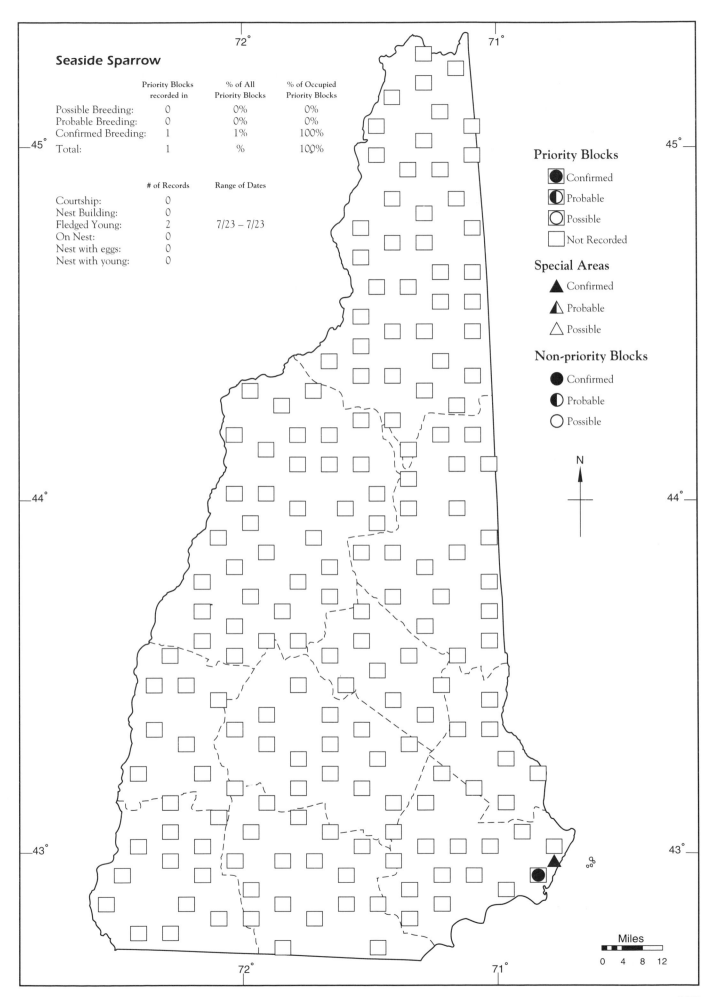

Seaside Sparrow

	Priority Blocks recorded in	% of All Priority Blocks	% of Occupied Priority Blocks
Possible Breeding:	0	0%	0%
Probable Breeding:	0	0%	0%
Confirmed Breeding:	1	1%	100%
Total:	1	%	100%

	# of Records	Range of Dates
Courtship:	0	
Nest Building:	0	
Fledged Young:	2	7/23 – 7/23
On Nest:	0	
Nest with eggs:	0	
Nest with young:	0	

Priority Blocks

- ● Confirmed
- ◖ Probable
- ○ Possible
- □ Not Recorded

Special Areas

- ▲ Confirmed
- ◣ Probable
- △ Possible

Non-priority Blocks

- ● Confirmed
- ◖ Probable
- ○ Possible

N

Miles
0 4 8 12

Song Sparrow
Melospiza melodia

This abundant sparrow's Latin name appropriately translates as "song finch with melodious song." It is best recognized by its heavily streaked white breast with a large dark spot in the center. Some Song Sparrows overwinter in southern New Hampshire, where spring migrants begin to appear in mid-March; further north, most migrants arrive during April (Elkins 1982). Most fall migrants depart during October, but stragglers remain through December.

Song Sparrows occupy a variety of habitats from moist thickets and wet, brushy areas to the shrubbery of residential neighborhoods. They occur throughout the state in back yards and gardens, along fence rows and lake and stream edges, and in marshes, swamps, and woods margins, nesting to elevations of 2,500 ft (760 m) (Dearborn 1903, Nolan 1968, Ridgely 1977).

This sparrow sings during much of its time in New Hampshire, occasionally into early fall. Upon first arrival, the male sings throughout the daylight hours from elevated perches in suitable breeding habitat (Samuels 1870, Forbush 1929). The song is a complex and highly variable series of notes and trills on different pitches, which Thoreau (1856 in Allen 1910) paraphrased as "maids! maids! maids! hang up your tea-kettle-ettle-ettle."

Atlas data indicate that breeding activities in the southern half of the state occur one to 2 weeks earlier than in the northern half, and suggest that the southwestern highlands lag behind the southeastern lowlands by approximately a week. The male establishes the territory, usually less than an acre in size, primarily by singing and by fighting with and chasing away intruding males (Nice 1937, Nolan 1968). During territorial conflicts, a male also may raise and lower one or both wings, fluff his feathers, and utter a muted warble (Nice 1943).

Once the female arrives, about 10 days after the male, he sings less frequently until they have begun nest building (White 1924, Nice 1943). During pairing and courtship a male frequently "pounces," darting down at a female, colliding, and flying away with a loud song (Townsend 1920, Nice 1943). During courtship, both male and female pick up and carry loose debris such as grasses and leaves before the female actually begins nest construction (Nice 1943). She builds the nest of grasses and weeds in 5 to 10 days (Nice 1943, Nolan 1968). In the Midwest, Nice (1937) found 90% of first nests on the ground, but only 66% of second and 33% of third nests at ground level. Nests are seldom higher than 12 ft (3.7 m) above the ground, and many above-ground nests are at heights of 2 to 4 ft (0.6 to 1.2 m) (Nolan 1968, Terres 1980).

The female incubates her 3 to 6 eggs for 10 to 14 days (Forbush 1929, Nolan 1968), leaving the nest for short periods every 20 to 30 minutes (Nice 1937). Song Sparrows raise 2 and sometimes 3 broods in a season (Harrison 1975), providing extended opportunity for confirming breeding. White (1937) reports eggs as early as 15 May and adults feeding fledglings as late as 5 August in Concord. Brown-headed Cowbirds frequently parasitize this species, reducing nesting success. Harrison (1975) reported as many as 7 cowbird eggs in one Song Sparrow nest.

The Song Sparrow utters a "tchenk" alarm note when disturbed near the nest (Forbush 1929). When alarmed, this sparrow usually skulks about in the underbrush (Nolan 1968). If an intruder approaches the nest too closely, the female may perform a distraction display, running about near the intruder with wings held stiffly erect and tail depressed (Nice 1943).

The young leave the nest about 10 days after hatching, but are not yet able to fly. They receive care from their parents for another 18 to 20 days (Nice 1937). Fledglings resemble the adults, but are more finely streaked.

Song Sparrows usually forage on or near the ground. During the nesting season, 34 to 50% of their diet consists of insects (Judd 1901 in Nolan 1968). Plant food includes berries and seeds, especially those of ragweeds, smartweeds, and grasses (Martin et al. 1961).

One can only speculate about the distribution of the Song Sparrow in New Hampshire before settlement by Europeans. It seems likely that the species was a summer resident in limited numbers at the edges of marshes and burns, around beaver flowages, and at other openings in the forest. It was here in 1792, if Allen is correct in assigning Belknap's "Spring bird, *Fringilla*" to this species. It has been very common in the state since at least the mid-1800s (Samuels 1867, Dearborn 1898, Allen 1903, Dearborn 1903, Wright 1911), and is still one of our most common birds.

Today, Song Sparrows occur throughout the state. Atlas records are lacking from only 5 priority blocks, all of which were predominantly 2,000 ft (610 m) or more in elevation. BBS data from 1966 to 1979 suggest a significant decline in Song Sparrow numbers in the Eastern region, attributed to severe winters in 1976–77 and 1977–78 (Robbins et al. 1986). Despite such periodic setbacks, this species likely will continue to be an abundant breeder in our state.

James McDermott

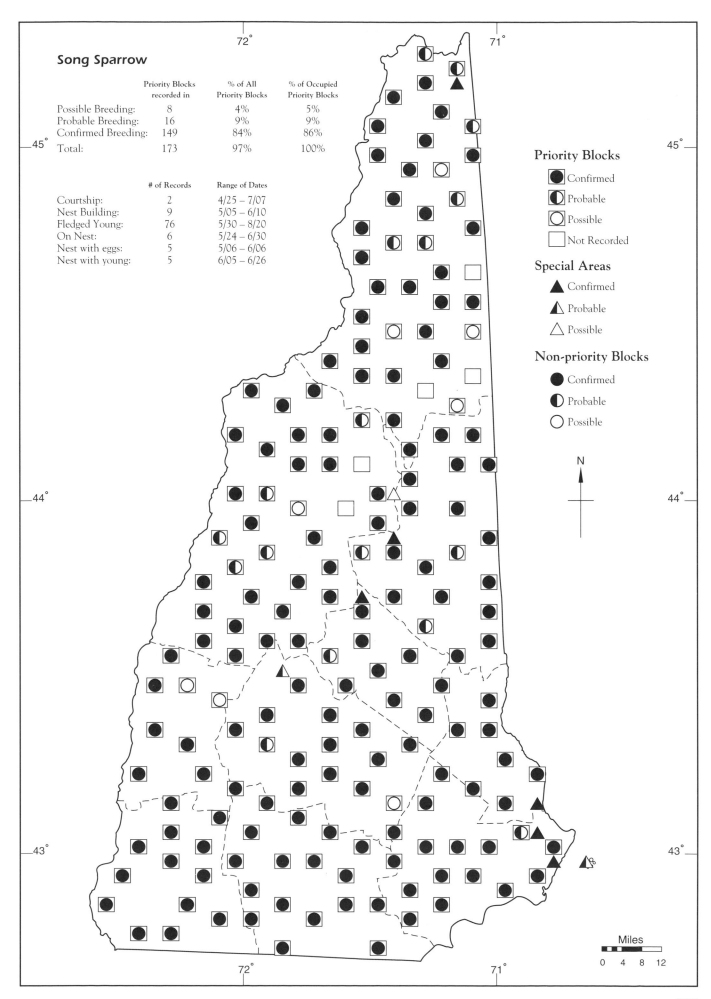

Song Sparrow

	Priority Blocks recorded in	% of All Priority Blocks	% of Occupied Priority Blocks
Possible Breeding:	8	4%	5%
Probable Breeding:	16	9%	9%
Confirmed Breeding:	149	84%	86%
Total:	173	97%	100%

	# of Records	Range of Dates
Courtship:	2	4/25 – 7/07
Nest Building:	9	5/05 – 6/10
Fledged Young:	76	5/30 – 8/20
On Nest:	6	5/24 – 6/30
Nest with eggs:	5	5/06 – 6/06
Nest with young:	5	6/05 – 6/26

Priority Blocks
- Confirmed
- Probable
- Possible
- Not Recorded

Special Areas
- Confirmed
- Probable
- Possible

Non-priority Blocks
- Confirmed
- Probable
- Possible

Miles
0 4 8 12

Lincoln's Sparrow
Melospiza lincolnii

This musical bird is a local summer resident in northern New Hampshire. Its favorite breeding haunts include semiopen tamarack and black spruce bogs, wet shrubby pastures, and cutover spruce-fir flats with scattered shrubs and small saplings (Richards, pers. obs.). The Lincoln's Sparrow somewhat resembles the slightly larger, more heavily striped Song Sparrow but has a finely streaked, buffy band across its upper breast. It is a shy species that flushes easily and flies away rapidly close to the ground (Richards, pers. obs.).

Audubon (*in* Speirs and Speirs 1968) provides an excellent account of a bird in Labrador (in 1832) which he recognized as new to science. He named it the Lincoln's Sparrow after his companion, Thomas Lincoln, who collected it. In summer, 2 subspecies of the Lincoln's Sparrow are confined to the mountains of the western U.S. The third subspecies, *M. lincolnii lincolnii*, breeds from Alaska to Labrador, south to Washington and northern New England. This subspecies winters from the southern U.S. south to El Salvador and Honduras (AOU 1957).

The Lincoln's Sparrow migrates inconspicuously through southern New Hampshire beginning in early May. The earliest Atlas dates for northern New Hampshire are 16, 23, and 25 May. Speirs and Speirs (1968) observed courtship from late May to early June and again in early July, even if there were young in the nest, suggesting that a second brood might follow. The female crouches, flutters, and utters a high-pitched note to attract the male, which then pounces on and copulates with her, often singing immediately afterwards (Speirs and Speirs 1968).

The usual song is a fine, musical trill that goes up the scale and then down a little. Song apparently is this species' only important territorial behavior (Speirs and Speirs 1968). Males may sing in flight or from the ground, but most often use a branch of a small tree as a song perch (Speirs and Speirs 1968). They sing most frequently before incubation and again after the young fledge (Speirs and Speirs 1968). Both sexes utter a scolding "tit" or "tic" note which they often repeat as a chatter when young are nearby.

Lincoln's Sparrows require low shrubs 4 to 8 ft (1.2 to 2.4 m) high with grass and sedge tussock openings, and tend to nest near wet areas. Nests are on the ground, in wet places usually on mounds, and are well hidden in vegetation (Speirs and Speirs 1968, Harrison 1975). They are cup-shaped, made of plant stems and dead leaves, and lined with fine grasses and a little hair (Harrison 1975). A well-concealed nest found in Pittsburg on 20 June 1959 was on the ground and built of fine sedges (Walkinshaw 1959). Clutch size varies from 3 to 6 eggs, but is usually 4 or 5, and the female incubates for 13 or 14 days (Harrison 1978). She sits very tight when an intruder approaches (Speirs and Speirs 1968). Both parents feed the nestlings, primarily with insects. Young leave the nest in 9 to 12 days (Speirs and Speirs 1968, Harrison 1978). Fledged young and postbreeding adults consume increasing amounts of seeds (Judd *in* Speirs and Speirs 1968).

Palmer (1949) describes Lincoln's Sparrows wandering outside of Maine nesting areas in late August. Southward movement begins by mid-September, with migration mainly from 24 September to 13 October. At Umbagog Lake, Brewster recorded migrants from 11 September to 16 October (Griscom 1938).

The Lincoln's Sparrow is a northern species which was unknown as a summer resident of New Hampshire in the last century, and has extended its range southward in recent decades. Allen (1903) termed it a migrant, but suggested that it might breed in northern New Hampshire, as it was well known to breed in the Adirondacks. Brewster, however, despite all his summer field work around Umbagog Lake in the period 1871–1909 and his special interest in the species, encountered the Lincoln's Sparrow there only in migration periods (Griscom 1938).

New Hampshire's first definite breeding season record of a Lincoln's Sparrow seems to be one flushed into Pittsburg from Chartierville, Quebec, on 5 July 1947 (Richards, unpubl. data). (Thayer's [1902 *in* Allison and Allison 1979] record from southwestern New Hampshire on 28 July 1900 is highly questionable.) Records followed in the next 8 years from 4 other Pittsburg locations, as well as Stratford, Cambridge, Columbia, Errol, and Albany (Richards, unpubl. data). The species was well established in northern New Hampshire by 1956, when Hebert recorded 24 Lincoln's Sparrows in Pittsburg, and McDade added a record for Lincoln (Hebert 1956). BBS data indicate a significant population increase in the Eastern region during 1966–79 (Robbins et al. 1986).

Atlas data suggest that the Lincoln's Sparrow is an uncommon to fairly common summer resident of New Hampshire's North Country but rare in and around the White Mountains. Church Pond Bog, Livermore, where the Lincoln's Sparrow has been a summer resident at least since 1955, is still its southernmost known nesting area in the state. There is only one other "confirmed" Atlas record south of Berlin and Lancaster. Further north, however, "confirmed" and "probable" breeding records are fairly well distributed. Distraction displays provided 7 out of 15 "confirmed" Atlas records, and observers found one nest with eggs. Vermont's 15 breeding "confirmations" included no nests (Nichols *in* Laughlin and Kibbe 1985).

This shy and little-known species is almost certainly more common than records indicate. A minor increase may have occurred in recent decades and seems likely for the future as long as logging and farm abandonment continue to create potential nesting habitat.

Tudor Richards

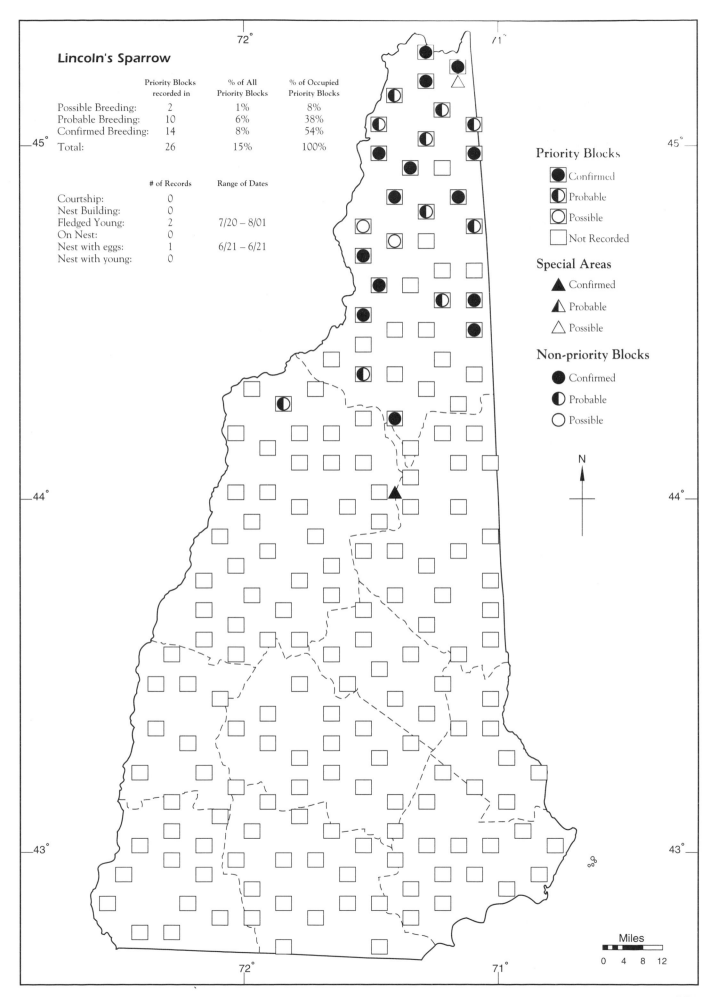

Lincoln's Sparrow

	Priority Blocks recorded in	% of All Priority Blocks	% of Occupied Priority Blocks
Possible Breeding:	2	1%	8%
Probable Breeding:	10	6%	38%
Confirmed Breeding:	14	8%	54%
Total:	26	15%	100%

	# of Records	Range of Dates
Courtship:	0	
Nest Building:	0	
Fledged Young:	2	7/20 – 8/01
On Nest:	0	
Nest with eggs:	1	6/21 – 6/21
Nest with young:	0	

Priority Blocks
- ● Confirmed
- ◐ Probable
- ○ Possible
- □ Not Recorded

Special Areas
- ▲ Confirmed
- ◤ Probable
- △ Possible

Non-priority Blocks
- ● Confirmed
- ◖ Probable
- ○ Possible

N

Miles
0 4 8 12

Swamp Sparrow

Melospiza georgiana

The Swamp Sparrow is a common and widespread but reclusive species in New Hampshire's freshwater swamps and marshes. It is usually distinguishable by its bright rusty cap, outlined white throat, and extensive chestnut edging on the wing feathers. Shy and retiring, the Swamp Sparrow is most easily observed when it is singing from an exposed perch.

Swamp Sparrows typically arrive in New Hampshire during April. Dearborn (1903) noted that they usually appeared about a week after Song Sparrows in the Durham area, and White (1937) stated that they usually reached Concord from 20 April on. Atlasers recorded singing males in mid-April at several locations. The song is a variable trill which resembles that of a Chipping Sparrow, but is generally louder, slower, and richer in tone. It sings particularly in early morning and evening and often well into the night until August.

Although little is known of courtship, White (1937) describes a flight song consisting of a prolonged trill with varying tone, delivered while moving slowly, but with rapidly beating wings, over a level flight path for up to about 25 yds (23 m). There is no evidence that males assist with nest building. The nest is usually over water (Reinert and Golet 1979) and often is placed between cattail stalks or in the tops of sedge clumps about 1 ft (0.3 m) above 6 to 24 in (15 to 60 cm) of water (Sutton *in* Wetherbee 1968). Along the Quahog River in central Massachusetts, however, the Swamp Sparrow consistently nests higher above the water in bushes, usually at heights reachable by standing in a boat (Wetherbee 1968). Occasional summer floods in local wetlands may cause failure of low nests and encourage such locally higher nest sites. The nest is a coarse but tightly woven outer cup surrounding a soft, grassy inner chamber. Some nests are domed with a side entrance, and some have an extension constructed of grass stems which protrudes about 3 in (8 cm) from one side (Hess 1910 *in* Wetherbee 1968).

The female usually lays 4 or 5 eggs, which are nearly identical to those of the Song Sparrow. White (1937) observed 2 nests containing 5 eggs in tussocks near Bela Brook in Concord in 1932. One set was about to hatch on 5 June, while incubation of the other was barely underway on 12 June. During early incubation, the female skulks away from the nest when disturbed by an intruder. Later in incubation, she usually sits tight, scolds when flushed, and is noisy when returning to the nest.

The female incubates for 12 or 13 days, and the male feeds her on the nest. The young leave the nest 7 to 11 days after hatching (Sutton 1935 *in* Wetherbee 1968). Forbush (1929) noted that nests often are so close to the water as to hamper the first flying attempts of the young. Struggling to fly, they sometimes fall into the water and become prey to large frogs, fish, or turtles.

Like Song Sparrows, Swamp Sparrows repeatedly pump their tails in flight. Their flights are relatively short, and they gain little altitude before plunging back into dense cover. They forage primarily on the ground and from the surface film while wading in shallow water. They are almost totally insectivorous in spring and early summer, but eat mostly seeds in the fall (Wetherbee 1968).

During fall migration in late September through October, Swamp Sparrows occur with other sparrows, often in grassy fields and hedgerows. White (1937) observed that Swamp Sparrows tend to be quieter than their compatriots at this time and to fly closer to the ground when flushed. Some Swamp Sparrows at least attempt to overwinter in New Hampshire (SRS, CBC data), and one did so successfully at a feeder in Kensington in 1986–87 and again in 1988–89 (Gavutis, pers. obs.).

Historically Swamp Sparrows were locally common nesting birds in southern New Hampshire (Dearborn 1898, Allen 1903, Dearborn 1903, Brewster 1924, White 1937, Thayer 1909 *in* Allison and Allison 1979). They were "plentiful in low, wet localities" in Belknap and Merrimack counties (Dearborn 1898) and "very common" in suitable habitat around Concord (White 1937). However, they were rare to uncommon in the northern Lakes Region (Faxon and Allen 1888, Allen 1889), and rare in the mountains (Allen 1903).

As the Atlas map indicates, Swamp Sparrows now occur throughout New Hampshire, apparently representing an increase from earlier times. Their thinner distribution in the northern and western parts of the state may result from less intensive field work in these areas, as well as a sparser distribution of wetlands. Although more common at lower elevations, these sparrows occur at elevations up to 2,500 ft (760 m) in the White Mountains (T. Richards, unpubl. data). Numbers of this species on New Hampshire BBS routes are among the highest recorded across the continent (Robbins et al. 1986).

As our state's human population continues to grow, draining and filling wetlands could have negative impacts on Swamp Sparrow populations. The Swamp Sparrow's future abundance in New Hampshire will reflect the extent and success of wetland protection efforts.

George W. Gavutis, Jr.

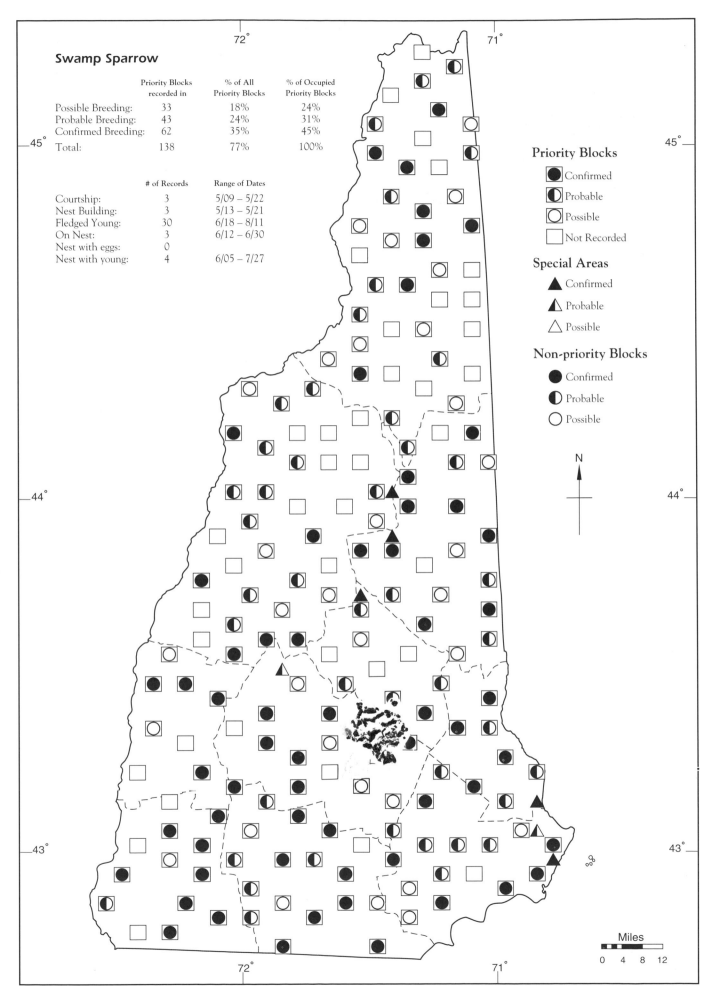

Swamp Sparrow

	Priority Blocks recorded in	% of All Priority Blocks	% of Occupied Priority Blocks
Possible Breeding:	33	18%	24%
Probable Breeding:	43	24%	31%
Confirmed Breeding:	62	35%	45%
Total:	138	77%	100%

	# of Records	Range of Dates
Courtship:	3	5/09 – 5/22
Nest Building:	3	5/13 – 5/21
Fledged Young:	30	6/18 – 8/11
On Nest:	3	6/12 – 6/30
Nest with eggs:	0	
Nest with young:	4	6/05 – 7/27

Priority Blocks

● Confirmed
◑ Probable
○ Possible
☐ Not Recorded

Special Areas

▲ Confirmed
◣ Probable
△ Possible

Non-priority Blocks

● Confirmed
◐ Probable
○ Possible

N

Miles
0 4 8 12

White-throated Sparrow
Zonotrichia albicollis

The White-throated Sparrow is a bird of northern forests, thickets, and mountain tops. The conspicuous white throat, black and white striped crown, and yellow spot between eye and bill identify this familiar bird, which breeds throughout northern New England. This large, abundant sparrow has increased recently in southern New Hampshire, and now winters there regularly in small numbers.

The clear, whistled song of the White-throated Sparrow carries widely through the woods. Songs often vary in length and pattern between individuals. Listeners sometimes render the well-known song as "Oh sweet Canada, Canada, Canada" or "Old Sam Peabody, Peabody, Peabody."

White-throats return to breeding areas about the third week of April (Lowther and Falls 1968). Males arrive about 2 weeks before females, establish territories, sing persistently before pairing, and chase intruders (Wasserman 1980). Pairs form by mid-May (Lowther and Falls 1968). Several distinct call notes of both sexes serve as contact and warning signals: "tseet" and a loud "pink!" are the most common (Lowther and Falls 1968). White-throats also may sing a brief and quavery version of their song in early August (Janeway, pers. obs.).

Breeding habitat includes brushy woods, fields, and clearings; overgrown clearcuts, thickets, and wetland edges; and krummholz. This sparrow nests above timberline to an elevation of 5,300 ft (1,620 m) in the White Mountains (Allen 1903), wherever there is suitable nesting cover. It seldom nests near thickly settled areas.

The female spends about a week in mid to late May building her nest of various plant materials (Forbush 1929). It is typically on the ground at the edge of a clearing, usually well concealed under low vegetation and sometimes in a small bush, a brush heap, or the roots of a fallen tree (Lowther and Falls 1968). The nest is a cup of twigs, rootlets, coarse grasses, mosses, bark fibers, wood chips, and pine needles and is lined with fine grasses, rootlets and hair (Harrison 1975, Harrison 1978). White-throats, especially males, may return to the same nest area each year. If the nest is destroyed, the female builds another near the first one (Lowther and Falls 1968).

The female White-throated Sparrow typically lays 4 eggs and incubates for 11 to 14 days (Harrison 1978). She is an infrequent host to cowbirds (Terres 1980). A Salisbury nest on the ground below the tip of a fallen dead spruce contained 4 eggs on 29 June, and another in a lowbush blueberry on Ragged Mtn., Danbury, held 3 eggs on 2 July (K. C. Elkins, pers. comm.). The female sits tight on her nest, but if flushed may run along the ground before taking flight, and scolds with loud chipping notes, which usually attract the male (Lowther and Falls 1968). During incubation the male sings a whisper song from the ground (Wasserman 1980).

Both parents tend the young, which remain in the nest 7 to 12 days, and fly 2 or 3 days later. The male remains on territory after the female and young leave together (Lowther and Falls 1968). White-throats often are locally abundant in New Hampshire during migration. On 4 October 1910, Wright (1911) counted 100 birds in 1 a (0.4 ha) in the Jefferson region.

White-throated Sparrows destroy many insect pests and weed seeds, and forage noisily on the ground, since they are active scratchers (Forbush 1929). The loud rustling of a foraging White-throat and its quick response to squeaking make it easy to locate even without its song and loud alarm note.

The White-throated Sparrow traditionally has been an abundant summer resident in the northern and higher areas of New Hampshire (Allen 1903, Wright 1911, Forbush 1929). This species formerly nested locally at higher elevations south of Lake Winnipesaukee (Allen 1903), but occurred only as a migrant near Durham (Dearborn 1903). As overgrown, brushy fields reverted to woods during the present century, this species has expanded its range southward in the state into newly available habitat.

As the Atlas map illustrates, this sparrow now breeds throughout New Hampshire. The only priority block lacking an Atlas record is in a largely urban area. BBS data suggest that the population of this species may undergo periodic fluctuations in the northeastern U.S., where it reaches the southern limit of its breeding range (Robbins et al. 1986). These data indicate an overall decreasing trend in the Northeastern states, possibly influenced by extremely cold winters in 1976–77 and 1977–78 (Robbins et al. 1986).

The downward trend likely will continue as breeding habitat grows into mature woods, or is developed. However, the White-throat's mountaintop habitat of thick, stunted spruce should continue to provide nesting places for the "nightingale" of our north woods.

Elizabeth C. Janeway

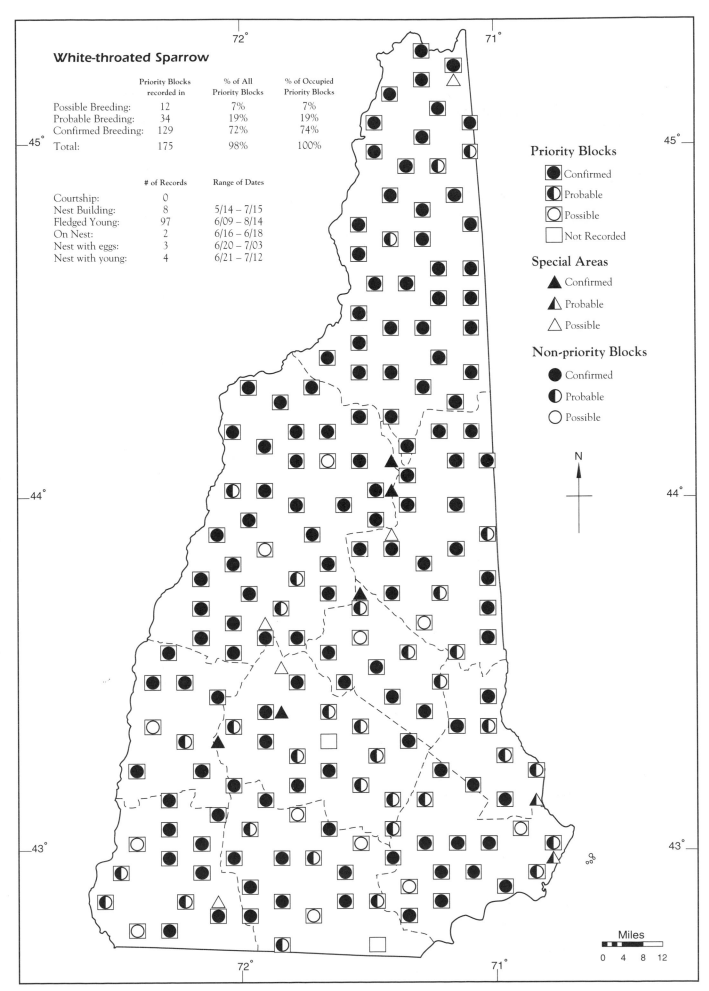

White-throated Sparrow

	Priority Blocks recorded in	% of All Priority Blocks	% of Occupied Priority Blocks
Possible Breeding:	12	7%	7%
Probable Breeding:	34	19%	19%
Confirmed Breeding:	129	72%	74%
Total:	175	98%	100%

	# of Records	Range of Dates
Courtship:	0	
Nest Building:	8	5/14 – 7/15
Fledged Young:	97	6/09 – 8/14
On Nest:	2	6/16 – 6/18
Nest with eggs:	3	6/20 – 7/03
Nest with young:	4	6/21 – 7/12

Priority Blocks

- ● Confirmed
- ◑ Probable
- ○ Possible
- ☐ Not Recorded

Special Areas

- ▲ Confirmed
- ◩ Probable
- △ Possible

Non-priority Blocks

- ● Confirmed
- ◖ Probable
- ○ Possible

N

Miles
0 4 8 12

Dark-eyed Junco
Junco hyemalis

This pert, gray and white songbird is one of the most abundant breeding birds in northern New Hampshire and nests at the highest elevations in the state. In 1973 the AOU (1973) grouped several former junco species into the Dark-eyed Junco. The widely distributed former "Slate-colored Junco" is the subspecies from the Northeast (Borror 1979). This junco is known to most of the U.S. as a winter visitor, but it nests throughout most of our state in coniferous or mixed woods and along forest edges. Allen (1903) describes New Hampshire breeding habitat as "coniferous woods and dry open pastures which have grown up to small pines or spruces."

The breeding range of the Dark-eyed Junco includes much of Canada and Alaska and the northern tier of states, and extends south in the larger mountain ranges. The winter range extends from southern Canada throughout most of the U.S. (NGS 1983).

Spring migration begins in mid-March and peaks in April (Borror 1979). Studies in Indiana indicate that the earliest migrants are adult females, followed by adult males, first year females, and finally, first year males (Nolan and Ketterson 1990). Juncos arrive on New Hampshire breeding grounds in mid-April (Allen 1903), nesting at elevations ranging from below 500 ft (150 m) to above 6,000 ft (1,830 m), but most commonly between 1,500 and 5,500 ft (460 and 1,680 m) (T. Richards, pers. comm.).

The male sings his "sleigh bell" trill from the tops of tall trees to establish a territory. Another song, heard during 11–13 June 1985 on Mt. Madison, Low and Burbanks Grant, is a "deeper, more metallic, insectlike 'zing, zing, zing, zing', quite different from the usual song" (E.C. Janeway, pers. comm.). White outer tail feathers, distinctive in flight, are used in tail-flicking displays during courtship (C.R. Foss, pers. comm.)

The female usually builds the nest of mosses, grasses, rootlets, and small twigs. It is lined with finer grasses and usually hair. The male may pick up nesting material during early courtship, but apparently does not assist with nest building (E. Ketterson, pers. comm.). Situated on the ground, the nest is usually in a well-hidden and well-drained location, such as on an embankment or among upturned tree roots (E. Ketterson, pers. comm.). Turner observed a female in Rochester carrying nesting material to a site behind a stone wall separating a hayfield from a young hardwood forest. A nest in Andover was located among ferns in the middle of a woods road (K. C. Elkins, pers. comm.). Another, just north of Wolf Mtn., Easton, was concealed neatly behind hanging green moss on an embankment about 10 in (25 cm) above a trail, and contained 4 eggs on 16 July 1985 (E.C. Janeway, pers. comm.). The late date suggests a second brood, which is common. The female flew from the nest and performed a distraction display, "hopping and fluttering along the trail". The high percentage of Atlas "confirmations" may result from the junco's tendency to nest near roads and trails and its highly visible distraction display.

The clutch usually contains 4 or 5 eggs, which the female incubates for 12 or 13 days (Harrison 1975, Harrison 1978). K. C. Elkins (pers. comm.) observed a nest containing 4 very small nestlings on 19 June 1973 in Andover; Allen (1903) found newly hatched young in Jackson on 16 June 1902. Both parents feed and defend nestlings (E. Ketterson, pers. comm.). Young leave the nest 10 to 13 days after hatching, and remain at least partly dependent on the adults for another 3 weeks (Harrison 1978). Fledged young provided the majority of "confirmed" records. The brown juveniles are heavily streaked and easily distinguishable from the brown-backed females.

Great waves of migrating juncos pass through New Hampshire in October. Although the vast majority continue southward, some "snowbirds" overwinter in the state. White (1937) notes their irregularity as winter residents in Concord, citing 5 "good" and 4 "poor" years from 1920 to 1934. Most juncos wintering in New Hampshire probably are males (Ketterson and Nolan 1983).

The name "*Junco*" comes from the Latin *juncus*, meaning "a seed." Juncos forage on the ground for forb and grass seeds and pick up seeds that chickadees and goldfinches have scattered beneath bird feeders. When they are feeding young in summer, however, almost half the diet consists of insects (Terres 1980).

The Dark-eyed Junco's breeding distribution in New Hampshire has changed little in the past century. Forbush (1929) and Allen (1903) considered it a common summer resident in the northern part of the state and less common south of Lake Winnipesaukee. Dearborn (1898) mentions nesting on Mt. Kearsarge, Warner, and Bean's Hill, Northfield, which apparently were the only breeding locations he knew of in Belknap and Merrimack counties. Dearborn (1903) considered it a bird of higher elevations and suspected nesting on the Blue Hills, Strafford. White (1937) considered it rare in Concord in summer, and mentions a few summer sightings but no nesting records.

The Atlas map largely follows the historical distribution. Only one northern priority block lacks a record, and southern blocks with records occur primarily at higher elevations. The scattered records in southeastern New Hampshire include 2 "confirmations" in southern Rockingham County, and one at an elevation of 600 ft (180 m) in Rochester. BBS data from 1966 to 1979 suggest significant decreases in junco populations in New Hampshire (Robbins et al. 1986). While still common in the state, this species will bear watching in the coming years.

Sandra B. Turner

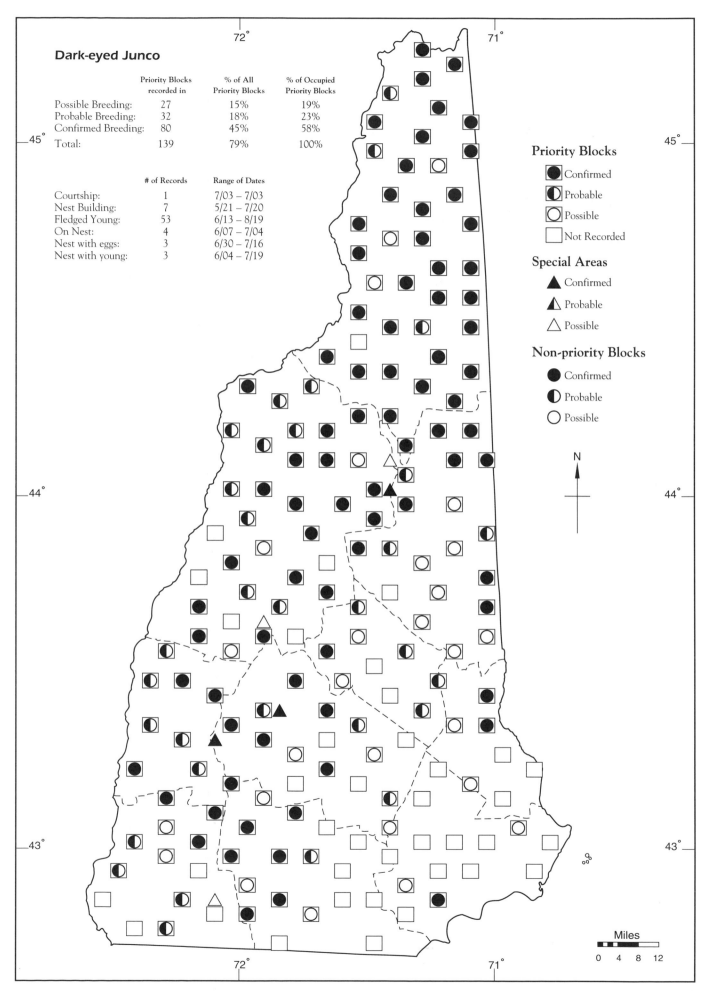

Dark-eyed Junco

	Priority Blocks recorded in	% of All Priority Blocks	% of Occupied Priority Blocks
Possible Breeding:	27	15%	19%
Probable Breeding:	32	18%	23%
Confirmed Breeding:	80	45%	58%
Total:	139	79%	100%

	# of Records	Range of Dates
Courtship:	1	7/03 – 7/03
Nest Building:	7	5/21 – 7/20
Fledged Young:	53	6/13 – 8/19
On Nest:	4	6/07 – 7/04
Nest with eggs:	3	6/30 – 7/16
Nest with young:	3	6/04 – 7/19

Priority Blocks

● Confirmed
◑ Probable
○ Possible
□ Not Recorded

Special Areas

▲ Confirmed
◤ Probable
△ Possible

Non-priority Blocks

● Confirmed
◐ Probable
○ Possible

N

Miles
0 4 8 12

Bobolink
Dolichonyx oryzivorus

Whether perched on a fence post or in flight over open fields, the Bobolink looks like a black bird whose back and wings have been splashed with a generous brush of white paint. Its song is loud and bubbling; and some say the Bobolink is singing its name. This striking member of the blackbird family breeds across southern Canada and south into Oregon, Colorado, Kentucky, and New Jersey (NGS 1983). The Bobolink winters from southwestern Brazil to northern Argentina (Forbush 1927).

Male Bobolinks return to New Hampshire in early to mid-May, often to the same area where they nested the previous year (Martin 1974, Gavin and Bollinger 1985). Their arrival is easily noticed, as they frequent large fields and pastures, often arising from the ground and flying low over the grass. The inconspicuous brown and tan streaked females arrive 10 to 12 days after the males. When courtship begins, males emit a torrent of song from the air or from a fence post or tree. On the ground they strut with tails spread, nape feathers erect, and wings partly open (Forbush 1927).

Bobolinks nest in tall, dense vegetation of hayfields or meadows, less often in pastures, and occasionally in large marshes and grassy swales along stream edges. These loosely colonial birds are polygynous, but males do form pair bonds and help to feed and care for the young (Terres 1980). Nests are on the ground and well concealed. Usually in depressions in the soil, occasionally they are raised slightly above the ground and attached to grass stems (Forbush 1927). They are loosely constructed of coarse grasses and plant stems and lined with fine grasses (Harrison 1975).

New Hampshire egg dates range from 21 May to 2 July (NHBBA data). Although haying operations start in the middle of June and probably destroy many nests, a nest in a depression may escape harm between the tractor wheels. The female incubates her 4 to 7, usually 5 or 6 eggs for 11 to 13 days (Harrison 1978), while the male remains in the vicinity of the nest, singing, giving the alarm if an intruder approaches, and distracting the intruder's attention. The female typically lands some distance from the nest and walks to it under cover of the lush vegetation. When disturbed at the nest, she runs away through the grass before taking flight (Harrison 1985). Both parents care for the young, which leave the nest 10 to 14 days after hatching, well before they can fly (Harrison 1978).

Bobolinks forage away from the nest site in the surrounding fields. They feed on grasshoppers, caterpillars, cutworms, crickets, and other insects, and whatever grass and forb seeds are available. Seeds become a more important part of the diet as they ripen in late summer and early fall (Forbush 1927).

By the middle of July, flocks of males, females, and young are forming and disbanding again, circling over meadows. Males molt into a drab plumage resembling the females' by the end of July. Bobolinks begin to move south in August, foraging in fields and marshes en route. Most have left New Hampshire by mid-September, but a few may linger into early October (Elkins 1982).

The "Boblincoln" occurred in New Hampshire long before the Eastern forests were cleared for agriculture (Belknap 1792), presumably occupying floodplain fields, streamside marshes, and large beaver meadows. Land clearing in the 1700s and 1800s created extensive areas of suitable habitat, enabling the species to expand considerably in both numbers and distribution. Samuels (1867) considered it common in New England, and "not rare in most of the northern sections" of the region.

Around the turn of the century it was common in much of New Hampshire, but less so north of the White Mountains (Dearborn 1898, Allen 1903, Dearborn 1903, Hoffmann 1904). Wright (1911) found it common in the Jefferson area, and estimated that 12 pairs inhabited fields at Jefferson Highlands, Jefferson, at 1,500-1,600 ft (460-490 m) elevation.

Breeding habitat declined as farmlands were abandoned after the mid-1800s. In addition, gunners in the middle Atlantic states shot great numbers of Bobolinks during migration to protect rice crops and for the food market (Forbush 1927, Bent 1958). The result was a general decrease in Bobolinks in New England after about 1875 (Forbush 1927). Changes in hay harvesting practices from hand mowing and raking to machine cutting and baling, and from July to June harvests continued to reduce populations in the 1900s (Bent 1958). Bobolinks persisted where suitable fields remained, and White (1937) found them still common in Concord in the late 1930s.

BBS data from 1966 to 1979 suggest that Bobolinks are nearly 4 times as common in New Hampshire as Eastern Meadowlarks. Bobolink numbers (mean birds per route) are almost twice as high in Vermont, where agricultural lands are still prevalent, as in much more heavily forested New Hampshire.

As the Atlas map indicates, Bobolinks still are well distributed in southern New Hampshire. They are absent from the core of the White Mountains and much of the North Country, where suitable habitat is lacking. Their distribution in Coos County clearly illustrates the locations of open lands along major valleys.

While a few Bobolinks still breed in some of New Hampshire's large marshes, the majority will continue to depend on hayfields and other human-maintained grasslands for breeding habitat. The future of agriculture, particularly dairy farming, in New Hampshire will largely shape future trends in the state's Bobolink population.

Frederic L. Steele

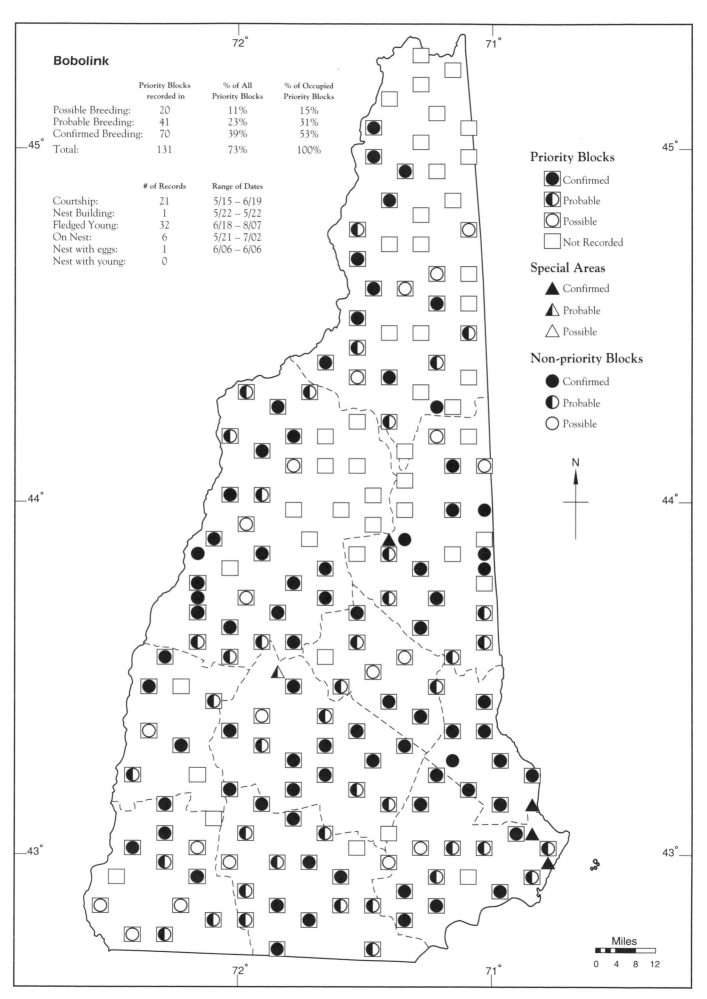

Bobolink

	Priority Blocks recorded in	% of All Priority Blocks	% of Occupied Priority Blocks
Possible Breeding:	20	11%	15%
Probable Breeding:	41	23%	31%
Confirmed Breeding:	70	39%	53%
Total:	131	73%	100%

	# of Records	Range of Dates
Courtship:	21	5/15 – 6/19
Nest Building:	1	5/22 – 5/22
Fledged Young:	32	6/18 – 8/07
On Nest:	6	5/21 – 7/02
Nest with eggs:	1	6/06 – 6/06
Nest with young:	0	

Priority Blocks
- Confirmed
- Probable
- Possible
- Not Recorded

Special Areas
- Confirmed
- Probable
- Possible

Non-priority Blocks
- Confirmed
- Probable
- Possible

N

Miles
0 4 8 12

Red-winged Blackbird
Agelaius phoeniceus

These handsome black birds with their flashing scarlet and gold "epaulettes" are widespread and abundant throughout North America, including New Hampshire. Their "conqueree," often given in chorus, is one of the most frequently heard bird songs. "Red-wings" are among the earliest birds to arrive here in spring. The first flocks of male Red-winged Blackbirds usually arrive before mid-March, sometimes as early as late February. The females, which are dark brown with heavily striped underparts, come a few weeks later.

Marshes and shrubby swamps are typical nesting habitats, but some Red-wings nest in upland fields and pastures. Upland nesting formerly was rare in New England (Forbush 1927), but now is rather common. Nests in marshes generally are more successful than those in uplands, where predation losses are greater (Robertson 1973). Farm machinery may destroy many nests in hayfields, depending on the harvest cycle (T. Engstrom, pers. comm.).

Soon after arrival some male Red-wings sing during early morning or late afternoon from conspicuous perches in their breeding marshes, which often are still frozen. These periods of territorial behavior are short, for the birds spend most of the day in flocks, often with grackles, cowbirds and starlings, feeding in fields and singing from nearby trees (White 1937, Orians 1980). Flocks are common in open country until at least late April.

By the second week in May most females have arrived, and the males are courting them (White 1937). Townsend (1920) aptly described the male Red-wing's display, in which he "spreads his tail, slightly opens his wings, puffs out all his feathers, and sings his quonkqueree or his still more watery and gurgling song . . . ogle-oggle-yer. Now . . . he especially puffs out, erects, and otherwise displays to their best advantage the gorgeous scarlet epaulettes."

A male may have up to 3 or more mates (Nero 1984). The males vigorously defend their territories, which are usually quite small in marshes (average 0.17 a [0.069 ha]), but larger (average 0.54 [0.22 ha]) in upland areas (Case and Hewitt 1963). The females establish and defend their own subterritories within a male's territory (Nero 1984). They make a display low in the vegetation which is similar to the male's, but accompanied by a different song (Nero 1984). Although males are more conspicuous, breeding females usually outnumber males in a marsh. Males usually do not breed until they are nearly 2 years old, but females breed as yearlings (Nero 1984).

The females build the nests, which are strong pouches with soft linings, usually in marsh vegetation over or near water. Nests in dry fields sometimes are on the ground (Bent 1965). Rarely, nests may be in trees (Harrison 1978). The females incubate the eggs for 11 or 12 days and do most feeding of the nestlings, which stay in the nest 10 or 11 days (Harrison 1978). Although male Red-winged Blackbirds aggressively defend their territories against large birds, even in marshes eggs and nestlings are often lost to crows, grackles, and other predators. Red-wings commonly replace lost clutches, but second broods probably are uncommon in New Hampshire (Forbush 1927, Nero 1984).

After fledging, the young stay in the marsh for about 2 weeks before moving to nearby uplands, where the female continues to feed them for another 2 weeks. The male usually stays in the marsh for a while longer (Nero 1984). Most Red-winged Blackbirds leave breeding marshes by the first of August, though some may return at night to roost (White 1937). From late July until the southward migration, large flocks frequent a few favored localities, such as the larger river meadows (White 1937). Some New England Red-wings move as much as 125 to 156 mi (200 to 250 km) by August (Dolbeer in Nero 1984), which may explain why they are scarce or absent over large areas of New Hampshire in most of August and in September.

However, most Red-wings migrate after molting in late August and September. During fall migration large blackbird concentrations are common in cornfields and marshes. Most depart in October, but in recent years a few often have lingered into winter, especially at bird feeders. Rarely, whole flocks winter in New Hampshire.

Red-winged Blackbirds have been at least locally common in New Hampshire throughout historical times (Goodhue 1877, Allen 1903, White 1937, Thayer 1907 in Allison and Allison 1979). Their numbers have increased extraordinarily in recent decades (T. Richards, pers. comm.). Old timers can remember when robins and bluebirds were the most conspicuous "harbingers of spring" (Elkins, pers. obs.). Now blackbirds, especially this species, usually come earlier. BBS data for New Hampshire from 1966 to 1984 suggest that Red-winged Blackbirds were more numerous in the 1970s than in the 1960s, but declined in the 1980s. Although Red-winged Blackbirds cause few problems in New England, they are serious agricultural pests in other parts of the country, where millions concentrate and consume great quantities of grain.

Atlas workers found Red-winged Blackbirds in all but 20 priority blocks, all of which are above 1,000 ft (300 m) elevation in the White Mountains or North Country and lack appropriate habitat. Elsewhere in the state these birds occur commonly above 1,000 feet (300 m), though rarely above 2,500 ft (760 m) (T. Richards, pers. comm.).

Kimball C. Elkins

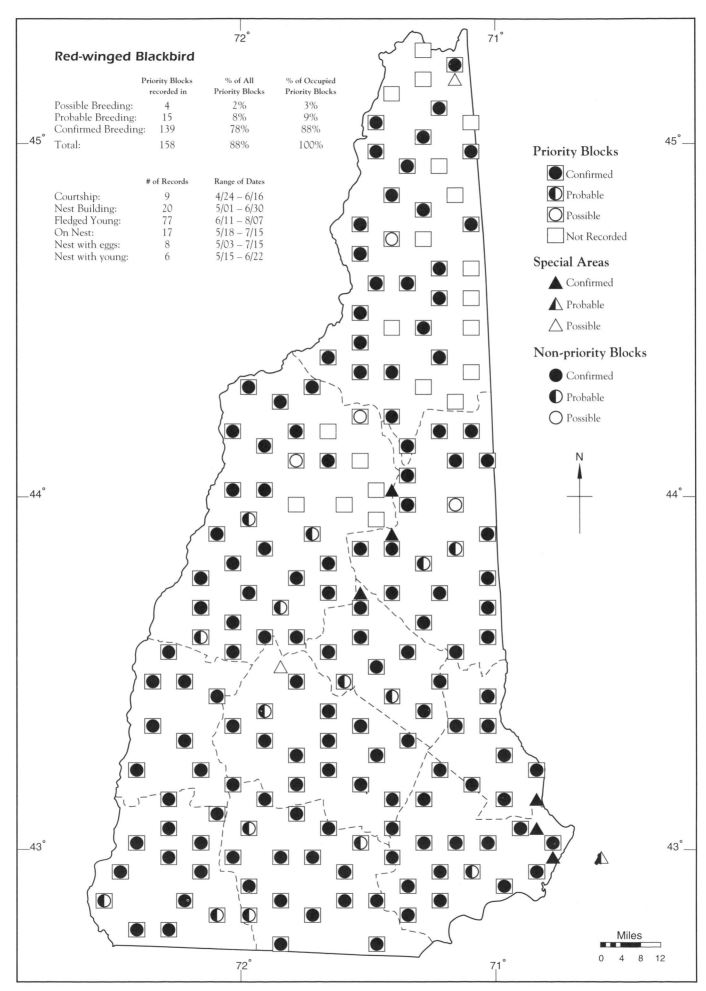

Red-winged Blackbird

	Priority Blocks recorded in	% of All Priority Blocks	% of Occupied Priority Blocks
Possible Breeding:	4	2%	3%
Probable Breeding:	15	8%	9%
Confirmed Breeding:	139	78%	88%
Total:	158	88%	100%

	# of Records	Range of Dates
Courtship:	9	4/24 – 6/16
Nest Building:	20	5/01 – 6/30
Fledged Young:	77	6/11 – 8/07
On Nest:	17	5/18 – 7/15
Nest with eggs:	8	5/03 – 7/15
Nest with young:	6	5/15 – 6/22

Priority Blocks

● Confirmed
◐ Probable
○ Possible
☐ Not Recorded

Special Areas

▲ Confirmed
◮ Probable
△ Possible

Non-priority Blocks

● Confirmed
◐ Probable
○ Possible

N

Miles
0 4 8 12

341

Eastern Meadowlark
Sturnella magna

The meadowlark's distinctive slurred whistle makes it an easy bird to detect in its preferred habitat of open fields. As it flies low over the grass, it alternates between flapping and gliding, and its white outer tail feathers are usually visible. Since it often flies away from the observer, the bright yellow breast and black necklace are seldom seen unless it alights in plain view.

Meadowlarks return to New Hampshire in late March or early April. The males arrive first and establish territories. They sing from exposed perches, such as trees, fence posts, and utility wires, engage in sometimes lengthy chases, and flutter several feet into the air with wings high, tails raised, and legs dangling. Males sing throughout the breeding season but most intensely before the females arrive, 2 to 3 weeks after the males. Males continue to defend territories until early August.

Once paired, mates engage in aerial chases and ground displays, and the female often answers her mate's song with a chattering call. The male usually is polygamous and has 2 or occasionally 3 females nesting on his territory. A male's females do not nest synchronously.

The domed nest, which opens on the side, is in a small hollow on the ground, well concealed in the grass. The female builds it, taking 3 to 8 days, and may add material after she has begun to lay eggs (Harrison 1978). The nest consists of grasses or forbs and is lined with finer plant material. Grasses form a loose dome over the nest cup, and the entrance may be roofed. Meadowlarks build their nests in early to mid-May, before heavy grass growth has developed (Ellis *in* Laughlin and Kibbe 1985). Mowing of hay typically begins in mid-June, and machinery may crush some nests. Atlas observers located only 3 nests.

The female incubates her 3 to 7 eggs for 13 to 15 days (Harrison 1978) while the male remains in the vicinity, singing frequently. The 5 eggs in one nest in Concord hatched on 30 or 31 May, and another nest held 5 eggs on 18 June (White 1937). Both parents tend the nestlings, which leave the nest after 11 or 12 days. The male then may take over care of the young while the female renests (Harrison 1978). Observations of fledged young provided nearly all "confirmed" Atlas records.

The summer diet consists primarily of insects, including cutworms, caterpillars, and grasshoppers. In the fall meadowlarks also eat some weed seeds (Forbush 1927). Meadowlarks begin to migrate south in late October or early November, but stragglers may remain longer or occasionally overwinter in southern New Hampshire (Elkins 1982).

Meadowlarks occupy breeding territories of 3 to 15 a (1 to 6 ha) (Lanyon 1957). Bobolinks often occur in the same fields, but also will use smaller fields than meadowlarks seem to require (Steele, pers. obs.). Although Weins (1969) found in Wisconsin that meadowlarks avoid fields with lush growth, this does not seem to be the case in New Hampshire. Both meadowlarks and bobolinks used a field for several years after it was seeded to brome and alfalfa, producing a heavy crop of hay (Steele, pers. obs.).

Known to Belknap (1792) as the "Marsh Lark," the meadowlark likely inhabited extensive beaver meadows in precolonial times. Subsequent land clearing for agriculture greatly increased available habitat and presumably enabled a population increase, but this species never has been as common in New Hampshire as it once was in southern New England. In Massachusetts, the meadowlark's abundance peaked in the 1800s when agriculture was at its height (Veit and Petersen 1993). The species has followed a similar pattern in New Hampshire, and Samuels (1867) considered it "not rare in northern New England." The first records in the White Mountains region are from Intervale (Bartlett/Conway) in the early 1890s (Allen 1903), Franconia in 1899 (Torrey 1900), and Lancaster in 1901 (Wright 1911).

Around the turn of the century it was uncommon in southern New Hampshire and rare further north (Allen 1903). Dearborn (1898) found it "common in some localities," and in the vicinity of Durham it occurred locally but was "nowhere abundant" (Dearborn 1903). Today meadowlarks are more common than Bobolinks in southern New England, but Bobolinks far outnumber them in Maine, New Hampshire, and Vermont (Robbins et al. 1986).

Robbins et al. (1986) document a population decline east of the Mississippi River during 1966-79 and note that the severe winter of 1976-77 had a dramatic, adverse impact on this species. The decline in New Hampshire apparently has continued during the Atlas period. Meadowlarks are now scarce or lacking in large fields where several were present only 6 years ago. They were common in some fields in northern New Hampshire in the first year of the Atlas, but have been declining in number since then (Steele, pers. obs.).

The Atlas map shows concentrations of meadowlark records in the Coastal Lowlands, the central Merrimack Valley, and western Grafton County, where extensive fields have persisted. Large fields are locally distributed in New Hampshire, occurring primarily in major river valleys. Many such fields have succumbed to development in recent years as agriculture has declined in the state.

Since human land uses have usurped areas where activity once created extensive meadows, the meadowlark's future in New Hampshire will be closely tied to that of the state's remaining agricultural lands. Recent efforts to protect and maintain productive farmlands provide hope that both can persist in an era of changing land use.

Frederic L. Steele

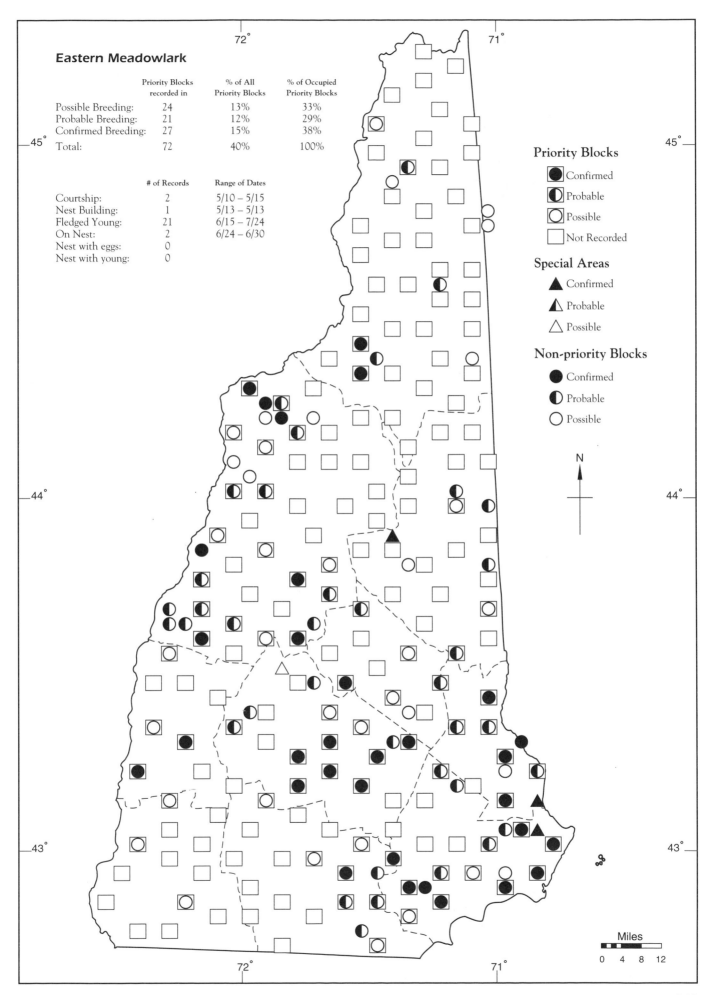

Eastern Meadowlark

	Priority Blocks recorded in	% of All Priority Blocks	% of Occupied Priority Blocks
Possible Breeding:	24	13%	33%
Probable Breeding:	21	12%	29%
Confirmed Breeding:	27	15%	38%
Total:	72	40%	100%

	# of Records	Range of Dates
Courtship:	2	5/10 – 5/15
Nest Building:	1	5/13 – 5/13
Fledged Young:	21	6/15 – 7/24
On Nest:	2	6/24 – 6/30
Nest with eggs:	0	
Nest with young:	0	

Priority Blocks

- ◐ Confirmed
- ◑ Probable
- ○ Possible
- ☐ Not Recorded

Special Areas

- ▲ Confirmed
- ◣ Probable
- △ Possible

Non-priority Blocks

- ● Confirmed
- ◑ Probable
- ○ Possible

N

Miles
0 4 8 12

Rusty Blackbird
Euphagus carolinus

The yellow-eyed, squeaky-voiced Rusty Blackbird is well named for its rusty-washed fall and winter plumage. During the breeding season the male is blackish, and his mate is grayer. This blackbird lacks the red "shoulders" of the similar-sized Red-wing and the colorful iridescence of the larger and longer-tailed grackle. Unlike other blackbirds, which have become so abundant as to be major pests in some regions, the Rusty is, at least in New Hampshire, an uncommon bird of wild places.

In New Hampshire the Rusty Blackbird is an uncommon to rare and local summer resident near northern wetlands, including beaver ponds, in the White Mountains and North Country. The species has nested in the mountains from slightly above 1,000 to about 4,000 ft (300 to 1,200 m) in elevation (Richards, pers. obs.). Its continental nesting range extends from northern Alaska to central Labrador in the north, and from central British Columbia to northern New England in the south. The species winters in the eastern U. S. from near the southern limit of the nesting range to the Gulf Coast (NGS 1983).

The Rusty Blackbird arrives in southern New Hampshire in late March or April, often in flocks with other blackbirds. It is soon on its breeding grounds at lower elevations. Unfavorable weather conditions may delay its arrival at higher elevations. The male's song is "a split creak like a rusty hinge: kush-a-lee alternating with ksh-lay"; the common call note is "a loud chack" (Peterson 1980). Courtship in one case involved a male spreading its tail and making a series of squeaky notes and a lower, sweeter note; in another case 2 males perched in a treetop stretching one wing downward and whistling a single note (Townsend 1920 and Munro 1947 *in* Bent 1958).

Kennard (1920 *in* Bent 1958) found nests in northern New England at heights of 2 to 20 ft (0.6 to 6.1 m), usually in spruces or firs beside streams but sometimes in deciduous shrubs. In the White Mountains, Rusties formerly preferred edges of permanent mountain ponds (Richards, pers. obs.), but recently seem to favor beaver ponds (B.J. Wicklow, pers. comm.).

This species never nests in colonies. Pairs require territories with nests at least 0.5 mi (0.8 km) apart, and return to the same nest site annually (Harrison 1975). The female builds a new nest each year, although nests persist for several years (Harrison 1975). A nest in Pittsburg, which resembled a robin's nest, was built of mud and sticks and lined with finer material (Dyer and Walkinsaw 1959). The female incubates the 4 or 5 eggs for about 14 days while the male feeds her. In one remarkable case, a pair built a fourth nest and raised 3 young after collectors removed their clutches from nests built on 24 May and 5 and 16 June (Bent 1958). Young usually leave the nest after about 13 days (Harrison 1978). After a complete late summer molt, juveniles emerge in winter plumage even rustier than adults. They gradually acquire their breeding plumage through feather wear (Bent 1958).

Both parents tend the young, and presumably feed them almost entirely on insects, which probably are the breeding season staple of adults. In other seasons Rusties eat crustaceans, snails, salamanders, small fish, insects, and vegetable matter, including waste grain and other seeds, mast, and fruit (Beal 1900 *in* Bent 1958).

Rusty Blackbirds may gather in groups long before heading south. Richards observed a flock of 16 on 8 July 1979 at East Inlet, Pittsburg. Brewster (1937) found flocks of presumably local birds at Umbagog Lake, Errol in late August and September, and at times of low water in early October recorded hundreds of presumed migrants.

The Rusty Blackbird nested in extreme northern New Hampshire around the turn of the century, but was unknown as a breeding species in the White Mountains (Allen 1903, Wright 1911, Forbush 1927). W. Taber (unpubl. data) apparently was the first to record a Rusty Blackbird in the White Mountains during the breeding season, at Lost River, Kinsman Notch, Woodstock on 17 June 1934. Taber also found 3 at Flat Mtn. Pond, Sandwich on 23 July 1939. In the meantime observers found 15 birds at Long Pond, Benton on 1 July 1938 (N.H. Nature Camp 1938). Since then Rusty Blackbirds have occurred in summer at 30 or more White Mountain locations, including Lonesome Lake, Lincoln; the Cherry ponds, Jefferson; Lily Pond and Greeley ponds, Waterville Valley; Hermit Lake, Sargents Purchase; and Lost Pond, Pinkhams Grant (Richards, unpubl. data).

On 16 June 1953, Richards saw a Rusty Blackbird nest with 4 recently hatched young at Lake Solitude on Mt. Sunapee, Newbury, about 3 ft (0.9 m) above the water in a small spruce. This apparently established the first New Hampshire breeding record south of the White Mountains. Observers found Rusties there in the next 3 summers but none thereafter. Richards also observed families at a beaver pond in Dublin on 19 July 1962 and 21 and 30 June 1963.

The Atlas project produced a concentration of records in northern Coos County and scattered records further south, primarily in the White Mountains. Rusty Blackbirds no longer occur in summer in many places, and are less common than previously at Umbagog Lake and perhaps even in Pittsburg (Richards, pers. obs.). BBS data for this species are too scant to indicate population trends. Here at the southern exteme of its breeding range, the numbers and distribution of Rusty Blackbirds may fluctuate over time. This will be an interesting species to monitor in the years ahead.

Tudor Richards

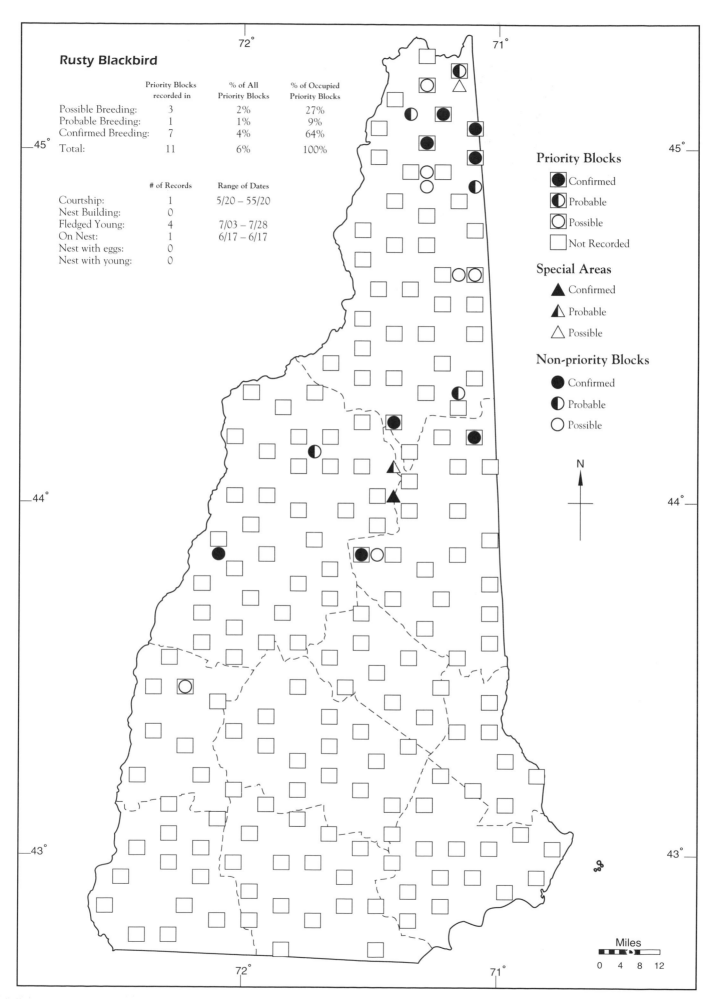

Rusty Blackbird

	Priority Blocks recorded in	% of All Priority Blocks	% of Occupied Priority Blocks
Possible Breeding:	3	2%	27%
Probable Breeding:	1	1%	9%
Confirmed Breeding:	7	4%	64%
Total:	11	6%	100%

	# of Records	Range of Dates
Courtship:	1	5/20 – 55/20
Nest Building:	0	
Fledged Young:	4	7/03 – 7/28
On Nest:	1	6/17 – 6/17
Nest with eggs:	0	
Nest with young:	0	

Priority Blocks
- ◐ Confirmed
- ◑ Probable
- ○ Possible
- ☐ Not Recorded

Special Areas
- ▲ Confirmed
- ◭ Probable
- △ Possible

Non-priority Blocks
- ● Confirmed
- ◑ Probable
- ○ Possible

N

Miles
0 4 8 12

Common Grackle
Quiscalus quiscula

The Common Grackle, New Hampshire's largest blackbird, is an omnivorous and gregarious opportunist. This common summer resident has iridescent black plumage, yellow eyes (dark in juveniles), and a long, wedge-shaped tail. The grackle occurs throughout New Hampshire in farmlands, parks, suburbs, marshes, and wooded swamps at elevations up to 2,500 ft (760 m) (Ridgely 1977). Habitat requirements include open foraging areas with nearby streams, swamps, ponds, or lakes (Ellison in Laughlin and Kibbe 1985).

Grackles forage on the ground in open areas and often scavenge along the shores of ponds and streams. They consume many insect pests, but can be destructive to corn, fruit, and other crops. They sometimes prey on crayfish, frogs, small fish, and eggs, nestlings, and even adults of other birds (Gross 1958).

The arrival of noisy grackle flocks in early to mid-March is one of New Hampshire's first signs of spring. Early flocks tend to be all males or all females, with the males arriving first (Gross 1958). At this time grackles feed with other blackbirds, which are smaller and have shorter tails. From arrival until incubation begins, grackles leave colonial nesting areas in the evening for communal night roosts (Widmann 1907 in Gross 1958).

Courtship begins soon after the females arrive. Four or 5 males may display to a single female in a tree (Petersen and Young 1950, Wiley 1976). Several males may pursue a flying female, with tails in characteristic V-shape. Upon landing, the males may display with feathers puffed out, wings opened, and tails spread or bills tilted upward (Gross 1958, Ficken 1963b, Wiley 1976). Their unmusical but distinctive song resembles the creaking of a rusty gate.

Atlas data suggest that most nest building takes place from mid-April through late May or even early June. During early stages both sexes carry long strands of nesting material to the site, though they may not construct the nest for several weeks. Construction time varies from 4 to 16 days (Petersen and Young 1950).

Grackles prefer conifers, including ornamentals, for nesting, but often nest in deciduous trees and shrubs after leaves have emerged. They also may use natural cavities, nest boxes, cattails, ledges, and buildings (Maxwell et al. 1976). Grackles frequently nest in loose colonies of 20 to 30 pairs, sometimes with up to 28 nests in one tree (Gross 1958). They defend only a small area immediately around the nest site (Ficken 1963b). The nest usually is near water and feeding areas, and often is in the same location year after year (Stokes 1979). The deeply cupped, bulky structure is made of sticks, grasses, weed stalks, roots, and leaves, often reinforced with mud and lined with fine grasses (Pough 1949, Gross 1958, Harrison 1975), and may be from 1 to 60 ft (0.3 to 18.3 m) above the ground.

The female incubates her 3 to 6, typically 4 or 5 eggs for 11 to 14 days (Gross 1958, Maxwell and Putnam 1972, Harrison 1975). New Hampshire atlasers observed grackles on the nest mainly during the second half of May and in early June. A late record on 21 July probably was a renesting attempt. Grackles normally raise a single brood annually (Ellison in Laughlin and Kibbe 1985).

During incubation the male may guard the nest while the female feeds or may pair with another female, leaving the first to raise the brood alone (Stokes 1979). Grackles fiercely defend their nests against intruders, and a male's alarm call may summon the entire colony (Gross 1958).

The nestling period lasts 10 to 18 days, usually about 12 (Gross 1958, Maxwell and Putnam 1972, Harrison 1978). Most Atlas records of nests with young came from late May through the third week of June. Both parents feed the young and remove fecal sacs. Feedings may be as frequent as 107 per nest per day (Maxwell and Putnam 1972), which may explain why adults carrying food accounted for 38% of Atlas "confirmations." Most FF records were from June.

Grackle fledglings are noisy and conspicuous, and accounted for 42% of Atlas "confirmations." Nearly three quarters of the fledgling records occurred between 15 June and 15 July. Fledglings depend on their parents for only 2 or 3 days (Harrison 1978) and soon form foraging parties. They join adults in communal night roosts by the first week of July (Gross 1958). The sooty brown juveniles acquire their first adult plumage in an August molt (Dwight 1900 in Gross 1958). Migration begins in September, and most grackles depart in huge flocks by the end of October. A few occasionally winter in southern New Hampshire.

The grackle apparently has expanded in distribution and abundance in New Hampshire during the last 80 to 90 years. Early sources reported the species as uncommon and local in areas where it is now common to abundant (Goodhue 1877, Dearborn 1903, Allen 1903, Wright 1911, Thayer 1909 in Allison and Allison 1979). Nesting was unknown in Durham (Dearborn 1903) and Manchester (Batchelder in Allen 1903) around the turn of the century. White (1937) observed that it had increased noticeably in Concord during the 1920s, and considered it a fairly common summer resident there.

As the Atlas map illustrates, the grackle now occurs throughout New Hampshire. It is more common in the southern part of the state than in the more extensively forested and mountainous areas further north. Of the 13 priority blocks lacking records, 12 are in the White Mountains and North Country.

BBS data from 1966 to 1979 show a recent peak of abundance in the East in 1975, followed by a steady decline which has resulted in part from severe winters and in part from blackbird control efforts in large winter roosts (Robbins et al. 1986).

Steve Smith

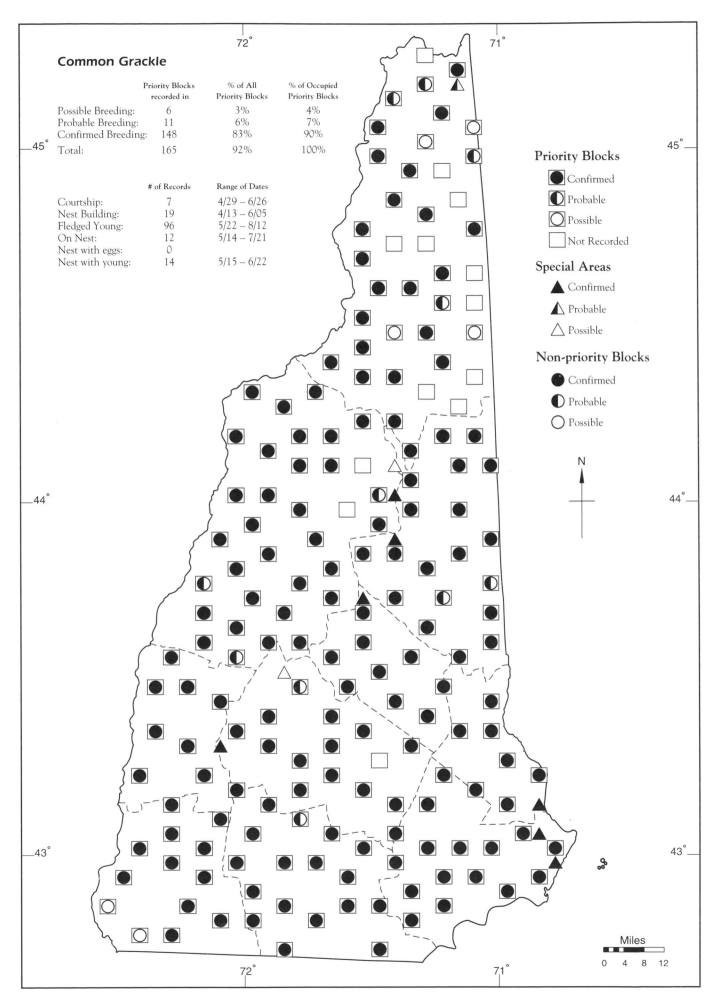

Common Grackle

	Priority Blocks recorded in	% of All Priority Blocks	% of Occupied Priority Blocks
Possible Breeding:	6	3%	4%
Probable Breeding:	11	6%	7%
Confirmed Breeding:	148	83%	90%
Total:	165	92%	100%

	# of Records	Range of Dates
Courtship:	7	4/29 – 6/26
Nest Building:	19	4/13 – 6/05
Fledged Young:	96	5/22 – 8/12
On Nest:	12	5/14 – 7/21
Nest with eggs:	0	
Nest with young:	14	5/15 – 6/22

Priority Blocks

● Confirmed
◐ Probable
○ Possible
□ Not Recorded

Special Areas

▲ Confirmed
◮ Probable
△ Possible

Non-priority Blocks

● Confirmed
◐ Probable
○ Possible

N

Miles
0 4 8 12

Brown-headed Cowbird

Molothrus ater

Cowbirds are the only North American birds that always lay their eggs in the nests of other species, which subsequently hatch the eggs and rear the young. Male Brown-headed Cowbirds have plain brown heads and shiny coal-black bodies; females are plain mouse-gray all over. Both sexes may occur in flocks throughout the year and often feed, roost, and migrate with Red-winged Blackbirds and Common Grackles. Cowbirds nest throughout New Hampshire except in the extensive northern forests and at high elevations. Although most common in farmlands, they also occur in residential areas.

Some cowbirds winter in New Hampshire, especially near the Coast, but most retreat to the middle and southern states by late October. Birds banded in New Hampshire during April–June have occurred in Connecticut, New York, New Jersey, Delaware, Virginia, North Carolina, and Florida during December–February (USFWS, unpubl. data). Males begin to arrive in New Hampshire in late March, and females follow a week or so later. The male's typical song is an inconspicuous thin whistle, "Sweet-Susie," given at infrequent intervals from a treetop perch or in flight. The female emits a low guttural rattle.

The mating and territorial behavior of cowbirds has long mystified observers. Three or more birds often loaf together on a high perch while one or more males display by ruffling their feathers, spreading their wings and tails, and vocalizing. The female cowbird generally lays one or 2 eggs in a host nest and often removes the same number of host eggs. She has a definite breeding area within which she lays her eggs (Friedmann 1929). Nice (1937) defined the home range in open floodplain habitat in Ohio as 20 to 30 a (8 to 12 ha). New Hampshire cowbirds most likely are monogamous like those studied by Dufty (1982) at Binghamton, N.Y.

A female may lay 6 or more eggs at dawn on successive days, often in different nests; she begins a second clutch after an interval of several days and may lay 3 or 4 clutches per season (Harrison 1975). Young develop very rapidly and leave the nest at 10 days; host parents feed them for another 2 weeks. The growth rate of a young cowbird typically exceeds that of the host's young, which frequently fail to survive. Most Atlas "confirmations" were from observations of the noisy fledged young.

The Brown-headed Cowbird is known to have parasitized 216 species, 139 of them successfully (Friedmann et al. 1977). The Yellow Warbler, Song Sparrow, Red-eyed Vireo, and Chipping Sparrow are by far the most frequently reported victims. Host species documented in New Hampshire include Yellow Warbler, Song Sparrow, Solitary and Red-eyed vireos, Black-and-white Warbler, American Redstart, Ovenbird, and Chipping Sparrow (White 1924, 1937, Friedmann 1929, 1963). Some species such as the Gray Catbird, American Robin, and Cedar Waxwing routinely remove cowbird eggs. Yellow Warblers often build a new nest on top of the parasitized nest, and other birds desert or attempt to rear the mixed brood.

Because cowbirds feed in pasture land and cropland, most of their nest parasitism occurs in and near open country. The majority of 1,645 parasitized nests in Ontario were in farmland habitats, especially dry, open, or semiopen areas with deciduous or mixed shrubs or small trees (Peck and James 1987). Cowbirds seldom bother birds nesting in the interior of extensive forests.

Seeds comprise half the cowbird's diet in summer and nearly all of it in winter. Bristle-grass, ragweed, and oats form the bulk of plant food in the Northeast. Grasshoppers, other insects, spiders, and myriapods also are important food items (Martin et al. 1951).

The Brown-headed Cowbird, originally a bird of the Great Plains, expanded its range eastward when the great Eastern forests were cut and is still expanding its range in the Northeast and Southeast. Although Belknap (1792) did not list this species for New Hampshire, the cowbird was a common summer resident south of the White Mountains and as far north as Warren by 1870 (Samuels 1865, Little 1870, Fox 1876, Goodhue 1877). At the turn of the century, it was an uncommon and local summer resident of valleys in southern and western New Hampshire, but rare north of Lake Winnipesaukee, with the northernmost known breeding records from Lancaster (Dearborn 1898, Allen 1903, Dearborn 1903, Hoffman 1904). White (1937) noted that this species decreased in numbers in the Concord area after 1930.

The cowbird apparently became established in northern New Hampshire in the mid-1900s. Wright (1911) had no record from Jefferson, but F. B. Spaulding found cowbirds fairly common at Lancaster in 1908 and 1909 (Wright, unpubl. note). Hebert (1958b) reported a "250% increase at Pittsburg," and "phenomenal numbers at Moultonboro." The species occurred on every New Hampshire BBS route in 1966, the first year of that survey. BBS data show a slight but significant decrease in cowbirds in the Northeast during 1966–79 (Robbins et al. 1986). New Hampshire's population was essentially stable during 1966–87 (BBS data).

As the Atlas map indicates, this species is now nearly ubiquitous south of the White Mountains and along the entire Connecticut Valley. It is scarce in the extensively forested areas of the White Mountains and North Country. The cowbird may increase in New Hampshire in coming decades as more forest gives way to other uses.

Chandler S. Robbins

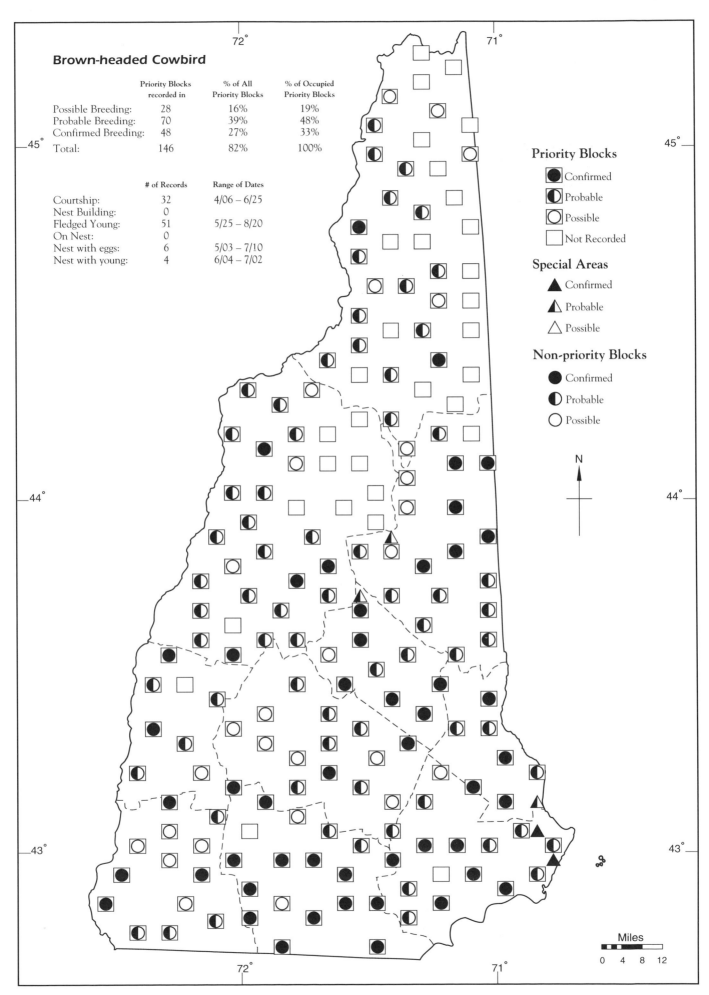

Brown-headed Cowbird

	Priority Blocks recorded in	% of All Priority Blocks	% of Occupied Priority Blocks
Possible Breeding:	28	16%	19%
Probable Breeding:	70	39%	48%
Confirmed Breeding:	48	27%	33%
Total:	146	82%	100%

	# of Records	Range of Dates
Courtship:	32	4/06 – 6/25
Nest Building:	0	
Fledged Young:	51	5/25 – 8/20
On Nest:	0	
Nest with eggs:	6	5/03 – 7/10
Nest with young:	4	6/04 – 7/02

Priority Blocks

● Confirmed
◐ Probable
○ Possible
☐ Not Recorded

Special Areas

▲ Confirmed
◮ Probable
△ Possible

Non-priority Blocks

● Confirmed
◐ Probable
○ Possible

N

Miles
0 4 8 12

349

Orchard Oriole

Icterus spurius

This species lacks the bright orange plumage of its well-known cousin, the Northern (Baltimore) Oriole, and is generally unfamiliar to New Englanders. The adult male is chestnut above and below with a black hood, wings, and tail; the female and immature male are yellowish green. The song is a short burst of robinlike notes delivered from the top of a small tree or often in flight. A common call is a blackbirdlike "chuck" (Pough 1946).

The normal breeding range of this oriole barely reaches the southern edge of New England (Peterson 1980), and Elkins (1982) designates it a "very rare to casual" summer resident in New Hampshire, arriving in early May and departing by the end of August. Although it is widespread and locally common in much of the eastern U.S., the 1986 *American Birds* Blue List (Tate 1986) considers it a Species of Special Concern due to reported declines in many areas since 1982. BBS data for 1966 to 1979 (Robbins et al. 1986) indicate a stable population in the Eastern region but a significant decline in the Central region.

In its primary breeding range, the Orchard Oriole often occurs in orchards as its name implies, but also frequents suburban shade trees, hedgerows, and woodland borders. Like the Northern Oriole it prefers open areas with small, scattered trees, often along streams and marshes, and shuns extensive, closed-canopy woodlands (Harrison 1975). Most of the few sightings of this species in New Hampshire have been in suburban areas along the Coast or in the lower Merrimack Valley at elevations of less than 300 ft (90 m).

In optimum habitat, pairs may nest so close together as to suggest a loose colony (Pough 1946). The nest, which the female constructs, is a cup-shaped structure (not pendant like the Northern Oriole's) woven mostly of fresh green grass stems and suspended from a forked branch 10 to 20 ft (3 to 6.1 m) above the ground (Pough 1946). The female incubates the 3 to 7 eggs for 12 to 14 days. The male often feeds her while she is on the nest (Harrison 1975). The young remain in the nest for about 2 weeks. Both parents feed them. New Hampshire breeding records include an immature male and 2 apparently adult females with a nest in a spruce tree observed in Hollis on 17 June 1966 (T. Richards, pers. comm.); a nest with young in Hampton on 20 June 1982 (NHBBA data); and adults with food for young in Rye on 22 June 1982, south Nashua on 28 June 1982, and New Hampton on 6 July 1968 (SRS). The young may remain near the nest for a week or more after fledging and then wander with their parents before migrating south (Sealy 1980). The birds depart for wintering areas in Central America very early, and New England records after August are scarce.

An unusual characteristic of this species is that the plumage of males in their first breeding season is distinctly different from that of adult males. The immature males resemble females, but have black chins and throats. These birds sing like adult males and often pair and nest successfully. Nearly half of the "confirmed" nestings in Vermont (Ellison *in* Laughlin and Kibbe 1985) and in New Hampshire during the respective Atlas periods involved males in immature plumage, which suggests that these young birds may be "pioneers" in range expansion.

There are several records of Orchard Orioles in New Hampshire in the early years of this century, but none of nesting. Abbott (1906) observed the species at 2 locations in the Concord area in late May 1903. Dearborn (1903) reported a specimen collected in an orchard near Dover, and Scott (1921) saw this oriole in orchards near Durham several times, usually in June. Records from the last 2 decades suggest that the species may undergo numerical and range-front fluctuations in New Hampshire similar to those reported by Sealy (1980) at the northwest edge of its breeding range in Manitoba, Can. After records of nesting birds in Hollis in 1966 and 1967, and in New Hampton in 1968, there were no nesting records until 1982 (SRS). Bagg and Eliot (1937) noted that the sporadic northward incursions of this bird seemed to follow the coastal plain into Maine much more readily than the river valleys into western New England.

There is some indication that when Orchard Orioles do nest in New Hampshire, more than one pair may nest in fairly close proximity and the birds may return in successive years. Observers reported a territorial pair on 13 and 19 June 1982 along Salmon Brook, south Nashua, but found no nest and did not see the birds after 19 June. However, a pair was carrying food for young less than a mile away on 28 June.

In recent years, one or more Orchard Orioles have occurred annually at Odiorne Point State Park, Rye, including an adult male carrying food, a female, and a second year male, on 22 June 1985 (NHBBA data). Similarly, a single bird or a pair have been sighted at the Amherst Country Club, Amherst, along the Souhegan River in at least 3 recent years (W. Goodwill, pers. comm.). The Atlas project also documented a pair in Newmarket in June 1985 and individual birds in Portsmouth and Dover. It seems likely that the Orchard Oriole will continue to be an uncommon and local breeding species in New Hampshire, primarily along the Coast and major river valleys.

Ralph Andrews

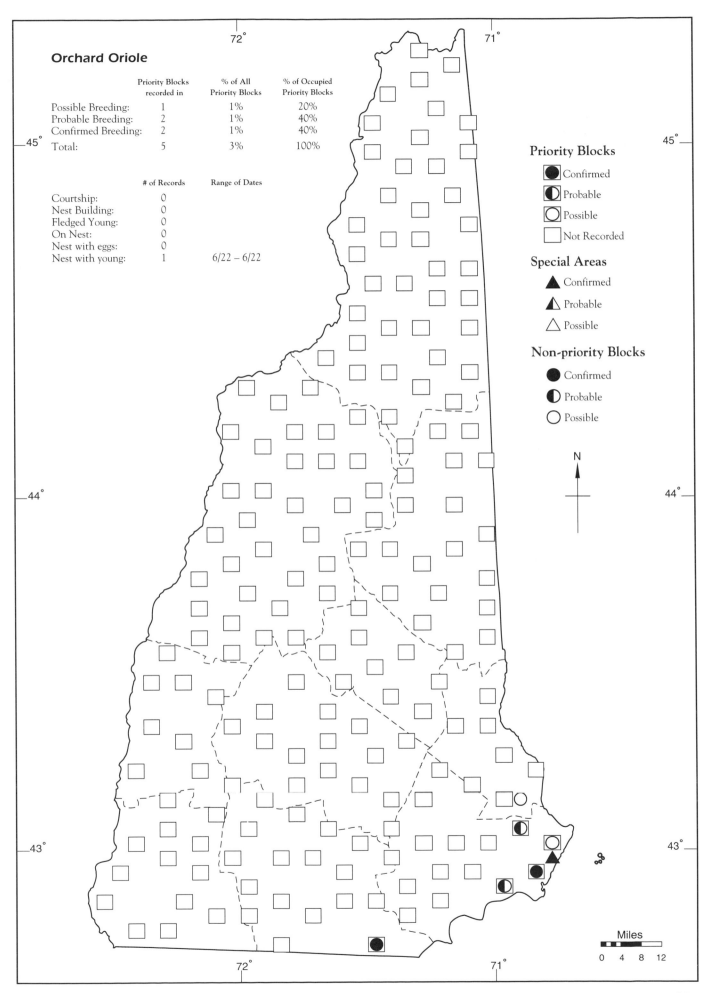

Orchard Oriole

	Priority Blocks recorded in	% of All Priority Blocks	% of Occupied Priority Blocks
Possible Breeding:	1	1%	20%
Probable Breeding:	2	1%	40%
Confirmed Breeding:	2	1%	40%
Total:	5	3%	100%

	# of Records	Range of Dates
Courtship:	0	
Nest Building:	0	
Fledged Young:	0	
On Nest:	0	
Nest with eggs:	0	
Nest with young:	1	6/22 – 6/22

Priority Blocks
- ● Confirmed
- ◐ Probable
- ○ Possible
- ☐ Not Recorded

Special Areas
- ▲ Confirmed
- ◤ Probable
- △ Possible

Non-priority Blocks
- ● Confirmed
- ◐ Probable
- ○ Possible

N

Miles
0 4 8 12

Northern Oriole
Icterus galbula

As cherry and apple trees come into bloom, Northern Orioles make a conspicuous return to New Hampshire with their animated song and unmistakable orange and black plumage. The males arrive here en masse in early May (White 1924), followed within days by the females. These birds are common summer residents of villages, suburbs, and open deciduous woodlands at elevations below 1,800 ft (550 m) (Ridgely 1988). They favor tall trees in or adjacent to open areas. Northern Orioles typically frequent treetops, and are most visible when singing or flying from one tree to another.

The Northern Oriole includes an Eastern subspecies, the "Baltimore" oriole, and a Western subspecies, the "Bullock's" oriole, which frequently interbreed, but were considered separate species until 1973 (AOU 1973). Adult male "Baltimore" Orioles are striking in their brilliant breeding plumage. It takes 2 years for young to attain full adult plumage. The orange plumage of first year males varies greatly in intensity, and the dark feathers are brownish rather than rich black. Females are orange below and grayish olive above, with rusty tails and dark heads and wings.

Courtship and nest building begin shortly after arrival and provide easy behavioral characteristics for atlasing. The male sings from the top of the selected nest tree, occasionally flies about the tree singing, and displays in front of the female by stretching himself into a vertical position, then quickly leaning forward and bowing deeply (Tyler 1958a).

The female collects long strips of plant fibers, grapevine bark, milkweed, and grasses in mid-May, and weaves them into a pensile nest in only 4 to 8 days (Harrison 1975). The tightly woven basket also may include (or consist entirely of) white yarn, string, or strands of rope. As trees leaf out, the nest becomes difficult to locate. It usually is 6.6 to 59 ft (2 to 18 m) above the ground (Harrison 1975) and near the end of a long drooping branch. The Northern Oriole always has preferred to nest in tall elms, but also will use other hardwood trees (Knight 1908 *in* Tyler 1958a). Ornithologists early in this century indicated that at least in some areas they then nested exclusively in elms (Forbush 1927, White 1937). Widespread loss of elms to Dutch elm disease may have forced them to accept other tree species. Nest trees in southern New Hampshire are often elms or maples, but also include locust, cottonwood, aspens, black willow, weeping willow, and an occasional white pine (J. Berry and R.A. Quinn, pers. comm.).

The female incubates her 3 to 6, usually 4 or 5 eggs for 12 to 14 days (Harrison 1975, Harrison 1978). Both parents tend the young, which fledge in about 2 weeks (Bendire 1895). Orioles are noisy neighbors and are quite vocal during their nesting period. The song is a series of loud, rollicking whistles, which varies between individuals (Dearborn 1903, Forbush 1927). Short, clear whistles constitute the call notes. The alarm call is an extended chattering.

Breeding confirmation is easy during June when adults are carrying food and young are calling ceaselessly, both before and after they fledge. In early July the male stops singing, and families move into maple swamps and overgrown pastures where they remain until the end of August (Forbush 1927, White 1937). Molt occurs during this period between the end of breeding activity and the beginning of fall migration (Rohwer and Manning 1990). The adult male may return to his territory in mid-August and may sing occasionally before departing at the end of the month or in early September. A few stragglers may remain at feeders in winter.

Orioles forage in treetops and shrubs for caterpillars, beetles, and other insects, including many injurious species (Forbush 1927). In late summer they frequent swamps and thickets, feeding on fruits and berries (Forbush 1927).

The Northern Oriole likely has increased in distribution and abundance in New Hampshire since European settlement. This is not a bird of dense forests, and its precolonial distribution may have been primarily in the relatively open bottomland forests along major floodplains and smaller stream banks, where elms abounded. The oriole readily occupied the elms planted as shade trees in villages, parks, cemeteries, and suburban neighborhoods, presumably expanding its distribution with the growing settlements. The species has been common in central and southern New Hampshire since the middle of the 19th century and probably earlier, but less common in the mountains and North Country where suitable habitat is scarce (Belknap 1792, Coues 1868, Maynard 1871, Goodhue 1877, Dearborn 1898, Allen 1903, Forbush 1927, White 1937, Ridgely 1977).

The Atlas documented the Northern Oriole in all but one priority block south of the White Mountains, but in less than half of those in Coos County, where suitable habitat occurs only in major valleys. Southern New Hampshire has undergone extensive residential and industrial development during the past 20 years, and Northern Orioles have benefited from the proliferation of shade trees along residential streets. New Hampshire's oriole population increased significantly during 1966–79 despite decreases in many other states (Robbins et al. 1986), and appears likely to thrive for the foreseeable future.

James McDermott

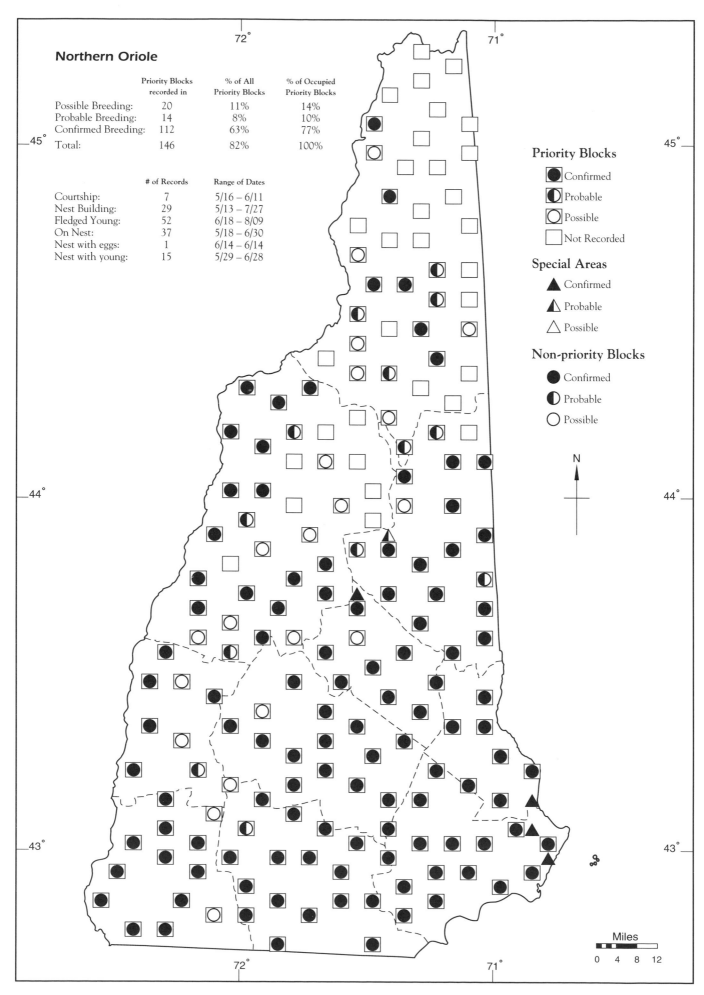

Northern Oriole

	Priority Blocks recorded in	% of All Priority Blocks	% of Occupied Priority Blocks
Possible Breeding:	20	11%	14%
Probable Breeding:	14	8%	10%
Confirmed Breeding:	112	63%	77%
Total:	146	82%	100%

	# of Records	Range of Dates
Courtship:	7	5/16 – 6/11
Nest Building:	29	5/13 – 7/27
Fledged Young:	52	6/18 – 8/09
On Nest:	37	5/18 – 6/30
Nest with eggs:	1	6/14 – 6/14
Nest with young:	15	5/29 – 6/28

Priority Blocks

● Confirmed
◑ Probable
○ Possible
☐ Not Recorded

Special Areas

▲ Confirmed
◮ Probable
△ Possible

Non-priority Blocks

● Confirmed
◑ Probable
○ Possible

N

Miles
0 4 8 12

Purple Finch
Carpodacus purpureus

Although our state bird is more pink than purple, the male's colors resemble the "royal purple" of old, which probably gave rise to the name. The adult male Purple Finch is largely rosy red, brightest on the top of its head and conspicuous on the rump, throat, and upper breast. Orange-red coloration on the similar male House Finch is restricted to the forehead, throat, and eyebrow; the rest of the bird is brown (Farrand 1983). The distinctive head of the female Purple Finch, with whitish eyebrow and face emphasizing dark brown cheeks and mustache, contrasts with the female House Finch's nondescript, finely streaked head.

The Purple Finch inhabits open mixed and coniferous woodlands, woodlots, and orchards (Godfrey 1979). It occurs throughout the state all year, but is less common in winter. Most Atlas "confirmations" were at elevations below 2,000 ft (610 m), but the species commonly occurs to 3,000 ft (Forbush 1929) and has been observed at elevations up to 5,000 ft (1,520 m) in the White Mountains during the breeding season (T. Richards, unpubl. data).

The diet of the Purple Finch is mainly seeds, fruits, and buds, but includes some insects, such as aphids and caterpillars. In early spring these finches may frequent orchards, eating flower buds of trees (Martin et al. 1951).

Our breeding population arrives mainly in April, and courtship occurs during late April and early May. Before and during nest building the male "dances" and sings in front of the female, either on the ground or on a branch. A "dancing" male hops around the female, dangling or vibrating his wings. He may pick up grass or straw in his bill and drop it. He parades in full song with beating wings, then rises straight in the air "a foot or so" (Bent 1968). Still singing, he drops beside her and postures with wings and tail spread, crest erect, and head and bill pointed upward. After copulation, the pair flies to a selected tree, the male still singing

(Wellman 1920 and Parkes 1940 *in* Bent 1968). The male also may perform an aerial display (Townsend 1920, Pearson 1936), in which he rises 200 to 300 ft (60 to 90 m) into the air singing, then sets his wings at a 45 angle and floats down in wide circles terminating where he began.

This species has 3 distinct songs and individual variations within them. The most commonly heard and recognized is the territorial and courtship song, a rapid warble, given from late April until July. Saunders (1929 *in* Bent 1968) describes the other 2 less common songs. Atlas records indicate peak song activity from mid-May to mid-June in southern New Hampshire, and continuing through June in the north.

The Purple Finch builds its nest in conifers, particularly spruce, 5 to 60 ft (1.5 to 18.3 m) from the ground (Bent 1968, Harrison 1975). The nest most commonly is located near the treetop on a horizontal branch, well hidden in thick foliage (Harrison 1975). The female builds it and incubates the 3 to 6, usually 4 or 5 eggs for 13 days, while the male feeds her on the nest (Bent 1968, Harrison 1975, Harrison 1978). Young birds spend 14 days in the nest and may fledge by 17 June (White 1924). Both adults tend the young for a considerable period after they have fledged, providing good opportunities for confirmations. Adults frequently bring their young to feeders. Juvenal plumage resembles that of the adult female, although the streaking is finer and the broad line over the eye is less distinct. The young utter a 2-note begging whistle while following the adults (Metcalf *in* Laughlin and Kibbe 1985). Southward migration begins in early September, peaks during October, and decreases rapidly in November. Banding data show that New Hampshire's summer residents move into New Jersey, Pennsylvania, Maryland, and Virginia for the winter and are replaced in our state by populations from further north (Kennard 1963). CBC data indicate that wintering populations have moved into New Hampshire by the end of December. The Purple Finch is erratic and relatively mobile during the winter months. Its distribution during winter and spring depends upon an available seed supply (Martin et al. 1951, Knight 1908 *in* Bent 1968).

This bird long has been a common summer resident of New Hampshire (Allen 1903, Forbush 1929, Thayer 1909 *in* Allison and Allison 1979). Several authors (Forbush 1929, Allen 1869 and Brewster 1906 *in* Bent 1968, Bent 1968) noted a decline of the species in the vicinity of Boston after starlings and House Sparrows became established there. Declines have occurred locally in New Hampshire's large urban centers as well, but habitat changes may be as important as interspecific competition.

Atlas workers documented the Purple Finch throughout New Hampshire, with only 5 priority blocks lacking records. The southernmost of these blocks are in relatively urban settings and truly may lack the species. Additional Atlas effort in the 2 northern blocks almost certainly would have produced Purple Finch records. Although some authors recently have expressed concern over possible displacement of Purple Finches by expanding populations of House Finches in the Northeast (Arbib 1982), BBS data from 1966 to 1979 indicate no declines in Purple Finch numbers in areas where House Finches also breed (Robbins et al. 1986). New Hampshire's state bird seems secure in its wooded habitats for the foreseeable future.

James McDermott

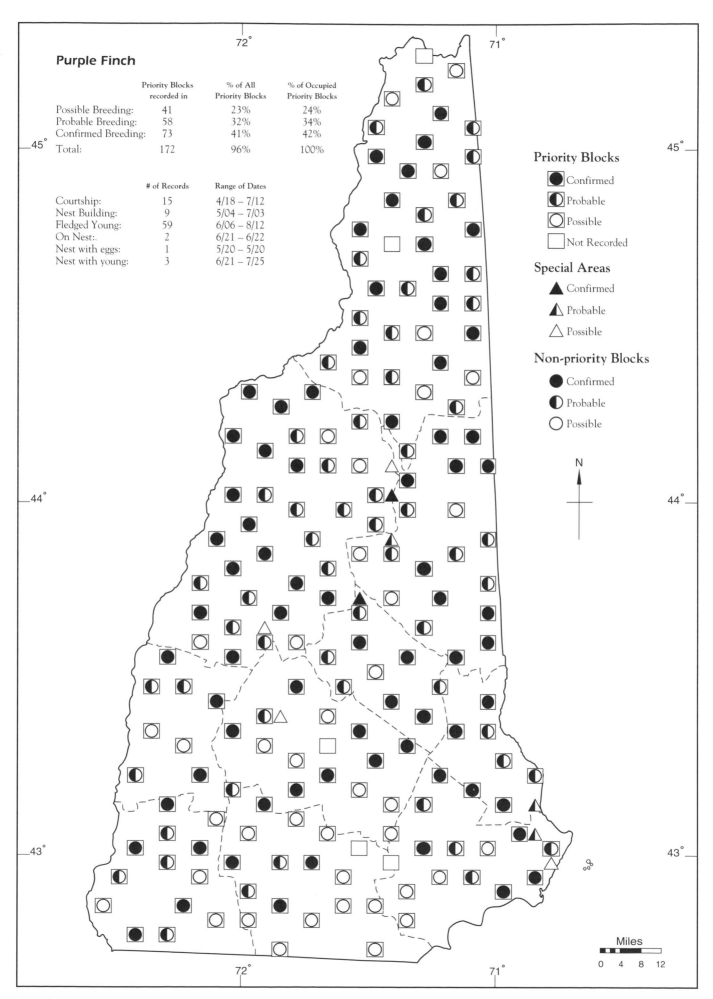

Purple Finch

	Priority Blocks recorded in	% of All Priority Blocks	% of Occupied Priority Blocks
Possible Breeding:	41	23%	24%
Probable Breeding:	58	32%	34%
Confirmed Breeding:	73	41%	42%
Total:	172	96%	100%

	# of Records	Range of Dates
Courtship:	15	4/18 – 7/12
Nest Building:	9	5/04 – 7/03
Fledged Young:	59	6/06 – 8/12
On Nest:	2	6/21 – 6/22
Nest with eggs:	1	5/20 – 5/20
Nest with young:	3	6/21 – 7/25

Priority Blocks

● Confirmed
◐ Probable
○ Possible
□ Not Recorded

Special Areas

▲ Confirmed
◣ Probable
△ Possible

Non-priority Blocks

● Confirmed
◐ Probable
○ Possible

N

Miles
0 4 8 12

House Finch
Carpodacus mexicanus

New Hampshire bird watchers are learning to distinguish this pretty Western finch from our state bird, the Purple Finch, as the House Finch crowds our bird feeders and fills our yards with its cheerful song. Compared to the raspberry-colored male Purple Finch, the male House Finch is smaller, with a flatter head and orange-red crown, breast, and rump. There are confusing color gradations between orange and red House Finch males, but the brown-streaked females of the 2 finch species are quite different. The pale, dull-plumaged female House Finch has a smaller bill and lacks the dark cheek patch of the female Purple Finch.

An increasingly abundant but local permanent resident since the first New Hampshire record in 1967, the House Finch frequents human habitations. It occurs at 1,500 ft (460 m) elevation in New Hampshire's highest town, Washington, Hillsborough County. In the West, where it is the most abundant finch, it nests at elevations up to 7,000 ft (2,150 m).

House Finches travel in pairs throughout the year, and may mate for life (Bergtold 1913 *in* Woods 1968). The breeding season begins in April. A courting male flutters its wings and sings with its "tail up, wings drooping, head up and crest feathers raised" (Hoffmann 1927 *in* Woods 1968). The long, variable song is a loud, rhythmic warbling, ending with an ascending buzzy note. It resembles the song of the Purple Finch, but is less musical. The female occasionally sings too.

In cities and suburbs, farmlands and parks, House Finches nest in trees and in a variety of other places including tree or building cavities, old hats, tin cans or stovepipes, and the abandoned nests of other birds such as orioles and phoebes (Woods 1968). They even nest in hanging planters on open porches. In April 1981, students at the University of New Hampshire, Durham, documented 17 pairs of House Finches on campus, and additional unmated birds at about 10 nest sites. These birds preferred buildings with ledges and thick vine

growth. They also used oaks, conifers, and evergreen shrubs next to buildings (Bowen et al. 1982).

The female House Finch builds a well-made nest of grass and twigs. One finch used string as a guy wire to fasten an insecure nest to a nail on a narrow joist (Woods 1968)! A female may use the same nest for subsequent broods and sometimes in successive years (Woods 1968). If the nest is destroyed, she usually rebuilds in the same site.

The female House Finch incubates her 2 to 6, usually 4 or 5 eggs for 12 to 14 days and produces 2 or more broods. The nestling period is 11 to 19 days (Terres 1980). Both parents tend their young and regurgitate food to the chicks. Because they do not remove fecal sacs after the first several days, excreta accumulates on the nest edge beginning in the second week after hatching (Evenden 1957). Fledglings perch in trees several days before flying and do not return to their nest (Woods 1968). Dandelion seeds are a common meal for young finches (Terres 1980).

After breeding, House Finch families gather in flocks in weedy fields or orchards, where they may damage fruit. The birds are fond of hemp seed, and, in the spring, of buds and maple sap from broken branches. Unlike House Sparrows they do not eat seeds from horse manure. They are gregarious, however, and gather throughout the year in flocks. Individuals show much variety in both plumage and personality, from tame to quarrelsome (Woods 1968). They choose high perches and usually fly over, rather than between, trees and buildings.

The House Finch is native to western North America, but was introduced on the East Coast. In 1940, California cage-bird dealers shipped illegally captured House Finches, glamorously named "Hollywood finches," to dealers in New York for sale as cage birds. Authorities stopped this traffic, which violated the Migratory Bird Treaty Act. To avoid prosecution, the dealers released the birds on Long Island. Although they had a difficult time surviving, the finches eventually adapted to the new climate and nested successfully in Babylon, N. Y., in 1943. After 1953 they began to spread westward, southward, and northward (Elliott and Arbib 1953, Terres 1980). House Finches have been increasing in the Eastern states ever since.

G. W. Cottrell reported New Hampshire's first House Finch on 8 April 1967 in Hillsboro; N. Struckoff spotted another bird 6 days later in Concord (SRS). D. Finch and C. Hess reported a single male in Errol in November and December 1969 (Smart 1970). In the summer of 1975, T.E. Harwood saw a pair with young in Manchester, and E. McCrillis found 2 pairs with young in Hampton (Hebert 1975).

The Seacoast CBC was the first in New Hampshire to report House Finches, with 3 in 1970 (Anderson 1971). In 1975, 105 House Finches doubled the Seacoast total for the previous year (Parker 1976). House Finches occurred on inland CBCs by 1980, and state CBC totals for House Finches were 201 in 1981 and 623 in 1986. BBS data suggest an average annual increase of 21% in the Eastern region from 1966 to 1979 (Robbins et al. 1986).

The Atlas documented House Finches in half (89) of the priority blocks. As the Atlas map indicates, New Hampshire's House Finch population currently exists largely in the southern half of the state, but is beginning to infiltrate the north. Although absent from boreal habitat and elevations above 2,000 ft (610 m), elsewhere in the state the House Finch clearly is here to stay.

Elizabeth C. Janeway

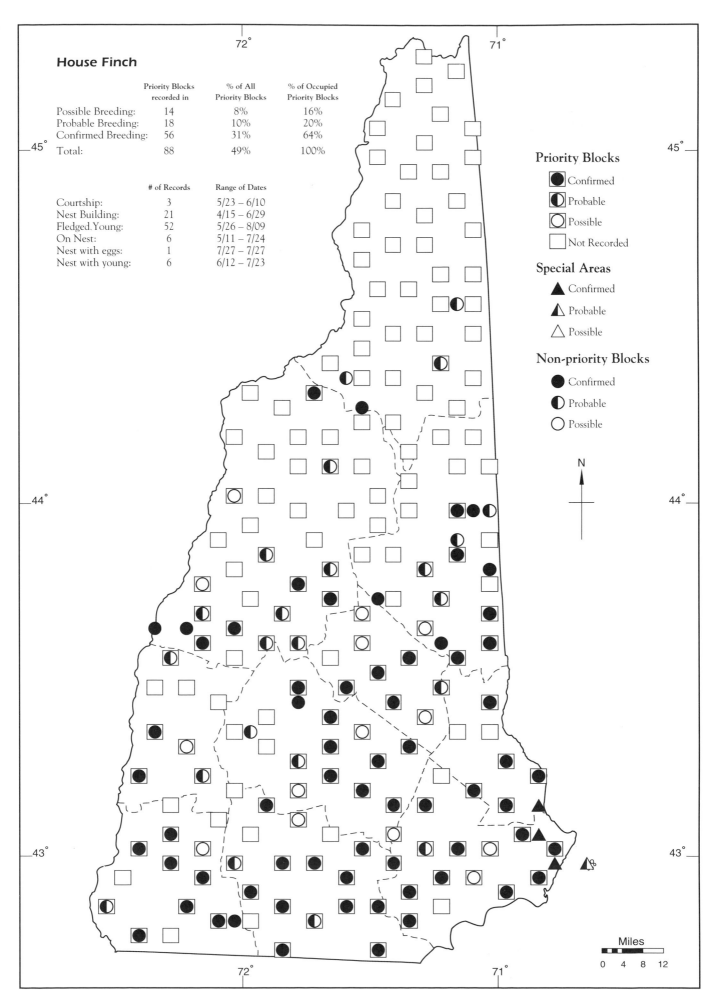

House Finch

	Priority Blocks recorded in	% of All Priority Blocks	% of Occupied Priority Blocks
Possible Breeding:	14	8%	16%
Probable Breeding:	18	10%	20%
Confirmed Breeding:	56	31%	64%
Total:	88	49%	100%

	# of Records	Range of Dates
Courtship:	3	5/23 – 6/10
Nest Building:	21	4/15 – 6/29
Fledged Young:	52	5/26 – 8/09
On Nest:	6	5/11 – 7/24
Nest with eggs:	1	7/27 – 7/27
Nest with young:	6	6/12 – 7/23

Priority Blocks
- ◐ Confirmed
- ◑ Probable
- ◯ Possible
- ☐ Not Recorded

Special Areas
- ▲ Confirmed
- ◩ Probable
- △ Possible

Non-priority Blocks
- ● Confirmed
- ◑ Probable
- ◯ Possible

N

Miles
0 4 8 12

Red Crossbill
Loxia curvirostra

The Red Crossbill is a sporadic inhabitant of coniferous and mixed forests, and is associated especially with pines (Newton 1973, AOU 1983). It occurs across Canada and the northern U.S. and southward in the western mountains into Mexico (NGS 1983). Populations of this species sporadically travel extraordinary distances from their "core range" to nest in suitable habitat thousands of miles from their usual breeding range, and subsequently disappear (Dickerman 1986a). Red Crossbills breed erratically in New Hampshire, and nesting dates and locations are unpredictable. They are less common in New Hampshire than White-winged Crossbills and nest further south in the state.

The division of North America's Red Crossbill population into subspecies has been complex and confusing. In an effort to clarify the nomenclature, Dickerman (1986a) described 6 subspecies with core ranges in Newfoundland, the central and eastern portions of southern Canada and the northern U.S. (including New England), the Pacific Northwest, the western U.S., the Southern Appalachians, and Mexico. New York invasions most commonly involve the Pacific Northwest subspecies (Dickerman 1986b).

Plumages of subspecies differ somewhat. However, a breeding adult male is generally brick red with a bright red rump, dusky wings, and a dark tail (Terres 1980). In summer, it may be duller, from pale rose to brownish scarlet (Forbush 1929). The breeding female is dusky yellow or yellowish olive with dark wings and tail, yellowish rump, and gray throat (Forbush 1929, Terres 1980). Uniformly dark wings distinguish the Red Crossbill from the White-winged Crossbill.

The Red Crossbill moves slowly and deliberately while feeding, using bill and feet to climb about the tree "like a little parrot" (Forbush 1929). A crossbill may hang by its beak or a foot, and when startled, may hide upside down in foliage (Forbush 1929). Red Crossbills eat seeds of pines, firs, spruces, hemlocks, and larches (Bent 1968), using their crossed, curved mandibles to pry open cone scales and their tongues to lift out the seeds (Terres 1980). The noise of opening cones sometimes reveals a flock's presence; the flock also may chatter or twitter while feeding (Forbush 1929). Red Crossbills also eat seeds of birches, alders, willows, poplars, elms, and maples; spruce buds; caterpillars, aphids, beetles, ants, and gall insects; and wild fruit (Forbush 1929, Bent 1968). Roadside salt and grit are important in the diet (Ridgely 1977). Rarely, the birds may come to feeders for sunflower seeds (Ridgely 1977).

Conifer seed abundance and availability determine where and when Red Crossbills nest (Forbush 1929). Pairs usually nest from mid-January to early spring, but may do so in any season. Forbush (1929) reported nesting from mid-January to July in Maine, and Bent (1968) cited a report of August nesting in Nova Scotia.

Male Red Crossbills have 2 songs, which they proclaim when pairing begins. They often sing from tall treetops. The perching song is loud but short, consisting of whistled notes interspersed with warbled phrases (Lawrence 1949). Crossbill flight is rapid and undulating, and the flight song is an elaborate series of "gyp" or "kip" notes (Forbush 1929). During the peak of courtship, the males mix perch and flight songs together in longer vocalizations (Lawrence 1949). The Red Crossbill's call is a "yip," "kip," "gyp," or "pip" note that resembles a chicken peep, and is often repeated as "kip-kip" or "kip-kip-kip" (Forbush 1929). Red Crossbills also produce a trill that sounds like the vibrating wings of the woodcock's display flight (Forbush 1929).

The nest is located 5 to 80 ft (1.5 to 24.4 m) from the ground on a conifer branch, some distance out from the trunk (Harrison 1975). The female incubates her 2 to 5, usually 3 or 4 eggs for 12 to 16 days, seldom leaving the nest (Newton 1973, Harrison 1975, Harrison 1978). The male's food deliveries, every 2 or 3 hours, can help a patient observer to locate the nest (Harrison 1975). Young leave the nest after 17 to 22 days and become independent 3 to 4 weeks later (Harrison 1978).

Since the late 1800s, observers throughout New Hampshire have recorded erratic visits of Red Crossbills in every month of the year. They were common at Umbagog Lake during the summer of 1870 (Maynard 1871). Dearborn (1903) observed them in the Durham area in April, May, August, September, and November of 1901, and mentions that they were abundant during the fall of 1899 until December. White (1924) observed flocks of 10 birds in May 1900 and June 1903 near Concord. Presumably these early records represented the "Old Northeastern" subspecies, which experienced a major population crash during 1905–12 (Dickerman 1986a).

New Hampshire records of Red Crossbills during 1938–68 indicate irruptions in 1948, 1953–54, 1960–61, and 1963–64 (RNEB, NHAQ, *passim*). The few New Hampshire nesting records have been from recent years. One nest was found at Squam Lake in 1972 (Ridgely 1977), and a record of a female at a feeder in Dublin on 2 June 1974 suggests possible nesting there (Allison and Allison 1979).

Nearly all Atlas observations and the only "confirmations" of Red Crossbills were in January and February 1985, and all "confirmations" are from the southern part of the state. BBS data from 1966 to 1979 reflect the local fluctuations in Red Crossbill numbers from year to year (Robbins et al. 1986). This crossbill's future distribution and abundance in New Hampshire will continue to be erratic and unpredictable, and a future Atlas project might produce a completely different pattern of distribution.

Susan Absalom Staats

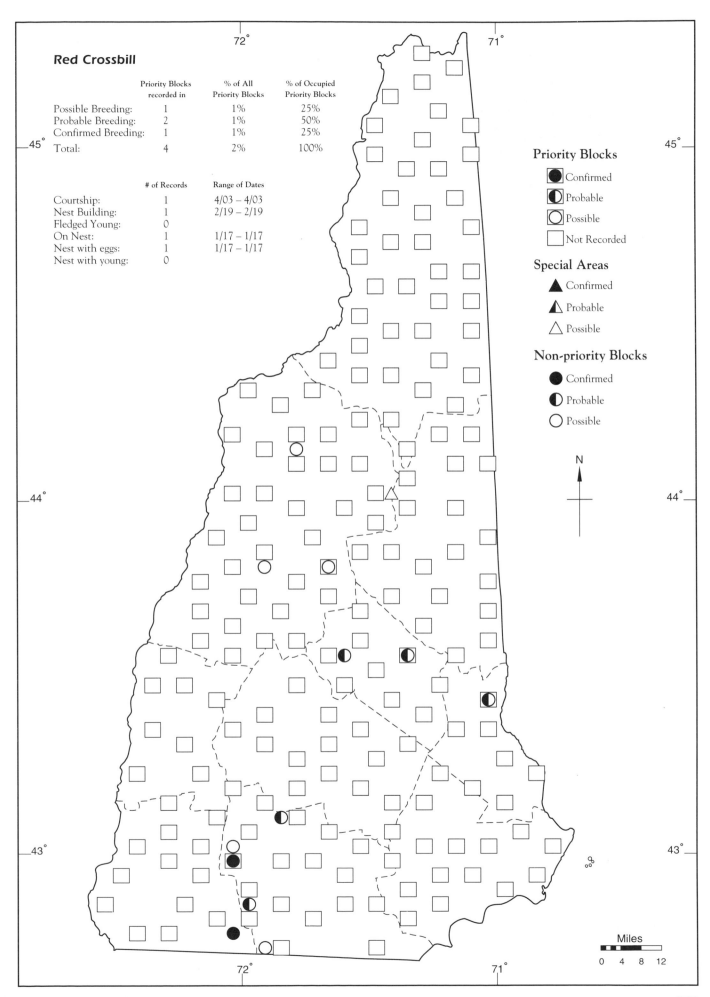

Red Crossbill

	Priority Blocks recorded in	% of All Priority Blocks	% of Occupied Priority Blocks
Possible Breeding:	1	1%	25%
Probable Breeding:	2	1%	50%
Confirmed Breeding:	1	1%	25%
Total:	4	2%	100%

	# of Records	Range of Dates
Courtship:	1	4/03 – 4/03
Nest Building:	1	2/19 – 2/19
Fledged Young:	0	
On Nest:	1	1/17 – 1/17
Nest with eggs:	1	1/17 – 1/17
Nest with young:	0	

Priority Blocks

● Confirmed
◐ Probable
○ Possible
□ Not Recorded

Special Areas

▲ Confirmed
◤ Probable
△ Possible

Non-priority Blocks

● Confirmed
◐ Probable
○ Possible

N

Miles
0 4 8 12

White-winged Crossbill
Loxia leucoptera

The White-winged Crossbill, like the Red Crossbill, is remarkable for its irregular wanderings and nesting times and for its scissorlike mandibles. Wing bars distinguish both White-wing sexes from Red Crossbills. While a small, permanent White-wing population may exist in the White Mountains and North Country, several years may pass with no reports of the species anywhere in New Hampshire. Nevertheless, it is sometimes common in the spruce-fir regions of the state (ASNH data). Its erratic distribution is associated with patterns of cone crop production by northern conifers (Lumsden and Smith *in* Cadman et al. 1987).

This circumpolar species includes Old and New world subspecies. The North American subspecies, *L. leucoptera leucoptera*, nests from Alaska to Labrador and south to the Lake states and northern New England, where it breeds sporadically (AOU 1957). It wanders, chiefly in winter, occasionally as far south as North Carolina (Forbush and May 1939). Males stay mostly in flocks throughout the year, separating only to perform courtship flights and feed incubating females (Forbush and May 1939).

White-winged Crossbills typically begin breeding in early February (Harrison 1978), but may nest in any month of the year (Godfrey 1966). Many breed between January and May (Harrison 1975), but most Ontario Atlas records during a 1984 irruption were from July to September (Cadman et al. 1987). Brewster found the species in breeding condition in August and September at Umbagog Lake (Griscom 1938). In one Nova Scotia locality, Tufts (*in* Taber 1968) found nests with young in January and both fully fledged young and nests with eggs in May.

Although nesting may be somewhat colonial (Taber 1968), each male claims 1 to 2 a (0.4 to 0.8 ha) around a particular spruce, which may contain the nest, singing from its tip (Messineo 1985). The male White-wing has a beautiful canarylike song, full of loud trills

and chips, and often sings in flight. Both sexes give chattering calls and "pink pink" notes. Courting males fly in circles above females with slowly beating wings, singing continuously, and finally settling on treetops with quivering, outstretched wings (Grinnell *in* Taber 1968). White-winged Crossbills may respond aggressively to tape-recorded calls of either crossbill species early in the breeding season (Messineo 1985).

White-wings build deep, cup-shaped nests in spruces, a few feet to 70 ft (21.3 m) above the ground on horizontal limbs (Harrison 1975). One nest in Maine consisted of plant stems, evergreen twigs, bits of moss, and a few insect cocoons, lined with rootlets and tendrils (Smith *in* Taber 1968). Another was 10 ft (3.0 m) from the ground and 2 to 3 ft (0.6 to 0.9 m) from the tree trunk in a spruce grove of about an acre. Both male and female worked on the nest, which was finished on 19 July 1889 (Hardy to Brewster *in* Palmer 1949). Apparently no one has observed a nest in New Hampshire.

A typical clutch includes 3 or 4 eggs (Harrison 1978). The male may feed an incubating female by regurgitation (Tufts *in* Taber 1968) but apparently does not always help feed the young (Bond *in* Taber 1968). An incubating female allows the male to approach no nearer than a few feet (Egan *in* Taber 1968) unless he is feeding her. The incubation and nestling periods are unknown (Harrison 1975, Harrison 1978). The young do not have crossed bills at fledging (Klugh *in* Taber 1968), but crossing may begin to develop within about 10 days (Messineo 1985). They acquire adult plumage in their second year (Dwight *in* Taber 1968).

Crossbills' mandibles may cross either way and are effective in extracting seeds from spruce, larch, and fir cones. These birds also eat carpels of undeveloped cones, various other seeds and fruits, and some insects (Taber 1968).

The White-winged Crossbill's history in New Hampshire is one of irregular fluctuations at all seasons. Allen (1903) considered the White-wing a permanent resident of spruce-fir forests at elevations above 3,000 ft (910 m) in the White Mountains and in the North Country. Brewster recorded it on visits to the Umbagog Lake area in 15 of 32 years from 1871 to 1909 (Griscom 1938), and Wright (1911) observed it in the Jefferson region in 5 years from 1904 to 1910. Thayer (1909 *in* Allison and Allison 1979) believed that the species probably nested on Mt. Monadnock, Jaffrey.

There appear to be few significant New Hampshire White-winged Crossbill records for several decades following 1909, when both observers and ornithological publications were generally lacking. Spruce-fir forest birds likely decreased in New Hampshire following extensive clearcutting and forest fires from 1870 to 1923. Since 1948 there have been more years with records than without (ASNH data). Most summer records are from the White Mountains or North Country, but some are from southern New Hampshire (ASNH data). New Hampshire data from RNEB (*passim*) indicate irruptions in 1948–49, 1953, 1958, and 1965, with the majority of irruption records from July to October.

Despite the lack of "confirmed" breeding records, this species probably nested in New Hampshire during the Atlas period. Nearly two-thirds of Atlas records for this species are from the irruption of 1984–85; nearly half are from 1984 alone. Most Atlas records are from the North Country, and the majority are from July and August. The status of the White-winged Crossbill in New Hampshire has changed little in recent decades. Barring disappearance of spruce-fir forests, the species likely will continue to be an irregular breeder in New Hampshire.

Tudor Richards

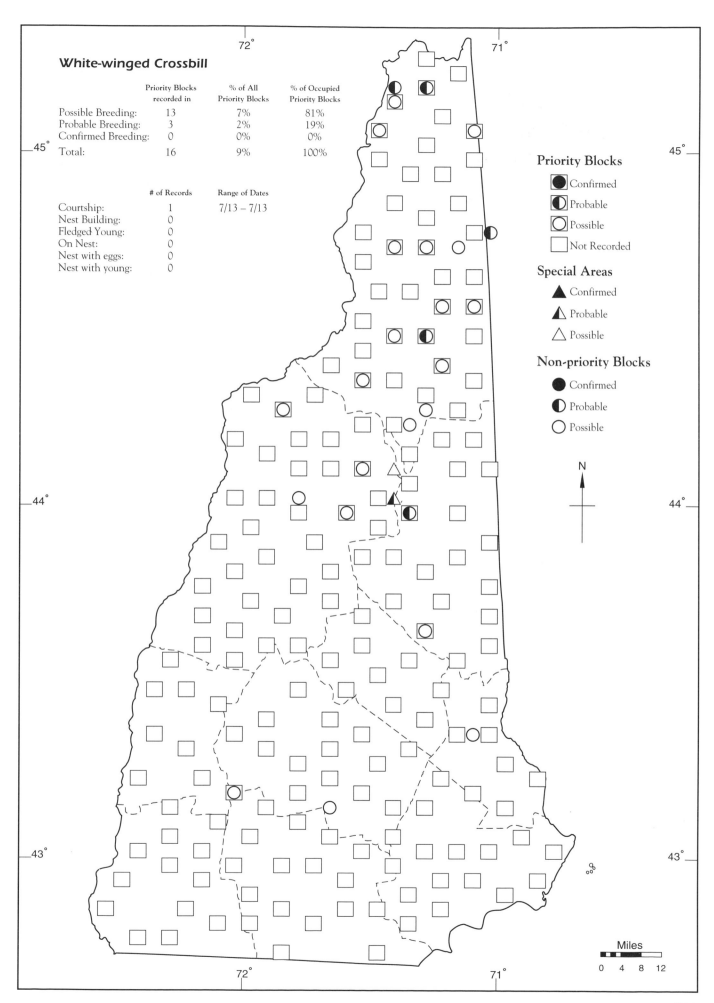

White-winged Crossbill

	Priority Blocks recorded in	% of All Priority Blocks	% of Occupied Priority Blocks
Possible Breeding:	13	7%	81%
Probable Breeding:	3	2%	19%
Confirmed Breeding:	0	0%	0%
Total:	16	9%	100%

	# of Records	Range of Dates
Courtship:	1	7/13 – 7/13
Nest Building:	0	
Fledged Young:	0	
On Nest:	0	
Nest with eggs:	0	
Nest with young:	0	

Priority Blocks

● Confirmed
◐ Probable
○ Possible
□ Not Recorded

Special Areas

▲ Confirmed
◢ Probable
△ Possible

Non-priority Blocks

● Confirmed
◐ Probable
○ Possible

N

Miles
0 4 8 12

Pine Siskin
Carduelis pinus

This heavily streaked, small finch, with its nasal calls and busy, nervous nature, is an unpredictable inhabitant of New Hampshire woodlands. The Pine Siskin's usual breeding range includes the coniferous forests of Canada, northern New England, and New York, but it sporadically nests further south during invasion years. In New Hampshire, this nomadic finch occurs somewhat irregularly even in the North County and at higher elevations in the mountains. South of the White Mountains, Pine Siskins are most common from March to May and October to December (Ridgely 1988), but are irregular even at these seasons, and more so as winter residents. Sporadic breeding in southern New Hampshire has been known since early in this century (Allen 1903, Thayer 1909 *in* Allison and Allison 1979). The proliferation of bird feeders may have contributed to an increased frequency of southern New Hampshire nesting records in recent years.

Primary breeding habitat includes coniferous and mixed forests, but siskins also nest in suburban shade trees. Breeding begins early, often when thick snows still blanket the forest floor. On crisp clear days in February the songs of male siskins create a chorus from frosted treetops as large flocks, often including goldfinches, roam through the canopy. The song is a succession of sweet notes with occasional "screeks." The call, given year round, is a thin, wheezy, rising "swee-ee-e-t," which resembles a call of the closely related American Goldfinch. The common flight note, "tit-a-tit" (Saunders 1935), readily identifies siskins overhead.

Pairs form and flocks separate into smaller groups during mid-March to May. Pair formation involves courtship feeding and flight song performances, in which a male circles a female. The groups form loose nesting colonies, in which nests may be only a few rods (16.5 ft [5.03 m]/1 rod) apart (Palmer 1968). A pair defends a small territory of 3 to 6 ft (0.9 to 1.8 m) around its nest (Weaver and West 1943).

The nest site is typically 6 to 35 ft (1.8 to 10.7 m) up in a large conifer (Harrison 1975), and well out on a lateral branch (Harrison 1978). Nest sites usually are in conifers (Palmer 1968). The male accompanies the female as she gathers twigs, rootlets, and other plant material to build the compact and well-concealed nest, lining it with hair, fur, and fine plant fibers. Siskins sometimes obtain nesting materials by dismantling old nests of other species (Dales and Bennett 1929, Weaver and West 1943). One nest in Hanover was completed on 31 March 1943, and another, begun on or shortly before 8 April 1941, was mostly finished 5 days later (Weaver and West 1943).

Egg laying may begin in mid-March and peaks in April. The clutch includes 2 to 6, commonly 3 or 4 eggs (Harrison 1975). Two nests in Hanover contained eggs on 17 and 18 April 1878 (Allen 1903), and egg laying at another began on 18 April 1941 (Weaver and West 1943). The female begins incubation with the first egg and incubates alone for about 13 days. In that time she rarely strays far from the nest, and the male feeds her directly or by regurgitation (Weaver and West 1943).

For about a week after hatching, the male continues to feed the female, and she regurgitates food to the young. Thereafter, the female begins to forage again, and both parents feed the young by regurgitating a mixture of insects and seeds (Weaver and West 1943, Palmer 1968). The female eats the fecal sacs before she begins to forage, but thereafter excrement builds up on the edge of the nest to form a characteristic rim, as with goldfinches (Weaver and West 1943). Young leave the nest at 14 to 16 days of age (Harrison 1978).

The siskin's sharply pointed bill enables it to feed on seed heads of many plant species. This finch tends to favor conifer seeds, hanging from cones like an acrobat while prying open the seed cases. It readily takes seeds of alder, birch, and several other hardwood species, as well as forbs. In the breeding season about one-sixth of the diet consists of insects, especially caterpillars, plant lice, aphids, scale insects, and grasshoppers (McAtee 1926 *in* Palmer 1968).

There is some evidence that Pine Siskins may be double-brooded (Brewster *in* Griscom 1938), and Atlas data include a late July record of an adult carrying food or fecal sacs. The scarcity of "confirmed" Atlas records for this species demonstrates the difficulty of observing this species at the nest. Historical accounts of the Pine Siskin in New Hampshire reflect its nomadic habits. Allen (1903) considered the species a common permanent resident of northern forests and elevations above 3,000 ft (910 m) in the White Mountains. However, Wright (1911) found it uncommon as a summer resident in the Jefferson region and nesting only sparingly on the Presidential Range. Brewster found it common in some years and absent in others in the vicinity of Umbagog Lake during his field work there in the late 1800s and early 1900s (Griscom 1938). Notable incursions in New Hampshire have occurred in 1873 (Griscom 1938), 1878 (Weaver and West 1943), 1899 (Dearborn 1903), 1941 (Weaver and West 1943), and 1958 to 1960 (RNEB, *passim*).

Atlas workers recorded Pine Siskins in 44% of New Hampshire's priority blocks, compared to only 8% of Vermont's (Laughlin and Kibbe 1985). Most New Hampshire records resulted from a major incursion in 1985, when many siskins lingered in southern New Hampshire into the summer. Lacking this incursion, our data for this species likely would have resembled Vermont's, which were collected during 1976–81.

Iain C. MacLeod

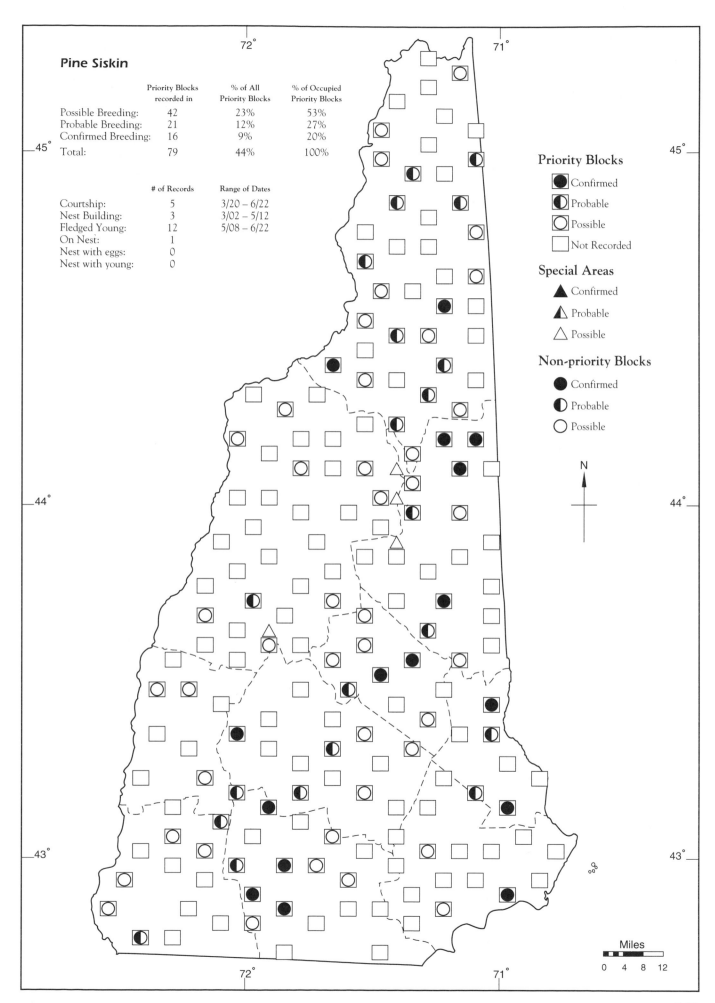

Pine Siskin

	Priority Blocks recorded in	% of All Priority Blocks	% of Occupied Priority Blocks
Possible Breeding:	42	23%	53%
Probable Breeding:	21	12%	27%
Confirmed Breeding:	16	9%	20%
Total:	79	44%	100%

	# of Records	Range of Dates
Courtship:	5	3/20 – 6/22
Nest Building:	3	3/02 – 5/12
Fledged Young:	12	5/08 – 6/22
On Nest:	1	
Nest with eggs:	0	
Nest with young:	0	

Priority Blocks
- ● Confirmed
- ◐ Probable
- ○ Possible
- ☐ Not Recorded

Special Areas
- ▲ Confirmed
- ◣ Probable
- △ Possible

Non-priority Blocks
- ● Confirmed
- ◐ Probable
- ○ Possible

N

Miles
0 4 8 12

American Goldfinch
Carduelis tristis

The male goldfinch is the only New Hampshire bird that appears all yellow except for black wings and tail. Close inspection reveals a small black cap. The female's colors are duller, and she lacks the black cap. This species can be recognized in the air by its undulating flight pattern. The song, which varies considerably among individuals, is a long, high, sweet warble, somewhat resembling that of the Purple Finch. Its call is often described as "per-chic-o-ree." The goldfinch is common throughout New Hampshire at elevations below 2,500 ft (760 m) (Ridgely 1988; T. Richards, unpubl. data). T. Richards (unpubl. data) has observed this species flying overhead in the White Mountains above 3,500 ft (1,070 m) elevation.

Goldfinches are most common in open country such as fields or pastures with hedgerows or scattered bushes, but also occur in open woods with scattered trees. Concentrations of goldfinches frequently occur in or near wetlands. They may nest near houses in residential areas (Nickell 1951).

Spring molt occurs in April and early May, and birds that arrive from the south during the mid-April to mid-May migration are in summer plumage. Upon arrival on the breeding grounds, males begin to sing from prominent perches. Despite their early arrival, goldfinches are among the last of our songbirds to begin nesting. They pair soon after returning, and then are quiet for several weeks to 2 months until they select a territory in June or July (Drum 1939, Stokes 1950). The males' territorial behavior includes display flights, short songs from prominent perches, and chasing intruding males (Stokes 1979).

The female begins nest building a few weeks after the territory is established. The male often accompanies her as she gathers fibrous nesting material (Walkinshaw 1938). Nesting is timed to coincide with the availability of down from cattails, thistles, and other flowers, which is used to line the densely woven,

compact nest (Nickell 1951, Harrison 1975). Goldfinch nests may be in a wide variety of trees and shrubs, and occasionally in tall, sturdy forbs such as thistles (Tyler 1968). Nests usually are in a fork of 2 or 3 branches from 4 to 20 ft (1.2 to 6.1 m) above the ground (Forbush 1929, Walkinshaw 1938). Walkinshaw (1938) found no cowbird parasitism in 111 nests observed, probably because goldfinches are such late nesters.

The female incubates her 4 or 5 eggs for 12 to 14 days (Walkinshaw 1938). The male remains in the vicinity of the nest and brings food to the incubating and brooding female. He circles conspicuously over the nest when he returns with food, and drops to feed her a regurgitated mash of plant seeds when she calls (Walkinshaw 1938). The female broods newly hatched young for the first several days and feeds them by regurgitation (Walkinshaw 1938). Both parents feed older nestlings. The parents do not remove fecal sacs after the young are a week old, and a distinctive rim of excrement builds up on the edge of the nest during the 10 to 17 day nestling period (Stokes 1950, Harrison 1978). Fledged young remain dependent on their parents for about 2 weeks (Stokes 1950) and often fly with them, giving a distinctive 2-syllable hunger call (Walkinshaw 1938).

Fall migration peaks from mid-August to mid-September. The fall molt starts in September, and males assume winter plumage, which is markedly duller than that of summer. The black wings remain to distinguish this species from other winter finches. Flocks of goldfinches often occur in New Hampshire through the winter, but their presence and movements are erratic. In some years they are common, but in other years, none are to be seen.

Although they are primarily seed eaters, goldfinches also eat buds and insects in spring when seeds are scarce. Dandelion seeds are an important source of food when they are mature. Later on, goldfinches consume many other kinds of seeds, especially those of goldenrods, asters, and other composites, as well as some garden weeds, especially amaranth and pigweed. Goldfinches also feed on filamentous algae, gathered from the surface of ponds, thereby obtaining a good source of protein (Kilham 1980). In winter, when weed seeds are covered by snow, they depend on birch and alder catkins and seeds of hemlock, spruce, and larch, as well as sunflower and other seeds available at bird feeders.

The American Goldfinch long has been a common summer resident in New Hampshire (Dearborn 1898, Allen 1903, Dearborn 1903, Forbush 1929, White 1937). Allen (1903) described this species as "a common permanent resident over most of the state save the deeply wooded portions above 3,000 ft" (909 m). Wright (1911) considered the goldfinch very common in the Jefferson area during the summer months, but absent in winter. Maynard (1871) also indicated that this species left northern New Hampshire for the winter.

As the Atlas map illustrates, the American Goldfinch breeds throughout southern New Hampshire. While observers may have missed the species in some priority blocks, records, suitable habitat is more locally distributed in the mountainous and extensively forested northern part of the state. Ten of the 15 blocks lacking records are in Coos County.

BBS data from 1966 to 1979 indicate a population decline east of the Mississippi River (Robbins et al. 1986). Although this trend was evident in New Hampshire through 1985 (C.S. Robbins, pers. comm.), the goldfinch remains common throughout the state. Some habitat loss has occurred as weedy fields have given way to woods or developments, but this species tolerates most human activity and likely will remain common here.

Frederic L. Steele

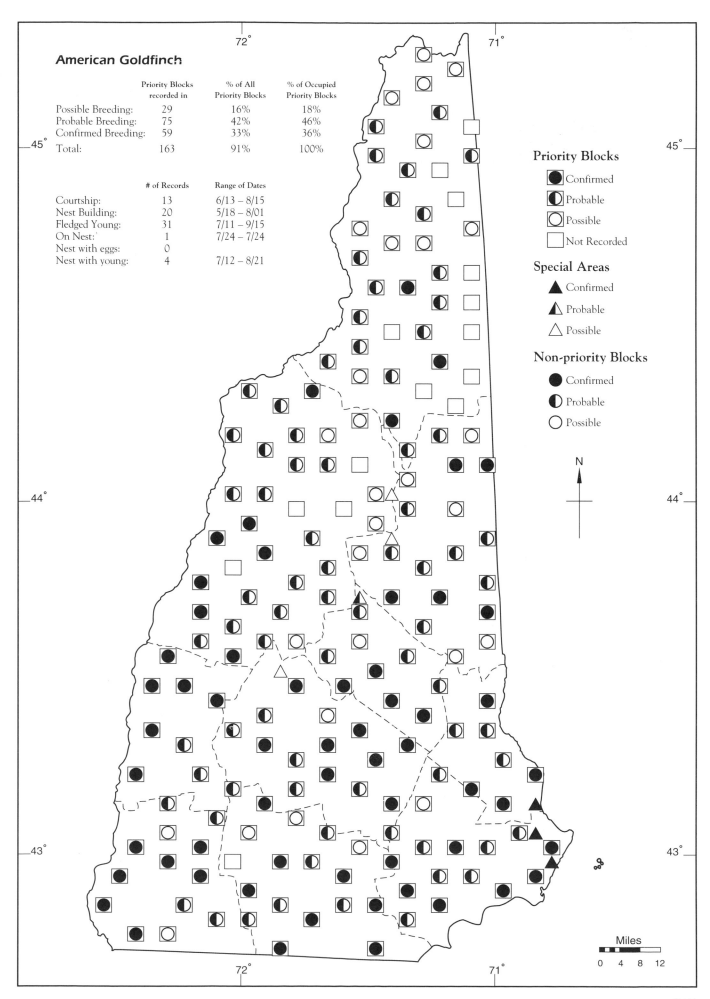

American Goldfinch

	Priority Blocks recorded in	% of All Priority Blocks	% of Occupied Priority Blocks
Possible Breeding:	29	16%	18%
Probable Breeding:	75	42%	46%
Confirmed Breeding:	59	33%	36%
Total:	163	91%	100%

	# of Records	Range of Dates
Courtship:	13	6/13 – 8/15
Nest Building:	20	5/18 – 8/01
Fledged Young:	31	7/11 – 9/15
On Nest:	1	7/24 – 7/24
Nest with eggs:	0	
Nest with young:	4	7/12 – 8/21

Priority Blocks
- ◐ Confirmed
- ◑ Probable
- ◯ Possible
- ☐ Not Recorded

Special Areas
- ▲ Confirmed
- ◤ Probable
- △ Possible

Non-priority Blocks
- ● Confirmed
- ◑ Probable
- ○ Possible

N

Miles
0 4 8 12

Evening Grosbeak
Coccothraustes vespertinus

These large finches are best known as common winter visitors to bird feeders, with voracious appetites for sunflower seeds. Despite their name, they are most active in the morning. As breeders, they are relatively recent in New Hampshire and much more numerous in the north than in the south. Males are yellow, black, and white with a large, thick, pale bill. Females are mostly gray with tinges of yellow and black, and white wings and tail. Partial albinos are not uncommon (Terres 1980).

Evening Grosbeaks are noisy, even in winter. Their most common call is a loud ringing "pteer" or "purreep." True songs are little known, but Speirs (1968) described them as a quiet "chip-up-chu-weer" and a high-pitched "whizz-whizz-tee-ee."

Seeds of the box elder or ash-leaved maple are a favorite food of Evening Grosbeaks. Grosbeaks also eat seeds of other maples and various conifers, tree buds, and fruits such as sumac, apple, and cherry. During the breeding season they take many insects, especially spruce budworms, when available (Speirs 1968). They often pick up sand and gravel along roads.

These birds wander so much when not breeding that early and late migration dates are difficult to determine. Spring migration runs from March until the end of May, but stragglers sometimes occur into early June. August and September records south of the regular breeding range are not unusual, but fall migration here occurs primarily from October well into winter (SRS).

Evening Grosbeaks breed most abundantly in spruce forests, but also will nest in deciduous trees and pines. Speirs (1968) describes an elaborate courtship observed in Hanover on 4 April 1937 in which a pair alternately bowed to each other "with great formality." The male's display features puffed-out body plumage and quivering wings. Courtship feeding also occurs.

The male accompanies the female while she gathers nesting material, but she alone builds the well-concealed nest, which typically is high in a tree (Speirs 1968). The nest is an oblong cup loosely made of sticks interwoven with moss or lichen and lined with rootlets (Harrison 1975). The female incubates for 12 to 14 days, and the nestlings fledge in 13 or 14 days (Harrison 1978). When foraging for the young, the parents usually leave and return to the nest together. The female usually feeds the nestlings, on regurgitated insects, while the male removes fecal sacs (Speirs 1968). In New Hampshire young may fledge as early as 16 June, but most fledglings are seen in July.

Few birds have experienced more spectacular range expansions than the Evening Grosbeak. Before 1889 this bird was known as a resident of forests north and west of the Great Lakes, although vagrants had been observed as far east as New York state. In the winter of 1889–90 a great flight brought many to every New England state except Rhode Island (Oatman *in* Laughlin and Kibbe 1985). New Hampshire specimens were taken in Milford, Henniker, Seabrook, Francestown, and Newmarket between 6 January and 1 May 1890 (Allen 1903). No further observations occurred until June 1903, when a small flock spent a few days in Franklin (Goodhue 1922). A specimen was taken in Dublin in December 1906 (Thayer 1909 *in* Allison and Allison 1979), and in January 1911 a few appeared in Lebanon (Storrs *in* Allen 1911) and Lancaster (Wright 1911). Evening Grosbeaks became rather frequent visitors thereafter, but were not reported every year until much later.

Widespread planting of box elders may have enticed Evening Grosbeaks to extend their winter range into the Eastern region, while the growing popularity of providing sunflower seeds at bird feeders induced them to return and linger. Their winter numbers still vary from abundant in some years to rather uncommon in others.

Evening Grosbeaks gradually extended their breeding range eastward. The first recorded breeding in New England was in Woodstock, Vt., in 1926 (Marble 1926). Although summer sightings occurred in New Hampshire as early as the 1920s (Forbush 1929), breeding was first confirmed in 1953 in Pittsburg (Wallace 1953). Evening Grosbeaks nested in the White Mountains in 1960 (Hebert 1960a), in New Hampton in 1963 (Bradley and Hebert 1963), and as far south as Dublin in 1967 (Allison and Allison 1979).

Evening Grosbeaks are still uncommon but widespread nesters throughout the North Country and White Mountains up to at least 3,000 ft (610 m) (T. Richards, unpubl. data). The Clarksville BBS route is the only one on which they occur consistently. South of the mountains, breeding apparently is sporadic.

Atlas records demonstrate a wide distribution in the 3 northern counties, and scattered occurrence further south, mostly in the Western Highlands. The presence of these birds on Mt. Monadnock, Jaffrey in July 1986 suggests that they may nest in spruce forests on our southern mountains, but "confirmed" breeding records in southern New Hampshire are at comparatively low elevations.

Grosbeaks may nest near feeders which provide a reliable food supply. When they abruptly appear with young at feeders in mid or late July, there is no way of telling how far they have moved from their nesting areas. However, if a pair frequents a feeder in June and early July and then brings fledglings, one can assume that the pair nested nearby. Almost all "confirmed" records are of adults with fledged young at bird feeders. Apparently no one ever has found a nest in New Hampshire.

Kimball C. Elkins

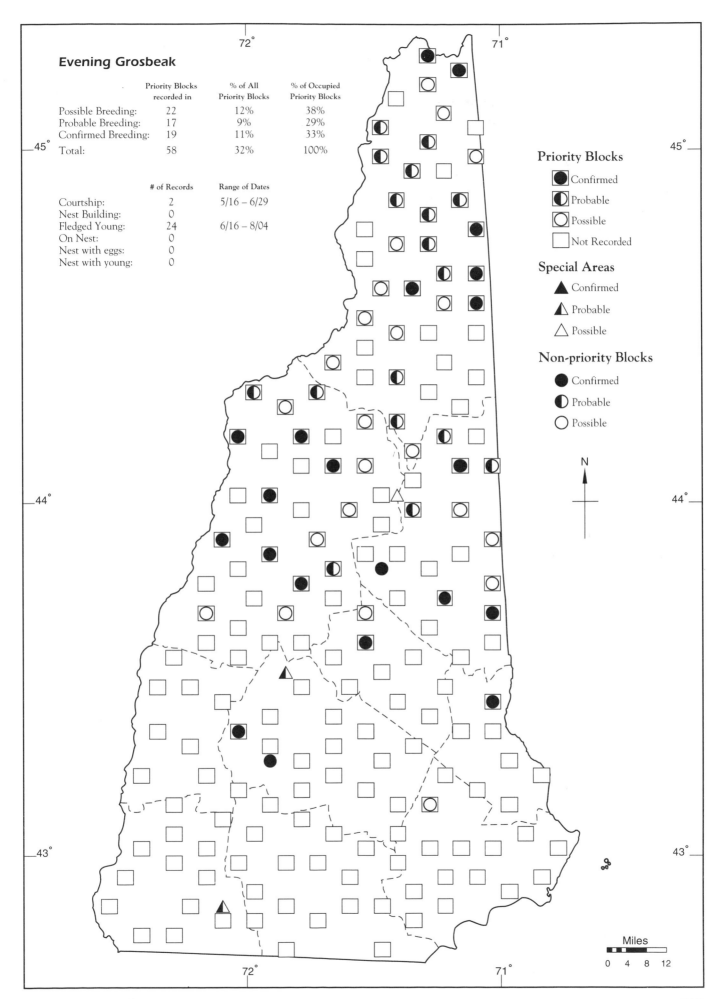

Evening Grosbeak

	Priority Blocks recorded in	% of All Priority Blocks	% of Occupied Priority Blocks
Possible Breeding:	22	12%	38%
Probable Breeding:	17	9%	29%
Confirmed Breeding:	19	11%	33%
Total:	58	32%	100%

	# of Records	Range of Dates
Courtship:	2	5/16 – 6/29
Nest Building:	0	
Fledged Young:	24	6/16 – 8/04
On Nest:	0	
Nest with eggs:	0	
Nest with young:	0	

Priority Blocks

● Confirmed
◐ Probable
○ Possible
☐ Not Recorded

Special Areas

▲ Confirmed
◮ Probable
△ Possible

Non-priority Blocks

● Confirmed
◐ Probable
○ Possible

N

Miles
0 4 8 12

House Sparrow
Passer domesticus

The noisy and belligerent House Sparrow, commonly called the "English sparrow," was introduced successfully to North America from England in 1853, and is now common on every continent except Antarctica (Merriam and Barrows 1889). This species is abundant in much of New Hampshire, and even occurs at the Mt. Washington Base Station, at 2,600 ft (790 m) elevation (T. Richards, pers. comm.). The male is distinctive, with black bib and white cheeks; the female is plain and drab.

The world's most widespread songbird does not have much of a song, only monotonous, shrill chirps. Full of nervous energy, adaptable and prolific, the House Sparrow is nonmigratory and forms an intense and persistent attachment to its nest site. The breeding season extends from April to September (Weaver 1943 *in* Bent 1958), with 2 and sometimes 3 broods a year. Noisy and frequent courtship is conspicuous in barnyard or city street. In courtship, a male will circle a female with drooping wings, or hop in front of her, bowing stiffly (Forbush 1929, Townsend 1909 *in* Bent 1958). Males fight aggressively.

House Sparrows may carry nesting material for several weeks before laying eggs (Harrison 1975). They aggressively usurp nest sites of native birds. In the decades following introduction, mobs of House Sparrows drove many songbirds from towns and villages by attacking adults and destroying eggs, nests, and young (Forbush 1929).

House Sparrows nest in farmyards, villages, towns, and cities, always close to human habitation. Nest sites include holes and crevices in buildings and trees, under eaves, behind shutters, on porch rafters, in birdhouses, and in swallow nests (Forbush 1929, Bent 1958). Occasionally these birds build a typical weaver finch nest, a huge ball in the fork of a tree with a side entrance (Harrison 1975).

Both sexes build the nest, but the male does most of the construction (Harrison 1975, Harrison 1978). The large, messy nest is made of grasses, weeds, and debris, and lined with hair and string (Forbush 1929, Harrison 1975). The female incubates the 3 to 7 eggs for 11 to 14 days (Harrison 1978). The male guards the eggs when the female leaves to feed (Forbush 1929). Several successive females may raise families in the same nest during a single breeding season (Weaver 1943 *in* Bent 1958). Adults feed fledged young for at least 2 weeks.

House Sparrows eat grain and other seeds, insects, seedlings, small fruits, and a variety of crops (Forbush 1929). Large flocks of House Sparrows feed and roost together in late summer. In late fall, they often return to their breeding grounds and claim sheltered sites such as cavities, open sheds, and thick vines for winter roosts (Forbush 1929).

After an unsuccessful attempt to introduce 8 pairs of House Sparrows into Brooklyn, N.Y., in 1850, a second release in 1853 established the species there (Merriam and Barrows 1889). Subsequent releases in New England (but apparently not New Hampshire) and many other locations across the continent over the next several decades produced a rapidly expanding and highly destructive population throughout much of North America (Merriam and Barrows 1889). Bostonians waged "the Great Sparrow War," an angry feud in the late 1880s (Merriam and Barrows 1889), over whether the species was a nuisance or a benefit. Spurred by its aggressive nature, the abundance of grain in cities and towns, and numerous nest sites in ornate Victorian buildings, this species had become extremely abundant by 1910 (Forbush 1929, Bent 1958). The population peaked between 1910 and 1915 and began to decrease noticeably as automobiles and tractors replaced horses, especially in the Eastern states (Forbush 1929, Bent 1958). More recently, a Western species, the House Finch, has displaced the House Sparrow from many of its city habitats (Kastner 1986).

The House Sparrow was a local resident in New Hampshire by the late 1860s (Coues 1868). Dearborn (1898) believed that numbers had peaked in Belknap and Merrimack counties, citing a stable population in Tilton for 7 years, and only rare sightings in rural areas. The 2 pairs Dearborn (1903) reported nesting in Durham are insignificant compared to the hundreds that nest there today. The species was "well established" in Dublin village by 1909 (Thayer 1909 *in* Allison and Allison 1979). At the same time it was "increasingly common" further north, with "several colonies" in Lancaster, where it took over Tree Swallow nests, and shared a house with Purple Martins (Wright 1911). By 1924, however, the species had declined noticeably in Concord (White 1924).

CBCs do not indicate dramatic changes in House Sparrow numbers during the past few decades, but A. C. Borror (pers. comm.) cautions that many CBC participants refuse to recognize these birds. BBS data indicate a significant decline in the Eastern region during 1966–79 (Robbins et al. 1986) and a continuing (but not statistically significant) decline in New Hampshire during the 1980s (S. Droege, pers. comm.).

Atlas data show this species to be widely distributed in southern New Hampshire, with records lacking for only 7 priority blocks in the 7 southern counties, and all but one of these blocks in the heavily forested Western Highlands. The House Sparrow is somewhat local from the White Mountains north, where open land and human habitations are relatively sparse. A few enormous blizzards might somewhat reduce its tenacious population, but otherwise this species will persist in suitable habitat.

Elizabeth C. Janeway

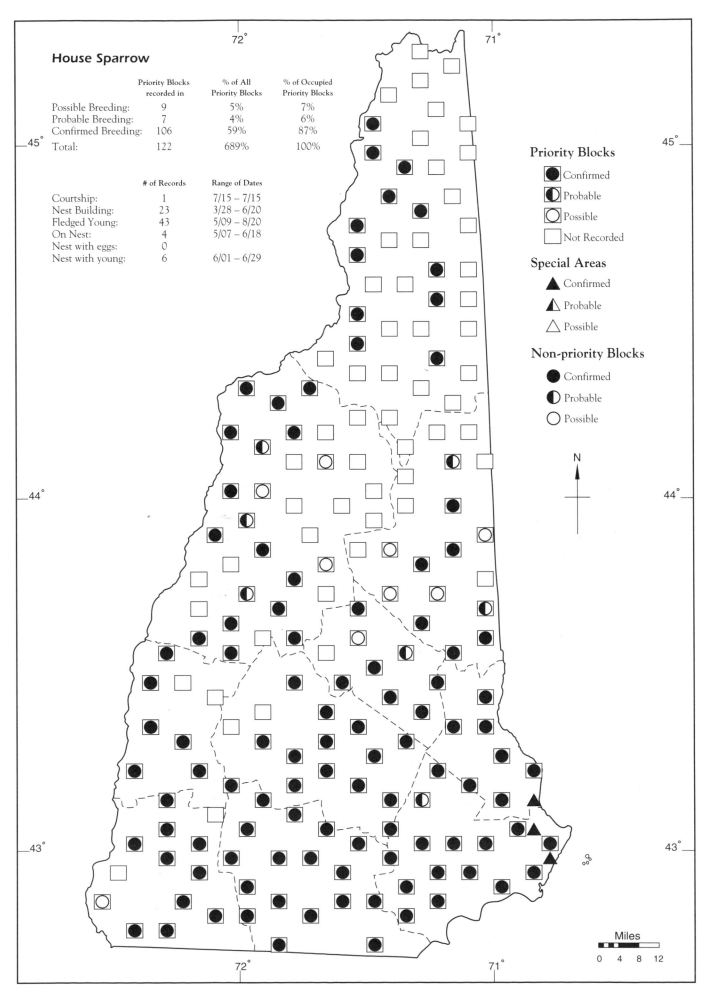

House Sparrow

	Priority Blocks recorded in	% of All Priority Blocks	% of Occupied Priority Blocks
Possible Breeding:	9	5%	7%
Probable Breeding:	7	4%	6%
Confirmed Breeding:	106	59%	87%
Total:	122	689%	100%

	# of Records	Range of Dates
Courtship:	1	7/15 – 7/15
Nest Building:	23	3/28 – 6/20
Fledged Young:	43	5/09 – 8/20
On Nest:	4	5/07 – 6/18
Nest with eggs:	0	
Nest with young:	6	6/01 – 6/29

Priority Blocks
- ◐ Confirmed
- ◑ Probable
- ○ Possible
- ☐ Not Recorded

Special Areas
- ▲ Confirmed
- ◣ Probable
- △ Possible

Non-priority Blocks
- ● Confirmed
- ◑ Probable
- ○ Possible

N

Miles
0 4 8 12

369

Accounts of Historically or Potentially Breeding Species

Least Bittern
Ixobrychus exilis

This secretive little bittern is rarely seen in New Hampshire, and finding one is cause for excitement. The Least Bittern is a relatively small marsh bird, less than half the length of the American Bittern, with a longer bill than a rail's. Large buffy patches on the chestnut wings distinguish this species from the slightly larger Green Heron. The Least Bittern breeds in large, open marshes and lakes with emergent vegetation. Such habitat is decreasing nationwide, and Least Bittern numbers have declined in many areas across the country.

The few observations documented in New Hampshire suggest that this bittern probably arrives here in May and leaves in September. One migrant perched in a pear tree on Star Island, Rye, on 19 September 1971! There are no documented breeding records for the state, although the species likely has nested here.

Once on its breeding grounds, this bird seldom flies, but climbs about on emergent vegetation, foraging for insects, small fish and frogs, tadpoles, snails, and leeches (Bent 1926). It can compress itself enough to squeeze between stems that are only an inch or so apart (Forbush 1925a). If threatened, it will freeze into an elongated posture, bill pointing straight up, and blend into its surroundings exceedingly well. When flushed, this species flies with an awkward, fluttering flight, legs dangling and neck outstretched, and soon drops down again into the vegetation (Bent 1926). On long flights, however, it draws in its head and extends its legs behind like a heron.

Least Bitterns nest in emergent vegetation that is 3 ft (0.9 m) or more in height over fresh water 1 to 3 ft (0.3 to 0.9 m) deep (Weller 1961). Nest site vegetation includes cattails, sedges, reeds, arrowhead, and buttonbush (Bent 1926). The flat, flimsy nest is 4 to 10 in (10 to 25 cm) across and is placed from water level up to 36 in (92 cm) above the water (Weller 1961, Ziebell 1990). Nests are located in clumps of previous years' vegetation, usually within about 8 ft (2.4 m) of open water (Weller 1961). The base is formed by bending down leaves and stems and then adding more stems on top. Nest construction, in which both sexes participate, peaks in late May and early June, and may continue until after hatching (Nero 1951, Palmer 1962).

The male utters a series of "coos" at a rate of 4 or 5 per second, all on the same pitch (Brewster *in* Bent 1926). When startled, this bittern may utter a loud, cackling "ca-ca, ca-ca." The male's cooing male often elicits an "uk-uk, uk" from the female (Allen *in* Bent 1926).

Both adults share incubation of the 2 to 6, usually 4 or 5 eggs, which lasts about 16 to 23 days (Ziebell 1990). Once the young hatch, both adults feed them partly digested food by regurgitation (Palmer 1962). By the time the young are 3 days old they can "freeze" with their bills pointing straight up. At 5 to 7 days they can assume an aggressive posture with head out, neck down, and wings partly opened (Weller 1961). Young generally remain

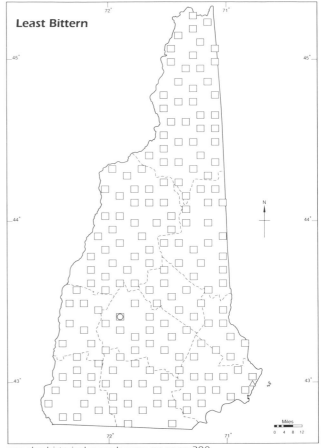

see also historical records map on page 390.

in the nest for about 10 to 14 days, but may leave for brief periods from the age of 5 days (Palmer 1962). Ages at first flight and independence are unknown. Juvenal plumage resembles that of the adult female, although the crown and back are somewhat lighter brown and the chest and throat more boldly striped (Bent 1926).

Least Bitterns are most readily observed in late June or early July. When feeding nestlings, adults may forage some distance from the nest and fly back just above the vegetation. After the young have fledged, family groups may feed together at the edge of an open area in an extensive marsh (R. Forster, pers. comm.).

The Least Bittern apparently always has been rare in New Hampshire (Coues 1868; Dearborn 1903; Allen 1903; Ridgely 1977; T. Richards, pers. comm.). There are few records of the species, and none from the northern third of the state. Dearborn (1903) considered it "an irregular and rather rare visitor in New Hampshire," and notes records from Hampton, Concord, and the Connecticut valley. Allen (1903) noted a specimen taken at Hampton Beach in 1869 and another taken at Seabrook, but knew of no breeding records for the state. White (1937) cited 2 specimens taken in Concord, which may well have been migrants. More recently, observers reported about 20 sightings from 8 locations during 1963–86, most from 31 May to 12 August (SRS).

As Forbush (1925) noted, however, the Least Bittern is extremely secretive and might not be as rare in some areas as is generally believed. Playing recordings of the song in likely habitat may help to locate it. A Least Bittern responded to broadcasts of King Rail calls in June 1984 in Sutton (Stephenson 1984).

Atlas efforts suggest that the Least Bittern is truly scarce in New Hampshire, but additional field work is needed to accurately assess its distribution in the state. The Atlas project produced "possible" breeding records near the Coast at Hampton, and at Cascade Marsh, Sutton, which covers about 70 a (28 ha) and includes extensive beds of cattails.

Atlas projects in neighboring states produced from 7 to 14 Least Bittern records (Laughlin and Kibbe 1985; Adamus 1988; Mass. BBA proj., unpubl.). Declines have been reported elsewhere in the country, and the species has been on the *American Birds* Blue List since 1979 (Tate 1986).

Robert C. Vernon

Snowy Egret
Egretta thula

These elegant, slender wading birds with their dark legs and golden slippers stalk patiently by day along tidal creeks in New Hampshire's coastal marshes, foraging for small fish and insect larvae. Snowy Egrets breed along the Atlantic Coast from Maine to Argentina, along the Pacific Coast from California to Chile, and at inland locations in parts of the range (Hancock and Kushlan 1984). Most of the North Atlantic population winters along the Gulf Coast, but some individuals winter as far north as New Jersey (Hancock and Kushlan 1984).

As the name implies, the plumage is white. Long white plumes on the head, neck, and back during the breeding season are especially evident when ruffled by a breeze. The bill is black. The immature Little Blue Heron is also white, but has greenish legs and feet, and a bluish bill with a dusky tip (Hancock and Kushlan 1984).

Snowy Egrets typically nest in colonies with other herons and egrets. Such colonies may be on islands, or near the shores of seacoasts, estuaries, or large inland water bodies with extensive shallows. There is no known nesting colony in New Hampshire, but Snowy Egrets nest nearby on Appledore Island, Kittery, Maine.

The Appledore heronry is in a thicket of shrubs and small trees dominated by choke cherry, winterberry, and shadbush. During 1961-75, Snowy Egrets nested only in shrubs at the north end of the island. Following human interference early in the 1976 nesting season, the birds moved to the southern end, where they continued to nest through the Atlas period.

The male selects the nest site and defends it vigorously with variety of displays (Palmer 1962, Hancock and Kushlan 1984). Noisy courtship performances begin in April in the shrubby nesting areas on Appledore Island (Reusch and Shambaugh 1977). These include vocal stretch displays, which males may perform in a group, and circle flights by pairs or individuals. After pair formation, the female may build a new nest with materials brought by her mate (Hancock and Kushlan 1984). Snowy Egrets often reuse nest platforms remaining from previous years, and nest trees often support multiple nests (Davis 1986).

Shoals Marine Laboratory personnel conduct a nest count at the Appledore heronry during late May of some years, when most birds either are still incubating or have young less than 2 weeks old. The range of egg dates is unknown for the Appledore Island egrets but eggs probably are laid in late April or early May, judging from the numbers of nests with eggs or small young in late May. Clutches usually include 3 to 5 eggs, laid on a bare stick platform.

Both sexes incubate, beginning with the first egg, and both parents tend the young (Harrison 1978). The incubation period in Plymouth, Mass., is about 3 weeks (W. E. Davis, pers. comm.). Physical factors apparently are major determinants of nesting success. Cold, wet weather when young are vulnerable in early June is likely to cause nest failures (Gaston and Johnson 1977). Adults sometimes abandon nests very early in the nesting season, so disturbance should be avoided in late April and early May (W. E. Davis, pers. comm.). At about 2 weeks of age, the white young can scramble away from the nest upon sight of a human. If they lose their grip and fall to the ground, they invariably perish unless placed back in the trees. Thus humans should avoid entering an egret colony until after the young have fledged, by mid-July.

Snowy Egrets feed on the mainland with other wading birds, mostly in tidal marshes. Each morning and evening they commute in groups from the nesting areas on Appledore Island to foraging areas on the mainland. Individual birds also come and go from the colony during the day when they are feeding young. Evening roosts at Appledore continue until early September, when the egrets depart for southern wintering areas.

During the late 19th and early 20th centuries, plume hunters nearly eradicated this species from North America (Hancock and Kushlan 1984). Reusch and Shambaugh (1977) compiled data showing that in 1832, prior to the plume-hunting era, the Snowy Egret bred as far north as Cape May, N.J. By 1900, it was restricted to Florida. With protection of breeding colonies and conservation laws in place, the Snowy Egret increased in numbers, and the breeding range expanded northward to Long Island by 1951. The first New Hampshire record is of one bird in Hampton Falls on 21 August 1947 (RNEB). The species staged a major invasion into southern New England in late summer of 1948, with one record for New Hampshire (RNEB), and was a regular visitor to New Hampshire tidal marshes by 1950 (Borror, pers. obs.).

The first discovery of Snowy Egrets nesting locally was at Appledore Island in 1961 (Bagg and Emery 1961), and O. Hewitt subsequently observed colonial nesting there during the 1960s. Since 1978, the nesting population of Snowy Egrets at Appledore has decreased from about 200 to 250 pairs in 1978-79 to only about 50 pairs in 1988.

In Maine the Snowy Egret also breeds regularly on Wood Island, Biddeford; Stratton Island, Old Orchard Beach; and Mark Island; Harpswell (Borror 1980). It breeds in at least 9 colonies in Massachusetts (Irwin and Korschgen 1979). Wooded swamps and thickets along the New Hampshire coast provide appropriate breeding habitat, and protection of such areas eventually may result in establishment of a New Hampshire breeding colony.

Arthur C. Borror

Little Blue Heron
Egretta caerulea

In a mixed flock of wading birds (egrets, herons, and ibises) along the New Hampshire tidal marshes, the adult Little Blue Heron stands out at a distance: it appears nearly black, is half again as big as a Green Heron, and is about the same size as a Snowy Egret. The adults, with blue-gray backs and dark brown necks and heads, differ markedly from the all white juvenile. A molting one-year-old heron appears strikingly dark and white blotched. In the Northeast this species is a coastal bird, but it is common inland in many parts of its range (Hancock and Kushlan 1984).

Although Little Blue Herons are not known to breed in New Hampshire, one or 2 pairs apparently nest each season on Appledore Island in the Isles of Shoals, Kittery, Maine (Borror 1980). The Little Blue Herons that occur singly along the New Hampshire coast during the nesting season are either nonbreeders or birds from the Appledore heronry. They arrive on the Coast in mid to late April, where they feed along the borders of tidal marsh pannes. Occasionally spring migrants appear at inland locations in New Hampshire. Their breeding range extends along the Atlantic and Gulf coasts of the U.S. from Texas to New England. They generally winter south of Cape Hatteras.

Little Blue Herons perform less elaborate courtship displays than many other egrets, and engage in stretching, bill-snapping, and wing preening displays as well as aggressive confrontations (Meyerriecks 1960). The male apparently gathers most of the nesting sticks and presents them to the female, who builds the flimsy nest in a tree or shrub 1.5 to 40 ft (0.5 to 12 m) above the ground (Hancock and Kushlan 1984). Clutches include 2 to 5 eggs (Telfair 1983), and both parents incubate, beginning after the second egg is laid, for a period of 21 to 23 days (Hancock and Kushlan 1984).

The Little Blue Heron's nest, eggs, and tiny (less than one week old) young are nearly identical in appearance to those of the Snowy Egret, so nest identification is difficult unless an adult is present. General timing of the breeding season seems to be the same as for the Snowy Egret. By late May at Appledore, this heron probably is still incubating or has young less than 2 weeks old. At an age of about 2 weeks, the white young are capable of scrambling out of the immediate area of the nest. People should avoid the nesting area from late April until after about mid-June, during which time human disturbance can cause nest desertion. Both parents feed the young until they are 50 days old (Hancock and Kushlan 1984).

Human exploitation held the range of the Little Blue Heron, along with that of the Snowy Egret, in check during most of the last century. However, the plume trade affected this species less than some other herons and egrets (Hancock and Kushlan 1984). The earliest record of this species in New Hampshire is of a specimen taken in Amherst on 28 April 1897 (Allen 1903). There are only scattered records for New England in the first half of the 20th century. These include one in Bow on 17 July 1902 (Abbott 1906). In 1948, however, the Little Blue Heron began a major expansion northward. In that year there were 5 in Epping on 27 July, one in Rindge on 7 August, and 34, including only one adult, in the Hampton marshes on 7 August (RNEB; T. Richards, unpubl. data). Observers reported scattered sightings during the 1950s, primarily from locations near the Coast (Hampton,

Kensington, Newmarket, Rye, Seabrook) but including a May record from New Hampton (RNEB, *passim*). Sightings increased along the Coast during the 1960s and 1970s, in April-May and July-October (RNEB, *passim*; SRS).

The first evidence of the Little Blue Heron nesting on Appledore was a large fledgling chasing an adult in the heronry on 20 July 1974 (O. Hewitt, pers. comm.). This may constitute the first nesting record for Maine. The Little Blue Heron also may breed occasionally in Maine heronries on Wood Island, Biddeford; Stratton Island, Old Orchard Beach; and Mark Island, Harpswell.

The Little Blue Heron is a potential breeding bird in New Hampshire, especially if a colony of Snowy Egrets becomes established here, since the 2 species often nest together in shrubby thickets near coastal marshes. The Little Blue Heron now breeds in at least 2 colonies on the Massachusetts coast. During the Atlas period, inland sightings of transients occurred in Mascoma Village (Lebanon) on 1 June 1981 and in Alton on 3 May 1981. Sightings along the coast at Hampton presumably involved birds from Appledore.

Arthur C. Borror

Glossy Ibis
Plegadis falcinellus

The Glossy Ibis presents a unique silhouette among New Hampshire's birds, flying with rapid, ducklike wing beats, its neck and long, drooping bill held outstretched. When feeding in wet coastal grasslands of New Hampshire, an ibis appears solidly dark at a distance. Its striking green and purple gloss is evident only under proper lighting conditions. Although the Glossy Ibis is not known to nest in New Hampshire, it nests regularly at the Isles of Shoals on Appledore Island, Kittery, Maine, just across the state line.

Ibises return to nest along the central New England coast in April. On Appledore Island, they occupy sites in dense stands of winterberry and either build a new nest of twigs or reuse a nest that has survived the previous winter. Whereas egrets nest throughout the colony area in a variety of shrubs and night-herons nest mostly in taller shrubs on drier sites, the nests of ibises appear to be restricted to the subcanopy area of winterberry in low, wet depressions. Ibises often line the nests with green leaves, which they tear from shrubs on other parts of the island; thus their nests contain more leafy vegetation than herons' nests.

Although precise egg dates and incubation times are unknown at this latitude, the nests usually contain 3 or 4 greenish eggs by late May. By late June and early July, the black, downy young with their stubby bills and white-streaked heads are visible. Both parents tend the young. According to Harrison (1978), one adult is always present for the first 5 days after hatching. Young move into the branches near the nest when 2 weeks old. They can fly a little and feed themselves at 6 weeks, but parents continue to feed them away from the nest (Harrison 1978). The young are full sized by early August, but their bills are less than full length. Young still accompany their parents when 7 weeks old (Harrison 1978).

Of all the wading birds on Appledore Island, Glossy Ibises are the most likely to stay and feed in wet open areas at the Isles of

Shoals. However, most ibises not tending eggs or small young leave the breeding and roosting area on Appledore at first light of morning and fly to the mainland. There, they feed around pannes in upper parts of tidal marshes and in wet pastures and meadows in coastal New Hampshire, and may venture farther inland than egrets. Ibises continue to return to the island to roost at night into early September, then gradually diminish in numbers and are gone by mid-September.

Until the late 1960s, the Glossy Ibis was a rare vagrant from the South, appearing chiefly after storms. The species began extending its range northward in the 1950s, reaching Cape Hatteras, N.C. by 1948; Cape May, N.J. by 1955; Jamaica Bay, Long Island, N.Y. by 1961; and Stratton Island, Scarborough, Maine by 1972 (Borror 1980). Shoals Marine Laboratory personnel reported the Glossy Ibis on Appledore Island in early June of 1973, so it may have nested on the island that year. In 1974 there were at least 6 young in the colony; no nest count was made. The ibis nesting population has since increased to about 30 pairs in the late 1970s, and about 50 pairs in 1988. The Glossy Ibis also has nested in at least 3 colonies in Massachusetts. This is a potential breeding bird in New Hampshire, perhaps in shrubby swamps adjacent to more remote sections of tidal marsh.

Arthur C. Borror

Bald Eagle
Haliaeetus leucocephalus

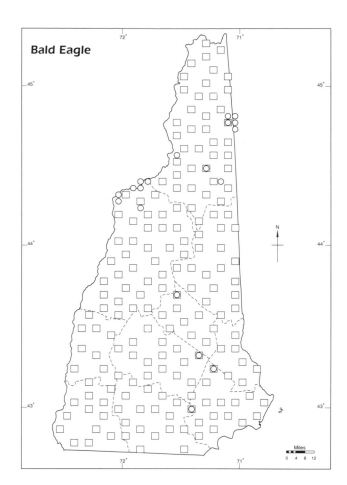

The invincible glare of yellow eyes as powerful wings lift to the sky belies the Bald Eagle's rather tenuous existence throughout much of its range. The "white-headed" eagle is a state and federally listed Endangered Species. It had ceased to nest here by 1950, but transients continued to occur in the state throughout the year (ASNH data). Bald Eagle activity in New Hampshire increased during the 1980s to include a substantial wintering population, consistent summer activity at 2 locations, and, in 1989, a nesting pair at Umbagog Lake, Errol. The wooded shorelines of the state's largest lakes, rivers, and estuaries support most of this activity.

The Bald Eagle's imposing size, protruding head and tail, and flat-winged profile distinguish it in flight. The adult's white head and tail are distinctive, but the dark-plumaged immature resembles other large raptors. A juvenile's annual molts progress to lighter head and tail feathers, with much variability in body plumage, usually producing adult plumage after 4 to 5 years (McCollough 1989).

Eagles arrive at breeding sites in the Northeast beginning in early March. Courtship may include spectacular talon-locked free falls or mutual soaring, but more frequently occurs on a perch as the birds sit side by side and stroke each other with their massive beaks (Gerrard and Bortolotti 1988; Evans, pers. obs.). The calls are relatively weak.

The nest typically is located one-third of the way down a live, towering white pine near the water's edge (Bent 1937). Both male and female add new sticks and fresh grasses throughout the nesting period. A structure 5 ft (1.5 m) wide by 3 ft (0.9 m) deep serves most pairs, but the nest may become immense over time. The largest eagle nest built by a single pair weighed 2 tons (1,818 kg) and was 20 ft (6.1 m) high (Brown and Amadon 1968).

Copulation takes place on a tree branch or similar site after the pair has perched side by side for some period of time (Gerrard et al. 1979). Egg laying occurs from the last 2 weeks in March to early April on the Maine coast; inland pairs and inexperienced nesters lag about 2 weeks behind (C. Todd, pers. comm.). The new nesting pair at Umbagog Lake were on eggs by 15 April 1989 (ASNH data).

Shared incubation begins when the first egg is laid and continues for about 35 days (Bent 1937, Gerrard and Bortolotti 1988). The clutch is usually 2 eggs. The young hatch asynchronously. Hatch dates for the Umbagog Lake pair were on or just prior to 19, 6, 15, and 14 May in the years 1990–93, respectively. The young spend 10 to 11 weeks in the nest. After fledging occurs in late July or early August, but the nest remains the focal point of activity for young and adults well into the fall. The bulk of the summer diet consists of fish, either plucked from the water or stolen from an Osprey, a frequent occurrence at Umbagog Lake. The Bald Eagle is an opportunistic feeder and often scavenges food.

Adults may remain near the nesting territory throughout the winter if open water persists. Northern and inland residents move to open rivers and bays, where fish and waterfowl are available. Bald Eagles often perch nearly motionless for hours at a time, especially in winter, when energy conservation is critical. Eagles can be gregarious at wintering areas, sharing carcasses and communal night roosts.

Young birds are highly transient during their 4 to 5 year development into adulthood. Juveniles may, however, show affinity for particular locations, providing early indications of subsequent breeding areas. Prime nest and perch sites are intrinsically attractive to the species and may support generations of use (Bent

1937). The nest tree of the recolonizing pair on Umbagog Lake had supported an active nest 40 years previously, and continued to be a preferred perch site for transients.

Historical records identify Umbagog, Squam, and Newfound lakes; Lake Wentworth, Wolfeboro; the Connecticut Lakes, Pittsburg; Lake Winnipesaukee; Great Bay; and Hampton Harbor as formerly occupied summer habitat (Dearborn 1898, Allen 1903, Scott 1921, ASNH data). Although the Bald Eagle may have been common along large water bodies in the mid-1800s (Coues 1868), numbers reportedly were declining by the turn of the century (Allen 1903, Brewster 1925). New Hampshire's last documented active nest, on Leonard Pond at Umbagog Lake, Errol, produced 2 young in 1949 (T. Richards, unpubl. data).

DDT caused a widespread decline through the 1950s and 1960s, which prompted national recovery efforts. Restoration programs in New York and Massachusetts and a growing breeding population in Maine have contributed to recently increased activity in New Hampshire. By the late 1980s, upwards of 50 individuals were passing through New Hampshire in winter, with 20 to 25 staying at wintering areas on Great Bay, the Merrimack and Connecticut rivers, and in the Lakes Region. Breeding season records during the Atlas period (NHESP data) reflect both transient nonbreeders and consistent summer activity at Umbagog Lake and on the Connecticut River.

Bald Eagles prefer a comfortable distance from potential disturbance and human activity when selecting nest sites (Fraser et al. 1985; Buehler et al., unpubl. rep.). Protection of remaining undeveloped shorelines on major water bodies will be a key to the species' future here. Although the number of Bald Eagle breeding pairs in New Hampshire is unlikely to regain historical levels, limited recolonization is likely to continue.

Diane Evans

Golden Eagle
Aquila chrysaetos

The powerful and majestic Golden Eagle is rare in New Hampshire. This enormous, dark brown raptor is not known to nest in the state at present, and is listed as Endangered both in New Hampshire and in Maine, where a few breeding pairs remain. Sightings of transients occur here annually, most often in the Connecticut River valley, White Mountains, and North Country.

Golden Eagles inhabit remote, mountainous terrain throughout the Northern Hemisphere and nest on cliffs well removed from human activity. In eastern North America, they forage over open areas such as bogs, old burns, and clearcuts. They are quite common in western North America, but are sparsely distributed east of the Mississippi River.

In flight, Golden Eagles are best distinguished from immature Bald Eagles by their proportionally shorter heads and necks. They often soar for long periods without flapping, usually holding their wings at a slightly upward angle.

Golden Eagles occur with Bald Eagles at wintering sites in Maine and Massachusetts, but have not appeared at New Hampshire's eagle wintering areas during the 1980s (ASNH data). New England pairs may remain in or near their breeding areas all year (Weik 1987). They advertise their territories si-

lently with undulating diving and swooping flights, which they may perform year round (Collopy and Edwards 1989). During winter months before the breeding season begins, pairs perform soaring displays, which typically begin with mutual soaring and develop into rolling, diving, and talon grappling (Brown 1976). Weik (1987) observed courtship flights in Maine on 7 March 1987 and 22 March 1986. Spofford (*in* Palmer 1988) once observed a female in northern New Hampshire that flew out from a mountainside and made dives and close circles before receiving prey from the male and bringing it to the nest to feed a month-old eaglet.

Although Golden Eagles occasionally nest in trees, cliff nests predominate in the Northeast (Spofford 1971, Weik 1987). They are made of thick branches and lined with deciduous or coniferous twigs (Harrison 1978). Golden Eagles spend much of their time perched near the nest, either on rock perches near the top of the cliff, or in live or dead pines (Weik 1987, Collopy and Edwards 1989).

Golden Eagles seldom vocalize. Mates may utter a series of slow 2-syllable yelps and sometimes yelp in concert; the distress call is "a shrill, chittering scream" (Palmer 1988). Captives have produced musical notes reminiscent of a Wild Turkey's (Brewster 1925, Hamerstrom *in* Palmer 1988).

In Maine, egg laying occurs from 26 March to 26 April (Weik 1987). Estimated nestling ages in historical New Hampshire nests suggest that incubation began in mid to late April (W.R. Spofford, pers. comm.). Incubation takes 43 to 45 days and usually involves only the female (Harrison 1978). There are usually 2 eggs.

Males supply food while females brood the young. Eaglets can feed themselves at about 40 days and fly 9 to 10 weeks after hatching (Brown and Amadon 1968). Maine young have hatched during 6 May – 6 June and have fledged between 15 July and 8 August (Weik 1987). The eaglets' chittering food calls ("Ki-ki-ki-ki-ki-ki-Yelp") help adults locate them after fledging (Palmer 1988).

Golden Eagles often fly low over woods, marshes, and open areas while hunting and may flush their prey at close range (Palmer 1949). Marsh birds, especially American Bittern and Great Blue Heron, predominate among prey in the Northeast, which also includes Double-crested Cormorant, Common Merganser, black duck, red fox, mink, and muskrat (Spofford 1971, Weik 1987).

Although Golden Eagles probably were uncommon in the Northeast at the time of European settlement, subsequent human persecution undoubtedly contributed to increasing rarity during the next 2 centuries. This species is extremely sensitive to human disturbance, even at considerable distances, and human-induced nest failure is common (Palmer 1988). Human disturbance of the few scattered pairs in the Northeast is of special concern (Spofford 1971, Weik 1987), and anyone who suspects a nest should remain at least a half mile away and avoid frequent visits.

Three documented nest sites in the state were active during the mid to late 1800s. One nest which held "partly fledged" young in July 1876 was unoccupied the following year (Allen 1903). Another site, in the Umbagog region, supported a pair in the late 1800s (Brewster 1925), and again during the 1950s, possibly as late as 1962 (W.R. Spofford, pers. comm.). There are no reports of young after 1956. The timing of this species' reproductive failure and subsequent disappearance coincides with that of the Peregrine in the Northeast, suggesting pesticide effects as a likely factor.

Recent activity includes various reports from the White Mountains in June and July 1966 and in the summer and fall of 1971. Golden Eagle records during the Atlas period include 16 sightings of adults or immatures.

Golden Eagle distribution in the Northeast always will be limited by availability of suitable remote nesting cliffs with adequate food resources within the species' 50 to 100 sq mi (130 to 260 sq km) home range (Spofford 1971). Weik (1987) recommends buffer zones of no human activity for a minimum of 3,280 ft (1,000 m) in front of Golden Eagles nesting cliffs. Increasing human intrusion into formerly remote northern forests may discourage successful nesting. The Golden Eagle's future in New Hampshire remains uncertain.

Carol R. Foss

Merlin
Falco columbarius

These small falcons of the north woods occur in New Hampshire primarily as migrants, but at least occasionally nest in northern Coos County. Formerly called Pigeon Hawks, Merlins are easily recognized as falcons by their rapid direct flight and long pointed wings. Only slightly longer than the more colorful kestrels, both sexes have darkly streaked white breasts and banded white-tipped tails.

Merlins are uncommon breeding residents of spruce-fir forests and northern prairies from Oregon and Wyoming east along the northern fringe of the contiguous U.S., north to tree line in Canada and Alaska (Palmer 1988). Most winter from the Gulf states to northern South America. They pass through New Hampshire during April to mid-May and again from late August through October, when they are especially common along the Coast and at sea (SRS).

Organochlorine pesticides caused Merlin population declines across North America during the 1950s and 1960s, and the Merlin was on the *American Birds* Blue List during 1972–81. Although the species' status has improved in recent years, populations have not recovered to pre-1950 levels, and the Merlin continues to be a Species of Special Concern (Tate 1986, DeSmet 1985 *in* Cadman et al. 1987).

Suitable breeding habitat in the East includes mixed or coniferous forests with nearby openings (Harrison 1975, Weir *in* Cadman et al. 1987). Merlins often nest near large lakes or rivers (L. Oliphant, pers. comm.). Males arrive on the breeding grounds in April or May, up to a month before females. Experienced pairs often return to their previous nesting territory, where they may have several alternate nest sites (Newton 1979, Weir *in* Cadman et al. 1987). In courtship, females solicit food with a loud, drawn-out whine. Nest sites often are old stick nests of other birds, but also include natural cavities in trees, old woodpecker holes, depressions on the ground, cliff ledges, and even holes in cut banks (Bent 1938, Harrison 1978, Terres 1980).

The female may lay her 4 or 5 (occasionally 2 to 7) eggs in a bare depression or may form a nest pad by pecking off nearby vegetation (Harrison 1978, Newton 1979). The female performs most of the incubation, which lasts 28 to 32 days, but the male may incubate for a few hours during the day. The male does all the hunting until the nestlings are old enough to be left alone (Harrison 1978, Newton 1979). He vocalizes when approaching the nest with prey, and usually transfers it to the female on a large horizontal branch (L. Oliphant, pers. comm.). Breeding Merlins are noisy, frequently uttering a shrill "kikikee" which is louder and harsher than that of the Sharp-shinned Hawk (Bent 1938, Weir *in* Cadman et al. 1987).

The young leave the nest at 26 to 32 days of age and remain nearby, dependent on their parents for up to a month after fledging (Harrison 1978, Newton 1979, Weir *in* Cadman et al. 1987). Juveniles resemble the female in plumage. They acquire adult plumage at 2 years of age, but may breed as one-year-olds (Newton 1979).

Merlins prey primarily on small birds, but also capture dragonflies, grasshoppers, and other insects, snakes, toads, rodents, and bats (Terres 1980, NGS 1983). These falcons hunt from an exposed perch or on the wing, typically in marshes, bogs, or other forest openings, or along the edges of ponds and streams (Terres 1980). Rather than stooping dramatically like Peregrines, Merlins overtake their quarry in direct flight with a sudden burst of speed (Bond 1936 *in* Terres 1980, NGS 1983). Foraging flights often are low and undulating and end in a sudden swoop up to a perch (Bent 1938).

Merlins typically occur locally in the southern portion of their breeding range in the East (NGS 1983), and their presence in northern New England appears to be sporadic as well as local. Allen (1903) cited a record by A. P. Chadbourne of a Merlin observed in the Great Gulf on Mt. Washington on 8 July 1886, which suggests the possibility of historical nesting in New Hampshire. Reports of Merlins nesting in a tree cavity on Carthaginia Island in the Merrimack River, Manchester, in May 1926, leave questions as to the accuracy of the record (McGowan *in* ASNH 1927, 1928).

Recent summer records include single individuals observed in Pittsburg on 15 June 1963 and 18 June 1967, and at Owls Head Cliff, Benton, on 11 July 1982 (SRS). Evidence for potential nesting in Pittsburg during and since the Atlas period includes observations of 2 small, dark falcons circling over a softwood stand in Pittsburg on 19 July 1986, and of one which vocalized continuously for about 15 minutes on the west side of East Inlet, Pittsburg, on 2 June 1987 (S. H. Wheeler, pers. comm.).

A succession of breeding season sightings at Umbagog Lake, Errol, in the early 1990s suggested the possibility of a nesting pair. Then, on 21 May 1994, Foss and H.P. Nevers observed a Merlin pair apparently copulating in Wentworth's Location and located the nest nearby. At least one young was visible on 11 July, and 2 fledglings were in the area on 30 July.

Most Merlin pairs in Ontario nest north of 45° N (Weir *in* Cadman et al. 1987), which crosses New Hampshire slightly south of Pittsburg. The future presence of these boreal raptors here may depend as much on their population densities further north as on conditions in northern New Hampshire.

Carol R. Foss

Clapper Rail

Rallus longirostris

The Clapper Rail is a chickenlike, brown marsh bird with a fairly long bill. It resembles the much more common Virginia Rail but is larger and is grayish brown rather than reddish. Compared to the Sora, it is larger and has a longer bill. It is seldom seen except in salt or brackish marshes, and on the Atlantic Coast probably never nests far from such places. Some ornithologists consider it a salt-marsh subspecies of the King Rail (Ripley 1977). It is a rare bird in New Hampshire, and there is no evidence that it ever has nested here. It was, however, present in the breeding season during the Atlas period, and it may nest here sporadically in the salt and brackish marshes of our Coast and major estuaries.

In the breeding season the Clapper Rail is a noisy bird, with a loud call that has been written as "cac, cac, cac, cac, ca, caha, caha" (Audubon 1840). Its common alarm note is a short "keck" (Ripley 1977).

Clapper Rails nest in the higher and drier parts of the salt marsh. Their nests are made of *Spartina* or other marsh vegetation, built up several inches above the ground, and often roofed over with green grass (Harrison 1975). They are not difficult to find (Bent 1926). Spring tides often flood them, but the birds will renest (Harrison 1978).

Both sexes incubate the clutch of 8 to 11 eggs for 20 to 24 days (Harrison 1978). The young are precocial and leave the nest soon after hatching. Both parents watch over them. Egg dates in New York range from 4 April to 4 August (Andrle and Carroll 1988).

These rails were once very abundant in the mid-Atlantic Coastal region of the U.S. (Audubon 1967) and are still common there. In New England they always have been uncommon. Although they nested in Connecticut as early as 1874 (Sage et al. 1913), nesting was not confirmed in Massachusetts until 1956 (Hill 1965). Clapper Rails now nest sporadically on Cape Cod (Veit and Petersen 1993) and occur on the northeastern coast of Massachusetts more frequently than in the past (Griscom and Snyder 1955).

A Clapper Rail was collected in Portsmouth sometime prior to 1902 (Allen 1903, Dearborn 1903). Breeding season records in our state in recent decades include: 2 seen in Hampton on 4 and 8 June 1961 (Hebert and Smart 1961); one in Seabrook on 10 May 1965 (ASNH 1965); and one seen and heard in Hampton on and after 23 May 1972 (Phinney 1972). There have been at least 3 other sightings: at Great Bay, 26 Dec 1953 (Wallace 1954a); on Star Island, Rye, 6 Oct 1968 (ASNH 1969); and in Rye, 24 Jan 1970 (Anderson 1970).

The only Atlas records of Clapper Rails were of single birds, perhaps the same individual, seen at Eel Pond, Rye, on 29 June and 9 July 1982 (E. W. Phinney and T. Bertrand, pers. comm.). New Hampshire's Coastal region includes a number of salt and brackish marshes which could provide suitable nesting habitat for these secretive birds. While the most extensive habitat exists in the Hampton Harbor estuary, smaller marshes further north along the Coast and associated with Great and Little bays and their tributaries also provide potential nesting areas. If Clapper Rails continue to extend their range northward, eventually they may become regular nesters in New Hampshire.

Kimball C. Elkins

Wilson's Phalarope

Phalaropus tricolor

In birddom, phalaropes epitomize "women's lib" because the smaller males are more drab than the females and they do all the nest building, incubating, and rearing of young. In spring, female Wilson's Phalaropes sport beautiful maroon, black, and orange stripes on their necks, sides, and backs. With their white rumps and dark wings, they may be confused with Lesser Yellowlegs and Stilt Sandpipers, but their exceedingly thin bills, heavier bellies, and light, graceful flight serve to distinguish them.

The Wilson's Phalarope is more terrestrial than either the Red or Northern phalarope, both of which occasionally occur along our Coast during migration. While Red and Northern phalaropes occur worldwide, the Wilson's is limited to the Western Hemisphere.

The Wilson's Phalarope traditionally nested in grasslands adjacent to wetlands in western and midwestern North America. By 1979, the species began nesting on the East Coast in Massachusetts. It may now nest in New Hampshire, at least in some years. The preferred East Coast habitat appears to be high salt marsh with lush marsh grasses and numerous salt pannes, especially areas that are relatively isolated from the mainland by deep channels. In such areas in Massachusetts, Gavutis has observed pairs where there is salt hay grass immediately adjacent to large salt panne systems and the grass grows on low mounds 1 to 2 in (2.5 to 5 cm) above the normal high tide line on the surrounding marsh. This habitat apparently resembles nesting habitat in the Midwest (Bent 1927). In 1986, a pair occupied a similar but

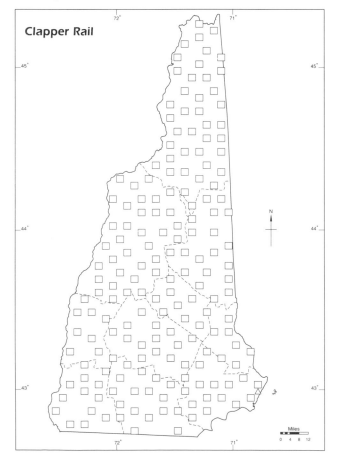

Clapper Rail

somewhat less isolated area in the Hampton Marsh, Hampton.

Wilson's Phalaropes begin to appear on the New England coast by early May, with peak counts occurring in mid-May (SRS). In the Midwest, where the species is common, the females tend to arrive first, soon followed by mixed flocks. Groups of 2 or 3 pairs then scatter to form small colonies at breeding sites. Apparently females typically outnumber males, thus putting males much in demand. Consequently, several females often pursue a single male during courtship flights. Pairs also bow to one another during courtship displays.

The nest of a Wilson's Phalarope is nearly impossible to detect unless the male flushes directly from it. It is usually well hidden in relatively short grass, and the eggs, of which there are usually 4, are cryptically colored for camouflage. Both sexes aggressively defend the nest and the precocious chicks, thus making it relatively easy to detect whether or not the pair actually is nesting (Bent 1927). Females remain near the nest during incubation and often will hover over an intruder's head (Bent 1927). Gavutis presumably was approaching a nest site or young when he observed a female in Newbury, Mass. that flew in wide arcs and circles while repeatedly uttering low calls. The male subsequently joined the female in protest.

A pair was present at Plum Island, Newburyport, Mass. during 17-21 June 1953, and individuals have occurred there regularly in June since the early 1960s. The first nests found in Massachusetts were in the Plum Island marshes on 22 June 1979, and at Monomoy NWR off Cape Cod, Mass. on 7 June 1980. Biologists suspect more or less continuous breeding, especially at Plum Island, since that time (Veit and Petersen 1993).

Apparently there are no New Hampshire records of Wilson's Phalarope between the 1870s and the 1950s (K. C. Elkins, pers. comm.). Since the 1950s they have been very uncommon migrants here, occurring chiefly in the fall (RNEB, *passim*; NHAQ, *passim*; SRS).

This phalarope's breeding debut in New Hampshire has been anticipated since the species began nesting in Massachusetts. During the 1970s, observers reported "evidence suggestive of breeding" in New Brunswick, New York, New Jersey, and Delaware (Veit and Petersen 1993).

The presence of an agitated male and female Wilson's Phalarope near a Common Tern colony in the Hampton marshes on 1 June 1986 (D.J. Abbott, pers. comm.) suddenly made this a "possible" breeding species in New Hampshire. Based on their agitated behavior, this pair may have had chicks or well-incubated eggs. Unfortunately no one was able to revisit the site until more than a month later, and the birds were not seen again. Between visits, the nest could have been destroyed or the young could have fledged.

Observers should monitor the Hampton marshes annually to determine the precise status of this species in New Hampshire. While it is difficult to predict its future breeding status in the state, it seems unlikely that it ever would become more than an uncommon breeder along the Coast.

George W. Gavutis, Jr.

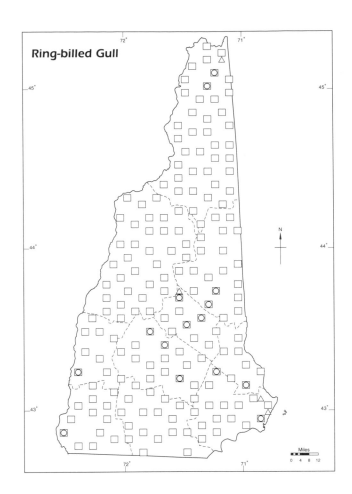

Ring-billed Gull
Larus delawarensis

In New Hampshire, the Ring-billed Gull is easily confused with the larger Herring Gull. Size is useful to distinguish them only when both species are present. The prominent black ring on the bill is a good visual cue for identifying the adult Ring-billed Gull. Both species have similar vocalizations, but the Ring-billed Gull's loud, mewing, buglelike cry is higher pitched than the Herring Gull's.

Ring-billed Gulls breed in the northwestern U.S., central Canada, and the Great Lakes and St. Lawrence region, and along the Maritime and Hudson Bay coasts (Blokpoel and Tessier 1986). They occur commonly in summer on many of New Hampshire's mid-sized to large lakes (Ridgely 1977) and on the Great Bay estuary (E. Miller, pers. comm.). Recently they have been fairly common spring and fall migrants along the New Hampshire coast. There apparently is no record of Ring-billed Gull breeding activity in New Hampshire, but the breeding population of this species has been expanding toward the state from the west.

Ring-billed Gulls breed primarily on islands in large inland lakes and rivers. They prefer to nest on islands with low, sparse vegetation, but have successfully colonized disturbed areas such as construction sites, harbor dikes, dredge spoils, piles of rubble, and slag dumps (Scharf 1981, Blokpoel and Tessier 1986). Ring-bills reportedly have nested on a garbage dump near Ottawa, Ont. (Weir 1983), and on a rooftop at Owen Sound, Ont. (Blokpoel and Smith 1988). Nesting substrates vary considerably, and include sand, sand/silt/clay aggregations, driftwood, concrete, slag, rocks, and boulders. Ring-bills rarely, if ever, nest on exposed sandy sites.

Adults apparently return to their colonial nesting sites already paired (Audubon 1840). Fidelity to both colony and nest area becomes well developed in stable colonies (Southern 1977, Southern and Southern 1980). The nest typically is a scrape lined with grasses and feathers (Bent 1921). The clutch most commonly includes 3 eggs (Bent 1921). Large clutches, called superclutches, are attributed to more than one female laying eggs in the same nest (Lagrenade and Mousseau 1983).

Egg laying at New Hampshire latitudes usually occurs in late April and May (Blokpoel and Tessier 1986). The incubation period ranges from 25 to 28 days (Nol and Blokpoel 1983). Both adults defend their nest with long calls, charges, and gape-jabs (Southern 1981). Both parents feed their young by regurgitating, initially presenting food to their chicks with the tips of their bills (Miller and Conover 1983). Young can fly about 35 days after hatching (Fetterolf 1983).

The Ring-billed Gull is an opportunistic feeder. This gull will plunge for fish, hawk for insects (Pettingill 1958, Lauro 1977), follow plows for earthworms and other invertebrates (Hailman 1960), beg food from people at beaches and fast food establishments, hunt for voles and other small mammals in fields, and scavenge at dumps and sanitary landfills (Bent 1921, Blokpoel and Tessier 1986).

Audubon (1967) described the Ring-billed Gull as "The Common American Gull" and observed nesting colonies on several islands in the Gulf of Maine. This gull was nearly extirpated from eastern North America by the early 1900s (Bent 1921). At that time Ring-bill breeding colonies were largely restricted to remote lakes of the northern prairie and far Western states and prairie provinces, where the species apparently suffered much less persecution from egg and plumage collectors and other human disturbances (Bent 1921).

Ring-bills reappeared on Lake Huron by 1926, after an absence of a quarter century (Ludwig 1943), and nested on Lake Ontario a year later (Ludwig 1974). By the mid-1930s, they also were nesting in New York on Lake Ontario and the upper St. Lawrence River (Hyde 1948). The first documented Ring-billed Gull nesting on Lake Champlain was in 1949 (Bull 1974).

Today, the Ring-bill flourishes throughout much of its former range. Dramatic population increases have resulted in a number of conflicts with human interests (Blokpoel 1980). A rapid population expansion began after a period of relative stability from about 1940 to the 1960s. Factors which may have contributed to the increase include: lowered water levels in the Great Lakes/St. Lawrence drainage, exposing new nesting habitat (Ludwig 1974); colonization of man-made spits and islands (Scharf 1981, Blokpoel 1983); invasion of alewives into the Great Lakes (Ludwig 1974); and abundant food supplies at landfills (Blokpoel and Tessier 1986, Jay 1986).

The Great Lakes and St. Lawrence River population more than doubled during 1976–84 to an estimated 700,000 nesting pairs, but has since stabilized (Blokpoel and Tessier 1986, Southern 1988). The nesting population on Lake Champlain was estimated at more than 27,000 nesting pairs in 1985, with an annual growth rate of 15.5% (Jay 1986). A pain nested on the Maine side of Umbagog Lake for the first time in 1981 (Adamus 1988).

The Atlas map shows a number of locations where

nonbreeding Ring-bills occur during the breeding season. The Lakes Region in particular attracts these gulls in summer, and provides potential breeding habitat. If neighboring gull populations continue to increase, Ring-billed Gulls may one day nest in New Hampshire, if they are not doing so already.

Dennis Slate

Arctic Tern
Sterna paradisaea

It takes a highly trained eye to distinguish this beautiful bird from its close relative, the Common Tern. The Arctic's bill is blood red rather than orange red, and lacks a black tip. Also, unlike the Common, the Arctic has a grayish breast, which contrasts with its white cheeks. Their calls are even more difficult to distinguish, although the Arctic's is less slurred and higher pitched. This species is the champion migrant of the bird world, often making an amazing 22,000 mi (35,200 km) annual round trip between the Arctic and the Antarctic.

This common circumpolar species approaches the southern limit of its U.S. nesting range in New Hampshire. Small but declining numbers nest in a few Massachusetts colonies of Common Terns on Cape Cod, and formerly nested off Cape Ann. The closest Maine colony in 1984 was on Outer Head Island, Georgetown (Andrews 1990) approximately 81 mi (135 km) from New Hampshire. NHFG listed the Arctic Tern as a Threatened Species in New Hampshire in 1980. It now apparently is extirpated, at least as a breeding species.

Arctic Terns usually nest in single species colonies in their northern range, but regularly nest in colonies of Common Terns

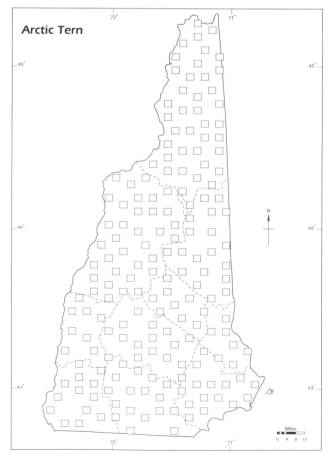

along the Maine coast, as they did historically in New Hampshire (ASNH data). In spring, both terns reach New England by mid-May (Elkins 1982). In fall, most Arctic Terns have departed by mid-September, but some Common Terns stay much later. Arctics usually choose sandy or rocky islands for nesting, and tend to nest in more open situations than Common Terns. Arctics may make a hollow in the sand, gravel, or moss, or may lay their eggs on bare rock, with a few pieces of granite, pebbles, or vegetation surrounding the nest (Townsend 1921). Arctics are even more likely than Common Terns to omit nesting material altogether. Their eggs are nearly identical to those of Common Terns, and a usual clutch is 2 or 3 eggs.

Although Arctic Terns were reportedly "abundant" in Massachusetts during the 19th century (Coues 1868), they never have been common on the New Hampshire coast. A few pair nested in Seabrook in 1926, and a single bird was observed in 1932 (White 1927, 1932b). Jackson (1947) found Arctic Terns breeding in a large colony of Common and Roseate terns on Londoners (Lunging) Island at the Isles of Shoals, Rye in the early 1930s. In 1936, 25 to 30 pairs of Arctics nested there among about 750 pairs of Common Terns (Wright 1937). There are no documented records of Arctics there since then, and all terns stopped nesting on Lunging Island after 1944 (Drury 1973, Taber 1955, Erwin and Korschgen 1979). Because of the similarity of the species, most historic accounts of nesting terns did not specify species or their proportions in colonies.

In 1965 and 1966, one pair nested on an island in Back Channel, New Castle/Portsmouth, and 2 pairs did so in 1967 (SRS). A single bird was present there in 1968, but observers found no nest. During the next 12 years, observers noted only occasional adults along the Coast during the breeding season. In 1981, A. C. Borror (pers. comm.) observed a courting pair at the Isles of Shoals, but noted no further breeding activity. On 21 June 1987, Gavutis observed an adult flying, calling, and sitting on a tidal creek bank just west of the Common Tern colony in the Hampton marshes.

The disappearance of nesting terns from the Isles of Shoals coincided with a rapid build-up of nesting gulls. Some Common Terns still nest on estuary islands and salt marshes, but Arctic Terns seldom accept such sites. No terns are likely to nest on the Isles of Shoals as long as gulls occupy the desirable nesting habitat. Removal of nesting gulls could lead to reestablishment of nesting Common Terns, and subsequently to a small but viable population of Arctic Terns.

George W. Gavutis, Jr.

Black Tern
Chlidonias niger

The small and beautiful Black Tern, a rare bird in New Hampshire, looks like a giant swallow as it gracefully hawks for insects over open water or marshes, alternately flapping and gliding and occasionally hovering. The sexes look alike, and during the breeding season have black heads, bills, and underparts (except for white undertail coverts), dark gray backs, notched tails, and wings that are nearly white below. At other seasons they have a somewhat mottled plumage (Peterson 1980). Their call note is a sharp "kik" (Pough 1951).

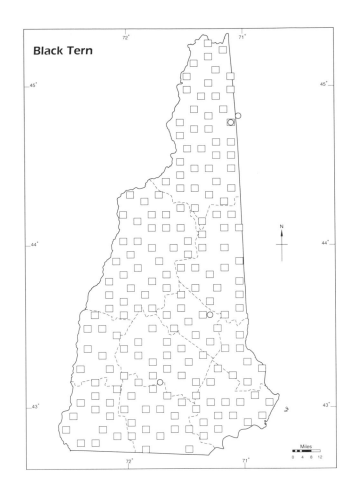

Black Tern

The Black Tern nests across the middle of North America as well as in the Old World, but never has been known to nest in New Hampshire. There are, however, several relatively recent breeding season records of the species for the state, and it is a regular though very local summer resident in Vermont, Maine, and the Maritime Provinces.

Black Terns of the Western Hemisphere winter mainly in South America (Pough 1951). Some reach their breeding grounds in Vermont in extensive cattail or shrub marshes by early May (Ellison *in* Laughlin and Kibbe 1985). Nesting tends to be loosely colonial (Harrison 1978), and nests often are in patches of sparse emergent vegetation (Bent 1921). They consist of bits of aquatic vegetation and sit on top of floating, rotted vegetation (Palmer 1949). An old grebe or duck nest or muskrat house may provide a foundation (Bent 1921, Pough 1951).

In the Northeast, 2 to 4, usually 3 eggs comprise a clutch. Both sexes incubate for a total of 20 to 22 days (Harrison 1978). Like other terns, they vigorously defend their nest sites and especially their eggs and young (Bent 1921). Day-old chicks may swim from the nest to escape danger, but young usually stay at the nest site for about 2 weeks. They can fly at about 3 weeks, and are fully fledged at about 4 weeks (Harrison 1978). Black Terns leave their nesting grounds as early as July, and southbound migrants are most common (though still rare) in New Hampshire in August (Elkins 1982).

While Black Terns sometimes feed on fish fry in the ocean in company with other terns, at inland localities they feed largely on insects caught in the air (Forbush 1925a). Their hawking over grasslands and marshes makes them conspicuous on the breeding grounds. They also eat spiders, small crayfish, and mollusks (Bent 1921).

The primary breeding range of the Black Tern in North America encompasses the prairie sloughs of the Midwest, but the overall range has expanded during the last century to include isolated patches of suitable habitat in the East. The species has been nesting in New York since at least 1903, though observers suspected nesting there as early as 1844 (Eaton 1910). As of the early 1920s, the species had not been known to nest in New England (Forbush 1925a). It was first found nesting in New Brunswick in 1936 (Tufts 1986), Vermont in 1937 (Ellison *in* Laughlin and Kibbe 1985), and Maine in 1946 (Palmer 1949).

In New Hampshire, Brewster (1924) found the Black Tern to be a "rare transient visitor" at Umbagog Lake during 18 August – 8 September in the years 1871 to 1909. An individual Goodhue saw on 10 June 1898 at Lake Winnipesaukee (Allen 1903) probably was a late spring migrant.

Apparently the first New Hampshire breeding season record of a Black Tern is of one T. Van Dyke observed on 29–30 June 1936, at the outlet of Umbagog Lake (Bagg and Eliot 1937). Three Black Terns seen next to an extensive cattail marsh at Lake Wantastiquet, Hinsdale on 25 August 1958, 3 there on 20 May 1959, and one on 4 May 1962 presumably were only migrants, but their occurrence in the same, seemingly potential nesting habitat may be significant (Richards, unpubl. data). More recent records are of 2 birds in apparently suitable nesting habitat at Cherry Pond, Jefferson, on 6 July 1978 (Richards and S.M. Sutcliffe, pers. obs.), 3 at the outlet of Umbagog Lake on 19 June 1987 (C.R. Foss, pers. comm.), another there on 13 July 1978 (E.C. Janeway, pers. comm.), and 2 there on 19 June 1988 (Evans, pers. obs.). Observers have reported single birds at 4 different locations in the state between 8 and 16 June during the period 1975–83 (SRS).

Records during the Atlas period were from Umbagog Lake, Elm Brook Marsh, Hopkinton, and Lake Winnipesaukee, Alton. It seems quite possible that the Black Tern, which only recently has begun nesting in New England, may nest somewhere in New Hampshire in the near future. Potential sites include Lake Wantastiquet, Cherry Pond, and Umbagog Lake, especially if these areas remain relatively undisturbed. The Maine Breeding Bird Atlas project documented 5 colonies, of which the closest to New Hampshire is in the Belgrade Lakes region (Adamus 1988). Of the 8 sites mentioned in the Vermont Atlas, all are extensive riparian marshlands on or near the state's 2 major lakes, Memphremagog and Champlain (Ellison *in* Laughlin and Kibbe 1985).

These terns are quite conspicuous during the breeding season, since nesting colonies generally are confined to extensive marshes over which adults spend much time in the air. Thus, any future establishment of a New Hampshire breeding colony is unlikely to escape detection for long.

Tudor Richards & Diane Evans

Passenger Pigeon
Ectopistes migratorius

The beautiful, long-extinct Passenger Pigeon is generally considered to have been North America's most abundant land bird within historical times. Wilson and Audubon, for example, saw flocks they calculated to exceed 2 billion and 1 billion birds, respectively (Forbush 1927).

This wild pigeon was the largest North American dove, about the size of a domestic pigeon. Its plumage resembled the Mourning Dove's but was darker, with a grayish blue head, fore wing, and rump, and a brighter violet neck mark. The male had a redder breast, and the somewhat duller female was paler below than the female Mourning Dove (Forbush 1927). Males made a loud, harsh "keck" note, chatterings, and a weak "keeho" cooing; females clucked and croaked (Craig 1911 *in* Forbush 1927).

Wild pigeons arrived in southern New Hampshire during late March or early April (Fox *in* Allen 1903, Goodhue *in* White 1937). Most continued on to nest in the northern counties and in Maine (Silver 1957). Passenger Pigeons nested in deciduous or coniferous upland or swampy woods, but preferred hardwoods (Forbush 1927).

The male's courtship consisted of wing flapping while simultaneously raising his body and making the "keck" and chattering notes. Nests were simple, frail structures of crossed twigs and sticks supported by branches, 10 to 50 ft (3 to 15.2 m) up in forest trees. There were reports of 100 or more nests in a tree. Both parents incubated the one or 2 eggs (Stevens *in* Brewster 1889) for 14 days (Deane 1896 *in* Townsend 1932). Both parents fed "pigeon milk" to the young pigeons, but forced them from the nests after 14 days or so (Brewster 1889). The adults then departed, often en masse, to nest again elsewhere, sometimes many miles away but always where food was plentiful (Forbush 1927).

Passenger Pigeons ate mostly seeds and insects early in the season, and fed mostly on mast and berries in late summer and fall (Townsend 1932). Enormous crops of acorns, beech nuts, chestnuts, and berries must have been necessary, especially to support the 3 broods a pair often raised each season (Forbush 1927).

Brewster (1925) mentioned Passenger Pigeons gathering in rather large flocks at Umbagog Lake on 1 September, probably not long before heading south. Late dates for Passenger Pigeons in New Hampshire are 8 and 10 October (Brewster 1925, Townsend 1932).

Native peoples used Passenger Pigeons extensively for food during many generations prior to European settlement, evidently without diminishing the population. For more than 200 years following the establishment of the first European settlements in eastern North America, wild pigeons were so abundant that migrating birds numbered in the millions if not billions and darkened the sky for hours and even days on end. They nested in colonies that stretched for miles and, with the weight of their numbers and their nests, often broke off even large branches from many of the trees (Forbush 1916, Forbush 1927, Townsend 1932).

From the time of the first European settlements, pigeons were killed for food, feather beds, and crop damage control. Although as early as 1672 Josselyn (*in* Silver 1957) claimed that pigeons had already diminished in numbers, Belknap (1792 *in* Allen 1903) described large flocks coming from the south and nesting in our woods with no mention of any decline. Crawford (1845 *in* Silver 1957) described felling beech trees against other trees so that the young pigeons would drop from nests. Single trees sometimes held as many as 40 nests, with 2 young per nest. Despite the early slaughter, pigeons remained abundant in many New England localities until market hunting became big business in the last century (Forbush 1927). Forbush (1927) mentioned great nestings in New England becoming fewer, but described a small one in northern Vermont during 1848-53 as consisting of 20 a (8 ha) or more of old-growth maple and yellow birch, with often 25 or more nests per tree. Pigeons remained abundant there at least until 1865 (Forbush 1927).

Passenger Pigeons still nested in Pembroke (Forbush 1927), Hollis, Webster, Conway (Allen 1903), and at Umbagog Lake (Brewster 1925) around 1870. A reliable observer reported that in Errol around 1850 they "were still so abundant that they appeared on wing in flocks a mile or more in length and had to be kept out of buckwheat fields by boys who watched the grain ceaselessly from daylight to dark" (Brewster 1925). To Brewster himself "they seemed plentiful enough about the Lake between 1871 and 1874." As late as 1874 he saw flocks of up to 30 birds but only one bird after that, in 1882, despite visits in 1876 and 1879-81. He obtained an 1890 record of one bird from another observer.

In Webster, Goodhue (unpubl.) saw "great flocks" in 1861, flocks of up to 50 in the early 1870s, and his last bird in 1884. In the Concord area, a General Battles saw his last pigeons in 1885, when he killed one out of a flock of 7 (White 1937). That may be the record Silver (1957) referred to as "the last official record for the state." Pigeons survived only a little longer in the Midwest, where they were hunted commercially almost to the end (Forbush 1927). No doubt land clearing had long-term, disastrous effects on pigeons, as did occasional severe storms (Silver 1957).

The last Passenger Pigeon died in the Cincinnati Zoo in 1914, with humans obviously to blame for the extinction of the species.

Tudor Richards

Barn Owl

Tyto alba

This distinctive-looking bird with its heart-shaped face has been known by many names, including Monkey-faced Owl and Common Barn Owl. It occurs on all continents except Antarctica, but not in cold climates. New Hampshire is on the northern edge of its range, and it occurs only rarely in our state.

This medium-sized owl is about the size of a crow, but has much longer wings. The female is larger than the male. Both sexes are tawny brown above, and white or pale tawny with small black spots below. The Barn Owl's legs are longer in proportion to its size than those of our other owls. The face is white, the eyes dark. The Barn Owl's flight is silent and wavering or "moth-like." Its vocalizations have been variously described: "a soft ascending wheezy cry" (Robbins et al. 1983), "a growling rattle" (Lippincott 1917), "a harsh blood-curdling screech" (Potter and Gillespie 1925). It sometimes snaps its bill loudly, and it calls "ick, ick" when bringing food to its young (Potter and Gillespie 1925). Nestlings hiss and make a "snoring" noise (Potter and Gillespie 1925).

As its name suggests, this owl often nests in barns, but it also will nest in silos, church steeples, towers, and many other sorts of buildings, as well as in hollow trees, burrows in the ground, and holes or crevices in banks or cliffs (Bendire *in* Bent 1938). It is typically a bird of open country, including farms, villages, and even cities, but sometimes roosts in the woods. The Barn Owl is one of the most nocturnal of owls, but it may hunt at dusk or dawn or on dark days to feed young or to survive during periods of severe weather (Prestt and Wagstaffe *in* Burton 1984). Rodents, especially voles, mice, and rats, constitute its principal prey (Johnsgard 1988). Its hearing is so acute that it can catch a mouse in complete darkness, guided by the rustling of the mouse as it moves (Payne 1962).

The height of the breeding season for Barn Owls is from March to September (Harrison 1975), but these birds may nest at any time of year. In New York eggs have been found in all months except January (Bull 1985). A pair may have 2 broods in a year. Clutches range from 2 to 11 eggs, which are laid at intervals of 2 or 3 days (Johnsgard 1988). The female incubates, beginning with the laying of the first egg. The incubation period usually cited is 32 to 34 days, but it is uncertain whether this is for a single egg or a clutch (Harrison 1975).

Nestlings are variable in size, as eggs hatch at 2 or 3 day intervals and thus young can differ in age by up to 3 weeks. Both parents feed the young, which can fly when about 60 days old but remain dependent for about 10 days or longer (Harrison 1978). Young raised in the northern U.S. may disperse in any direction, but more go south than go east, west, or north, and those that go south are likely to go farther (Stewart 1952). The species appears to be migratory at the northern edge of its range (Johnsgard 1988).

Barn Owls nested in Connecticut at least as early as 1892 (Sage et al. 1913). In Massachusetts, though there are many earlier records of occurrence, the first confirmed nesting was in 1925 (Griscom and Snyder 1955). Recently published reports suggest that these owls may have nested in Vermont as early as the 1890s and again in the 1920s, but "confirmed" breeding was first documented there (4 times from 1976 to 1980) as a result of the Vermont Breeding Bird Atlas project (Laughlin *in* Laughlin and Kibbe 1985). Palmer (1949) presented no evidence that Barn Owls ever had nested in Maine, though he considered the species "perhaps a very rare resident." These owls did nest in Maine in 1960 (Hebert 1960a).

Neither Forbush (1927) nor Bent (1938) mentions the occurrence of the Barn Owl in New Hampshire. The state's first published record for the species is of one observed in Belmont on 10 August 1948 (RNEB). Since then observers have reported this owl in the following towns: Wolfeboro (17–18 August 1960), Windsor (2 April 1966), Bradford (8 October 1970), Meredith (16 October 1971), Plainfield (20 December 1972) (SRS). The first, and so far the only documented nesting record is of a pair with 7 young in a silo in Hollis in August 1977 (Elkins 1978). The only record of Barn Owls during the period of Atlas field work was of an injured bird, which later died, picked up in Winchester in April 1981 (Abbott 1981).

Barn Owls slowly have been extending their range northward during this century (Stewart 1952). They are more sensitive to low temperatures than our other owls and have been known to perish of cold or hunger during severe winters (Speirs 1940, Griscom and Snyder 1955). They have nested regularly in Massachusetts since 1928 (Griscom and Snyder 1955, Keith 1964). The Massachusetts BBA project (unpubl.) produced 11 records of "confirmed" nesting, all but one of which were near the coast, and only 2 of which were north of Boston. Barn Owls almost surely will be found nesting again in New Hampshire, but perhaps only sporadically, during years when their populations are high. If our climate becomes warmer, they may become regular breeding birds.

Kimball C. Elkins

Long-eared Owl
Asio otus

This secretive owl resembles the Great Horned Owl, but is much smaller and slimmer, lacks a white "bib," and has long, close-set ear tufts. The Long-eared Owl prefers dense stands of coniferous or mixed woods with open land nearby for hunting. Apparently suitable habitat is widespread in this state, but although these owls may be year-round residents, sightings are few and far between. Long-eareds are almost exclusively nocturnal and spend daylight hours roosting in dense foliage, usually near tree trunks. The scarcity of records may result from their secretive habits or from true rarity.

Long-eareds produce a wide variety of vocalizations, including catlike meows, doglike barks, shrieks, whistles, and various hoots (Forbush 1927, Bent 1938). They are most vociferous during the breeding season and in close proximity to their nests (Bent 1938). The male's usual song is a series of evenly spaced, low-pitched hoots, most often given between dusk and midnight. Nocturnal display flights involve flying erratically through the woods and occasionally clapping the wings below the body. Females utter a nasal, buzzy call, often from the nest tree (Johnsgard 1988).

The nest is most often an old one built by crows, hawks, or squirrels (Bent 1938). Occasionally the owls will nest in a tree cavity or, very rarely, on the ground (Bent 1938). Incubation of the 3 to 8, usually 4 or 5 eggs begins when the first egg is laid and lasts between 25 and 30 days (Harrison 1975). Bent (1938) cites egg dates for New England and New York from 31 March to 31 May, with 7 of the 13 during 19 April to 15 May. A nest found in the Jefferson region on 25 May 1905 contained 5 half-grown young (Wright 1911).

The female sits very tight on the nest, while the male roosts nearby and brings her food at night (Harrison 1975). Much of the diet consists of rodents (Bent 1938). Prey also include shrews, moles, small birds, frogs, snakes, and insects. Both parents participate in rearing the young. Long-eared owlets leave the nest as "branchers" at 20 to 26 days of age, and begin to fly when they are 30 to 40 days old. They begin to become more independent at about 2 months of age, but may continue to beg until about 50 days old (Johnsgard 1988).

When approached, Long-eareds assume an elongated freeze posture, in which their cryptically colored bodies resemble a broken-off branch or a piece of loose tree bark. If their young are in danger, however, the adults perform distraction displays or assume threat postures with widespread wings, glaring eyes, and swaying heads.

Unlike many other owls, Long-eareds exhibit at least some migrational tendencies. Considerable numbers migrate past banding stations along the lower Great Lakes, and migrations through northern New England likely occur during October and March (Bent 1938). The majority of New Hampshire records during 1939-66 are from October to January; winter records are exclusively from towns along or near the coast (RNEB, NHAQ, *passim*). In winter, communal roosts are not uncommon. As many as 50 to 75 Long-eared Owls have shared a single woodlot in southern Ontario during the winter (Cadman et al. 1987).

Some early ornithologists considered Long-eared Owls species common to abundant in New Hampshire (Coues 1868, Maynard 1871). Minot (1895) even described them as "perhaps the most

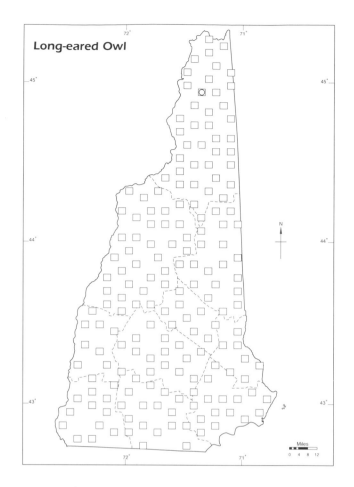

Long-eared Owl

numerous of American Owls." Dearborn (1903) thought them rather common in the Durham area and mentioned a local nest. The only other definitive breeding season record from that era seems to be an individual Brewster (1925) encountered near the shores of Umbagog Lake in Cambridge on 11 June 1879. Forbush (1927) considered them rather common in northern New England and stated that "formerly it was a common bird throughout most of the forested region within its breeding range, and it is more common still than most of us realize." However, all sources since that time (and even some early sources) have considered Long-eared Owls uncommon to rare, or even absent as a nesting species over much of New Hampshire (Dearborn 1898, Allen 1903, Hoffman 1904, White 1937, Allison and Allison 1979). Some impressions of their abundance may have resulted from observations of communal winter roosts, rather than of breeding pairs (K. Elkins, pers. comm.).

The Maine Atlas produced only 4 records, all "confirmed" (Adamus 1988), and the Vermont Atlas only 5 records, 3 of which are "confirmed" (Laughlin and Kibbe 1985). Even in New York, where Eaton (1914) proclaimed the species "not very uncommon ... in most parts of the State" early in the century, only 2% of atlas blocks produced records (Andrle and Carroll 1988). Was this owl really common to abundant in the Northeast 100 years ago? If so, the reasons for its decline are unknown.

Breeding season records in New Hampshire are nearly non-existent over the past 60 years. They include Eaton (May 1949), Hanover (May 1958), New Hampton (May 1968), Gilford (March 1971), Kensington (reported nest in May 1972) and Dixville (June 1972) (ASNH data). G. and A. Robbins heard the only Long-eared Owl of the 6 year Atlas project in Stewartstown, Coos County. ASNH has received no breeding season records since 1985.

It would take special effort to investigate the true distribution and abundance of Long-eared Owls in this state, for the lack of sightings is probably not entirely due to the secrecy of the species. Long-eareds just might be nearly as rare as they appear. If so, and if they have experienced a significant decline during the present century as anecdotal evidence suggests, their status and problems deserve prompt research attention.

George C. Robbins

American Pipit

Anthus spinoletta

The inconspicuous American Pipit nests on alpine and Arctic tundra in the Northern Hemisphere and frequents short grass and exposed soil during migration. This species breeds across North America from Alaska to Newfoundland and south in western mountains to California and New Mexico (Terres 1980). A small breeding population occurs on Mt. Katahdin, Maine, and a nest discovered on Mt. Washington in 1991 (C.C. Rimmer, pers. comm.) provides the first New Hampshire nesting record. The winter range extends from Maryland to Guatemala (Terres 1980).

American Pipits are slender, sparrow-sized birds, gray brown above and buffy below. Their long, slender bills and long legs distinguish them from Dark-eyed Juncos and White-throated Sparrows, which also frequent New Hampshire's alpine habitat. They frequently wag their white-edged tails up and down.

Spring migration through Maine and New Hampshire occurs primarily during May (Palmer 1949, SRS). Spring flocks are typically small (Palmer 1949) but occasionally approach 100 (SRS). Arrival in breeding habitat on Mt. Katahdin, Maine apparently occurs in mid to late May (Palmer 1949). Alpine nesting habitat encompasses level to steep terrain and well vegetated to completely bare sites, but must include features such as eroded turf, tussocks, or tilted rocks in areas which become snow-free by mid to late June (Verbeek 1970).

Verbeek's (1970) study of American Pipits on Wyoming's Beartooth Plateau provides most of the following information on breeding behavior. Pipits forage for wind-blown insects on alpine snowfields for several weeks after arrival. They establish territories with ground and flight displays and considerable chasing when the weather improves. Pairs may abandon newly established territories and move to lower elevations during severe weather.

Although the sexes have identical plumage, territorial behavior distinguishes males from females early in the breeding season. Males droop their wings in ground displays, bobbing their tails or holding them elevated. The conspicuous flight display involves rising about 130 ft (40 m) into the air, then descending to the ground with wings fully extended and tail raised and widely spread. The male sings a tinkling "tjwee, tjwee" continuously during the flight display, and sometimes on the ground.

Nest building begins in mid-June and takes 4 to 5 days. The nest, constructed of grass and occasionally lined with hair, is built in or at the base of a tussock, in a clump of vegetation, under a rock's edge, or in a bare spot. Often it is partly recessed and faces away from prevailing winds, sun, and drifting snow (Verbeek 1970).

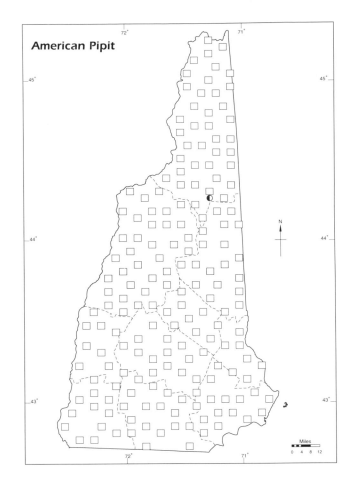

Clutches vary from 3 to 6 but usually include 4 or 5 eggs. Laying begins about 4 days after a rise in temperature, sometimes only 4 days after the nest site is free of snow, and can extend into early July. The female incubates for about 14 days. The male forages for insects, walking slowly through thick vegetation after the snow melts, and feeds the female at some distance from the nest. He announces his approach with a "tjueet" call, repeating it until she arrives. She answers "peet" from the nest, and calls "wee-wee-wee-wee" as she flies to him and displays with frenzied wing vibrations. After accepting food, she usually walks back to the nest, catching additional insects on the way. She also may leave the nest to forage for herself.

The female broods the young for about the first 5 days, and they remain in the nest 14 or 15 days. The well-camouflaged fledglings frequent rock slides and stone stripes. The adults feed them for 14 days after fledging.

Pipits associate in loose flocks after family groups disperse in early September (Verbeek 1970). Migrants appear in northern New England by 16 September and peak during late September and October (Palmer 1949, SRS). During fall migration they are locally common, especially in major river valleys and along the Coast (Forbush 1929). Fall flocks in New Hampshire may number 200+ birds and sometimes occur into mid-November (SRS). The pipit is much more common as a migrant here in fall than in spring (Dearborn 1898, 1903, Allen 1903, Thayer 1909 *in* Allison and Allison 1979).

The first breeding season records of pipits in potential breeding habitat were of 2 individuals near the summit of Mt. Madison, Thompson and Meserves Purchase/Low and Burbanks Grant, on 20 July 1937 (Palmer and Taber 1946) and another 2 on Mt. Washington on 19 June 1965 (SRS). The next alpine sightings occurred in the 1980s, and provided evidence of possible breeding on Mt. Washington. T. Richards observed a pipit at about 5,500 ft (1,680 m) elevation on 15 September 1984 (SRS). Although this bird may have been a migrant, individuals have remained on Wyoming breeding grounds as late as 22 September (Verbeek 1970). Subsequently, S. and W. Fogelman (pers. comm.) observed 2 pipits interacting above timberline on Mt. Washington on 9 June 1985; H. M. Cadot (pers. comm.) heard a pipit near the summit on 2 July 1987; and C. Lewey (pers. comm.) observed single pipits performing aerial displays below the summit on 7 July 1988 and on 23 June 1989, and saw an apparent pair on the ground in potential nesting habitat on 7 July 1988. Finally, on 29 June 1991, C.C. Rimmer (pers. comm.) observed 3 pairs of pipits and located a nest with 5 eggs just above 5,400 ft (1,650 m) elevation in a sloping sedge meadow. This newly discovered breeding population provides an exciting opportunity for future study.

Carol R. Foss

Loggerhead Shrike
Lanius ludoicianus

The stocky "butcher bird" moved into New Hampshire during the late 1800s and was an uncommon and local summer resident for several decades before retreating from New England as a nesting species. It occurs across much of the U.S. and south central Canada, but remains essentially absent from New England and the Appalachians and is more common in the southern part of its range (Robbins et al 1986). It winters in the southern U.S and Mexico (Farrand 1983). This predator inhabits open country with scattered trees and shrubs (especially hawthorns), hedges, or orchards.

Shrikes secure their prey on thorns or barbed wire or in the forks of trees while eating. Loggerhead Shrikes hunt from relatively low perches in open or brushy areas, scanning the ground for large insects, rodents, snakes, and small birds, and sometimes hover a few feet above potential prey (Vandercook 1921 in Graber et al. 1973). Their flight, often low to the ground, is undulating with very rapid wing beats; they frequently drop low from one perch and rise abruptly to the next (Farrand 1983, NGS 1983).

This shrike seldom sings. Its unmusical song of repeated and widely separated phrases is low and harsh (Forbush 1929, Farrand 1983). Territorial defense includes an aggressive wing-fluttering display (Smith 1973). Courtship includes wing fluttering, tail expanding, and erratic chase flights (Sprunt 1950).

The Loggerhead Shrike could be expected to occur here during April to October, while the slightly larger and lighter Northern Shrike is present mostly from November through March (Elkins 1982). Loggerheads begin nest construction soon after arrival and may complete their nest within 11 days (Todd 1940, Graber et al. 1973). Both male and female collect nesting materials, but the female does most of the construction, fashioning a bulky nest from twigs, plant stems, and grass, and lining it with feathers, plant fibers, and other cottony materials (Graber et al. 1973, Harrison 1975, Harrison 1978). A nest in Lancaster contained white twine and pieces of white cloth (Wright 1911).

The nest typically is located 3 to 50 ft (0.9 to 15.2 m) above ground in a dense shrub or low tree (Harrison 1975, Harrison 1978). One New Hampshire nest was on an elm branch 10 ft (3 m) above the ground and near the trunk, 3 others were in stunted spruces (Wright 1911), and yet another in a back yard fir (Allen 1903). Dearborn (1903) noted that nests in the Durham area were "likely to be in an apple or other scrubby tree."

The female lays 4 to 7 eggs and incubates for 14 to 17 days, while the male brings her food (Graber et al. 1973, Harrison 1975, Harrison 1978). New Hampshire Loggerhead Shrikes lay eggs by late April or early May. A pair in Hanover had 6 eggs in a nest on 4 May 1885 (Allen 1903). Other New Hampshire egg dates are 26 April 1898 in Charlestown (6 eggs) (Allen 1903) and May 1897 in Tilton (Dearborn 1898). The adults may swoop boldly at intruders to defend their nest (Todd 1940).

Both parents tend the young, which leave the nest after 16 to 20 days and spend several days nearby. They become independent at 26 to 36 days and begin to impale insects at 30 to 40 days (Graber et al. 1973, Harrison 1978, Miller 1931 in Terres 1980). A nest in Hanover contained 6 young on 30 May 1884 (Allen 1903); 5 nestlings observed in Lancaster on 8 June 1909 had moved to nearby branches on 15 June (Wright 1911).

Resident shrikes are most conspicuous in July and August after the young have fledged, when they often perch on roadside wires and branches (Dearborn 1903, Wright 1911). Fall sightings in New Hampshire during 1953–75 occurred from 10 August to 31 October, especially during 16 to 31 August (RNEB, *passim*; SRS).

This species extended its range eastward as forests were cleared for agriculture during the century following European settlement (Eaton 1914 in Bull 1974). The first New England record was in West Newton, Mass., on 21 October 1872 (Bagg and Eliot 1937). Pairs nested in Vermont and Maine in 1877, in Massachusetts in 1883, and in New Hampshire in 1884 (Bagg and Eliot 1937). The population in New Hampshire may have peaked between 1885 and 1910, when nesting occurred in Charlestown, Hanover, Tilton, Jefferson, Lancaster, and the Durham area (Dearborn 1898, Allen 1903, Dearborn 1903, Wright 1911).

No New Hampshire nests are known since 1910, and observers have reported only occasional sightings of individuals, primarily migrants. Between 1960 and 1980, the only reported breeding season sightings occurred in Lancaster (1963), Shelburne (1971), Canterbury (1974), and Hebron (1980) (ASNH records). During the Atlas project, observers reported individuals in the Sunapee area on 8 April 1982, in Bridgewater in May 1983, and in Carroll on 5 April 1986.

Loggerhead Shrikes have declined almost steadily since about 1910 throughout much of their range, but especially in the eastern U.S. (Graber et al. 1973, Milburn 1981, Tate 1986). BBS data from 1966 to 1979 document a significant decrease throughout the continent (Robbins et al. 1986). Possible explanations include loss of breeding and foraging habitat, high incidence of road kills, and contaminated prey (Graber et al. 1973, Bull 1974, Robbins et al. 1986), but the true causes remain a mystery. The Loggerhead Shrike is unlikely to become reestablished as a breeding species in New Hampshire in the foreseeable future.

Carol R. Foss

Palm Warbler

Dendroica palmarum

The tail-wagging Palm Warbler could have been named the Bog Warbler, as it nests mostly in bogs across much of Canada and the extreme northern U.S. The Eastern subspecies, the Yellow Palm Warbler (*D. palmarum hypochrysea*), nests from Ontario east to Newfoundland and south to northeastern New England, and winters principally from Tennessee and North Carolina to the Gulf Coast (AOU 1957). Breeding habitat consists of bogs and boggy heaths with scattered black spruce (Welsh *in* Cadman et al. 1987).

The Palm Warbler is a very rare breeding bird in New Hampshire, which is at the southeastern limit of its nesting range. Although observers confirmed breeding in the state in 1957, 1980, and 1988 (Richards, unpubl. data), the Atlas produced only 2 "possible" breeding records. One came from the edge of the same bog in Errol where all but one of several previous summer records were obtained.

The almost constant, vigorous pumping of the Palm Warbler's tail is often the first thing that attracts one's attention to this bird. Olive brown above, with a reddish brown cap, yellow stripe over the eye, and bright yellow underparts with chestnut side streaking, the breeding male is rather handsome. The female is only slightly duller. The male's song is a weak trill, which is less emphatic than that of the Chipping Sparrow (Farrand 1983).

Next to the Pine Warbler, the Palm Warbler is the earliest warbler to arrive in spring, generally passing through New Hampshire between mid-April and early May. It is also one of the last to leave in fall. In Maine, and presumably in New Hampshire, nesting may start in early May (Palmer 1949).

In New Hampshire observers have found the Palm Warbler breeding in northern, semiopen bogs, but in Maine it also nests in drier heaths and tends to be colonial (Palmer 1949). The presence of sphagnum, shrub openings, and a spruce or tamarack overstory apparently are key habitat characteristics (Welsh *in* Cadman et al. 1987). The cup-shaped nest, made of bark shreds, dry grasses, and shredded weed stems and lined with finer grasses and feathers, is usually on the ground, but may be up to 4 ft (1.2 m) above the ground in a small spruce (Harrison 1984).

The clutch contains 4 or 5 eggs (Tyler 1953c). The male feeds the incubating female (Harrison 1975). Maine egg dates are 27 May (2 warbler and 2 cowbird eggs) to 26 June, but 4 nestlings have been found as early as 30 May (Knight *in* Palmer 1949). The incubation and nestling periods are each 12 days, and juveniles can fly short distances a day or so after leaving the nest (Tyler 1953c). Young hide in vegetation after leaving the nest, and are incapable of sustained flight for several days (Harrison 1978). Both parents feed the young (Brower *in* Palmer 1949).

On the breeding grounds Palm Warblers catch small beetles, gnats, mosquitoes, and flies in the air or on vegetation. They also eat small seeds in late summer and fall (Knight *in* Tyler 1953c). Palm Warblers generally start south in mid to late September, but Brewster (*in* Griscom 1938) observed one at Umbagog Lake as late as 19 October.

The Palm Warbler's short history as a summer resident of New Hampshire began deep in the extensive Floating Island Bog at Harper's Meadow, Errol, on 6 July 1955, when Richards (*in* Hebert 1955) heard one singing and then attracted 2 to within 2 ft (0.6 m) by "squeaking." Exactly 2 years later he observed 2 Palm Warblers in the same bog, one with food in its mouth, which established the first reasonably sure breeding record for the state (Richards *in* Hebert 1957). Two individuals were present there on 25 June 1960 (Hebert 1960a). Due to the bog's inaccessibility and difficult walking conditions, apparently no one made further thorough searches until 2 August 1980, when Richards (unpubl. data) observed an adult and a juvenile, with down on either side of its breast, in the same area. On 2 August 1988, Richards and J. McIlwaine saw an adult feeding a young bird in the same bog but closer to Harper's Meadow. These sightings occurred on a sphagnum mat with black spruces and tamaracks about 20 ft (6.1 m) high and 40 ft (12.2 m) apart, and many sedge tussocks and shrubs. Further north, participants in an ASNH field trip heard and saw a Palm Warbler on 29 June 1975 in a fairly densely wooded section of a small bog near Back Lake, Pittsburg (Richards *in* Hebert 1975).

The Atlas produced no "confirmed" or "probable" breeding records. Atlas workers documented Palm Warblers at a bog in Dummer, observing a singing bird on 4 May 1985. On 2 August 1985 Richards (unpubl. data) saw an adult Palm Warbler in a stand of northern white cedar on a low, narrow ridge separating the Floating Island Bog from the Androscoggin River. M. Cohn-Haft (pers. comm.) found an adult Palm Warbler with food in its beak on 2 June 1986 in a bog a few rods into Maine from Second College Grant.

Since the Palm Warbler is at the extreme southern limit of its nesting range in northern New Hampshire and is rare here in summer, it may be unable to hold its own indefinitely. On the other hand, even though the species hasn't been found in various locations with apparently suitable nesting habitat, it may occur at other inaccessible sites. Continued monitoring of suitable habitat will be needed to assess future trends in this warbler's numbers and distribution.

Tudor Richards

Cerulean Warbler

Dendroica cerulea

Bluest of all wood warblers, the Cerulean Warbler is a denizen of bottomland forests in the east central U.S. and is expanding its range northeastward into New England. This warbler is extremely rare in New Hampshire, and to date breeding in the state has not been confirmed. The male is azure blue above and white below, with a distinct black band on its breast. The female is bluish green above, with creamy eyebrow stripe and underparts. Both sexes have white wing bars. The Cerulean Warbler's breeding range encompasses the eastern central area of the U.S. and southern Ontario, from the Great Lakes south to the northern counties of the Gulf states and from central New England west to Iowa and eastern Oklahoma (Peck and James 1987). This species winters in humid evergreen forests in the Andean foothills from Venezuela to Peru (Robbins et al. 1992).

The Cerulean Warbler apparently migrates singly or in small groups, seldom with other warblers (Rathbun *in* Bent 1953). It may arrive in New Hampshire as early as 10 May, and is easily overlooked but for the male's enthusiastic singing. The loud song, very similar to those of Black-throated Blue Warblers and Northern Parulas, consists of 2 short notes followed by a rising series of buzzy notes. The male sings from dawn to dusk during May and June (Harrison 1984), but stops in early July (Forbush 1929). The alarm note is a sharp "chip" (Forbush 1929).

Cerulean Warblers nest in tall deciduous trees in extensive, open, mature riparian forests (Robbins et al. 1992). Favored nest trees include elms, maples, oaks, basswood, and sycamore (Bull 1974, Peck and James 1987). The dominant trees in Vermont's only known nesting area are silver maple and cottonwood (Ellison *in* Laughlin and Kibbe 1985).

These treetop warblers tend to nest in small colonies where suitable habitat exists (Pough 1951). In May, males aggressively defend their territories and "fight furiously and persistently" (Forbush 1929). Mating and nest building begin soon after arrival on the breeding grounds (Rathbun *in* Bent 1953). The female builds her nest on a horizontal limb 15 to 65 ft (4.5 to 20 m) above ground, far out from the trunk, and often above an opening (Bent 1953, Peck and James 1987). The compact, shallow nest, built of bark strips and grasses and decorated with spider webs and lichen, resembles nests of the Eastern Wood-Pewee and the Blue-gray Gnatcatcher (Harrison 1975).

The female incubates for 12 or 13 days (Harrison 1975). Documented egg dates in Vermont range from 23 May to 12 June (Laughlin and Kibbe 1985). The nestling period is unknown (Harrison 1978). Both parents tend the young, and families forage together after the young fledge (Bent 1953). Fall migration begins in July (NGS 1983).

The Cerulean Warbler's known range has expanded into the Northeast since the late 1800s. The species nested locally in western and central New York in the early 1900s (Eaton 1914), and was nesting along the Hudson River in Dutchess County, N. Y. by 1922 (Bull 1974). Sightings occurred in Connecticut and Massachusetts before 1900 (Forbush 1929) and became regular there by the 1950s (Griscom and Sprunt 1957). The first New England nesting record is from Connecticut in 1972 (Finch 1972).

The Vermont Atlas "confirmed" nesting in 1977 in the Champlain Valley, where a population of 4 to 6 pairs inhabits an area of tall riparian forest (Ellison *in* Laughlin and Kibbe 1985). Massachusetts now has a breeding population of about 5 to 10 pairs (Veit and Petersen 1993). The species also occurs in southern Quebec (Ouellet 1967).

The first New Hampshire record is of a bird observed in Peterborough on 27 May 1918, and the next is of one seen near Holderness on 5 June and collected on 8 June 1929 (Harding 1930, Bagg and Eliot 1937). Subsequent records include a male seen and heard at Lees Mills, Moultonborough on 28 May 1970 (Ridgely 1977), and a male observed within 150 yd (135 m) of this spot on 10 May 1980 (SRS). Other sightings in 1980 include a bird singing on 24 June in the tops of a large stand of 75 to 90 ft (22.9 to 27.4 m) oaks and birches about 300 ft (91.5 m) from the shore of Granite Lake, Stoddard; a male observed daily near Tower Hill Pond, Candia during 27-31 May; and 2 reported from Canaan on 11 May.

The only verified record during the Atlas project is of 2 males singing at the Tower Hill Pond location on 26 May 1981 (SRS). Unverified reports of a singing male in tall, mixed second-growth woodland just west of Mountain Pond, Chatham, on 18 May 1982, and a young Cerulean Warbler in the same area on 14 July suggest the possibility of occasional nesting in New Hampshire. More recent records include singing males in Hinsdale on 20

June 1987, in Salisbury on 21 May 1988, in Webster on 15 June 1989, and in Nottingham on 16 May 1992 (SRS). While the Cerulean Warbler has gradually extended its range northward, BBS data indicate a serious recent population decline in this species (Robbins et al. 1986, Robbins et al. 1989). Both breeding and wintering habitats have experienced widespread destruction during the past 50 years, and the USFWS considers the Cerulean Warbler a Species of Management Concern (Robbins et al. 1992). This species deserves careful watching in the coming years.

Elizabeth C. Janeway

Henslow's Sparrow
Ammodramus henslowii

This little sparrow, with its insectlike song and mouselike behavior, has a certain glamour owing to its rarity, since it has nearly vanished from northern New England. It is not very difficult to recognize when well seen; the flat, largely olive-colored head, finely streaked breast and reddish wings make it distinctive. It is primarily a bird of wet meadows and low-lying neglected fields where the herbaceous vegetation is dense and a foot or more high (Graber 1968, Robins 1971), but it sometimes occurs in "well-drained hayfields or even in hill-top pastures" (Bagg and Eliot 1937) and in grassy swamps (Allen 1903). In Concord, White (1937) found this species in "low-lying hayfields that are wet early in the season or have wet hollows in them," "bogs with marsh grass," and "swamps with bushes amid the tussocks." Territories are often clumped, perhaps in response to subtle patchiness in habitat. Several pairs may nest in one meadow, while nearby areas are unoccupied (Robins 1971). When they occurred regularly in New England, the first Henslow's Sparrows arrived in late April and early May (Griscom and Snyder 1955). Some stayed into October, but they were hard to find after singing ceased in late August (Goodhue 1922).

Male Henslow's Sparrows are not difficult to observe, for they sing persistently, usually from the tops of weeds or low bushes. They defend territories, which average a little less than an acre, by singing from perches on shrubs or weeds, or hidden on the ground (Hyde 1939, Robins 1971). If closely approached, they do not fly far, but soon drop into the grass where they run like mice. The song is an unmusical "sel-lick," and night singing is common in some populations. Observed courtship behavior has been unceremonious: the male holds dead grass in his bill (Hyde 1939). Some Henslow's Sparrows shift their territories locally during the breeding season. In a Michigan study area the adult population was more than twice as large in July as in May, perhaps as a result of such shifting (Robins 1971).

The nest is typically well hidden at the base of a thick clump of grass, one to several inches above the ground, resting on dead herbaceous vegetation (Graber 1968, Robins 1971). Goodhue (*in* Deane 1878, Goodhue 1922) found the first and possibly the only documented nest of Henslow's Sparrow in New Hampshire, containing 4 nearly grown young on 16 August 1877. It was "in a low place in a large meadow" in Salisbury, in a thick bunch of cut grass over almost 2 in (5 cm) of water and about 6 in (15 cm) above the level of the surrounding ground. The nest was "quite large and bulky, and made of coarse dry grass and lined with finer

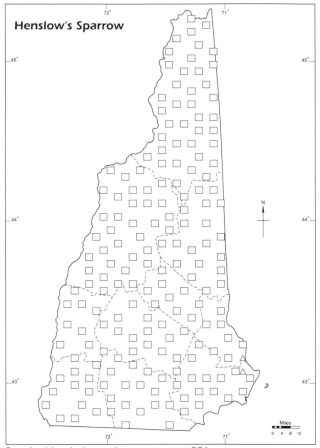

Henslow's Sparrow

See also historical records map on page 391.

of the same."

The female builds the nest and incubates the 3 to 5 eggs for 11 days (Hyde 1939). The young leave the nest when 9 or 10 days old (Graber 1968), and there are usually 2 broods (Harrison 1975). The nest is difficult to find, for the female sits very close and leaves and approaches it on foot (Graber 1968). The male does not sing much during the day while nestlings are being fed (Robins 1971).

During the breeding season the food of Henslow's Sparrows is more than 80% animal matter (insects, spiders, etc.) (Hyde 1939). The vegetable matter consists mainly of grass and weed seeds (Hyde 1939).

Goodhue (1922) took the first New Hampshire specimen of Henslow's Sparrow in Webster on 17 April 1874 and found the species regularly after that, noting its presence in Boscawen and Salisbury. He considered it merely uncommon. Allen (1903) regarded this sparrow as a "local summer resident" of the lowlands and river valleys south of the White Mountains and mentioned its occurrence in 6 additional towns. In 1909, Thayer (in Allison and Allison 1979) reported it to be "fairly common in the big Hancock meadow," but rare in Dublin. White (1937) found it at 4 localities in Concord during the breeding season, and notes a young-of-the-year taken there on 12 July. From the late 1930s through the 1960s the species was found at 12 locations, including 4 towns in the Connecticut River valley north to Charlestown, 4 towns in the central part of the state north to Meredith, and 4 towns in the coastal plain (Elkins, unpubl. data; T. Richards, pers. comm.; NHAQ, passim). Since 1970, it has been exceedingly rare in New Hampshire. A singing male was observed at Whiteface Intervale, Sandwich, during 2-8 Sept. 1971, the northernmost record for the state (Ridgely 1988).

The sole Atlas record is of a male heard and seen in Newington from 24 May to 5 June 1983 (T. Butler et al., NHBBA data), after which it could not be found. Since no female was observed, it seems best to regard this as a "possible" rather than a "probable" breeding record, but considering the female sparrow's secretiveness, a pair may have been present and already nesting.

The recent decline of Henslow's Sparrows is not restricted to New Hampshire. The Massachusetts Atlas project (1970-75) recorded the species in only 3 localities and did not "confirm" breeding, while the Vermont Atlas project recorded it as a "possible" breeder in only 2 localities (Laughlin and Kibbe 1985). The reason for the decline is not known. Apparently suitable habitat remains unoccupied, but the species may have some special habitat requirements of which we are unaware. Additional study of this elusive species might offer an explanation for its decline.

Kimball C. Elkins

Pine Grosbeak
Pinicola enucleator

The beautiful and remarkably tame Pine Grosbeak is a stocky, robin-sized bird, the largest member of its family in North America. Its fairly large, stubby bill is, however, smaller than those of other New England grosbeaks. Both the rosy male and largely gray female have prominent white wing bars. This species is a very rare summer resident of New Hampshire and reaches the extreme southern limit of its breeding range in the White Mountains, where it apparently does not nest regularly. A circumpolar species, the Pine Grosbeak has several subspecies in North America. *P. e. eschatosus*, native to New Hampshire and once called the Newfoundland Pine Grosbeak, breeds from central Quebec and Newfoundland south, sporadically, to northern New England. It occasionally winters as far south as Virginia (AOU 1957).

A bird of spruce-fir forests, this grosbeak occasionally occurs in New Hampshire in summer, on mountain slopes and in northern wooded bogs. It may be absent from New Hampshire in some winters, but in most years is present in small numbers. Very rarely, the Pine Grosbeak is at least locally abundant. More than 3,000 were present in Hanover during 10–12 January 1950 (Wade and Forsyth in Richards 1950).

The loud, musical song has a wide range of clear, whistled, separate notes (Taber in Bent 1968) and a ventriloquial quality (Forbush and May 1939). When flying high overhead, the Pine Grosbeak often is identifiable by its markedly undulating flight and loud, musical call of 2 to 4 notes, sometimes suggestive of yellowlegs calls, with the second note lower than the first (Richards, pers. obs.).

In one courtship sequence, the male offered an unidentifiable large, white object to his mate, who accepted it. Both birds then flicked their tails, and the female pecked her mate under his tail (Speirs in Bent 1968).

The female builds a loosely woven nest of twigs with an inner cup of moss, grass and fine roots, 2 to 10 ft (0.6 to 3 m) up in a conifer or birch (Harrison 1978). A nest in Maine was lined with hare's fur and located about 4 ft (1.2 m) above ground in a fir in a pasture (Knight 1897 in Palmer 1949). The male feeds the female while she incubates the 2 to 5, usually 4 eggs for 13 or 14 days (Harrison 1975). Both parents feed the young (Austin in Bent 1968), which leave the nest 14 to 20 days after hatching (Maddox in Bent 1968, Harrison 1978).

Pine Grosbeak diets change with the seasons. Buds, seeds, and berries of many kinds, especially mountain ash berries, pine and ash seeds, and maple buds, but also some insects are the principal foods (Knight in Bent 1968). Apples and crab apples seem particularly attractive in winter (Richards, pers. obs.).

The first summer records of Pine Grosbeaks in New Hampshire appear to be those of Cabot (in Allen 1903), who observed one or more birds in the White Mountains in August 1857, and Thoreau (1910), who observed a pair on Mt. Lafayette, Franconia on 15 July 1858. Brewster (in Griscom 1938) collected juveniles in the Umbagog Lake area in late August and early September 1874, to establish what may be New Hampshire's first breeding record. In many other visits to the region until 1909, Brewster only observed individuals on 13 May and 26 August 1896, and one or more birds in late September of 3 other years.

Allen (1903) cites a number of summer records between 1876 and 1902, including adults feeding young in the Connecticut Lakes region, Pittsburg, on 31 July 1876; an adult male in full song on 12 July 1884 and an immature bird on 13 July 1886 near the Halfway House on Mt. Washington, circa 3,800 ft (1,160 m); 2 "bright males" and a dull-plumaged bird on 19 and 28 June 1889 at Eagle Lakes, Mt. Lafayette, at about 4,000 ft (1,220 m); and an adult male on 14 June 1902, in Carter Notch, Beans Purchase, at about 4,500 ft (1,370 m).

Apparently the first summer record after 1902 is of a young male on 2 July 1938 on Mt. Kinsman, Lincoln (RNEB). A few recent records, all from June or July, include a singing male in the Pemigewasset Wilderness, Lincoln (Hebert 1958a); 3 apparent young on 10 June 1962 in the Moose Pasture Bog, Pittsburg (Hebert 1962; Richards, unpubl. data); one or more on Mt.

Lafayette, Franconia (Bradley and Hebert 1963); and a pair on the east side of East Inlet, Pittsburg (Hebert 1979). M. Cohn-Haft provided the only Atlas record, a female at the Second College Grant on 9 July 1982.

While the New York Atlas project produced no Pine Grosbeak records (Andrle and Carroll 1988), the Vermont Atlas reported 2 singing males on Mt. Mansfield (Fichtel in Laughlin and Kibbe 1985). The Maine Atlas included 31 breeding records, of which 7 were "probable" and 2 "confirmed" (Adamus 1988). New Hampshire atlasers produced 2 sightings and one "possible" breeding record.

We will never know whether the breeding records of the 1800s represented a resident population or merely periodic southern range extensions in years of unusually high breeding populations further north or following high winter populations in New Hampshire. In either case, the Pine Grosbeak has been known to nest here very infrequently during the present century, and it is doubtful that a resident population currently exists in the state.

Although heavy logging and devastating spruce budworm outbreaks in recent decades have greatly reduced favorable habitat in northern New Hampshire, extensive areas of good habitat remain, especially in the high elevation forests of the White Mountains. Further research will be needed to clarify the status and population trends of this colorful finch in northern New England.

Tudor Richards

Appendices
&
Reference Cited

Appendix A: Historical Records for Selected Species (1963 to 1980)

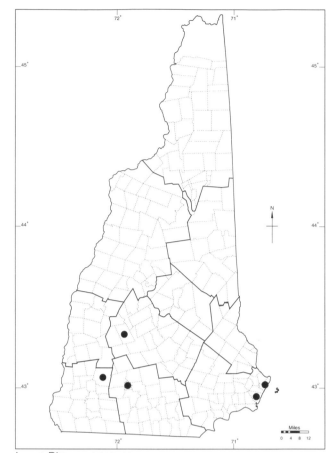

Pied-billed Grebe (1963–80, June, July records)

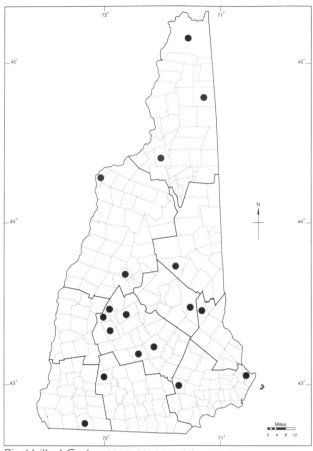

Least Bittern (1963–80, May, June, July records)

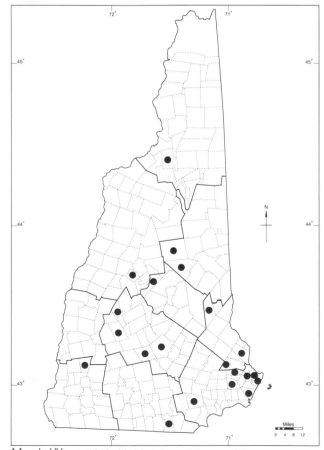

Marsh Wren (1963–80, May, June, July records)

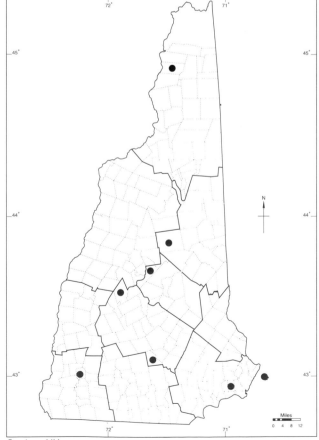

Sedge Wren (1963–80, June, July, August records)

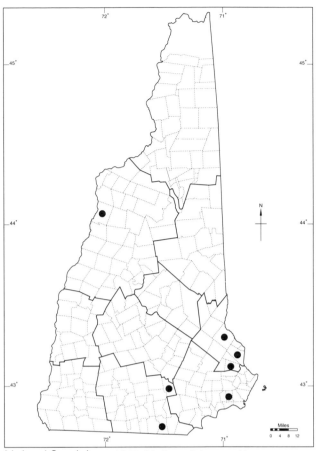

Upland Sandpiper (1963–80, June, July records)

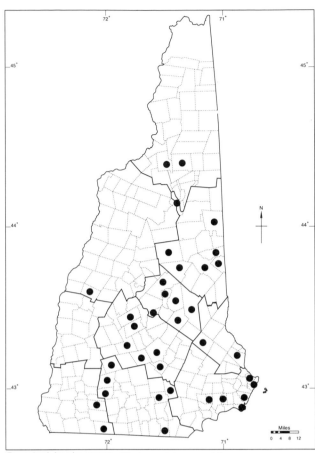

Purple Martin (1963–80, June, July records)

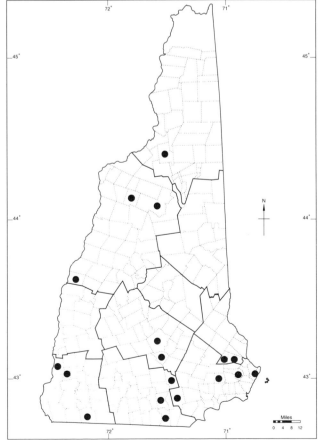

Grasshopper Sparrow (1963–80, May – July records)

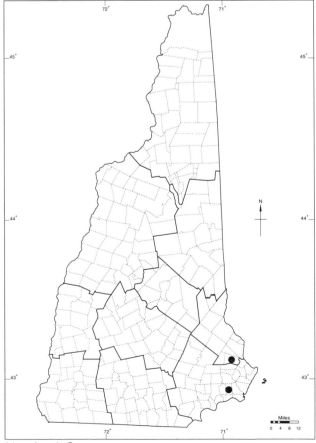

Henslow's Sparrow (1963–80, May – July records)

Appendix B: Winter Distribution Maps of Selected Species (1983 to 1985)

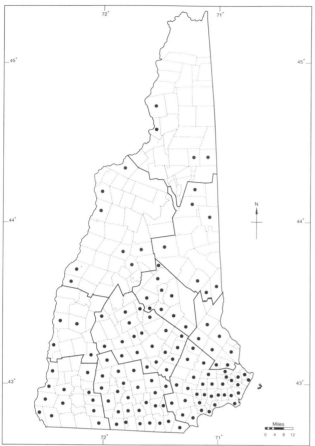

Figure B-1: Mourning Dove (winter distribution 1983–1985)

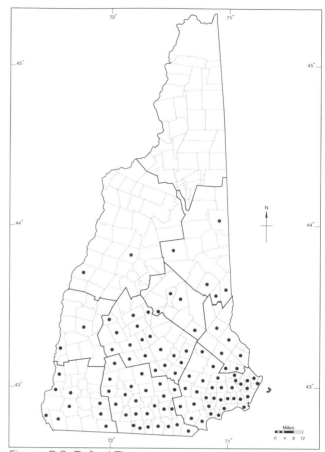

Figure B-2: Tufted Titmouse (winter distribution 1983–1985)

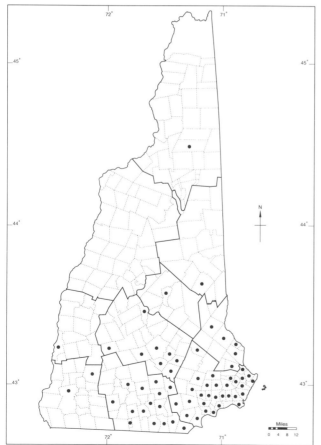

Figure B-3: Northern Mockingbird (winter distribution 1983–1985)

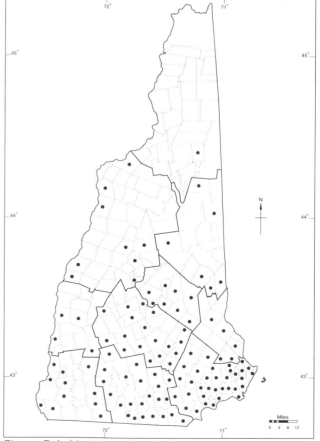

Figure B-4: Northern Cardinal (winter distribution 1983–1985)

Appendix C: Level of Atlas Effort by Priority Block

Priority Block #	CO	PR	PO	Total	Hours Atlased	# of Yrs. Visited	Months Visited
1646	30	11	15	56	8.75	2	JUL
2616	22	13	28	63	25.00	2	MAY–JUL
2622	45	36	19	100	60.00	3	MAY–AUG
2635	22	14	40	76	32.00	2	MAY–JUL
2646	34	10	35	79	25.25	3	JUN–AUG
2714	29	14	40	83	26.50	5	JUN–JUL
2721	39	19	27	85	23.25	5	MAY–JUL
2742	26	11	31	68	23.00	3	JUN–JUL
3546	43	19	13	75	44.75	4	APR–AUG
3611	42	37	14	93	42.50	2	APR–AUG
3624	53	34	8	95	73.00	3	APR–AUG
3632	48	37	16	101	61.50	4	APR–AUG
3645	45	30	5	80	35.50	2	APR–JUL
3712	13	9	16	38	26.00	1	JUN
3724	22	19	24	65	11.50	2	MAY–AUG
3731	35	24	19	78	20.00	2	JUN–AUG
3743	55	15	37	107	109.00	4	MAR, MAY–AUG
4535	47	20	10	77	42.00	4	APR–JUN
4546	39	34	11	84	49.25	3	APR, JUN–JUL
4614	22	16	28	66	31.50	3	JUN–AUG
4621	36	22	31	89	39.25	3	JUN–JUL
4634	42	9	11	62	24.75	2	JUL
4641	38	18	35	91	45.00	3	JUN–AUG
4713	44	17	42	103	66.25	3	APR–SEP
4722	35	18	26	79	38.50	3	MAY–JUL
4733	22	13	20	55	25.50	3	JUN–JUL
4742	39	8	20	67	47.00	3	JUL
5422	39	33	13	85	16.25	5	MAY–AUG
5443	42	38	21	101	23.00	5	APR–JUL
5516	42	29	11	82	38.25	3	JUN–JUL
5522	41	29	13	83	30.00	4	APR, JUN–JUL
5535	39	22	15	76	21.50	3	MAR, MAY–AUG
5544	48	13	35	96	43.50	5	APR–SEP
5614	14	8	32	54	59.00	3	MAY–AUG
5624	30	27	29	86	63.75	3	JUN–AUG
5634	37	13	39	89	80.50	5	JUN–AUG
5645	13	9	20	42	76.25	5	MAY–AUG
5713	53	24	11	88	222.75	4	APR–AUG
5726	14	7	22	43	23.50	3	JUN–JUL
5731	35	6	24	65	93.00	3	JUN–JUL
5741	20	14	19	53	40.25	4	JUN–JUL
6335	43	33	11	87	16.50	2	MAY–JUL
6346	38	30	21	89	19.50	4	APR–AUG
6416	39	27	13	79	6. +	3	APR–JUL
6426	42	28	23	93	?	4	MAR–AUG
6435	38	45	13	96	7.00	2	APR–JUL
6444	39	21	18	78	82.25	3	MAY–AUG
6515	29	15	16	60	60.25	3	MAR–AUG
6521	27	20	16	63	44.00	3	MAY–SEP
6534	28	11	30	69	72.00	5	JUN–AUG
6544	21	8	23	52	61.75	3	JUN–AUG
6614	52	37	20	109	143.50	4	MAR–SEP
6623	15	12	31	58	22.00	5	MAY–JUL
6633	36	17	25	78	49.50	4	MAR–JUL
6642	35	13	29	77	39.50	4	APR–JUL
6712	43	8	29	80	100.00	6	MAY–JUL
6724	62	15	16	93	70.50	5	MAR–JUL
6732	54	10	25	89	132.75	6	APR–JUL
6744	48	5	33	86	39.00	3	MAY–JUL
7326	39	29	11	79	3 +	2	MAY–JUL, OCT
7333	36	24	15	75	6 +	3	MAR–AUG
7345	28	16	20	64	?	3	MAY–AUG

Priority Block #	CO	PR	PO	Total	Hours Atlased	# of Yrs. Visited	Months Visited
7412	38	27	20	85	18 +	3	MAY–JUN
7424	43	10	46	99	?	4	FEB, APR–AUG
7434	20	19	14	53	15.50 +	4	MAY–JUL
7446	62	15	22	99	100.00	4	APR–AUG
7513	37	25	20	82	39.50	5	APR–JUL
7525	36	29	24	89	16.25	5	APR–JUL, OCT
7531	26	14	21	61	42.25	5	MAY–AUG
7544	46	22	21	89	67.50	6	MAR, MAY–JUL
7612	25	11	22	58	35.00	4	JUN–JUL
7624	48	22	26	96	90.50	5	MAY–AUG
7631	36	30	13	79	23.75	3	MAY–JUN, AUG
7645	38	22	17	77	32.00	1	MAY–JUL
7714	35	11	40	86	6.75	3	MAY–AUG
7724	39	22	24	85	33.25	4	MAY–AUG
7736	37	27	24	88	24.25	4	MAY–AUG
7746	39	23	24	86	34.25	5	APR–AUG
8245	64	9	24	97	57.25	6	MAY–JUL
8315	51	27	16	94	64.25	6	APR–AUG
8324	35	21	19	75	73.75	5	MAY–JUL
8336	31	25	27	83	54.25	5	MAY–AUG
8345	39	33	12	84	40.75	5	MAR–JUL, SEP
8411	36	21	19	76	21.50	5	APR–JUL
8424	34	21	32	87	19.25	4	MAY–JUL
8432	35	27	24	86	10.50	4	APR–AUG
8444	38	18	29	85	12.50	3	MAY–JUL
8514	45	35	19	99	22.50	5	MAY–AUG
8525	35	23	15	73	26.50	2	MAY–JUL
8535	36	36	35	107	48.75	3	MAR, MAY–AUG
8544	37	8	55	100	32.50	3	APR–AUG
8614	36	16	27	79	14.50	1	MAY–JUL
8623	53	15	12	80	41.00	2	MAR–JUL
8636	39	28	35	102	5.50 +	5	FEB–AUG
8642	51	26	14	94	46.00	2	MAR–JUL
8711	47	18	26	91	6.00 +	5	APR–AUG
8725	36	32	21	89	61.25	4	MAR–JUL
8735	53	18	17	88	42.00	4	MAR–SEP
8744	38	30	9	77	16.00	3	MAR, MAY–JUL
9231	48	11	30	89	48.75	5	MAY–AUG
9241	45	4	31	80	4.50 +	3	APR–AUG
9311	24	7	34	65	?	1	APR–MAY, JUL
9322	35	25	20	80	26.50	3	JUN–JUL
9332	42	18	25	85	106.50	5	FEB–AUG
9344	39	27	17	83	52.50	5	APR–AUG
9416	41	31	35	107	88.50	6	MAR–SEP
9425	45	18	32	95	191.00	4	FEB–AUG
9434	45	32	26	103	196.00	5	MAR–AUG
9446	43	29	31	103	103.00	5	MAR–AUG
9516	46	25	34	105	113.75	5	APR–AUG
9525	42	20	25	87	30.50	4	MAR JUL
9531	44	31	27	102	77.00	2	APR–AUG
9544	38	22	33	93	74.00	4	APR–AUG
9615	48	27	10	85	64.50	2	MAR–JUL
9623	48	23	14	85	103.75	3	MAR–JUL
9636	58	20	21	99	58.75	4	APR–AUG
9642	76	21	21	118	174.25	5	APR–AUG
9711	43	41	9	93	38.00	5	APR–JUL
9724	51	33	10	94	39.50	4	MAR–JUL
9735	77	20	12	109	145.00	5	MAR–AUG
9744	42	42	14	98	34.00	5	APR–JUL
9823	57	32	18	107	101.50	5	FEB–AUG
10214	38	20	23	81	10.75	3	MAY–JUN
10226	38	11	29	78	18.00	3	MAY–JUL

Level of Atlas Effort by Priority Block (Continued)

Priority Block #	CO	PR	PO	Total	Hours Atlased	# of Yrs. Visited	Months Visited
10236	37	26	11	74	10.00	2	MAY–JUL
10245	43	7	29	79	28.75	1	JUN–JUL
10314	38	29	17	84	49.00	2	MAR–APR, JUN–JUL
10326	44	16	30	90	36.25	2	MAR–JUL, DEC
10335	37	33	24	94	92.50	4	MAY–JUL
10341	39	17	19	75	59.50	2	MAY–JUL
10416	54	19	20	93	25.50	4	MAR–AUG
10422	29	32	21	82	54.00	2	APR–SEP
10435	55	24	15	94	82.25	2	MAR–AUG
10444	36	32	20	88	80.25	5	APR–AUG
10514	63	30	7	100	171.50	5	FEB, APR–JUL
10525	41	19	27	87	12.50 +	4	APR–AUG
10535	40	24	26	90	106.00	4	MAR–AUG
10546	35	16	23	74	21.50	3	MAR, MAY–JUL
10616	38	9	33	80	69.50	3	APR–AUG
10625	31	27	20	78	54.75	1	MAY–JUL
10636	55	19	9	83	71.50	4	APR–JUL
10646	46	20	16	82	53.25	5	APR–JUN
10711	64	17	16	97	55.50	3	MAR–JUL
10726	53	25	10	88	46.50	5	MAR–AUG
10732	84	11	7	102	320.00	5	FEB–AUG
10746	40	23	19	82	48.00	5	MAR–JUL
10813	86	8	13	107	288.50	5	FEB–JUL
10825	38	23	31	92	53.25	4	MAR–AUG
10831	41	45	10	96	64.75	5	
10846	54	21	9	84	257.00	5	MAR–JUL
11144	35	23	32	90	23.50	3	APR–AUG, APR–MAY, JUL, OCT

Priority Block #	CO	PR	PO	Total	Hours Atlased	# of Yrs. Visited	Months Visited
11212	29	19	21	69	6.50	3	APR–MAY, JUL–AUG
11226	39	11	27	77	11.50	3	MAY–JUL
11234	55	17	29	101	73.25	2	MAY–AUG
11246	40	16	19	75	28.00	2	MAY–JUL
11315	38	18	19	75	104.75	4	APR–JUL
11321	37	22	27	86	17.75	2	MAY–JUL
11334	54	26	16	96	130.00	5	FEB–SEP
11342	42	13	28	83	42.00	5	APR–AUG
11413	40	28	18	86	26.50	4	MAR–AUG
11422	38	9	33	80	73.50	5	FEB, APR–AUG
11431	42	21	21	84	27.00	4	APR–AUG
11441	35	37	18	90	35.50	4	MAR–JUL
11511	46	25	20	91	44.50	5	MAR–JUL
11522	51	21	20	92	124.50	5	APR–AUG
11532	53	18	25	96	28.00	5	APR–JUL
11541	54	24	8	86	10.50	5	APR–JUL
11614	64	8	14	86	100.75	4	APR–AUG
11621	45	29	20	94	54.00	6	APR–JUL, SEP
11633	43	19	28	90	35.00	6	APR–JUL
11642	39	20	26	85	41.00	5	APR–JUL
11712	41	15	23	79	14.75	5	MAY–JUL
11721	50	11	7	68	61.25	5	MAR–AUG
11732	39	21	29	89	24.75	3	MAR–JUL
11813	92	9	16	117	173.75	5	FEB–AUG
11832	63	15	13	91	96.00	5	FEB–AUG
12431	34	18	26	78	35.50	4	APR–AUG
12611	46	20	21	87	41.50	5	MAR–AUG

TOTAL # OF HOURS: 9,757.25

Appendix D: Plants Cited in the Text

Woody Plants

alder *Alnus rugosa, A. serrulata, A. crispa*
alder, speckled *Alnus rugosa*
apple *Pyrus malus*
ash *Fraxinus* spp.
ash, mountain *Sorbus americana, S. decora*
aspen *Populus tremuloides, P. grandidentata*
basswood *Tilia americana*
barberry *Berberis vulgaris, B.thunbergii*
bayberry *Myrica pensylvanica*
beech, American *Fagus grandifolia*
birch *Betula* spp.
birch, black *Betula lenta*
birch, gray *Betula populifolia*
birch, heart-leaved *Betula papyrifera*
   var. *cordifolia*
birch, Ontario
birch, paper (white) *Betula papyrifera*
birch, yellow *Betula lutea (alleghaniensis)*
blackberry (brambles) *Rubus* spp.
blueberry *Vaccinium* spp.
blueberry, lowbush *Vaccinium augustifolium*
boxelder *Acer negundo*
buttonbush *Cephalanthus occidentalis*
cedar, red *Juniperus virginiana*
ceder, white (northern white) *Thuja occidentalis*
cherry *Prunus* spp.
cherry, black *Prunus serotina*
cherry, choke *Prunus virginiana*
cherry, pin *Prunus pensylvanica*
chestnut, American *Castanea dentata*
cottonwood *Populus deltoides*
crabapple *Pyrus prunifolia, P. baccata,* etc.
cranberry *Vaccinium* macrocarpon, V. Oxycoccus
dogwood, gray *Cornus racemosa*
dogwood, red-osier *Cornus stolonifera*
elderberry *Sambucus canadensis*
elm, American *Ulnus americana*
fir, balsam *Abies balsamea*
grapes, wild *Vitis* spp.
hawthorn *Crataegus* spp.
hemlock *Tsuga canadensis*
hickory *Carya* spp.
hobblebush *Viburnum alnifolia*
honeysuckle, tartarian *Lonicera tartarica*
huckleberry *Gaylussacia baccata, G. frondosa,*
   G. dumosa
ironwood *Ostrya virginiana*
juniper *Juniperus communis*
larch *Larix laricina/decidua*
laurel, mountain *Kalmia latifolia*
lilac *Syringa vulgaris*
locust *Robinia pseudacacia, Gleditsia triacanthos*
maple *Acer* spp.
maple, ash-leaved *Acer negundo*
maple, mountain *Acer spicatum*
maple, red *Acer rubens*
maple, silver *Acer saccharinum*
maple, striped *Acer pensylvanicum*
maple, sugar *Acer saccharum*
meadowsweet *Spirea alba, S. latifolia*
mountain ash, European *Pyrus aucuparia*
oak *Quercus* spp.
oak, bear (scrub) *Quercus ilicifolia*
oak, red *Quercus rubra*
pear *Pyrus communis*
pine, pitch *Pinus rigida*
pine, red *Pinus resinosa*
pine, white *Pinus strobus*

poplar *Populus* spp.
raspberry *Rubus idaeus*
rhododendron *Rhododendron maximum*
rose, multiflora *Rosa multiflora*
rose, salt-spray *Rosa rugosa*
rose, swamp *Rosa palustris*
rose, wild *Rosa* spp.
shadbush (serviceberry) *Amelanchier* spp.
spirea *Spiraca* spp.
spruce, black *Picea mariana*
spruce, Norway *Picea abies*
spruce, red *Picea rubens*
sumac *Rhus* spp.
sumac, smooth *Rhus glabra*
sycamore *Platanus occidentalis*
tamarack *Latrix laricina*
virburnum *Virburnum* spp.
virginia creeper *Parthenocissus quinquefolia,*
   P. inserta
willow *Salix* spp.
willow, black *Salix nigra*
willow, weeping *Salix babylonica*
winterberry *Ilex verticillata*
yew (creeping yew) *Taxus canadensis*

Herbaceous Plants

alfalfa *Medicago sativa*
amaranth *Amaranthus* spp.
arrowhead *Sagittaria* spp.
aster *Aster* spp.
bee balm *Monarda didyma*
black rush *Juncus geradi*
bristle-grass *Seteria* spp.
brome *Bromus* spp.
broom sedge *Andropogon scopanus, A. gerardii*
buckwheat *Fagopyrum sagittatum*
bulrush, hard-stemmed *Scirpus fluviatilis*
cattail *Typha* spp.
canary-grass, reed *Phalaris arundinacea*
clover *Trifolium* spp.
columbine *Aquilegia canadensis*
corn *Zea mays*
crab grass *Digitaria* spp.
dandelion *Taraxacum officinale*
daylily *Hemerocallis flava*
duckweed *Lemna* spp.
fern Osmundaceae/Polypodiaceae
fern, cinnamon *Osmunda cinnamomea*
fern, sensitive *Onoclea sensibilis*
fireweed *Epilobium angustifolium*
fungus, false tinder *Fomes igniarius*
goldenrod *Solidago* spp.
grass Graminidae
grass, beach *Panicum* spp.
grass, blue-joint *Calamagrostis canadensis*
heart-rot, fungal *Spongipellis pachyodon*
hemp Cannabinaceae
jewelweed *Impatiens capensis*
joe pyeweed, spotted *Eupatorium maculatum*
legume Leguminosae
lichen Ascomycetes/Lecanorales
lichen, Usnea *Usnea* spp.
lily pad *Nymphaea odorata, Nuphar* spp.
loosestrife, purple *Lythrum salicaria*
milkweed *Asclepias* spp.
moss, hairy cap *Polytrichum* spp.
moss, sphagnum *Sphagnum* spp.
nettles Urticaceae
nut grass *Cyperus rotundus*

oats *Avena fatua, A. sativa, A. pubescens*
onion *Allium* spp.
partridge berry *Mitchella repens*
pea *Lathyrus sativum*
peat *Sphagnum* spp.
phragmites *Phragmites communis*
pigweed *Chenopodium* spp.
poison ivy *Rhus radicans*
pondweed *Potamogeton* spp.
Queen Anne's lace *Daucus carota*
ragweed *Ambrosia* spp.
reed *Phragmites communis*
rice, cultivated *Oryza sativa*
rice, wild *Zizania aquatica*
rush Juncaceae
salt hay grass *Spartina patens*
sedge *Carex* spp.
sedge, tussock *Carex stricta*
sedge, water *Carex aquatilis*
smartweed *Polygonum* spp.
saltmarsh cordgrass *Spartina alterniflora*
sunflower *Helianthus annuus*
thistle *Cirsium* spp.
trillium *Trillium* spp.
trumpet-vine (trumpet-creeper) *Campsis*
   radicans

References

Fernald, M.L. 1950. Gray's manual of botany. 8th
   ed. American Book, NewYork.

Appendix E: Animals Cited in the Text

Mammals

bat Chiroptera
beaver *Castor canadensis*
cat, domestic *Felis catus*
chipmunk, eastern *Tamias striatus*
cow *Bos taurus*
coyote *Canus latrans*
dog, domestic *Canus familiaris*
fisher *Martes pennanti*
fox *Vulpes vulpes, Urocyon cinereoargenteus*
fox, red *Vulpes vulpes*
hare, snowshoe *Lepus americanus*
horse *Equus* spp.
mink *Mustela vison*
mouse *Mus, Peromyscus* spp.
muskrat *Ondatra zibethicus*
porcupine *Erethizon dorsatum*
rabbit *Sylvilagus floridanus, S. transitionalis*
raccoon *Procyon lotor*
rat, Norway *Rattus norvegicus*
rodent Rodentia
sheep *Ovis aries*
shrew *Sorex* spp., *Blarina brevicauda*
skunk, striped *Mephitis mephitis*
squirrel *Sciurus/Tamiasciurus/Glaucomys* spp.
squirrel, red *Tamiasciurus hudsonicus*
vole *Microtus/Clethrionomys* spp.
vole, meadow *Microtus pennsylvanicus*
woodchuck *Marmota monax*
weasel *Mustela* spp.

Other Vertebrates

bluefish *Pomotomus saltatrix*
cunner *Tautogolabrus adspersus*
eel, American *Anguilla rostrata*
flounder, summer *Paralichthys dentatus*
frog Ranidae/Hylidae
goldfish *Carassius auratus*
killifish *Fundulus diaphanus*
mackerel *Scomber scombrus*
minnow Cyprinidae
pickerel *Esox niger, E. americanus americanus*
rock gunnel *Pholis gunnellus*
salamander Caudata
sand lance *Ammodytes americanus*
snake Serpentes
snake, garter *Thamnophis sirtalis*
snake, water *Nerodia sipedon*
tadpole Anura
toad *Bufo americanus*
trout *Salmo/Salvelinus* spp.
turtle Chelonia
turtle, snapping *Chelydra serpentina*

Invertebrates: Insects

ant Formicidae
aphid (plant lice) Aphidoidea
bee Apoidea
bee, honey *Apis mellifera*
beetle Coleoptera
beetle, carabid Carabidae
beetle, engraver (bark) Scolytidae
beetle, Japanese *Popillia japonica*
beetle, June Melolonthinae
beetle, potato *Leptinotarsa decemlineata*

beetle, wood boring Coleoptera
budworm, spruce *Choristoneura fumiferana*
bug Hemiptera
butterfly Lepidoptera
caddisfly Trichoptera
cankerworm Geometridae
caterpillar Lepidoptera
caterpillar, tent *Malacosoma americanum*
centipede Chilopoda
coccid Coccoidea
cranefly Tipulidae
cricket Gryllidae
cutworm Noctuidae
damselfly Zygoptera
dragonfly Anistoptera
flea Siphonaptera
fly Diptera
fly, black Simuliidae
stonefly Plecoptera
gnat Diptera
grasshopper Orthoptera
grub Melolonthinae
hornet Vespidae
inchworm Geometridae
insects, scale Coccoidea
leafhopper Cicadellidae
lice, spruce gall Aphidoidea
locust Acrididae
mayfly Ephemeroptera
mealworm Tenebrionidae
midge Chironomidae
mosquito Culicidae
moth Heterocera
moth, brown-tail *Nygmia phaeorrhoea*
moth, gypsy *Porthetria dispar*
plant hoppers Fulgoroidea
sawfly Symphyta
sawfly, larch *Pristiphora erichsonii*
wasp Hymenoptera
wasp, parasitic Ichneumonoidea/Chaleidoidea
webworm (fall) *Hyphantria cunea*
weevil Cucurlionidae

Other invertebrates

bivalves Bivalvia
crab, fiddler *Uca* spp.
crab, mud Brachyura
crayfish Decapoda
daddy-longlegs Phalangiidae
earthworm Lumbricidae
leech Hirudinea
mussel, blue *Mytilus edulis*
shellfish Mollusca
slug Styllommatophora
snail Mesogastropoda
spider Araneae

References

American Fisheries Society. 1970. Common and scientific names of fishes from the United States and Canada. 3rd ed.

Barnes, R.D. 1974. Invertebrate zoology. 3rd. ed. W.B. Saunders Company, Philadelphia.

Borror, D.J. and D.M. DeLong. 1971. An introduction to the study of insects, 3rd ed. Holt, Rinehart and Winston,

Franq, E.N. 1981. Key to land mammals of New Hampshire. Univ. N.H., Durham. Mimeogr.

Div. Fish and Wildl., N.Y. Dept. of Environ. Conserv. 1987. Checklist of the amphibians, reptiles, birds and mammals of New York State, including their protective status. N.Y.D.E.C. Nongame Unit, Delmar, N.Y.

Scarola, J.F. 1987. Freshwater fishes of New Hampshire. N.H. Fish and Game Dept., Concord.

Taylor, J. 1993. The amphibians and reptiles of New Hampshire. N.H. Fish and Game Dept., Concord.

References Cited in the Text

In general, unpublished data from various sources, and data from "Records of New England Birds" (RNEB), Species Report Slips (SRS) submitted to ASNH, Asterisk Species Report Forms from this Atlas project, and the Cornell Laboratory of Ornithology Nest Record Program are cited in the text only. Christmas Bird Count (CBC) data is published annually in American Birds, and Breeding Bird Census (BBC) data is published annually as a supplement to the Journal of Field Ornithology. Species Report Slips, Asterisk Species Report forms, and data from the N.H. Endangered Species Program and NHBBA project are housed at ASNH headquarters in Concord, N.H. Breeding Bird Survey data (BBS) is avaiable from the Patuxent Wildlife Research Center, Laurel, Md. Computerized data from the NHBBA is housed at NHFG headquarters in Concord, N.H.

Citations reflecting information from multiple issues or volumes of a publication are denoted by the term "passim," and are not included in the bibliography. Cites of "RNEB, passim" refer to a succession of publications:

"Bulletin of New England Bird-life", published monthlyfrom 1936 to 1944 by the New England Museum of Natural History, Boston,
"Records of New England Birds," published monthly from 1945to 1955 by the Massachusetts Audubon Society in their" Bulletin of the Massachusetts Audubon Society," and
"Records of New England Birds," published monthly as aseparate publication from 1956 through 1960, and 1964 through 1968.

Citations of "NHAQ, passim" refer to seasonal bird records published in a succession of Audubon Society of New Hampshire publications:
ASNH Bulletin, 1921–28,
Bull. of the Audubon Society of N.H., 1925–49,
NH Bird News, 1951–60, and
NH Audubon Quarterly, 1961–61.

Subsequent ASNH records are cited as SRS, the collection of which began in 1963 and continues to the present. Many of these records have been published in the NH Audubon Quarterly (1963–76), NH Audubon (1977-82), and NH Bird Records (1982 to present). The above publications, as well as many other historical refernces on New Hampshire birds, are avaiable in the F.B. White Library at the Audubon Society of New Hampshire in Concord.

Abbott, F. M. 1906. Birds and flowers around Concord, New Hampshire. Rumford Printing Company, Concord.

Abbott, J. M. 1942. Louisiana Water-thrush breeding in New Hampshire. Auk 59:114–115.

Abbott, D. J. 1976. 1976 spring migration. N.H. Audubon Quar. 29:82–87.

Abbott, D. J. 1981. The spring migration, March 1 to May 31, 1981. N.H. Audubon 17(6):3–6.

Adam, C. I. G. 1987. Status of the Eastern Screech Owl in Saskachewan with reference to adjacent areas, pp. 268–276. In R. W. Nero, R. J. Clark, R. J. Knapton, and R. H. Hamre, Biology and conservation of northern forest owls; symposium proceedings. USDA Forest Serv. Gen. Tech. Rep. RM-142.

Adams, R. J., Jr., and R. Brewer. 1981. Autumn selection of breeding location by field sparrows. Auk 98:629–631.

Adamus, P. R. 1988. Atlas of breeding birds in Maine, 1978–1983. Maine Dept. Inland Fish. and Wildl., Augusta.

Adkisson, C. S., and R. N. Conner. 1978. Interspecific voice imitation in the White-eyed Vireo. Auk 95:602–606.

Akerley, C. 1968. Tiger of the air. N.H. Audubon Quar. 21:51.

Allen, F. H. 1889. Summer birds at Bridgewater and Moultonboro, New Hampshire. Auk 6:76–79.

Allen, G. M. 1902. A list of the birds of New Hampshire. Proc. Manchester Inst. Arts and Scien. 4. Manchester, N.H.

Allen, G. M. 1903. A list of the birds of New Hampshire. Nature Study Press, Manchester, N.H.

Allen, G. M. 1909. Fauna of New England: Aves. Occas. Papers Boston Soc. Nat. Hist. Vol. 7. Boston.

Allen, F. H., [ed]. 1910. Thoreau's bird-lore, being notes on New England birds from the journal of Henry D. Thoreau. Houghton Mifflin, Boston.

Allen, G. M. 1921. The Wild Turkey in New England. Bull. Essex County Ornithol. Club Mass. 3(1):5–18.

Allen, F. H. 1922. Some little known songs of common birds. Nat. Hist. 22:235–242.

Allen, D. L. 1954. Our wildlife legacy. Funk & Wagnalls, New York.

Allen, D. 1956. Pheasants in North America. Stackpole Books, Washington, D.C.

Allison, E., and K. Allison. 1957. Owl incident. N.H. Bird News 10:44–45.

Allison, E. and K. Allison. 1979. Birds of Dublin, New Hampshire, 1909–1979, including Gerald H. Thayer's list of 1909. Dublin Cons. Comm., Dublin, N.H.

Alway, J. H., and D. A. Boag. 1979. Behavior of captive Spruce Grouse at the time broods break up and juveniles disperse. Can. J. Zool. 57:1311–1317.

Anderson, H. C. 1970. Winter season 1969–1970: Dec 1, 1969 to Feb. 28, 1970. N.H. Audubon Quar. 23:67–74.

Anderson, H. C. 1971. Winter Season 1970–71. N.H. Audubon Quar. 24:63–69.

Andrews, R., [comp.]. 1990. Coastal waterbird colonies: Maine to Virginia, 1984–85: an update of an atlas based on 1977 data, showing colony locations and species composition at both time periods, with examination of changes in regional populations. Pt. 1. Maine to Connecticut. Pt. 2. New York to Virginia. U.S. Fish and Wildl. Serv., Newton Corner, Mass.

Andrle, R. F. and J. R. Carroll, [eds.]. 1988. The atlas of breeding birds in New York state. Cornell Univ. Press, Ithaca.

American Ornithologists' Union. 1957. Check-list of North American birds. 5th ed. Am. Ornithol. Union, Washington, D.C.

American Ornithologists' Union. 1973. Thirty-second supplement to the AOU check-list of North American birds. Auk 90:411–419.

American Ornithologists' Union. 1983. Check-list of North American birds. 6th ed. Am. Ornithol. Union, Washington, D.C.

American Ornithologists Union. 1987. Thirty-sixth supplement to the AOU check-list of North American birds. Auk 104:591–595.

Arbib, R. 1977. The 1978 blue list. Am. Birds 31:1087–1096.

Arbib, R. 1982. The blue list for 1982. Am. Birds 36:129–135.

Armstrong, J. T. 1965. Breeding home range in the nighthawk and other birds: its evolution and ecological significance. Ecology 46:619–629.

ASNH. 1920. Checklist of birds of New Hampshire. Audubon Soc. N.H., Concord.

ASNH. 1927. Unusual records for New Hampshire. Bull. Audubon Soc. N.H. 6(3):34–35.

ASNH. 1928. Further report on a pigeon hawk nesting in New Hampshire. Bull. Audubon Soc. N.H. 8(2):14–15.

ASNH. 1950a. A plea for hawks and owls. Newsl. Audubon Soc. N.H. 3(2):1–9.

ASNH. 1950b. Spring migration records from members. Newsl. Audubon Soc. N.H. 3(3):6–13.

ASNH. 1950c. Bird records of the nesting season. Newsl. Audubon Soc. N.H. 3(4):8–13.

ASNH. 1952. Summer nesting records. N.H. Bird News 5(4):10–15.

ASNH. 1954. 1954 nesting season. N.H. Bird News 7(4):18–23.

ASNH. 1965. 1965 nesting season. N.H. Audubon Quar. 18:94–108.

ASNH. 1969. 1968 fall migration. N.H. Audubon Quar. 22:32–41.

Audubon, J. J. 1967. The birds of America. 7 vols. (Original publication 1840–1844.) Dover Publ., New York.

Bagg, A. C., and S. A. Eliot. 1937. Birds of the Connecticut valley in Massachusetts. Hampshire Bookstore, Northampton, Mass.

Bagg, A. M., and R. P. Emery. 1961. Regional reports: nesting season, June 1 to August 15, 1961, Northeastern Maritime Region. Aud. Field Notes 15:450–453.

Bagg, A. M., and H. M. Parker. 1951. The Turkey Vulture in New England and eastern Canada up to 1950. Auk 68:315–333.

Baird, J. 1968. Savannah Sparrow, pp. 678–696. In A. C. Bent, Life histories of North American cardinals, grosbeaks, buntings, towhees, finches, sparrows and allies, Pt. 2. O. L. Austin, Jr., [ed.], U.S. Natl. Mus. Bull. 237. Washington, D.C.

Baird, S. F., T. M. Brewer, and R. Ridgway. 1884. The water birds of North America. Vol. 2. Mem. Mus. Comp. Zool. Harvard 13.

Baldwin, H. I. 1970. Mount Monadnock guide. Soc. Protection N.H. For., Concord.

Balfour, E., and M. A. MacDonald. 1970. Food and feeding behavior of the hen harrier in Orkney, Scotland. Scot. Birds 6:157–166.

Balgooyen, T. G. 1976. Behavior and ecology of the American Kestrel (Falco sparverius) in the Sierra Nevada of California. Univ. Cal. Publ. Zool. 103:1–83.

Barlow, J. C., and D. M. Power. 1970. An analysis of character variation in Red-eyed and Philadelphia vireos (Aves: Vireonidae) in Canada. Can. J. Zool. 48:673–680.

Barlow, J. C., and J. C. Rice. 1977. Aspects of the comparative behavior of Red-eyed and Philadelphia vireos. Can. J. Zool. 55:528–542.

Batchelder, F. W. 1902. Additions to the preliminary list of birds [resident, visitant, migrant or accidental, observed in the vicinity of Manchester, New Hampshire]. Proc. Manchester Inst. Arts and Scien. 3:73–74. Manchester, N.H.

Beal, F. E. L. 1918. Food habits of the swallows, a family of vulnerable native birds. USDA Bull. 619.

Beaver, D. L. 1980. Recovery of an American Robin (Turdus migratorius) population after earlier DDT use. J. Field Ornithol. 51:220–228.

Bednarz, J. C., and J. J. Dinsmore. 1982. Nest sites and habitat of Red-shouldered and Red-tailed hawks in Iowa. Wilson Bull. 94:31–45.

Bednarz, J. C., D. Klem, Jr., L. J. Goodrich, and S. E. Senner. 1990. Migration counts of raptors at Hawk Mountain, Pennsylvania, as indicators of population trends, 1934–1986. Auk 107:96–109.

Beecher, M. D., I. M. Beecher, and S. Lumpkin. 1981a. Parent offspring recognition in Bank Swallows (Riparia riparia). Pt. 1. Anim. Behav. 29:86–94.

Beecher, M. D., I. M. Beecher, and S. Hahn. 1981b. Parent offspring recognition in Bank Swallows (Riparia riparia). Pt. 2: development and acoustic basis. Anim. Behav. 29:95–101.

Belknap, J. 1792. The history of New Hampshire. Bradford and Read, Boston.

Belle-Isles, J.C., and J. Picman. 1986. House Wren nest-destroying behavior. Condor 88:190–193.

Bellrose, F. C. 1976. Ducks, geese, and swans of North America. 2d ed. Stackpole Books, Harrisburg, Pa.

Bellrose, F. C. 1978. Ducks, geese and swans of North America. Stackpole Books. Harrisburg, Pa. 2nd printing, rev.

Bellrose, F. C. 1980. Ducks, geese, and swans of North America. 3d ed. Stackpole Books, Harrisburg, Pa.

Belthoff, J. R., and G. Ritchison. 1986. Natal dispersal and mortality of juvenile Eastern Screech-Owls in central Kentucky. Proc. Ann. Meeting, Raptor Res. Found., 20–23 Nov., Gainesville, Fla. abstract.

Bendire, C. E. 1895. Life histories of North American birds. U.S. Natl. Mus. Spec. Bull. 3. Washington, D.C.

Bent, A. C. 1919. Life histories of North American diving birds. U.S. Natl. Mus. Bull. 107. Washington, D.C. Reprinted 1963, Dover Publ., New York.

Bent, A. C. 1921. Life histories of North American gulls and terns. U.S. Natl. Mus. Bull. 113. Washington, D.C. Reprinted 1963, Dover Publ., New York.

Bent, A. C. 1923. Life histories of North American wild fowl. Pt. 1. U.S. Natl. Mus. Bull. 126. Washington, D.C. Reprinted 1962, Dover Publ., New York.

Bent, A. C. 1925. Life histories of North American wild fowl. Pt. 2. U.S. Natl. Mus. Bull. 130. Washington, D.C. Reprinted 1963, Dover Publ., New York.

Bent, A. C. 1926. Life histories of North American marsh birds. U.S. Natl. Mus. Bull. 135. Washington, D.C. Reprinted 1963, Dover Publ., New York.

Bent, A. C. 1927. Life histories of North American shore birds. Pt. 1. U.S. Natl. Mus. Bull. 142. Washington, D.C. Reprinted 1962, Dover Publ., New York.

Bent, A. C. 1929. Life histories of North American shore birds. Pt. 2. U.S. Natl. Mus. Bull. 146. Washington, D.C. Reprinted 1963, Dover Publ., New York.

Bent, A. C. 1932. Life histories of North American gallinaceous birds. U.S. Natl. Mus. Bull. 162. Washington, D.C. Reprinted 1963, Dover Publ., New York.

Bent, A. C. 1937. Life histories of North American birds of prey. Pt. 1. U.S. Natl. Mus. Bull. 170. Washington, D.C. Reprinted 1961, Dover Publ., New York.

Bent, A. C. 1938. Life histories of North American birds

of prey. Pt. II. U.S. Natl. Mus. Bull. 170. Washington, D.C. Reprinted 1961, Dover Publ., New York.

Bent, A. C. 1939. Life histories of North American woodpeckers. U.S. Natl. Mus. Bull. 174. Washington, D.C. Reprinted 1964, Dover Publ., New York.

Bent, A. C. 1940. Life histories of North American cuckoos, goatsuckers, hummingbirds and their allies. U.S. Natl. Mus. Bull. 176. Washington, D.C. Reprinted in 2 pts., 1964, Dover Publ., New York.

Bent, A. C. 1942. Life histories of North American flycatchers, larks, swallows, and their allies. U.S. Natl. Mus. Bull. 179. Washington, D.C. Reprinted 1963, Dover Publ., New York.

Bent, A. C. 1946. Life histories of North American jays, crows, and titmice. U.S. Natl. Mus. Bull. 191. Washington, D.C. Reprinted in 2 pts., 1964, Dover Publ., New York.

Bent, A. C. 1948. Life histories of North American nuthatches, wrens, thrashers and their allies. U.S. Natl. Mus. Bull. 195. Washington, D.C. Reprinted 1964, Dover Publ., New York.

Bent, A. C. 1949. Life Histories of North American thrushes, kinglets, and their allies. U.S. Natl. Mus. Bull. 196. Washington, D.C. Reprinted 1964, Dover Publ., New York.

Bent, A. C. 1950. Life histories of North American wagtails, shrikes, vireos and their allies. U.S. Natl. Mus. Bull. 197. Washington, D.C. Reprinted 1965, Dover Publ., New York.

Bent, A. C. 1953. Life histories of North American wood warblers. U.S. Natl. Mus. Bull. 203. Washington, D.C. Reprinted in 2 pts., 1963, Dover Publ., New York.

Bent, A. C. 1958. Life histories of North American blackbirds, orioles, tanagers, and allies. U.S. Natl. Mus. Bull. 211. Washington, D.C. Reprinted 1963, Dover Publ., New York.

Bent, A. C. 1965. Life histories of North American wagtails, shrikes, vireos, and their allies. U.S. Natl. Mus. Bull. 197. Washington, D.C. Reprinted 1965, Dover Publ., New York.

Bent, A. C. 1968. Life histories of North American cardinals, grosbeaks, buntings, towhees, finches, sparrows, and allies. Pts. 1–3. O. L. Austin, Jr., [ed.] U.S. Natl. Mus. Bull. 237. Washington, D.C. Reprinted 1968, Dover Publ., New York.

Berger, A. J. 1968. Eastern Vesper Sparrow, pp. 868–871. In A. C. Bent, Life histories of North American cardinals, grosbeaks, buntings, towhees, finches, sparrows and allies, pt. 2. O. L. Austin, Jr., [ed.] U.S. Natl. Mus. Bull. 237. Washington, D.C.

Bertin, R. L. 1977. Breeding habitats of the Wood Thrush and Veery. Condor 79:308–311.

Bertrand, T. 1984. Manchester nighthawk report 1984. Prep. for Audubon Soc. N.H., Concord. Mimeogr.

Best, L. B. 1977. Territory quality and mating success in the Field Sparrow. Condor 79:192–204.

Biermann, G. C., and S. G. Sealy. 1982. Parental feeding of nestling Yellow Warblers in relation to brood size and prey availability. Auk 99:332–341.

Bildstein, K. L. 1988. Northern Harrier, pp. 251–303. In R. S. Palmer, [ed.], Handbook of North American birds. Vol 4. Yale Univ. Press, New Haven.

Black, C. P. 1975. The ecology and bioenergetics of the Black-throated Blue Warbler (Dendroica caerulescens caerulescens). Ph.D. diss., Dartmouth Coll., Hanover, N.H.

Blaisdell, M. E. 1919. Birds of Goffstown. In G. P. Hadley, [ed.], History of the town of Goffstown, 1733–1920. Vol. I. Goffstown, N.H.

Blaisdell, M. E. 1934. The Grasshopper Sparrow in Goffstown. Spec. Bull. Audubon Soc. N.H. 1:6–7.

Blanchan, N. 1898. Bird neighbors. Doubleday & McClure, Garden City, N.Y.

Blanchard, G. C. 1904. The Christmas bird census, Wilton, New Hampshire. Bird-Lore 6:8.

Blokpoel, H. 1980. Gull problems at Ontario airports: no

magic solutions, pp. 1–30. In Proc. First Meeting Bird Strike Prevention Workshop, Ottawa.

Blokpoel, H., and B. Smith. 1988. First records of roof nesting by Ring-billed Gulls and Herring Gulls in Ontario. Ont. Birds.

Blokpoel, H., and G. D. Tessier. 1986. The Ring-billed Gull in Ontario: a review of a new problem species. Can. Wildl. Serv. Occas. Paper 57:1–34.

Boag, D. A., and M. A. Schroeder. 1992. Spruce Grouse. In A. Poole, P. Stettenheim, and F. Gill, [eds.], The birds of North America. No. 5. Acad. Nat. Scien., Philadelphia, and Am. Ornithol. Union, Washington, D.C.

Bock, C. E., and L. W. Lepthien. 1972. Winter irruptions of Red-breasted Nuthatches in North America, 1950–1970. Am. Birds 26:558–561.

Bollengier, R. M., Jr. 1979. Eastern Peregrine Falcon recovery plan. USDI Fish & Wildl. Serv, Newton Corner, Mass.

Bollengier, R. M. 1984. Gull population and movements in the Concord/Manchester area. U.S. Dept. Agric., Animal Damage Control Unit, Concord, N.H.

Bolles, F. 1890. Snake skins in the nests of Myiarchus crinitus. Auk 7:288.

Bolles, F. 1893. At the north of Bearcamp Water. Houghton Mifflin, Boston.

Bond, J. 1937. The Cape May Warbler in Maine. Auk 54:306–308.

Bond, J. 1971. Birds of the West Indies. Houghton Mifflin, Boston.

Borror, D. J. 1961. Intraspecific variation in passerine bird songs. Wilson Bull. 73:52–78.

Borror, A. C. 1979. Laboratory guide to bird study. Univ. N.H., Durham.

Borror, A. C. 1980. Breeding birds of the Isles of Shoals. Shoals Marine Lab., Cornell Univ., Ithaca, N.Y.

Borror, D. J. 1987. Song in the White-eyed Vireo. Wilson Bull. 99:377–397.

Borror, A. C., and D. Holmes. 1990. Birds of the Isles of Shoals. Shoals Marine Lab., Cornell Univ., Ithaca, N.Y.

Bortner, J. B. 1987. American Woodcock harvest and breeding population status, 1987. U.S. Fish and Wildl. Serv., Off. Migratory Bird Manage., Laurel, Md.

Bortner, J. B. 1988. American Woodcock harvest and breeding population status, 1988. U.S. Fish and Wildl. Serv., Off. Migratory Bird Manage., Laurel, Md.

Bowen, B., C. Nolan, and A. C. Borror. 1982. House Finch range extension and breeding distribution on the U.N.H. campus, April 1981. Univ. N.H., Durham. Unpubl. rep.

Bowles, J. H. 1895. Notes on the Blackburnian Warbler. Oologist 12:64–65.

Boxall, P. C. 1983. Observations suggesting parental division of labor by American Redstarts. Wilson Bull. 95:673–674.

Boyd, E. M. 1962. A half-century's changes in the bird-life around Springfield, Massachusetts. Bird-Banding 33:137–148.

Brackbill, H. 1958. Nesting behavior of the Wood Thrush. Wilson Bull. 70:70–89.

Brackbill, H. 1970. Tufted Titmouse breeding behavior. Auk 87:522–536.

Bradley, R. A. 1980. Vocal and territorial behavior in the White-eyed Vireo. Wilson Bull. 92:302–311.

Bradley, R., and V. H. Hebert. 1963. 1963 nesting season. N.H. Audubon Quar. 16:132–140.

Brainard, D. 1953. 1952 fall migration. N.H. Bird News 6(1):20–30.

Brainard, D. 1960. Cardinals nesting in Hanover. N.H. Bird News 13:140.

Breckenridge, W. J. 1956. Measurements of the habitat niche of the Least Flycatcher. Wilson Bull. 68:47–51.

Brewer, R. 1961. Comparative notes on the life history of

the Carolina Chickadee. Wilson Bull. 73:348–373.

Brewster, W. 1879. Breeding habits of the American Brown Creeper (*Certhia familiaris americana*). Bull. Nuttall Ornithol. Club 4:199–209.

Brewster, W. 1880. Notes on the habits and distribution of the Philadelphia Vireo (*Vireo philadelphicus*). Bull. Nuttall Ornithol. Club 5:1–7.

Brewster, W. 1883. Bicknell's Thrush (*Turdus aliciae Bicknelli*) in New England. Bull. Nuttall Ornithol. Club 8:12–17.

Brewster, W. 1889. The present status of the wild pigeon (*Ectopistes migratorius*) as a bird of the United States, with some notes on its habits. Auk 6:285–291.

Brewster, W. 1891. A study of Florida Gallinules with some notes on a nest found at Cambridge, Massachusetts. Auk 8:1–7.

Brewster, W. 1906. The birds of the Cambridge region of Massachusetts. Mem. of the Nuttall Orithol. Club 4. Cambridge, Mass.

Brewster, W. 1924. The birds of Lake Umbagog region of Maine. Pt. 1. Bull. Mus. Comp. Zool. 66. Harvard Coll., Cambridge.

Brewster, W. 1925. The birds of Lake Umbagog region of Maine. Pt. 2. Bull. Mus. Comp. Zool. 66. Harvard Coll., Cambridge.

Brewster, W. 1937. The birds of Lake Umbagog region of Maine. Pt. 3. L. Griscom, [comp.]. Bull. Mus. Comp. Zool. 66. Harvard Coll., Cambridge.

Brewster, W. 1938. The birds of Lake Umbagog region of Maine. Pt. 4. L. Griscom, [comp.]. Bull. Mus. Comp. Zool. 66. Harvard Coll., Cambridge.

Brown, L. 1976. Eagles of the world. Universe Books, New York.

Brown, L., and D. Amadon. 1968. Eagles, hawks and falcons of the world. McGraw-Hill, New York.

Buckley, P. A., and F. G. Buckley. 1981. The endangered status of North American Roseate Terns. Colonial Waterbirds 4:166–173.

Bull, J. 1974. Birds of New York state. Doubleday, Garden City, N.Y.

Bull, J. 1985. Birds of New York state, including the 1976 supplement. Comstock Publ. Assoc. of Cornell Univ. Press, Ithaca and London.

Bull, John, and John Farrand, Jr. 1977. The Audubon Society field guide to North American birds: eastern region. Alfred A. Knopf, New York.

Burger, J. 1978. Great Black-backed Gulls breeding in salt marsh in New Jersey. Wilson Bull. 90:304–305.

Burger, J. 1987. Physical and social determinants of nest-site selection in Piping Plover in New Jersey. Condor 89:811–818.

Burns, F. L. 1911. A monograph of the Broad-winged Hawk (*Buteo platypterus*). Wilson Bull. 23:139–320.

Burns, F. L. 1915. Comparative periods of deposition and incubation of some North American birds. Wilson Bull. 27:275–286.

Burns, F. L. 1921a. Comparative periods of nestling life of some North American Nidicolae. Wilson Bull. 33:90–99.

Burns, F. L. 1921b. Comparative periods of nestling life of some North American Nidicolae. Wilson Bull. 33:177–182.

Burns, J. T. 1982. Nests, territories, and reproduction of Sedge Wrens (*Cistothorus platensis*). Wilson Bull. 94:338–349.

Burton, J. A., [ed.]. 1984. Owls of the world; their evolution, structure, and ecology. Rev. ed. Tanager Books, Dover, N.H.

Busby, D. G., and S. G. Sealy. 1979. Feeding ecology of a population of nesting Yellow Warblers. Can. J. Zool. 57:1670–1681.

Buss, I. O. and A. S. Hawkins. 1939. The Upland Plover at Faville Grove, Wisconsin. Wilson Bull. 51:202–220.

Butler, R. G., and S. Janes-Butler. 1983. Sexual differences in the behavior of adult Great Black-backed Gulls (*Larus marinus*) during the pre- and post-hatch periods. Auk 100:63–75.

Cade, T. 1982. The falcons of the world. Cornell Univ. Press, Ithaca, N.Y.

Cade, T. J., and J. L. Lincer, C. M. White, D. G.Roseneau, and L. G. Swartz. 1971. DDE residues and eggshell dangers in Alaskan falcons and hawks. Science 172:955–957.

Cadman, M. D., P. F. J. Eagles, and F. M. Helleiner, [comps.]. 1987. Atlas of the breeding birds of Ontario. Univ. of Waterloo Press, Waterloo.

Cairns, W. E. 1982. Biology and behavior of breeding Piping Plovers. Wilson Bull. 94:531–545.

Case, H. A., and O. H. Hewitt. 1963. Nesting and productivity of the Red-winged Blackbird in relation to habitat. Living Bird 2:7–20.

Catesby, M. 1731. The natural history of Carolina, Florida and the Bahama islands. Vol. I. London (priv. publ.).

Chabreck, R. H. 1963. Breeding habits of the Pied-billed Grebe in an impounded coastal marsh in Louisiana. Auk 80:447–452.

Chadbourne, A. P. 1887. A list of the summer birds of the Presidential Range of the White Mountains, New Hampshire. Auk 4:100–108.

Chamberlain, D. R., and G. W. Cornwell. 1971. Selected vocalizations of the common crow. Auk 88:613–634.

Chamberlain-Auger, J. A., P. J. Auger, and E. G. Strauss. 1990. Breeding biology of American Crows. Wilson Bull. 102:615–622.

Chambers, R. E. 1983. Integrating timber and wildlife management handbook. State Univ. N.Y., Syracuse and N.Y. Dept. Environ. Conserv., Albany.

Chapman, F. M. 1906. Handbook of birds of eastern North America. D. Appleton & Co., New York.

Chapman, F. M. 1907. The warblers of North America. D. Appleton & Co., New York.

Cherrington, B. 1985. Manchester nighthawk report 1985. Prep. for Audubon Soc. N.H., Concord. Mimeogr.

Christy, R. H. 1939. Northern Pileated Woodpecker, pp. 171–191. *In* A. C. Bent, Life histories of North American woodpeckers. U.S. Natl. Mus. Bull. 174. Washington, D.C.

Clark, J. N. 1899. Eight days among the birds of northern New Hampshire. Osprey 4:2–3.

Clark, R. J. 1972. Observations of nesting Marsh Hawks in Manitoba. Blue Jay 30:43–48.

Clark, K. L., and R. J. Robertson. 1981. Cowbird parasitism and evolution of anti-parasite strategies in the Yellow Warbler. Wilson Bull. 93:249–258.

Clark, W. S., and B. K. Wheeler. 1987. A field guide to hawks - North America. Houghton Mifflin, Boston.

Coleman, J. S. 1985. Home range, habitat use, behavior, and morphology of the Gettysburg vultures. M.S. thesis, VPI and State Univ., Blacksburg, Va.

Coleman, J. S., and J. D. Fraser. 1987. Food habits of Black and Turkey vultures in Pennsylvania and Maryland. J. Wildl. Manage. 51:733–739.

Coleman, J. S, and D. J. Fraser. 1989. Habitat use and home ranges of Black and Turkey vultures. J. Wildl. Manage. 53:782–792.

Collins, S. L. 1983. Geographic variation in habitat structure of the Black-throated Green Warbler (*Dendroica virens*). Auk 100:382–389.

Collopy, M. W., and T. C. Edwards, Jr. 1989. Territory size, activity budget, and role of undulating flight in nesting Golden Eagles. J. Field Ornithol. 60(1):43–51.

Comey, A. C. 1904. A partial list of the summer birds of Holderness, New Hampshire. Wilson Bull. 16:5–9 (new series); Vol. 46 (old series).

Confer, J. L., and K. Knapp. 1979. The changing proportion of Blue-winged and Golden-winged warblers in Tompkins County and their habitat selection. Kingbird 29:8–14.

Confer, J. L., and P. Paicos. 1985. Downy Woodpecker predation at goldenrod galls. J. Field Ornithol. 56(1):56–64.

Conner, R. N. 1975. Orientation of entrances to woodpecker nest cavities. Auk 92:371–374.

Conner, R. N., and C. S. Adkisson. 1974. Eastern Bluebirds nesting in clearcuts. J. Wildl. Manage. 38:934–935.

Conner, R. N., and C. S. Adkisson. 1977. Principal component analysis of woodpecker nesting habitat. Wilson Bull. 89:122–129.

Conner, R. N., O. K. Miller, Jr., and C. S. Adkisson. 1976. Woodpecker dependence on trees infected by fungal heart rots. Wilson Bull. 88:575–581.

Connett, E. V. 1947. Duck shooting along the Atlantic tidewater. William Morrow and Co, New York.

Coues, E. 1868. A list of the birds of New England. Proc. Essex Inst. 5. Salem, Mass.

Cox, G. W. 1960. A life history of the Mourning Warbler. Wilson Bull. 72:5–28.

Craig, R. J. 1984. Comparative foraging ecology of Louisiana and Northern waterthrushes. Wilson Bull. 96:173–183.

Craig, R. J. 1987. Different prey selection in two species of waterthrushes (*Seiurus*). Auk 104:180–187.

Craighead, J. J., and F. C. Craighead, Jr. 1956. Hawks, owls and wildlife. Stackpole Co., Harrisburg, Pa. and Wildl. Manage. Inst., Washington, D.C. Reprinted 1969, Dover Publ., New York.

Cringan, A. T. 1970. Reproductive biology of Ruffed Grouse in southern Ontario, 1964–69. J. Wildl. Manage. 34:756–761.

Crocoll, S. T., and J. W. Parker. 1989. The breeding biology of Broad-winged and Red-shouldered hawks in western New York. J. Raptor Res. 23(4):125–139.

Crouch, J. E. 1936. Nesting habits of the Cedar Waxwing. Auk 53:1–8.

Cruickshank, A. D. 1950. Summer birds of Lincoln County, Maine. Natl. Audubon Soc., New York.

Davie, O. 1898. Nests and eggs of North American birds. 5th ed. David McKay, Philadelphia.

Davis, D. E. 1959. Observations on territorial behavior of Least Flycatchers. Wilson Bull. 71:73–85.

Davis, C. M. 1978. A nesting study of the Brown Creeper. Living Bird 17:237–263.

Davis, D. 1983. Breeding behavior of Turkey Vultures. *In* S. R. Wilbur and J. A. Jackson, [eds.], Vulture biology and management. Univ. Calif. Press, Los Angeles.

Davis, W. E. 1986. Effects of old nests on nest-site selection in Black-crowned Night-Herons and Snowy Egrets. Wilson Bull. 98:300–303.

Deane, R. 1878. *Cotuiniculus henslowii* in New Hampshire. Bull. Nuttall Ornithol. Club 3:39.

Dearborn, N. 1898. A preliminary list of the birds of Belknap and Merrimack counties, New Hampshire, with notes. M.S. thesis, N.H. Coll. Agric. and Mechanic Arts, Durham.

Dearborn, N. 1903. The birds of Durham and vicinity. Contrib. Zool. Lab. 6. N.H. Coll. Agric. and Mechanic Arts, Durham.

DeGraff, R. M., and D. D. Rudis. 1986. New England wildlife: habitat, natural history and distribution. USDA For. Serv. Gen. Tech. Rep. NE-108.

DeGraaf, R. M., B. J. Hill, J. M. Keniston, J. W. Lanier, and G. M. Whitman. 1980. Forest habitat for birds of the northeast. USDA For. Serv., Northeast For. Exp. Station and Eastern Region. Earlier version of DeGraaf and Rudis 1986.

de Kiriline, L. 1954. The voluble singer in the tree tops. Audubon 56:109–111.

DeLuca, D. 1991. The 1991 Upland Sandpiper project final report to New Hampshire Fish and Game Department. Audubon Soc. N.H., Concord. Unpubl. rep.

Deusing, M. 1939. Nesting habits of the Pied-billed Grebe. Auk 56:367–373.

Dexter, R. W. 1981. Nesting success of Chimney Swifts related to age and the number of adults at the nest, and the subsequent fate of the visitors. J. Field Ornithol. 52:228–232.

Dickerman, R. W. 1986a. A review of the Red Crossbill in New York state. Pt. 1. Historical and nomenclatural background. Kingbird 36:73–78.

Dickerman, R. W. 1986b. A review of the Red Crossbill in New York state. Pt. 2. Identification of specimens from New York. Kingbird 36:127–134.

Dilger, W. C. 1956a. Adaptive modifications and ecological isolating mechanisms in the thrush genera Catharus and Hylocichla. Wilson Bull. 68:171–199.

Dilger, W. C. 1956b. Hostile behavior and reproductive isolating mechanisms in the avian genera Catharus and Hylocichla. Auk 73:313–353.

Dixon, C. L. 1978. Breeding biology of the Savannah Sparrow on Kent Island. Auk 95:235–246.

Dolton, D. D. 1985. 1985 Mourning Dove breeding population status. USDI Fish and Wildl. Serv. Adm. Rep., Off. Migratory Bird Manage., Laurel, Md.

Dow, D. D. 1965. The role of saliva in food storage by the Gray Jay. Auk 82:139–154.

Drum, M. 1939. Territorial studies on the Eastern Goldfinch. Wilson Bull. 51:69–77.

Drury, W. H. 1973. Population changes in New England seabirds. Bird-Banding 44:267–313; 45:1–15.

Duebbert, H. F., and J. T. Lokemoen. 1977. Upland nesting of American Bitterns, Marsh Hawks, and Short-eared Owls. Prairie Nat. 9:33–40.

Dufty, A. M. 1982. Movements and activities of radio-tracked Brown-headed Cowbirds. Auk 99:316–27.

Dunham, D. W. 1964. Reproductive displays of the Warbling Vireo. Wilson Bull. 76:170–173.

Dunham, D. W. 1966. Territorial and sexual behavior in the Rose-breasted Grosbeak Pheucticus ludovicianus (L.). Z. Tierpsychol. 23:438–51.

Dunn, E. 1975. Caloric intake of nesting Double-crested Cormorant on the coast of Maine. Auk 62:241–256.

Dunne, P., D. Sibley, and C. Sutton. 1988. Hawks in flight. Houghton Mifflin, Boston.

Dwight, J. 1887. A new race of the Sharp-tailed Sparrow (Ammodramus caudacutus). Auk 4:232–239.

Dyer, W. A. and L. H. Walkinsaw [sic]. 1959. Birds observed in Coos County, New Hampshire, June 1959. Mimeogr.

Eaton, E. H. 1910. Birds of New York. Pt. 1. Univ. State N.Y., Albany.

Eaton, E. H. 1914. Birds of New York. Pt. 2. Univ. State N.Y., Albany.

Eaton, S. W. 1957. A life history study of Seiurus noveboracensis (with notes on Seiurus aurocapillus and the species of Seiurus compared). St. Bonaventure Univ. Scien. Stud. 19:7–36.

Eaton, S. W. 1958. A life history study of the Louisiana Waterthrush. Wilson Bull. 70:211–36.

Edminster, F. C. 1947. The Ruffed Grouse. Macmillan, New York.

Ehrlich, P., D. S. Dobkin, and D. Wheye. 1988. The birder's handbook: a field guide to the natural history of North American birds. Simon and Schuster, New York.

Eiserer, L. A. 1980. Effects of grass length and mowing on foraging behavior of the American Robin (Turdus migratorius). Auk 97:576–580.

Eliason, B. C. 1986. Female site fidelity and polygyny in Blackpoll Warbler (Dendroica striata). Auk 103:782–790.

Elkins, K. C. 1957. The Wood Thrush in New Hampshire. N.H. Bird News 10(2):33–36.

Elkins, K. C. 1961. Birds of Webster and vicinity in the 1870's and today. N.H. Audubon Quar. 14:2–13.

Elkins, K. C. 1978. The fall migration, August 1 – November 30, 1977. NH Audubon 14(2):2–6.

Elkins, K.C. 1982. A checklist of the birds of New Hampshire. Audubon Soc. N.H., Concord.

Elliott, J. J., and R. S. Arbib, Jr. 1953. Origin and status of the House Finch in the eastern United States. Auk 70:31–37.

Ellison, L. N. 1971. Territoriality in Alaskan Spruce Grouse. Auk 88:652–664.

Emlen, J. T., Jr. 1954. Territory, nest building, and pair formation in the Cliff Swallow. Auk 21:16–35.

Emlen, S. T., and N. J. DeJong. 1975. Adaptive significance of synchronized breeding in a colonial bird; a new hypothesis. Science 188:1029–1031.

Erskine, A. J. 1977. Birds in boreal Canada. Can. Wildl. Serv. Rep. Ser. 41:1–73.

Erwin, A. M. 1979. The breeding success of two sympatric species of gulls, the Herring and the Great Black-backed Gull. Wilson Bull. 83:152–158.

Erwin, R. M., and C. E. Korschgen. 1979. Coastal waterbird colonies, Maine to Virginia, 1977. USDI Fish and Wildl. Serv. FWS/OBS—79/10.

Evans, E. W. 1978. Nesting responses of Field Sparrows (Spizella pusilla) to plant succession on a Michigan old field. Condor 80:34–40.

Evenden, F. G. 1957. Observations on nesting behavior of the House Finch. Condor 59:112–117.

Farmer, A. M. 1892. Camping out. Ornithol. and Oologist 17:136.

Farmer, A. M. 1895. The Yellow-throated Vireo. Nidiologist 2:80.

A.M. Farmer, Jr., 1897. Nidiologist 4.

Farrand, J., [ed.]. 1983. The Audubon Society master guide to birding. Vols. 1–3. Alfred A. Knopf, New York.

Farrand, J., Jr. 1988. Eastern birds. McGraw Hill, New York.

Faxon, W. 1892. The Prairie Horned Lark (Otocoris alpestris practicola) breeding in New Hampshire and Massachusetts. Auk 9:201–202.

Faxon, W., and J. A. Allen. 1888. Notes on the summer birds of Holderness, Bethlehem, and Franconia, New Hampshire. Auk 5:149–155.

Feare, C. 1984. The Starling. Oxford Univ. Press, New York.

Fenn, R. 1940. Red-headed Woodpecker nesting in New Hampshire. Auk 57:254.

Fetterolf, P. M. 1983. Effects of investigator activity on Ring-billed Gull behavior and reproductive performance. Wilson Bull. 95:23–41.

Ficken, M. S. 1962. Agonistic behavior and territory in the American Redstart. Auk 79:607–632.

Ficken, M. S. 1963a. Courtship of the American Redstart. Auk 80:307–317.

Ficken, R. W. 1963b. Courtship and agonistic behavior of the Common Grackle. Auk 80:52–72.

Ficken, M. S., and R. W. Ficken. 1965. Comparative ethology of the Yellow Warbler, Chestnut-sided Warbler, and American Redstart. Wilson Bull. 77:363–375.

Ficken, M. S., and R. W. Ficken. 1968a. Courtship of Blue-winged Warblers, Golden-winged Warblers, and their hybirds. Wilson Bull. 80:161–172.

Ficken, M. S., and R. W. Ficken. 1968b. Territorial relationships of Blue-winged Warblers, Golden-winged Warblers, and their hybrids. Wilson Bull. 80:442–457.

Ficken, M. S., R. W. Ficken, and S. R. Witkin. 1978. Vocal repertoire of the Black-capped Chickadee. Auk 95:34–48.

Finch, D. W. 1972. Northeastern maritime region. Am. Birds 26:832–837.

Fisher, J., and R. M. Lockley. 1954. Sea-birds. Houghton Mifflin, Boston.

Fitch, H. S. 1974. Observations on the food and nesting of the Broad-winged Hawk (Buteo platypterus) in northeastern Kansas. Condor 76:331–333.

Fogarty, M. J., K. A. Arnold, L. McKibben, L. B. Pospichal, and R. J. Tully. 1977. Common Snipe, pp. 189–209. In Glen C. Sanderson, [ed.], Management of migratory shore and upland game birds in North America. Internat. Assoc. Fish and Wildl. Agencies, Washington, D.C.

Forbes, M. R. L., and C. D. Ankney. 1987. Hatching asynchrony and food allocation within broods of Pied-billed Grebes, Podilymbus podiceps. Can. J. Zool. 65:2872–2877.

Forbes, M. R. L., and C. D. Ankney. 1988. Nest attendance by adult Pied-billed Grebes, Podilymbus podiceps (L.). Can. J. Zool. 66:2019–2023.

Forbes, J. E., and D. W. Warner. 1974. Behavior of a radio-tagged Saw-whet Owl. Wilson Bull. 92:475–488.

Forbush, E. H. 1912. A history of the game birds, wild-fowl and shore birds of Massachusetts and adjacent states. Mass. State Board Agric.

Forbush, E. H. 1916. A history of the game birds, wild-fowl and shore birds of Massachusetts and adjacent states. 2d ed. Mass. State Board Agric.

Forbush, E. H. 1925a. Birds of Massachusetts and other New England states. Vol. I. Mass. Dept. Agric., Boston.

Forbush, E. H. 1925b. A natural history of American birds of eastern and central North America. Houghton Mifflin, Boston.

Forbush, E. H. 1927. Birds of Massachusetts and other New England states. Vol. II. Mass. Dept. Agric., Boston.

Forbush, E. H. 1929. Birds of Massachusetts and other New England states. Vol. III. Mass. Dept. Agric., Boston.

Forbush, E. H., and J. B. May. 1939. A natural history of American birds of eastern and central North America. Houghton Mifflin, Boston.

Foss, C. R., and D. DeLuca. 1990. Habitat use of Upland Sandpipers and Bald Eagles at Pease A.F.B., Portsmouth/Newington, New Hampshire. Prep. for the Nature Conservancy. Audubon Soc. N.H., Concord, Unpubl. rep.

Foster, W. L., and J. Tate, Jr. 1966. The activities and coactions of animals at sapsucker trees. Living Bird 5:87–114.

Fox, W. H. 1876. Three migrations compared. Forest and Stream 6:354.

Fraser, J. D., L. D. Frenzel, and J. E. Mathisen. 1985. The impact of human activities on breeding Bald Eagles in north central Minnesota. J. Wildl. Manage. 49:585–592.

Fredrickson, L. H. 1971. Common Gallinule breeding biology and development. Auk 88:914–919.

Freer, V. M. 1979. Factors affecting site tenacity in New York Bank Swallows. Bird-Banding 50:349–357.

Friedmann, H. 1929. The cowbirds, a study in the biology of social parasitism. C. C. Thomas, Springfield, Ill.

Friedmann, H. 1963. Host relations of the parasitic cowbirds. U.S. Nat. Mus. Bull. 233. Washington, D.C.

Friedmann, H., L. F. Kiff, and S. I. Rothstein. 1977. A further contribution to knowledge of the host relations of the parasitic cowbirds. Smithsonian Contrib. to Zool. 235.

Gabrielson, I. N. 1915. The home of the great crest. Wilson Bull. 27:421–434.

Galli, A. E., C. F. Leck, and T. T. Forman. 1976. Avian distribution patterns in forest islands of different sizes in central New Jersey. Auk 93:356–364.

Gaston, G. R., and P. G. Johnson. 1977. Nesting success and mortality of nestlings in a coastal Alabama heron-egret colony, 1976. Northeast Gulf Scien. 1:14–22.

Gates, J. M. 1972. Red-tailed Hawk populations and ecology in east-central Wisconsin. Wilson Bull. 84:421–433.

Gerrard, J., and G. R. Bortolotti. 1988. The Bald Eagle — haunts and habits of a wilderness monarch. Smithsonian Inst. Press, Washington, D.C. and London.

Gerrard, P. N., S. N. Wienmayer, and J. M. Gerrard. 1979. Bald Eagle nesting behavior. Raptor Res. 13:57–64.

Gibbs, J. P., and S. M. Melvin. 1990. An assessment of wading birds and other wetlands avifauna and their habitats in Maine. Maine Dept. Inland Fish. and Wildl., Bangor. Unpubl. rep.

Gill, F. B. 1980. Historical aspects of hybridization between Blue-winged and Golden-winged warblers. Auk 97:1–18.

Gill, F. B. 1985. Whither two warblers? Living Bird Quar. 4(4):4–7.

Gillespie, M. 1930. Behavior and local distribution of Tufted Titmice in winter and spring. Bird-Banding 1:113–127.

Glover, F. A. 1953. Nesting ecology of the Pied-billed Grebe in north-western Iowa. Wilson Bull. 65:32–39.

Godfrey, W. E. 1966. The birds of Canada. Natl. Mus. Can. Bull. 203, Biolo. Ser. 73. Ottawa.

Godfrey, W. E. 1979. The birds of Canada. Natl. Mus. Nat. Scien., Ottawa.

Goff, G. R., D. J. Decker, J. W. Kelley, and R. A. Howard, Jr. 1981. Ring-necked Pheasant (*Phasianus colchicus*). N.Y. Wildl. Resour. 6. Extension publ. Dept. Nat. Resour., N.Y. State Coll. Agric. and Life Scien., Cornell Univ., Ithaca.

Gollop, J. B., and W. H. Marshall. 1954. A guide for aging duck broods in the field. Miss. Flyway Counc. Tech. Sect.

Goodhue, C. F. 1877. The birds of Webster and adjoining towns. Forest and Stream 8:33–34,49,96,113,146.

Goodhue, C. F. 1922. Fifty years among the birds of New Hampshire. Concord Public Library, Concord, N.H. Unpubl. ms.

Goodwin, D. 1976. Crows of the world. Cornell Univ. Press, Ithaca, N.Y.

Goossen, J. P., and S. G. Sealy. 1982. Production of young in a dense nesting population of Yellow Warblers, *Dendroica petechia*, in Manitoba. Can. Field-Nat. 96:189–199.

Graber, J. W. 1968. Western Henslow's Sparrow, pp. 779–794. *In* A. C. Bent, Life histories of North American cardinals, grosbeaks, buntings, towhees, finches, sparrows and allies, pt. 2. O. L. Austin, Jr., [ed.]. U.S. Natl. Mus. Bull. 237. Washington, D.C.

Graber, R. R., and J. W. Graber. 1951. Nesting of the Parula Warbler in Michigan. Wilson Bull. 63:75–83.

Graber, R. R., J. W. Graber, and E. L. Kirk. 1973. Illinois birds: Laniidae. Biol. Notes 83. Ill. Nat. Hist. Survey, Urbana, Ill.

Grandy, J. W. 1983. The North American Black Duck (Anas rubripes): a case study of 28 years of failure in American wildlife management. Internatl. J. Study Anim. Problems 4(4):supplement. Humane Soc. U.S., Washington, D.C.

Greenlaw, J. S. 1983. Microgeographic distribution of breeding Seaside Sparrows on New York salt marshes, pp. 99–114. In The Seaside Sparrow, its biology and management. N.C. Biol. Surv. and N.C. State Mus., Raleigh.

Greenwald, M. R. 1984. Some notes on Spruce Grouse. Bird Observer Eastern Mass. 12:249–266.

Griscom, L. 1929. Changes in the status of certain birds in the New York region. Auk 46:45–47.

Griscom, L. 1938. Birds of the Lake Umbagog region of Maine. Pt. IV. Mus. Comp. Zool. Harvard Coll., Cambridge.

Griscom, L. 1949. The birds of Concord [Massachusetts]. Harvard Univ. Press, Cambridge.

Griscom, L., and D. E. Snyder. 1955. The birds of Massachusetts: an annotated and revised checklist. Peabody Mus., Salem, Mass.

Griscom, L. and A. Sprunt, Jr., [eds.]. 1957. The warblers of America. Devin-Adair, New York.

Griscom, L., and A. Sprunt, Jr. 1979. The warblers of America. Rev. E. M. Reilly, Jr. Doubleday, Garden City, N.Y.

Gross, A. O. 1940. Eastern Nighthawk, pp. 206–234. *In* A. C. Bent, Life histories of North American cuckoos, goatsuckers, hummingbirds and their allies. U.S. Natl. Mus. Bull. 176. Washington, D.C.

Gross, A. O. 1942a. Bank Swallow, pp. 400–424. *In* A. C. Bent, Life histories of North American flycatchers, larks, swallows and their allies. U.S. Natl. Mus. Bull. 179. Washington, D.C.

Gross, A. O. 1942b. Northern Cliff Swallow, pp. 463–484. *In* A. C. Bent, Life histories of North American flycatchers, larks, swallows and their allies. U.S. Natl. Mus. Bull. 179. Washington, D.C.

Gross, A. O. 1945. The present status of the Great Black-backed Gull on the coast of Maine. Auk 62:241–256.

Gross, A. O. 1946. Eastern Crow, pp. 226–259. *In* A. C. Bent, Life histories of North American jays, crows, and titmice. U.S. Natl. Mus. Bull. 191. Washington, D.C.

Gross, A. O. 1949. Eastern Hermit Thrush, pp. 143–162. *In* A. C. Bent, Life histories of North American thrushes, kinglets and their allies. U.S. Natl. Mus. Bull. 196. Washington, D.C.

Gross, A. O. 1953a. Black-polled Warbler, pp. 389–408. *In* A. C. Bent, Life histories of North American wood warblers, pt. 2. U.S. Natl. Mus. Bull. 203. Washington, D.C.

Gross, A. O. 1953b. Northern and Maryland Yellowthroats, pp. 542–565. *In* A. C. Bent, Life histories of North American wood warblers, pt. 2. U.S. Natl. Mus. Bull. 203. Washington, D.C.

Gross, A. O. 1958. Bronzed Grackle, pp. 395–421. *In* A. C. Bent, Life histories of North American blackbirds, orioles, tanagers and allies. U.S. Natl. Mus. Bull. 211. Washington, D.C.

Gullion, G. W. 1972. Improving your forested lands for Ruffed Grouse. Misc. J. Ser. Publ. 1439. Minn. Agric. Exp. Station, St. Paul, and Ruffed Grouse Soc., Corapolis, Pa.

Hager, D. C., Jr. 1957. Nesting populations of Red-tailed Hawks and Horned Owls in central New York State. Wilson Bull. 69:263–272.

Hailman, J. P. 1960. Ring-billed Gulls following the plow. Raven 31:109.

Halberg, E., and H. Halberg. 1956. Guide to summer birding in the Connecticut Lakes region. N.H. Bird News 9:39–49.

Hall, G. A. 1983. Birds of West Virginia: distribution and ecology. Carnegie Mus. Nat. Hist. Spec. Publ. 7. Pittsburg.

Halla, B. F. 1966. The Mute Swan in Rhode Island. *In* 23rd Trans. Northeast Sect. Wildl. Soc.

Hamas, M. J. 1975. Ecological and physiological adaptations for breeding in the Belted Kingfisher (*Megaceryle alcyon*). Ph.D. diss., Univ. Minn.

Hamerstrom, F. 1969. A harrier population study, pp. 367–383. *In* J. J. Hickey, [ed.], Peregrine Falcon populations: their biology and decline. Univ. Wisc. Press, Madison.

Hamerstrom, F. 1986. Harrier hawk of the marshes. Smithsonian Inst. Press, Washington, D.C.

Hamerstrom, F. N., F. Hamerstrom, and J. Hart. 1973. Nest boxes: an effective management tool for kestrels. J. Wildl. Manage. 37:400–403.

Hamilton, W. J., Jr. 1943. Nesting of the Eastern Bluebird. Auk 60:91–94.

Hancock, J., and J. Kushlan. 1984. The herons handbook. Harper and Row, New York.

Hann, H. W. 1937. Life history of the Ovenbird in southern Michigan. Wilson Bull. 49:145–237.

Harding, K. C. 1925. Semi-colonizations of Veeries. Bull. Northeastern Bird-banding Assoc. 1:4–7.

Harding, K. C. 1930. Cerulean Warbler in Holderness, New Hampshire. Auk 47:90.

Harding, K. C. 1931. Nesting habits of the Black-throated Blue Warbler. Auk 48:512–522.

Harlow, R. C. 1922. The breeding habits of the northern raven in Pennsylvania. Auk 39:399–410.

Harrison, H. H. 1951. Notes and observations on the Wilson's Warbler. Wilson Bull. 63:143–148.

Harrison, H. H. 1975. A field guide to birds' nests in the United States east of the Mississippi River. Houghton Mifflin, Boston.

Harrison, C. 1978. A field guide to the nests, eggs, and nestlings of North American birds. Collins and Sons, Glasgow.

Harrison, P. 1983. Seabirds: an identification guide. Croom Helm Ltd., Beckenham, Kent.

Harrison, H. H. 1984. Wood warbler's world. Simon and Schuster, New York.

Hatch, J. 1982. The cormorants of Boston harbor and Massachusetts bay. Bird Observer Eastern Mass. 10:65–73.

Hays, H. 1972. Polyandry in the Spotted Sandpiper. Living Bird Quar. 11:43–57.

Hays, Helen. 1984. The vole that roared. Nat. Hist. 93(5):7–16.

Hebert, V. H. 1955. 1955 nesting season. N.H. Bird News 8(4):118–122.

Hebert, V. H. 1956. 1956 nesting season. N.H. Bird News 9(4):120–123.

Hebert, V. H. 1957. 1957 summer records. N.H. Bird News 10(4):112–116.

Hebert, V. H. 1958a. 1958 nesting season. N.H. Bird News 11:33–40.

Hebert, V. H. 1958b. Twin state 1957 fall migration. N.H. Bird News 11:24–368.

Hebert, V. H. 1958c. 1957–58 winter season. N.H. Bird News 11(2):12–17.

Hebert, V. H. 1960a. 1960 nesting season. N.H. Bird News 13:143–154.

Hebert, V. H. 1960b. Purple Martins in New Hampshire. N.H. Bird News 13:155.

Hebert, V. H. 1962. 1962 nesting season. N.H. Audubon Quar. 15:116–122.

Hebert, V. H. 1967. 1967 spring migration. N.H. Audubon Quar. 20:105–116.

Hebert, V. H. 1972. 1972 nesting season. N.H. Audubon Quar. 25:145–152.

Hebert, V. H. 1973. 1973 nesting season. N.H. Audubon Quar. 26:131–137.

Hebert, V. H. 1974. The summer season. N.H. Audubon Quar. 27:105–112.

Hebert, V. H. 1975. The summer season, 1975. N.H. Audubon Quar. 28:113–120.

Hebert, V. H. 1978. Seasonal bird records: 1978 nesting season. N.H. Audubon 13(8):3–6.

Hebert, V. H. 1979. Seasonal bird records: summer report 1979. N.H. Audubon 15(8):3–5.

Hebert, V. H., and R. W. Smart. 1961. 1961 spring migration season. N.H. Audubon Quar. 14:84–104.

Hecht, W. R. 1951. Nesting of the Marsh Hawk at Delta, Manitoba. Wilson Bull. 63:167–176.

Henny, C. J., and W. Van Velzen. 1972. Migration patterns and wintering localities of American Ospreys. J. Wildl. Manage. 36:1133–1141.

Henny, C. J., and H. M. Wight. 1969. Population ecology and environmental pollution: Red-tailed and Cooper's hawks. *In* Population ecology of migratory birds. Papers from symposium held at Laurel, Md., 9–10 Oct. 1969. U.S. Bur. Sport Fish. and Wildl. Res. Rep. 2.

Henny, C. J., F. C. Schmid, E. M. Martin, and L. L. Hood. 1973. Territorial behavior, pesticides, and the population ecology of Red-shouldered Hawks in central Maryland, 1943–1971. Ecology 54:545–554.

Herrick, F. H. 1883. Prairie Warbler in New Hampshire. Science 2(31):309 (ser. 1).

Hessler, E., J. R. Tester, E. B. Siniff, and M. M. Nelson. 1970. A biotelemetry study of survival of pen-reared pheasants released in selected habitats. J. Wildl. Manage. 34:267–74.

Heusmann, H. W. 1974. Mallard-Black duck relationships in the northeast. Wildl. Soc. Bull. 2:171–177.

Hickey, J. J. 1943. A guide to bird watching. Doubleday, New York.

Hickey, J. J., and L. B. Hunt. 1960. Initial songbird mortality following a Dutch elm disease control program. J. Wildl. Manage. 24:259–265.

Higgins, K. F. and L. M. Kirsch. 1975. Some aspects of the breeding biology of the Upland Sandpiper in North Dakota. Wilson Bull. 87:96–102.

Higgins, K. F., H. F. Duebbert, and R. B. Oetting. 1969. Nesting of the Upland Plover on the Missouri Coteau. Prairie Nat. 1(3):45–48.

Hill, W. P. 1956. Birds between the Monadnocks. Transcript Printing, Peterborough, N.H.

Hill, N. P. 1965. The birds of Cape Cod, Massachusetts. William Morrow, New York.

Hill, N. P. 1968. Eastern Sharp-tailed Sparrow, pp. 795–812. In A. C. Bent, Life histories of North American cardinals, grosbeaks, buntings, towhees, finches, sparrows and allies, pt. 2. O. L. Austin, Jr., [ed.]. U.S. Natl. Mus. Bull. 237. Washington, D.C.

Hjertaas, D. G., P. Hjertaas, and W. J. Maher. 1988. Colony size and reproductive biology of the Bank Swallow (Riparia riparia) in Saskatchewan Canada. Can. Field-Nat. 102:465–470.

Hochbaum, H. A. 1944. The canvasback on a prairie marsh. Wildl. Manage. Inst., Harrisburg, Pa.

Hoffman, R. 1904. A guide to the birds of New England and eastern New York. Houghton Mifflin, Boston.

Hofslund, P. B. 1957. A life history of the yellowthroat, Geothlypis trichas. Proc. Minn. Acad. Scien. 27:144–174.

Hofslund, P. B. 1959. Fall migration of Herring Gulls from Knife Island, Minnesota. Bird-Banding 30:104–113.

Holmes, R. T. 1986. Foraging patterns of forest birds: male-female differences. Wilson Bull. 98:196–213.

Holmes, R. T., R. E. Bonney, Jr., and S. W. Pacala. 1979. Guild structure of the Hubbard Brook bird community: a multivariate approach. Ecology 60:512–520.

Holmes, R. T., T. W. Sherry, and F. W. Sturges. 1986. Bird community dynamics in a temperate deciduous forest: long-term trends at Hubbard Brook. Ecol. Monogr. 56:201–220.

Holmes, R. T., T. W. Sherry, P. P. Marra, and K. E. Petit. 1992. Multiple-brooding and productivity of a Neotropical migrant, the Black-throated Blue Warbler (Dendroica caerulescens), in an unfragmented temperate forest. Auk 109:321–333.

Hoogland, J. L., and P. W. Sherman. 1976. Advantages and disadvantages of Bank Swallow (Riparia riparia) coloniality. Ecol. Monogr. 46:33–58.

Horak, G. J. 1970. A comparative study of the foods of the Sora and Virginia Rail. Wilson Bull. 82:206–213.

Horton, F. B. 1903. Mortality of Purple Martins (Progne subis) at Brattleboro, Vermont. Auk 20:435–436.

Hotchkiss, F. R. 1967. Red-shafted Flicker in New Hampshire chimney. N.H. Audubon Quar. 20:98.

Howard, D. V. 1967. Variation in the breeding season and clutch size of the robin in the northeastern United States and the maritime provinces of Canada. Wilson Bull. 79:432–440.

Howard, D. V. 1968. Range expansion of the cardinal into New Hampshire. N.H. Audubon Quar. 21:2–6.

Howe, M. A. 1982. Social organization in a nesting population of Eastern Willets (Catoptrophorus semipalmatus). Auk 99:88–102.

Howe, R. H., Jr., and G. M. Allen. 1901. The birds of Massachusetts. Cambridge, Mass. (priv. publ.).

Howes-Jones, D. 1985. Nesting habits and activity patterns of the Warbling Vireo, Vireo gilvus, in southern Ontario. Can. Field-Nat. 99:484–489.

Hurley, R. J., and E. C. Franks. 1976. Changes in the breeding ranges of two grassland birds. Auk 93:108–115.

Hussell, D. J. T. 1980. The timing of fall migration and molt in Least Flycatchers. J. Field Ornithol. 51:65–71.

Hyde, A. S. 1939. The life history of Henslow's Sparrow, Passerherbulus henslowii (Audubon). Univ. Mich. Mus. Zool. Misc. Publ. 41. Ann Arbor.

Hyde, A. A. 1948. Breeding of the Ring-billed Gull in New York in 1936. Auk 65:317.

Ickes, R. A., and M. S. Ficken. 1970. An investigation of territorial behavior in the American Redstart utilizing recorded songs. Wilson Bull. 82:167–176.

Irwin, R., and C. Korschgen. 1979. Coastal waterbird colonies: Maine to Virginia, 1977. USDI Fish and Wildl. Serv. Biol. Surv. Prog. FWS/OBS–79/08.

Jackson, C. F. 1947. Notes on the bird population at the Isles of Shoals. Bull. Audubon Soc. N.H. 18:49–54, 63–64.

Jackson, J. A. 1970a. A quantitative study of the foraging ecology of Downy Woodpeckers. Ecology 51:318–323.

Jackson, J. A. 1970b. Observations at the nest of the Red-headed Woodpecker, pp. 3–10. In Niobrara, 1968–1969. Ann. Rep., Univ. Kan. Mus. Natl. Hist.

Jackson, J. A. 1976. A comparison of some aspects of the breeding ecology of Red-headed and Red-bellied woodpeckers in Kansas. Condor 78:67–76.

Jackson, J. A. 1983. Nesting phenology, nest site selection, and reproductive success of the Black and Turkey vultures. In S. R. Wilbur and J. A. Jackson, [eds.], Vulture biology and management. Univ. Calif. Press, Los Angeles.

Jackson, C. F., and P. F. Allan. 1931. Experiment in the recolonization of the Common Tern (Sterna hirundo). Auk 48:17–21.

Jackson, C. F., and P. F. Allan. 1932. Additional note on the breeding in Maine of the Great Black-backed Gull (Larus marinus). Auk 49:349–350.

Jacobs, J. P., E. A. Jacobs, and T. C. Erdman. 1988. Nesting ecology of Red-shouldered Hawks in Wisconsin. Proc. Ann. Meeting, Raptor Res. Found., Oct. 27–29, Minneapolis. Abstract.

James, R. D. 1973. Ethological and ecological relationships of the Yellow-throated and Solitary vireos (Aves: Vireonidae) in Ontario. Unpubl. Ph.D. thesis, Univ. Toronto.

James, R. D. 1976. Foraging behavior and habitat selection of three species of vireos in southern Ontario. Wilson Bull. 88:62–75.

James, R. D. 1979. The comparative foraging behavior of Yellow-throated and Solitary vireos: the effect of habitat and sympatry, pp. 137–163. In J. G. Dickson, R. N. Connor, R. R. Fleet, J. A. Jackson, and J. C. Kroll, [eds.], The role of insectivorous birds in forest ecosystems. Academic Press, New York.

James, R. D. 1984. Structure, frequency of usage and apparent learning in the primary song of the Yellow-throated Vireo, with comparative notes on Solitary Vireo. Can. J. Zool. 62:468–472.

Janik, C. A., and J. A. Mosher. 1981. Breeding biology of raptors in the central Appalachians. Raptor Res. 16:18–24.

Jay, D. P. 1986. A population study of Ring-billed Gulls on Lake Champlain. M.S. thesis, Univ. Vt., Burlington.

Johnsgard, P. A. 1973. Grouse and quails of North America. Univ. Nebr. Press, Lincoln.

Johnsgard, P. A. 1975a. North American game birds of upland and shoreline. Univ. Nebr. Press, Lincoln.

Johnsgard, P. A. 1975b. The waterfowl of North America. Indiana Univ. Press, Bloomington.

Johnsgard, P. A. 1978. Ducks, geese and swans of the world. Univ. Nebr. Press, Lincoln.

Johnsgard, P. A. 1980. Short communications: copulatory behavior of the American Bittern. Auk 97:868–869.

Johnsgard, P. A. 1981. The plovers, sandpipers, and snipes of the world. Univ. Nebr. Press, Lincoln.

Johnsgard, P. A. 1988. North American owls: biology and natural history. Smithsonian Inst. Press, Washington, D.C.

Johnsgard, P. A. 1990. Hawks, eagles, and falcons of North America. Smithsonian Inst. Press, Washington, D.C.

Johnson, D. H. 1987. Barred Owls and nest boxes; results of a five-year study in Minnesota, pp. 129–134. In Biology and conservation of northern forest owls. Symposium proc., Winnipeg, Man. USDA For. Serv. Gen. Tech. Rep. RM-142.

Johnson, E. J., and L. B. Best. 1982. Factors affecting feeding and brooding of Gray Catbird nestlings. Auk 99:148–156.

Kale, H. W., II. 1965. Ecology and bioenergetics of the Long-billed Marsh Wren in Georgia salt marshes. Nuttall Ornithol. Club Publ. 5. Cambridge, Mass.

Kastner, J. 1986. A world of watchers. Knopf, New York.

Kaufman, K. 1990. A field guide to advanced birding. Houghton Mifflin, Boston.

Kaufmann, G. W. 1987. Growth and development of Sora and Virginia Rail chicks. Wilson Bull. 99:432–440.

Keeler, J. E., C. C. Allin, J. M. Anderson, S. Gallizioli, K. E. Gamble, D. W. Hayne, W. H. Kiel, Jr., F. W. Martin, J. L. Ruos, K. C. Sadler, L. D. Soileau, C. E. Braun, and H. D. Funk. 1977. Mourning Dove (Zenaida macroura), pp. 275–298. In G. C. Sanderson, [ed.], Management of migratory shore and upland game birds in North America. Internat. Assoc. of Fish and Wildl. Agencies, Washington, D.C.

Keith, A. R. 1964. A thirty-year summary of the nesting of the Barn Owl on Martha's Vineyard, Massachusetts. Bird-Banding 35:22–31.

Kemper, D. L., and J. M. Taylor. 1981. Seasonal reproductive changes in the American Robin (Turdus migratorius) of the Pacific Northwest. Can. J. Zool. 59:212–217.

Kendeigh, S. C. 1945a. Nesting behavior of wood warblers. Wilson Bull. 57:145–164.

Kendeigh, S. C. 1945b. Community selection by birds on the Helderberg Plateau in New York. Auk 62:418–436.

Kendeigh, S. C. 1947. Bird population studies in the coniferous forest biome during a spruce budworm outbreak. Ontario Dept. Lands and For. Biol. Bull. 1:1–100.

Kennard, J. H. 1963. Ten years birdbanding experience in New Hampshire. N.H. Audubon Quar. 16:2–8.

Ketterson, E. D., and V. Nolan, Jr. 1983. The evolution of differential bird migration. Curr. Ornithol. 1:357–402.

Kilham, L. 1959a. Bark-eating of Red-headed Woodpeckers. Condor 61:371–373.

Kilham, L. 1959b. Early reproductive behavior of flickers. Wilson Bull. 71:323–336.

Kilham, L. 1959c. Mutual tapping of Red-headed Woodpecker. Auk 76:235–236.

Kilham, L. 1959d. Territorial behavior of wintering Red-headed Woodpeckers. Wilson Bull. 70:347–358.

Kilham, L. 1959e. Behavior and methods of communication of Pileated Woodpeckers. Condor 61:377–387.

Kilham, L. 1962a. Breeding behavior of Yellow-bellied Sapsuckers. Auk 79:31–43.

Kilham, L. 1962b. Nest sanitation of the Yellow-bellied Sapsucker. Wilson Bull. 74:96–97.

Kilham, L. 1964. The relations of Yellow-bellied Sapsuckers to wounded birches and other trees. Auk 81:520–527.

Kilham, L. 1965. Differences in feeding behavior of male and female Hairy Woodpeckers. Wilson Bull. 77:134–145.

Kilham, L. 1966a. Nesting activities of Black-backed Woodpeckers. Condor 68:308–310.

Kilham, L. 1966b. Reproductive behavior of Hairy Woodpeckers: I. pair formation and courtship. Wilson Bull. 78:251–265.

Kilham, L. 1968. Reproductive behavior of White-breasted Nuthatches: I. distraction display, bill-sweeping, and nest hole defense. Auk 85:477–492.

Kilham, L. 1969. Reproductive behavior of Hairy Woodpeckers: III. agonistic behavior in relation to courtship and territory. Wilson Bull. 81:169–183.

Kilham, L. 1970. Feeding behavior of Downy Woodpeckers: I. preference for paper birches and sexual differences. Auk 87:544–556.

Kilham, L. 1971a. Reproductive behavior of Yellow-bellied Sapsuckers: I. preference for nesting in Fomes-infected aspens and nest hole interrelations with flying squirrels, raccoons and other animals. Wilson Bull. 83:159–171.

Kilham, L. 1971b. Roosting habits of White-breasted Nuthatches. Condor 73:113–114.

Kilham, L. 1972a. Death of Red-breasted Nuthatch from pitch around nest hole. Auk 89:451–452.

Kilham, L. 1972b. Reproductive behavior of White-breasted Nuthatches: II. courtship. Auk 89:115–129.

Kilham, L. 1973. Reproductive behavior of the Red-breasted Nuthatch: I. courtship. Auk 90:597–609.

Kilham, L. 1974. Early breeding season behavior of Downy Woodpeckers. Wilson Bull. 86:407–418.

Kilham, L. 1976a. Kingfisher in the garden. N.H. Audubon Quar. 29:99–103.

Kilham, L. 1976b. Winter foraging and associated behavior of Pileated Woodpeckers in Georgia and Florida. Auk 93:15–24.

Kilham, L. 1979. Courtship and the pair-bond of Pileated Woodpeckers. Auk 96:587–594.

Kilham, L. 1980. Goldfinches feeding on filamentous algae. Oriole 45:48.

Kilham, L. 1981. Agonistic behavior of the White-breasted Nuthatch. Wilson Bull. 93:271–274.

Kilham, L. 1983. Life history studies of the woodpeckers of eastern North America. Nuttall Ornithol. Club Publ. 20. Cambridge, Mass.

Kilham, L. 1984a. Cooperative breeding of American Crows in Florida. J. Field Ornithol. 55:349–356.

Kilham, L. 1984b. Intra- and extrapair copulatory behavior of American Crows. Wilson Bull. 96:716–717.

Kilham, L. 1985a. Territorial behavior of American Crows. Wilson Bull. 97:389–390.

Kilham, L. 1985b. Behavior of American Crows in the early part of the breeding cycle. Fla. Field Nat. 13:25–48.

Kilham, L. 1985c. Common Raven, Corvus corax, robs American Crow, Corvus brachyrynchos, in aerial chase. Can. Field-Nat. 99:372.

Kirsch, L. M. and K. F. Higgins. 1976. Upland Sandpiper nesting and management in North Dakota. Wildl. Soc. Bull. 4(1):16–20.

Knight, O. W. 1897. A list of the birds of Maine. Univ. Maine Dept. Nat. Hist. Bull. 3. Augusta.

Knupp, D. M., R. B. Owen, Jr., and J. B. Dimond. 1977. Reproductive biology of American Robins in northern Maine. Auk 94:80–85.

Korschgen, C. E. 1979. Coastal waterbird colonies: Maine. Biol. Serv. Prog., USDI Fish and Wildl. Serv. FWS/OBS–79/O9.

Kortright, F. H. 1942. The ducks, geese and swans of North America. Stackpole Books, Harrisburg, Pa., and Wildl. Manage. Inst., Washington, D.C.

Kortright, F. H. 1953. The ducks, geese and swans of North America. Stackpole Books, Harrisburg, Pa., and Wildl. Manage. Inst., Washington, D.C. 2nd printing.

Kricher, J. C. 1981. Range expansion of the Tufted Titmouse (Parus bicolor) in Massachusetts. Am. Birds 35:750–753.

Krohn, W. B. 1973. Banded Maine woodcock. Maine Fish and Game 15(2):4–7.

Kroodsma, D. E. 1989. What, when, where, and why warblers warble. Nat. Hist. 5/89: 51–59.

Kury, C., and R. Gochfeld. 1975. Human interference and gull predation in cormorant colonies. Biol. Conserv. 8:23–34.

Lacaillade, H. C. 1975. Waterfowl and their management in New Hampshire. N.H. Fish and Game Dept. Survey Rep. 11.

Laerm, J., and J. C. Haney. 1984. Observations on the thermoregulatory behavior of a roof-nesting Common Nighthawk (C. minor). Oriole 49:7–10.

Lagrenade, M. C., and P. Mousseau. 1983. Female-female pairs and polygynous associations in a Quebec Ring-billed Gull colony. Auk 100:210–212.

Lanyon, W. E. 1957. The comparative biology of the meadowlarks (Sturnella) in Wisconsin. Nuttal Ornithol. Club. Publ. Cambridge, Mass.

Laskey, A. R. 1957. Some Tufted Titmouse life history. Bird-Banding 28:135–145.

Laskey, A. R. 1962. Breeding biology of mockingbirds. Auk 79:596–606.

Laughlin, S. B., and D. P. Kibbe. 1985. The atlas of breeding birds of Vermont. Univ. Press New Eng., Hanover, N.H.

Lauro, A. J. 1977. Gull predation on an ant swarm. Kingbird 27:87–88.

Lawrence, L. de K. 1948. Comparative study of the nesting behavior of Chestnut-sided and Nashville warblers. Auk 65:204–219.

Lawrence, L. de K. 1949. The Red Crossbill at Pisimi Bay, Ontario. Can. Field-Nat. 63:147–160.

Lawrence, L. de K. 1953. Nesting life and behavior of the Red-eyed Vireo. Can. Field-Nat. 67:47–77.

Lawrence, L. de K. 1961. Five days with a pair of nesting Canada Jays. Can. Field-Nat. 61:1–12.

Lawrence, L. de K. 1967. A comparative life-history of four species of woodpeckers. Ornithol. Monogr. 5:1–167.

Lee, J. A. 1980. Survival of the smallest nestling in Goshawks. Raptor Res. 14:70–73.

Lein, M. R. 1981. Display behavior of Ovenbirds (Seiurus aurocapillus): II. Song variation and singing behavior. Wilson Bull. 93:21–41.

Lemon, R. E., R. Cotter, R. C. MacNally, and S. Monette. 1985. Song repetoires and song sharing by American Redstarts. Condor 87:457–470.

Lenington, S. 1980. Bi-parental care in Killdeer; an adaptive hypothesis. Wilson Bull. 92:8–20.

Lett, D. W., and D. M. Bird. 1987. Postfledging behavior of American Kestrels in southwestern Quebec. Wilson Bull. 99:77–82.

Levi, W. 1963. The pigeon. Levi Publishing, Sumter, S.C.

Lincer, J. L., and J. A. Sherburn. 1974. Organochlorines in kestrel prey: a north-south dichotomy. J. Wildl. Manage. 38:427–434.

Lippincott, J. W. 1917. The Barn Owl's voice. Bird-Lore 19:275.

Lisi, G. 1988. A field study of Black-backed Woodpeckers in Vermont. Vt. Fish and Wildl. Dept. Nongame and Endangered Species Prog. Tech. Rep. 3.

Little, W. 1870. The history of Warren; a mountain hamlet, located among the White Hills of New Hampshire. Wm. E. Moore, printer, Manchester, N.H.

Lowther, J. K., and J. B. Falls. 1968. White-throated Sparrow, pp. 1364–1392. In A. C. Bent, Life histories of North American cardinals, grosbeaks, buntings, towhees, finches, sparrows and allies, pt. 3. O. L. Austin, Jr., [ed.]. U.S. Natl. Mus. Bull. 237. Washington, D.C.

LPC. 1991. Turning points: The Loon Preservation Committee 15 year report. Audubon Soc. N.H., Concord.

Ludwig, F. E. 1943. Ring-billed Gulls of the Great Lakes. Wilson Bull. 55:234–243.

Ludwig, J. P. 1974. Recent changes in the Ring-billed Gull population and biology in the Laurentian Great Lakes. Auk 91:575–594.

Lunk, W. A. 1962. The Rough-winged Swallow, stelgidopteryx ruficollis (Vieillot); a study based on its breeding biology in Michigan. Nuttall Ornithol. Club Publ. 4. Cambridge, Mass.

Lynch, P. J., and D. G. Smith. 1984. Census of Eastern Screech-Owls (Otus asio) in urban open-space areas using tape-recorded song. Am. Birds 38:388–391.

Lyons, D. M., and J. A. Mosher. 1987. Morphological growth, behavioral development, and parental care of Broad-winged Hawks. J. Field Ornithol. 58:334–344.

Lyons, D. M., K. Titus, and J. A. Mosher. 1986. Sprig delivery by Broad-winged Hawks. Wilson Bull. 93:469–471.

MacArthur, R. H. 1958. Population ecology of some warblers of northeastern coniferous forests. Ecology 39:599–619.

MacClintock, L., B. L. Whitcomb, and R. G. Whitcomb. 1977. Evidence for the value of corridors and minimization of isolation in preservation of biotic diversity. Am. Birds 31:6–12.

MacIver, L. 1990. Population dynamics, breeding ecology, and management of Piping Plovers on outer Cape Cod, Massachusetts. M.S. thesis, Univ. Mass., Amherst.

MacNally, R. C., and R. E. Lemon. 1985. Repeat and serial singing modes in American Redstarts (Setophaga ruticilla): a test of functional hypotheses. Zeitschrift Tierpsychologie 69:191–202.

MacQueen, P. M. 1950. Territory and song in the Least Flycatcher. Wilson Bull. 62:194–205.

Madson, J. 1978. The Mourning Dove. Conserv. Dept., Winchester Group, Olin Corp. Winchester Press, East Alton, Ill.

Mallett, Sandy. 1978. A year with New England's birds. N.H. Publishing, Somersworth.

Marble, R. M. 1907. List of birds found within a radius of one mile from the Crawford House, New Hampshire, July, August and September during the past 5 years. Crawford House (Priv. printed).

Marble, R. M. 1926. Nesting of Evening Grosbeak at Woodstock, Vermont. Auk 43:549.

Marchand, P. J. 1987. North Woods. Appalachian Mountain Club, Boston.

Marshall, J. R., Jr. 1967. Parallel variation in North and Middle American screech-owls. Monogr. West. Found. Vert. Zool. 1:1–72.

Martin, A. C., H. S. Zim, and A. L. Nelson. 1951. American wildlife and plants: a guide to wildlife food habits. McGraw-Hill, New York. Reprinted 1961, Dover Publ., New York.

Martin, A. C., H. S. Zim, and A. L. Nelson. 1961. American wildlife and plants: a guide to wildlife food habits. Dover Publ., New York.

Maslowski, K. 1983. The Blue-Gray Gnatcatcher: sure sign of spring. Bird Watchers Digest 5(4):28–29.

Matray, P. F. 1974. Broad-winged Hawk nesting and ecology. Auk 91:307–324.

Maxwell, G. R., II, and S. P. Putnam. 1972. Incubation, care of young, and nest success of the Common Grackle in northern Ohio. Auk 89:349–359.

Maxwell, G. R., II, J. M. Nocilly, and R. I. Shearer. 1976. Observations at a cavity nest of the Common Grackle and an analysis of grackle nest sites. Wilson Bull. 88:505–507.

May, J. B. 1929. Rough-winged Swallow, pp. 161–164. In E. H. Forbush, Birds of Massachusetts and other New England states. Vol. III. Mass. Dept. Agric., Boston.

Maynard, C. J. 1871. A catalogue of the birds of Coos County, New Hampshire, and Oxford County, Maine. Proc. Boston Soc. Nat. Hist. 14:357–395.

McAllister, N. M., and R. W. Storer. 1963. Copulation in the Pied-billed Grebe. Wilson Bull. 75:166–173.

McAtee, W. L. 1911. Woodpeckers in relation to trees and wood products. USDA Biol. Survey Bull. 39:1–99.

McCollough, M. A. 1989. Molting sequence and aging of Bald Eagles. Wilson Bull. 101:1–10.

McConnell, J. 1981. Distraction display of Chestnut-sided Warbler. Chat 45(4):103.

McDade, H. C. 1963. Notes on the Northern Raven. N.H. Audubon Quar. 16:117–118.

McGarigal, K., and J. D. Fraser. 1984. The effect of forest stand age on owl distribution in southwestern Virginia. J. Wildl. Manage. 48:1393–1398.

McGill, P. A. 1977. Breeding ecology and competition between Great Black-backed and Herring gulls. Cornell Univ. Press, Ithaca, N.Y.

McIntyre, J. W. 1988. The Common Loon, spirit of northern lakes. Univ. Minn. Press, Minneapolis.

McLaren, M. A. 1975. Breeding biology of the Boreal Chickadee. Wilson Bull. 87:344–354.

McLean, I. G., J. N. M. Smith, and K. G. Stewart. 1986. Mobbing behavior, nest exposure and breeding success in the American Robin (Turdus migratorius). Behaviour 96:171–186.

McNair, D. B., and R. A. Forster. 1983. Heterospecific vocal mimicry by six oscines. Can. Field-Nat. 97:321–322.

Mendall, H. L. 1937. Nesting of the Bay-Breasted Warbler. Auk 54:429–439.

Mendall, H. L. 1958. The Ring-necked Duck in the northeast. Univ. of Maine Bull. 60(16).

Meng, H. K. 1951. Food habits of nesting Cooper's Hawks and Goshawks in New York and Pennsylvania. Wilson Bull. 79:169–174.

Merriam, H. F. 1917. Nesting of the Cape May Warbler at Lake Edward, Quebec. Auk 34:410–413.

Merriam, T. L. 1983. Food habits of nestling Seaside Sparrows in unaltered and ditched salt marshes on Long Island, New York, pp. 115–122. In The Seaside Sparrow, its biology and management. N.C. Biol. Surv. and N.C. State Mus., Raleigh.

Merriam, C. H., and W. E. Barrows. 1889. The English Sparrow in North America, especially in its relations to agriculture. USDA Bull. 1. Washington, D.C.

Messineo, D. J. 1985. The 1985 nesting of Pine Siskin, Red Crossbill, and White-winged Crossbill in Chenango Country, New York. Kingbird 35:233–237.

Meyerriecks, A. J. 1960. The comparative breeding behaviour of four species of North American herons. Nuttall Ornithol. Club Publ. 2. Cambridge, Mass.

Milburn, T. 1981. Status and distribution of the Loggerhead Shrike, Lanius ludovicianus, in the northeastern United States. Off. Endangered Species, USDI Fish and Wildl. Serv., Washington, D.C.

Miller, D. E., and M. R. Conover. 1983. Chick vocal patterns and non-vocal stimulation as factors instigating parental feeding behavior in the Ring-billed Gull. Anim. Behav. 31:145–151.

Miller, J. R., and J. T. Miller. 1948. Nesting of the Spotted Sandpiper at Detroit, Michigan. Auk 65:558–567.

Minot, H. D. 1875. Nesting of the Prairie Warbler in New Hampshire. Am. Nat. 9:520.

Minot, H. D. 1876. The summer birds of the White Mountain region. Am. Nat. 10:75–80.

Minot, H. D. 1895. The land-birds and game-birds of New England. Riverside Press, Cambridge, Mass.

Morris, M. M. J., and R. E. Lemon. 1988. American Redstart nest placement in southwestern New Brunswick. Can. J. Zool. 66:212–216.

Morrison, L. 1883. History of Windham, New Hampshire. Cupples-Upham and Co., Boston.

Morse, D. H. 1967a. The contexts of songs in Black-throated Green and Blackburnian warblers. Wilson Bull. 79:64–74.

Morse, D. H. 1967b. Competitive relationships between Parula Warblers and other species during the breeding season. Auk 84:490–502.

Morse, D. H. 1968. A quantitative study of foraging of male and female spruce-woods warblers. Ecology 49:779–784.

Morse, D. H. 1971. Effects of the arrival of a new species upon habitat utilization by two forest thrushes in

Maine. Wilson Bull. 83:57–65.

Morse, D. H. 1972. Habitat differences of Swainson's and Hermit thrushes. Wilson Bull. 84:206–208.

Morse, D. H. 1976. Variables affecting the density and territory size of breeding spruce-woods warblers. Ecology 57:290–301.

Morse, D. H. 1978. Populations of Bay-Breasted and Cape May warblers during an outbreak of the spruce budworm. Wilson Bull. 90:404–413.

Morse, D. H. 1979. Habitat use by the Blackpoll Warbler. Wilson Bull. 91:234–243.

Morse, D. H. 1989. American warblers: an ecological and behavioral perspective. Harvard Univ. Press, Cambridge.

Mosher, J. A., and C. Henny. 1976. Thermal adaptiveness of plumage color in screech-owls. Auk 93:614–19.

Mountjoy, D. J., and R. J. Robertson. 1988. Nest construction tactics in the Cedar Waxwing. Wilson Bull. 100:128–130.

Mousley, H. 1934a. A study of the home life of the Northern Crested Flycatcher (Myiarchus crinitus boreus). Auk 51:207–216.

Mousley, H. 1934b. A study of the home life of the Short-billed Marsh Wren (Cistothorus stellaris). Auk 51:439–445.

Mueller, H. C., D. D. Bergen, and G. Allez. 1979. The identification of North American accipiters. Am. Birds 33:236–240.

Murray, B. G., Jr., and F. B. Gill. 1976. Behavioral interactions of Blue-winged and Golden-winged warblers. Wilson Bull. 88:231–254.

Myers, G. R., and D. W. Waller. 1977. Helpers at the nest in Barn Swallows. Auk 94:596.

Nelson, B. 1979. Seabirds, their biology and ecology. A & W Publ., New York.

Nelson, B., and K. Titus. 1989. Silviculture practices and raptor habitat associations in the northeast. Proc. Northeast Raptor Manage. Symposium and Workshop. Natl. Wildl. Fed. Scien. and Tech. Ser. 13.

Nero, R. W. 1951. Notes on nesting of the Least Bittern. Pass. Pigeon 13:5–8.

Nero, R. W. 1984. Redwings. Smithsonian Inst. Press, Washington, D.C.

Nettleship, D. N., and T. R. Birkhead. 1985. The Atlantic Alcidae. Academic Press, New York.

Nevers, H. P. 1968. Waterfowl utilization of beaver impoundments in southeastern New Hampshire, pp. 105–120. In 25th Trans. Northeast Sect. Wildl. Soc.

Newton, I. 1973. Finches. Taplinger Publ., New York.

Newton, I. 1979. Population ecology of raptors. Buteo Books, Vermillion, S.D.

National Geographic Society. 1983. Field guide to the birds of North America. Natl. Geogr. Soc., Washington, D.C.

NHFG. 1975. Federal aid performance report, Proj. W-75-R. N.H. Fish and Game Dept., Concord.

NHFG. 1985. Bad news for black duck and woodcock. Field Notes 37(3).

NHFG. 1989a. Estimated bags of waterfowl in New Hampshire 1980–89. N.H. Fish and Game Dept., Concord.

NHFG. 1989b. Use of nest boxes by Hooded Mergansers and Wood Ducks in New Hampshire 1980–89. N.H. Fish and Game Dept., Concord.

N.H. Nature Camp. 1938. A list of the birds recorded by the New Hampshire Nature Camp. Soc. Protection N.H. For., Concord.

Nice, M. M. 1930. A study of a nesting of Black-throated Blue Warblers. Auk 47:338–345.

Nice, M. M. 1937. Studies in the life history of the Song Sparrow. Pt. 1. Trans. Linnean Soc. N.Y. 4:1–247. Reprinted 1964, Dover Publ., New York.

Nice, M. M. 1943. Studies in the life history of the Song Sparrow. Pt. 2. Trans. Linnean Soc. N.Y. 6.

Reprinted 1964, Dover Publ., New York.

Nichols, T. H., and D. W. Warner. 1972. Barred Owl habitat use as determined by radiotelemetry. J. Wildl. Manage. 36:213–224.

Nickell, W. P. 1943. Observations on the nesting of the Killdeer. Wilson Bull. 55:23–28.

Nickell, W. P. 1951. Studies of habitats, territory, and nests of the Eastern Goldfinch. Auk 68:447–470.

Nickell, W. P. 1965. Habitats, territory, and nesting of the catbird. Am. Midl. Nat. 73:433–478.

Nisbet, I. C. T. 1989. Status and biology of the northeastern population of the Roseate Tern (Sterna dougalli): a literature survey and update: 1981–1989. Unpubl. rep. to the U.S. Fish and Wildl. Serv., Newton Corner, Mass.

Nisbet, I. C. T., and M. J. Welton. 1984. Seasonal variations in breeding success of Common Terns: consequences of predation. Condor 86:53–60.

Nolan, V. 1968. Eastern Song Sparrow, pp. 1492–1512. In A. C. Bent, Life histories of North American cardinals, grosbeaks, buntings, towhees, finches, sparrows and allies, pt. 3. O. L. Austin, [ed.]. U.S. Natl. Mus. Bull. 237. Washington, D.C.

Nolan, V., Jr. 1978. The ecology and behavior of the Prairie Warbler Dendroica discolor. Ornithol. Monogr. 26.

Nolan, V., Jr., and E. D. Ketterson. 1990. Timing of autumn migration and its relation to winter distribution of Dark-eyed Juncos. Ecology 71:1267–1278.

Nol, E., and H. Blokpoel. 1983. Incubation period of Ring-billed Gull and the egg immersion technique. Wilson Bull. 95:283–286.

Noon, B. R. 1981. The distribution of an avian guild along a temperate elevational gradient: the importance and expression of competition. Ecol. Monogr. 51:105–124.

Noon, J. 1990. The Squam lakes and their loons. Loon Preservation Committee, Meredith, N.H.

Norton, A. H., and R. P. Allen. 1931. Breeding of the Great Black-backed Gull and Double-crested Cormorant in Maine. Auk 48:589–592.

Nuttall, T. 1903. A popular handbook of the birds of the United States and Canada. Rev. and annot. by M. Chamberlin. Little, Brown, Boston.

Odum, E. P. 1941. Annual cycle of the Black-capped Chickadee - 1,2. Auk 58:314–333, 518–535.

Odum, E. P. 1942. Annual cycle of the Black-capped Chickadee - 3. Auk 59:499–531.

Odum, R. R. 1977. Sora, pp. 57–65. In G.C. Sanderson [ed.], Management of migratory shore and upland game birds in North America. Internat. Assoc. Fish and Wildl. Agencies, Washington, D.C.

Ogden, J. C., [ed.]. 1977. Transactions of the North American Osprey research conference, College of William and Mary, Williamsburg, Virginia, 10–12 February 1972. USDI Natl. Park Serv., Trans. and Proc. Ser. 2.

Oliver, D. L. 1902. The catbird wintering at Concord, New Hampshire. Auk 19:208–209.

Orians, G. H. 1980. Some adaptations of marsh-nesting blackbirds. Princeton Univ. Press, Princeton, N.J.

Orians, G. H., and F. Kuhlman. 1956. Red-tailed Hawk and Horned Owl populations in Wisconsin. Condor 58:371–385.

Oring, L. W., and M. L. Knudsen. 1972. Monogamy and polyandry in the Spotted Sandpiper. Living Bird 11:59–73.

Oring, L. W., and D. B. Lank. 1982. Sexual selection arrival times, philopatry, and site fidelity in the polyandrous Spotted Sandpiper. Behav. Ecol. and Sociobiol. 10:185–191.

Ouellet, H. 1967. The distribution of the Cerulean Warbler in the province of Quebec, Canada. Auk 84:272–274.

Ouellet, H. 1970. Further observations on the food and

predatory habits of the Gray Jay. Can. J. Zool. 48:327–330.

Ouellet, H. 1991. Is Bicknell's Thrush a Gray-cheeked Thrush? Ann. meeting of Am. Ornithol. Union, Montreal. Abstract 15.

Overtree, L., D. Evans, and C. R. Foss. 1989. 1989 Upland Sandpiper project: final report. Prep. for Audubon Soc. of N.H., Concord.

Owen, D. F. 1963. Polymorphism in the screech-owl in eastern North America. Wilson Bull. 75: 183–190.

Owen, R. B., Jr., J. M. Anderson, J. W. Artmann, E. R. Clark, J. G. Oilworth, L. E. Gregg, F. W. Martin, J. O. Newsom, and S. R. Pursglove. 1977. American Woodcock, pp. 149–186. In G. C. Sanderson, [ed.], Management of migratory shore and upland game birds in North America. Internat. Assoc. of Fish and Wildl. Agencies, Washington, D.C.

Palmer, R. S. 1949. Maine birds. Bull. Mus. Comp. Zool. 102. Harvard Coll., Cambridge.

Palmer, R. S., [ed.]. 1962. Handbook of North American birds. Vol. 1: loons through flamingos. Yale Univ. Press, New Haven.

Palmer, R. S. 1968. Pine Siskin, pp. 424–447. In A. C. Bent, Life histories of North American Cardinals, Grosbeaks, Buntings, Towhees, Finches, Sparrows, and Allies, pt. 1. O. L. Austin, Jr., [ed.]. U.S. Natl. Mus. Bull. 237. Washington, D.C.

Palmer, R. S., [ed.]. 1976. Handbook of North American birds. Vols. 2 and 3. Yale Univ. Press, New Haven.

Palmer, R. S. 1988. Handbook of North American birds. Vol. 4: duirnal raptors. Pt. II. Yale Univ. Press, New Haven.

Palmer, R. S., and W. Taber. 1946. Birds of the Mt. Katahdin region of Maine. Auk 63:299–314.

Parker, H. W. 1976. Summary - winter season 1975–76. N.H. Audubon Quar. 29:59–64.

Parnell, J. F., and R. F. Soots. 1975. Herring and Great Black-backed gulls nesting in North Carolina. Auk 92:154–157.

Paszkowski, C. A. 1984. Macrohabitat use, microhabitat use, and foraging behavior of the Hermit Thrush and Veery in a northern Wisconsin forest. Wilson Bull. 96:286–292.

Payne, R. S. 1962. How the Barn Owl locates prey by hearing. Living Bird 1:150–159.

Pearson, T. G. 1936. Birds of America. Doubleday, Doran, Garden City, N.Y.

Peck, G. K., and R. D. James. 1987. Breeding birds of Ontario: nidology and distribution. Vol 2: Passerines. Life Scien. Misc. Publ. Royal Ontario Museum, Ont.

Peters, J. L. 1953. Northern American Redstart, pp. 681–689. In A. C. Bent, Life histories of North American wood warblers. U.S. Natl. Mus. Bull. 203. Washington, D.C.

Petersen, A. J. 1955. The breeding cycle of the Bank Swallow. Wilson Bull. 67:235–86.

Petersen, L. R. 1979. Ecology of Great Horned Owls and Red-tailed Hawks in southeastern Wisconsin. Wisc. Dept. Nat. Resour. Tech. Bull. 111. Madison.

Petersen, A., and H. Young. 1950. A nesting study of the Bronzed Grackle. Auk 67:466–475.

Peterson, R. T. 1947. A field guide to the birds east of the Rockies. 2nd ed. Houghton Mifflin, Boston.

Peterson, R. T. 1980. A field guide to the birds east of the 'Rockies. 4th ed. Houghton Mifflin, Boston.

Pettingill, O. S., Jr. 1936. The American Woodcock. Mem. Boston Soc. Nat. Hist. 9:169–391.

Pettingill, O. S. 1958. Ring-billed Gulls hawking may-flies. Jack-Pine Warbler 36:154.

Phillips, J. C. 1922. A natural history of ducks. Vol. 2. Houghton Mifflin, Boston.

Phinney, E. W. 1968. Spring migration 1968. N.H. Audubon Quar. 21:107–116.

Phinney, E. W. 1972. Spring migration, March 1 – May 31, 1972. N.H. Audubon Quar. 25:105–120.

Pickwell, G. 1925. The nesting of the Killdeer. Auk 42:485–496.

Pitelka, F. A. 1940. Breeding behavior of the Black-throated Green Warbler. Wilson Bull. 52:3–18.

Platt, J. B. 1976. Sharp-shinned Hawk nesting and nest site selection in Utah. Condor 78:102–103.

Poole, A. F. 1989. Ospreys: a natural and unnatural history. Cambridge Univ. Press, Cambridge.

Porter, H. E. 1903. A list of birds seen in Franconia, New Hampshire, and vicinity during August and September, 1903. Wilson Bull. 2:107–110.

Porter, E. H., and H. E. Porter. 1904. 'Kearsarge' birds. Wilson Bull. 11:97–100.

Portnoy, J. W., and W. E. Dodge. 1979. Red-shouldered Hawk nesting ecology and behavior. Wilson Bull. 91:104–17.

Pospichal, L. B. 1952. A field study of Sora Rail (Porzana carolina) and Virginia Rail (Rallus limicola) populations in central Minnesota. M.S. thesis, Univ. Minn.

Post, W., and J. S. Greenlaw. 1975. Seaside Sparrow displays: their function in social organization and habitat. Auk 92:461–492.

Potter, E. F. 1980. Notes on nesting Yellow-billed Cuckoos. J. Field Ornithol. 17–29.

Potter, J. K., and J. A. Gillespie. 1925. Observations on the domestic behavior of the Barn Owl Tyto pratincola. Auk 42:177–192.

Pough, R. H. 1946. Audubon bird guides: small land birds of east and central North America from southern Texas to central Greenland. Doubleday, Garden City, N.Y.

Pough, R. H. 1949. Audubon bird guide: eastern land birds. Doubleday, Garden City, N.Y.

Pough, R. H. 1951. Audubon water bird guide. Doubleday, Garden City, N.Y.

Putnam, L. S. 1949. The life history of the Cedar Waxwing. Wilson Bull. 61:141–182.

Quinn, R. A. 1981. Seasonal bird records: summer report 1980. N.H. Audubon 17(1):6–10.

Quinn, R. A. 1982. Seasonal bird nesting records, summer 1981. N.H. Audubon 18(1):8–10.

Rappole, J. H., and D. W. Warner. 1980. Ecological aspects of migrant bird behavior in Veracruz, Mexico. In A. Keast and E. S. Morton, [eds.], Migrant birds in the Neotropics: ecology, behavior, distribution, and conservation. Smithsonian Inst. Press, Washington, D.C.

Rappole, J. H., E. S. Morton, T. E. Lovejoy, and J. L. Ruos. 1983. Nearctic avian migrants in the Neotropics. USDI Fish and Wildl. Serv., Washington, D.C.

Reed, C. A. 1965. North American bird eggs. Dover Publ., New York.

Reilly, E. M., Jr., [ed.]. 1979. The warblers of North America. Doubleday, Garden City, N.Y. Rev. ed.

Reinert, S., and F. Golet. 1979. Breeding ecology of the Swamp Sparrow in a southern Rhode Island peatland. Trans. Northeast Sect. Wildl. Soc. 36:1–13.

Reusch, C., and N. Shambaugh. 1977. Courtship behavior and range extension of the Glossy Ibis (Plegadis falcinellus) and the Snowy Egret (Egretta thula) on the eastern seaboard of the United States. Unpubl. res., Univ. N.H., Durham.

Reynolds, R. T., and H. M. Wight. 1978. Distribution, density, and productivity of Accipiter hawks breeding in Oregon. Wilson Bull. 90:182–196.

Rice, J. 1978a. Behavioral interactions of interspecifically territorial vireos: I. Song discrimination and natural interactions. Anim. Behav. 26:527–549.

Rice, J. 1978b. Ecological relationships of two interspecifically territorial vireos. Ecology 59:526–538.

Richards, T. 1950. Bird records from members. Audubon Soc. N.H. Newsl. 3(2):9–16.

Richards, T. 1951. Odd birds at odd places and odd times. N.H. Bird News 4(1):19.

Richards, T. 1952. The waterfowl of New Hampshire: their history and present status. M.S. thesis, Univ. Mich., Ann Arbor.

Richards, T. 1954. Our changing bird life. N.H. Bird News 7(1):3–16.

Richards, T. 1956. Our changing bird life — concluding part II, 1900–1955. N.H. Bird News 9(2):34–38.

Richards, T. 1958. A list of the birds of New Hampshire. Audubon Soc. N.H., Concord.

Richards, T. 1967. Birds of the White Mountain region. In Natural history of the White Mountains. Audubon Soc. N.H., Concord.

Richards, T. 1980. A brief history of New Hampshire's coastal bird life, pp. 13–21. In N.H. Audubon Ann., Concord.

Ridgely, B. S. 1977. Birds of the Squam Lakes region. Squam Lakes Assoc., Plymouth, N.H.

Ridgely, B. S. 1988. Birds of the Squam Lakes region. 2nd ed. Squam Lakes Assoc., Holderness, N.H.

Ripley, S. D. 1977. Rails of the world. David R. Godine, Boston.

Robbins, C. A. 1919. A colony of Cape Cod Piping Plovers. Auk 36:351–355.

Robbins, C. S. 1950. Ecological distribution of the breeding Parulidae of Maryland. M.S. thesis, Geo. Wash. Univ., Washington, D.C.

Robbins, C. S., B. Bruun, and H. S. Zim. 1966. Birds of North America: a guide to field identification. Golden Press, New York.

Robbins, C. S., B. Bruun, and H. S. Zim. 1983. Birds of North America: a guide to field identification. Rev. ed. Golden Press, New York.

Robbins, C. S., D. Bystrak, and P. H. Geissler. 1986. The breeding bird survey: its first fifteen years, 1965–1979. USDI Fish and Wildl. Serv. Resour. Publ. 157.

Robbins, C. S., J. R. Saver, R. S. Greenberg, and S. Droege. 1989. Population declines in North American birds that migrate to the Neotropics. Proc. Natl. Acad. Scien. USA 86:7658–7662.

Robbins, C. S., J. W. Fitzpatrick, and P. B. Hamel. 1992. A warbler in trouble: Dendroica cerulea, pp. 549–562. In J. M. Hagan III and D. W. Johnston, [eds.]. Ecology and conservation of Neotropical migrant landbirds. Smithsonian Inst. Press, Washington, D.C.

Roberts, T. S. 1932. The birds of Minnesota. 2 vols. Univ. Minn. Press, Minneapolis.

Roberts, A. 1963. Breeding bird census of two pine forests with special reference to the Pine Warbler. Oriole 28:63–71.

Robertson, R. J. 1973. Optimal niche space of the Red-winged Blackbird: 3. Growth rate and food of nestlings in marsh and upland habitat. Wilson Bull. 85:209–22.

Robins, J. D. 1971. A study of Henslow's Sparrow in Michigan. Wilson Bull. 83:39–48.

Robinson, S. K., and R. T. Holmes. 1982. Foraging behavior of forest birds: the relationships among search tactics, diet, and habitat structure. Ecology 63:1918–1931.

Robinson, S. K., and R. T. Holmes. 1984. Effects of plant species and foliage structure on the foraging behavior of forest birds. Auk 101:672–684.

Robinson, W. L., and D. E. Maxwell. 1968. Ecological study of the Spruce Grouse on the Yellow Dog Plains. Jack-Pine Warbler 46:75–83.

Roest, A. I. 1957. Notes on the American Sparrow Hawk. Auk 74:1–19.

Rohwer, S., and J. Manning. 1990. Differences in timing and number of molts for Baltimore and Bullock's orioles: Implications to hybrid fitness and theories of delayed plumage maturation. Condor 92:125–140.

Root, R. B. 1969. The behavior and reproductive success of the Blue-gray Gnatcatcher. Condor 71:16–31.

Root, T. 1988. Atlas of wintering North American birds, an analysis of Christmas Bird Count data. Univ. Chicago Press, Chicago.

Roth, J. L. 1977. Breeding biology of the Nashville Warbler in northern Michigan. Jack-Pine Warbler 55:129–141.

Ruge, K. 1971. Zur biologie des Dreizehnspechtes Picoides tridactylus. L. Ornithol. Beob. 68:256–271.

Ruge, K. 1975. Die lautausserungen adulter Dreizehnspechte Picoides tridactylus und ihre bedeutung beider beurteilung der systematischer stellung von Picoides. Ornithol. Beob. 72:75–82.

Ryden, H. 1979. God's Dog. Penguin Books, New York.

Sabo, S. R. 1980. Niche and habitat relations in subalpine bird communities of the White Mountains of New Hampshire. Ecol. Monogr. 50:241–259.

Sage, J. H., L. Bennett, and W. P. Bliss. 1913. The birds of Connecticut. Bull. Conn. Geolog. and Nat. Hist. Survey 20(1):1–370.

Samuel, D. E. 1971. The breeding biology of Barn and Cliff swallows in West Virginia. Wilson Bull. 83:284–301.

Samuels, E. A. 1865. Oology of some of the land birds of New England, pp. 386–429. In Rep. of Commissioner Agric. for the year 1864. Gov. Printing Off., Washington, D.C.

Samuels, E. A. 1867. Ornithology and oology of New England: containing full descriptions of the birds of New England and adjacent states and provinces. Nichols and Noyes, Boston.

Samuels, E. A. 1870. The birds of New England. Noyes, Holmes, and Co., Boston.

Samuels, E. A. 1883. Birds of New England and adjacent states. Lockwood, Brooks, and Co., Boston.

Saunders, A. A. 1935. A guide to bird songs. D. Appleton-Century, New York.

Savard, J. P., and J. B. Falls. 1987. Influence of habitat on the nesting height of birds in urban areas. Can. J. Zool. 59:924–932.

Sawyer, D. 1947. Nesting of Chestnut-sided Warbler. Auk 64:136–137.

Scharf, W. C. 1981. The significance of deteriorating man-made island habitats to Common Terns and Ring-billed Gulls in the St. Mary's River, Michigan. Colonial Waterbirds 4:155–159.

Scharf, W. C., and E. Balfour. 1971. Growth and development of nestling hen harriers. Ibis 113:323–329.

Schorger, A. W. 1952. Introduction of the domestic pigeon. Auk 69:462–463.

Schroeder, R. L. 1983. Habitat suitability index models: Downy Woodpecker. USDI Fish and Wildl. Serv. FWS/OBS–82/10.38.

Scott, C. F. 1921. Notes on land birds of southern New Hampshire. M.S. thesis, Univ. N.H., Durham.

Scott, T. G. 1938. Some Saw-whet Owls in central Iowa. Wilson Bull. 50:239–242.

Sealy, S. G. 1967. Notes on the breeding biology of the Marsh Hawk in Alberta and Saskatchewan. Blue Jay 25:63–69.

Sealy, S. G. 1980. Breeding biology of Orchard Orioles in a new population in Manitoba. Can. Field-Nat. 94:154–158.

Secunda, R. C., and T. W. Sherry. 1991. Polyterritorial polygyny in the American Redstart. Wilson Bull. 103:190–203.

Selleck, G. H. 1902. Nighthawk notes. Bird-Lore 4:114.

Serrentino, P. 1987. The breeding behavior and ecology of the Northern Harrier in New Hampshire. M.S. thesis, Univ. R.I., Kingston.

Seutin, G. 1991. The Grey-cheeked Thrush: one species or two? An analysis of mtDNA. Ann. meeting, Am. Ornithol. Union, Montreal. Abstract 14.

Shedd, D. H. 1982. Seasonal variation and function of mobbing and related anti-predator behaviors of the American Robin (Turdus migratorius). Auk 99:342–346.

Shedd, D. H. 1985. A propensity to mob. Living Bird Quar. 4(4):8–11.

Sheldon, W. G. 1967. The book of the American Woodcock. Univ. Mass. Press, Amherst.

Shelley, L. O. 1925. A sandpiper's wooing. Bird-Lore 27:107.

Shelley, L. O. 1932. Gulling along the New Hampshire coast. Bull. Audubon Soc. N.H. 11:23–25.

Shelley, L. O. 1933. Blue-winged Teal breeding in Cheshire County, New Hampshire. Auk 50:354–355.

Sherman, M. S. 1889. Birds of Grafton County, New Hampshire. Oologist 6:74.

Sherrod, S. K. 1978. Diets of North American Falconiformes. Raptor Res. 12:49–121.

Sherrod, S. K. 1983. Behavior of fledgling peregrines. Pioneer Impressions, Ft. Collins, Colo.

Sherry, T. W. 1979. Competitive interactions and adaptive strategies of American Redstarts and Least Flycatchers in a northern hardwood forest. Auk 96:265–283.

Sherry, T. W. 1985. Adaptation to a novel environment: food, foraging, and morphology of the Cocos Island Flycatcher, pp. 908–920. In P. A. Buckley, M. S. Foster, E. S. Morton, R. S. Ridgely, and F. G. Buckley, [eds.], Neotropical ornithology. Ornithol. Monogr. 36. Am. Ornithol. Union, Washington, D.C.

Sherry, T. W., and R. T. Holmes. 1985. Dispersion and habitat responses of birds in northern hardwood forests. In M. Cody, [ed.], Habitat selection in birds. Academic Press, New York.

Sherry, T. W., and R. T. Holmes. 1988. Habitat selection by breeding American Redstarts in response to a dominant competitor, the Least Flycatcher. Auk 105:350–364.

Sherry, T. W., and R. T. Holmes. 1992. Population fluctuations in a long-distance Neotropical migrant: demographic evidence for the importance of breeding season events in the American Redstart, pp. 431–442. In J. M. Hagan III and D. W. Johnston, [eds.], Ecology and conservation of neotropical migrant landbirds. Smithsonian Inst. Press, Washington, D.C.

Shields, W. M. 1984. Factors affecting nest and site fidelity in Adirondack Barn Swallows. Auk 101:780–789.

Shigo, A. L., and L. Kilham. 1968. Sapsuckers and Fomes igniarius var. populinus. USDA For. Serv. Res. Note NE 84. NE For. Exp. Station, Upper Darby, Pa.

Short, L. L., Jr. 1964. Extra helpers feeding young of Blue-winged and Golden-winged warblers. Auk 81:428–430.

Short, L. L. 1974. Habits and interactions of North American Three-toed Woodpeckers (Picoides arcticus) and (Picoides tridactylus). Am. Mus. Novit. 2547:1–42.

Siegler, H. R. 1949. The Ring-necked Pheasant in New Hampshire. N.H. Fish and Game Dept., Concord.

Silver, H. 1957. A history of New Hampshire game and furbearers. N.H. Fish and Game Dept., Survey Rep. 6. Concord.

Skutch, A. F. 1945. Incubation and nestling periods of Central American birds. Auk 62:8–37.

Skutch, A. F. 1976. Parent birds and their young. Univ. Texas Press, Austin.

Skutch, A. F. 1979. Parent birds and their young. Univ. Texas Press, Austin. 2nd printing.

Smart, R. 1970. 1969 fall migration. N.H. Audubon Quar. 23:27–37.

Smith, R. L. 1959. The songs of the Grasshopper Sparrow. Wilson Bull. 71:143–151.

Smith, R. L. 1968. Grasshopper Sparrow, pp. 725–745. In A. C. Bent, Life histories of North American cardinals, grosbeaks, buntings, towhees, finches, sparrows and allies, pt. 2. O. L. Austin, Jr., [ed.]. U.S. Natl. Mus. Bull. 237. Washington, D.C.

Smith, S. M. 1973. An aggressive display and related behavior in the Loggerhead Shrike. Auk 90:287–298.

Smith, C. F. 1979. Proceedings of the endangered species conference. USDI Fish and Wildl. Serv., Newton Corner, Mass.

Smith, C. F. 1980. Owls in New Hampshire: an historical perspective. N.H. Audubon Ann.: 27–35.

Smith, C. F., and R. Choate, [eds.]. 1985. Proposed revision of New Hampshire list of threatened and endangered species: documentation for revision and comments. USDI Fish and Wildl. Serv., Newton Corner, Mass.

Smith, D. G., A. Devine, and D. Walsh. 1987. Censusing Screech-Owls in southern Connecticut, pp. 255–267. In R. W. Nero, R. J. Clark, R. J. Knapton, and R. H. Hamre, [eds.], Biology and conservation of northern forest owls; symposium proceedings. USDA Forest Serv. Gen. Tech. Rep. RM-142.

Snyder, N. F., and J. W. Wiley. 1976. Sexual size dimorphism in hawks and owls of North America. Am. Ornithol. Union, Washington, D.C.

Snyder, N. F. R., H. A. Snyder, J. L. Lincer, and R. T. Reynolds. 1973. Organochlorines, heavy metals and the biology of North American Accipiters. Bio. Scien. 32:300–305.

Sorrie, B. 1975. Atlassing for Alder and Willow flycatchers. Breeding Bird Atlas Newsl. 3. Mass. Audubon Soc., Lincoln.

Southern, W. E. 1977. Colony selection and colony site tenacity in Ring-billed Gulls at a stable colony. Auk 94:469–478.

Southern, L. K. 1981. Sex-related differences in territorial aggression by Ring-billed Gulls. Auk 98:179–181.

Southern, W. E. 1988. Response to H. Blokpoel and G. D. Tessier. Auk 105:398.

Southern, L. K., and W. E. Southern. 1980. Philopatry in Ring-billed Gulls. Proc. Colonial Waterbird Group 3:27–32.

Speirs, J. M. 1940. Mortality of Barn Owls at Champaign, Illinois. Auk 57:571.

Speirs, D. H. 1968. Eastern Evening Grosbeak, pp. 206–237. In A. C. Bent, Life histories of North American cardinals, grosbeaks, towhees, finches, sparrows and allies, pt. 1. O. L. Austin, Jr., [ed.]. U.S. Natl. Mus. Bull. 237. Washington, D.C.

Speirs, J. M., and D. H. Speirs. 1968. Lincoln's Sparrow, pp. 1434–1467. In A. C. Bent, Life histories of North American cardinals, grosbeaks, buntings, towhees, finches, sparrows and allies, pt. 3. O. L. Austin, Jr., [ed.]. U.S. Natl. Mus. Bull. 237. Washington, D.C.

Speiser, R., and T. Bosakowski. 1988. Nest site preference of the Red-tailed Hawks in the highlands of southeastern New York and northern New Jersey. J. Field Ornithol. 59:361–368.

Spofford, W. R. 1971. The breeding status of the Golden Eagle in the Appalachians. Am. Birds 25:3–7.

Sprunt, A., Jr. 1950. Loggerhead Shrike, pp. 131–148. In A. C. Bent, Life histories of North American wagtails, shrikes, vireos and their allies. U.S. Natl. Mus. Bull. 197. Washington, D.C.

Stallcup, R. 1985. Yellowish warblers. Point Reyes Bird Observatory Newsl. 68.

Stanwood, C. J. 1913. The Olive-backed Thrush (Hylocichla ustulata swainsoni) at his summer home. Wilson Bull. 25:118–137.

Stein, R. C. 1958. The behavioral, ecological, and morphological characteristics of two flycatchers (Empidonax traillii). N.Y. State Mus. and Scien. Serv. Bull. 371:1–63.

Stein, R. C. 1963. Isolating mechanisms between populations of Traill's flycatchers. Proc. Am. Philosophical Soc. 107:21–50.

Stenger, J. 1958. Food habits and available food of Ovenbirds in relation to territory size. Auk 75:335–346.

Stenger, J., and J. B. Falls. 1959. The utilized territory of the Ovenbird. Wilson Bull. 71:125–140.

Stephenson, R. W. 1984. Unpubl. rep. on the Least Bittern in New Hampshire. N.H. Dept. Resour. and Econ. Dev., Nat. Heritage Inventory, Concord.

Stewart, P. A. 1952. Dispersal, breeding behavior, and longevity of banded Barn Owls in North America.

Auk 69:227–245.

Stewart, R. E. 1953. Life history of the Yellowthroat. Wilson Bull. 65:99–115.

Stewart, R. E., and C. S. Robbins. 1958. Birds of Maryland and the District of Columbia. North Am. Fauna 62. USDI Fish and Wildl. Serv., Washington, D.C.

Stiehl, R. B. 1985. Brood chronology of the Common Raven. Wilson Bull. 97:78–87.

Stoddard, H. L. 1931. The bobwhite quail, its habits, preservation and increase. C. Scribner's Sons, New York.

Stokes, A. W. 1950. Breeding behavior of the goldfinch. Wilson Bull. 62:107–127.

Stokes, D. W. 1979. A guide to the behavior of common birds. Little, Brown, Boston.

Stokes, D. W., and L. Q. Stokes. 1983. A guide to bird behavior. Vol 2. Little, Brown, Boston.

Stokes, D. W., and L. Q. Stokes. 1989. A guide to bird behavior. Vol. III. Little, Brown, Boston.

Stone, W. 1937. Bird studies at Old Cape May. Noyes, Holmes, and Co., Boston.

Stoner, D. 1936. Studies on the Bank Swallow, *Riparia riparia riparia* (Linnaeus), in the Oneida Lake region. Bull. N.Y. State Coll. For., Syracuse Univ. 9(2):120–233.

Storrs, C. H. 1911. The Evening Grosbeak in New Hampshire. Auk 28:267.

Stott, R. S., and D. P. Olson. 1974. Sea duck populations on the New Hampshire coastline. N.H. Agric. Exp. Station Res. Rep. 33. Durham.

Stout, G. D., [ed.]. 1967. The shorebirds of North America. Viking Press, New York.

Strohmeyer, D. L. 1977. Common Gallinule, pp. 110–117. In G. C. Sanderson, [ed.], Management of migratory shore and upland game birds. Internat. Assoc. Fish and Wildl. Agencies, Washington, D.C.

Stull, W. D. 1968. Eastern and Canadian Chipping Sparrows, pp. 1166–1184. In A. C. Bent, Life histories of North American cardinals, grosbeaks, buntings, towhees, finches, sparrows and allies, pt. 2. O. L. Austin, Jr., [ed.]. U.S. Natl. Mus. Bull. 237. Washington, D.C.

Sturm, L. 1945. A study of the nesting activities of the American Redstart. Auk 62:189–206.

Sutcliffe, S. 1980. Aspects of the nesting ecology of Common Loons in New Hampshire. M.S. thesis, Univ. N.H., Durham.

Sutherland, C. A. 1963. Notes on the behavior of Common Nighthawks in Florida. Living Bird 2:31–39.

Taber, W. 1950. The ravens and hawks of Katahdin and their behavior. Bull. Maine Audubon Soc. 6:3–8.

Taber, W. 1953. Fitzwilliam birds. N.H. Bird News 6(2):4–10.

Taber, W. 1955. The Isles of Shoals. Bull. Maine Audubon Soc. 11:58–66.

Taber, W. 1968. White-winged Crossbill, pp. 527–544. In A. C. Bent, Life histories of North American cardinals, grosbeaks, buntings, towhees, finches, sparrows and allies, pt. 1. O. L. Austin, Jr., [ed.]. U.S. Natl. Mus. Bull. 237. Washington, D.C.

Taber, W., and D. W. Johnston. 1968. Indigo Bunting, pp. 80–111. In A. C. Bent, Life histories of North American cardinals, grosbeaks, buntings, towhees, finches, sparrows and allies, pt. 1. O. L. Austin, Jr., [ed.]. U.S. Natl. Mus. Bull. 237. Washington, D.C.

Tate, J., Jr. 1970. Nesting and development of the Chestnut-sided Warbler. Jack-Pine Warbler 48:57–65.

Tate, J., Jr. 1981. The blue list for 1981: the first decade, a summary of the first ten years of the annual "early warning list" of declining, threatened, or vulnerable species. Am. Birds 35:3–10.

Tate, J., Jr. 1986. The blue list for 1986. Am. Birds 40:227–236.

Telfair, R. C., II. 1983. Atypically colored Little Blue Heron eggs. Wilson Bull. 95:481–482.

Terres, John K., [ed.]. 1980. The Audubon Society encyclopedia of North American birds. Alfred A. Knopf, New York.

Terrill, L. Mc I. 1931. Nesting of the Saw-whet Owl in the Montreal district. Auk 48:169–174.

Thayer, G. 1902. Some southern New Hampshire and western Massachusetts notes. Auk 19:294–297.

Thomas, G. E. 1989. Nesting ecology and survival of hen and poult eastern Wild Turkeys in southern New Hampshire. M.S. thesis, Univ. N.H., Durham.

Thomas, J. W., R. Anderson, C. Maser, and E. Bull. 1979. Wildlife habitats in managed forests—the Blue Mountains of Oregon and Washington. USDA Agric. Handbook 553.

Thoreau, H. D. 1910. Notes on New England birds. F. H. Allen, [ed.]. Houghton Mifflin, Boston.

Tinbergen, N. 1953. The Herring Gull's world. Collins, London.

Tingley, S. I. 1982. Northeastern maritime region. In "The Nesting Season." Am. Birds 36:954–956.

Titus, K., and M. R. Fuller. 1990. Recent trends in counts of migrant hawks from northeastern North America. J. Wildl. Manage. 54:463–470.

Titus, K., and J. A. Mosher. 1981. Nest-site habitat selected by woodland hawks in the Central Appalachians. Auk 98:270–281.

Titus, K., M. R. Fuller, D. F. Stauffer, and J. R. Sauer. 1989. Buteos, pp. 53–64. In Proc. Northeast Raptor Manage. Symposium and Workshop. Natl. Wildl. Fed., Washington, D.C.

Todd, W. E. C. 1940. Birds of western Pennsylvania. Univ. Pittsburgh Press, Pittsburg.

Toland, B. R. 1985. Nest site selection, productivity, and food habits of Northern Harriers in southwest Missouri. Nat. Areas J. 5:22–27.

Toland, B. R. 1987. The effect of vegetative cover on foraging strategies, hunting success and nesting distribution of American Kestrels in Central Missouri. J. Raptor Res. 21:14–20.

Torrey, B. 1885. Birds in the bush. Houghton Mifflin, Boston.

Torrey, B. 1890. June in Franconia. Atlantic Monthly 77:198–207.

Torrey, B. 1892. The foot-path way. Houghton Mifflin, Boston.

Torrey, B. 1900. May in Franconia. Atlantic Monthly 85:628–639.

Torrey, B. 1905. The Prairie Horned Lark on Mt. Washington. Auk 22:414–415.

Townsend, C. W. 1916. Wilson Bull. 28.

Townsend, C. W. 1920. Supplement to the birds of Essex County, Massachusetts. Mem. Nuttall Ornithol. Club. Cambridge, Mass.

Townsend, C. W. 1921. Arctic Tern, pp. 249–255. In A. C. Bent, Life histories of North American gulls and terns. U.S. Natl. Mus. Bull. 113. Washington, D.C.

Townsend, C. W. 1926. Virginia Rail, pp. 292–301. In A. C. Bent, Life histories of North American marsh birds. U.S. Natl. Mus. Bull. 135. Washington, D.C.

Townsend, C. W. 1929. Killdeer, pp. 202–217. In A. C. Bent, Life histories of North American shorebirds, pt. 2. U.S. Natl. Mus. Bull. 146. Washington, D.C.

Townsend, C. W. 1932. Passenger Pigeon, pp. 379–402. In A. C. Bent, Life histories of North American gallinaceous birds. U.S. Natl. Mus. Bull. 162. Washington, D.C.

Tufts, R. W. 1986. Birds of Nova Scotia. 3rd ed. Nova Scotia Mus., Halifax.

Tyler, W. M. 1929. Piping Plover, pp. 236–246. In A. C. Bent, Life histories of North American shore birds, pt. 2. U.S. Natl. Mus. Bull. 146. Washington, D.C.

Tyler, W. M. 1939. Northern Downy Woodpecker, pp. 52–68. In A. C. Bent, Life histories of North American woodpeckers. U.S. Natl. Mus. Bull. 174. Washington, D.C.

Tyler, W. M. 1940a. Chimney Swift, pp. 271–293. In A. C. Bent, Life histories of North American cuckoos, goatsuckers, hummingbirds and their allies, pt. 2. U.S. Natl. Mus. Bull. 176. Washington, D.C.

Tyler, W. M. 1940b. Ruby-throated Hummingbird, pp. 332–352. In A. C. Bent, Life histories of North American cuckoos, goatsuckers, hummingbirds and their allies. U.S. Natl. Mus. Bull. 176. Washington, D.C.

Tyler, W. M. 1942a. Eastern Kingbird, pp. 11–29. In A. C. Bent, Life histories of North American flycatchers, larks, swallows and their allies. U.S. Natl. Mus. Bull. 179. Washington, D.C.

Tyler, W. M. 1942b. Eastern Wood Pewee, pp. 266–279. In A. C. Bent, Life histories of North American flycatchers, larks, swallows and their allies. U.S. Natl. Mus. Bull. 179. Washington, D.C.

Tyler, W. M. 1942c. Eastern Phoebe, pp. 140–154. In A. C. Bent, Life histories of North American flycatchers, larks, swallows, and their allies. U.S. Natl. Mus. Bull. 179. Washington, D.C.

Tyler, W. M. 1942d. Tree Swallow, pp. 384–340. In A. C. Bent, Life histories of North American flycatchers, larks, swallows and their allies. U.S. Natl. Mus. Bull. 179. Washington, D.C.

Tyler, W. M. 1946. Northern Blue Jay, pp. 32–52. In A. C. Bent, Life histories of North American jays, crows, and titmice. U.S. Natl. Mus. Bull. 191. Washington, D.C.

Tyler, W. M. 1948a. Brown Creeper, p. 56–70. In A. C. Bent, Life histories of North American nuthatches, wrens, thrashers and their allies. U.S. Natl. Mus. Bull. 195. Washington, D.C.

Tyler, W. M. 1948b. Red-breasted Nuthatch, pp. 22–35. In A. C. Bent, Life histories of North American nuthatches, wrens, thrashers and their allies. U.S. Natl. Mus. Bull. 195. Washington, D.C.

Tyler, W. M. 1948c. White-breasted Nuthatch, pp. 1–12. In A. C. Bent, Life histories of North American nuthatches, wrens, thrashers and their allies. U.S. Natl. Mus. Bull. 195. Washington, D.C.

Tyler, W. M. 1950a. Eastern Warbling Vireo, pp. 362–373. In A. C. Bent, Life histories of North American wagtails, shrikes, vireos and their allies. U.S. Natl. Mus. Bull. 197. Washington, D.C.

Tyler, W. M. 1950b. Red-eyed Vireo, p. 335–348. In A. C. Bent, Life histories of North American wagtails, shrikes, vireos and their allies. U.S. Natl. Mus. Bull. 197. Washington, D.C.

Tyler, W. M. 1950c. Cedar Waxwing, pp. 79–102. In A. C. Bent, Life histories of North American wagtails, shrikes, vireos and their allies. U.S. Natl. Mus. Bull. 197. Washington, D.C.

Tyler, W. M. 1953a. Golden-winged Warbler, pp. 47–57. In A. C. Bent, Life histories of North American wood warblers. U.S. Natl. Mus. Bull. 203. Washington, D.C.

Tyler, W. M. 1953b. Wilson's Pileolated Warbler, pp. 626–639. In A. C. Bent, Life histories of North American wood warblers. U.S. Natl. Mus. Bull. 203. Washington, D.C.

Tyler, W. M. 1953c. Yellow Palm Warbler, pp. 450–456. In A. C. Bent, Life histories of North American wood warblers. U.S. Natl. Mus. Bull. 203. Washington, D.C.

Tyler, W. M. 1958a. Baltimore Oriole, p. 247–270. In A. C. Bent, Life histories of North American blackbirds, orioles, tanagers and their allies. U.S. Natl. Mus. Bull. 211. Washington, D.C.

Tyler, W. M. 1958b. Scarlet Tanager, pp. 479–491. In A. C. Bent, Life histories of North American blackbirds, orioles, tanagers and their allies. U.S. Natl. Mus. Bull. 211. Washington, D.C.

Tyler, W. M. 1968. Eastern American Goldfinch, pp. 447–466. In A. C. Bent, Life histories of North American cardinals, grosbeaks, buntings, finches, sparrows and allies, pt. 1. O. L. Austin, Jr., [ed.]. U.S. Natl. Mus. Bull. 237. Washington, D.C.

Tyrell, E. Q. 1984. Hummingbirds: their life and

behavior. Crown Publishers, New York.

Urner, C. A. 1925. Notes on two ground-nesting birds of prey. Auk 42:31–41.

USFWS. 1988a. Flyway summary—midwinter waterfowl survey. Patuxent Wildl. Res. Center, Laurel, Md.

USFWS. 1988b. Atlantic coast Piping Plover recovery plan. USDI Fish and Wildl. Serv., Newton Corner, Mass.

USFWS. 1990. Waterfowl harvest and population survey data. Patuxent Wildl. Res. Center., Laurel, Md.

USFWS and CWS. 1986. Status of waterfowl and fall flight forecasts. USDI Fish and Wildl. Serv. in coop. with Can. Wildl. Serv., Washington, D.C.

VanCamp, L. F., and C. J. Henny. 1975. The screech-owl: its life history and population ecology in northern Ohio. North Am. Fauna 71. USDI Fish and Wildl. Serv., Washington, D.C.

Varick, W. R. 1917. A mockingbird in New Hampshire. Auk 34:91.

Veit, R., and W. R. Peterson. 1993. Birds of Massachusetts. Mass. Audubon Soc., Lincoln.

Verbeek, N. A. M. 1970. Breeding ecology of the Water Pipit. Auk 87:425–451.

Vt. Fish & Wildlife Dept. 1986. Model habitat management guidelines for deer, bear, hare, grouse, turkey, woodcock, and non-game wildlife. Leahy Press, Montpelier, Vt.

Wade, D. E. 1947. What is distribution of Ruby-crowned Kinglet in New Hampshire?. Bull. Audubon Soc. N.H. 18:36.

Walkinshaw, L. H. 1935. Studies of the Short-billed Marsh Wren (Cistothorus stellaris) in Michigan. Auk 52:362–369.

Walkinshaw, L. H. 1937. The Virginia Rail in Michigan. Auk 54:464–475.

Walkinshaw, L. H. 1938. Life history studies of the Eastern Goldfinch. Pt. I. Jack-Pine Warbler 16:3–11, 14–15.

Walkinshaw, L. H. 1940. Summer life of the Sora rail. Auk 57:153–168.

Walkinshaw, L. H. 1944. The eastern Chipping Sparrow in Michigan. Wilson Bull. 56:193–205.

Walkinshaw, L. H. 1959. The Prairie Warbler in Michigan. Jack-Pine Warbler 37:54–63.

Walkinshaw, L. H. 1960. Some Coos County, New Hampshire bird experiences. N.H. Bird News 13:54–58.

Walkinshaw, L. H. 1968. Eastern Field Sparrow, pp. 1217–1235. In A. C. Bent, Life histories of North American cardinals, grosbeaks, buntings, towhees, finches sparrows and allies, pt. 2. O. L. Austin, Jr., [ed.]. U.S. Natl. Mus. Bull. 237. Washington, D.C.

Wallace, G. W. 1939. Bicknell's Thrush, its taxonomy, distribution, and life history. Proc. Boston Soc. Nat. Hist. 41:211–402.

Wallace, V. H. 1949a. Breeding bird census: 9. Partially cut-over northern hardwood slope. Audubon Field Notes:258–259.

Wallace, V. H. 1949b. Bird notes at New Hampton. Audubon Soc. N.H. Newsl. 2(1):14.

Wallace, V. H. 1953. 1953 nesting season. N.H. Bird News 6(4):17–23.

Wallace, V. H. 1954a. The winter season. N.H. Bird News 7(2):13–17.

Wallace, V. H. 1954b. Nesting season. N.H. Bird News 7(4):18–23.

Wasserman, F. E. 1980. Territorial behavior in a pair of White-throated Sparrows. Wilson Bull. 92:74–87.

Wayne, A. T. 1910. Birds of South Carolina. Contrib. Charleston Mus. 1.

Weaver, F. G. 1939. Studies in the life history of the Wood Thrush. Bird-Banding 10:16–23.

Weaver, R. 1941. Mockingbird in New Hampshire in midsummer. Auk 58:264.

Weaver, F. G. 1949. Wood Thrush, pp. 101–123. In A. C. Bent, Life histories of North American thrushes, kinglets and their allies. U.S. Natl. Mus. Bull. 196. Washington, D.C.

Weeks, H. P. 1984. Importance and management of riparian bridges and culverts for nesting passerines, pp. 163–175. In W. C. McComb, [ed.], Management of nongame species and ecological communities. Univ. Ky., Lexington.

Weik, A. P. 1987. The status of Golden Eagles in Maine. Honors thesis, Univ. Maine, Ororno.

Weins, J. A. 1969. An approach to the study of ecological relationships among grassland birds. Ornithol. Monogr. 8:1–93.

Weir, R. D. 1983. Ontario region. Am. Birds 37:982–985.

Weir, R. D., F. Cooke, M. H. Edwards, and R. B. Stewart. 1980. Fall migration of Saw-whet Owls at Prince Edward Point, Ontario. Wilson Bull. 92:475–488.

Weller, M. W. 1958. Observations on the incubation behavior of a Common Nighthawk. Auk 75:48–59.

Weller, M. W. 1961. Breeding biology of the Least Bittern. Wilson Bull. 73:11–35.

Welsh, D. A. 1975. Savannah Sparrow breeding and territoriality on a Nova Scotia dune beach. Auk 92:235–251.

Welter, W. A. 1935. The natural history of the Long-billed Marsh Wren. Wilson Bull. 47:3–34.

Westemeier, R. L. 1989. Upland Sandpipers on Illinois prairie-chicken sanctuaries. Ill. Nat. Hist. Rep. 284:1–2.

Weston, F. M. 1949. Blue-gray Gnatcatcher, pp. 344–364. In A. C. Bent, Life histories of North American thrushes, kinglets, and their allies. U.S. Natl. Mus. Bull. 196. Washington, D.C.

Wetherbee, D. K. 1968. Southern Swamp Sparrow, pp. 1475–1490. In A. C. Bent, Life histories of North American cardinals, grosbeaks, buntings, towhees, finches, sparrows and allies, pt. 3. O. L. Austin, Jr., [ed.]. U.S. Natl. Mus. Bull. 237. Washington, D.C.

Weydemeyer, W. 1933. Nesting of the Rough-winged Swallow in Montana. Auk 50:362–363.

Weyden, W. J. 1975. Scops and screech-owls: vocal evidence for a basic subdivision of the genus Otus (Strigidae). Ardea 63:65–77.

Wheeler, S. 1979. New Hampshire kestrels, pp. 25–27. In N.H. Audubon Ann.

Wheelwright, N. T. 1986. Diet of American Robins: an analysis of U. S. Biological Survey records. Auk 103:710–725.

Whitcomb, R. F. 1977. Island biogeography and "habitat islands" of eastern forests. Am. Birds 31:3–5.

White, F. B. 1924. A preliminary list of birds of Concord, N.H. Rumford Press, Concord.

White, F. B. 1927. Common and Arctic terns at Seabrook, New Hampshire. Audubon Soc. N.H. Bull. 6:42–43.

White, F. B. 1928. Seabrook beach. Bull. Audubon Soc. N.H. 8:13.

White, F. B. 1929. Marsh, beach, and ledge. Audubon Soc. N.H. Bull. 9:3–5.

White, F. B. 1931. Notes on birds at Seabrook in 1930. Audubon Soc. N.H. Bull. 10:29–30.

White, F. B. 1932a. Notes from Seabrook beach, 1931. Audubon Soc. N.H. Bull. 11:7.

White, F. B. 1932b. Seabrook beach, New Hampshire. Audubon Soc. N.H. Bull. 11:31–32.

White, F. B. 1935. Notes from Concord and Seabrook. Spec. Bull. Audubon Soc. N.H. 2:11–12.

White, F. B. 1937. Local notes on the birds at Concord, New Hampshire. Rumford Press, Concord.

White, R. P. 1988. Wintering grounds and migration patterns of the Upland Sandpiper. Am. Birds 42:1247–1253.

Whittle, C. L. 1920. A colony of Three-toed Woodpeckers. Bird-Lore 22:351–352.

Whittle, H. G. 1923a. Early migratory movements of Seiurus n. noveboracensis. Auk 40:669–700.

Whittle, H. G. 1923b. Recent experiences with nesting catbirds. Auk 40:603–606.

Wilcox, L. 1944. Great Black-backed Gull breeding in New York. Auk 61:653–654.

Wilcox, L. 1959. A twenty year banding study of the Piping Plover. Auk 76:129–152.

Wiley, R. H. 1976. Communication and spatial relationships in a colony of Common Grackles. Anim. Behav. 24:570–584.

Willey, C. H. 1968. The ecological significance of the Mute Swan in Rhode Island, pp. 121–134. In 25th Trans. Northeastern Sect. Wildl. Soc., Northeastern Fish and Wildl. Conf.

Williamson, P. 1971. Feeding ecology of the Red-eyed Vireo (Vireo olivaceus) and associated foliage-gleaning birds. Ecol. Monogr. 41:129–152.

Willoughby, E. J., and T. J. Cade. 1964. Breeding behavior of the American Kestrel (Sparrow Hawk). Living Bird 3:75–96.

Wood, R., and W. L. Gelston. 1972. Preliminary report: the Mute Swans of Michigan's Grand Traverse Bay region. Mich. Dept. Nat. Resour. Lansing, Mich.

Woods, R. S. 1968. House Finch, pp. 290–314. In A. C. Bent, Life histories of North American cardinals, grosbeaks, buntings, towhees, finches, sparrows and allies, pt. 1. O. L. Austin, Jr., [ed.]. U.S. Natl. Mus. Bull. 237. Washington, D.C.

Wolfenden, G. E. 1968. Northern Seaside Sparrow, pp. 819–831. In A. C. Bent, Life histories of North American cardinals, grosbeaks, buntings, towhees, finches, sparrows and allies, pt. 2. O. L. Austin, Jr., [ed.]. U.S. Natl. Mus. Bull. 237. Washington, D.C.

Worthen, T. W. D. 1891. A list of the vertebrates found within thirty miles of Hanover, N.H. Hanover, N.H.

Wright, H. W. 1911. The birds of the Jefferson region in the White Mountains, New Hampshire. Proc. Manchester Inst. Arts and Scien. 5. Pt 1. Manchester, N.H.

Wright, H. W. 1921. The mockingbird in the Boston region and in New England and Canada. Auk 38:422.

Wright, P. L. 1937. The birds of the Isles of Shoals. M.S. thesis, Univ. N.H., Durham.

Young, H. 1955. Breeding behavior and nesting of the Eastern Robin. Am. Midl. Nat. 53:329–352.

Zack, R., and J. B. Falls. 1975. Response of the Ovenbird (Aves: Parulidae) to an outbreak of the spruce budworm. Can. J. Zool. 53:1669–1672.

Zeleny, L. 1978. The Bluebird. Indiana Univ. Press, Bloomington.

Ziebell, T. J. 1990. Nesting Least Bitterns on Rush Lake, Wisconsin. Passenger Pigeon 52:19–28.

Zimmerman, J. L. 1977. Virginia Rail (Rallus limnicola), pp. 46–560. In G. C. Sanderson, [ed.], Management of migratory shore and upland game birds in North America. Internat. Assoc. of Fish and Wildl. Agencies, Washington, D.C.

Zumeta, D. C., and R. T. Holmes. 1978. Habitat shifts and roadside mortality of Scarlet Tanagers during a cold wet New England spring. Wilson Bull. 90:575–586.

Index of
Common & Scientific
Bird Names

Index

Accipiter cooperii. *See* Hawk, Cooper's

Accipiter gentilis. *See* Goshawk, Northern

Accipiter striatus. *See* Hawk, Sharp-shinned

Actitis macularia. *See* Sandpiper, Spotted

Aegolius acadicus. *See* Owl, Northern Saw-whet

Agelaius phoeniceus. *See* Blackbird, Red-winged

Aquila chrysaetos. *See* Eagle, Golden

Aix sponsa. *See* Duck, Wood

Ammodramus caudacutus. *See* Sparrow, Sharp-tailed

Ammodramus henslowii. *See* Sparrow, Henslow's

Ammodramus maritimus. *See* Sparrow, Seaside

Ammodramus savannarum. *See* Sparrow, Grasshopper

Anas acuta. *See* Pintail, Northern

Anas clypeata. *See* Shoveler, Northern

Anas crecca. *See* Teal, Green-winged

Anas discors. *See* Teal, Blue-winged

Anas platyrhynchos. *See* Mallard

Anas rubripes. *See* Duck, American Black

Anas strepera. *See* Gadwall

Anthus spinoletta. *See* Pipit, American

Archilochus colubris. *See* Hummingbird, Ruby-throated

Ardea herodias. *See* Heron, Great Blue

Asio flammeus. *See* Owl, Short-eared

Asio otus. *See* Owl, Long-eared

Auk, Great I-19

Aythya collaris. *See* Duck, Ring-necked

Bartramia longicauda. *See* Sandpiper, Upland

Bittern, American I-20, I-27, 10–11, 370, 374

Bittern, Least I-4, I-7, I-20, 370, 390

Blackbird, Red-winged I-8, I-27, I-28, I-29, 340–341, 344, 348

Blackbird, Rusty I-22, I-27, I-29, I-31, 344–345

Bluebird, Eastern I-8, I-22, 140, 168, 214–215, 222, 236, 276

Bobolink I-8, I-18, I-19, I-22, 44, 322, 338–339, 342

Bobwhite, Northern I-4, I-7, I-18, I-22, 70–71

Bombycilla cedrorum. *See* Waxwing, Cedar

Bonasa umbellus, *See* Grouse, Ruffed

Botaurus lentiginosus. *See* Bittern, American

Branta canadensis. *See* Goose, Canada

Bubo virginianus. *See* Owl, Great Horned

Bubuculus ibis. *See* Egret, Cattle

Bucephala clangula. *See* Goldeneye, Common

Bucephala islandica. *See* Goldeneye, Barrow's

Bunting, Indigo I-8, 296, 310–311

Bunting, Snow 164

Buteo jamaicensis. *See* Hawk, Red-tailed

Buteo lineatus. *See* Hawk, Red-shouldered

Buteo platypterus. *See* Hawk, Broad-winged

Butorides striatus. *See* Night-Heron, Black-crowned

Calidris himantopus. *See* Sandpiper, Stilt

Calcarius lapponicus. *See* Longspur, Lapland

Camptolaimus labradorius. *See* Duck, Labrador

Caprimulgus vociferus. *See* Whip-poor-will

Cardinal, Northern I-22, I-23, I-26, 306–307, 392

Cardinalis cardinalis. *See* Cardinal, Northern

Carduelis pinus. *See* Siskin, Pine

Carduelis tristis. *See* Goldfinch, American

Carpodacus mexicanus. *See* Finch, House

Carpodacus purpureus. *See* Finch, Purple

Casmerodius albus. *See* Egret, Great

Catbird, Gray I-8, I-27, 228–229, 232, 348

Cathartes aura. *See* Vulture, Turkey

Catharus fuscescens. *See* Veery

Catharus guttatus. *See* Thrush, Hermit

Catharus minimus. *See* Thrush, Gray-cheeked

Catharus ustulatus. *See* Thrush, Swainson's

Catoptrophorus semipalmatus. *See* Willet

Cepphus grylle. *See* Guillemot, Black

Certhia americana. *See* Creeper, Brown

Ceryle torquata. *See* Kingfisher, Belted

Chaetura pelagica. *See* Swift, Chimney

Charadrius melodus. *See* Plover, Piping

Charadrius vociferus. *See* Killdeer

Chickadee, Black-capped I-7, I-8, I-31, 158, 188–189, 190, 192, 196, 272

Chickadee, Boreal I-19, I-25, I-27, I-28, I-29, I-30, I-31, 188, 190–191

Chickadee, Hudson Bay. *See* Chickadee, Boreal

Chlidonias niger. *See* Tern, Black

Chordeiles minor. *See* Nighthawk, Common

Circus cyaneus. *See* Harrier, Northern

Cistothorus palustris. *See* Wren, Marsh

Cistothorus platensis. *See* Wren, Sedge

Coccothraustes vespertinus. *See* Grosbeak, Evening

Coccyzus americanus. *See* Cuckoo, Yellow-billed

Coccyzus erythropthalmus. *See* Cuckoo, Black-billed

Colaptes auratus. *See* Flicker, Northern

Colinus virginianus. *See* Bobwhite, Northern

Columba livia. *See* Dove, Rock

Contopus borealis. *See* Flycatcher, Olive-sided

Contopus virens. *See* Wood-pewee, Eastern

Cormorant, Double-crested I-20, I-26, I-18, I-19, 6–7, 374

Corvus brachyrhynchos. *See* Crow, American

Corvus corax. *See* Raven, Common

Corvus ossifragus. *See* Crow, Fish

Coturnicops noveboracensis. *See* Rail, Yellow

Cowbird, Brown-headed I-8, 158, 212, 260, 262, 284, 290, 298, 312, 314, 328, 348–349

Creeper, Brown I-8, 196, 198–199, 208, 284

Crossbill, Red I-4, I-22, I-27, I-29, I-31, 358–359, 360

Crossbill, White-winged I-7, I-25, I-27, I-29, I-31, 358, 360–361

Crow, American I-8, 172, 182–183, 184

Crow, Fish I-7, I-26, 182, 184–185

Cuckoo, Black-billed 106–107, 108

Cuckoo, Yellow-billed I-26, 106, 108–109

Cyanocitta cristata. *See* Jay, Blue

Cygnus columbianus. *See* Swan, Tundra

Cygnus olor. *See* Swan, Mute

Dendragapus canadensis. *See* Grouse, Spruce

Dendroica caerulescens. *See* Warbler, Black-throated Blue

Dendroica castanea. *See* Warbler, Bay-breasted

Dendroica cerulea. *See* Warbler, Cerulean

Dendroica coronata. *See* Warbler, Yellow-rumped

Dendroica discolor. *See* Warbler, Prairie

Dendroica fusca. *See* Warbler, Blackburnian

Dendroica magnolia. *See* Warbler, Magnolia

Dendroica palmarum. *See* Warbler, Palm

Dendroica pensylvanica. *See* Warbler, Chestnut-sided

Dendroica petechia. *See* Warbler, Yellow

Dendroica pinus. *See* Warbler, Pine

Dendroica striata. *See* Warbler, Blackpoll

Dendroica tigrina. *See* Warbler, Cape May

Dendroica virens. *See* Warbler, Black-throated Green

Dolichonyx oryzivorus. *See* Bobolink

Dove, Mourning I-8, I-18, I-19, I-22, 60, 104–105, 392

Dove, Rock I-21, I-23, 102–103

Dryocopus pileatus. *See* Woodpecker, Pileated

Duck, American Black I-8, I-18, I-20, I-27, I-31, 22, 24–25, 26, 374

Duck, Labrador I-19

Duck, Ring-necked I-20, I-31, 30–31, 36

Duck, Wood I-5, I-8, I-19, I-20, I-27, I-31, 20–21, 36

Dumetella carolinensis. *See* Catbird, Gray

Eagle, Bald I-4, I-5, I-7, I-19, I-21, 42, 373–374

Eagle, Golden I-4, I-7, 374

Ectopistes migratorius. *See* Pigeon, Passenger

Egret, Cattle I-4

Egret, Great I-4

Egret, Snowy I-4, I-7, I-20, I-26, 371–372

Egretta caerulea. *See* Heron, Little Blue

Egretta thula. *See* Egret, Snowy

Egretta tricolor. *See* Heron, Tricolored

Eider, Common I-18, I-19, I-20, I-26, 32–33

Empidonax alnorum. *See* Flycatcher, Alder

Empidonax flaviventris. *See* Flycatcher, Yellow-bellied

Empidonax minimus. *See* Flycatcher, Least

Empidonax traillii. *See* Flycatcher, Willow

Empidonax virescens. *See* Flycatcher, Acadian

Eremophila alpestris. *See* Lark, Horned

Euphagus carolinus. *See* Blackbird, Rusty

Falco columbarius. *See* Merlin

Falco peregrinus. *See* Falcon, Peregrine

Falco sparverius. *See* Kestrel, American

Falcon, Peregrine I-4, I-5, I-22, 60–61, 84, 102, 186

Finch, House I-22, I-26, 230, 354, 356–357, 368

Finch, Purple I-8, I-22, I-29, I-30, I-31, 354–355, 356, 364

Flicker, Northern I-8, 44, 60, 116, 132, 140–141, 142, 230

Flycatcher, Acadian I-7, 150–151

Flycatcher, Alder I-8, I-4, 152–153, 154

Flycatcher, Great Crested I-8, 160–161, 236

Flycatcher, Least I-8, 148, 156–157

Flycatcher, Olive-sided I-31, 144–145

Flycatcher, Willow I-4, 152, 154–155

Flycatcher, Yellow-bellied I-28, I-29, I-30, I-31, 148–149

Gadwall I-4

Gallinago gallinago. *See* Snipe, Common

Gallinula chloropus. *See* Moorhen, Common

Gallinule, Common. *See* Moorhen, Common

Gallinule, Florida. *See* Moorhen, Common

Gavia immer. *See* Loon, Common

Geothlypis trichas. *See* Yellowthroat, Common

Gnatcatcher, Blue-gray I-4, I-22, 212–213, 386

Goldeneye, Barrow's 34

Goldeneye, Common I-5, I-20, I-31, 34–35, 36

Goldfinch, American I-8, 362, 364–365

Goose, Canada I-20, 18–19

Goshawk, Northern I-21, 48, 50–51

Grackle, Common I-8, I-23, I-28, I-29, 226, 316, 344, 346–347, 348

Grebe, Pied-billed I-4, I-27, 4–5, 390

Grosbeak, Evening I-22, 366–367

Grosbeak, Pine I-4, I-7, I-22, I-29, I-31, 387

Grosbeak, Rose-breasted I-8, I-27, 308–309

Grouse, Ruffed I-8, I-18, 44, 64, 66–67, 114, 270

Grouse, Spruce I-19, I-27, I-29, I-30, I-31, 64–65

Guillemot, Black I-4, I-7, 100–101

Gull, Great Black-backed I-21, I-26, I-27, 2, 6, 32, 92, 94–95, 96, 100

Gull, Herring I-21, I-26, I-27, 32, 92–93, 94, 96, 377

Gull, Ring-billed I-4, I-7, I-27, I-21, 377

Haematopus palliatus. *See* Oystercatcher, American

Haliaeetus leucocephalus. *See* Eagle, Bald

Harrier, Northern I-4, I-5, I-19, I-21, 44–45

Hawk, Broad-winged I-8, I-19, I-21, I-23, 48, 52, 54–55, 180

Hawk, Cooper's I-4, I-21, 46, 48–49, 50, 102

Hawk, Red-shouldered I-21, 52–53, 54, 112, 114, 180

Hawk, Red-tailed I-8, I-21, 52, 56–57, 102, 112

Hawk, Sharp-shinned I-4, I-21, 46–47, 48

Helmitheros vermivorus. *See* Warbler, Worm-eating

Heron, Great Blue I-5, I-8, I-19, I-20, I-27, 8–9, 14, 40, 112, 374

Heron, Green I-4, I-28, 8–9, 12, 370, 372

Heron, Little Blue I-4, I-7, 371–372

Heron, Tricolored I-4

Hirundo pyrrhonota. *See* Swallow, Cliff

Hirundo rustica. *See* Swallow, Barn

Hummingbird, Ruby-throated I-8, 124–125

Hylocichla mustelina. *See* Thrush, Wood

Ibis, Glossy I-4, I-7, I-20, I-26, 372

Icterus galbula. See Oriole, Northern

Icterus spurius. See Oriole, Orchard

Ixobrychus exilis. See Bittern, Least

Jay, Blue I-7, I-8, I-22, 60, 180–181, 226, 286, 316

Jay, Gray I-19, I-22, I-27, I-29, I-31, 178–179

Junco, Dark-eyed I-8, I-25, I-27, I-28, I-29, I-30, I-31, 336–337, 383

Junco hyemalis. See Junco, Dark-eyed

Kestrel, American I-8, I-21, I-29, 58–59, 172

Killdeer I-8, I-18, I-19, I-20, I-23, 80–81, 230

Kingbird, Eastern I-8, I-28, I-29, 162–163

Kingfisher, Belted I-8, I-28, 126–127, 132, 170

Kinglet, Golden-crowned I-25, I-29, I-30, I-31, 208–209, 210

Kinglet, Ruby-crowned I-22, I-27, I-28, I-29, I-30, I-31, 146, 208, 210–211

Lanius ludoicianus. See Shrike, Loggerhead

Lark, Horned I-4, I-20, 164–165

Larus argentatus. See Gull, Herring

Larus delawarensis. See Gull, Ring-billed

Larus marinus. See Gull, Great Black-backed

Longspur, Lapland 164

Loon, Common I-5, I-19, I-20, I-27, 2–3

Lophodytes cucullatus. See Merganser, Hooded

Loxia curvirostra. See Crossbill, Red

Loxia leucoptera. See Crossbill, White-winged

Mallard I-8, I-20, I-27, I-31, 24, 26–27

Martin, Purple I-4, I-22, I-23, 166–167, 368, 391

Meadowlark, Eastern I-18, I-19, I-22, 322, 338, 342–343

Melanerpes carolinus. See Woodpecker, Red-bellied

Melanerpes erythrocephalus. See Woodpecker, Red-headed

Meleagris gallapavo sylvestris. See Turkey, Wild

Melospiza georgiana. See Sparrow, Swamp

Melospiza lincolnii. See Sparrow, Lincoln's

Melospiza melodia. See Sparrow, Song

Merganser, Common I-20, I-27, 2, 38–39, 374

Merganser, Hooded I-5, I-19, I-20, I-23, I-27, I-31, 20, 36–37

Merganser, Red-breasted I-4, 38

Mergus merganser. See Merganser, Common

Mergus serrator. See Merganser, Red-breasted

Merlin I-4, I-7, I-21, 375–378

Mimus polyglottos. See Mockingbird, Northern

Mniotilta varia. See Warbler, Black-and-white

Mockingbird, Northern I-26, 230–231, 232, 392

Molothrus ater. See Cowbird, Brown-headed

Moorhen, Common I-4, I-26, 76–77

Myiarchus crinitus. See Flycatcher, Great Crested

Night-Heron, Black-crowned I-4, I-7, I-20, I-26, 10, 12–13, 14

Nighthawk, Common I-4, I-5, I-22, 118–119, 120

Northern, Goshawk 50–51, 102

Nuthatch, Red-breasted I-8, I-29, I-31, 194–195

Nuthatch, White-breasted I-8, 192, 194, 196–197

Nycticorax nycticorax. See Heron, Green

Oceanodroma leucorhoa. See Storm-Petrel, Leach's

Oporornis philadelphia. See Warbler, Mourning

Oriole, Baltimore. *See* Oriole, Northern

Oriole, Northern I-8, 350, 352–353

Oriole, Orchard I-22, I-26, 350–351

Osprey I-5, I-19, I-21, 42–43, 373

Otis asio. See Screech-Owl, Eastern

Ovenbird I-8, I-27, I-28, I-29, I-30, 288, 290–291, 348

Owl, Barn I-4, 381

Owl, Barred I-8, I-31, 112, 114–115, 116

Owl, Eastern Screech. *See* Screech-Owl, Eastern

Owl, Great Horned I-26, 48, 112–113, 114, 116, 382

Owl, Long-eared I-4, I-7, 382

Owl, Northern Saw-whet 116–117, 230

Owl, Short-eared I-4

Oystercatcher, American I-18

Pandion haliaetus. See Osprey

partridge. *See* Grouse, Ruffed

Parula americana. See Parula, Northern

Parula, Northern I-25, I-27, I-31, 258–259, 274, 385

Parus atricapillus. See Chickadee, Black-capped

Parus bicolor. See Titmouse, Tufted

Parus hudsonicus. See Chickadee, Boreal

Passer domesticus. See Sparrow, House

Passerculus sandwichensis. See Sparrow, Savannah

Passerina cyanea. See Bunting, Indigo

Perisoreus canadensis. See Jay, Gray

Phalacrocorax auritus. See Cormorant, Double-crested

Phalarope, Northern. *See* Phalarope, Red-necked

Phalarope, Red 376

Phalarope, Red-necked 376

Phalarope, Wilson's I-4, I-7, 376–377

Phalaropus fulicaria. See Phalarope, Red

Phalaropus lobatus. See Phalarope, Red-necked

Phalaropus tricolor. See Phalarope, Wilson's

Phasianus colchicus. See Pheasant, Ring-necked

Pheasant, Chinese Ring-necked. *See* Pheasant, Ring-necked

Pheasant, Ring-necked 62–63

Pheucticus ludovicianus. See Grosbeak, Rose-breasted

Philohela minor. See Woodcock, American

Phoebe, Eastern I-8, 146–147, 158

Picoides arcticus. See Woodpecker, Black-backed

Picoides pubescens. See Woodpecker, Downy

Picoides tridactylus. See Woodpecker, Three-toed

Picoides villosus. See Woodpecker, Hairy

pigeon *See* Dove, Rock

Pigeon, Passenger I-18, I-19, 380

Pinicola enucleator. See Grosbeak, Pine

Pintail, Northern I-20

Pipilo erythrophthalmus. See Towhee, Rufous-sided

Pipit, American I-4, I-7, I-22, 383

Pipit, Water. See Pipit, American

Piranga olivacea. See Tanager, Scarlet

Plautus impennis. See Auk, Great

Plectrophenax nivalis. See Bunting, Snow

Plegadis falcinellus. See Ibis, Glossy

Plover, Piping I-4, I-20, I-26, 78–79

Podilymbus podiceps. See Grebe, Pied-billed

Polioptila caerulea. See Gnatcatcher, Blue-gray

Pooecetes gramineus. See Sparrow, Vesper

Porzana carolina. See Sora

Progne subis. See Martin, Purple

Quiscalus quiscula. See Grackle, Common

Rail, Clapper I-4, I-7, 376

Rail, King I-4, 376

Rail, Virginia I-4, 72–73, 74, 376

Rail, Yellow I-4

Rallus elegans. See Rail, King

Rallus limicola. See Rail, Virginia

Rallus longirostris. See Rail, Clapper

Raven, Common I-4, I-8, I-18, I-22, I-29, I-30, 60, 182, 186–187, 226

Redstart, American I-8, I-27, I-28, I-29, I-31, 286–287, 348

Regulus calendula. See Kinglet, Ruby-crowned

Regulus satrapa. See Kinglet, Golden-crowned

Riparia riparia. See Swallow, Bank

Robin, American I-7, I-8, I-27, I-28, I-29, I-30, 44, 136, 222, 226–227, 304, 348

Sandpiper, Spotted I-8, I-27, I-28, 84–85, 292

Sandpiper, Stilt 376

Sandpiper, Upland I-4, I-5, I-19, I-20, I-23, 86–87, 391

Sapsucker, Yellow-bellied I-8, 124, 130–131, 162

Sayornis phoebe. See Phoebe, Eastern

Screech-Owl, Eastern I-4, I-19, I-22, I-26, 110–111, 116

Seiurus aurocapillus. See Ovenbird

Seiurus motacilla. See Waterthrush, Louisiana

Seiurus noveboracensis. See Waterthrush, Northern

Setophaga ruticilla. See Redstart, American

Shoveler, Northern I-4

Shrike, Loggerhead I-4, I-7, I-22, 384

Sialia sialis. See Bluebird, Eastern

Siskin, Pine I-29, I-30, 362–363

Sitta canadensis. See Nuthatch, Red-breasted

Sitta carolinensis. See Nuthatch, White-breasted

Snipe, Common I-4, I-21, 88–89

Snipe, Eurasian 88

Somateria mollissima. See Eider, Common

Sora I-4, 72, 74–75, 376

Sparrow, Chipping I-8, 276, 288, 314–315, 332, 348, 385

Sparrow, Field I-8, 316–317

Sparrow, Grasshopper I-4, I-19, I-22, 322–323, 391

Sparrow, Henslow's I-4, I-7, I-19, I-22, 386, 391

Sparrow, House I-8, I-21, I-23, 140, 166, 168, 174, 188, 214, 354, 368–369

Sparrow, Lincoln's I-22, I-31, 330–331

Sparrow, Savannah I-19, 320–321, 322

Sparrow, Seaside I-4, I-7, I-22, I-26, 324, 326–327

Sparrow, Sharp-tailed I-4, I-26, 324–325, 326

Sparrow, Song I-8, I-27, I-28, I-29, 298, 318, 328–329, 330, 332, 348

Sparrow, Swamp I-8, I-27, I-29, 332–333

Sparrow, Vesper I-4, I-19, I-22, I-23, I-28, 318–319, 320

Sparrow, White-throated I-8, I-19, I-23, I-27, I-28, I-29, I-30, I-31, 264, 334–335, 383

Sphyrapicus varius. See Sapsucker, Yellow-bellied

Spizella passerina. See Sparrow, Chipping

Spizella pusilla. See Sparrow, Field

Starling, European I-8, I-21, I-23, 166, 214, 236–237, 354

Stelgidopteryx serripennis. See Swallow, Northern Rough-winged

Sterna antillarum. See Tern, Least

Sterna dougallii. See Tern, Roseate

Sterna hirundo. See Tern, Common

Sterna paradisaea. See Tern, Arctic

Storm-Petrel, Leach's I-18

Strix varia. See Owl, Barred

Sturnella magna. See Meadowlark, Eastern

Sturnus vulgaris. See Starling, European

Swallow, Bank I-8, I-28, I-29, 126, 170, 172–173, 174

Swallow, Barn I-8, I-18, I-22, I-29, 174, 176–177

Swallow, Cliff I-4, I-22, 174–175, 176

Swallow, Northern Rough-winged I-4, I-20, I-22, 126, 170–171, 172

Swallow, Tree I-8, I-29, 140, 168–169, 214, 368

Swan, Mute 16–17

Swan, Tundra 16

Swift, Chimney I-8, I-18, I-29, I-31, 122–123

Tachycineta bicolor. See Swallow, Tree

Tanager, Scarlet I-8, 242, 304–305, 308

Teal, Blue-winged I-4, I-20, 22, 28–29

Teal, Green-winged I-4, I-7, I-20, 22–23

Tern, Arctic I-4, I-7, I-21, 378

Tern, Black I-4, I-7, 379

Tern, Common I-4, I-5, I-21, I-26, 82, 96–97, 377, 378

Tern, Least I-4, I-7, I-21, I-26, 98–99

Tern, Roseate I-4, I-21

Thrasher, Brown I-8, 228, 232–233

Thrush, Bicknell's. See Thrush, Gray-cheeked

Thrush, Gray-cheeked I-25, I-27, I-29, I-30, 218–219, 220

Thrush, Hermit I-8, I-23, I-25, I-30, 216, 220, 222–223, 224

Thrush, Olive-backed. See Thrush, Swainson's

Thrush, Swainson's I-25, I-27, I-28, I-29, I-30, I-31, 216, 218, 220–221, 222

Thrush, Wood I-8, I-19, I-20, I-22, I-23, I-29, 216, 218, 220, 222, 224–225

Thryothorus ludovicianus. See Wren, Carolina

Titmouse, Tufted I-22, 192–193, 230, 306, 392

Towhee, Rufous-sided I-27, I-28, 312–313

Toxostoma rufum. See Thrasher, Brown

Tringa flavipes. See Yellowlegs, Lesser

Tringa melanoleuca. See Yellowlegs, Greater

Troglodytes aedon. See Wren, House

Troglodytes troglodytes. See Wren, Winter

Turdus migratorius. See Robin, American

Turkey, Wild I-5, I-18, I-22, 68–69

Tyrannus tyrannus. See Kingbird, Eastern

Tyto alba. See Owl, Barn

Veery I-8, I-27, I-28, I-29, 216–217, 220, 222, 224

Vermivora chrysoptera. See Warbler, Golden-winged

Vermivora peregrina. See Warbler, Tennessee

Vermivora pinus. See Warbler, Blue-winged

Vermivora ruficapilla. See Warbler, Nashville

Vireo flavifrons. See Vireo, Yellow-throated

Vireo gilvus. See Vireo, Warbling

Vireo griseus. See Vireo, White-eyed

Vireo olivaceus. See Vireo, Red-eyed

Vireo, Philadelphia I-4, I-27, I-29, I-30, I-31, 240, 246–247, 248

Vireo philadelphicus. See Vireo, Philadelphia

Vireo, Red-eyed I-7, I-8, I-25, I-27, I-28, I-29, I-30, 240, 244, 246, 248–249, 348

Vireo solitarius. See Vireo, Solitary

Vireo, Solitary I-8, I-31, 238, 240–241, 242, 348

Vireo, Warbling I-8, I-28, 244–245, 246, 248

Vireo, White-eyed I-4, I-7, I-22, I-26, 230, 238–239

Vireo, Yellow-throated I-28, 238, 240, 242–243, 244, 304

Vulture, Turkey I-4, I-7, I-21, 40–41

Warbler, Bay-breasted I-27, I-29, I-31, 254, 266, 280–281

Warbler, Black-and-white I-8, I-25, I-27, 266, 272, 282, 284–285, 348

Warbler, Black-throated Blue I-8, I-25, I-28, I-30, I-31, 268–269, 274, 385

Warbler, Black-throated Green I-8, I-19, I-25, I-27, I-29, I-30, I-31, 264, 272–273

Warbler, Blackburnian I-8, I-27, I-28, I-31, 266, 274–275, 280, 288

Warbler, Blackpoll I-25, I-27, I-29, I-30, I-31, 280, 282–283

Warbler, Blue-winged I-4, I-22, I-26, 250–251, 252

Warbler, Brewster's 250, 251, 252

Warbler, Canada I-8, I-25, I-27, I-28, I-29, I-31, 274, 302–303

Warbler, Cape May I-4, 254, 266–267, 280

Warbler, Cerulean I-4, I-7, 385

Warbler, Chestnut-sided I-8, I-19, I-25, I-27, I-29, I-31, 256, 262–263

Warbler, Golden-winged I-4, I-26, 250, 252–253

Warbler, Lawrence's 250, 252, 253

Warbler, Magnolia I-8, I-25, I-28, I-29, I-30, I-31, 264–265

Warbler, Mourning I-19, I-27, 296–297

Warbler, Myrtle. *See* Warbler, Yellow-rumped

Warbler, Nashville I-8, I-25, I-28, I-29, I-30, I-31, 254, 256–257, 300

Warbler, Palm I-4, I-7, I-22, I-31, 385

Warbler, Pine I-27, 276–277, 385

Warbler, Prairie I-22, I-26, 278–279

Warbler, Tennessee I-4, I-22, I-27, I-29, I-31, 246, 254–255, 280

Warbler, Wilson's I-28, I-31, 300–301

Warbler, Worm-eating I-4, I-7, 288–289

Warbler, Yellow I-8, I-27, I-28, I-29, 162, 260–261, 348

Warbler, Yellow-rumped I-8, I-25, I-27, I-28, I-29, I-30, I-31, 270–271, 272, 282

Waterthrush, Louisiana I-4, I-20, I-22, I-27, 292, 294–295

Waterthrush, Northern I-8, I-25, I-27, 292–293, 294

Waxwing, Cedar I-7, I-8, I-29, I-31, 234–235, 348

Whip-poor-will I-5, I-22, 120–121

Willet I-7, I-18, I-21, I-26, 82–83

Wilsonia canadensis. See Warbler, Canada

Wilsonia pusilla. See Warbler, Wilson's

Wood-pewee, Eastern I-8, 146–147, 386

Woodcock, American I-5, I-8, 90–91, 358

Woodpecker, Black-backed I-4, I-27, I-29, I-31, 136, 138–139

Woodpecker, Downy I-8, I-31, 132–133, 136, 196

Woodpecker, Hairy I-8, 132, 134–135, 136

Woodpecker, Pileated I-8, I-18, I-19, I-22, 132, 140, 142–143

Woodpecker, Red-bellied I-4, I-22

Woodpecker, Red-headed I-4, 128–129

Woodpecker, Three-toed I-4, I-7, I-19, I-29, I-31, 136–137, 138

Wren, Carolina I-4, I-22, I-26

Wren, House I-8, 168, 200–201, 316

Wren, Marsh I-4, I-7, 204, 206–207, 390

Wren, Sedge I-4, I-22, 204–205, 206, 390

Wren, Winter I-8, I-29, I-30, I-31, 200, 202–203

yellowlegs spp. 230

Yellowlegs, Greater 82

Yellowlegs, Lesser 376

Yellowthroat, Common I-8, I-19, I-27, I-28, I-29, I-31, 296, 298–299

Zenaida macroura. See Dove, Mourning

Zonotrichia albicollis. See Sparrow, White-throated